THE VITAMIN B COMPLEX

F. A. ROBINSON

M.Sc.Tech. (Manchester), LL.B. (London), F.R.I.C.

THE VITAMIN B

COMPLEX

NEW YORK

JOHN WILEY & SONS INC

440 FOURTH AVENUE

1951

First Published 1951

PRINTED IN GREAT BRITAIN AT
THE UNIVERSITY PRESS
ABERDEEN

PREFACE

MANY excellent books on vitamins have already been published, but so rapid is the expansion of knowledge in this field that constant revision is necessary to keep them up to date. The task of assimilating new knowledge becomes progressively more difficult with each year that passes and a complete survey must necessarily become more and more voluminous. In the absence of some method of regularly revising existing monographs, the scientific worker must keep himself informed of new developments by a close study of the original literature, abstracts or periodical summaries such as the *Annual Reports* of the Chemical Society, or he must be content to rely on the publication of occasional reviews or symposia in which particular aspects of the subjects are discussed.

Hitherto, no book devoted exclusively to a study of the vitamin B complex has been published. Yet there is much to be said in favour of thus restricting the field of inquiry. Perhaps the strongest argument is the impossibility of adequately surveying the whole group of vitamins within the compass of one volume. And what more natural, in this event, than to confine the study to the group of water-soluble vitamins now known as the vitamin B complex which, after all, contains all the newly characterised vitamins ? Apart from a historical connection, the members of this group have little in common with the fat-soluble vitamins or with vitamins C and P, whereas nearly all of them have a strong family likeness, resembling one another closely in their distribution in foodstuffs, in their biological effects on animals, plants, insects and micro-organisms, and in their biochemical functions. One of the main objects of this book is to stress this close relationship, although the mode of treatment adopted, that is, the discussion of each vitamin in turn, tends perhaps to stress the distinctive characteristics of each rather than their similarities.

I first became interested in the vitamin B complex about the year 1935 or 1936, when the synthesis of vitamins B_1 and B_2 was reported, and I have maintained this interest ever since. I have followed closely every development in this field and have myself been engaged in the isolation, production and assay of the most important members of the complex and, in recent years, I have been particularly concerned with the relation between the B vitamins and chemotherapy. My qualifications for writing this monograph are therefore an intimate association with various aspects of the vitamin B complex, a conviction that it forms a group of substances of outstanding biological

v

importance, and, I must confess, an urge to systematise the heterogeneous, rather untidy, array of data, so that others, not so intimately acquainted with the field, may have an over-all picture of what the vitamin B complex is and why it is of such significance in human and animal nutrition and in the economy of micro-organisms.

The task has not been an easy one, but I hope I have succeeded in presenting a coherent story in a form that others will find useful. I have tried to include all that is essential, and exclude all that is non-essential, but I am certain that my choice will not always meet with approval, especially as the subject is of interest to such a large number of specialists in so many branches of pure and applied science— chemists, zoologists, physiologists and bacteriologists, clinicians, nutritionists and agriculturists. Obviously it is impossible to give in one book all the information that workers in these diverse fields require, and it is to assist those who wish to have more detailed information in any particular field that I have included, at the end of each section, references to the original literature.

The story of the vitamin B complex, as will be evident in the pages that follow, has been compiled from many sources, some having no obvious connection with human nutrition. It would not be surprising, in view of the paramount importance of these substances in the metabolism of all living organisms, if further fascinating discoveries remain to be made, with consequences of perhaps even greater significance than any we have so far witnessed. I hope that this monograph may help to sustain the interest of research workers in these important substances.

F. A. ROBINSON.

" Waldrons ",
    Tewin Wood, Herts.

CONTENTS

CONTENTS

CONTENTS

Chapter I

INTRODUCTION

Research workers are usually so busy piling brick on brick on the edifice of human knowledge that there is never time for them to stand back and survey what has been built and how it has been done.

NATURE, *Sept.* 20, 1947.

THE WAR OF 1939-45 focused attention on the vital importance of food and nutrition, and showed how vulnerable are the food supplies of a large industrialised nation to enemy attack. The weapon of blockade was used alongside weapons of offence, and precautions against starvation were given the same high priority as air-raid precautions. It was fortunate indeed for this country—the most dependent of all the Western nations on external sources of food supplies—that so much was known concerning the nutritional value of foodstuffs. This knowledge enabled substitutes to be found for foods in short supply ; it enabled a sound rationing system to be built up which, although reducing food intake well below the level considered by nutritionists to be optimal, prevented any serious symptoms of malnutrition developing in the population as a whole, and gave to " priority " classes—children, expectant and nursing mothers and certain types of manual workers—a generous allowance of special foodstuffs to take the additional strain of growth, pregnancy, lactation and heavy work ; it assisted in the development of new methods of preserving and storing foodstuffs to reduce to a minimum the loss of food value ; and it helped to determine what foodstuffs should be selected to ensure the best possible use of the limited shipping space available for bringing imports into this country.

Although hostilities have now ceased, the importance of the science and technology of nutrition remains as great as ever, for a large proportion of the world's population is underfed. Even in this country we were until recently subsisting on a diet only just adequate for ordinary activity. For some sections of the population, particularly adolescents, it is probably less than adequate. Sir Jack Drummond has stated in a monograph published by the Royal Institute of Chemistry (1948) that adolescents " are often the first among the population to reveal signs of inadequate feeding. In Western Europe in 1940-45 that was true, and it is also true that this ' red light ' is showing here today. Many of these young people who were well nourished for most of the war period are not gaining weight today as they should ; some are even losing weight." If this is a picture of the state of nutrition in this country today, what is the picture like in less fortunate countries ? The problem of adequately feeding the world's population has by no means ceased to exist with the cessation of hostilities. Indeed, now is the time to examine the problem afresh in the light of the vast experiment carried out in this country between 1939 and 1945. The theories of nutritionists were then put to the test in a way that had not previously been possible, and as a result many widely-accepted generalisations had to be modified.

In order to feed everyone properly it is obviously necessary to know the nature of the substances present in food, how much of each is needed to maintain a certain level of activity, and how much is present in the foods commonly consumed. Investigations carried out during the last forty years have gone a long way towards supplying complete information on these points and, as already stated, this was used in formulating the food policy of this country during the 1939-45 war. With the additional information accumulated during the war and since, we have an even more complete picture of what is necessary for proper nutrition. What is now lacking is the machinery for applying this knowledge to rid the world once and for all of the spectre of famine.

The foundations of the science of nutrition were laid during the nineteenth century, when Liebig demonstrated that foods consisted of three main elements—proteins, carbohydrates and fats—and Voit and his colleagues showed that carbohydrates were burnt in the body to produce energy ; that proteins were used for building up the tissues of the body ; and that fats provided a reserve of food on which the body could draw in an emergency. It is difficult to say when this simple concept came to be recognised as inadequate as a basis for assessing the importance of different foodstuffs, for even in the eighteenth century sailors knew that scurvy could be prevented by lime-juice and fresh vegetables, while in 1885 a Japanese admiral, Takaki, eliminated beriberi from the Japanese navy by improving the sailors' diet. Perhaps the most significant date is the year 1897, in which Dr. C. Eijkman, a Dutchman employed in his country's colonial service in Java, began to study beriberi, a common disease of the tropics, which had hitherto been attributed to a bacterial infection. He noticed that hens in the prison yard suffered from a kind of leg weakness similar to the paralysis of beriberi from which the prisoners themselves were suffering. If anyone else had noticed this similarity, they had drawn from it the obvious conclusion that the hens had caught the infection from the men ! Eijkman, however, made a urther observation ; he noticed that when the food of the hens was inadvertently changed from polished rice, on which the prisoners were fed, to unmilled rice the paralysed hens recovered. This suggested to him that beriberi was in some way connected with food and not with infection. Forthwith, Eijkman began to experiment, and found that he could induce paralysis in hens by feeding them on polished rice and could then cure the paralysis by adding rice polishings to their diet. His colleague, Grijns, subsequently showed that beans also prevented paralysis in birds, and that an extract of beans or rice polishings cured both paralysed birds and beriberi patients. The factor thus shown to be present in these materials was later known as vitamin B. Thus a fourth dietary essential—vitamins—was added to the three elements —carbohydrate, fat and protein—recognised by the nineteenth-century nutritionists. The main materials for building this particular " edifice of human knowledge " were now available, but the story of how it is being erected—for it is not yet finished—is a long and complicated one. It has been built, like any other house, brick by brick and plank by plank. Sometimes progress has been rapid and one individual or, more often, a team of workers has contributed several courses to the brickwork. Sometimes, indeed, the building has assumed a distinctly lop-sided appearance with one wing completed almost before the foundations of another have been laid.

This book is concerned with only one aspect of the story of nutrition, and does not even set out to tell the story of all the vitamins, but only the story of those water-soluble vitamins which we now call the vitamin B complex. Progress in this field has been so rapid, and so much information has accumulated in recent years, that a complete review of all that is known about the vitamins would fill more than one volume. Besides, the story of the vitamin B complex is a coherent one and the pattern which it follows gains in clarity when this group of vitamins is considered apart from the other factors of nutritional importance. This review of the vitamin B complex is an attempt, in the words of the quotation at the heading of this chapter, " to stand back and survey what has been built and how it has been done ", even though the building is still surrounded by scaffolding and the workers are still actively engaged in completing various parts of it.

Recent research has made it more and more evident that the members of the vitamin B complex, although chemically diverse, constitute a group of biologically related substances, responsible for effecting transformations of fundamental importance to the life of organisms ranging in complexity from men to bacteria. They are, in fact, some of the building blocks around which the fabric of all living structures is built. It is to emphasise this one-ness of function that a book dealing with the vitamin B complex alone appeared to be desirable.

3

As already stated, the existence of vitamin B_1 or, as it is now called in this country, aneurine or, in the U.S.A., thiamine, was first demonstrated by feeding experiments on birds and human beings suffering from a deficiency disease. The same method was used for four other members of the vitamin B complex. The biological importance of nicotinic acid, for instance, was discovered as the result of Goldberger's study of pellagra in negroes and " poor whites " in the Southern States of the U.S.A. and his subsequent experiments on humans and dogs. Riboflavine was similarly identified as a vitamin necessary for the growth of rats, pyridoxine as a factor that cured a dermatitis in rats, and pantothenic acid as a factor that cured a dermatitis in chicks. Up to this point, the isolation of the several members of the vitamin B complex had followed an invariable routine —first, the observation that an experimental animal developed characteristic symptoms when maintained on a certain type of purified diet, then the discovery that an extract of some foodstuff, more often than not yeast or liver, would cure the symptoms, and finally attempts to purify the factor using the deficient animal for following the progress of the purification steps. With pantothenic acid, however, events took a different course and one that had an important influence on the subsequent history of vitamin science.

It had been observed in 1901 by a Belgian microbiologist, E. Wildiers, that certain yeasts failed to develop on a medium made up of purified constituents, but that they grew satisfactorily when an extract of yeast was added. He concluded that these organisms required for their growth a factor derived from living cells, and he gave this hypothetical factor the name " bios ". Many years later it was shown that bios was not one single substance, but a mixture of several substances. Various components were shown to be identical with aneurine, riboflavine, nicotinic acid and pyridoxine. Thus, the substances that stimulated the growth of yeasts proved to be the same as those that stimulated the growth of animals. In other words, the bios complex and the vitamin B complex, if not actually identical with one another, showed considerable overlap. One member of the bios complex, not at that time identified with any member of the vitamin B complex, was a substance to which the name pantothenic acid had been given. Concentrates of this substance prepared from liver showed chemical properties similar to those of the filtrate factor that cured chick dermatitis, and an interchange of specimens by the workers concerned showed that pantothenic acid cured dermatitis in chicks, whilst the filtrate factor stimulated the growth of yeast. Shortly afterwards the identity of the two substances was established by degradation and synthesis. Here indeed was striking confirmation that the bios complex and the vitamin B complex had much in common and that substances essential for the growth of unicellular organisms were also necessary for the growth of their multicellular relatives. The clue thus provided was followed up, with spectacular results. Another member of the bios complex is a substance called biotin, which has a demonstrable biological activity in extremely high dilution. When biotin was administered to animals suffering from so-called vitamin H deficiency the symptoms disappeared, and thus another link was forged between the two groups. In almost exactly the same way folic acid, a factor essential for the growth of certain bacteria, was shown to be identical with a factor, termed vitamin B_c, necessary for the well-being of chicks. In this instance, however, there exists a group of at least four closely related factors exhibiting similar biological properties—a folic acid complex within the vitamin B complex. Other examples of the identity of growth factors for higher and lower organisms are provided by p-aminobenzoic acid and inositol, both of which are essential growth factors for many bacteria and yeasts and also essential vitamins for certain species of animals.

The discovery that p-aminobenzoic acid was a growth factor for bacteria led to another discovery of great theoretical significance although not apparently of great practical importance. The discovery of the growth-promoting properties of p-aminobenzoic acid followed the observation that it counteracted the antibacterial action of sulphanilamide, to which it is structurally analogous. This led to a theory that bacterial growth may be inhibited by the addition to the medium of a substance which antagonised the growth-promoting action of an essential metabolite.

Now every theory, to be of any value, should enable predictions to be made, and the fulfilment of these predictions greatly strengthens the theory from which they are derived. If, then, sulphanilamide could reverse the growth-promoting effect of p-aminobenzoic acid, would substances chemically related to other members of the bios or vitamin B complex inhibit bacterial growth by competing with these vitamins in the metabolic processes going on within the bacterial cell ? This question was asked—and answered in the affirmative—by groups of workers in Great Britain, the U.S.A. and Germany. Pyridine-β-sulphonic acid was shown to antagonise the effects of nicotinic acid, isoriboflavine those of riboflavine, desoxypyridoxine those of pyridoxine, pantoyltaurine and many other related substances those of pantothenic acid, and oxybiotin those of biotin. The use of such antagonists has thrown a great deal of light on the function of the vitamin B complex.

Another important phenomenon that has recently come to light as the result of work with sulphanilamide and related sulphonamides is that of intestinal synthesis. When certain sulphonamides, not readily absorbed from the gut, were given to experimental animals, symptoms of vitamin B complex deficiency developed, and investigation showed that the sulphonamide had checked the growth of the intestinal flora which normally synthesised certain members of the vitamin B complex. Many animals are able to utilise the vitamins thus formed and are therefore independent of external sources of supply. The phenomenon undoubtedly occurs in man, but normally only in respect of certain vitamins, and it is not known what the conditions are for stimulating the growth of the appropriate organisms in man and whether the vitamins so formed are invariably available to the host or are only available under special circumstances.

The names of those whose labours have contributed to the accumulation of the vast amount of knowledge we now possess about these substances, those who, so to speak, have " piled brick on brick on the edifice ", is legion. In some instances, a particular individual may have contributed only one little item of knowledge and then transferred his energies to other spheres. In other instances, the contribution of one individual may have extended over a period of years, indeed over a whole life-time. There are others again who have built up large schools of vitamin research and have carried out elaborate programmes of investigation as leaders of teams of specialists. There are also industrial organisations, who have used their research laboratories and development departments for the improvement of manufacturing processes and testing techniques, and who have often made discoveries of outstanding importance.

Of those who have thus contributed to the advance of vitamin science, only a few can be referred to specifically. Mention has already been made of Dr. C. Eijkman, the pioneer in the field, who showed that beriberi was a deficiency disease caused by the absence from the diet of the factor we now call aneurine or thiamine ; in 1930, a few months before his death, Eijkman was awarded the Nobel prize in recognition of his discoveries. He shared it with another pioneer of vitamin science, Sir Frederick Gowland Hopkins, one-time President of the Royal Society, who showed that the growth rate of rats maintained on a purified diet rapidly declined until the animals died, and that the addition of milk to the diet, in amounts that supplied only negligible amounts of protein and carbohydrate, checked the fall in growth and enabled the animals to live and thrive. Hopkins' classical experiments have been repeated, with appropriate modifications, by all subsequent investigators who have studied growth factors for higher animals. Another name closely associated with vitamin science is that of Casimir Funk, a Pole working at the Lister Institute, London, who in 1912 coined the word " vitamine " to describe the then

6

mysterious factors responsible for curing deficiency diseases. He it was who brought Eijkman's work to the notice of a larger scientific public and who predicted the existence of other deficiency diseases. This prediction was fulfilled within a few years, when Dr. J. Goldberger proved, contrary to all previous opinion, that pellagra was a deficiency disease. Goldberger was appointed in 1913 by the U.S. Bureau of Public Health to investigate the outbreak of pellagra in the Southern States of the U.S.A. He was struck by the fact that nurses and doctors attending pellagra patients in an asylum never contracted the disease, and came to the conclusion that it was due to the particular diet on which the patients, invariably poor, had to maintain themselves. He proved his point, first, by adding milk and eggs to an orphanage diet and thereby eliminating pellagra from that particular institution and, secondly, by giving them diets consisting solely of deficient foods ; this diet was in fact similar to that eaten regularly by thousands of poor farmers in the areas in which pellagra was endemic.

The years immediately following the work of these pioneers saw few developments of scientific importance, although the empirical knowledge gained as the result of their labours was used in various parts of the world in the prevention and cure of both beriberi and pellagra. In 1926, however, events began to move more rapidly, and in that year pure crystalline aneurine was isolated. It was synthesised ten years later by Prof. R. R. Williams of Columbia University in collaboration with a group of chemists employed by Merck & Co., Rahway. A year earlier, in 1935, riboflavine had been synthesised independently by Prof. R. Kuhn of the University of Heidelberg and Prof. P. Karrer of the University of Zurich, and in 1937 nicotinic acid, known since 1867 as a chemical of no particular importance, was recognised as the pellagra-preventive factor. Pyridoxine was characterised as a vitamin in 1938 and in the following year was synthesised independently by Prof. R. Kuhn and the Merck workers who had already achieved fame in connection with the synthesis of aneurine, and who were to enhance their reputation still further by the successful synthesis of other vitamins. Shortly afterwards, they collaborated with Prof. R. J. Williams, then of Oregon State College and later of the University of Texas and brother of Prof. R. R. Williams, in studying the constitution of pantothenic acid, which they synthesised in 1940. This was followed by an investigation into the structure of biotin in collaboration with Prof. V. du Vigneaud of Cornell University ; they synthesised biotin in 1943. Another name associated with biotin is that of Prof. F. Kögl of the University of Utrecht, who isolated it from egg-yolk in 1936, studied its constitution under particularly difficult conditions during the

German occupation of Holland and suggested a formula which he subsequently admitted, in the light of du Vigneaud's results, to be erroneous. Actually, Kögl's biotin is probably different from, although closely related to, du Vigneaud's, and what is believed to be the correct formula for egg-yolk biotin was suggested by Kögl in 1944. Folic acid was isolated in 1941 from spinach leaves by Prof. R. J. Williams, of pantothenic acid fame, and Dr. E. E. Snell, who had already carried out a large amount of microbiological work in connection with members of the vitamin B complex. Similar substances were subsequently isolated from yeast and liver, and synthesised in 1946 by research chemists employed by the Lederle Labs. Inc., Pearl River, New York, and the American Cyanamid Co., Bound Brook, New Jersey. The latest member of the vitamin B complex to be discovered, vitamin B_{12}, was obtained in crystalline form in 1948 by the Merck group already referred to and by Dr. E. Lester Smith of Glaxo Laboratories Ltd., Greenford.

This is the story in briefest outline of the vitamin B complex. In the chapters that follow, details are given of the isolation, chemistry, biological properties and functions of each vitamin in turn, and in a final chapter an attempt is made to show the close biological relationship that exists between these substances by indicating the different stages of metabolism in which each participates.

Chapter II

ANEURINE (THIAMINE)

1. HISTORICAL

Beriberi

The existence in foodstuffs of substances essential for the proper functioning of the animal organism was first recognised by C. Eijkman and H. Grijns, two Dutch medical officers working in the Dutch East Indies. They suggested that beriberi was not caused by a toxic principle or by infection, as had been supposed, but by a nutritional deficiency.

Discovery of the Vitamins

In 1911, C. Funk[1] published a series of papers describing the isolation from rice polishings of a substance capable of curing beri-beri. In the following year he wrote:[2] " The deficient substances, which are of the nature of organic bases, we will call ' vitamines ', and we will speak of a beriberi or scurvy vitamine, which means a substance preventing the special disease." The word " vitamine " remained in use until 1920, by which time it had become clear that only a few of these substances were organic bases. It was then proposed[3] that the name should be changed to " vitamin " with the implication that a vitamin is " a neutral substance of undefined composition ".

Although several of the vitamins contain nitrogen atoms and are basic, only one or two contain the amino group, NH_2, characteristic of a primary amine. One of these is vitamin B_1, now known in this country as aneurine hydrochloride and in America as thiamine hydrochloride. At first it was called vitamin B, and it is the absence of this substance that is responsible for beriberi, which, as already mentioned above, was the first deficiency disease to be recognised as such. The condition is due to the use of polished rice as a major article of diet, the bulk of the vitamin being contained in the outer layers of the grain which are removed in the processing. The resulting rice polishings have a marked curative effect on the course of the disease and an aqueous extract possesses similar activity.

Complex Nature of Vitamin B

That vitamin B was not a single substance was first shown in 1920 by A. D. Emmett and G. O. Luros,[4] who found that the growth-promoting water-soluble vitamin B and the antineuritic vitamin B were not equally susceptible to heat, the latter being more labile than the former. Six years later, Goldberger *et al.*[5] stated that " investigators using the rat-growth test must hereafter recognise—and take due account of at least two essentials "—the antineuritic vitamin B and the pellagra-preventive factor. In the following year the British Accessory Food Factors Committee recommended the adoption of vitamin B_1 and vitamin B_2 as the names of these two factors, whilst the American Society of Biological Chemists, on the other hand, adopted a different nomenclature, reserving the name vitamin B for the antineuritic factor and assigning the name vitamin G to the anti-pellagra factor. When other water-soluble factors came to be isolated from liver and yeast, however, the British system was found more flexible as it could be extended to cover these new factors, which were designated vitamin B_3, vitamin B_4, etc. The name aneurin was proposed in 1935 by B. C. P. Jansen,[6] who first isolated the vitamin in the pure state. Though generally accepted in Europe this name was rejected in the U.S.A. on the ground of " therapeutic implication " and the name thiamine was adopted instead. Aneurine is now accepted as the official name in the British Pharmacopoeia, the addition of the " e " being an interesting reversal of the change from " vitamine " to " vitamin ".

References to Section 1

1. C. Funk, *J. Physiol.*, 1911, **43**, 395.
2. C. Funk, *J. State Med.*, 1912, **20**, 341.
3. J. C. Drummond, *Biochem. J.*, 1920, **14**, 660.
4. A. D. Emmett and G. O. Luros, *J. Biol. Chem.*, 1920, **43**, 265.
5. J. Goldberger, G. A. Wheeler, R. D. Lillie and L. M. Rogers, *U.S. Publ. Health Rep.*, 1926, **41**, 297.
6. B. C. P. Jansen, *Nature*, 1935, **135**, 267.

2. ISOLATION OF ANEURINE

The first attempt to concentrate the antineuritic factor was made in 1912 by Suzuki *et al.*[1] who used an aqueous extract of rice polishings as the raw material ; they tested their concentrates, which they termed " oryzanin ", on pigeons maintained on a vitamin B-free diet, noting the amount required to prevent the head retraction (opisthotonus) characteristic of these birds in the polyneuritic condition. In the same year, Edie *et al.*[2] prepared a concentrate from yeast ('' torulin ''), also using the pigeon as test animal, whilst C. Funk [3] prepared concentrates from both rice-polishings and yeast. Several other workers investigated the problem during the next twelve years or so, but no further advance was made until 1926 when B. C. P. Jansen and W. F. Donath,[4] working in Java, effected a much greater concentration than earlier workers by treatment with acid clay ; this adsorbed the vitamin from an aqueous solution of pH 4·5, and it was then recovered by elution with baryta. To detect activity, they used rice-birds (*Munia maja*) which, like pigeons, readily develop polyneuritis when maintained on a vitamin B-free diet. By a series of operations terminating in the formation of a platinic chloride complex, Jansen and Donath eventually obtained the vitamin in the form of a crystalline hydrochloride, m.p. 250° C.

The vitamin was also isolated from yeast by H. W. Kinnersley and R. A. Peters,[5] from wheat germ by B. C. Guha and J. C. Drummond,[6] and from rice polishings by an improved method by R. R. Williams *et al.*[7] This led to the production of sufficient aneurine to enable its constitution to be worked out.

The details of the methods of isolation used by different workers vary greatly, a method applicable to one source being not necessarily applicable to a different source. The method of Williams *et al.*, in which rice polishings were used as the starting material, was to prepare an aqueous extract, adsorb the vitamin on to fullers' earth (Cerecedo *et al.*[8] recommend synthetic zeolites), elute with aqueous pyridine or quinine, the latter giving a much better recovery, and then treat the aqueous solution with benzoyl chloride in dilute alkali to benzoylate impurities. These were removed by chloroform extraction, and the vitamin was precipitated with silver nitrate, barium hydroxide and phosphotungstic acid. Finally the aneurine was recrystallised from acidified organic solvents, *e.g.* phenol and butanol or alcoholic hydrochloric acid. From one ton of rice polishings, Williams *et al.* obtained 5 to 10 g. of aneurine hydrochloride.

D. S. Herr [9] has described a method of isolating aneurine and of separating it from riboflavine by means of synthetic ion exchange resins. Amberlite IR-100 in the acid form adsorbed 168 mg. of aneurine per g. of dry resin and, provided the rate of flow through the column of resin was not too high, recovery was complete ; the adsorbed aneurine was completely eluted by 18 % or, better, 37 % hydrochloric acid. It appears that elution was not due to true chemical exchange, as a considerable excess of hydrochloric acid was necessary. This is supported by the observation that when aneurine was adsorbed on the basic form of Amberlite IR-100, it was recovered to the extent of only 30 % by hot sodium chloride solution.

Riboflavine was adsorbed much less strongly than aneurine by Amberlite IR-100 and was readily eluted by a more dilute acid; the two vitamins were thus readily separated by adjusting the time of contact with the resin.

References to Section 2

1. U. Suzuki, T. Shamimura and S. Okade, *Biochem. Z.*, 1912, **43**, 89.
2. E. S. Edie, W. H. Evans, B. Moore, G. C. E. Simpson and A. Webster, *Biochem. J.*, 1912, **6**, 234.
3. C. Funk, *J. Physiol.*, 1913, **46**, 487; *Brit. Med. J.*, 1913, **1**, 814.
4. B. C. P. Jansen and W. F. Donath, *Proc. K. Akad. Wetensch. Amsterdam*, 1926, **29**, 1390.
5. H. W. Kinnersley and R. A. Peters, *Biochem. J.*, 1928, **22**, 419; 1933, **27**, 225, 232.
6. B. C. Guha and J. C. Drummond, *ibid.*, 1929, **23**, 880.
7. R. R. Williams, R. E. Waterman and J. C. Keresztesy, *J. Amer. Chem. Soc.*, 1934, **56**, 1187.
8. L. R. Cerecedo and D. J. Hennessy, *ibid.*, 1937, **59**, 1617; L. R. Cerecedo and F. J. Kaszuba, *ibid.*, 1619; L. R. Cerecedo and J. J. Thornton, *ibid.*, 1621.
9. D. S. Herr, *Ind. Eng. Chem.*, 1945, **37**, 631.

3. CHEMICAL CONSTITUTION OF ANEURINE

The chemical nature of vitamin B_1 was elucidated by a brilliant series of investigations carried out by R. R. Williams and his colleagues; these have been described in a monograph by Prof. Williams.[1] The key to the structure of vitamin B_1 was found in the action of neutral sodium sulphite solution; at room temperature[2] this cleaved the molecule into two halves according to the equation:

$$C_{12}H_{18}N_4SOCl_2 + Na_2SO_3 \rightarrow C_6H_9N_3SO_3 + C_6H_9NSO + 2NaCl.$$

The substance, $C_6H_9N_3SO_3$, on hydrolysis with acid[3] yielded ammonia and another substance, $C_6H_8N_2SO_4$. Both these substances on treatment with water at 200° C. yielded sulphuric acid and, with alkali, sulphurous acid, proving the presence of a sulphonic acid group in both. The two compounds gave ultra-violet absorption spectra characteristic of a pyrimidine nucleus, and this was confirmed by the conversion[4] of the compound, $C_6H_9N_3SO_3$, into 4-amino-2 : 5-dimethylpyrimidine:

$$
\begin{array}{c}
\text{N}=\text{C}-\text{NH}_2 \\
| \quad | \\
\text{CH}_3-\text{C} \quad \text{C}-\text{CH}_3 \\
\| \quad \| \\
\text{N}-\text{CH}
\end{array}
$$

by the action of sodium in liquid ammonia. The constitution of the pyrimidine was established by synthesis.[5] By a similar synthesis,[6] 5-ethoxymethyl-4-hydroxy-2-methyl-pyrimidine was prepared and this, on treatment with sodium sulphite, yielded 4-hydroxy-2-methyl-pyrimidyl-5-methane-sulphonic acid, identical with the compound, $C_6H_8N_2SO_4$. The primary cleavage product, $C_6H_9N_3SO_3$,was therefore presumed to be 4-amino-2-methyl-pyrimidyl-5-methane-sulphonic acid :

$$
\begin{array}{c}
\text{N}\!=\!\text{C}\!-\!\text{NH}_2 \\
| \quad | \\
\text{CH}_3\!-\!\text{C} \quad \text{C}\!-\!\text{CH}_2\!-\!\text{SO}_3\text{H} \\
\| \quad \| \\
\text{N}\!-\!\text{CH}
\end{array}
$$

The other primary cleavage product, C_6H_9NSO, was oxidised with nitric acid,[7] giving 4-methyl-thiazole-5-carboxylic acid, identical with a compound prepared in 1890 by M. Wöhmann.[8] This substance had also been obtained by A. Windaus and his colleagues [9] by the oxidation of aneurine with nitric acid, but they failed to recognise the presence of the thiazole nucleus.

Since the compound, C_6H_9NSO, contained an alcoholic hydroxyl group that could be readily replaced by chlorine,[7] it was assumed to be 5-β-hydroxyethyl-4-methyl-thiazole and the correctness of this assumption was established by H. T. Clarke and S. Gurin,[10] who synthesised it by a method described below.

The first formula for aneurine, suggested by Williams before the constitution of the pyrimidine half was known, was

$$
\begin{array}{c}
\text{N}\!=\!\text{C}\!-\!\text{NH}_2 \qquad\qquad \text{CH}_3 \\
| \quad | \qquad\qquad\qquad |\\
\text{CH} \ \text{C}\!-\!\!-\!\!-\!\!-\!\!-\!\!-\!\text{N}\!\!\stackrel{\displaystyle /\text{C}\!=\!\text{C}\!-\!\text{CH}_2\!-\!\text{CH}_2\text{OH}}{\underset{\text{Cl} \ \ \searrow\!\text{CH}\!-\!\text{S}}{}} \\
\| \quad \| \\
\text{N}\!-\!\text{C}\!-\!\text{C}_2\text{H}_5 \qquad\qquad\qquad \text{HCl}
\end{array}
$$

This was subsequently revised but, in the meantime, A. Windaus and his colleagues [11] put forward a very similar formula :

$$
\begin{array}{c}
\text{N}\!=\!\text{C}\!-\!\text{NH}_2 \qquad\qquad \text{CH}_3 \\
| \quad | \qquad\qquad\qquad | \\
\text{CH}_3\!-\!\text{C} \ \text{C}\!-\!\!-\!\!-\!\!-\!\!-\!\!-\!\text{N}\!\!\stackrel{\displaystyle /\text{C}\!=\!\text{C}\!-\!\text{CH}_2\!-\!\text{CH}_2\text{OH}}{\underset{\text{Cl} \ \ \searrow\!\text{CH}\!-\!\text{S}}{}} \\
\| \quad \| \\
\text{N}\!-\!\text{C}\!-\!\text{CH}_3 \qquad\qquad\qquad \text{HCl}
\end{array}
$$

This formula was also erroneous, though in an I.G. patent [12] protecting the preparation of a substance of this structure it is claimed to have vitamin B_1 activity !

The formula now known to be correct :

$$
\begin{array}{c}
\text{N}\!=\!\text{C}\!-\!\text{NH}_2 \\
| \quad | \\
\text{CH}_3\!-\!\text{C} \quad \text{C}\!-\!\text{CH}_2 \\
\| \quad \| \\
\text{N}\!-\!\text{CH}
\end{array}
\qquad
\begin{array}{c}
\text{CH}_3 \\
\text{C}\!=\!\text{C}\!-\!\text{CH}_2\!-\!\text{CH}_2\text{OH} \\
\text{N} \quad | \\
\quad \text{CH}\!-\!\text{S} \\
\text{Cl} \qquad\qquad\qquad \text{HCl}
\end{array}
$$

and subsequently proposed by R. R. Williams,[13] takes into account the revised formula for the pyrimidine half. The point of attachment to the pyrimidine ring was settled by the position of the sulphonic group in the sulphite cleavage product, whilst the point of attachment to the thiazole ring was established by titration experiments.

When aneurine chloride was titrated with alkali,[14] one mole was taken up in a normal manner and therefore the pH failed to increase, except transitorily, almost immediately recovering its former value. This continued until a total of three moles of alkali had been added when a steady rise in pH occurred. This curious and unexpected behaviour was interpreted to indicate an intramolecular rearrangement. It was found [15] that 5-β-hydroxyethyl-4-methyl-thiazole methiodide behaved similarly on titration, whence it was concluded that aneurine chloride was also a quaternary ammonium salt. The explanation of the titration results is that the thiazole ring is opened according to the following series of changes :

$$
\begin{array}{c}
\text{CH}_2\!-\!\text{P} \\
| \\
\text{Cl . N}\!-\!\!-\!\text{C}\!- \\
\| \quad \| \\
\text{CH} \quad \text{C}\!- \\
\diagdown \;\; \diagup \\
\text{S}
\end{array}
\;\longrightarrow\;
\begin{array}{c}
\text{CH}_2\!-\!\text{P} \\
| \\
\text{HO . N}\!-\!\!-\!\text{C}\!- \\
\| \quad \| \\
\text{CH} \quad \text{C}\!- \\
\diagdown \;\; \diagup \\
\text{S}
\end{array}
\;\longrightarrow\;
\begin{array}{c}
\text{CH}_2\!-\!\text{P} \\
| \\
\text{N}\!-\!\!-\!\text{C}\!- \\
| \quad \| \\
\text{HO . CH} \quad \text{C}\!- \\
\diagdown \;\; \diagup \\
\text{S}
\end{array}
\;\longrightarrow\;
\begin{array}{c}
\text{CH}_2\!-\!\text{P} \\
| \\
\text{N}\!-\!\!-\!\text{C}\!- \\
| \quad \| \\
\text{CHO} \quad \text{C}\!- \\
| \\
\text{SH}
\end{array}
$$

(where P = the pyrimidine ring). The third molecule of sodium hydroxide is required to neutralise the mercapto group.

References to Section 3

1. R. R. Williams, " Vitamin B_1 and its use in Medicine," Macmillan, 1938.
2. R. R. Williams, *J. Amer. Chem. Soc.*, 1935, **57,** 229 ; R. R. Williams, R. E. Waterman, J. C. Keresztesy and E. R. Buchman, *ibid.*, 536.
3. R. R. Williams, E. R. Buchman and A. E. Ruehle, *ibid.*, 1093.
4. R. R. Williams, *ibid.*, 1936, **58,** 1063 ; J. K. Cline, R. R. Williams, A. E. Ruehle and R. E. Waterman, *ibid.*, 1937, **59,** 530.
5. R. R. Williams, A. E. Ruehle and J. Finkelstein, *ibid.*, 526.

6. J. K. Cline, R. R. Williams and J. Finkelstein, *ibid.*, 1052.
7. E. R. Buchman, R. R. Williams and J. C. Keresztesy, *J. Amer. Chem. Soc.*, 1935, **57**, 1849.
8. M. Wöhmann, *Annalen*, 1890, **259**, 299.
9. A. Windaus, R. Tschesche and R. Grewe, *Z. physiol. Chem.*, 1934, **228**, 27.
10. H. T. Clarke and S. Gurin, *J. Amer. Chem. Soc.*, 1935, **57**, 1876.
11. A. Windaus, R. Tschesche and R. Grewe, *Z. physiol. Chem.*, 1935, **237**, 98.
12. I.G., B.P. 456735.
13. R. R. Williams, *J. Amer. Chem. Soc.*, 1936, **58**, 1063.
14. R. R. Williams and A. E. Ruehle, *ibid.*, 1935, **57**, 1856.
15. E. R. Buchman, R. R. Williams and J. C. Keresztesy, *ibid.*, 1849.

4. SYNTHESIS OF ANEURINE

The complete synthesis of aneurine was first announced by R. R. Williams and his co-workers in America, but important contributions were made by A. R. Todd and his collaborators in England, by A. Windaus and his school in Germany, and by K. Makino and T. Imai in Japan. The subject is one of some complexity and papers of fundamental importance appeared within a few weeks or even days of one another, so that it is well-nigh impossible to give a strictly chronological account of the course of events.

The matter is further complicated by the policy of the German workers of withholding publication until patent protection had been adequately effected. Thus H. Hörlein [1] states " the priority of the synthesis of the product undoubtedly rests with Andersag and Westphal ". This may very well be true, for the I.G. began to file patents as early as 1935. Since, however, the paper by H. Andersag and K. Westphal [2] was not published until 1937, over a year after Williams' publication, this belated claim to priority seems rather like an attempt to secure the academic cake as well as the economic half-penny !

It will simplify matters if the method of synthesis adopted by each group of workers is discussed in turn.

American Method

R. R. Williams and J. K. Cline [3] condensed ethyl α-formyl-β-ethoxy-propionate with acetamidine, and converted the resulting 5-ethoxymethyl-4-hydroxy-2-methyl-pyrimidine into 4-amino-5-bromomethyl-2-methyl-pyrimidine by the following series of reactions :

$$C_2H_5O.CH_2.CH_2.COOC_2H_5 \xrightarrow{\text{H.COOC}_2\text{H}_5} C_2H_5O.CH_2.\underset{\underset{CHO}{|}}{CH}.COOC_2H_5 \xrightarrow{\text{NH}_2.\text{C(CH}_3):\text{NH}}$$

$$CH_3.\underset{\overset{\|}{N}}{\underset{}{C}}\quad\underset{\overset{\|}{—CH}}{\underset{}{C}}.CH_2.OC_2H_5 \xrightarrow{\text{POCl}_3} CH_3.\underset{\overset{\|}{N}}{\underset{}{C}}\quad\underset{\overset{\|}{—CH}}{\underset{}{C}}.CH_2.OC_2H_5 \xrightarrow{\text{alc. NH}_3}$$

(N=C.OH ... N—CH) → (N=C.Cl ... N—CH)

$$CH_3.\underset{\overset{\|}{N}}{\underset{}{C}}\quad\underset{\overset{\|}{—CH}}{\underset{}{C}}.CH_2.OC_2H_5 \xrightarrow{\text{HBr}} CH_3.\underset{\overset{\|}{N}}{\underset{}{C}}\quad\underset{\overset{\|}{—CH}}{\underset{}{C}}.CH_2Br$$

(N=C.NH₂ ... N—CH) → (N=C.NH₂ ... N—CH)

The final product, in the form of its hydrobromide, was reacted with 5-β-hydroxyethyl-4-methyl-thiazole, obtained by E. R. Buchman [4] from α-aceto-γ-butyrolactone by the following series of reactions :

$$CH_3.CO.CH_2.COOC_2H_5 \xrightarrow{\overset{CH_2—CH_2}{\diagdown\underset{O}{}\diagup}} CH_3.CO.\underset{\underset{CO——O}{|\qquad|}}{CH.CH_2.CH_2} \xrightarrow{\text{SO}_2\text{Cl}_2}$$

$$CH_3.CO.\underset{\underset{CO——O}{|\qquad|}}{CCl.CH_2.CH_2} \xrightarrow{\text{dil. HCl}} CH_3.CO.CHCl.CH_2.CH_2OH$$

Aneurine bromide hydrobromide was formed and this was converted into the chloride hydrochloride by shaking with silver chloride. Attempts to prepare the pyrimidine half by other methods [5] such as by Curtius, Hoffman or Loessen degradations of the appropriate derivatives of 4-hydroxy-2-methyl-pyrimidine-5-acetic acid (obtained from hydroxymethyl malonic ester) were not very successful.

The method of Williams et al. has been adopted for the large scale manufacture of vitamin B_1 by Merck & Co., Rahway, and a large number of patents have been filed in this country, in the U.S.A. and elsewhere to protect this process. The first group [6] describes the preparation of halogenated acetopropyl alcohols, esters and similar derivatives, which are required in the synthesis of the thiazole half, by halogenation of acetopropyl alcohol or the appropriate derivative or by hydrolysis and decarboxylation of halogenated α-aceto-γ-butyrolactone. The second group,[7] comprising a single patent, protects the condensation of halogenated acetopropyl alcohol with thioformamide to give 4-alkyl-5-hydroxyalkyl thiazoles. The third group [8] covers the condensation of acetamidine with α-formyl-β-ethoxypropionic ester to give 5-ethoxymethyl-4-hydroxy-2-methyl-pyrimidine, and the preparation from this compound of the corresponding 4-halogeno-derivatives and thence the 4-amino-compound. The preparation of the 2-methyl-5-halogenomethyl-4-amino-pyrimidine is also described.

The last group [9] covers the formation of aneurine by condensation of 5-β-hydroxyethyl-4-methyl-thiazole with 4-amino-5-bromomethyl-2-methyl-pyrimidine or with 5-alkyloxymethyl-2-methyl-4-amino-pyrimidine, or with (4-amino-2-methyl-pyrimidyl-5-)-bromoacetic acid.

5-β-Hydroxyethyl-4-methylthiazole has also been prepared by reducing ethyl 4-methylthiazole-5-acetate with lithium aluminium hydride, the ester being prepared by the reaction of ethyl α-bromo-laevulinate with thioformamide. [9a]

British Method

The method of synthesis discovered by Todd *et al.* differs in one important respect from that of Williams : the thiazole ring is formed as the last stage of the synthesis, being produced by the action of 3-aceto-3-chloro-propyl alcohol on the appropriate thioformamido-methyl-pyrimidine. The preparation of such thioformamido compounds was first described by Todd *et al.*,[10] who showed that 5-amino-pyrimidine yielded the corresponding thioformyl derivative on treatment with a solution of potassium dithioformate ; the reaction does not occur with 2-, 4- or 6-amino-pyrimidine. By reacting 4-amino-6-ethyl-5-thioformamido-pyrimidine with 3-aceto-3-chloro-propyl alcohol, an isomer of aneurine was obtained, identical with the compound represented by Williams' first formula (page 13). The fact that it was biologically inactive helped towards the rejection of this formula. Potassium dithioformate was subsequently used by A. R. Todd and F. Bergel [11] to prepare aneurine itself, the complete series of reactions being as follows :

$$
\begin{array}{ccccc}
\mathrm{NH_2} & \mathrm{C_2H_5O.OC} & \mathrm{N{=}C.OH} & \mathrm{N{=}C.Cl} \\
| & | & |\ \| & |\ | \\
\mathrm{CH_3.C} + & \cdot\ \mathrm{C.CN} \longrightarrow \mathrm{CH_3.C}\ \ \mathrm{C.CN} \longrightarrow \mathrm{CH_3.C}\ \ \mathrm{C.CN} \longrightarrow \\
\| & \| & \|\ \| & \|\ \| \\
\mathrm{NH} & \mathrm{C_2H_5{-}CH} & \mathrm{N{-}CH} & \mathrm{N{-}CH}
\end{array}
$$

$$
\begin{array}{ccc}
\mathrm{N{=}C.NH_2} & \mathrm{N{=}C.NH_2} & \mathrm{N{=}C.NH_2} \\
|\ | & |\ | & |\ | \\
\mathrm{CH_3.C}\ \ \mathrm{C.CN} \longrightarrow \mathrm{CH_3.C}\ \ \mathrm{C.CH_2.NH_2} \longrightarrow \mathrm{CH_3.C}\ \ \mathrm{C.CH_2.NH.CSH} \\
\|\ \| & \|\ \| & \|\ \| \\
\mathrm{N{-}CH} & \mathrm{N{-}CH} & \mathrm{N{-}CH}
\end{array}
$$

$\longrightarrow$ Aneurine

In an alternative process, acetamidine was coupled, not with ethoxymethylene-cyanacetic ester, but with ethoxymethylene-malonic ester. This gave the 5-carboxylic ester which was converted to the corresponding amide, and thence to the nitrile.

The use of potassium dithioformate was patented by Hoffmann-La Roche,[12] who also patented a number of other reactions enabling them to synthesise aneurine by a unique process which was used for its large-scale manufacture. The requisite pyrimidine compounds were synthesised [13] from acetimino-ethyl ether hydrochloride and aminomethylene malondinitrile, the preparation of the latter being described in a later patent.[14]

$$
\begin{array}{ccc}
\underset{\displaystyle |}{OC_2H_5} & \underset{\displaystyle ||}{NH_2-CH} & \underset{\displaystyle |\ |}{N=CH} \\
CH_3.C & + \quad C.CN & \longrightarrow \quad CH_3.C \quad C.CN \\
\underset{\displaystyle NH}{||} & \underset{\displaystyle CN}{|} & \underset{\displaystyle N-C.NH_2}{||\ ||}
\end{array}
$$

The product was reduced, as in Todd's process, to the aminomethyl compound, which was then converted [12] by treatment with potassium dithioformate into the thioformamidomethyl derivative. This was treated,[15] not with 3-aceto-3-halogenopropyl alcohols or their esters, but with 3-chloro-2-ethoxy-2-methyl-tetrahydrofurane to yield aneurine. The relation between the two types of compound is evident from the following formulae :

$$
\begin{array}{cc}
Cl.CH-CH_2 & Cl.CH-CH_2 \\
CH_3-C \quad CH_2 & CH_3.CO \quad CH_2 \\
C_2H_5O \quad O & OH
\end{array}
$$

The preparation of this furane derivative, due to Klingenfuss, was covered in another patent.[16] A variant of this process, due to Chinoin,[16a] comprises the treatment of 2 : 3-dihalogeno-2-methyl-tetrahydrofurane with an agent capable of removing hydrogen chloride and then condensing the product with the thioformamidomethyl compound. The constitution of halogenated acetopropyl alcohols has been the subject of extensive investigation, and J. R. Stevens and G. A. Stein[17] showed that halogenated acetopropyl alcohols, more especially the bromo-derivative, exist in the form of a dimeride of the formula :

$$
\begin{array}{l}
CH_2-CH.Cl \\
| \qquad | \quad CH_3 \\
CH_2 \quad C< \\
\quad O \qquad O.CH_2.CH_2.CHCl.CO.CH_3
\end{array}
$$

It is thus the acetochloropropyl ether of 3-chloro-1-hydroxy-1-methyl-tetrahydrofurane. The preparation of this compound has been patented.[18]

Roche Products patented the preparation of keto-alcohol acetates such as 3-aceto-propyl acetate, by heating lactones, such as α-aceto-γ-butyrolacetone, with glacial acetic acid in presence of anhydrous sodium acetate [19]

$$CH_3.CO.CH.CH_2.CH_2 \overset{CH_3.COOH}{\longrightarrow} CH_3.CO.CH_2.CH_2.CH_2.O.OC.CH_3$$

though the conversion can be effected by means of sulphuric or phosphoric acid.[20] The latter procedure can also be used for the formation of the 3-chloro- or 3-bromo-acetates. Roche Products also protected the bromination of 3-acetopropyl acetate by the action of sulphuryl chloride in presence of an alkali metal bromide at 60° C., with silica as catalyst,[21] and also [22] by reacting 3-acetopropyl alcohol or its acetate with (a) a dibromide of a salt of pyridine or quinoline ; (b) bromine and a salt of pyridine or quinoline ; and (c) chlorine, a salt of pyridine or quinoline and an alkali metal bromide. The crude products obtained from these reactions can be used for the preparation of aneurine directly by condensation with 4-amino-2-methyl-5-thio-formamidomethyl-pyrimidine.[23]

The preparation of 5-alkoxymethyl-4-amino-2-methyl-pyrimidines by reacting 4-amino-5-aminomethyl-2-methyl-pyrimidine with an alkyl nitrite has also been patented.[24]

German Method

The methods of synthesis devised by the German workers are described mainly in patent specifications. The first publication, however, was a paper by R. Grewe [25] describing the condensation of acetamidine with ethoxymethylene-malondinitrile to give 4-amino-5-cyano-2-methyl-pyrimidine, which on hydrogenation with a palladium-charcoal catalyst gave the corresponding 5-aminomethyl compound.

$$CH_3.\underset{NH}{\overset{NH_2}{C}} + \underset{C_2H_5O.CH}{\overset{CN}{C.CN}} \rightarrow CH_3.\underset{N-CH}{\overset{N=C.NH_2}{C}}\overset{}{C.CN} \rightarrow CH_3.\underset{N-CH}{\overset{N=C.NH_2}{C}}\overset{}{C.CH_2NH_2}$$

He stated that Prof. Hörlein had informed him that Andersag and Westphal had already synthesised the vitamin in the laboratories of the I.G.Farbenindustrie, and that as a result he had decided to abandon his own investigations. A publication by H. Andersag and K. Westphal [26] appeared in 1937; in this paper they described the synthesis of the pyrimidine half from acetamidine and formyl-succinic ester as follows :

$$\begin{matrix} & NH_2 & CHO \\ CH_3.\,C & + & CH.CH_2.COOC_2H_5 & \longrightarrow \\ & NH & COOC_2H_5 \end{matrix}$$

$$\begin{matrix} & N{=}CH \\ CH_3.\,C & C.CH_2.COOC_2H_5 & \longrightarrow \\ & N{-}C.OH \end{matrix}$$

$$\begin{matrix} & N{=}CH \\ CH_3.\,C & C.CH_2.COOC_2H_5 & \longrightarrow \\ & N{-}C.Cl \end{matrix}$$

$$\begin{matrix} & N{=}CH \\ CH_3.\,C & C.CH_2.CONH_2 & \longrightarrow \\ & N{-}C.NH_2 \end{matrix}$$

$$\begin{matrix} & N{=}CH \\ CH_3.\,C & C.CH_2.NH_2 & \longrightarrow \\ & N{-}C.NH_2 \end{matrix}$$

$$\begin{matrix} & N{=}CH \\ CH_3.\,C & C.CH_2Br \\ & N{-}C.NH_2 \end{matrix}$$

They synthesised the thiazole half by condensing 3-bromo-3-aceto-propyl acetate with barium thiocyanate to give 2-hydroxy-5-β-hydroxyethyl-4-methyl-thiazole from which the hydroxyl group was removed by chlorination, followed by reduction. The product was condensed with 4-amino-5-bromomethyl-2-methyl-pyrimidine, giving aneurine bromide hydrobromide.

The I.G. patents based on this work cover, not only the direct coupling of the thiazole half and the pyrimidine half, but also the preparation of aneurine from the thioformamidomethyl-pyrimidine. One group of patents [27] covers the preparation of pyrimidine compounds by combining acetamidine with a great variety of formyl- and alkoxymethylene-acetic esters and acetonitriles substituted by a group convertible into the aminomethyl group.

The preparation of the thiazole compound by Andersag and Westphal's barium thiocyanate method was the subject of another patent,[28] which mentions incidentally the preparation of the necessary 3-bromo-3-acetopropyl alcohol esters. The final stage of the synthesis was described in another patent,[29] which includes both the direct coupling of the two halves and the condensation of 4-amino-2-methyl-5-thioformamidomethyl-pyrimidine with γ-aceto-γ-bromopropyl benzoate.

A variant of the I.G. method of preparing the pyrimidine half of the molecule was described by Chinoin,[30] who condensed alkoxyme-thylene-cyanoacetic esters with a base such as acetamidine to form the intermediate α-cyano-β-amidino-acrylic acid which, on heating with water or acidulated water, yielded the amino-pyrimidine :

$$\begin{array}{ccc}
\overset{\text{NH}}{\underset{\text{NH}_2}{\text{CH}_3 . \overset{\|}{\underset{|}{\text{C}}}}} + \overset{\text{CN}}{\underset{\text{CHOC}_2\text{H}_5}{\overset{|}{\underset{\|}{\text{C . COOC}_2\text{H}_5}}}} & \longrightarrow & \overset{\text{NH} \quad \text{CN}}{\underset{\text{NH}\!-\!\text{CH}}{\text{CH}_3 . \overset{\|}{\underset{|}{\text{C}}} \quad \overset{|}{\underset{\|}{\text{C . COOC}_2\text{H}_5}}}}
\end{array}$$

$$\longrightarrow \quad \overset{\text{N}\!-\!\text{C . NH}_2}{\underset{\text{N}\!=\!\text{CH}}{\text{CH}_3 . \overset{\|}{\underset{|}{\text{C}}} \quad \overset{\|}{\underset{|}{\text{C . COOC}_2\text{H}_5}}}}$$

Another variant is provided by the following series of reactions : [31]

$$\text{HOCH}_2 . \text{CH}_2 . \text{CN} \longrightarrow \text{C}_2\text{H}_5\text{OCH}_2 . \text{CH}_2 . \text{CN}$$

$$\xrightarrow{\text{H . COOC}_2\text{H}_5} \overset{\text{CN}}{\underset{\text{CHONa}}{\text{C}_2\text{H}_5\text{O . CH}_2 . \overset{|}{\underset{\|}{\text{C}}}}} \xrightarrow{\text{CH}_3 . \text{COCl}} \overset{\text{CN}}{\underset{\text{CHOOC . CH}_3}{\text{C}_2\text{H}_5\text{O . CH}_2 . \overset{|}{\underset{\|}{\text{C}}}}}$$

$$\xrightarrow{\text{CH}_3 . \text{C(NH}_2) : \text{NH}} \overset{\text{N}\!=\!\text{C . NH}_2}{\underset{\text{N}\!-\!\text{CH}}{\text{CH}_3 . \overset{|}{\underset{\|}{\text{C}}} \quad \overset{|}{\underset{\|}{\text{C . CH}_2\text{OC}_2\text{H}_5}}}} \longrightarrow \overset{\text{N}\!=\!\text{C . NH}_2}{\underset{\text{N}\!-\!\text{CH}}{\text{CH}_3 . \overset{|}{\underset{\|}{\text{C}}} \quad \overset{|}{\underset{\|}{\text{C . CH}_2\text{Br}}}}}$$

References to Section 4

1. H. Hörlein, *Z. physiol. Chem.*, 1938, **253**, 82.
2. E. Andersag and K. Westphal, *Ber.*, 1937, **70**, 2035.
3. R. R. Williams and J. K. Cline, *J. Amer. Chem. Soc.*, 1936, **58**, 1504.
4. E. R. Buchman, *ibid.*, 1936, **58**, 1803.
5. J. K. Cline, R. R. Williams and J. Finkelstein, *ibid.*, 1937, **59**, 1052.
6. Research Corporation, B.P. 472396, 490571 ; U.S.P. 2216574, 2223885, 2218349, 2218350.
7. Research Corporation, B.P. 472459.
8. Research Corporation, B.P. 496738, 522531.
9. Research Corporation, B.P. 496726, 507918 ; U.S.P. 2166233.
9a. A. J. Eusebi, E. V. Brown and L. R. Cerecedo, *J. Amer. Chem. Soc.*, 1949, **71**, 2931.
10. A. R. Todd, F. Bergel and Karimullah, *J. Chem. Soc.*, 1936, 1557.
11. A. R. Todd and F. Bergel, *ibid.*, 1937, 364.
12. Hoffmann-La Roche, B.P. 478993.
13. Hoffmann-La Roche, B.P. 486414.
14. Hoffmann-La Roche, B.P. 542403.
15. Hoffmann-La Roche, B.P. 500519.
16. Hoffmann-La Roche, B.P. 496801.
16a. Chinoin, B.P. 615404.

17. J. R. Stevens and G. A. Stein, *J. Amer. Chem. Soc.*, 1940, **62**, 1045.
18. Research Corporation, B.P. 547664.
19. Roche Products, B.P. 549306.
20. I.C.I., B.P. 552617.
21. Roche Products, B.P. 550197.
22. Roche Products, B.P. 554428 ; U.S.P. 2397333.
23. Roche Products, B.P. 559106.
24. Roche Products, B.P. 588806.
25. R. Grewe, *Z. physiol. Chem.*, 1936, **242**, 89.
26. H. Andersag and K. Westphal, *Ber.*, 1937, **70**, 2035.
27. I.G., B.P. 473193, 475559, 475507.
28. I.G., B.P. 456751.
29. I.G., B.P. 471416.
30. Chinoin, B.P. 538743.
31. G. V. Tschelintzev and Z. V. Benevolevskaja, *J. Gen. Chem. Russ.*, 1944, **14**, 1142.

5. PROPERTIES OF ANEURINE

Aneurine hydrochloride is 3-(4'-amino-2'-methyl-pyrimidyl-5'-methyl)-5-β-hydroxyethyl-4-methyl thiazolium chloride hydrochloride. It forms white monoclinic plates generally in rosette-like clusters. It is said to be odourless when pure, but generally has a slight smell of bran. It is readily soluble in water (*ca.* 1 g. per ml.), less soluble in methyl alcohol, 95 % ethyl alcohol (1 g. per 100 ml.) and absolute ethyl alcohol (1 g. in 315 ml.), and insoluble in ether, acetone, chloroform and benzene. It crystallises from aqueous alcohol as the hemihydrate, m.p. 248° to 250° C. with decomposition. The crystals were originally described as monoclinic,[1] but subsequently three different crystalline forms were described.[2] Form I is orthorhombic and form II monoclinic, and the latter is converted into the former in solutions up to 80° C. The reverse change occurs in the solid phase at 182° C. Form III has the same optical properties as form II, but the crystals have a different shape ; this is the least stable form.

Aneurine hydrochloride has a characteristic absorption spectrum in 0·005 N hydrochloric acid, with a maximum at 247 mμ, at which wave-length $E_{1 cm.}^{1 \%}$ is 425 to 450. It is optically inactive.

When a solution of aneurine hydrochloride is allowed to stand for two or three days with a solution of sodium bisulphite, it gives a quantitative yield of the sparingly soluble 4-amino-2-methyl-pyrimidyl-5-methane-sulphonic acid. When a solution of aneurine hydrochloride in dilute hydrochloric acid is treated with formaldehyde and diazotised aniline, a pink colour slowly develops and when the solution is shaken with isobutyl alcohol, the colour passes into the alcoholic phase. This is the basis of Peters' formaldehyde-azo test (see page 37). When a slightly alkaline solution of aneurine is treated with potassium ferricyanide solution, thiochrome is formed and the solution acquires a blue fluorescence extractable into isobutyl alcohol. This reaction also forms the basis of a method of estimating aneurine (see page 38).

Aneurine hydrochloride was included in the Third Addendum (1941) to the British Pharmacopoeia 1932, which laid down tests for identity and purity. Each gram contains 320,000 international units. The monograph was slightly modified in the Seventh Addendum (1945), and revised in the British Pharmacopoeia, 1948. The prophylactic and therapeutic doses are given as 1 to 3 mg. and 10 to 30 mg. daily respectively. Injection of aneurine and tablets of aneurine were made official in 1948.

References to Section 5

1. J. D. Bernal and D. Crowfoot, *Nature*, 1933, **131**, 911.
2. Armour Research Foundation, *Anal. Chem.*, 1948, **20**, 683.

6. STABILITY OF ANEURINE

Aneurine hydrochloride is stable in the dry state, and acid solutions can be stored for some time without loss of activity. It is unstable in neutral or alkaline solution, however, especially when exposed to air. Gastric juice, which is of course acid, has little or no effect on aneurine, but when antacids have been used, some destruction may occur.[1] Gastric juice from patients with achlorhydria did not cause destruction, but bile and duodenal pancreatic juice, which are slightly alkaline, rapidly destroyed aneurine.

According to K. T. H. Farrer[2] aneurine is completely destroyed in fifteen minutes at 100° C. at pH 9, whilst at pH 8, 7, 6, 5, 4, and 3, the proportions destroyed within one hour are 100, 67·8, 53·4, 40·0, 20·3 and 16·0 % respectively and within three hours 100, 96·4, 86·3, 67·4, 44·5, and 29·1 % respectively. No loss of activity occurred in 1 % hydrochloric acid solution in seven hours. The stability is not solely determined by the pH of the solution, however, but depends on the nature of the buffer employed, for Beadle *et al.*[3] showed that on heating a solution of aneurine of pH 5·4 for one hour at 100° C., 100 % destruction occurred with a borate buffer, 10 % with an acetate buffer, 3 % with a phosphate buffer and 57 % in an unbuffered solution. In general, the destruction increased as the pH increased. The protective action of the phosphate buffer was confirmed by R. G. Booth,[4] who showed that less vitamin was lost in phosphate buffer than in phthalate buffer, whilst Myrbäck *et al.*[5] showed that the pyrophosphate ion had a marked stabilising effect at pH 2 to 6·5 ; the optimal pH for stability on sterilisation was 6·5.

K. T. H. Farrer [6] subsequently showed that a linear relationship existed between the reaction velocity of the destruction of aneurine and the hydrogen ion concentration for any given buffer in the pH range 3 to 8. The relationship varied for each buffer, however, and the slope of the curve changed as the ionic constitution of the solution altered ; where this was accompanied by a large change in pH there was a correspondingly large change in the slope of the curve obtained by plotting pH against the logarithm of the velocity coefficient. The reaction velocity increased as the pH rose. R. G. Booth [4] also showed that copper (2 p.p.m.) catalysed the destruction of aneurine, whereas iron, aluminium, zinc and tin had no effect. According to K. T. H. Farrer,[7] however, the effect of copper is variable and, whilst destruction is more rapid in presence of copper in phosphate or phosphate-phthalate solutions, the rate of destruction may actually be decreased by the addition of copper to phosphate solutions containing tartrate, citrate or glycine. Arising out of this work, it was noticed that aneurine was destroyed more slowly in buffer solutions considerably more dilute than those used in earlier experiments, and further investigation showed [8] that in phosphate buffer the concentration of buffer salts affected the rate of destruction of aneurine below pH 6 ; the addition of citric acid eliminated this effect, whereas phthalate enhanced it. The rate of destruction was also dependent on the initial concentration of aneurine, being higher the more concentrated the solution, irrespective of the nature of the buffer solution.[8a]

Stabilisation of Aneurine Solutions

F. C. McIntire and D. V. Frost [9] claimed that aneurine solutions could be stabilised by α- or β-amino acids, and that the effect was lost when the amino group was acetylated or the amino acid was converted into a betaine, but, rather surprisingly, not when the carboxyl group was converted into an amino group or when one or two methyl groups were introduced into the amino group. Removal of the amino group farther from the carboxyl group than the β-position gave compounds that promoted the destruction of aneurine, although lysine was said to be as effective as glycine. Anthranilic acid had a protective action, *m*-aminobenzoic acid was without effect, whilst *p*-aminobenzoic acid had a destructive effect. Taurine, benzylamine, diallylamine and tri-*n*-butylamine were protective and all other amines tested proved to be destructive. Nicotinic acid and nicotinamide were also destructive.

Thiaminase

C. A. Elvehjem and his co-workers [10] appear to have been the first to correlate the effect of feeding raw fish with aneurine deficiency. They observed that the addition of 25 % of raw carp to a diet adequate for the chick caused vitamin B_1 deficiency, and that incubation of aneurine with raw carp intestines for fifteen minutes resulted in a loss of 50 to 100 % of the biological activity. C. A. Evans *et al.*[11] showed that the so-called Chastek paralysis of foxes, caused by feeding 10 % or more of fresh whole fish in the diet, and of which the characteristic symptoms are injuries to the liver and brain, could be prevented by administration of 10 mg. of aneurine per day. The paralysis was caused by feeding the skin, scales, skeleton and heads, but not the muscle tissue, of carp. The viscera were particularly rich in the responsible factor, which was shown to be a protein, probably enzymic in character. The same conclusion was reached by P. S. Owen and J. W. Ferrebee,[12] who showed that the factor was destroyed by cooking. The enzymic nature of the factor was confirmed by R. R. Sealock and R. L. Goodland,[13] who showed that its destructive effect on the vitamin was inhibited by certain inorganic substances, *e.g.* copper, zinc and iron salts, potassium cyanide, sodium fluoride and sodium sulphate, by certain organic compounds such as iodoacetic acid and cysteine, known to inhibit enzymes and, most interesting of all, by a number of thiazole and pyrimidine derivatives related to aneurine. These included the 3-*o*-aminobenzyl, 3-β-aminoethyl, 3-β-phthalimidoethyl, 3-ethyl and 3-phenyl derivatives of 4-methyl-thiazolium chloride and the 5-bromomethyl, 5-ethoxymethyl and 5-methylene sulphonic acid derivatives of 4-amino-2-methylpyrimidine. 3-*o*-Aminobenzyl-4-methyl-thiazolium chloride actually competed with aneurine for the enzyme of the Chastek principle. Other thiazole compounds of this type were the benzyl, *o*-, *m*- and *p*-nitrobenzyl and the *o*-, *m*-, and *p*-aminobenzyl quaternary ammonium salts of 2- and 4-methyl- and 2 : 4-dimethyl-5-β-hydroxyethyl thiazole.[14] 3-*m*-Amino-benzyl-4-methyl-thiazolium chloride, however, accelerated the destruction of aneurine by the enzyme ; so did *m*-nitraniline and *m*-amino-benzoic acid.[14a] This result was shown to be due to combination of the amino group with the 5-methylene group of the pyrimidine moiety formed by destruction of the aneurine, since N-(6-amino-2-methyl-pyrimidyl-5-methyl)-*m*-nitraniline was isolated from the product formed by inactivation in the presence of *m*-nitraniline.

The enzyme was shown [15] to be present in raw herring as well as in carp ; feeding either to cats resulted in the onset of vitamin B_1 deficiency with convulsions in twenty-three to forty days, followed by death. The enzyme, to which the name thiaminase has been given,

25

also appears to be present in raw clams.[16]   According to L. O. Krampitz and D. W. Woolley,[17] the enzyme consists of a heat-labile, non-dialysable portion and a heat-stable dialysable portion. It appears to effect a hydrolytic cleavage of the aneurine molecule into the thiazole and pyrimidine halves : [18]

$$
\begin{array}{c}
\underset{\substack{| \quad | \\ \text{N---CH} \quad \text{Cl}}}{\overset{\substack{\text{N==C . NH}_2 \\ | \quad |}}{\text{CH}_3\text{---C} \quad \text{C---CH}_2\text{---N}}} \quad \overset{\text{CH}_3}{\underset{\text{CH---S}}{\text{C===C . CH}_2 . \text{CH}_2\text{OH}}} \longrightarrow \underset{\substack{|| \quad || \\ \text{N---CH}}}{\overset{\substack{\text{N==C . NH}_2 \\ | \quad |}}{\text{CH}_3 . \text{C} \quad \text{C . CH}_2\text{OH}}}
\end{array}
$$

$$
+ \quad \text{N} \overset{\text{CH}_3}{\underset{\text{CH---S}}{\text{C===C . CH}_2 . \text{CH}_2\text{OH}}}
$$

$$
+ \quad \text{HCl}
$$

The presence of thiaminase in raw carp tissues and blood was confirmed by K. Bhagvat and P. Devi,[19] who also demonstrated the existence of another anti-aneurine factor in certain cereals and oil seeds. This second factor was soluble in water, but not in salt solutions, and could be extracted from cereals by means of a water-chloroform mixture. It was stated not to be enzymic in nature, but it could be separated by dialysis into a heat-labile, non-dialysable part and a heat-stable, dialysable part, both of which inactivated aneurine. The inactivated aneurine could be utilised by mosquito larvae, but not by rats or pigeons.

Thiaminase is also present in the tissues of shrimps and some mussels, but it appears to be absent from crabs and some salt-water fish.[20]

The existence of another natural product capable of producing vitamin B_1 deficiency on a vitamin B_1 rich diet was reported by Weswig et al.,[21] who showed that bracken, which causes " fern-poisoning " in cattle, also poisons rats when given to the extent of 40 % of the diet ; the animals died after twenty days with symptoms of vitamin B_1 deficiency. Animals given aneurine recovered. Bracken inactivated aneurine in vitro and so to a smaller extent did the faeces of rats fed on a diet containing bracken.[21a]

Stability of Cocarboxylase

Aneurine pyrophosphate, or cocarboxylase (see page 93) is the form in which aneurine functions as a co-enzyme. It is somewhat more stable than aneurine when the two are compared at the same

pH values,[3, 4] but is more sensitive to changes of pH.[22] Between 3·5 and 7·0, the increase in sensitivity is proportional to the logarithm of the velocity coefficient for the destruction of cocarboxylase minus the logarithm of the coefficient for the destruction of aneurine at any given pH. The rate of thermal destruction, like that of aneurine, is higher the greater the initial concentration.[8a]

References to Section 6

1. D. Melnick, W. D. Robinson and H. Field, *J. Biol. Chem.*, 1941, **138**, 49.
2. K. T. H. Farrer, *J. Proc. Austral. Chem. Inst.*, 1941, **8**, 113.
3. B. W. Beadle, D. A. Greenwood and H. R. Kraybill, *J. Biol. Chem.*, 1943, **149**, 339, 349.
4. R. G. Booth, *Biochem. J.*, 1943, **37**, 518.
5. K. Myrbäck, I. Vallin and B. Kihlberg, *Svensk Kem. Tidskr.*, 1942, **54**, 97.
6. K. T. H. Farrer, *Biochem. J.*, 1945, **39**, 128.
7. K. T. H. Farrer, *ibid.*, 1947, **41**, 162.
8. K. T. H. Farrer, *ibid.*, 167.
8a. K. T. H. Farrer, *Brit. J. Nutr.*, 1948, **2**, 242.
9. F. C. McIntire and D. V. Frost, *J. Amer. Chem. Soc.*, 1944, **66**, 1317.
10. E. H. Spitzer, A. I. Coombus, C. A. Elvehjem and W. Wisnicky, *Proc. Soc. Exp. Biol. Med.*, 1941, **48**, 376.
11. C. A. Evans, W. E. Carlson and R. G. Green, *Amer. J. Path.*, 1942, **18**, 79 ; R. G. Green, W. E. Carlson and C. A. Evans, *J. Nutrition*, 1942, **23**, 165 ; R. R. Sealock, A. H. Livermore and C. A. Evans, *J. Amer. Chem. Soc.*, 1943, **65**, 935.
12. P. S. Owen and J. W. Ferrebee, *New England J. Med.*, 1946, **162**, 267.
13. R. R. Sealock and R. L. Goodland, *J. Amer. Chem. Soc.*, 1944, **66**, 507.
14. A. H. Livermore and R. R. Sealock, *J. Biol. Chem.*, 1947, **167**, 699.
14a. R. R. Sealock and A. H. Livermore, *ibid.*, 1949, **177**, 553 ; R. R. Sealock and N. C. Davis, *ibid.*, 987.
15. D. C. Smith and L. M. Prout, *Proc. Soc. Exp. Biol. Med.*, 1944, **56**, 1.
16. D. Melnick, M. Hochberg and B. L. Oser, *J. Nutrition*, 1945, **30**, 81.
17. L. O. Krampitz and D. W. Woolley, *J. Biol. Chem.*, 1944, **152**, 9.
18. R. R. Sealock and A. H. Livermore, *ibid.*, 1944, **156**, 379.
19. K. Bhagvat and P. Devi, *Indian J. Med. Res.*, 1944, **32**, 123, 131, 139.
20. K. P. Jacobsohn and M. D. Azevedo, *Arch. Biochem.*, 1947, **14**, 83.
21. P. H. Weswig, A. M. Freed and J. R. Haag, *J. Biol. Chem.*, 1946, **165**, 737.
21a. B. Thomas and H. F. Walker, *J. Soc. Chem. Ind.*, 1949, **68**, 6.
22. K. T. H. Farrer, *Biochem. J.*, 1945, **39**, 261.

7. BIOLOGICAL ESTIMATION OF ANEURINE

Polyneuritic Pigeons

A few of the methods used in the estimation of vitamin B_1 in natural substances have been referred to above when discussing the isolation of the vitamin. The prevention or cure of polyneuritis in ricebirds was used by B. C. P. Jansen and W. F. Donath,[1] whilst Edie et al.,[2] H. W. Kinnersley and R. A. Peters,[3] and K. H. Coward et al.[4] used polyneuritic pigeons, comparing the amount of test substance required to cure the symptoms in one group of birds with the amount of a standard preparation required to cure those in another group. Alternatively the minimum amount of substance required to maintain the weight of a standard bird on a polished rice diet was sometimes estimated, as in Seidell's method.[5] K. H. Coward and B. G. E. Morgan [6] found that there was a direct relationship between the dose and the percentage of birds cured, but not between the dose and the duration of cure, thus confirming the earlier work of Kinnersley and Peters.

Catatorulin Test

An interesting variant of the pigeon method is the catatorulin test, proposed by Peters et al.,[7] in which the oxygen uptake of avitaminous pigeons' brain was measured before and after the addition of the test solution.

Chick Method

A method of estimating aneurine, in which chicks are used, was described by T. H. Jukes and H. Heitman.[8] The basal diet consisted of polished rice, fish meal and autoclaved yeast, and the results were evaluated from a curve obtained by plotting the " polyneuritic mortality index ", i.e. the length of the test period (twenty-eight days) minus the number of days' survival, against the amounts of aneurine added to the diet. Chicks required 135 to 150 μg. of aneurine per 100 g. of diet to maintain normal health.

Rat Weight Test

The pigeon has been supplanted as a test animal by the rat. H. C. Sherman and A. Spohn [9] devised a method that was in general use for some years and is similar in principle to that of Guha and Drummond [10] already referred to. The success of the method depends to a considerable extent on the selection of the experimental animals. An inbred strain is preferred, many would say is essential, and the groups of animals used for testing the unknown sample and the standard are made up of pairs of litter-mates of the same sex and of approximately the same weight, so that as far as possible differences in response due to variations in animals are eliminated. The quantity of aneurine fed is so chosen that the rate of growth will be maximal. It is the normal practice to give the test material at at least three dose levels and the standard at two levels.

Sherman and Spohn originally recommended a test period of eight weeks, subsequently reduced to four weeks, whilst K. H. Coward [11] claimed that satisfactory results were obtained after only two weeks and F. W. Schultz and E. M. Knott [12] believe that results can be obtained in ten days. When the test is complete, a dose-response curve is plotted, the smoothness of which is a check on the reliability of the assay. The vitamin content of the test substance is calculated by reference to this curve. According to Coward the accuracy of the vitamin B_1 assay is high for a biological method. The sensitivity is also high, differences between doses of one μg. being detectable. Care has to be taken to prevent refection [13] (see page 75).

A curative method using rats, similar in principle to the original test with pigeons, was proposed by M. I. Smith.[14] In this method, the rats were fed a basal vitamin B_1-free diet until depleted, and the weight gain on the basal diet, to which had been added graded doses of the test solution, was compared with the gain in weight of animals fed on the same basal diet supplemented with known amounts of a standard solution of vitamin B_1. Young rats on a vitamin B_1-deficient diet were found to develop polyneuritis in fifty to eighty days. Oral administration or injection of aneurine resulted in improvement within three to five hours and definite cure in eighteen to twenty-four hours. After a certain time the effects wore off, symptoms of polyneuritis recurred and were again alleviated by another dose of the vitamin. Although the curative response was proportional to the dose, Smith did not believe the relationship to be quantitative, and he therefore made his comparisons on the basis of the minimum curative dose. Other workers, although confirming Smith's general conclusions, found considerable variations in the occurrence of polyneuritis but these, it is suggested, can be reduced by the use of a sufficiently large number of animals.

Of the four procedures considered by the Committee of Revision of the U.S. Pharmacopoeia, only the rat curative method was recommended. The preferred procedure is substantially that of Smith, the main variation being a more adequate diet, which is claimed to give a 100 % incidence of polyneuritis in rats, and repeated production and cure of polyneuritis in the same animal ; as many as ten such periods are said to be possible.

With pure aneurine, the duration of cure increases with increasing dosage and is linear over a considerable range, so that aneurine preparations can be assayed by comparing the duration of cure resulting from the test dose with that of a dose of standard.

Other criteria besides duration of cure have been used with the rat curative method, *e.g.* the time required for the rat to return to the weight it had when the vitamin B_1 injection was given [15] and the number of day doses per gram of material,[16] analogous to the pigeon method.

Bradycardia and Convulsion Methods

T. W. Birch and L. J. Harris [17] compared Smith's method with two other methods in which the rat is used. The first of these, the bradycardia method, is based on the observation that the heart rate of the vitamin B_1-deficient rat is lower than that of the normal animal, but is increased on administration of vitamin B_1, the increase being proportional to the dose given. Thus the heart-beat of a rat fed on a vitamin B_1-deficient diet for three weeks is measured by means of an electrocardiograph, and again twenty-four hours after giving a single measured dose of the test solution. The result is compared with that obtained after the administration of known amounts of a standard vitamin preparation to control animals.

The second method depends on the cure of convulsions which develop in rats fed a diet almost, but not quite, free from aneurine. The number of days which elapse between the administration of the test solution and the onset of the next convulsion is taken to be a measure of the amount of vitamin present. Birch and Harris recommend the bradycardia method as being quicker and easier than the other methods and as being no less reliable ; they have used it extensively, but in the hands of other workers it has not given good results.

B.P. Method

The weight method is the method of assay most widely employed in this country and the one adopted as official in the Addendum 1936 to the British Pharmacopoeia 1932. About ten young rats, each weighing 40 to 50 g., are fed immediately after weaning on the following basal diet, which is cooked by steaming for about three hours :

Sodium caseinate	100 g.
Rice starch	300 g.
Arachis or cottonseed oil . . .	75 g.
Salt mixture	25 g.
Water	500 g.

The salt mixture consists of : NaCl, 23·4 ; $MgSO_4 . 7H_2O$, 24·6 ; $Na_2 HPO_4$, 35·8 ; $K_2H PO_4$, 69·6 ; $Ca(H_2PO_4)_2$, 68·8 ; calcium lactate, 15·4 ; iron citrate, 6·0 ; KI, 0·2 parts.

Each rat receives daily, in addition, 3 to 5 drops of cod liver oil to provide vitamins A and D and 1 ml. of autoclaved yeast extract to provide vitamin B_2 complex. The rats are placed in separate cages with wire screens to prevent access to the faeces. Growth continues for two to three weeks and then stops. When the weight has been stationary for not less than five days or has begun to decline, the rats are divided into two groups. Each rat of one group receives daily, for four weeks, 10 mg. of the substance to be tested and each rat of the other group, 1 unit of the Standard Preparation. This was formerly a fuller's earth adsorbate kept at the National Institute for Medical Research, Hampstead (now Mill Hill), and the Unit of Anti-neuritic Activity (Vitamin B_1) for Great Britain and Northern Ireland, which was the same as the international unit, was defined as the specific antineuritic activity contained in 10 mg. of the Standard Preparation. In 1945, after the pure vitamin had become available, the Standard Preparation was changed to a specimen of pure crystalline synthetic aneurine hydrochloride now kept at Mill Hill, and the unit was defined as the specific antineuritic activity contained in 3·125 μg. of the Standard Preparation (Seventh Addendum to the British Pharma-copoeia 1932, Appendix XXIII).

The average increase in weight of the rats is determined for each group. If the average increase in weight is approximately the same for both groups, the vitamin B_1 activity of the test substance is equal to that of the standard. If the increase in weight in the group receiving the test substance is less or greater than in the group receiving the standard, the test is repeated, using a larger or smaller dose of the test substance. Alternatively, for the first trial, two doses of the substance being tested may be given and fourteen rats may be used. In each trial there should be at least two rats receiving no dose ; these should show a gradual decline in weight, ending usually in convulsions caused by vitamin B_1 deficiency. In an experiment in which five rats receive the Standard Preparation and five rats receive the test substance, and in which the mean responses are equal, the limits of error (P = 0·99) are 65 and 154 %.

Another method of assessing the response of vitamin B_1-deficient rats to graded doses of aneurine was suggested by K. H. Coward and B. G. E. Morgan,[18] who observed that the oestrus cycle was inter-rupted in vitamin B_1 deficiency, and that the time required to complete three cycles in rats previously deprived of aneurine was inversely proportional to the daily dose of vitamin B_1. The method is not of practical importance, however, being less accurate than the growth method. Moreover, riboflavine deficiency has a similar effect on the oestrus cycle, and the presence of riboflavine in the test substance would presumably interfere with aneurine assays.

References to Section 7

1. B. C. P. Jansen and W. F. Donath, *Proc. K. Akad. Wetensch. Amsterdam*, 1926, **29**, 1390.
2. E. S. Edie, W. H. Evans, B. Moore, G. C. E. Simpson and A. Webster, *Biochem. J.*, 1912, **6**, 234.
3. H. W. Kinnersley and R. A. Peters, *ibid.*, 1928, **22**, 419; 1933, **27**, 225, 232.
4. K. H. Coward, J. H. Burn, H. W. Ling and B. G. E. Morgan, *ibid.*, 1933, **27**, 1719.
5. A. Seidell, *U.S. Publ. Health Rep.*, 1922, **37**, 1519.
6. K. H. Coward and B. G. E. Morgan, *Biochem. J.*, 1939, **38**, 658.
7. R. Passmore, R. A. Peters and H. M. Sinclair, *ibid.*, 1933, **27**, 842; R. A. Peters, H. Rydin and R. H. S. Thompson, *ibid.*, 1935, **29**, 53; 1938, **32**, 2031.
8. T. H. Jukes and H. Heitman, *J. Nutrition*, 1940, **19**, 21.
9. H. C. Sherman and A. Spohn, *J. Amer. Chem. Soc.*, 1923, **45**, 2719.
10. B. C. Guha and J. C. Drummond, *Biochem. J.*, 1929, **23**, 880.
11. K. H. Coward, *ibid.*, 1936, **30**, 2012.
12. F. W. Schultz and E. M. Knott, *J. Nutrition*, 1936, **12**, 583.
13. L. S. Fridericia, P. Freudenthal, S. Gudjonnsson, G. Johansen and N. Schoubye, *J. Hygiene*, 1927, **27**, 70.
14. M. I. Smith, *U.S. Publ. Health Rep.*, 1930, **45**, 116.
15. F. F. Heyroth, *Bull. Basic Science Rep.*, 1932, **4**, 1.
16. H. W. Kinnersley, R. A. Peters and V. Reader, *Biochem. J.*, 1930, **24**, 1820.
17. T. W. Birch and L. J. Harris, *ibid.*, 1934, **28**, 602.
18. K. H. Coward and B. G. E. Morgan, *ibid.*, 1941, **35**, 974.

8. MICROBIOLOGICAL ASSAY OF ANEURINE

An entirely different method of assaying aneurine preparations from the foregoing are fermentation tests ; these are carried out with micro-organisms for which aneurine is an essential growth factor. The principle of the method is that the selected organism is grown on a medium that gives optimal growth on addition of aneurine, and the amount of growth obtained with the test solution is then compared with that given by a control containing known amounts of aneurine. The amount of growth is measured in some suitable way, *e.g.* turbidimetrically or by the amount of carbon dioxide, lactic acid or other metabolite formed.

Yeast Fermentation Method

In the methods of A. S. Schultz et al.,[1] of K. Heyns [2] and of H. H. Bunzell,[3] a sugar solution is fermented with yeast and the carbon dioxide produced is measured. Schultz et al.,[4] however, found that other yeast-stimulating substances were present in urine and therefore modified their original method by carrying out two fermentations, one before and one after oxidation with potassium ferricyanide to convert the aneurine into thiochrome ; the difference between the two results was proportional to the true aneurine content. For the estimation of aneurine in wheat, yeast, bread, liver, milk and orange juice, they used another modification,[5] the aneurine being destroyed by treatment with sodium sulphite solution at 100° C. for thirty minutes at pH 5 to 6. Again, the difference between the results before and after this treatment was claimed to be proportional to the aneurine content ; interfering substances were said to be unaffected by sulphite, and the sulphite degradation products were supposed not to stimulate the growth of the yeast.[6]

A modification of this method was used by R. J. Williams et al.,[7] who employed the " old process " strain of Saccharomyces cerevisiae, which was grown on a medium supplemented with yeast and liver extracts freed from aneurine by adsorption on fuller's earth. This method is said to be simpler than the original method and to be capable of estimating as little as 0·00005 μg. of aneurine per 2·5 ml. of medium. Unfortunately it is not specific, the thiazole moiety (5-β-hydroxyethyl-4-methyl-thiazole) of aneurine and the pyrimidine moiety (4-amino-5-ethoxymethyl-2-methyl-pyrimidine) giving 60 and 30 % respectively of the response given by aneurine hydrochloride. Cocarboxylase does not stimulate the growth of the organism under these conditions.

N. S. Scrimshaw and W. B. Stewart [8] also found that the method of Schultz et al. lacked specificity ; for instance, it gave poor results when used for the assay of meat and egg products. They claimed to have eliminated the sources of error in the method by first carrying out a preliminary assay with graded amounts of aneurine added to the blank to determine the range over which the response was linear and then in the main assay using three tubes, one containing the sample, another the blank and the third a blank plus a suitable amount of aneurine. The aneurine content of the sample was calculated by comparing the amount of gas liberated in the first tube (after correcting for the value obtained for the blank) with that produced in the third tube similarly corrected. The effectiveness of sulphite cleavage of a known amount of aneurine added to the blank was determined for each type of substance and, if necessary,

3

a correction was applied for the activity of any cleavage products present in the sample.

The lack of specificity was confirmed by H. F. Deutsch,[9] who found that the pyrimidine half of aneurine was more active than aneurine itself on yeast at low concentrations, but less active at high concentrations. The pyrimidine and thiazole halves together were almost as active as aneurine, whilst the thiazole half alone or 4-amino-2-methyl-pyrimidyl-5-methane sulphonic acid were less active. These results are therefore not in complete agreement with those of Schultz *et al.*, who stated that the sulphite-cleavage products did not stimulate the growth of yeasts ; the discrepancy may be due to the use of different strains. It is evident therefore that the yeast growth method must be used with caution, especially when the test solution is suspected to contain degradation products of aneurine. H. G. Obermeyer and L. Chen,[10] for example, showed that substantial amounts of biologically available thiazole or pyrimidine derivatives remained in foodstuffs in which aneurine had decomposed.

Westenbrink *et al.*[11] used the yeast fermentation method in rather a novel form for the estimation of cocarboxylase in blood. The blood was acidified to pH 3 and heated to $100°$ C. for $1\frac{1}{2}$ minutes, neutralised to pH 6·2 and centrifuged. Alkali-washed brewers' yeast was added to an aliquot portion of the solution, aneurine and a manganese salt were then added and the suspension was incubated at $27·5°$ C. for fifteen minutes to re-synthesise carboxylase. The yeast was then centrifuged off, re-suspended in acetate buffer solution, pH 5·6, and reacted at $27·5°$ C. with sodium pyruvate. The amount of carbon dioxide liberated was proportional to the cocarboxylase in the blood.

Although the yeast growth method, as generally used, is an aerobic fermentation, aneurine can also be estimated by an anaerobic fermentation. This was first demonstrated by L. Atkin *et al.*,[12] who found that the addition of 0·01 to 0·04 μg. of aneurine to 5 mg. of yeast suspended in 3 ml. of medium considerably raised the anaerobic carbon dioxide output during the second hour of incubation and that the increase in fermentation by 0·01 to 0·02 μg. of aneurine was proportional to the vitamin concentration. The observation was confirmed by H. Laser,[13] who also showed that different yeasts behaved differently, bakers' yeast giving a regular response and *Torula utilis* no response at all. He also noted that in yeasts that responded with an increase in anaerobic fermentation, aerobic fermentation was also increased quantitatively by the same minute amounts of aneurine. E. S. Josephson and R. S. Harris,[14] using a Warburg manometer, were able to estimate the aneurine content of tissue extracts containing as little as 10^{-8} g. per ml.

Phycomyces Assay Method

Although yeast is the micro-organism most commonly used for the estimation of aneurine, other micro-organisms have been used. Next in importance to yeast is the mould, *Phycomyces Blakesleeanus*, which was employed by W. H. Schopfer,[15] A. P. Meiklejohn,[16] H. M. Sinclair [17] and T. Morell.[18] A suitable aneurine-free medium to which graded amounts of the test solution have been added is inoculated with mould spores, incubated for seven days and the mycelium then removed, dried and weighed. The results are compared with those obtained using the same basal medium to which have been added known amounts of aneurine, and the aneurine content of the unknown solution is calculated from the dose-response curve obtained with the standard. The method has been used to estimate the aneurine and cocarboxylase contents of blood plasma and cerebrospinal fluid [19] and for the routine assay of vegetable extracts.[20] A. P. Meiklejohn [21] used the *Phycomyces* method to estimate the aneurine content of potatoes and found that the green sprouts contained a factor toxic for the mould, whilst the centre of the tubers from April to August, and the skin layer always, contained an adjuvant factor that stimulated the growth of the mould only in presence of aneurine.

Assays with Other Organisms

Lactobacillus fermenti was suggested by H. P. Sarett and V. H. Cheldelin,[22] growth being measured turbidimetrically sixteen to eighteen hours after inoculation. Cocarboxylase was 30 % more active than aneurine. *Staphylococcus aureus* was used by P. M. West and P. W. Wilson,[23] *Glaucoma piriforme* by L. Emerique-Blum and A. Lwoff,[24] *Streptococcus salivarius* by C. F. Niven and K. L. Smiley,[25] and a yeast, *Saccharomyces macedoniensis*, by Emery *et al.*[26]

Probably the most satisfactory of these methods is that of Sarett and Cheldelin. Under the conditions prescribed by the authors, the organism, *Lactobacillus fermenti* 36, does not respond to the pyrimidine and thiazole components of aneurine, alone, together or in presence of aneurine. A quantitative response is obtained in presence of 0·005 to 0·04 μg. of aneurine per 10 ml. of medium. Unfortunately, the basal medium is rather complicated, consisting of alkali-treated peptone, acid-hydrolysed casein, glucose, sodium acetate, cystine, adenine, guanine and uracil, with the usual inorganic salts and the following members of the vitamin B complex : riboflavine, calcium pantothenate, *p*-aminobenzoic acid, nicotinic acid, pyridoxine, biotin and folic acid. The growth-response is measured turbidimetrically.

The original method of Sarett and Cheldelin gave unsatisfactory results with some materials containing inhibitory or stimulatory substances, and E. E. Fitzgerald and E. B. Hughes [27] eliminated this particular source of error by subtracting from the response to the test solution, the response to another portion of the solution in which the aneurine had been inactivated by autoclaving with sulphite.

Some of the difficulties of the *L. fermenti* turbidimetric method are said to be overcome by using a plate method of assay, similar in principle to that used for the assay of antibiotics, except that the zones formed around the holes cut in the agar are zones of stimulation and not of inhibition.[28] The method is not very sensitive, but with yeast and yeast products the results are at least as accurate as those obtainable by other methods.[29] Takadiastase was used to liberate the aneurine from the yeast.

References to Section 8

1. A. S. Schultz, L. Atkin and C. N. Frey, *J. Amer. Chem. Soc.*, 1937, **59,** 948, 2457 ; 1938, **60,** 1514.
2. K. Heyns, *Z. physiol. Chem.*, 1939, **258,** 219.
3. H. H. Bunzell, *Ind. Eng. Chem., Anal. Ed.*, 1942, **14,** 279.
4. A. S. Schultz, L. Atkin and C. N. Frey, *J. Biol. Chem.*, 1940, **136,** 713.
5. A. S. Schultz, L. Atkin and C. N. Frey, *Ind. Eng. Chem., Anal. Ed.*, 1942, **14,** 35.
6. A. S. Schultz, L. Atkin, C. N. Frey and R. R. Williams, *J. Amer. Chem. Soc.*, 1941, **63,** 632.
7. R. J. Williams, J. R. McMahan and R. E. Eakin, *Univ. Texas Publ.*, 1941, No. 4137, 31.
8. N. S. Scrimshaw and W. B. Stewart, *J. Biol. Chem.*, 1944, **155,** 79.
9. H. F. Deutsch, *ibid.*, 1944, **152,** 431.
10. H. G. Obermeyer and L. Chen, *ibid.*, 1945, **159,** 117.
11. H. G. K. Westenbrink, E. P. S. Parvé, A. C. van den Linden and W. A. van den Broek, *Z. Vitaminforsch.*, 1943, **63,** 218.
12. L. Atkin, A. S. Schultz and C. N. Frey, *J. Biol. Chem.*, 1939, **129,** 471.
13. H. Laser, *Biochem. J.*, 1941, **35,** 488.
14. E. S. Josephson and R. S. Harris, *Ind. Eng. Chem., Anal. Ed.*, 1942, **14,** 755.
15. W. H. Schopfer, *Z. Vitaminforsch.*, 1935, **4,** 67.
16. A. P. Meiklejohn, *Biochem. J.*, 1937, **31,** 1441.
17. H. M. Sinclair, *ibid.*, 1938, **32,** 2185 ; 1939, **33,** 1816, 2027.
18. T. Morell, *Deut. med. Woch.*, 1938, **64,** 1722.
19. A. P. Meiklejohn, *Biochem. J.*, 1937, **31,** 1441 ; H. M. Sinclair, *ibid.*, 1938, **32,** 2185; 1939, **33,** 1816, 2127 ; E. N. Rowlands and J. F. Wilkinson, *Brit. Med. J.*, 1938, **2,** 878 ; T. Morell, *Deut. med. Woch.*, 1938, **64,** 1722 ; G. Guhr, *Klin. Woch.*, 1939, **18,** 1028 ; R. Goodhart and H. M. Sinclair, *J. Biol. Chem.*, 1940, **132,** 11.

20. K. C. Hamner, W. S. Stewart and G. Matrone, *Food Res.*, 1943, **8**, 444.
21. A. P. Meiklejohn, *Biochem. J.*, 1943, **37**, 340.
22. H. P. Sarett and V. H. Cheldelin, *J. Biol. Chem.*, 1944, **155**, 153.
23. P. M. West and P. W. Wilson, *Science*, 1938, **88**, 334.
24. L. Emerique-Blum and A. Lwoff, *Bull. Soc. Chim. biol.*, 1940, **22**, 179.
25. C. F. Niven and K. L. Smiley, *J. Biol. Chem.*, 1943, **150**, 1.
26. W. B. Emery, N. McLeod and F. A. Robinson, *Biochem. J.*, 1946, **40**, 426.
27. E. E. Fitzgerald and E. B. Hughes, *Analyst*, 1949, **74**, 340.
28. A. L. Bacharach and W. F. J. Cuthbertson, *ibid.*, 1948, **73**, 334.
29. A. Jones and S. Morris, *ibid.*, 1949, **74**, 333.

9. CHEMICAL ESTIMATION OF ANEURINE

Azo Method

The first chemical test proposed for vitamin B_1 was the so-called formaldehyde-azo test of H. W. Kinnersley and R. A. Peters,[1] who found that vitamin B_1 concentrates gave a pink colour with diazotised sulphanilic acid and formaldehyde solution and that the colour increased slowly in intensity for thirty to sixty minutes, thereafter remaining constant for a considerable time. The method was later modified by them [2] to make it quantitative ; the error was stated to be not greater than 5 %. H. J. Prebluda and E. V. McCollum [3] and D. Melnick and H. Field [4] used diazotised p-aminoacetophenone (without formaldehyde) for estimating aneurine. The latter authors extracted the coloured product with xylene to make the test more specific, and thereby reduced the error to 2 %. By hydrolysing cocarboxylase preparations with yeast phosphatase the test was made applicable to the estimation of the coenzyme. In a later paper, Melnick and Field [5] introduced adsorption on Permutit, followed by elution with potassium chloride solution, to effect purification.

The azo method is now one of the standard methods of estimating aneurine, and has been modified by various workers to eliminate interference from other compounds present in the material to be assayed (*cf.* Emmett *et al.*[6]). Diazotised p-aminoacetophenone was used by L. J. Harris and W. D. Raymond,[7] by E. F. Yang and B. S. Platt,[8] and by Y. Sakurai *et al.*[9] The last-named group of workers purified the sample by adsorption of the aneurine on " acid clay " and elution of the adsorbate with alcoholic phenol. H. Willstaedt [10] used diazotised 2 : 4-dichloroaniline, which gives a yellowish-red colour, as the reagent. E. R. Kirch and O. Bergeim [11] used p-carbethoxybenzene trichloroacetate and extracted the colour with isoamyl alcohol ; both vitamin A and vitamin C interfere, however, and must be removed, the former by extraction with isoamyl alcohol before addition of the reagent, and the latter by oxidation. Cocarboxylase gave no colour and could be estimated separately after hydrolysis with phosphatase. B. Alexander and J. E. Levi [12] found that uric acid and vitamin C interfered with the estimation of aneurine by means of the Prebluda-McCollum reagent ; they removed uric acid by precipitation with zinc at pH 7·4 and vitamin C by precipitation with lead acetate at pH 8·2.

Thiochrome Method

The other reaction on which is based a chemical test for aneurine was also discovered by R. A. Peters.[13] He observed that when aneurine was oxidised with potassium permanganate or manganese dioxide at a pH not exceeding 6, a blue fluorescent substance was produced. G. Barger et al.[14] prepared this fluorescent substance by oxidation of aneurine with potassium ferricyanide solution and obtained it in the pure state as pale yellow crystals having the formula, $C_{12}H_{14}N_4OS . 2HCl$. It showed an intense blue fluorescence in neutral or alkaline solution and had all the other properties of thiochrome described by R. Kuhn et al.[15] Its constitution was established and its synthesis worked out by Bergel et al.[16]

The conversion of aneurine into thiochrome was studied by B. C. P. Jansen,[17] who established the optimal conditions for the oxidation with potassium ferricyanide ; he extracted the thiochrome with isobutanol and measured the fluorescence of the extract in a fluorimeter calibrated against standard solutions of quinine. The method has been extensively employed for the estimation of vitamin B_1 in foodstuffs and urine, and indeed may be said to be the most important method of assay. It was officially adopted in the Seventh Addendum (1945) to the British Pharmacopoeia 1932.

According to D. J. Hennessy,[18] it is more sensitive than the colorimetric method and capable of estimating lower potencies. This was confirmed by Brown et al.,[19] who also obtained good agreement between the two methods. They stated, however, that neither method was satisfactory with very low potencies, only the rat growth or pigeon weight maintenance methods giving reliable results in such instances. Hennessy et al.[20] found little difference between the results obtained by means of the thiochrome test, the rat growth test and the fermentation test when pharmaceutical preparations were assayed by these methods.

J. C. Moyer and D. K. Tressler [21] obtained good agreement between the thiochrome method and the sulphite-cleavage modification of the fermentation method.

The method has been modified by individual workers to meet their particular requirements and there is, therefore, a bewildering array of methods to choose from. The objects of these various modifications are, of course, to eliminate interference from other substances present in the sample being assayed. Some substances prevent the formation of thiochrome, leading to low results, whilst others enhance the fluorescence and produce high results.

Perhaps the most important modification is that introduced by D. J. Hennessy and L. R. Cerecedo,[22] in which the aneurine is adsorbed on a zeolite, Decalso, and eluted with hot potassium chloride solution. This method, which is analogous to Melnick and Field's modified procedure, has been adopted by the majority of workers. Perlzweig et al.[23] used Superfiltrol for removing aneurine from urine, and a mixture of pyridine, ethanol and hydrochloric acid for elution.

Even when adsorbents of this type are used, interfering substances may remain. H. L. Mason and R. D. Williams [24] experienced trouble in assaying urines owing to the presence of fluorescent derivatives of nicotinic acid. Satisfactory results were obtained only when the amount of aneurine in the sample exceeded 100 μg. When the excretion was low or when 300 to 500 mg. of nicotinic acid were ingested per day, the non-thiochrome material accounted for most of the fluorescence. They suggested that the difficulty could be overcome by repeating the fluorimetric assay after destroying the aneurine in the urine by heating with sodium sulphite at pH 5 for fifteen minutes and then subtracting the intensity of the fluorescence from that given by the untreated solution.

V. A. Najjar and K. C. Ketron,[25] however, showed that the fluorescent metabolite of nicotinic acid, " F_2 " (see page 254), which was responsible for this phenomenon, was attacked by sodium sulphite, so that Mason and Williams' procedure did not give a true blank. They recommended Hennessy and Cerecedo's method with the rather unsatisfactory expedient of assuming that 21 % of the fluorescence was due to " F_2 ". Y. L. Wang and L. J. Harris [26] destroyed interfering fluorescent substances in extracts prepared from foodstuffs by oxidation with hydrogen peroxide before extraction with isobutanol.

Another group of substances that may cause interference in the fluorimetric assay of urines are salicylates ; these may be removed [27] by acidification and extraction with isobutanol before oxidation.

J. G. Organ and F. Wokes [28] experienced a reverse effect in estimating the aneurine content of cereal extracts. These appeared to contain substances that " quenched " the fluorescence, and interference from this source was only satisfactorily overcome by adding known amounts of aneurine equal to at least four times that originally present and then subtracting the amount added from the results.

P. Ellinger and M. Holden [29] found that certain inorganic salts also had a marked quenching effect on the fluorescence of thiochrome in isobutanol. Maximum fluorescence occurred at pH 11. D. F. Clausen and R. E. Brown [30] attributed certain of the errors in the thiochrome method to the effect of dissolved oxygen and changes of temperature on the quinine standard generally employed, and advocated the use of glass standards and a constant temperature. Certain foodstuffs may contain substances that interfere with the quantitative adsorption of aneurine on Decalso.[31]

An alternative oxidising agent to potassium ferricyanide was suggested by W. I. M. Holman,[32] who claimed that a saturated solution of mercuric oxide in alkaline potassium chloride solution gave more satisfactory results, especially when applied to Decalso eluates.

C. A. P. Carbajal,[33] instead of estimating the thiochrome fluorimetrically measured the ferrocyanide simultaneously formed by titration with ceric sulphate solution. Little information is available as to the merits of this method, which is claimed to be capable of estimating as little as 5 μg. of aneurine.

In addition to ensuring that the conversion of aneurine into thiochrome is not inhibited or the fluorescence enhanced by the presence of other impurities, satisfactory assays also necessitate the complete extraction of the aneurine from the material being tested with, at the same time, the minimum of substances likely to interfere with the development of the fluorescence. A large variety of methods exist for extracting aneurine from foodstuffs but, in general, these resolve themselves into extraction with acid, digestion with enzymes or a combination of the two. According to R. G. Booth,[34] extraction with acid is as efficient as is enzymic digestion, but most workers appear to prefer the latter method. L. J. Harris and Y. L. Wang [35] used a combination of takadiastase and papain, whilst takadiastase alone was used by E. C. Slater [36] for milk and cereal products, by Brown et al.,[37] who claimed it to be the best of the enzymes for cereal products, and by A. Z. Hodson [38] for milk. R. T. Connor and G. J. Straub [39] digested the material for one hour with dilute sulphuric acid and then incubated with clarase.

The thiochrome method can also be used for the estimation of aneurine pyrophosphate (cocarboxylase), and it is possible to obtain an estimate of the free and combined aneurine in the same solution. On oxidation with ferricyanide, aneurine pyrophosphate and orthophosphate give derivatives insoluble in isobutanol,[22] but by incubation with a kidney phosphatase preparation, both esters are converted into free aneurine, which can then be estimated by conversion to thiochrome. H. G. K. Westenbrink and B. C. P. Jansen [40] used a different method for the fluorimetric estimation of aneurine pyrophosphate ; after oxidation with ferricyanide, they evaluated the fluorescence in the isobutanol layer to estimate the free aneurine, and the fluorescence in the aqueous layer to estimate the cocarboxylase. This method obviously suffers from severe limitations, and is only applicable when the aqueous phase is free from coloured impurities and other fluorescent substances.

A simplified base-exchange method, not involving adsorption columns, was used by E. Papageorge and M. V. Lamar [41] for the estimation of aneurine in urine by three different thiochrome methods ; agreement was generally good. The use of benzene sulphonyl chloride to destroy aneurine is recommended for the estimation of non-thiochrome fluorescent impurities.

A different principle was used for the estimation of aneurine by H. Wachsmuth.[42] On adding potassium mercuric iodide solution to a weakly acid solution of aneurine a crystalline precipitate of aneurine iodomercurate was formed. The iodine in this precipitate or in the excess of the reagent was titrated after oxidation to iodate by treatment with bromine.

Physico-chemical Method

Although aneurine exhibits characteristic absorption bands in the ultra-violet region of the spectrum, these can only be used for estimating the vitamin when relatively pure solutions are available. The only physical method of estimating aneurine that appears to be promising is the polarographic method, although it does not seem to have been generally adopted. J. J. Lingane and O. L. Davis [43] discovered that, with potassium chloride as base solution, aneurine gave a step with a half-wave potential of $-1\cdot25$ volts *vs.* the saturated calomel electrode, and that riboflavine and nicotinic acid gave steps at other voltages, so that it was possible to estimate all three vitamins in one and the same solution at the same time.

When electrolysed in a very dilute solution containing ammonium chloride, boric acid and potassium chloride or in a phosphate buffer solution, aneurine gave a current-voltage curve with a prominent maximum at $1\cdot7$ volts *vs.* the saturated calomel electrode ; [44] this is believed to arise from a catalytic effect of the aneurine.

References to Section 9

1. H. W. Kinnersley and R. A. Peters, *Biochem. J.*, 1934, **28**, 867.
2. H. W. Kinnersley and R. A. Peters, *ibid.*, 1938, **32**, 1516.
3. H. J. Prebluda and E. V. McCollum, *Science*, 1936, **84**, 488 ; *J. Biol. Chem.*, 1939, **127**, 495.
4. D. Melnick and H. Field, *J. Biol. Chem.*, 1939, **127**, 505, 531.
5. D. Melnick and H. Field, *ibid.*, 1939, **130**, 97.
6. A. D. Emmett, G. Peacock and R. A. Brown, *ibid.*, 1940, **135**, 131.
7. L. J. Harris and W. D. Raymond, *Biochem. J.*, 1939, **33**, 2037.

8. E. F. Yang and B. S. Platt, *Chinese J. Physiol.*, 1939, **14,** 259.
9. Y. Sakurai, T. Inagaki and S. Omori, *J. Agric. Chem. Soc. Japan*, 1940, **16,** 331.
10. H. Willstaedt, *Naturwiss.*, 1937, **25,** 682.
11. E. R. Kirch and O. Bergeim, *J. Biol. Chem.*, 1942, **143,** 575.
12. B. Alexander and J. E. Levi, *ibid.*, 1942, **146,** 399.
13. R. A. Peters, *Nature*, 1935, **135,** 107.
14. G. Barger, F. Bergel and A. R. Todd, *ibid.*, 1935, **136,** 259 ; *Ber.*, 1935, **68,** 2257.
15. R. Kuhn, T. Wagner-Jauregg, F. W. van Klaveren and H. Vetter, *Z. physiol. Chem.*, 1935, **234,** 196.
16. F. Bergel, A. R. Todd, H. Fraenkel-Conrat and A. Jacob, *Nature*, 1936, **138,** 76, 406.
17. B. C. P. Jansen, *Rec. trav. Chim.*, 1936, **55,** 1046.
18. D. J. Hennessy, *Ind. Eng. Chem.*, *Anal. Ed.*, 1941, **13,** 216.
19. R. A. Brown, E. Hartzler, G. Peacock and A. D. Emmett, *ibid.*, 1943, **15,** 494.
20. D. J. Hennessy, S. Wapner and J. Truhlar, *ibid.*, 1944, **16,** 479.
21. J. C. Moyer and D. K. Tressler, *ibid.*, 1942, **14,** 788.
22. D. J. Hennessy and L. R. Cerecedo, *J. Amer. Chem. Soc.*, 1939, **61,** 179.
23. W. A. Perlzweig, H. Kamin, I. Gue and J. V. Blalock, *Arch. Biochem.*, 1945, **6,** 97.
24. H. L. Mason and R. D. Williams, *J. Biol. Chem.*, 1941, **140,** 417 ; 1942, **146,** 589.
25. V. A. Najjar and K. C. Ketron, *ibid.*, 1944, **152,** 579.
26. Y. L. Wang and L. J. Harris, *Chem. and Ind.*, 1942, 27.
27. J. B. Cleland, *Austral. J. Exp. Biol.*, 1943, **21,** 153.
28. J. G. Organ and F. Wokes, *J. Soc. Chem. Ind.*, 1944, **63,** 165.
29. P. Ellinger and M. Holden, *Biochem. J.*, 1944, **38,** 147.
30. D. F. Clausen and R. E. Brown, *Ind. Eng. Chem.*, *Anal. Ed.*, 1944, **16,** 572.
31. M. A. Eppright and R. J. Williams, *ibid.*, 576.
32. W. I. M. Holman, *Biochem. J.*, 1944, **38,** 388.
33. C. A. P. Carbajal, *Bol. Soc. Quim.*, *Peru*, 1942, **8,** 105.
34. R. G. Booth, *Analyst*, 1942, **67,** 162.
35. L. J. Harris and Y. L. Wang, *Biochem. J.*, 1941, **35,** 1050, 1068.
36. E. C. Slater, *Austral. J. Exp. Biol.*, 1941, **19,** 29.
37. E. B. Brown, J. C. Hamm and H. E. Harrison, *J. Biol. Chem.*, 1943, **151,** 153.
38. A. Z. Hodson, *Food Res.*, 1945, **10,** 351.
39. R. T. Connor and G. J. Straub, *Ind. Eng. Chem.*, *Anal. Ed.*, 1941, **13,** 380.
40. H. G. K. Westenbrink and B. C. P. Jansen, *Acta brev. Neerl. Physiol.*, 1938, **8,** 119.
41. E. Papageorge and M. V. Lamar, *Arch. Biochem.*, 1947, **14,** 315.
42. H. Wachsmuth, *Natuurwetensch. Tijds.*, 1942, **23,** 157.
43. J. J. Lingane and O. L. Davis, *J. Biol. Chem.*, 1941, **137,** 567.
44. A. Wollenberger, *Science*, 1945, **101,** 386.

10. OCCURRENCE OF ANEURINE IN FOODSTUFFS

The occurrence of aneurine in foodstuffs is of considerable importance in nutrition, and many thousands of assays have been reported. Those published prior to 1938 have been collected in the form of tables by M. A. Boas-Fixsen and M. H. Roscoe [1] (which should be consulted for the older references) and are only summarised here, together with the more important recent results. Wheat bread contains from 0·07 to 0·4 mg. per 100 g. according to the type. White bread contains the smallest amount and brown and whole grain bread the most, the amount progressively decreasing as the percentage extraction is reduced. Breads from 70, 80 and 100 % extraction flour, for example, contained 0·13, 0·24 and 0·26 mg. per 100 g. respectively.[2] Germ bread is richer than white bread, containing 0·24 to 0·5 mg. per 100 g. Rye bread contains 0·06 to 0·25 mg. per 100 g., again depending on the percentage extraction.

Of cereal products, wheat germ is the richest source, containing 1·2 to 6·6 mg. per 100 g. Whole wheat grain contains 0·35 to 1·0 mg. per 100 g. ;[3] middlings about 1·5 and bran 0·4 to 1·0 mg. per 100 g. Wheat flour contains 0·12 to 0·48 mg. per 100 g., depending on the percentage extraction. Barley (whole grain) contains 0·07 to 0·6 ; barley germ, 4·2 ; maize (whole grain), 0·015 to 0·18 ; maize germ, 1·5 ; oats (whole grain), 0·18 to 1·0 ; rye (whole grain), 0·3 to 0·4 ; rye (germ), 0·9 to 2·2 ; rice (whole or ground), 0·05 to 0·27 ; and rice bran, 1·7 to 2·3 mg. per 100 g.

Fruits do not, in general, contain much aneurine. Apples, pears, peaches, bananas, dates, grapefruit, orange, pineapple, plum and tangerine contain between 0·09 and 0·15 mg. per 100 g. Soft fruits, such as blackberries, red and blackcurrants and raspberries, are poorer sources. Prunes contain 0·2 to 0·27 and raisins and sultanas 0·2 to 0·3 mg. per 100 g. Orange juice contains 0·065 to 0·070, grapefruit juice 0·032 to 0·035 and tangerine juice 0·07 mg. of aneurine per 100 ml.[4]

Most nuts contain more aneurine than do fruits :[5] almond, 0·24 ; pecan, 0·7 to 1·0 ; barcelona, 0·11 ; brazil, 1·0 ; pine kernels, 0·5 ; chestnut, 0·27 ; hazel, 0·6 ; peanut, 0·3 to 1·0 and walnut, 0·45 mg. per 100 g. Cocoanut contains only 0·03 to 0·06 mg. per 100 g. Peanut butter contains about 0·38 mg. per 100 g.[6]

Vegetables vary considerably in their aneurine content. Among the richest sources are the cauliflower, 0·33 ; butter bean (dry), 0·48, haricot bean, 0·15 to 0·36 ; runner bean, 0·07 to 0·22 ; soya bean (meal), 0·24 to 1·2 ; lentil, 0·12 to 0·63 ; pea (fresh), 0·2 to 0·8 ; pea (dried), 0·12 to 1·5 ; beetroot, 0·2 ; savoy, 0·24 ; carrot, 0·18 ; lettuce, 0·27 ; mushroom, 0·15 ; onion, 0·12 ; asparagus, 0·19 ; spinach, 0·06 to 0·2 ; brussels sprout, 0·18 ; tomato, 0·12 ; turnip, 0·12 ; watercress, 0·18 ; and potato,[7] 0·09 to 0·18 mg. per 100 g.

Cow's milk contains 0·03 to 0·07 mg. per 100 ml. ; cheese, 0 to 0·09 ; and egg yolk,[8] 0·3 mg. per 100 g. About 60 % of the aneurine in milk is in the free state.[9] Cow's colostrum contains 0·06 and ewe's colostrum and milk, 0·11 and 0·06 mg. per 100 ml.[10]

Muscle from various kinds of fish contains 0·06 to 0·12 and hard roe, 1 to 2 mg. per 100 g. Soft roes contain much less (0·15 to 0·2 mg. per 100 g.). Beef contains 0·09 to 0·3 ; mutton, 0·18 ; pork,[11] 0·54 ; ham, 0·8 to 1·5 ; and chicken, 0·15 to 0·18 mg. per 100 g. Ox liver contains 0·45, pig kidney, 1·0 and sheep's kidney 0·57 mg. per 100 g.

Dried yeast is the richest of all known sources, containing 1·8 to 36 mg. per 100 g. Royal jelly and bee bread, although of no importance from the standpoint of human nutrition, are relatively rich sources of aneurine, containing 0·9 and 0·64 mg. per 100 g. of dry matter respectively.[12] According to Kitzes et al.,[13] honey, pollen and royal jelly contain 0·0044, 0·6 and 1·8 mg. per 100 g. respectively.

Ordinary beer contains only traces of aneurine [14] (1 to 6 I.U. per ml.), although riboflavine and nicotinic acid may be present in appreciable quantities. Malt beers contain up to 100 μg. per litre of aneurine. It is believed [15] on the basis of an examination of nineteenth-century buns made from " good ale yeast " that nineteenth-century ale must have been very much richer in aneurine than present-day beer or ale, most of the vitamin being lost from bright beer by removal with the yeast.

Tea, although rich in nicotinic acid, does not contain appreciable amounts of aneurine. Maté leaves contain [16] 0·167 mg. per 100 g.

Effect of Processing on Aneurine Content of Foodstuffs

Much intensive work, especially during the 1939-45 war, has been carried out on the effect of storage on the vitamin content of foodstuffs and on the losses resulting from different methods of cooking vegetables and cereals. A detailed account of this cannot be given but the general conclusions are as follows. Heat treatment reduced the vitamin B_1 content of milk,[17] and rice,[18] but not of peas,[19, 20] unless sodium bicarbonate was added to the cooking water. Dehydrated vegetables lost only small amounts of aneurine by the ordinary method of dehydration, but when sulphite was used the loss was considerable.[21] The amount of aneurine retained on cooking depended on the method used and with dehydrated cabbage amounted to 42 to 76 %. The maximum amount of aneurine lost in cooking potatoes was about 30 %, and no further loss occurred on keeping the potatoes warm as occurs with vitamin C.[22] Freezing caused no loss of vitamin B_1, and appears to be an excellent way of preserving the vitamin content of vegetables. Storage at temperatures below 0° C. was better than storage at normal temperatures [20, 23]. The rate of destruction of the vitamin B_1 in dehydrated products at elevated temperatures (above 37° C.) appeared to be affected by a number of factors, and could not be prevented by storage in vacuum, nitrogen or carbon dioxide or by addition of an antioxidant.[24]

References to Section 10

1. M. A. Boas-Fixsen and M. H. Roscoe, *Nutr. Abs.*, 1937-38, **7**, 837 ; 1939-40, **9**, 815.
2. D. I. Allen, *J. Nutrition*, 1943, **25**, 521.
3. For the aneurine content of different varieties of wheat, see also E. C. Slater and E. J. Rial, *J. Proc. Austral. Chem. Inst.*, 1941, **8**, 71 ; R. G. Booth, *J. Soc. Chem. Ind.*, 1940, **59**, 181 ; for the distribution of aneurine in the wheat grain, see G. F. Somers, M. H. Coolidge and K. C. Hamner, *Cereal Chem.*, 1945, **22**, 333 ; J. J. C. Hinton, *Biochem. J.*, 1943, **37**, 585 ; L. H. Pulkki and K. Puutula, *Biochem. Z.*, 1941, **308**, 122 ; for the distribution in the rice grain, see J. J. C. Hinton, *Brit. J. Nutrition*, 1948, **2**, 237.
4. M. I. Bailey and A. W. Thomas, *J. Nutrition*, 1942, **24**, 85.
5. R. Melville, *Chem. and Ind.*, 1947, 304.
6. C. D. Miller, L. Louis and C. Peterson, *Food Res.*, 1943, **8**, 27.
7. For variations in the aneurine content of potatoes according to variety and season, see J. Meiklejohn, *Biochem. J.*, 1943, **37**, 340.
8. For the aneurine content of eggs from different varieties of hens, see N. S. Scrimshaw, F. B. Hatt and M. W. Scrimshaw, *J. Nutrition*, 1945, **30**, 375 ; for the distribution of aneurine in the embryonated egg, see N. S. Scrimshaw, W. E. Porter and M. W. Scrimshaw, *ibid.*, 1949, **38**, 237, 267.
9. N. Halliday and H. J. Deuel, *J. Biol. Chem.*, 1941, **140**, 555.
10. P. B. Pearson and A. L. Darnell, *J. Nutrition*, 1946, **31**, 51.
11. For the aneurine content of different animal tissues, see also M. Pyke, *Biochem. J.*, 1940, **34**, 1341 ; R. C. Miller, J. W. Pence, R. A. Dutcher, P. T. Ziegler and M. A. McCarty, *J. Nutrition*, 1943, **26**, 261.
12. M. H. Haydak and L. S. Palmer, *J. Econ. Entom.*, 1940, **33**, 396.
13. G. Kitzes, H. A. Schuette and C. A. Elvehjem, *J. Nutrition*, 1943, **26**, 241.
14. H. Fink and F. Just, *Wochsch. Brau.*, 1941, **58**, 17, 79 ; R. H. Hopkins, *Nature*, 1943, **152**, 274.
15. E. C. Barton-Wright, T. Moran and H. S. Sarson, *ibid.*, 273.
16. J. M. Chaves, *Rev. Alimenta*, 1944, **8**, 173.
17. A. L. Daniels, *Amer. J. Dis. Child.*, 1941, **62**, 127 ; A. D. Holmes, C. P. Jones, A. W. Wertz and J. W. Kuzmeski, *J. Nutrition*, 1943, **26**, 337.

18. Y. Sakurai, S. Omori and S. Huzita, *Bull. Inst. Phys.-Chem. Res.,
    Japan*, 1941, **20**, 308 ; M. Swaminathan, *Indian J. Med. Res.,*
    1942, **30**, 409.
19. M. L. Fincke, R. Little, E. Redelings and J. Perkins, *Food Res.,*
    1943, **8**, 123.
20. B. Barnes, D. K. Tressler and F. Fenton, *ibid.,* 420.
21. F. Fenton, B. Barnes, J. C. Moyer, K. A. Wheeler and D. K.
    Tressler, *Amer. J. Publ. Health*, 1943, **33**, 799 ; F. Fenton,
    E. Gleim, M. Albury, J. R. McCartney and K. Visnyei, *Food
    Res.,* 1946, **11**, 468 ; F. Fenton, E. Gleim, A. Arnason, J. F.
    Thompson, M. Albury and M. Phillips, *ibid.,* 475.
22. E. Gleim, M. Albury, J. R. McCartney, K. Visnyei and F. Fenton,
    ibid., 461.
23. E. Gleim, D. K. Tressler and F. Fenton, *ibid.,* 1944, **9**, 471.
24. G. E. Rice, J. F. Benk, F. L. Kauffman, H. W. Schultz and H. E.
    Robinson, *ibid.,* 491.

II. EFFECT OF ANEURINE DEFICIENCY IN ANIMALS

Effect in Pigeons

Incidental reference has already been made to some of the symptoms associated with vitamin B_1 deficiency in experimental animals. One of the first recorded signs of vitamin B_1 deficiency, actually used to follow the isolation of the vitamin, was the characteristic head retraction of the pigeon, termed opisthotonus ; [1] this is a form of convulsion, and is analogous to the convulsions produced in rats and other animals by vitamin B_1 deficiency. Vitamin B_1-deficient pigeons also show ataxia and leg weakness, cardiac failure with tachycardia, abnormalities of the electrocardiograph and necrosis of the heart muscle. Starvation alone produces bradycardia and variable heart block.[2] In most instances, the symptoms rapidly disappear on administration of aneurine, unless the deficiency is severe ; recovery from leg weakness is slow, however. R. L. Swank and O. A. Bessey [2] consider paralysis to be a characteristic symptom of vitamin B_1 deficiency, and maintain that it is unnecessary to postulate the existence of vitamin B_4 (see page 612). Nerve degeneration is also characteristic of vitamin B_1 deficiency in pigeons,[3] and leads to mild myelin degeneration in the peripheral nerves of the spinal cord, the extent of the degeneration depending on the severity of the deficiency.[4] Incidentally, aneurine can be detected in the myelin sheaths of peripheral nerves by fluorescence micro-spectrography.[5]

In vitamin B_1-deficient pigeons, alcohol disappears from the blood at the same rate as in normal pigeons,[6] whilst the onset of acute vitamin B_1 deficiency symptoms in pigeons is delayed by the substitution of alcohol for the fat and carbohydrate of the diet in isocaloric quantities ; the vitamin B_1 requirements for metabolising fat appear to be intermediate between those required for carbohydrates and alcohol.[7]

Finally, E. Sárfy [8] reported that in vitamin B_1-deficient pigeons the adrenals show a small increase in adrenaline content, whilst that of the blood undergoes a decrease, followed later by a reduction in the amount in the adrenals and an increase in the amount in the blood. Reversal of these changes occurs on administering aneurine.

Effect in Chicks

Chicks respond to aneurine deficiency in a very similar way to pigeons and exhibit opisthotonus, owing to functional impairment of the inhibitory fibre from the upper to the lower brain. In chronic deficiency, leg weakness and nerve degeneration occur, the axis cylinder degenerating and then the myelin sheath ; finally the cell undergoes chromatolysis.[9] Myelin degeneration in the peripheral nerves and spinal cord is not observed in acute aneurine deficiency in chicks.[4] Heart failure is shown by some birds, with necrosis of the myocardial fibres. Actually, changes in the electrocardiogram occur two days before the other symptoms of vitamin B_1 deficiency make their appearance,[10] the changes becoming more pronounced as the deficiency progresses. On administration of aneurine, the symptoms rapidly improve, but the electrocardiogram only slowly returns to normal.

The blood-sugar of chicks is reduced during the first ten to fourteen days on a vitamin B_1-deficient diet ; [11] it then increases and when convulsions occur it may have twice the normal value. Injection of aneurine restores the blood-sugar level to normal. Changes in the nerves due to vitamin B_1 deficiency have been demonstrated in tissue culture experiments,[12] the length and density of nerve fibres in embryos grown in plasma from vitamin B_1-deficient chicks and the density of the spindle cells being less than in embryos grown in normal plasma ; the density of the macrophages was not significantly affected. Addition of aneurine to the deficient plasma increased the spindle cell density, but did not affect the fibre length or density. In blood clots washed with sulphite to destroy aneurine, normal axon growth occurred, however, and the abnormal growth in vitamin B_1-deficient plasma may be due to the greater fluidity of deficient plasma.

Effect in Rats

Rats, when fed a diet inadequate in vitamin B_1, show a steady decline in weight, once the tissues have been depleted of their stores of the vitamin ; this change in weight, as already mentioned (see page 28), is used for the biological assay of vitamin B_1 preparations. Rats also develop convulsions and slowing of the heart-beat (bradycardia) on diets low in aneurine ; these symptoms have also been proposed as the basis of bio-assay methods (see page 30). The electrocardiogram shows a good response to aneurine treatment within twenty-four to seventy-two hours. Changes in the electrocardiogram can be observed about a week before other signs become evident.[13] In addition, a condition of anoestrus is produced and can be cured by administration of aneurine ;[14] the accompanying disturbances of reproduction and lactation, however, are not cured until the stock diet is given. Riboflavine deficiency also causes anoestrus, and administration of riboflavine restores both the normal cycle and normal reproduction and lactation. Attempts to use this condition as the basis of a method of assaying aneurine were not very successful ;[15] it is not considered specific for aneurine.

Other symptoms of vitamin B_1 deficiency observed in rats are :[16] loss of appetite, without affecting the gain in weight per unit of food, a decrease in the fat and energy output, a lower body temperature, decreased efficiency in the utilisation of metabolisable energy, an increased loss of energy as heat and by excretion in the urine, an increased C : N ratio in the urine and an apparent depression of the oxidative processes of the body. In addition achlorhydria, loss of muscular tone and lesions of the nervous system may develop.[17]

Vitamin B_1 deficiency resulted in a rapid and marked deterioration of the work performance of swimming rats, and this was promptly restored by the administration of aneurine ;[18] reduction of the food intake without rendering the diet deficient in aneurine did not decrease the work performance.

When young rats were allowed to develop acute deficiency symptoms, which were then cured by a small amount of aneurine and the process repeated several times, most of the animals at autopsy showed enlarged hearts due to dilatation of the right auricle ; a few rats showed pleural effusions and ascites.[19] The auricles generally showed necrosis of the muscle fibres, cellular infiltration and proliferation or a decreased number of muscle fibres and fibrosis. Changes in the ventricle were uncommon or slight. Half the rats showed pathological changes in the pulmonary veins.

Different strains of rats may behave differently towards aneurine, a point to be carefully considered in bio-assay work. For example, one highly inbred strain was observed[20] to develop polyneuritis in fifty-eight days, whilst another strain showed only mild deficiency after ninety days. One result of vitamin B_1 deficiency in rats is marked creatinuria,[21] a correlation being observed between the excretion of creatinine and the bodyweight. Even in mild chronic deficiency, the blood urea and non-protein nitrogen increase considerably. Only mild creatinuria was observed in animals deficient in riboflavine, pyridoxine or pantothenic acid.

Aneurine and Riboflavine

A connection between aneurine deficiency and riboflavine has been remarked upon by several workers. Although no change in the excretion of riboflavine occurs in the early stages of aneurine deficiency, in the later stages rapid excretion occurs ; [22] this is believed to be due to the rapid metabolism of tissue, e.g. shrinkage of the liver. It has also been shown that the concentration of riboflavine in the liver is increased in aneurine deficiency and *vice versa*.[23] A deficiency of pyridoxine, pantothenic acid, biotin or vitamin A had no effect on the concentration of aneurine or riboflavine in the liver. Chronic aneurine deficiency does not affect the riboflavine content of the body tissues,[24] but riboflavine is not utilised so well in this condition as in normal rats on an isocaloric diet.

Aneurine and Fat Metabolism

Some workers appear to have established a connection between aneurine and fat metabolism. This was first suggested by H. G. K. Westenbrink,[25] who found that fat in the diet conserved the vitamin B_1 present in the tissues. This sparing action of fat was confirmed by H. M. Evans *et al.*,[26] who showed furthermore that fats differed in their ability to inhibit the onset of deficiency symptoms, the optimal effect being obtained with fats containing C_8-fatty acids. The nutritive value of fats was different for vitamin B_1-deficient and normal rats. A. R. Kemmerer and H. Steinbock,[27] on the other hand, could find no support for this hypothesis, the vitamin B_1 contents of the tissues being the same whether the animals were fed a high carbohydrate diet or a high fat diet. Nor was any evidence in favour of the vitamin sparing action of fat obtained by Reinhold *et al.*[28] from experiments on humans. The subjects were maintained from ten to fifteen days on a basal diet, then for the same period on a diet high in fat and then on one high in carbohydrate ; aneurine was estimated in the urine, faeces and food. Urinary excretion of aneurine decreased in five out of the six women when the carbohydrate to fat ratio was increased. The high fat diet had the same effect on urinary aneurine as had the basal diet. Faecal excretion of aneurine was not affected by the change in diet.

Another and somewhat different connection between vitamin B_1 and fats was reported by Longenecker *et al.*,[29] who found that loss of body fat occurred when rats were being depleted of aneurine and that the iodine value of the total fatty acids was increased, indicating that the more saturated fatty acids were preferentially metabolised ; addition of aneurine caused rapid decomposition of body fat. Le R. Voris and H. P. Moore [30] reported finding the exact opposite, however, namely an increase in body fat in vitamin B_1 deficiency, but this is contrary to the experience of other workers. F. W. Quackenbush et al.[31] found that on a high carbohydrate, low fat diet, the normal deposition of fat was prevented by a deficiency of pyridoxine or pantothenic acid, as well as of aneurine, and suggested that the production of fat in the body is not a function of any one dietary factor ; aneurine did not prevent the rapid loss of fat that resulted from a deficiency of other members of the vitamin B complex, nor was it more effective than any of these in increasing the total fat content.

G. E. Boxer and D. Stetten [32] also observed a decrease in the deposition of fatty acids when rats were fed a high carbohydrate, fat-free diet low in aneurine ; they attributed the phenomenon to low food intake rather than to a specific effect of aneurine.

On the whole, therefore, one must conclude that no case has been made out for a connection between aneurine and fat utilisation, and that claims to have obtained evidence for such a connection depend not on a specific effect of aneurine, but rather on reduced food intake due to loss of appetite or to the deliberate restriction of the diet.

Aneurine and Carbohydrate Metabolism

On the other hand, there is no doubt as to the connection between aneurine and carbohydrate metabolism, first pointed out as early as 1914 by C. Funk,[33] for the symptoms of vitamin B_1 deficiency are accentuated or, alternatively, the aneurine requirements are increased, by conditions that demand a greater output of work, e.g. by exercise.[34] The effect of raising the environmental temperature is controversial, C. A. Mills [35] stating that rats require twice as much and chicks four times as much aneurine at 91° F. as at 68° and 70° F. respectively, whilst Kline et al.[36] declare that the aneurine requirements are reduced. The relation between aneurine and carbohydrate metabolism has been elucidated largely by the brilliant researches of R. A. Peters, and is more fully discussed in a later section (see page 90).

According to J. B. Leonards and A. H. Free,[37] the rate of intestinal absorption of galactose by normal rats is 66 % greater than in vitamin B_1-deficient rats and 12 % greater than in pyridoxine deficiency, although the absorption was unaffected by riboflavine deficiency. These workers [38] found that there was no change in the rate of metabolism of galactose as a result of chronic vitamin B_1 deficiency.

Effect on Infected Animals

Rats and mice have been used to study the effect of aneurine deficiency on resistance to infection. Mice apparently became more susceptible to *Pneumococcus* Type I infection when made deficient in aneurine or riboflavine, and administration of several times the normal intake of either vitamin at the time of infection did not affect the mortality.[39] Similarly, administration of aneurine markedly increased the resistance of mice to respiratory infections by *Streptococcus haemolyticus*.[40] Aneurine-deficient rats and mice were more susceptible to *Salmonella typhi murium* than were animals fed an adequate diet ; this was a primary result of aneurine deficiency in the mouse, but secondary to inanition in the rat.[41]

Vitamin B_1-deficient mice showed a lower incidence of infection than normal mice to the murine strain of poliomyelitis virus, though the vitamin B_1-deficient survivors became paralysed after a prolonged incubation period when given adequate aneurine.[42] A similar increase in resistance to the Lansing strain of poliomyelitis virus was observed when mice were maintained on a vitamin B_1-deficient diet, both the mortality rate and incidence of paralysis being lower than in normal animals.[43] Restriction of the caloric intake to 40 % of the normal was, however, equally effective, even when extra aneurine was given so that this striking effect of aneurine on susceptibility to virus infection would appear to be quite illusory. In spite of this the effect of an aneurine antagonist, "oxythiamine" (see page 127), on poliomyelitis was tested ; it afforded some protection but not as much as that given by a vitamin B_1-free diet.[43a] Vitamin B_1 deficiency did not appear to make rats more susceptible to Flexner's MV cotton rat-adapted strain of poliomyelitis virus,[44] but with the Lansing strain a group of rats receiving an excess of aneurine showed a higher incidence of paralysis than a group of vitamin B_1-deficient animals ; on a second passage, however, there was no difference between the two groups.

The resistance of aneurine-deficient mice to the Lansing strain of poliomyelitis virus or to Theiler's encephalomyelitis virus was only partly due to the accumulation of pyruvic acid or similar metabolite (see page 90), for the addition of pyruvic acid to a diet containing aneurine did increase the resistance of man to these virus infections, but not to the same extent as did aneurine deficiency.[45] Chicks, on the other hand, were protected against avian encephalomyelitis to the greatest degree when given large doses of aneurine throughout life.[46] If, however, the chicks were fed on an optimal diet for two weeks, and then with different levels of aneurine, those on the lowest level were protected. Monkeys (*Macaca mulatta*) showed no increase in resistance to poliomyelitis virus when deficient in aneurine,[47] and aneurine deficiency had no significant effect on susceptibility to influenza virus.[40]

Vitamin B_1-deficient rats are said to be more susceptible than normal animals to rat leprosy,[48] whilst rats rendered deficient in aneurine or riboflavine have been claimed to be less resistant to infection with the worm, *Nippostrongylus muris*.[49] Plasma from an aneurine- (or riboflavine-) deficient animal did not give such adequate protection as did immune plasma from normally fed animals.

A moderate impairment in the antibody response to inoculation with human erythrocytes was observed in aneurine-deficient rats.[49a]

Other Animals

The phalanger, *Trichosurus vulpicula*, appears to be unique in being able to synthesise aneurine,[50] though in the light of work on intestinal synthesis published since the appearance of this suggestion, it must not be concluded that this animal is capable of synthesising the vitamin in the actual tissues or body fluids.

Vitamin B_1 deficiency in pigs follows the same general pattern as in rats, and the main symptoms are anorexia, vomiting, dyspnoea, cyanosis and general weakness.[51, 52] Cardiac dilatation without hypertrophy occurs, together with a local and diffuse myocardial necrosis.[53] Neurological symptoms, however, are absent.[51, 54] The blood shows increased pyruvate.[51] The symptoms are cured by administration of about 125 mg. of aneurine per 100 g. of carbohydrate plus protein.[55] The aneurine content of the blood is directly related to the proportion in the diet and the muscle tissue ; it increased within a week from 21 to 30 μg. per 100 g. when the diet was supplemented by 25 to 50 mg. of aneurine per day.[56] Deposition of aneurine in the tissues is dependent on the dietary intake.[52] Pigs rapidly store supplementary doses of aneurine in the muscle tissue, the effect being detectable within eight days of feeding an additional 50 mg. per day. Maximum storage occurred within thirty-five days and beyond this period no further increase occurred.[57] Owing to storage of aneurine, pigs can be maintained for about three months on an aneurine-deficient diet before loss of appetite occurs.[58]

Vitamin B_1-deficient dogs show tachycardia, hypotension and changes in the electrocardiogram,[59] and these disappear on administration of aneurine. The pyruvic acid content of the blood is increased and the lactate-pyruvate ratio is decreased.[60] Administration of alcohol to vitamin B_1-deficient dogs decreased the pyruvate and increased the lactate, whereas in normal animals both were decreased.[60] Injection of glucose had the reverse effect, increasing the pyruvate and lactate of normal animals and the lactate-pyruvate ratio of vitamin B_1-deficient dogs, following an initial decrease.[61] Anaemia is not a symptom of vitamin B_1 deficiency in dogs.[62]

Cats exhibit three stages in the development of vitamin B_1 deficiency : [63] (a) an induction stage, with development of anorexia ; (b) a cortical stage with neurological disturbances, particularly of postural, mechanical and tonic convulsive seizures ; and (c) a terminal stage in which the animal is prostrate ; this is followed by death in one to two days. The first and second stages, but not the third, are reversed by injection of aneurine. After one to two weeks on a vitamin B_1-deficient diet, cats showed a 50 % increase in the length of time they were able to maintain respiration in 3·25 % oxygen.[64]

The symptoms exhibited by monkeys (Macaca mulatta) on a diet deficient in aneurine were : [65] loss in weight, decreased food consumption, general muscle weakness, loss of reflexes, convulsions, inco-ordination, increased cachexia, signs of cardiac insufficiency, prostration and, finally, death. No vomiting or opisthotonus was observed. About 15 μg. of aneurine per kg. of bodyweight per day were required to prevent the onset of deficiency and 25 to 50 μg. for adequate growth. The pyruvic acid content of the blood in normal monkeys was found to be higher than in normal human or pig blood ; it increased in aneurine deficiency.

Vitamin B_1 deficiency in the calf results in weakness, inco-ordination of the legs, convulsions, head retraction and sometimes scouring, anorexia and dehydration ; the blood and urinary pyruvate are increased above the normal levels.[65a]

Aneurine and the Alimentary Tract

It was at one time supposed that absence of vitamin B_1 produced adverse changes in the alimentary tract, but this is now known not to be the case. For example, two groups of workers [66] observed gastric ulcers in a large proportion of rats on a vitamin B_1-deficient diet, but these are now believed to be due to a secondary and not a direct effect of the lack of vitamin B_1. B. P. Babkin [67] appears to have obtained evidence that absence of some member of the vitamin B complex reduces the response of the gastric glands to the normal stimuli provided by the right kind of food. Feeding yeast restored the response to normal but unfortunately no attempt was made to establish the nature of the responsible factor. It is possible that Babkin's observations provide an explanation of the association between vitamin B_1 and anorexia.

Aneurine had no effect on the movements of the intestine either *in vitro* or *in vivo*.[68] It is readily absorbed from the large and small intestine and in chronic diarrhoea appreciable losses may occur through faulty absorption.

References to Section 11

1. U. Suzuki, T. Shamimura and S. Okade, *Biochem. Z.*, 1912, **43**, 89.
2. R. L. Swank and O. A. Bessey, *J. Nutrition*, 1941, **22**, 77 ; *Arch. intern. Med.*, 1942, **70**, 763.
3. R. L. Swank and M. Prados, *Arch. Neurol. Psychiat.*, 1942, **47**, 97.
4. J. H. Shaw and P. H. Phillips, *J. Nutrition*, 1945, **29**, 113.
5. F. Sjöstrand, *Nature*, 1946, **157**, 698.
6. R. L. Berg, E. Stotz and W. W. Westerfeld, *J. Biol. Chem.*, 1944, **152**, 51.
7. W. W. Westerfeld and E. A. Doisy, *J. Nutrition*, 1945, **30**, 127.
8. E. Sárfy, *Z. physiol. Chem.*, 1939, **262**, 87.
9. R. L. Swank, *J. Exp. Med.*, 1940, **71**, 683.
10. M. L. De Finis and J. B. Odoriz, *Rev. Soc. argent. Biol.*, 1943, **19**, 314.
11. L. I. Nitzcscu and V. Isanid, *Compt. rend. Soc. Biol.*, 1940, **133**, 490, 492.
12. A. S. Burt, *J. Cell. Comp. Physiol.*, 1943, **21**, 145 ; 1943, **22**, 205.
13. J. M. Hundley, L. L. Ashburn and W. H. Sebrell, *Amer. J. Physiol.*, 1945, **144**, 404 ; J. M. Hundley and W. H. Sebrell, *U.S. Publ. Health Rep.*, 1946, **61**, 847.
14. K. H. Coward, B. G. E. Morgan and L. Wahler, *J. Physiol.*, 1942, **100**, 423 ; V. A. Drill and M. W. Burrill, *Endocrin.*, 1944, **35**, 187.
15. K. H. Coward and B. G. E. Morgan, *Biochem. J.*, 1941, **35**, 974.
16. F. J. McClure, Le R. Voris and E. B. Forbes, *J. Nutrition*, 1934, **8**, 295.
17. D. Glick and W. Antopol, *J. Pharm. Exp. Ther.*, 1939, **65**, 389.
18. M. Kniazuk and H. Molitor, *ibid.*, 1944, **80**, 362.
19. L. L. Ashburn and J. V. Lowry, *Arch. Path.*, 1944, **37**, 27.
20. R. W. Luecke, L. S. Palmer and C. Kennedy, *Arch. Biochem.*, 1944, **5**, 395.
21. B. Sure and Z. W. Ford, *J. Nutrition*, 1942, **24**, 405.
22. J. W. Ferrebee and N. Weissman, *ibid.*, 1943, **26**, 459 ; B. Sure, *ibid.*, 1944, **27**, 447 ; R. W. Luecke, L. S. Palmer and C. Kennedy, *Arch. Biochem.*, 1944, **5**, 395.
23. H. O. Singher, C. J. Kensler, H. Levy, E. Poore, C. P. Rhoads and K. Unna, *J. Biol. Chem.*, 1944, **154**, 69.
24. B. Sure, *ibid.*, 1945, **157**, 543.
25. H. G. K. Westenbrink, *Acta brev. Neerland.*, 1933, **3**, 95.
26. H. M. Evans, S. Lepkovsky and E. A. Murphy, *J. Biol. Chem.*, 1934, **107**, 437.
27. A. R. Kemmerer and H. Steinbock, *ibid.*, 1933, **103**, 353.

28. J. G. Reinhold, J. T. L. Nicholson and K. O'S. Elsom, *J. Nutrition*, 1944, **28**, 51.
29. H. E. Longenecker, G. Gavin and E. W. McHenry, *J. Biol. Chem.*, 1940, **134**, 693.
30. Le R. Voris and H. P. Moore, *J. Nutrition*, 1943, **25**, 7.
31. F. W. Quackenbush, H. Steinbock and B. R. Platz, *J. Biol. Chem.*, 1942, **145**, 163.
32. G. E. Boxer and D. Stetten, *ibid.*, 1944, **153**, 607.
33. C. Funk, *Z. physiol. Chem.*, 1914, **89**, 378.
34. N. B. Guerrant and R. A. Dutcher, *J. Nutrition*, 1940, **20**, 589.
35. C. A. Mills, *Arch. Biochem.*, 1942, **1**, 73.
36. O. L. Kline, L. Friedman and E. M. Nelson, *J. Nutrition*, 1945, **29**, 35.
37. J. B. Leonards and A. H. Free, *ibid.*, 1943, **26**, 499.
38. J. B. Leonards and A. H. Free, *ibid.*, 1944, **28**, 197.
39. J. G. Wooley and W. H. Sebrell, *U.S. Publ. Health Rep.*, 1942, **57**, 149.
40. J. W. Riddle, *Ohio State Univ. Abs., Doctoral Diss.*, 1943, **43**, 143 ; *Biol. Abs.*, 1945, **19**, 1408.
41. E. Guggenheim and E. Buechler, *Proc. Soc. Exp. Biol. Med.*, 1946, **61**, 413.
42. A. F. Rasmussen, H. A. Waisman, C. A. Elvehjem and P. F. Clark, *J. Infect. Dis.*, 1944, **74**, 41.
43. C. Foster, J. H. Jones, W. Heube and F. Dorfman, *J. Exp. Med.*, 1944, **29**, 221.
43a. J. H. Jones, C. Foster and W. Henle, *Proc. Soc. Exp. Biol. Med.*, 1948, **69**, 454.
44. J. A. Toomey, W. O. Frohring and W. S. Takacs, *Proc. Soc. Exp. Biol. Med.*, 1943, **54**, 153 ; *Yale J. Biol. Med.*, 1944, **16**, 477.
45. H. A. Waisman, H. C. Lichstein, C. A. Elvehjem and P. F. Clark, *Arch. Biochem.*, 1945, **8**, 203.
46. J. M. Cooperman, H. C. Lichstein, P. F. Clark and C. A. Elvehjem, *J. Bact.*, 1946, **52**, 467.
47. P. F. Clark, H. A. Waisman, H. C. Lichstein and E. S. Jones, *Proc. Soc. Exp. Biol. Med.*, 1945, **58**, 42.
48. L. F. Badger, E. Masunaga and D. Wolf, *U.S. Publ. Health Rep.*, 1940, **55**, 1027.
49. J. Y. C. Watt, *Amer. J. Hyg.*, 1944, **39**, 145.
49a. B. B. Carter and A. E. Axelrod, *Proc. Soc. Exp. Biol. Med.*, 1948, **67**, 416.
50. A. Bolliger and C. R. Austin, *J. Proc. Roy. Soc. N.S.W.*, 1941, **75**, 118.
51. M. M. Wintrobe, H. J. Stein, M. H. Miller, R. H. Follis, V. Najjar and S. Humphreys, *Johns Hopkins Hosp. Bull.*, 1942, **71**, 141.
52. W. W. Heinemann, M. E. Ensminger, T. J. Cunha and E. C. McCulloch, *J. Nutrition*, 1946, **31**, 107.
53. R. H. Follis, M. H. Miller, M. M. Wintrobe and H. J. Stein, *Amer. J. Path.*, 1943, **19**, 341.

54. M. M. Wintrobe, R. H. Follis, S. Humphreys, H. Stein and M. Lauritsen, *J. Nutrition*, 1944, **28**, 283.
55. C. van Etten, N. R. Ellis and L. L. Madsen, *ibid.*, 1940, **20**, 607 ; N. R. Ellis and L. L. Madsen, *ibid.*, 1944, **27**, 253.
56. J. W. Pence, R. C. Miller, R. A. Dutcher and W. T. S. Thorp, *J. Biol. Chem.*, 1945, **158**, 647.
57. J. W. Pence, R. C. Miller, R. A. Dutcher and P. T. Ziegler, *J. Animal Sci.*, 1945, **4**, 141.
58. M. E. Ensminger, W. W. Heinemann, T. J. Cunha and E. C. McCulloch, *Washington Agric. Exp. Sta.*, 1945, *Bull.* 468.
59. L. de Soldati, *Compt. rend. Soc. Biol.*, 1940, **133**, 323.
60. R. L. Berg, E. Stotz and W. W. Westerfeld, *J. Biol. Chem.*, 1944, **152**, 51.
61. A. Chesler, E. Homberger and H. E. Himwick, *ibid.*, 1944, **153**, 219.
62. A. R. Maass, L. Michaud, H. Spector, C. A. Elvehjem and E. B. Hart, *Arch. Biochem.*, 1944, **4**, 105.
63. G. M. Everitt, *Amer. J. Physiol.*, 1944, **141**, 439.
64. D. C. Smith, R. H. Orter and J. E. P. Toman, *ibid.*, 1944, **140**, 603.
65. H. A. Waisman and K. B. McCall, *Arch. Biochem.*, 1944, **4**, 265.
65a. B. C. Johnson, T. S. Hamilton, W. B. Nevens and L. E. Boley, *J. Nutrition*, 1948, **35**, 137.
66. G. Dalldorf and M. Kellogg, *J. Exp. Med.*, 1932, **56**, 391 ; B. Sure and H. S. Thatcher, *Arch. Path.*, 1933, **16**, 809.
67. B. P. Babkin, *Canad. Med. Assoc. J.*, 1933, **29**, 5.
68. H. Molitor and W. L. Sampson, *E. Merck's Jahresber.*, 1936, **50**, 51.

12. EFFECT OF ANEURINE DEFICIENCY IN MAN

Beriberi

The classical pathological condition arising from vitamin B_1 deficiency in man is beriberi. This condition occurs extensively in the Far East, where it has been known for centuries, according to T. Lee[1] since the fourth century A.D., but has only recently been recognised in the West. It is characterised by degenerative changes in the nervous system, including a multiple peripheral neuritis. This is often accompanied by generalised oedema and serous effusions, with a tendency to cardiac hypertrophy and dilatation.

Death in cases of beriberi is not due to the neuritis but to cardiac hypertrophy. On autopsy the heart is found to be greatly enlarged, especially on the right side, with a thin wall and a generalised arteriolar or capillary dilatation. Pulmonary oedema frequently occurs as a result of the back-pressure caused by the failure of this side of the heart ; the liver, spleen and kidneys may also be affected.

The nerve changes are generally detectable only by microscopic examination. In the spinal cord, degeneration of the medullary sheath is the most usual finding, but in some cases the axis cylinder itself is fragmented. Changes may also be seen in the posterior ganglion and anterior horn cells. Degeneration is found as a constant factor in all peripheral nerves ; it generally starts in the legs, spreading to the arms later, and then to other parts of the body. The myelin of the sheath is broken up into balls or threads and eventually disappears. In this last event the axis cylinders appear to be coiled, and may be fragmented and atrophied. Parallel with these nerve changes, hyperaesthesia and then anaesthesia occur in the legs, and the leg and thigh muscles become atrophied, with loss of cross-striation and shrinkage of the sarcoplasm. Later the hands and arms, and even other parts of the body, become affected in the same way. These nerve and muscle changes are, of course, not peculiar to beriberi, but occur in all forms of polyneuritis.

In cases where oedema occurs, it is first observed in the legs and thighs, and may later spread to other parts of the body, oedema of the lungs being a frequent symptom. At autopsy, serous fluid may be found in the subcutaneous tissue, usually the pericardium, the pleura and the peritoneum. The oedema is probably due to generalised capillary dilatation with increased permeability to plasma, and may disappear quite suddenly after a sudden diuresis.

In Europe and the U.S.A., classical beriberi is rarely seen, and vitamin B_1 deficiency occurs in the form of polyneuritis induced by special circumstances. Alcoholic polyneuritis [2] is a vitamin B_1 deficiency arising in chronic alcoholics whose high intake of calories in the form of alcohol increases their vitamin B_1 requirements. The condition is often aggravated by the gastro-intestinal disturbances that arise in such cases ; these lead to defective absorption of such vitamin B_1 as is taken in the form of food. Polyneuritis of pregnancy [3] may arise through the increased metabolic requirements of the foetus, and lack of the vitamin may be aggravated by loss of food in vomiting.

Beriberi was encountered in Japanese prisoner-of-war camps during the war of 1939-45.[4] It was characterised by anorexia, nervous manifestations, tachycardia and arrhythmia. The symptoms were cured by aneurine, but a vitamin B complex preparation was even more effective.

Other Conditions Associated with Vitamin B_1 Deficiency

Aneurine deficiency may also be associated with pregnancy accompanied by a poor diet, pregnancy anaemia, pernicious anaemia accompanied by myxoedema, steatorrhoea, idiopathic hypochromic anaemia, scurvy, carcinoma and ulcer of the stomach, fatal pulmonary tuberculosis, anorexia nervosa and following gastrectomy.[5] In some forms of anaemia, in certain cardiovascular disturbances and in subacute combined degeneration of the cord, aneurine deficiency is usually associated with deficiencies of other members of the vitamin B complex.[6]

Aneurine is probably of no value in diabetes,[7] diabetic neuritis,[8] or pre-eclamptic toxaemia.[9]

Wernicke's encephalopathy, characterised by anorexia, vomiting, nystagmus, and emotional changes with, subsequently, mental and eye changes, was observed in a Japanese prisoner-of-war camp,[10] and was cured rapidly and completely by injections of aneurine. As acute aneurine deficiency appeared to be the sole cause of the condition, the name cerebral beriberi is suggested.

In pyloric stenosis, colitis and fevers, the diet may be limited with reduction of the vitamin B_1 intake to a figure below that essential for adequate metabolism, which is generally taken to be 2 to 3 mg. a day, so that vitamin B_1 deficiency may accompany these conditions.

The symptoms present in these special types of polyneuritis are similar in every respect to those described above as characteristic of beriberi. They differ in detail from those encountered in other polyneuritides.

A deficiency of aneurine leads almost invariably to gastro-intestinal symptoms, especially anorexia and nausea, and administration of aneurine produces immediate relief, though it should be borne in mind that not all forms of anorexia are due to vitamin B_1 deficiency. Occasional symptoms of vitamin B_1 deficiency are glossitis, achlorhydria, anaemia and diarrhoea.

Treatment

Aneurine hydrochloride is a specific remedy for beriberi and the polyneuritides arising from vitamin B_1 deficiency, and its administration in such conditions is generally followed by a quick recovery. From 20 to 50 mg. of crystalline aneurine hydrochloride are given in cases of beriberi by intramuscular or intravenous injection and, after about a fortnight, the same dose may be given orally until the symptoms are completely relieved. Since patients suffering from vitamin B_1 deficiency may also be suffering from other deficiencies, it is frequently necessary to give other vitamins in addition to aneurine, sometimes in the form of liver or yeast extracts. The time required for recovery depends on the extent to which the disease has progressed. Peripheral nerves are capable of regeneration as long as the cell body in the spinal cord or posterior ganglion remains viable. Where the cells and axis cylinders of the central nervous system have degenerated, however, restoration cannot take place. The heart condition and oedema generally respond dramatically to vitamin B_1, these being assisted by the diuretic effect of the vitamin, which helps to remove accumulated fluid from the tissues.

Experimental Vitamin B_1 Deficiency

Perhaps the simplest picture of uncomplicated vitamin B_1 deficiency is obtained in experiments with human volunteers, though it must be confessed that the results are not always as consistent or clearcut as might be desired, perhaps for reasons that will be referred to later (see page 76).

Jolliffe et al.[11] produced aneurine deficiency artificially in four out of five subjects by maintenance on a diet low in vitamin B_1. Subjective symptoms were observed on the fourth day and objective signs on the fifth. One subject, however, developed no symptoms or signs after thirty days on a diet containing 60 % of his calculated aneurine requirement. Addition of aneurine cured all the symptoms within three days and the objective signs within five days. Between 7 and 25 % of the ingested aneurine was excreted in the urine. Urinary excretion appeared to be well correlated with the aneurine intake (see page 63), though the amount excreted varied from one individual to another with the same intake.

Oedema was reported by Elsom et al.[12] to be an early symptom of experimental human aneurine deficiency. The changes in carbohydrate metabolism included failure of the blood-sugar to return to normal within three to four hours of ingestion of glucose, and maintenance of a high pyruvic acid content in the blood. The blood lactic acid also increased, the R.Q. was unaltered and the response to insulin decreased as the deficiency progressed. The abnormalities disappeared on administration of aneurine.

A considerable number of experiments of this kind were carried out over a number of years by R. D. Williams and his colleagues.[13] Anorexia, fatigue, loss of weight, absence of or low free gastric acidity, constipation, tenderness of the muscles of the calves and abnormalities in the electrocardiogram were more or less constant findings, but no oedema, cardiac dilatation or peripheral pain, such as are encountered in classical beriberi, were observed. Subjective symptoms were usually experienced by the patients before objective signs became manifest. The first of these signs, which appeared about the thirtieth day with subjects maintained on a daily intake of 0·2 mg. (i.e. about 10 % of the normal intake) was a diminished aneurine excretion, and by the fiftieth day the urinary excretion following administration of the test dose was also reduced (see page 63). After this stage was reached administration of glucose raised the blood-pyruvic and lactic acid levels, and anorexia and increased weakness and paraesthesia of the legs appeared. Only after 110 days on this regimen did signs of polyneuropathy appear, with sensory loss, loss of tendon reflexes and paralysis of the leg muscles, so that this sign of aneurine deficiency is particularly late in making its appearance ; it can only be cured by weeks of treatment with high doses of aneurine.

Experiments on the simultaneous administration of aneurine and desiccated thyroid showed [14] that the latter was less efficient in promoting metabolic activity in a state of vitamin B_1 deficiency. This may be connected with the observation of other workers [15] that thyrotoxic patients are unable to store aneurine but excrete large amounts in the urine, faeces and sweat, and the claim that aneurine is of benefit in such cases.

A comparison of the effects of acute and mild chronic aneurine plus riboflavine deficiency was made by Horwitt et al.[16] They divided their subjects into three groups. The first received a daily diet containing 2200 cals. and sufficient vitamins, with the exception of aneurine (400 μg. per day) and riboflavine (900 μg. per day). The second group had the same diet, but with 6 mg. of aneurine and 1·3 mg. of riboflavine per day. The third group served as a control. In the first group, some dulling of interest and restriction of activity was observed and, within nine months, an abnormally high level of lactic and pyruvic acid was found in the blood after administration of glucose. After two years, the members of the second group were transferred to a diet that supplied 250 μg. of aneurine and 800 μg. of riboflavine daily ; within three months, the blood lactic and pyruvic acids had risen higher than in the first group. Shortly afterwards, clinical symptoms developed—non-pitting oedema of the facial skin, budding of the blood vessels into the cornea with plexus formation, decreased vibration sense in the legs and some loss of inhibitory control with exaggeration of psychotic symptoms. Immediate recovery occurred when 6 mg. of aneurine per day were administered.

The effects of a combined deficiency of aneurine, riboflavine and nicotinic acid were studied by Keys et al.[17] One group of young men lived for 161 days on a diet that supplied only 0·61 mg. of aneurine, 0·95 mg. of riboflavine and 12·2 mg. of nicotinic acid per day, whilst another group subsisted on a diet that supplied rather more of the vitamins. No serious deficiency symptoms developed. When the vitamin intake of some of the subjects was reduced to 0·032 mg. of aneurine, 0·052 mg. of riboflavine and 0·4 mg. of nicotinic acid per day, however, symptoms of vitamin B_1 deficiency appeared, and were quickly relieved by administration of aneurine. Thus, aneurine deficiency is probably the first to manifest itself in a multiple vitamin deficiency (see page 607).

Aneurine and Cancer

J. E. Ayre and W. A. G. Bauld [18] noted that abnormal oestrogenic activity in cases of menorrhagia and uterine cancer was often associated with a vitamin B_1 deficiency, though not with a deficiency of other vitamins. They therefore suggested that aneurine deficiency over a prolonged period may pre-dispose either to menorrhagia or to malignancy. It is suggested that the finding of a vitamin B_1 deficiency together with an abnormally high level of oestrogen may be indicative of a dangerous pre-cancerous state.

References to Section 12

1. T. Lee, *Chinese Med. J.*, 1940, **58**, 314.
2. G. R. Minot, M. B. Strauss and S. Cobb, *New England J. Med.*, 1933, **208**, 1244 ; N. Jolliffe and P. M. Joffe, *Proc. Soc. Exp. Biol. Med.*, 1935, **32**, 1161 ; N. Jolliffe, C. N. Colbert and P. M. Joffe, *Amer. J. Med. Sci.*, 1936, **191**, 515.
3. E. D. Plass and W. F. Meugert, *J. Amer. Med. Assoc.*, 1933, **101**, 2020 ; M. R. Strauss and W. J. Macdonald, *ibid.*, 1933, **100**, 1320.
4. R. E. Hibbs, *Ann. Int. Med.*, 1946, **25**, 270.
5. H. M. Sinclair, *Proc. Roy. Soc. Med.*, 1939, **32**, 807.
6. R. Goodhart and H. M. Sinclair, *J. Biol. Chem.*, 1940, **132**, 11.
7. K. A. Smith and H. L. Mason, *Proc. Staff Meetings Mayo Clinic*, 1940, **15**, 529.
8. W. Needles, *J. Amer. Med. Assoc.*, 1943, **121**, 914.
9. R. Kapeller-Adler and J. A. Cartwright, *Edinburgh Med. J.*, 1943, **50**, 305.
10. H. E. de Wardener and B. Lennox, *Lancet*, 1947, **1**, 11.
11. N. Jolliffe, R. Goodhart, J. Gennis and J. K. Cline, *Amer. J. Med. Sci.*, 1939, **198**, 198.
12. K. O. Elsom, F. D. W. Lukens, W. H. Montgomery and L. Jonas, *J. Clin. Invest.*, 1940, **19**, 153.
13. R. D. Williams, H. L. Mason and B. F. Smith, *Proc. Staff Meetings Mayo Clinic*, 1939, **14**, 787 ; R. D. Williams, H. L. Mason, R. M. Wilder and B. F. Smith, *Arch. intern. Med.*, 1940, **66**, 785 ; R. D. Williams, H. L. Mason, B. F. Smith and R. M. Wilder, *ibid.*, 1942, **69**, 721 ; R. D. Williams, H. L. Mason, M. H. Power and R. M. Wilder, *ibid.*, 1943, **71**, 38.
14. R. D. Williams and E. C. Kendall, *ibid.*, 1943, **72**, 185.
15. R. H. Williams, E. Egana, P. Robinson, S. P. Asher and C. Dutoit, *ibid.*, 1943, **72**, 353.
16. M. K. Horwitt, E. Liebert, O. Kreisler and P. Wittman, *Science*, 1946, **104**, 407.
17. A. Keys, A. F. Henschel, H. L. Taylor, O. Mickelsen and J. Brozek, *Amer. J. Physiol.*, 1945, **144**, 5.
18. J. E. Ayre and W. A. G. Bauld, *Science*, 1946, **103**, 441.

13. EFFECT OF EXCESSIVE DOSAGE WITH ANEURINE

According to C. L. Steinberg,[1] daily doses of 100 μg. of aneurine given to rats caused sterility in the second generation females, whilst daily doses of 200 and 400 μg. resulted in the appearance of a toxic factor in the milk of the third generation females and in complete failure of lactation respectively. This observation was confirmed by M. B. Richards,[2] who found that failure of lactation was more severe the higher the intake of aneurine, and that litters from does with a high aneurine intake (plus calcium carbonate) failed to survive, were in a poor condition or showed convulsive fits due to pyridoxine deficiency. Excess of aneurine, in fact, appeared to precipitate pyridoxine deficiency. L. R. Cerecedo and L. J. Vinson,[3] on the other hand, failed to find evidence that amounts of the order of 625 to 700 μg. per day had any harmful effects on the fertility or lactation of rats. According to C. Mano,[4] the respiration of mice was stimulated by small doses, whilst respiratory arrest and chronic cramps were produced by large doses.

C. L. Steinberg [1] also reported that, in humans, overdosage with aneurine may give rise to herpes zoster, and C. A. Mills [5] and Z. A. Leitner [6] found that an intake of more than 5 mg. per day produced symptoms of hyperthyroidism, *e.g.* nervousness, tremors, tachycardia and sweating. It was suggested that these were due to overdosage or, more correctly, to supersaturation. When the vitamin was withdrawn, the nervousness and other symptoms disappeared.

Several cases of sensitivity resembling allergic reactions have also been reported ; [6,7] in at least one instance the patient was desensitised by the conventional procedure. As, according to F. Kalz,[8] injection of aneurine hydrochloride intradermally invariably causes a histamine-like reaction, the intradermal test cannot be used to test sensitivity towards aneurine. Anaphylaxis plays no part in aneurine toxicity as seen in rabbits,[9] but the injection of a sensitising dose of 100 mg. increased the resistance of the animals to toxic injections of the vitamin, increasing the lethal dose from 126 to 238 mg. per kg. H. Molitor [10] was unable to sensitise dogs and guinea-pigs so that anaphylactic phenomena appeared. Anaphylactic shock has been reported in man.[11]

Aneurine is usually regarded as non-toxic. N. Joliffe,[12] for instance, observed no toxic effects in over 3000 patients ; he also reported that Borsook treated seventy patients for three years with 100 mg. of aneurine hydrochloride per day without untoward results. It seems to be generally accepted that aneurine can safely be given by mouth, but should be given by injection only in severe intestinal dysfunction and acute beriberi. In the rare instances in which parenteral administration is resorted to, the possibility of anaphylaxis must be kept in mind and the dose given slowly. C. A. Mills,[5] however, suggests that parenteral administration should never be used.

References to Section 13

1. C. L. Steinberg, *Amer. J. Digest. Dis. Nutr.*, 1938, **5**, 680.
2. M. B. Richards, *Brit. Med. J.*, 1945, **1**, 433.
3. L. R. Cerecedo and L. J. Vinson, *Proc. Soc. Exp. Biol. Med.*, 1944, **55**, 139.
4. C. Mano, *Japan J. Med. Sci.*, IV, 1940, **12**, *Proc.*, 98.
5. C. A. Mills, *J. Amer. Med. Assoc.*, 1941, **116**, 2101 ; 1941, **117**, 1501.
6. Z. A. Leitner, *Lancet*, 1943, **2**, 474.
7. M. H. Stiles, *J. Allergy*, 1941, **12**, 507 ; L. Scheff, *J. Amer. Med. Assoc.*, 1941, **117**, 609 ; C. L. Laws, *ibid.*, 176 ; W. S. Eisenstadt, *Minn. Med.*, 1942, **25**, 861 ; M. M. Mitrani, *J. Allergy*, 1944, **15**, 150 ; W. Stein and M. Morgenstein, *Ann. Int. Med.*, 1944, **20**, 826.
8. F. Kalz, *J. Invest. Dermat.*, 1942, **5**, 135.
9. T. J. Haley and A. M. Flesher, *Science*, 1946, **104**, 567.
10. H. Molitor, *Proc. Fed. Amer. Soc. Exp. Biol.*, 1942, **1**, 309.
11. I. M. Reingold and F. R. Webb, *J. Amer. Med. Assoc.*, 1946, **130**, 491.
12. N. Jolliffe, *ibid.*, 1941, **117**, 1496, 1501.

14. METABOLISM OF ANEURINE

Both microbiological and chemical assays have been used to measure the amount of aneurine in the blood and urine of normal and avitaminous humans and animals. The results indicated that the blood and urine concentrations were lower in vitamin B_1-deficient than in normal subjects, and quite early in the history of aneurine therapy it was recognised that low concentrations of aneurine in both body fluids supported a diagnosis of vitamin B_1 deficiency.

Urinary excretion and the Test-Dose Method of Assessing Nutritional Status

L. J. Harris and P. C. Leong [1] introduced a method of assessing the nutritional status of an individual with respect to aneurine that was more reliable than a simple measurement of the urinary concentration. The concentration of aneurine in the urine before and after administration of a test dose was estimated by the thiochrome method ; in vitamin B_1 deficiency, very little of the test dose was excreted, whereas well-nourished subjects excreted a relatively large proportion.

Using this method, Y. L. Wang and L. J. Harris [2] found that normal humans excreted 36 to 105 (average 65) μg. of aneurine per day and that, on administration of a test dose of just over 1 mg. of aneurine hydrochloride per 10 stones of bodyweight, this increased to over 105 μg. per day. Excretions of less than 30 μg. per day, rising to not more than 45 μg. after giving the test dose, were taken to indicate sub-optimal levels of intake, whilst values of 15 μg. per day or less were regarded as indicative of more or less severe vitamin B_1 deficiency.

A somewhat similar method was used by G. M. Hills [3] with similar, though somewhat higher, results. He found that normal humans excreted 50 to 170 (average 100) μg. per day and that, except in thyrotoxicosis, oral administration of a 1-mg. test dose of aneurine hydrochloride resulted in the excretion, three hours later, of 26 to 110 (average 65) μg. In a fully saturated individual, 200 μg. of the test dose were excreted within three hours. H. C. Hou and E. F. Yang,[4] using a modification of the test devised by E. F. Yang and B. S. Platt,[5] in which diazotised p-aminoacetophenone is the reagent, obtained values of 28 to 170 and 0 to 16 μg. for the daily urinary excretion of normal Chinese adults and beriberi patients respectively. R. C. Guha and B. Ahmad [6] reported values of 84 to 228 μg. for the daily output of normal Indian adults ; this was computed to be 6 to 19 % of the intake.

The test-dose method has been used extensively by various workers in different parts of the world. Some have employed the thiochrome method for estimating the aneurine, some various modifications of the azo reaction and others the yeast growth or the *Phycomyces* method. Different routes of administration, different test doses and different criteria for assessing the response have also been proposed ; some workers have suggested estimating the aneurine output within twenty-four hours of giving the test dose, others within three hours, and yet others within four hours.[7] Again, some workers have recorded the absolute amounts excreted and others the percentage of the test dose excreted.

Melnick *et al.*,[8] using diazotised p-aminoacetophenone, found that the average daily excretions by well-nourished men and women were 198 and 93 μg. respectively, and that, after oral administration of a 5-mg. test dose, 14 and 12 % respectively were excreted within twenty-four hours. Elderly men (66 to 75 years of age) excreted slightly more aneurine than women of the same age.[9] I. Magyar [10] claimed that the excretion within twenty-four hours of less than 18 % of a 2- to 10-mg. test dose administered intravenously was indicative of vitamin B_1 deficiency. W. Neuweiler [11] found that the daily urinary excretion of normal women was 45 to 665 μg., of pregnant women on a normal diet, 120 to 930 μg., of pregnant women on a diet supplemented with 2 mg. of aneurine hydrochloride daily, 400 to 780 μg., of nursing mothers, 145 to 1070 μg., and of cases of complicated pregnancy, 210 to 765 μg. Intramuscular injection of 10 mg. of aneurine hydrochloride resulted in the retention of 32 to 70 % by the normal women and the pregnant women given the aneurine-supplemented diet, whereas more than 70 % was retained by the pregnant women on an ordinary diet, by those with neuralgic complaints and by the nursing mothers ; 100 % was retained in subjects with pregnancy toxaemia. A. C. Siddall and J. W. Mull [12] stated that the average daily excretions of forty-two pregnant women were 286, 263 and 249 μg. in the first, second and third trimesters respectively ; these excretions were doubled on administration of 750 μg. of aneurine hydrochloride daily by mouth.

Much lower values were reported by K. V. Toverud [13] for pregnant and non-pregnant women. Normal women were found to excrete 80 μg. per day by the thiochrome method or 137·5 μg. by the azo method, and 2·6 to 16·1 % of a 5-mg. test dose was excreted within twenty-four hours. Pregnant women excreted on the average only 38 μg. per day, but nearly half of the group excreted none at all, and only 2 % of the test dose was excreted within twenty-four hours. Lactating women excreted 70 μg. per day and the response to a test dose was intermediate between that of pregnant and normal women.

H. L. Mason and R. D. Williams [14] stated that the diet prior to carrying out a test for aneurine deficiency should provide 800 to 900 μg. of aneurine per day, that a test dose of 1 mg., equivalent to 0·4 mg. per 1000 cals., should be used and that the excretion of over 100 μg. in the urine in twenty-four hours, increasing to at least 20 % of the test dose, was evidence of an adequate intake of aneurine.

Y. L. Wang and J. Yudkin [15] showed that aneurine excretion decreased rapidly in subjects fed a vitamin B_1-deficient diet and reached a steady value in six days. When vitamin B_1 was restored to the diet, the excretion rapidly increased and, with a normal intake of about 900 μg. per day, it rose to 137 to 233 μg. per day. Benson et al.[16] gave the urinary excretion of children, aged 4 to 10 years, as 92 to 602 (average 268) μg. per day, and claimed that on an adequate diet, supplying at least 990 μg. per day, 27 % of the ingested aneurine was excreted. The excretion of less than 20 % of the daily intake was claimed to indicate vitamin B_1 deficiency.

According to Kraut et al.,[17] some of the aneurine in urine is generally present in the form of cocarboxylase, 10 to 210 μg. of aneurine and 0 to 180 μg. of cocarboxylase being excreted per day ; the average of thirty-eight estimations was 100 μg. of free and 40 μg. of bound aneurine. The ratio of free to bound aneurine in individual instances varied enormously—from 1 : 9 to 9 : 1. Administration of aneurine increased the excretion of both forms and generally left the ratio substantially unaffected.

The presence in urine of a pyrimidine compound capable of stimulating the growth of yeast in a manner similar to aneurine was reported by Pollack et al.[18] They found that on depriving a subject of aneurine for ten days the ratio of aneurine to pyrimidine changed from 9 : 1 to 1 : 9, the absolute amount of the pyrimidine excreted remaining substantially constant. The intravenous injection of 100 mg. of aneurine was followed by an enormous increase in the excretion of urinary pyrimidine.

A novel method of studying the metabolism of aneurine was introduced by Borsook et al.[19] They injected aneurine containing radioactive sulphur, S^{35}, intramuscularly into a man who had been deprived of aneurine for thirty-six days, and found that there was a rapid increase in the excretion of S^{35} in the urine, indicating that significant amounts of aneurine remained in the tissues after prolonged ingestion of a vitamin B_1-free diet. The results also showed that injected aneurine interacted very quickly with pre-existing aneurine in the blood and tissues, and that metabolism was very rapid, yielding neutral sulphur compounds and inorganic sulphate in the urine.

The efficiency with which different amounts of aneurine are utilised in the rat varies, but doses of 5 to 50 μg. per day were the levels most effectively utilised.[20] The efficiencies for doses of 50, 100 and 1000 μg. per day were 92, 83, and 52 % respectively. The results indicate that appreciable destruction of aneurine occurs in the body. Such destruction was shown to take place when aneurine was incubated with liver, lung, heart, stomach and intestinal tissue. Comparable figures are not available for humans, but it has been shown [21] that in normal subjects the urinary excretion is directly related to the dose given and, with intakes of 50 mg., approximates to 100 %. On a synthetic diet yielding 1 mg. of aneurine per day and on a natural diet containing 0·84 mg., the daily urinary outputs were 113 to 147 and 90 to 112 μg. respectively.[22]

Doubt was thrown on the validity of the excretion test method of assessing aneurine status by E. C. Allbone and E. Finch,[23] who found that children on an ordinary diet excreted in the urine 10 to 14 % of their intake of aneurine and that after giving 0·5 to 1·0 mg. by mouth, the output in different individuals varied considerably—from 0 to 41 %—but the average was still only 14 %. Many recently ill children excreted amounts of aneurine considerably less than the accepted levels without showing signs of beriberi.

Somewhat disturbing results were also obtained by H. H. Gifft and H. M. Hauck,[24] who compared four different methods of assessing aneurine status. Normal adults were maintained for forty-four days on a diet that provided 600 μg. of aneurine per 1000 cals., and the following estimations were carried out : (a) the twenty-four-hourly excretion for the last four weeks of the period ; (b) the percentage recovery of a 5-mg. oral test dose given at the end of the period ; (c) the recovery of a 1-mg. intramuscular dose at the beginning, and (d) at the end, of the period. The twenty-four-hourly excretion was found to be equivalent to 9 to 13 % of the intake, the recovery from the 5-mg. dose to 15 to 22 % of the dose and from the two 1-mg. doses to 15 to 24 % and 8 to 21 % respectively. Each test in fact gave a result that indicated a different nutritional status in the same individual. E. Papageorge and G. T. Lewis [25] compared the twenty-four-hourly urinary output of aneurine in normal young adults with : (a) the percentage recovery from a 1-mg. oral test dose after four hours ; and (b) the urinary output in a " fasting hour " specimen collected in the hour immediately following the completion of a twenty-four-hourly period and after an overnight fast. Satisfactory correlation was obtained between the twenty-four-hour output on the one hand and the " fasting hour " sample and the response to the 1-mg. test dose on the other, but the " fasting hour " test did not agree so well with the response to the test dose. Nevertheless, the " fasting hour " test was recommended as being the most convenient for nutritional surveys. The excretion of less than 4 μg. in the " fasting hour " test was regarded as indicative of aneurine deficiency.

Possibly the most critical study of the test-dose method is that carried out by Mickelsen et al.,[26] who made a statistical examination of the values obtained for the aneurine excretion of groups of " normal " young men. They showed that with dietary intakes of 0·6, 1·0, 1·8 and 2·0 mg. of aneurine per day, the amount of aneurine (as determined by the thiochrome method) excreted in the urine was linearly related to the intake, although one individual might excrete twice or three times as much as another individual on the same diet. The variations between individuals and groups increased with increased excretion. These workers also studied the excretion of the pyrimidine half of the aneurine molecule, which for brevity they term " pyramin ". This was estimated by the yeast fermentation method of Schultz et al. The excretion of pyramin was found to bear an exponential relationship to the aneurine intake, a plateau being formed at high intakes corresponding to an excretion of 400 μg. of pyramin per day. At more normal levels, however, i.e. 1 to 2 mg. per day, the relationship was linear. Moreover, the pyramin excretion was less variable than the aneurine excretion, and statistical treatment was therefore easier. The results suggest that insufficient attention has been given in the past to the statistical significance of the values obtained in aneurine excretion tests. Another factor that appears to have been ignored by previous workers is that, when the aneurine intake is changed, the rate of response in the urinary excretion is such that only half the change is completed in ten days. Mickelsen *et al.* recommended that at intakes between 0·7 and 1 mg. of aneurine per day, the aneurine excretion is a better indicator of nutritional status than the pyramin excretion, but that outside these limits the pyramin excretion is the more reliable.

The urinary excretion of aneurine by human subjects maintained on a diet rich in aneurine was reduced when viable fresh bakers' yeast was added to the diet,[27] and pure aneurine hydrochloride ingested with live yeast was not recovered in the urine.[27a] No such depression occurred when the yeast had been boiled in water.

Blood Concentrations and their Value in Assessing Nutritional Status

Although urinary excretion following the administration of a test dose has until recently been the accepted procedure for assessing the degree of vitamin B_1 deficiency, attempts have also been made to use blood concentrations for assessing nutritional status. Among the first papers reporting the aneurine content of blood were those of A. P. Meiklejohn [28] and H. M. Sinclair,[29] who employed the *Phycomyces* test. The concentration of aneurine in plasma and cerebrospinal fluid varied from 0 to 1·3 μg. per 100 ml. and in both instances the aneurine was present in the free state and not as cocarboxylase. The amount of aneurine present in the whole blood of healthy adults was 7·4 ± 1·4 μg. per 100 ml. ; values less than 4·5 μg. per 100 ml. were taken to indicate vitamin B_1 deficiency. E. N. Rowlands and J. F. Wilkinson,[30] using substantially the same method, obtained similar values. They found normal blood to contain 6·5 to 16·5 μg. per 100 ml. and the blood of subjects with alcoholic neuritis, nutritional neuritis, scurvy and malnutrition 5 μg. per 100 ml. or less. I. Magyar [31] obtained values ranging from 1 to 15 with an average of 7·6 μg. per 100 ml. for blood serum, and confirmed that the level depended on the dietary intake of aneurine.

According to R. Goodhart and T. Nitzberg,[32] normal blood contains 3·1 to 9·2 with an average of 5·4 μg. per 100 ml., and a value of less than 3 μg. per 100 ml. is indicative of vitamin B_1 deficiency. They used the yeast-growth method of Atkin, Schultz and Frey, and found that a heat labile factor was present in blood which enhanced the stimulatory activity of aneurine on yeast ; they were able to eliminate interference from this source by heating the blood at 100° C. for four to five minutes.

Benson *et al.*[33] obtained values ranging from 4·8 to 12·3 with an average of 7·8 μg. per 100 ml. for the aneurine content of the blood of healthy children, values not differing appreciably from those obtained by other workers for adults. They commented on the fact that daily variations in the blood aneurine of an individual did not follow the daily urinary aneurine outputs of the same individual, and that the blood concentration bore no relationship to the absolute amount or proportion of the dietary aneurine excreted in the urine.

It has been reported [34] that the amount of free aneurine in the maternal blood decreases during parturition, whereas the " bound " aneurine concentration remains unchanged. It is suggested that the decrease in the free aneurine concentration is due to an increase in the amount of acetylcholine hydrolysed, to changes in the nervous action and to increased passage through the placenta.

When aneurine hydrochloride (1 mg. per kg.) was injected intravenously into normal dogs, a temporary increase in the blood cocarboxylase occurred.[35] The injection of insulin (1 I.U. per kg.) into a normal animal was also followed by a rise in the blood cocarboxylase. If aneurine hydrochloride was injected into an insulin-treated animal, a still greater increase in the blood concentration of cocarboxylase, together with a decrease in the concentration of inorganic phosphate, occurred. No significant changes of this type, however, resulted from the injection of aneurine hydrochloride into depancreatised hyperglycemic dogs, and these responded normally when controlled with insulin, except that the blood inorganic phosphate remained constant. The results suggest that insulin increases the phosphorylation of aneurine.

Because the administration of aneurine to rabbits or humans was found to increase the capacity of their serum to inhibit the haemolytic action of digitonin, D. L. Farley [36] suggested that antihaemolytic activity could be used as an index of aneurine status, but the observation does not appear to have been made use of for this purpose.

Distribution of Aneurine in Blood Elements

A number of workers have studied the distribution of aneurine in the blood elements. The low proportion of aneurine in the plasma has already been noted. This was confirmed by E. Deutsch,[37] who obtained values of 9 to 16 μg. per 100 ml. for normal blood ; of this only 3 to 10 % was present in the plasma. The aneurine content of leucocytes and platelets were reported [38] to be ten-fold that of the erythrocytes. In leukemias, the concentration in leucocytes and platelets increased five-fold.[39] The yeast fermentation method estimates in addition to aneurine a pyrimidine compound (see page 106), presumed to be a metabolite, and the abnormaily high concentration of aneurine in the leucocytes in leukemia is attributed to impaired utilisation of the vitamin in this condition, since the amount of the pyrimidine metabolite present was found to be substantially the same as in normal individuals.

The red cells of humans and rats contain 2·1 and 1·4 μg. of aneurine pyrophosphate per 10^{11} cells respectively and white cells 340 and 280 μg. per 10^{11} cells.[39a]

Phosphorylation of Aneurine

The phosphorylation of aneurine (see page 93) is extremely rapid,[40] intravenous administration of the hydrochloride into normal human subjects being almost immediately followed by an increase in the aneurine pyrophosphate content of the blood ; this fell to normal again after about six minutes. Hepatic cirrhosis, but not nephritis, impaired the phosphorylation of aneurine. Similarly, the intravenous injection of cocarboxylase was followed by an increase in the plasma and red cell aneurine diphosphate and free aneurine ; the level of the latter rapidly returned to normal, but the diphosphate remained at an abnormally high level for more than one hour. Patients with advanced cirrhosis showed no immediate increase in the amount of free aneurine in the blood, and exhibited a smaller rise in the diphosphate than that observed in normal subjects.

Aneurine in Faeces

The amount of aneurine excreted in the faeces by rats was constant, whether the rats received 0, 5 or 50 μg. of aneurine daily [41] but, in deficient animals, the volume of faeces was greatly reduced ; the aneurine was largely present in the form of cocarboxylase. The faeces of aneurine-deficient rats did not alleviate symptoms of aneurine deficiency when given to other rats.

The amount of free aneurine excreted by humans on a synthetic diet containing 1 mg. of aneurine per day or on a natural diet containing 0·84 mg. was 13 to 17 and 25 to 49 μg. respectively ; the combined faecal aneurine was 2·4 to 5·1 times as high on the natural diet as on the synthetic diet.[42] The faecal excretion of aneurine is relatively constant, and independent of the dietary intake,[43, 44, 45] most of the aneurine in the faeces resulting from bacterial synthesis.[43, 44] It is present within the bacterial cells.

Faecal excretion is discussed more fully on page 76.

Aneurine in Sweat

Ordinarily, no appreciable quantities of aneurine are excreted in the sweat, whether this is produced thermally or as the result of exercise.[46] The sweat produced by exercise following the injection of 50 mg. of aneurine hydrochloride, however, contained a much greater concentration (4·5 mg. per litre) than the urine excreted by the same subjects (63 μg. per litre).[47]

Foetal Aneurine

Aneurine appears to be incapable of passing the placenta, although it accumulates in this organ, which thus serves to regulate the supply of aneurine to the foetus.[48] The concentrations of aneurine in the venous and arterial blood of the umbilical cord were found to be 7·5 and 5 μg. per 100 ml. respectively, compared with 2 to 12 μg. per 100 ml. in the maternal venous blood, and 2·7 to 10 μg. per 100 g. in the placenta. When 50 μg. of aneurine hydrochloride were given intravenously before parturition, the aneurine contents of both the cord blood and maternal blood and of the placenta increased, but the injected aneurine disappeared rapidly except in the placenta.

Aneurine only passes into the placenta when free,[49] although bound aneurine is present in this organ in concentrations greater than that of free aneurine ; the placenta contains 18 to 38 μg. per 100 g. of total aneurine, of which 4 to 8 μg. per 100 g. is in the free state. Oral administration of aneurine to newborn babes resulted in its excretion in the urine, but administration to the mother had little effect, because it was stopped by the placental barrier.[50]

Aneurine Content of Milk

The aneurine content of breast milk can be increased by increasing the amount of aneurine in the diet, but only to a maximum of 25 to 32 μg. per 100 ml.[13, 51] Breast-fed infants do not excrete aneurine, and require less aneurine than do artificially fed infants.[52] According to E. C. Slater and E. J. Rial,[53] breast milk contains about 9 μg. of aneurine per 100 ml. in the second week of lactation, rising to about 15 μg. per 100 ml. after twenty weeks and then gradually falling. Free aneurine is maximal in the third or fourth week, but a large proportion of the aneurine is present in phosphorylated form. Knott et al.,[54] from an analysis of 111 samples of milk from fifty women, record an average concentration of 15 μg. per 100 ml. None was present in the colostrum but the concentration in the later milk increased gradually to a maximum of 20 μg. per 100 ml. in the first three weeks, thereafter falling to 9·3 μg. per 100 ml. at weaning. This was confirmed by Roderuck et al.,[55] who obtained low aneurine values for the first few days after parturition, and rapidly increasing amounts during the first few weeks, rising to a maximum value of 14·0 to 14·7 μg. per day. The diet was the principal factor in determining the concentration in the milk.

Intramuscular injection of aneurine during labour, or oral administration after parturition, accelerated the increase in the milk aneurine during lactation.

Aneurine Content of Tissues

Aneurine is fairly uniformly distributed throughout the tissues of the human body. Brain, liver and kidney contain approximately [56] 1 μg. per g., heart muscle 2 to 3 μg. per g., and skeletal muscle 0·5 μg. : higher values are obtained immediately after administration of aneurine. Unlike other tissues, the brain maintained its vitamin B_1 content in face of a deficit of the vitamin for a considerable time.[56a]

Westenbrink et al.[57] studied the distribution of aneurine pyrophosphate in the tissues of man and of the rat, pig, duck, chick, pigeon, goose, blackheaded gull and frog. Compared with other animals, the amounts present in human liver and kidney were low and the amount in the heart muscle was high. In most animals, with the exception of the pig, little difference was found in the amounts present in the liver, kidney and heart muscle. In general, the spleen, adrenals, pancreas, thymus and sex organs contained less than the liver, kidney and heart, though rat testicles contained an exceptionally large amount. Except in the pig, lung tissue had only a low aneurine content. The amount present in the nervous system was low, both in man and the pig. Pig skeletal muscle contained an exceptionally large amount of aneurine pyrophosphate, and there was a marked difference between the amounts present in skeletal and in smooth muscle.

According to B. Alexander,[58] most of the aneurine in animal tissue is present as pyrophosphate.

The concentration of aneurine in the skeletal muscle of infants increases somewhat with age. A value of 20 μg. per 100 g. was recorded for a premature foetus, somewhat higher values for a full-term foetus and a value of 147 μg. per 100 g. for a seven-year old child.[59] More aneurine was present in the combined than in the free state ; for example, foetal organs from the third to the ninth month of pregnancy contained 3 to 7 μg. per 100 g. of free aneurine, and 20 to 50 μg. per 100 g. of total aneurine.[49] The concentration was highest in muscular organs.

References to Section 14

1. L. J. Harris and P. C. Leong, *Lancet*, 1936, **1**, 886.
2. Y. L. Wang and L. J. Harris, *Biochem. J.*, 1939, **33**, 1356.
3. G. M. Hills, *ibid.*, 1966.
4. H. C. Hou and E. F. Yang, *Chinese J. Physiol.*, 1939, **14**, 269.
5. E. F. Yang and B. S. Platt, *ibid.*, 259.
6. R. C. Guha and B. Ahmad, *Indian J. Med. Res.*, 1939, **27**, 465.
7. V. A. Najjar and L. E. Holt, *Johns Hopkins Hosp. Bull.*, 1940, **67**, 107.
8. D. Melnick, H. Field and W. D. Robinson, *J. Nutrition*, 1939, **18**, 593.
9. L. W. Weitz and H. S. Mitchell, *Proc. Soc. Exp. Biol. Med.*, 1941, **48**, 259.
10. I. Magyar, *Z. Vitaminforsch.*, 1940, **10**, 32.
11. W. Neuweiler, *Arch. Gynäk.*, 1939, **169**, 19.
12. A. C. Siddall and J. W. Mull, *Amer. J. Obstet. Gynec.*, 1945, **49**, 672.
13. K. V. Toverud, *Z. Vitaminforsch.*, 1940, **10**, 255.
14. H. L. Mason and R. D. Williams, *J. Clin. Invest.*, 1942, **21**, 247.
15. Y. L. Wang and J. Yudkin, *Biochem. J.*, 1940, **24**, 343.
16. R. A. Benson, C. M. Witzberger and L. B. Slobody, *J. Pediat.*, 1941, **18**, 617 ; R. A. Benson, L. B. Slobody, C. M. Witzberger and L. Lewis, *ibid.*, 1942, **20**, 454.
17. H. Kraut, A. Weischer and G. Stumpff, *Biochem. Z.*, 1941, **308**, 309.
18. H. Pollack, M. Ellenberg and H. Dolger, *J. Nutrition*, 1941, **21**, *Suppl.*, 10.
19. H. Borsook, E. R. Buchman, J. B. Hatcher, D. M. Yost and E. McMillan, *Proc. Nat. Acad. Sci.*, 1940, **28**, 412.
20. B. Sure and Z. W. Ford, *J. Nutrition*, 1943, **26**, 659.
21. B. Alexander, G. Landwehr and F. Mitchell, *J. Clin. Invest.*, 1946, **25**, 294.
22. M. L. Hathaway and J. E. Strom, *J. Nutrition*, 1946, **32**, 1.
23. E. C. Allbone and E. Finch, *Arch. Dis. Childhood*, 1945, **20**, 169.
24. H. H. Gifft and H. M. Hauck, *J. Nutrition*, 1946, **31**, 635.
25. E. Papageorge and G. T. Lewis, *ibid.*, 1947, **34**, 301.
26. O. Mickelsen, W. O. Caster and A. Keys, *Proc. Soc. Exp. Biol. Med.*, 1946, **62**, 254 ; *J. Biol. Chem.*, 1947, **168**, 415.
27. H. T. Ness, E. L. Price and H. T. Parsons, *Science*, 1946, **103**, 198.
27a. M. Garber, M. M. Marquette and H. T. Parsons, *J. Nutrition*, 1949, **38**, 225.
28. A. P. Meiklejohn, *Biochem. J.*, 1937, **31**, 1441.
29. H. M. Sinclair, *ibid.*, 1938, **32**, 2185 ; 1939, **33**, 1816, 2027.
30. E. N. Rowlands and J. F. Wilkinson, *Brit. Med. J.*, 1938, **2**, 818.
31. I. Magyar, *Z. Vitaminforsch.*, 1940, **10**, 32.
32. R. Goodhart and T. Nitzberg, *J. Clin. Invest.*, 1941, **20**, 625.
33. R. A. Benson, C. M. Witzberger, L. B. Slobody and L. Lewis, *J. Pediat.*, 1942, **21**, 659.
34. W. Neuweiler, *Z. Vitaminforsch.*, 1942, **12**, 329.

35. P. P. Foà, J. A. Smith and H. R. Weinstein, *Arch. Biochem.*, 1947, **13**, 449.
36. D. L. Farley, *Surg., Gynec., Obstet.*, 1942, **74**, 1154.
37. E. Deutsch, *Schweiz. Med. Woch.*, 1942, **72**, 895.
38. A. T. Gorham, J. C. Abels, A. L. Robins and C. P. Rhoads, *J. Clin. Invest.*, 1942, **21**, 161.
39. J. C. Abels, A. T. Gorham, L. Carver and C. P. Rhoads, *ibid.*, 177.
39a. G. Smits and E. Florijn, *Biochim. et Biophys. Acta*, 1949, **3**, 44.
40. R. H. Williams, G. W. Bissell and J. B. Peters, *Arch. intern. Med.*, 1944, **73**, 203.
41. G. A. Emerson and H. G. Obermeyer, *Proc. Soc. Exp. Biol. Med.*, 1945, **59**, 299.
42. M. L. Hathaway and J. E. Strom, *J. Nutrition*, 1946, **32**, 1.
43. L. Wildemann, *Biochem. Z.*, 1941, **308**, 10.
44. B. Alexander, G. Landwehr and F. Mitchell, *J. Clin. Invest.*, 1946, **25**, 287.
45. H. G. Oldham, M. V. Davis and L. J. Roberts, *J. Nutrition*, 1946, **32**, 163.
46. D. M. Tennant and R. H. Silber, *J. Biol. Chem.*, 1943, **148**, 159.
47. E. L. Hardt and E. V. Still, *Proc. Soc. Exp. Biol. Med.*, 1941, **48**, 704.
48. W. Neuweiler, *Z. Vitaminforsch.*, 1940, **10**, 40.
49. W. Neuweiler, *ibid.*, 1941, **11**, 88.
50. W. Neuweiler, *ibid.*, 1943, **13**, 280.
51. A. F. Morgan and E. G. Haynes, *J. Nutrition*, 1939, **18**, 105.
52. F. Widenbauer and H. Krüger, *Z. Kinderheilk.*, 1939, **61**, 52.
53. E. C. Slater and E. J. Rial, *Med. J. Australia*, 1942, **1**, 3.
54. E. M. Knott, S. C. Kleiger and F. Torres-Bracamonte, *J. Nutrition*, 1943, **25**, 49.
55. C. E. Roderuck, H. H. Williams and I. G. Macy, *Amer. J. Dis. Child.*, 1945, **70**, 162 ; *J. Nutrition*, 1946, **32**, 249.
56. J. W. Ferrebee, N. Weissman, D. Parker and P. S. Owen, *J. Clin. Invest.*, 1942, **21**, 401.
56a. J. Salcedo, V. A. Najjar, L. E. Holt and E. W. Hutzler, *J. Nutrition*, 1948, **36**, 307.
57. H. G. K. Westenbrink, E. P. S. Parvé and H. J. Thomasson, *Z. Vitaminforsch.*, 1943, **13**, 101.
58. B. Alexander, *J. Biol. Chem.*, 1943, **151**, 455.
59. M. C. Hulse, N. Weissman, V. Rowland, R. Gross and J. W. Ferrebee, *Amer. J. Dis. Child.*, 1944, **67**, 30.

15. INTESTINAL SYNTHESIS OF ANEURINE

As long ago as 1915 it was observed by Theiler *et al.*[1] that ruminants could be maintained for long periods of time on a diet low in certain vitamins, and they therefore suggested that " the vitamin requirements of cattle are so low that they may even be covered indirectly by synthesis carried out by the extensive bacterial flora of the intestines ".

Thirteen years later, Bechdel et al.[2] showed that calves developed normally on a diet low in " vitamin B ", and they therefore supported the hypothesis put forward by Theiler et al. Later work, however, indicated that the source of the vitamin B in ruminants is the bacterial flora not of the intestine, but of the rumen. Nevertheless, recent work has confirmed in a most dramatic manner the prophetic words of the South African workers in respect of other species of animals.

Most of the early results on aneurine excretion in animals were confined to estimates of urinary excretion, and no reports appear to have been made of the amounts excreted in faeces until 1935, when Guerrant et al.[3] showed that vitamin B_1 was present in the faeces of rats owing to bacterial synthesis in the caecum. In the rat the nature of the ingested carbohydrate had a marked effect on the elaboration of the vitamin, readily assimilable carbohydrates such as sucrose and glucose being ineffective. Dextrin, however, was assimilated at a much slower rate, enabling it to reach the caecum where organisms had an opportunity of multiplying. For many years it was believed that rats could only benefit from this microbiological synthesis by ingesting their faeces [4] and, in fact, they may do this in vitamin B_1 deficiency tests unless prevented from gaining access to their faeces, for instance, by using cages with wire-screens ; many experiments have been invalidated through failure to take precautions against this contingency.

Refection

In 1926 it was reported by L. S. Fridericia [5] in Denmark that a young rat on a " vitamin B "-deficient diet containing rice starch had begun to grow at a normal rate, after its weight had declined in the anticipated manner. At the same time, the faeces became white and bulky owing to the presence of undigested starch. The phenomenon was termed refection, and appeared spontaneously some months later in a group of rats at the Lister Institute, London.[6] It could be induced in any rats by feeding the bulky white faeces. The phenomenon is due to the sudden loss by the rat of the ability to digest starch, though why this should happen is still a mystery. It has been suggested [7] that the presence of undigested starch and of starch-splitting organisms in the caecum leads to a vigorous fermentation with the development of an acid pH that favours the growth of organisms capable of synthesising members of the vitamin B complex. These then become available to the rat by virtue of the acid pH of the caecum, and the caecal region therefore behaves like the rumen in ruminants (see page 79). Refected rats excrete more vitamin B than non-refective rats on the same vitamin B-deficient diet.

Refection has also been observed in the pigeon,[8] whilst the rabbit may derive some, and possibly most, of its vitamin B supply from the consumption of its faeces. Rabbits excrete two types of faeces, one normal, voided during the day-time, the other, softer and produced during the night. The latter are normally swallowed by the rabbit directly from the anus.[9] They swarm with bacteria, and are presumably rich in the vitamin B complex.

Rôle of the Intestinal Flora

The presence in rat faeces of components of the vitamin B complex was demonstrated by Light et al.,[10] who found that the animals lost weight when sulphaguanidine was added to the diet, and that growth was restored either by giving the vitamin B complex or faeces from normal rats. They concluded that the sulphonamide inhibited the bacterial synthesis of essential factors belonging to the complex.

The aneurine content of human faeces was shown to be independent of the aneurine intake by L. Wildemann,[11] who ascribed this to synthesis of the vitamin by bacteria in the intestine. He put forward these results rather to prove that faecal excretion, in contrast to urinary excretion, is not a measure of the nutritional status of an individual. His conclusions have since been confirmed by Alexander et al.[12]

The possible significance of the independence of faecal excretion and diet was not appreciated until the publication in 1943 of a paper by V. A. Najjar and L. E. Holt [13] who, in an attempt to establish the aneurine requirements of man with greater accuracy than had hitherto been possible, maintained nine young male volunteers for several months on a diet supplying only 0·1 to 0·2 mg. per day. Five showed the anticipated signs of aneurine deficiency, but four showed no signs at all, even after the complete exclusion of aneurine from the diet for a further seven weeks. Free aneurine was found to be present in the faeces, and on giving one of these four anomalous subjects sulphasuxidine the faecal aneurine fell to zero, rising again to the original value when the administration of the sulphonamide was stopped.

This appeared to indicate that aneurine formed by the flora of the intestine could, under certain conditions, be absorbed in sufficient quantities to prevent the development of aneurine deficiency. That it was probably absorbed from the large intestine was demonstrated by giving a retention enema containing aneurine ; a pronounced rise in the urinary excretion of aneurine followed.

What conditions are necessary for intestinal synthesis and why the phenomenon had not previously been discovered in the course of the innumerable experiments that have been carried out is still a mystery, although some of the factors that affect the phenomenon are now known. The authors conclude their paper with these very significant words : " The demonstration that intestinal bacteria can synthesise thiamine carries interesting implications for human nutrition. This phenomenon may explain the discrepancies in thiamine requirements found by different observers. Since it is likely that the biosynthesis of thiamine is greatly affected by diet, as is known to be the case in animals, it follows that we must think in terms of requirements on particular diets rather than of requirements in general."

In fact, the result appears to call into question the fundamental concept of a vitamin as a substance that must be present in the diet to enable animals to remain healthy. For why, if man can derive his aneurine requirements from his intestinal flora, should vitamin B_1 deficiency ever be observed ? The complete answer to this question has not yet been found, but similar observations in respect of other members of the vitamin B complex have been made, with results even more striking than those obtained with aneurine.

Although their results anticipate much that should properly be reserved for later chapters, it is useful at this stage to refer to the work of Denko et al.[14] These workers measured the faecal and urinary excretions of seven healthy young men maintained on a normal diet containing p-aminobenzoic acid, biotin, folic acid, pantothenic acid, pyridoxine, aneurine, riboflavine and nicotinic acid, the amount of each of these factors in the diet being measured. The following results were obtained (μg. per day) for the range of the averages of the seven subjects and the mean of the averages :

	Urine	Faeces
p-Aminobenzoic acid	131-198 (148)	183-361 (246)
Biotin	27·5-35·6 (31·7)	114-201 (133)
Folic acid	2·94-4·99 (3·99)	222-393 (304)
Pantothenic acid	2·68-3·46 (3·04)	0·89-3·66 (2·20)
Pyridoxine	0·57-0·69 (0·63)	0·33-0·42 (0·38)
Nicotinic acid	1·31-1·39 (1·21)	2·14-5·41 (3·63)
Aneurine	144-323 (227)	109-895 (548)
Riboflavine	543-913 (678)	823-1313 (1029)

They indicate that the faecal excretion was higher than the urinary excretion in every instance except pantothenic acid and pyridoxine.

A comparison was then made of the ranges and means of the average daily vitamin intakes with the ranges and means of the average urinary and faecal excretions :

	Intake	Urinary and Faecal Excretion	Excretion a Per Cent. Intake (Mean)
p-Aminobenzoic acid	97-220 (188)	331-398 (373)	230
Biotin	37-54 (44)	136-236 (163)	378
Folic acid	43-86 (62)	226-397 (310)	542
Pantothenic acid	4·19-5·30 (4·73)	4·07-6·72 (5·25)	112
Pyridoxine	1·32-2·46 (1·76)	0·94-1·07 (1·01)	57
Nicotinic acid	12·4-20·9 (15·6)	3·32-6·64 (4·82)	31
Aneurine	1·24-1·63 (1·44)	0·36-1·02 (0·78)	57
Riboflavine	1·74-1·98 (1·84)	1·74-1·98 (1·84)	91

A similar series of tests was carried out on five young men maintained on a diet containing limited amounts of all the members of the vitamin B complex. Two other men were given the same diet supplemented with amounts of each vitamin equal to or greater than the amounts contained in the normal diet previously given. With the restricted vitamin intake, the faecal excretion of aneurine and of the other vitamins was at least as high as that on the normal diet, and was unaffected by vitamin supplementation. The faecal excretion of aneurine actually exceeded the dietary intake. The urinary excretion of aneurine, on the other hand, and of riboflavine, N^1-methylnicotinamide and pantothenic acid decreased markedly on the restricted diet, but returned to normal on supplementation. With the other vitamins the urinary excretion was affected to a smaller extent.

It is evident from these results that all the B vitamins are synthesised by the intestinal flora, but that the requirements of aneurine, riboflavine and nicotinic acid as reflected in the urinary excretion must be met from the vitamins supplied in the diet. Possibly with the other vitamins absorption takes place to a sufficient extent to prevent the development of deficiency symptoms. This may be the reason why deficiencies of p-aminobenzoic acid, folic acid, biotin, pantothenic acid and, probably, pyridoxine are virtually unknown except in experimental subjects. Only with aneurine, riboflavine and nicotinic acid are characteristic deficiency symptoms produced when the diet contains inadequate amounts. It must be presumed that although bacterial synthesis of these three vitamins may occur in the intestine they are not normally absorbed, although sometimes, as in Najjar's experiment, animals may be able to make use of the aneurine, riboflavine or nicotinic acid produced by bacterial action. That no absorption of bacterial aneurine normally occurs was the conclusion reached by B. Alexander and G. Landwehr,[15] for neither aneurine nor cocarboxylase was absorbed from the large intestine when administered by retention enema. This is a complete contradiction of the result obtained by Najjar and Holt.

It is possible that the results of intestinal synthesis have been noted previously without the real explanation having been appreciated. F. M. Meyers,[16] for example, reported that healthy Javanese excreted from o to 63 μg. of aneurine per day compared with 40 to 3000 μg. for the inhabitants of temperate climates. He concluded that a chronic low vitamin B_1 intake may produce an adaptation of the body. Might it not rather be that the needs of the body were being met in such instances by the bacteria of the gut ?

A little information is available concerning the effect of certain factors on faecal excretion. Increased amounts of aneurine, for example, were excreted in the faeces of humans when large amounts of plant fibre were ingested,[17] although no change occurred in the faecal excretion on altering the carbohydrate : fat ratio.[18] The nature of the carbohydrate may also be a factor affecting the bacterial synthesis of aneurine, for Schweigert et al.[19] observed that the amount of aneurine excreted in the urine increased when the sucrose in the diet was replaced by lactose. Feeding live yeast stimulated bacterial synthesis, and Parsons et al.[20] found that compressed bakers' yeast increased the faecal excretion in humans ; at the same time the urinary excretion was reduced, showing that the vitamin B_1 in the yeast was not being absorbed. Better absorption was obtained after the yeast had been boiled with water. A similar result was obtained with rats.[21]

Of considerable interest in relation to bacterial synthesis in the intestine are the results obtained by R. C. Thompson,[22] who found that the intestinal micro-organism B. proteus vulgaris synthesised inter alia aneurine, and by P. R. Burkholder and I. McVeigh,[23] who found that aneurine was also synthesised on synthetic media by the intestinal organisms, Escherichia coli, Bacillus lactis aerogenes, B. mesentericus, B. vulgatus and B. faecalis alcaligenes.

Synthesis of Aneurine in the Rumen

Closely related to the phenomenon of bacterial synthesis in the intestine of man is that of bacterial synthesis in the rumen of ruminants. As already noted, Theiler et al.,[1] in 1915, observed that ruminants could be maintained on diets low in certain vitamins, and their results were confirmed by Bechdel et al.[2] Several years later, Wegner et al.[24] and Hunt et al.[25] found that the rumen contents of a calf, obtained by means of a fistula, had a higher vitamin B_1 content than the diet. L. W. McElroy and H. Goss [26] reported a value of 7 μg. per g. for the concentration of aneurine in the dried rumen and reticulum contents of a sheep that had been fed on a diet containing only 0·4 μg. per g. of the vitamin. They concluded that the vitamin in the rumen was derived from microbial growth and not by concentration of the vitamin already present in the diet. On the other hand, the rumen of a cow maintained on the same diet contained no aneurine, but the milk contained 2 to 2·5 μg. per g. The conclusion was therefore reached that aneurine was not a dietary essential for the ruminant. A later report by Hunt *et al.*[27] failed to confirm the earlier result, since no evidence could be obtained that aneurine was synthesised in the rumen of a steer, the amount present being less than that present in the diet. This may have been due to the nature of the diet, however, since on increasing the amount of maize or carbohydrate in the feeding-stuff, the difference between the two values tended to decrease.

References to Section 15

1. A. Theiler, H. H. Green and P. R. Viljoen, *Rep. vet. Res. S. Afr.*, 1915, **3-4**, 9.
2. S. L. Bechdel, H. E. Honeywell, R. A. Dutcher and M. H. Knutsen, *J. Biol. Chem.*, 1928, **80**, 231.
3. N. B. Guerrant, R. A. Dutcher and L. F. Tomey, *ibid.*, 1935, **110**, 233 ; N. B. Guerrant, R. A. Dutcher and R. A. Brown, *J. Nutrition*, 1937, **13**, 305.
4. T. B. Osborne and L. B. Mendel, *Publ. Carnegie Inst.*, 1911, No. 156, part 2, p. 59.
5. L. S. Fridericia, *Skand. Arch. Physiol.*, 1926, **49**, 55 ; L. S. Fridericia, P. Freudenthal, S. Gudjonnsson, G. Johansen and N. Schoubye, *J. Hygiene*, 1927-28, **27**, 70.
6. M. H. Roscoe, *ibid.*, 103.
7. P. M. Kon, *A Bacteriological and Physiological Study of the Phenomenon of Potato Starch Refection in the Rat*, Ph.D. Thesis, Univ. of Reading, 1935 ; P. M. Kon, S. K. Kon and A. T. R. Mattick, *J. Hygiene*, 1938, **38**, 1 ; S. K. Kon, *Proc. Nutr. Soc.*, 1945, **3**, 217.
8. J. Taylor and U. Thant, *Indian J. Med. Res.*, 1919, **16**, 747.
9. H. Madsen, *Nature*, 1939, **143**, 981 ; E. L. Taylor, *ibid.*, 1939, **143**, 982 ; A. Eden, *ibid.*, 1940, **145**, 36, 628.
10. R. F. Light, L. J. Cracas, C. T. Olcott and C. N. Frey, *J. Nutrition*, 1942, **24**, 427.
11. L. Wildemann, *Biochem. Z.*, 1941, **308**, 10.
12. B. Alexander, G. Landwehr and F. Mitchell, *J. Clin. Invest.*, 1946, **25**, 287.
13. V. A. Najjar and L. E. Holt, *Science*, 1943, **98**, 456 ; *J. Amer. Med. Assoc.*, 1943, **123**, 683.
14. C. W. Denko, W. E. Grundy, J. W. Porter, G. H. Berryman, T. E. Friedemann and J. B. Youmans, *Arch. Biochem.*, 1946, **10**, 33 ; C. W. Denko, W. E. Grundy, N. C. Wheeler, C. R. Henderson, G. H. Berryman, T. E. Friedemann and J. B. Youmans, *ibid.*, 1946, **11**, 109.

15. B. Alexander and G. Landwehr, *Science*, 1945, **101,** 229.
16. F. M. Meyers, *Amer. J. Med. Sci.*, 1941, **201,** 785.
17. A. Williamson and H. T. Parsons, *J. Nutrition*, 1945, **29,** 51.
18. J. G. Reinhold, J. T. L. Nicholson and K. O'S. Elsom, *ibid.*, 1944, **28,** 51.
19. B. S. Schweigert, J. M. McIntire, L. M. Henderson and C. A. Elvehjem, *Arch. Biochem.*, 1945, **6,** 403.
20. H. T. Parsons, A. Williamson and M. L. Johnson, *J. Nutrition*, 1945, **29,** 373.
21. H. T. Parsons, A. Foeste and H. Gilberg, *ibid.*, 383.
22. R. C. Thompson, *Univ. Texas Publ.*, 1942, No. 4237, p. 87.
23. P. R. Burkholder and I. McVeigh, *Proc. Nat. Acad. Sci.*, 1942, **28,** 285.
24. M. I. Wegner, A. N. Booth, C. A. Elvehjem and E. B. Hart, *Proc. Soc. Exp. Biol. Med.*, 1940, **45,** 769.
25. C. H. Hunt, C. H. Kirk, E. W. Burroughs, R. M. Bethke, A. F. Schalk and P. Gerlaugh, *J. Nutrition*, 1941, **21,** 85.
26. L. W. McElroy and H. Goss, *J. Biol. Chem.*, 1939, **130,** 437 ; *J. Nutrition*, 1941, **21,** 163.
27. C. H. Hunt, E. W. Burroughs, R. M. Bethke, A. F. Schalk and P. Gerlaugh, *ibid.*, 1943, **25,** 207.

16. ANIMAL AND HUMAN REQUIREMENTS OF ANEURINE

It is clear that from what has been said in the preceding section on bacterial synthesis in the intestine that animal and human requirements for aneurine may well be affected—possibly to a very considerable degree—by the incidence of this phenomenon. Unfortunately, no precise information is available at present to indicate how common intestinal synthesis is in man or in other animals, or to what extent the aneurine thus provided is available to meet the requirements of the host.

One can only suspect, from the fact that it was discovered comparatively recently, that intestinal synthesis is an infrequent and circumscribed source of aneurine, and that the values arrived at for human requirements before the phenomenon came to light still remain generally valid, although possibly wide of the mark in exceptional instances. This supposition is believed not to hold good with some other members of the vitamin B complex.

The first attempts to determine the amounts of aneurine needed by an animal were carried out by T. B. Osborne and L. B. Mendel,[1] who showed that the amount required increased with the weight of the animal. This was confirmed by G. R. Cowgill,[2] who studied the aneurine requirements of four different species of animals and obtained the following results :

Species	Weight (g.)	Daily Requirement (µg.)
Mouse . .	20	3
	26	6
Rat . . .	97	3
	153	7
Pigeon . .	300	6
	400	12
	500	18
Dog . .	6000	25
	8000	35
	10,000	54

He concluded that the requirements for man would be proportionately lower. Young rats required twice as much aneurine for growth when maintained at 90° F. as they required at 68° F.[3]

The first calculations made for the human requirements of vitamin B_1 were based on an examination of diets known to have been associated with epidemics of beriberi and of diets known to be associated with the absence of beriberi. G. R. Cowgill[2] set out the available data in detail and summarised the results in a graph relating body-weight to the vitamin : calorie ratio. It can be deduced from this that a 60-kg. man consuming 2500 cals. per day would require not less than 210 I.U. of vitamin B_1 per day. A. Z. Baker and M. D. Wright[4] and A. G. van Veen[5] arrived at values of 200 to 500 and 150 I.U. per day respectively as the minimum intake to prevent beriberi in man ; these are equivalent to 0·7 to 1·7 and 0·5 mg. per day.

The difference between these estimates may be due to the smaller average weight of Indonesians, on whom van Veen made his observations, compared with Europeans. Stepp et al.[6] gave the requirements as 0·25 to 0·75 mg. per day, whilst Vorhaus et al.[7] estimated that the normal American adult requires about 1 mg. of pure aneurine daily, although they did not imply that this was the minimum necessary for health.

More recent results have been based on controlled experiments with human volunteers, or on saturation tests with individuals on different diets, or on nutritional surveys of particular sections of the population. An example of investigations of the first type is provided by the work of Elsom et al.[8] They maintained six volunteers on a diet containing just enough aneurine to satisfy the "theoretical" requirements and three others on a diet containing half this amount. Three of those on the higher level developed typical signs of aneurine deficiency, whence it was concluded that the *minimum* intake to maintain health was 0·65 mg. per day.

Saturation tests were used by D. Melnick,[9] who stated that adults required 0·35 mg. of aneurine per 1000 cals. or 0·875 mg. per day, assuming a calorie intake of 2500 cals. per day. He recommended a minimum intake of 0·5 mg. per 1000 cals., however. Of the subjects tested (Americans) only 73 % excreted sufficient aneurine to pass all clearance tests. Saturation tests were also employed by R. D. Williams *et al.*[10] who found that an intake of 0·1 to 0·175 mg. of aneurine per 1000 cals. caused a rapid, and one of 0·22 mg. per 1000 cals. a slow, depletion of the tissue reserves, whereas an intake of 0·45 mg. per 1000 cals. was associated with only a slight depletion of cocarboxylase. H. Oldham *et al.*[11] found that 0·5 mg. per 1000 cals. satisfied the aneurine requirements of adults.

As an example of the third type of investigation, the results of T. Moran and R. G. Booth[12] may be cited. After carrying out a dietary survey, they concluded that 50 % of the population of Britain in the early days of the 1939-45 war had an inadequate intake of the vitamin ; they gave the average requirement of the population as a whole as 2·3 mg. per day on a diet supplying 2810 cals. per day ; this is equivalent to 2·05 mg. per 2500 cals. Excluding lactating women and young children, the aneurine requirement was estimated at 1·4 mg. per day or 1·25 mg. per 2500 cals., a value identical with the intake recommended by Melnick. M. D. Wright,[13] however, considered this value to be inadequate, and stated that 1·9 mg. per day should be regarded as the minimum. E. G. Young[14] made a dietary survey among Canadian families with incomes ranging from $450 to $1500 per annum, and found that the average consumption of aneurine was 0·20 mg. per 1000 cals. for men, 0·19 mg. per 1000 cals. for women and 0·22 mg. per 1000 cals. for children, considerably lower values than those generally accepted as desirable. Yet no evidence of clinical aneurine deficiency was observed.

Lane *et al.*[15] stated that, prior to the introduction of enriched flour, the average vitamin B_1 content of the American diet—due in the main to lean pork, bread and milk—was 0·8 mg. per 2500 cals., a much lower figure than the minimum standard suggested by Melnick and by Wright. The use of enriched flour increased the value to 1·3 mg. per 2500 cals., a figure just above Melnick's minimum, but below Wright's.

On the whole, there is a surprising unanimity about the minimum human requirement for aneurine, and we may safely assert that at least 1·25 mg. per 2500 cals. should be given in order to maintain health. The optimal quantity, that is, the amount required to ensure full activity, is probably much higher, probably in the region of 2·5 mg. per 2500 cals.

Infants of about six months of age require at least 200 mg. of aneurine daily,[16] and this can normally be supplied when the mother's milk contains 20 mg. or more of aneurine per 100 ml.

An attempt to evaluate the effect on the aneurine requirements of man of bacterial synthesis in the intestine was made by Alexander *et al.*[17] They defined the minimum aneurine requirement as the amount utilised or otherwise altered in body metabolism plus the amount required to cover uncontrollable losses from the body. When subjects were maintained on a restricted intake of aneurine, excretion of the vitamin fell to a point where its concentration was too small to be measured. In computing the daily minimum requirement, therefore, the urinary aneurine can be deducted from the intake. The minimum requirement for a male consuming 2400 cals. per day was in this way found to be 0·44 mg. per 1000 cals. or 1·06 mg. per day. An increase in the intake of aneurine increased the urinary excretion of aneurine and of a related factor that accelerated yeast fermentation. When the intake exceeded 1·3 mg. the increase of this second factor must also be subtracted from the aneurine intake, because it represents aneurine breakdown. Alexander *et al.* suggested that the amount of aneurine and cocarboxylase in the faeces could be ignored, since they are the result of bacterial synthesis and exist within the cells of the micro-organisms.

M. L. Hathaway and J. E. Strom [18] recommended a daily allowance for women of 1·1 to 1·2 mg., whilst Oldham *et al.*[19] recommended a total daily intake for young women of 20 μg. per kg. of body weight, say, 1·2 mg. per day.

It is instructive to compare these estimates with the actual intake of aneurine in this country during the 1939-45 war. The civilian consumption per head per day was about 1·2 mg. in 1939 and rose steadily to a value of 1·87 mg. in 1947.[20] Experience showed that 0·35 mg. per 1000 cals. was marginal and that signs of vitamin B_1 deficiency appeared with 0·25 mg. per 1000 cals. Deficiency was rarely encountered in the Netherlands, however, during 1944-45, when the inhabitants were subsisting on a starvation diet, because the aneurine/calorie ratio remained above the limiting value, whereas a deficiency was common in Japanese prison camps where white rice was the basic cereal and the diet contained less than 0·2 mg. of aneurine per 1000 cals.[21]

References to Section 16

1. T. B. Osborne, L. B. Mendel and H. C. Cannon, *J. Biol. Chem.*, 1922, **54,** 739.
2. G. R. Cowgill, " The Vitamin B Requirement of Man ", New Haven, Yale Univ. Press, 1934.

3. C. A. Mills, *Proc. Soc. Exp. Biol. Med.*, 1943, **54**, 265.

4. A. Z. Baker and M. D. Wright, *Proc. Roy. Soc. Med.*, 1936, **29**, 1145.

5. A. G. van Veen, *Geneesh. Tijdschr. Nederl.-Ind.*, 1935, **75**, 2050.

6. W. Stepp, J. Kuhnau and H. Schroeder, *Die Vitamine*, Stuttgart, F. Enhe, 1937.

7. M. G. Vorhaus, R. R. Williams and R. E. Waterman, *J. Amer. Med. Assoc.*, 1935, **105**, 1580.

8. K. O'S. Elsom, J. G. Reinhold, J. T. L. Nicholson and C. Chornock, *Amer. J. Med. Sci.*, 1942, **203**, 569.

9. D. Melnick, *J. Nutrition*, 1942, **24**, 139.

10. R. D. Williams, H. L. Mason and R. M. Wilder, *ibid.*, 1943, **25**, 71.

11. H. Oldham, F. Johnston, S. Kleiger and H. H. Arismendi, *ibid.*, 1944, **27**, 435.

12. T. Moran and R. G. Booth, *Chem. and Ind.*, 1940, 533.

13. M. D. Wright, *ibid.*, 578.

14. E. G. Young, *Canadian Med. Assoc. J.*, 1945, **53**, 527.

15. R. L. Lane, E. Johnson and R. R. Williams, *J. Nutrition*, 1942, **23**, 613.

16. E. M. Knott, *Proc. Soc. Exp. Biol. Med.*, 1940, **45**, 765 ; E. M. Knott, S. C. Kleiger, F. W. Schultz and G. Collins, *J. Pediat.*, 1943, **22**, 43 ; L. E. Holt, R. L. Nemir, S. E. Snyderman, A. A. Albanese, K. C. Ketron, L. P. Guy and R. Carreters, *J. Nutrition*, 1949, **37**, 53.

17. B. Alexander, G. Landwehr and F. Mitchell, *J. Clin. Invest.*, 1946, **25**, 287.

18. M. L. Hathaway and J. E. Strom, *J. Nutrition*, 1946, **32**, 1.

19. H. G. Oldham, M. V. Davis and L. J. Roberts, *ibid.*, 163.

20. *Food Consumption Levels in the United Kingdom*, Cmd. 7203, H.M.S.O. 1947.

21. J. C. Drummond, " Nutritional Requirements of Man in the Light of Wartime Experience ", Royal Institute of Chemistry, 1948.

17. PHARMACOLOGICAL ACTION OF ANEURINE

Toxicity

The acute fatal doses of aneurine hydrochloride for the mouse, rat, rabbit and dog were found to be [1,2] 125, 250, 300 and 350 mg. per kg. respectively by the intravenous route, and six and forty times these values when given subcutaneously and orally.   Death occurred from respiratory failure.   G. Hecht and H. Weese,[3] however, reported that 160 mg. per kg. caused the death of rabbits by paralysis of the central nervous system, whilst T. J. Haley and A. M. Flesher [4] found that the lethal dose for rabbits was 126 mg. per kg. but, after a sensitising dose of 100 mg. of aneurine hydrochloride, this increased to 238 mg. per kg. E. L. Stern [5] found that 600 mg. administered by cisternal puncture killed a cat.

According to T. J. Haley,[5a] aneurine nitrate had approximately the same acute toxicity for mice and rabbits as had the hydrochloride.

Effect on Isolated Tissues and Organs

The effect of solutions of aneurine on isolated tissues and organs has been studied by many workers. A dilution of 1 in 1000 to 10,000 produced acceleration and an increase in the amplitude of the isolated frog's heart.[6] A dilution of 1 in 1000 increased the tonus of the exposed frog's heart, but at higher concentrations,[7] aneurine acted as a cardiac depressant due to acidity and hypertonicity. A dilution of 1 in 1000 depressed the frog's ventricle to stoppage at pH 5·2 to 6·0, and a similar, though less marked, effect was produced by a dilution of 1 in 10,000 ; 1 in 100,000 had no effect. Cocarboxylase also had a depressant effect at pH values up to 7·6. The depressant effect was not annulled by atropine.[8] Dilutions of 1 in 1000 to 10,000 produced coronary dilatation and an increase in the amplitude of the perfused rabbit's heart.[6]

The movements of the perfused isolated rabbit's intestine were increased and the rhythm of the isolated rabbit's uterus was inhibited by dilutions of 1 in 100 to 10,000, but augmented by a dilution of 1 in 100,000. The contractions of skeletal muscle were decreased by aneurine in a dilution of 1 in 1000.[6] Aneurine and cocarboxylase inhibited the action of nicotine on the isolated rabbit and guinea-pig intestine and on the isolated striated muscle of the frog ; these effects were not influenced by prostigmine.[9] The total work output of frog's gastrocnemius muscle, when perfused with Ringer's solution and stimulated electrically, was significantly increased by the addition of aneurine [10] up to concentrations of 0·001 millimoles per litre. Aneurine pyrophosphate had a greater effect at lower concentrations, and an equal effect at 0·001 millimoles per litre. When the sciatic nerve of a frog was stimulated and frozen in liquid air, the stimulated nerve liberated aneurine, as shown by rat bradycardia.[11] The total aneurine in frog's nerve after poisoning with iodoacetate remained the same after stimulation, but the free aneurine fell to half the amount present in the non-stimulated nerve.[12] This difference is believed to be due to the effect of iodoacetate on phosphorylation.

The aneurine content of guinea-pig's sciatic nerve diminished after cutting the nerve and in fifty to seventy hours fell to 40 to 50 % of the amount present in a control nerve.[13] Stimulation of the branch of the vago-sympathetic nerve fibres supplying the heart of the frog led to the liberation of aneurine, or a compound resembling it, as well as to liberation of acetyl choline.[14] The substance exhibited a different polarographic behaviour from aneurine and is believed to be a reserve substance connected with the disappearance of acetyl choline.

Aneurine, in a dilution of 1 in 10,000, inhibited the vasoconstrictor action of nicotine in frog vessels.[15] The action was due to the thiazole moiety, and the site of the action was the myoneural junction in striated muscles and the postganglionic nerve endings or muscle elements of the vessel walls in smooth muscles.

Effect on Intact Animals

In the intact frog, aneurine produced central motor and respiratory paralysis and pupillary constriction. In mice, small doses stimulated respiration, whilst large doses produced chronic cramps and respiratory arrest. In rabbits, intravenous injection of 0·05 to 1 mg. stimulated respiration and raised the blood pressure.[6] Aneurine did not increase the purgative effect of phenolphthalein in monkeys.[16]

The toxic symptoms observed in rabbits were :[4] peripheral vasodilatation, decreased respiration due to a direct action on the respiratory centre in the medulla, asphyxial convulsions due to anoxia resulting from decreased oxygenation of the blood, death by paralysis of the respiratory centre and cardiac arrhythmias, probably due to anoxia and not to a direct action on the cardiac muscle of the conduction system. In dogs, intravenous injection of aneurine hydrochloride solution caused a marked but transient fall in blood pressure, bradycardia, transitory vasodilatation and transitory changes in the electrocardiogram ; death was due to respiratory arrest.[16a]

When applied directly to the cerebral cortex, aneurine produced motor reactions, consisting of rhythmic contractions of the muscle corresponding to the cortical " motor " point at which it was applied.[17] The reaction was at first weak, but subsequently increased in intensity. When all the skeletal musculature was involved, generalised epileptiform convulsions took place with a tonic-clonic sequence. Epileptiform convulsions were produced in thirty-four out of forty-five dogs by means of a 2 to 10 % solution applied in this way, but in eleven of the dogs only localised muscular clonic reactions could be obtained. Identical results were obtained with cocarboxylase, but the pyrimidine and thiazole halves of the molecule had no effect.

Relation between Aneurine and Acetyl Choline

An association of a different type between aneurine and acetyl choline was indicated by Kuhn et al.[18] Like choline, aneurine is a quaternary ammonium base and a primary alcohol, and its acetyl derivative was found to behave like acetyl choline in stimulating the rat intestine. The question as to whether acetyl aneurine is an additional nerve messenger has not yet been answered, but the idea is an interesting one, because if it is essential for the proper functioning of the nervous system, its absence may result in atrophy of the nerves, a characteristic feature of vitamin B_1 deficiency that is not explicable if aneurine acts simply as a metabolic catalyst of pyruvic acid oxidation or decarboxylation. Further work on the connection between aneurine and the nervous system is highly desirable.

An attempt to explain the connection between aneurine deficiency and the appearance of nerve lesions was made by D. Glick and W. Antopol.[19] They noted that many of the symptoms of vitamin B_1 deficiency, such as hypochlorhydria, loss of muscular tone, certain forms of nerve dysfunction and tachycardia, were relieved by administration of choline esters, and that certain symptoms of hyperthyroidism were alleviated by aneurine and choline esters. They suggested, therefore, that aneurine might inhibit choline esterase activity so that a deficiency of the vitamin might result in enhanced enzyme activity and a reduced concentration of acetyl choline.

This suggestion, if true, might also explain McHenry's observation that aneurine cured fatty livers in rats kept on a low choline diet, for the increased choline esterase activity produced by administration of the vitamin might lead to an increased availability of free choline, which would tend to reduce the amount of fat in the liver. When this ingenious hypothesis was tested, it was found that aneurine did inhibit choline esterase, but only in concentrations far in excess of the normal. Thus, whereas the blood rarely contains more than 1 μg. of aneurine per ml., detectable inhibition was produced by 1000 μg. per ml. of serum. The authors conclude : " the possibility that thiamine may be histologically localised in some tissue should be borne in mind, for then it might exert its enzyme inhibition *in vivo* ".

Aneurine appears to have a curious effect on acetyl choline. V. Erspamer[20] observed that *in vitro* aneurine in concentrations greater than 10 p.p.m. reduced the effect of acetyl choline on isolated tissues, and that the intravenous injection into rats of 30 to 100 mg. per kg. of bodyweight increased, and 100 to 500 mg. per kg. decreased, the toxicity of sublethal doses of acetyl choline previously injected subcutaneously. Moderate aneurine deficiency in pigeons enabled them to resist the effect of twice the minimum fatal dose of acetyl choline, and twice the usual concentration of acetyl choline was required to stimulate the isolated gut of such pigeons. After the deficiency symptoms had been cured by treatment with aneurine, the response to acetyl choline was normal. The opposite effect was noted by E. A. Zeller and H. Birkhauser[21] in avitaminous rats, the liver of which contained less choline esterase than normal, although the brain was unaffected. In such animals the effects of acetyl choline would presumably be prolonged. C. Torda and H. G. Wolff,[22] on the other hand, failed to observe any inhibitory or potentiating effect of aneurine hydrochloride, aneurine pyrophosphate or acetyl aneurine on the response of frog's rectus muscle to acetyl choline. Aneurine hydrochloride and pyrophosphate increased acetyl choline synthesis by about 10 % in concentrations of $3 \times 10^{-6}\ M$ and $2 \times 10^{-6}\ M$ respectively. Higher concentrations decreased the synthesis of acetyl choline, whilst adrenaline increased the synthesis 40 to 150 %.

E. M. Boyd and R. W. Dingwall[7] reported that concentrations of 100 to 250 mg. per 100 ml. prevented bradycardia in the exposed frog's heart due to acetyl choline and other drugs.

B. Jackson and G. Wald[8] found that aneurine in dilutions of 1 in 1000 to 100,000 progressively antagonised acetyl choline ; the effect was not shown by cocarboxylase.

References to Section 17

1. H. Molitor and W. L. Sampson, *E. Merck's Jahresber.*, 1936, **50,** 51.
2. V. Erspamer, *Arch. int. Pharmacodyn.*, 1940, **64,** 1.
3. G. Hecht and H. Weese, *Klin. Woch.*, 1937, **16,** 414.
4. T. J. Haley and A. M. Flesher, *Science*, 1946, **104,** 567.
5. E. L. Stern, *Amer. J. Surg.*, 1938, **39,** 495.
5a. T. J. Haley, *Proc. Soc. Exp. Biol. Med.*, 1948, **68,** 153.
6. C. Mano, *Japan. J. Med. Sci.*, IV, 1940, **12,** *Proc.*, 98.
7. E. M. Boyd and R. W. Dingwall, *Quart. J. Pharm.*, 1941, **14,** 209.
8. B. Jackson and G. Wald, *Amer. J. Physiol.*, 1942, **135,** 464.
9. K. Unna and E. P. Pick, *J. Pharmacol.*, 1944, **81,** 294.
10. N. W. Shock and W. H. Sebrell, *Amer. J. Physiol.*, 1944, **142,** 265 ; *Proc. Soc. Exp. Biol. Med.*, 1945, **59,** 212.
11. A. Liechti, A. von Muralt and M. Reinert, *Helv. Physiol. Pharm. Acta*, 1943, **1,** 79.
12. A. and F. Wyss, *Experientia*, 1945, **1,** 160.
13. A. von Muralt and F. Wyss, *ibid.*, 1944, **2,** 445.
14. A. von Muralt, *Nature*, 1944, **154,** 767.
15. H. Haimovici and E. P. Pick, *Proc. Soc. Exp. Biol. Med.*, 1946, **62,** 234.
16. S. Loewe, I. Loewe and R. Knox, *Amer. J. Digest. Dis.*, 1943, **10,** 65.
16a. J. A. Smith, P. P. Foa, H. R. Weinstein, A. S. Ludwig and J. M. Wertheim, *J. Pharmacol.*, 1948, **93,** 294.
17. M. V. Dias, *Science*, 1947, **105,** 211.
18. R. Kuhn, T. Wieland and H. Huenschmann, *Z. physiol. Chem.*, 1939, **259,** 48.
19. D. Glick and W. Antopol, *J. Pharmacol.*, 1939, **65,** 389.
20. V. Erspamer, *Boll. Soc. ital. Biol. sperim.*, 1939, **14,** 655 ; *Arch. int. Pharmacodyn.*, 1939, **63,** 385.
21. E. A. Zeller and H. Birkhauser, *Helv. Chim. Acta*, 1940, **23,** 1457.
22. C. Torda and H. G. Wolff, *Proc. Soc. Exp. Biol. Med.*, 1944, **56,** 88, 89.

18. FUNCTION OF ANEURINE

Lactic Acid

As long ago as 1914, C. Funk [1] suggested that vitamin B_1 was concerned with carbohydrate metabolism, and the first step towards an understanding of its more precise function was taken in 1929 when H. W. Kinnersley and R. A. Peters [2] showed that avitaminous pigeon brain contained more lactic acid than did normal brain. T. W. Birch and L. J. Harris [3] suggested that the bradycardia of vitamin B_1-deficient animals was correlated with the accumulation of lactic acid in the organism, although they did not consider that the symptoms were directly attributable to the presence of the acid, since bradycardia was not produced by injection of sodium lactate solution.

H. G. K. Westenbrink, [4] however, claimed that either pyruvic acid or lactic acid was the toxic metabolite responsible for some of the symptoms of vitamin B_1 deficiency, and in a more recent paper, it has been claimed [5] that convulsions similar to those resulting from vitamin B_1 deficiency are produced in pigeons by injection of lactate or pyruvate solution and that, provided not more than 0·15 ml. of a 2 % solution has been administered, the symptoms can be relieved by the intravenous injection of 2000 to 5000 I.U. of vitamin B_1.

Whether the physiological effects observed in vitamin B_1 deficiency are due to an accumulation of lactic or pyruvic acid or of some other substance, the fact that these substances do accumulate both in the blood and the urine, instead of being further metabolised, cannot now be questioned.

Pyruvic Acid

B. S. Platt and G. D. Lu [6] showed that the blood of beriberi patients contained not only pyruvic acid, but other ketonic substances as well. The amount of ketone bodies increased on exertion and the increase was accompanied by clinical manifestations of fulminating beriberi with cardiac symptoms. They did not believe that these cardiac symptoms were directly attributable to the accumulation of pyruvic acid, however.

Bisulphite-binding Substances in Blood

Attempts have been made to use the increase in ketonic substances in the blood to assess the degree of vitamin B_1 deficiency. Thus Shils et al. [7] observed that in rats on a diet low in vitamin B_1, the increase in bisulphite-binding substances (B.B.S.) in the blood was proportional to the extent of the deficiency. The increase was stated to be due mainly to the accumulation of pyruvic acid. A. Göth [8] claimed to be able to detect incipient hypovitaminosis by measuring the B.B.S. in blood ; when the nutritional status was such that 11.4 % of a test dose of aneurine was excreted, the B.B.S. were 7.8 mg. per 100 ml., whereas when the excretion fell to 3.6 % the B.B.S. had risen to 13.4 mg. per 100 ml. Similarly, H. A. Harper and H. J. Deuel [9] found that during aneurine depletion the urinary excretion of pyruvate increased, more in males than in females. The excretion was reduced when optimal amounts of aneurine were given, although not when amounts adequate for minimum growth were given. They did not claim that the phenomenon could be used for diagnosing vitamin B_1 deficiency. Shils et al.,[10] on the other hand, failed to observe any increase in B.B.S. in the urine of subjects fed a vitamin B_1-deficient diet.

The method of assessing vitamin B_1 deficiency by measuring the bisulphite-binding substances in the blood never met with general approval, however, and was explicitly rejected by Robinson et al.,[11] by Wortis et al.[12] and by H. A. Davis and F. K. Bauer.[13] The last-named workers compared the blood pyruvic acid in various diseases with that of controls. The normal level was 0.5 to 1.3 mg. per 100 ml., but in various hepatic disorders it increased up to 4.25 and in toxic goitre to 3.5 mg. per 100 ml. No increase was observed in non-toxic goitre or in renal disease, but an increase occurred in some malignant diseases. It was estimated that half the cases of infection examined also had increased pyruvic acid levels in the blood. Obviously, therefore, elevation of the blood pyruvic acid cannot be used for the diagnosis and evaluation of vitamin B_1 deficiency without excluding other conditions that might equally well be responsible.

M. K. Horwitt and O. Kreisler,[13a] however, claim that the levels of lactate and pyruvate in the blood can be used to diagnose vitamin B_1 deficiency under the combined " metabolic load " of ingestion of glucose and exercise, although quite useless in the fasting state.

Methylglyoxal

Another substance that was at one time implicated as the toxic product responsible for the symptoms of vitamin B_1 deficiency is methylglyoxal (pyruvic aldehyde), $CH_3 . CO . CHO$. The presence of this substance in the urine of vitamin B_1-deficient infants was reported by A. Geiger and A. Rosenberg,[14] and in the milk of women with beri-beri by several Japanese workers.[15]

Infantile beriberi is a condition in breast-fed infants first described towards the end of last century by Japanese clinicians and, because the infant recovered when removed from the breast, the condition was attributed to a toxin in the milk. The presence of a toxin was, in fact, demonstrated by T. Suzuki and A. Takamatsu,[16] who showed that it was methylglyoxal and that the administration of vitamin B_1 diminished the methylglyoxal content of the milk. R. Orimo [17] showed that the milk of vitamin B_1-deficient women was low in glyoxalase, the concentration of which could, however, be raised by giving the vitamin, whilst A. Takamatsu and A. Sato [18] showed that methylglyoxal induced pathological changes in rabbits similar to those in infantile beriberi.

J. Vogt-Möller [19] suggested that the symptoms of beriberi were due to poisoning by methylglyoxal which accumulated as the result of some breakdown in the action of the enzyme glyoxalase or its coenzyme, glutathione (glutamyl-cysteyl-glycine) ; he favoured the latter alternative. B. S. Platt and G. D. Lu,[20] however, could find no evidence that methylglyoxal was responsible for the symptoms of beriberi.

Unfortunately, it appears never to have been decided whether the cure of infantile beriberi was due to the administration of vitamin B_1 or to administration of glutathione, as no information is available as to the nature of the vitamin B supplements used. In many instances these were probably concentrates prepared from liver or yeast and therefore likely to contain both.

There is no real proof that aneurine deficiency leads to an accumulation of methylglyoxal, although there is convincing evidence that methylglyoxal is responsible for infantile beriberi. In the light of present knowledge, however, this is just as likely to be produced by a deficiency of glutathione as of aneurine.

Experiments on the Respiration of Brain Tissue

The explanation of the relationship between vitamin B_1 deficiency and the accumulation of lactic or pyruvic acid in the blood was discovered by R. A. Peters,[21] who, in a paper of fundamental importance, showed that normal pigeon brain slices in Ringer phosphate solution containing glucose as substrate had a higher oxygen uptake than avitaminous brain slices. The same results were obtained when sodium lactate or sodium pyruvate were used as substrates. When aneurine was added to the solutions, the oxygen uptake of the avitaminous tissue was raised to the normal value in all three instances. The reaction was extremely sensitive and highly specific. It was described as the catatorulin effect, and was made the basis of a method of assaying vitamin B_1 (see page 28). Peters was able to show also that, with sodium succinate as substrate, normal and avitaminous brain tissue respired at the same rate, and he therefore concluded that the vitamin was concerned with the oxidation of pyruvic acid, but not of succinic acid.

The accumulation of lactic acid as well as pyruvic acid in the blood and tissues of avitaminous animals was at first sight puzzling, but the difficulty was disposed of by W. C. Sherman and C. A. Elvehjem,[22] who pointed out that pyruvic acid completely inhibited lactic dehydrogenase activity, so that lactic acid accumulated in the tissues instead of being metabolised. By removing pyruvic acid, vitamin B_1 thus indirectly brought about the normal metabolism of lactic acid. It has been suggested that the accumulation of methylglyoxal might similarly be due to the inhibition of methylglyoxalase by pyruvate, but there appears to be no direct evidence on this point.

Pyruvic Acid Metabolism

Pyruvic acid can be metabolised in various ways. In the presence of air, the acid is oxidised to acetic acid and carbon dioxide :

$$(1) \quad CH_3 . CO . COOH + O \rightarrow CH_3 . COOH + CO_2,$$

and many workers have maintained that this is the reaction catalysed by aneurine. K. Lohmann and P. Schuster [23] and others, however, hold that in yeast at all events aneurine catalyses the anaerobic decarboxylation to acetaldehyde and carbon dioxide :

$$(2) \quad CH_3 . CO . COOH . \rightarrow CH_3 . CHO + CO_2,$$

whilst others, *e.g.* H. A. Krebs,[24] H. A. Krebs and W. A. Johnson,[25] and G. M. Hills,[26] believe that it catalyses a dismutation of the type :

$$(3) \quad 2CH_3 . CO . COOH \rightarrow CH_3 . CHOH . COOH + CH_3 . COOH + CO_2 .$$

Aneurine Pyrophosphate

Actually, aneurine itself is not the catalyst responsible for pyruvic acid metabolism. H. G. K. Westenbrink and J. J. Pollak [27] observed that a period of ten minutes elapsed after the addition of aneurine to polyneuritic brain tissue extract before any uptake of oxygen occurred, and they interpreted this as an indication that aneurine underwent a change before it could function as a catalyst. The nature of this change was revealed by K. Lohmann and P. Schuster,[23] who isolated from yeast a coenzyme, cocarboxylase, which was found to be the pyrophosphate of aneurine :

93

This structure was confirmed by K. G. Stern and J. W. Hofer,[28] who synthesised aneurine pyrophosphate by treating aneurine with two molecular proportions or more of phosphorus oxychloride. Both groups of workers found that the substance produced carbon dioxide from pyruvic acid in the presence of yeast cells freed from natural cocarboxylase. Enzymic methods of preparing cocarboxylase from aneurine were subsequently described by H. Tauber,[29] by H. von Euler and R. Vestin [30] and by M. Silverman and C. H. Werkman,[31] whilst an improved synthetic method was described by H. Weil-Malherbe,[32] in which the 5-bromoethyl-thiazole analogue of aneurine hydrobromide was treated with silver pyrophosphate in pyrophosphoric acid solution at 100° C. for fifteen hours. The cocarboxylase was isolated after conversion to the silver salt, precipitation with phosphotungstic acid and recrystallisation from dilute alcohol.

Phosphorylation of aneurine *in vivo* apparently takes place in the upper part of the digestive tract,[33] although attempts to convert aneurine into cocarboxylase by incubation with juices from the stomach, pancreas, duodenum or jejunum of dogs, or by mixtures of the juices with mucosa extracts were unsuccessful. The reverse change, however, that is, the hydrolysis of cocarboxylase to aneurine, was readily effected by incubation with duodenal or jejunal juice. The hydrolysis of aneurine monophosphate could also be effected by phosphatase preparations, at a rate comparable with the hydrolysis of cocarboxylase. H. Weil-Malherbe [34] showed that neither aneurine nor aneurine monophosphate functioned *per se* as coenzymes of carboxylase ; the latter has a longer induction period than the former, presumably due to the fact that it must first be hydrolysed to free aneurine. Aneurine could be converted into cocarboxylase by the action of adenosine triphosphate. That aneurine monophosphate was not an intermediate in the formation of cocarboxylase was confirmed by the fact that, although it reduced the pyruvic acid content of the blood of aneurine-deficient rats,[35] it had a somewhat lower activity than aneurine itself. The conversion of aneurine into cocarboxylase by adenosine triphosphate was confirmed by Elvehjem and his colleagues,[36] who also showed that cocarboxylase was formed from aneurine in presence of washed dried yeast, hexose diphosphate and boiled tissue extract.

F. Lipmann [37] reported that Lohmann's pure cocarboxylase functioned as a coenzyme in the oxidation of pyruvic acid, and suggested that aneurine was first converted into cocarboxylase which then acted as the coenzyme of a system capable of catalysing the liberation of carbon dioxide from pyruvic acid with formation of either acetaldehyde or acetic acid. This theory was not at first generally accepted, however, for R. A. Peters [38] had found that pure cocarboxylase had only 10 % of the activity of vitamin B_1 in the catatorulin test. Later, however, I. Banga, S. Ochoa and R. A. Peters [39] obtained evidence confirming Lohmann and Schuster's hypothesis ; brain preparations that responded to aneurine apparently synthesised cocarboxylase sufficiently rapidly to account for the oxygen uptakes observed, whilst the inferior activity of cocarboxylase in the catatorulin effect was due to its failure to reach the active centre, as it was much less permeable than aneurine itself ; with finely minced brain dispersions, cocarboxylase was very much more active.

I. Banga, S. Ochoa and R. A. Peters [40] were further able to show that the oxidative decarboxylation of pyruvate in brain, and probably in other animal tissues, was not so simple as reaction (1) above indicates and required the presence of inorganic phosphate, C_4-dicarboxylic acids (e.g. succinate, fumarate, malate, etc.), adenine nucleotide, magnesium ions and probably cozymase. They did not, however, believe that the oxidation of pyruvate in brain involved the Krebs' tricarboxylic acid cycle (see page 626).

Aneurine Triphosphate

When aneurine was phosphorylated with phosphoric acid that had been desiccated at 350° C., the triphosphoric ester was formed. This reduced or abolished the bradycardia produced by electrical stimulation and increased the amplitude and regularised the rhythm of heart-beats affected by fatigue or potassium chloride. Cocarboxylase had no such effect, whilst adenosine triphosphate only affected the rhythm and not the bradycardia. Aneurine triphosphate restored the carboxylase activity of washed yeast cells, but had only about one-quarter the activity of cocarboxylase.[40a]

Dismutation of Pyruvic Acid

A considerable body of evidence has now accumulated to suggest that aneurine in the form of its pyrophosphate is concerned with the dismutation reaction (3) rather than with reactions (1) or (2). G. M. Hills [26] reached this conclusion from a study of the oxygen uptake of Staphylococcus aureus in presence and absence of aneurine, and his results were confirmed by Kligler et al.,[41] who also found that, under aerobic conditions, S. aureus produced pyruvic and lactic acids from glucose in the absence of aneurine. Under anaerobic conditions the presence or absence of aneurine made no difference, the reaction being purely glycolytic. When pyruvate was used instead of glucose the absence of aneurine resulted in dismutation, producing equimolecular amounts of lactic acid, acetic acid and carbon dioxide. This reaction was obscured under aerobic conditions, owing to partial oxidation of the lactic acid. Lactate was utilised as a substrate only under aerobic conditions and, in the presence of aneurine and nicotinic acid, was completely oxidised to acetic acid and carbon dioxide ; in the absence of aneurine, oxidation was incomplete, 25 % of the lactic acid being converted to pyruvic acid.

H. A. Krebs and L. V. Eggleston [42] and H. A. Krebs,[43] suggested that reaction (3) actually occurs in two stages, in which oxaloacetic acid acts as a hydrogen carrier :

(4) $CH_3 . CO . COOH + HOOC . CH_2 . CO . COOH \xrightarrow{+ H_2O}$
$$CH_3 . COOH + HOOC . CH_2 . CHOH . COOH + CO_2$$

(5) $CH_3 . CO . COOH + HOOC . CH_2 . CHOH . COOH \longrightarrow$
$$CH_3 . CHOH . COOH + HOOC . CH_2 . CO . COOH$$

The net result of these reactions is, of course, reaction (3).

The formation of oxaloacetic acid, which cannot be isolated owing to its instability, was demonstrated indirectly by E. A. Evans and L. Slotin [44] and H. G. Wood et al.,[45] using carbon dioxide containing radioactive carbon. Furthermore, D. H. Smyth [46] showed that the catalytic effect of aneurine on the oxygen uptake of " avitaminous " *Staphylococcus aureus* could be reproduced by oxaloacetic acid, and R. W. Benham [47] observed that oxaloacetate produced the same effect as aneurine on the growth of the mould, *Pityrosporum ovale*. Krebs suggested that aneurine catalyses not the oxidation of pyruvic acid, but the formation of oxaloacetic acid from pyruvic acid :

(6) $CH_3 . CO . COOH + CO_2 \rightarrow HOOC . CH_2 . CO . COOH.$

So far this hypothesis has not been tested on animals, but, if true, it would provide a more than adequate explanation of the importance of aneurine, since oxaloacetic acid has been shown to act as a hydrogen carrier and to take part in the synthesis of citric, α-ketoglutaric, succinic, fumaric and malic acids, glutamic and aspartic acids and their corresponding amides, glutamine and asparagine (Krebs et al.[48]).

Citric Acid

A number of papers have been published claiming a connection between aneurine on the one hand and citric acid and various amino acids on the other. It has been observed,[49] for example, that rats on a vitamin B_1-deficient diet low in citric acid, excreted less and less citric acid as the deficiency became acute, but that on administration of aneurine, the citric acid excretion increased to a maximum after four to six days. It was therefore suggested that cocarboxylase was an essential factor in the synthesis of endogenous citric acid from precursors, but A. H. Smith and C. E. Meyer [50] claimed that the reduced citric acid excretion in vitamin B_1 deficiency was merely the result of a lower intake of food and not a direct result of the absence of aneurine.

Amino-acid Metabolism

The connection between aneurine and amino acids is even more obscure, although rats receiving 5 μg. of aneurine per day were said to utilise protein more efficiently than rats receiving half this amount.[50a] When extra phenylalanine was administered to vitamin B_1-deficient rats, phenylpyruvic acid was found in the urine,[51] but no evidence is available [52] to suggest that aneurine-deficient rats are less able than normal rats to metabolise either phenylalanine or tyrosine. On the other hand, it has been claimed [53] that in vitamin B_1 deficiency there is an increased enzymatic degradation of histidine due to a disturbance of the intermediary carbohydrate metabolism, whilst the administration of aneurine to normal rats has been said [54] to reduce the excretion of histidine ; this returned to normal on stopping the administration of aneurine. An attempt has also been made [55] to associate aneurine with transamination, as it had been found that tissues from vitamin B_1-deficient rats were much less effective than tissues from normal rats in transferring the amino group from L-glutamic acid to pyruvic acid. It is now known, however, that this reaction is brought about by a coenzyme that contains, not aneurine, but pyridoxine (see page 333).

Oxaloacetic Acid

The hypothesis that cocarboxylase catalyses the formation of oxaloacetic acid is apparently directly opposed to the results of L. O. Krampitz and C. H. Werkman,[56] who prepared from *Micrococcus lysodeikticus* an enzyme that catalysed the reverse of reaction (6). This decarboxylation required magnesium ions, but not cocarboxylase or aneurine. Moreover, contrary to Smyth's observations with *Staphylococcus*, oxaloacetic acid did not replace aneurine in the dismutation of pyruvate with a culture of *M. lysodeikticus* from which cocarboxylase and magnesium had been removed.

Further data of this type were reported by J. H. Quastel and D. M. Webley,[57] who worked with vitamin B_1-deficient propionic acid bacteria. They found that the oxidation of acetate and propionate was accelerated by aneurine only in presence of magnesium and potassium ions, whereas the oxidation of pyruvate was accelerated by aneurine alone and not by magnesium or potassium ions alone. The rate of disappearance of pyruvate, however, was increased by the addition of magnesium and potassium ions even in the absence of vitamin B_1, but the oxygen uptake was not increased. This observation probably explains the acceleration that takes place in the oxidation of lactate by vitamin B_1-deficient bacteria in the presence of magnesium and potassium ions and in the absence of aneurine, since the removal of pyruvic acid by these ions would enhance the oxidation of lactate, which it is known to inhibit. The oxygen uptake, with succinate and fumarate as substrates, was also greatly increased by magnesium and potassium ions, even in the absence of aneurine. This is explained by the fact that these ions accelerate the breakdown by propionic acid bacteria of oxaloacetate, which inhibits succinate oxidation. Since it is known that oxaloacetate inhibits succinic dehydrogenase, this also explains the effects of cozymase and nicotinamide on succinate oxidation by animal tissues. Thus the breakdown of both oxaloacetate and of pyruvate by propionic acid bacteria is catalysed by a mixture of magnesium and potassium ions independently of the presence of vitamin B_1. The accelerating effects of vitamin B_1 in the absence of magnesium and potassium ions are explained as due to the catalysed oxidation of pyruvate or acetate formed from the substrate as intermediaries.

Quastel and Webley also found that the rate of oxidation of acetate, succinate, etc., by vitamin B_1-deficient propionic acid bacteria could be increased not only by the addition to these substrates of magnesium and potassium ions or hexosediphosphate ions (which had the same effect), but also by previously incubating the organisms with these ions, followed by thorough washing. They suggested that the ions completed or induced the formation in the bacterial cell of a system essential for the oxidation of the substrates.

These results may be accounted for on the assumption that incubation of the propionic acid bacteria with hexosediphosphate enriches the cells with adenosine triphosphate and that such cells then have the ability to phosphorylate vitamin B_1 ; the cocarboxylase so formed then catalyses the oxidation of pyruvate and acetate. The magnesium ions are believed to be necessary for effecting phosphorylation.

The fact that succinate, fumarate and ethyl and propyl alcohols do not require aneurine for their oxidation is explained by assuming that adenosine triphosphate is essential either for their complete oxidation or for their oxidation to pyruvate or acetate, where cocarboxylase becomes necessary. Thus, adenosine triphosphate is a coenzyme for the oxidation of fumarate, ethyl and propyl alcohols.

The suggestion made by Krebs and Eggleston and by Smyth that vitamin B_1 catalysed the formation of oxaloacetate was regarded by

Quastel and Webley as untenable because oxaloacetate cannot replace aneurine as an accelerator of acetate and propionate oxidation by propionic acid bacteria. Thus, aneurine exerts its catalytic effect on acetate and pyruvate oxidations by a process other than by the formation of oxaloacetate as suggested by Krampitz and Werkman.

Aneurine, a Catalyst for Several Reactions

The most recent results favour the view, which now enjoys wide support, that aneurine, or rather cocarboxylase, is capable of catalysing more than one reaction involving pyruvic acid. F. Lipmann,[58] for example, suggested that in lactic acid bacteria, such as *B. delbrückii*, it functioned as a dehydrogenating catalyst promoting reaction (1), whereas in yeast it catalysed reaction (2). He showed [59] that, on hydrogenation in presence of platinum black or on reduction by sodium dithionite, hydrogen was taken up by the quaternary nitrogen atom of the thiazole ring, giving dihydroaneurine pyrophosphate :

$$\text{CH}_3 . \underset{\substack{\| \\ \text{N---CH}}}{\overset{\substack{\text{N}=\text{C} . \text{NH}_2 \\ \|}}{\text{C}}} \underset{}{\text{C---CH}_2\text{---N}} + \underset{\substack{| \\ \text{CH---S}}}{\overset{\substack{\text{CH}_3 \\ | \\ \text{C}=\text{C} . \text{CH}_2 . \text{CH}_2 . \text{OP}_2\text{O}_6\text{H}_3}}{}} \xrightarrow{+2\text{H}}$$

$$\text{CH}_3\text{---}\underset{\substack{\| \\ \text{N---CH}}}{\overset{\substack{\text{N}=\text{C} . \text{NH}_2 \\ \|}}{\text{C}}} \underset{}{\text{C---CH}_2\text{---N}} \underset{\substack{| \\ \text{CH}_2\text{---S}}}{\overset{\substack{\text{CH}_3 \\ | \\ \text{C}=\text{C} . \text{CH}_2 . \text{CH}_2 . \text{OP}_2\text{O}_6\text{H}_3}}{}}$$

He drew an analogy with the reduction of Warburg's yellow enzyme and suggested that such a change may occur *in vivo* as well as *in vitro*. In pigeon brain tissue, however, cocarboxylase appears [60] to catalyse the dismutation reaction (3).

Lipmann's views were supported by E. S. G. Barron and C. M. Lyman,[61] who observed that the extent to which cocarboxylase catalysed the oxidation of pyruvic acid on the one hand, and its dismutation on the other, varied with different organisms according to the oxygen tension. Thus, under optimal conditions for oxidation, pyruvic acid was directly oxidised to acetic acid and carbon dioxide ; under optimal conditions for reduction it might be reduced to lactic acid or split by dismutation into acetic acid and formic acid :

$$\text{CH}_3 . \text{CO} . \text{COOH} + \text{H}_2\text{O} \rightarrow \text{CH}_3 . \text{COOH} + \text{H} . \text{COOH}$$

The " oxydismutation coefficients ", *i.e.* the ratio between the amount of pyruvic acid used by the cell under conditions optimal for oxidation and the amount used under conditions optimal for dismutation, were determined for gonococci, *Streptococcus haemolyticus* and for several strains of *Staphylococcus aureus*. Only with the strain of *S. haemolyticus* and with one strain of *S. aureus* was the rate of pyruvic acid disappearance greater in the absence than in the presence of oxygen. In rat tissues also anaerobic metabolism was lower than aerobic metabolism, whilst in goose erythrocytes, pyruvic acid was not utilised at all in the absence of oxygen. Further results by E. S. G. Barron and C. M. Lyman [62] confirmed these views. They showed that kidney slices from normal rats produced an increased amount of glucose when incubated with pyruvate, whereas kidney slices from vitamin B_1-deficient rats did not give such a marked increase until aneurine was added. Heart slices from vitamin B_1-deficient rats produced less citrate from pyruvate and oxaloacetate than did normal heart slices. In this instance, however, no increase occurred on addition of aneurine, due to a failure to phosphorylate the aneurine during the short time of incubation. This evidence strengthens the view that aneurine catalyses not only the oxidation and dismutation of pyruvate, but other reactions involving it. It is therefore suggested that cocarboxylase is an integral part of an enzyme system concerned with the activation of pyruvate, enabling it to take part in a number of reactions.

The problem was also studied by K. G. Stern and J. L. Melnick, [63] who showed that pyruvic acid was not decarboxylated via the "Langenbeck cycle", *i.e.* by combination with cocarboxylase to form a catalytically active substituted imino acid :

$$
\begin{array}{c}
CH_3 . CHO \quad\nwarrow\nearrow\quad CH_3 . C . COOH \quad\nwarrow\qquad CH_3 . CO . COOH + R . NH_2 \\
\qquad\qquad\qquad \|\qquad\qquad\qquad\qquad\qquad\qquad\qquad\qquad \\
\qquad\qquad\qquad N . R \\
CH_3 . CO . COOH \quad\swarrow\nwarrow\quad CH_3 . CH : NR \quad\swarrow\qquad CO_2
\end{array}
$$

and confirmed Lipmann's results on the reduction of aneurine. They pointed out, however, that no evidence was advanced by Lipmann to support his view that aneurine acts as a *reversible* oxidation-reduction system in the same way as pyridine coenzyme. Stern and Melnick claimed that dihydro-aneurine was devoid of biological activity, but that dihydro-cocarboxylase was as active as the oxidised form in both the polyneuritic pigeon and in yeast. In a re-investigation of the problem, however, they found [64] that the supposed biological activity of reduced cocarboxylase was due to the presence of traces of unchanged coenzyme. Fully reduced cocarboxylase, like reduced aneurine, had no biological activity.

Barron and Lyman and their collaborators [65] showed that cocarboxylase was more resistant than aneurine to the action of oxidising and reducing agents, the rate of reduction of aneurine by sodium dithionite and by hydrogen in presence of colloidal palladium or platinum black being three times as fast as the rate of reduction of cocarboxylase ; a similar relationship was observed for the rates of re-oxidation of the two reduction products. The reduced cocarboxylase had neither vitamin nor enzyme-component activity, nor had the substance formed by re-oxidation by means of histidine and ferri-protoporphyrin, thus confirming the later result of Stern and Melnick. It was concluded, therefore, that cocarboxylase is an integral part of the activating protein when acting as a component of an enzyme system, and that it does not owe its activity to reversible oxidation and reduction.

This was confirmed by *in vitro* experiments with tissues from avitaminous animals, in which it was found that the addition of aneurine accelerated condensation reactions of pyruvate leading to the synthesis of carbohydrate, α-ketoglutarate, citrate, acetoacetate and succinate. All these reactions start as condensation reactions of pyruvate and in all of them there is a step in which an oxidative decarboxylation occurs. Thus in the synthesis of carbohydrate, aneurine pyrophosphate may catalyse either the carboxylation of phosphopyruvate to phospho-enoloxaloacetate or the decarboxylation of this compound to phosphoenolpyruvate, and it is impossible to determine whether aneurine is a component of a condensation enzyme or of an oxidative decarboxylation enzyme. The increased stability of aneurine to reduction and oxidation following phosphorylation rather argues against the latter alternative.

The addition of aneurine also increased the oxidation and utilisation of α-ketoglutarate by the tissues of avitaminous rats, but only when the aneurine had previously been incubated with the tissue to make its phosphorylation possible. It was therefore concluded that the activating protein of α-ketoglutarate oxidase is, like that of pyruvate oxidase, an aneurine pyrophosphate-protein.

The possibility that aneurine might be an oxidation catalyst has been considered by other workers, and O. Zima and R. R. Williams [66] suggested a mechanism different from that proposed by Lipmann. They pointed out that aneurine chloride hydrochloride could only exist in solutions far more strongly acid than living tissue, and suggested that in the cell the vitamin probably exists as a hemichloride ; this can be obtained from the chloride hydrochloride by treatment with excess potassium chloride. Two well-defined crystalline sodium salts were obtained from aneurine chloride hydrochloride by addition of alkali ; the one, obtained with sodium ethoxide, was deep yellow in colour and the other, obtained with strong aqueous sodium hydroxide solution, was white. These were assigned the structures :

$$
\begin{array}{c}
N\!=\!\!C\!-\!N\!=\!\!CH \\
| \quad | \quad \quad | \\
CH_3 . C \quad C\!-\!CH_2\!-\!N\!-\!C\!=\!\!C . CH_2 . CH_2OH \\
\| \quad \| \qquad \quad | \quad | \\
N\!-\!CH \qquad \quad CH_3 \; SNa
\end{array}
$$

and

$$
\begin{array}{c}
N\!=\!\!C . NH_2 \\
| \quad | \\
CH_3 . C \quad C\!-\!CH_2\!-\!N\!-\!\!-\!\!-\!C\!=\!\!C . CH_2 . CH_2OH \\
\| \quad \| \qquad \qquad | \quad | \quad | \\
N\!-\!CH \qquad CHO \; CH_3 \; SNa
\end{array}
$$

respectively. On treatment with iodine, a disulphide was obtained, which, on reduction with tin and hydrochloric acid, was reconverted into aneurine. This disulphide was antineuritic, having 60 to 70 % of the activity of aneurine.

Zima et al.,[67] discussing the implications of this discovery, suggested that aneurine and this disulphide might function as a bio-catalyst for oxidations and reductions in the same way as do cysteine and cystine. Aneurine was oxidised to the disulphide by treatment with dilute hydrogen peroxide at pH 7·5, whilst the disulphide was reduced back to aneurine or to the corresponding thiol by cysteine or glutathione, though not by ascorbic acid.

So far, however, no conclusive evidence has been put forward to indicate that the disulphide is ever formed *in vivo*. On the contrary, it has been shown [68] that cocarboxylase and its thiol form liberated carbon dioxide from pyruvic acid at about the same rate, whereas the disulphide pyrophosphate was inactive. The suggestion that vitamin B_1 is part of a redox system must therefore be rejected.

This conclusion is supported by R. A. Peters,[69] who found that aneurine disulphide was at least as active as aneurine in the catatorulin test, and that, in presence of SH-compounds, aneurine disulphide pyrophosphate was able to effect the decarboxylation of pyruvic acid by washed yeast. Cysteine, for example, was very effective, whereas cystine was inert. Presumably, aneurine disulphide pyrophosphate must first be reduced to aneurine by SH-compounds before it is active in the catatorulin effect.

Aneurine, a Catalyst Activating Pyruvic Acid

Doubtless the final word has not yet been said as to the precise rôle played by aneurine pyrophosphate in pyruvate metabolism, but the most satisfactory hypothesis at the present time is undoubtedly that of E. S. G. Barron, C. M. Lyman, M. A. Lipton and J. M. Goldinger,[70] who suggested that aneurine activates the pyruvic acid molecule in a manner that can be represented schematically as follows :

$$CH_3 . C\mathrel{\substack{\nearrow O\\\searrow COOH}} \xrightarrow{\text{cocarboxylase}} CH_3 . C\mathrel{\substack{\nearrow O^+\\\searrow COOH}}$$

The activated pyruvic acid is then able to react with catalysts for its oxidation to acetic acid, reduction to lactic acid, decarboxylation to acetaldehyde, dismutation to lactic and acetic acids or carboxylation to oxaloacetic acid. By inhibiting the activation of pyruvic acid, the absence of aneurine resulting from vitamin B_1 deficiency would interfere with all the chemical transformations in which pyruvic acid plays a part.

Aneurine and Vitamin C

According to Roy et al.,[71] narcotics such as chloretone stimulated the synthesis of vitamin C by rats, but the effect was reduced if the animals were made aneurine- or riboflavine-deficient. Since pyruvic and lactic dehydrogenases are known to be affected by chloretone, it was suggested that pyruvic acid might be utilised in the synthesis of ascorbic acid and that both aneurine and riboflavine might be necessary for effecting this transformation.

References to Section 18

1. C. Funk, *Z. physiol. Chem.*, 1914, **89**, 378.
2. H. W. Kinnersley and R. A. Peters, *Biochem. J.*, 1929, **23**, 1126 ; 1930, **24**, 711.
3. T. W. Birch and L. J. Harris, *ibid.*, 1934, **28**, 602.
4. H. G. K. Westenbrink, *Arch. neer. physiol.*, 1934, **19**, 94.
5. I. Nitzescu and C. Angelescu, *Z. Vitaminforsch.*, 1942, **12**, 82.
6. B. S. Platt and G. D. Lu, *Quart. J. Med.*, 1936, **5**, 355 ; *Biochem. J.*, 1939, **33**, 1523, 1538.
7. M. E. Shils, H. G. Day and E. V. McCollum, *J. Biol. Chem.*, 1941, **139**, 145.
8. A. Göth, *Z. Vitaminforsch.*, 1944, **14**, 231.
9. H. A. Harper and H. J. Deuel, *J. Biol. Chem.*, 1941, **137**, 233.
10. M. E. Shils, H. G. Day and E. V. McCollum, *Amer. J. Med. Sci.*, 1941, **201**, 561.
11. W. D. Robinson, D. Melnick and H. Field, *J. Clin. Invest.*, 1940, **19**, 483.
12. H. Wortis, E. Beuding and W. E. Wilson, *Proc. Soc. Exp. Biol. Med.*, 1940, **43**, 279.
13. H. A. Davis and F. K. Bauer, *Arch. Surg.*, 1944, **48**, 185, 190, 193.
13a. M. K. Horwitt and O. Kreisler, *J. Nutrition*, 1949, **37**, 411.
14. A. Geiger and A. Rosenberg, *Klin. Woch.*, 1933, **12**, 1258.

15. M. Chiba, *Tohoku J. Exp. Med.*, 1932, **19**, 486.
16. T. Suzuki and A. Takamatsu, *ibid.*, 1934, **24**, 202 ; see also L. Fehily, *Brit. Med. J.*, 1944, **2**, 590.
17. R. Orimo, *Tohoku J. Exp. Med.*, 1939, **35**, 374.
18. A. Takamatsu and A. Sato, *ibid.*, 1934, **23**, 506.
19. J. Vogt-Möller, *Biochem. Z.*, 1931, **233**, 248.
20. B. S. Platt and G. D. Lu, *Biochem. J.*, 1939, **33**, 1523, 1538.
21. R. A. Peters, *Lancet*, 1936, **1**, 1161.
22. W. C. Sherman and C. A. Elvehjem, *Biochem. J.*, 1936, **30**, 785.
23. K. Lohmann and P. Schuster, *Naturwiss.*, 1937, **25**, 26 ; *Biochem. Z.*, 1937, **294**, 188.
24. H. A. Krebs, *Nature*, 1936, **138**, 288.
25. H. A. Krebs and W. A. Johnson, *Biochem. J.*, 1937, **31**, 645.
26. G. M. Hills, *ibid.*, 1938, **32**, 383.
27. H. G. K. Westenbrink and J. J. Pollak, *Rec. trav. chim. Pays Bas*, 1937, **56**, 315.
28. K. G. Stern and J. W. Hofer, *Science*, 1937, **85**, 483.
29. H. Tauber, *ibid.*, 1937, **86**, 180.
30. H. von Euler and R. Vestin, *Naturwiss.*, 1937, **25**, 416.
31. M. Silverman and C. H. Werkman, *Proc. Soc. Exp. Biol. Med.*, 1939, **40**, 369.
32. H. Weil-Malherbe, *Biochem. J.*, 1940, **34**, 980.
33. E. S. Nasset and J. F. Waldo, *J. Nutrition*, 1941, **21**, *Suppl.*, 10.
34. H. Weil-Malherbe, *Biochem. J.*, 1939, **33**, 1997.
35. F. Schlenk, R. B. Vowles and H. von Euler, *Arkiv Kemi, Min., Geol.*, 1940, **13B**, No. 20.
36. M. A. Lipton and C. A. Elvehjem, *Nature*, 1940, **145**, 226 ; M. A. Lipschitz, V. R. Potter and C. A. Elvehjem, *Biochem. J.*, 1938, **32**, 474 ; *J. Biol. Chem.*, 1938, **124**, 147.
37. F. Lipmann, *Nature*, 1937, **140**, 25.
38. R. A. Peters, *Biochem. J.*, 1937, **31**, 2240.
39. I. Banga, S. Ochoa and R. A. Peters, *ibid.*, 1939, **33**, 1109.
40. I. Banga, S. Ochoa and R. A. Peters, *ibid.*, 1980.
40a. L. Velluz, G. Amiard and J. Bartos, *Bull. Soc. Chim.*, 1948 [v], **15**, 871 ; *J. Biol. Chem.*, 1949, **180**, 1137 ; L. Velluz, R. Jequier and C. Plotka, *C. R. Acad. Sci.*, 1948, **226**, 1855.
41. L. J. Kligler, N. Grossowicz and S. Bergner, *J. Bact.*, 1943, **46**, 399.
42. H. A. Krebs and L. V. Eggleston, *Biochem. J.*, 1940, **34**, 1383.
43. H. A. Krebs, *Nature*, 1941, **147**, 560.
44. E. A. Evans and L. Slotin, *J. Biol. Chem.*, 1940, **136**, 301.
45. H. G. Wood, C. H. Werkman, A. Hemingway and A. O. Nier, *ibid.*, 1942, **142**, 31.
46. D. H. Smyth, *Biochem. J.*, 1940, **34**, 1598.
47. R. W. Benham, *Proc. Soc. Exp. Biol. Med.*, 1945, **58**, 199.
48. H. A. Krebs, L. V. Eggleston, A. Kleinzeller and D. H. Smyth, *Biochem. J.*, 1940, **34**, 1234.
49. H. A. Sober, M. A. Lipton and C. A. Elvehjem, *J. Biol. Chem.*, 1944, **134**, 605.
50. A. H. Smith and C. E. Meyer, *ibid.*, 1941, **139**, 277.

50a. H. L. Mayfield and M. T. Hedrick, *J. Nutrition*, 1949, **37**, 475.

51. K. Closs and A. Fälling, *Z. physiol. Chem.*, 1938, **254**, 258.

52. M. M. Kaser and W. J. Darby, *J. Biol. Chem.*, 1945, **161**, 279.

53. S. Edlbacher and G. Viollier, *Helv. Chim. Acta*, 1943, **26**, 1978.

54. J. Dawson, *Biochem. J.*, 1944, **38**, Proc., xv.

55. M. G. Kritzman, *Biochimia*, 1943, **8**, 85.

56. L. O. Krampitz and C. H. Werkman, *Biochem. J.*, 1941, **35**, 595.

57. J. H. Quastel and D. M. Webley, *ibid.*, 1942, **36**, 8.

58. F. Lipmann, *Nature*, 1937, **140**, 25 ; *Enzymologia*, 1937, **4**, 65.

59. F. Lipmann, *Nature*, 1936, **138**, 1097.

60. F. Lipmann, *Skand. Arch. Physiol.*, 1937, **76**, 255.

61. E. S. G. Barron and C. M. Lyman, *J. Biol. Chem.*, 1939, **127**, 143.

62. E. S. G. Barron and C. M. Lyman, *Science*, 1940, **92**, 337.

63. K. G. Stern and J. L. Melnick, *J. Biol. Chem.*, 1939, **131**, 597.

64. K. G. Stern and J. L. Melnick, *ibid.*, 1940, **135**, 365.

65. E. S. G. Barron and C. M. Lyman, *ibid.*, 1941, **141**, 951 ; E. S. G. Barron, C. M. Lyman, M. A. Lipton and J. M. Goldinger, *ibid.*, 957 ; E. S. G. Barron, J. M. Goldinger, M. A. Lipton and C. M. Lyman, *ibid.*, 975.

66. O. Zima and R. R. Williams, *Ber.*, 1940, **73**, 941.

67. O. Zima, K. Ritsert and T. Moll, *Z. physiol. Chem.*, 1941, **267**, 210.

68. P. Karrer and M. Viscontini, *Helv. Chim. Acta*, 1946, **29**, 711.

69. R. A. Peters, *Nature*, 1946, **158**, 707.

70. E. S. G. Barron, C. M. Lyman, M. A. Lipton and J. M. Goldinger, *J. Biol. Chem.*, 1941, **140**, xi.

71. S. C. Roy, S. K. Roy and B. C. Guha, *Nature*, 1946, **158**, 238.

19. ANEURINE IN THE NUTRITION OF MICRO-ORGANISMS

Aneurine is not only a vitamin for animals, but it is also a " vitamin" for many micro-organisms. E. Wildiers [1] in 1901 postulated that yeasts required in addition to sugar and inorganic salts a hypothetical organic substance which he called " bios ". This was subsequently shown to be, not one single entity, but a mixture of several different substances. One of these, which had provisionally been designated " Bios V ", was ultimately shown to be identical with aneurine.[2] Since then, a considerable amount of work has been carried out on the aneurine requirements of a large variety of yeasts and other fungi and bacteria. Some of these micro-organisms have been used for the assay of aneurine.

Yeasts

Reference has already been made (page 33), for example, to the yeast fermentation method of estimating aneurine, in which a strain of yeast that fails to produce carbon dioxide in the absence of aneurine is employed. If such an organism is grown on a medium containing aneurine, the amount of gas produced is, within limits, proportional to the aneurine concentration. The chief disadvantage, already referred to, is that other substances may be present that stimulate the fermentation. Such substances are said to be present in urine, and both the thiazole and the pyrimidine moieties of aneurine enhance gas production. The organisms used in this microbiological method of assay were certain strains of *Saccharomyces cerevisiae :* but not all yeasts, and not even all *Saccharomyces*, require added aneurine before growth occurs. In an examination of thirty-six kinds of yeast, P. R. Burkholder [3] found that fifteen kinds required aneurine, whilst of a further thirty-three yeasts examined by P. R. Burkholder and D. Moyer,[4] twenty-four required aneurine. The most marked deficiencies were observed with *Candida suaveolens* and *C. deformans, Chalara mycoderma, Mycoderma lipolytica, M. valida* and *M. vini, Pichia belgica* and *P. Drombrowskii, Saccharomyces fragilis, S. globosus, S. macedoniensis, S. muciparus, S. validus, Saccharomycodes ludwigii, Torulopsis laurentii, T. dattila* and *Zygosaccharomyces mandshuricus.* In a third paper, Burkholder and his colleagues [5] examined 110 further species and varieties of yeast and found that thirty-three required aneurine. These comprised strains of the following additional species : *Saccharomyces cerevisiae* var. *ellipsoideus, Kloeckera brevis, Zygosaccharomyces japonicus, Z. priorianus* and *Torulopsis stellata. K. brevis* was of particular interest, as it responded to six different vitamins. Emery *et al.*[6] confirmed the observations of Burkholder *et al.* regarding the requirement of *S. macedoniensis* and *K. brevis* for aneurine, and used the former for assaying aneurine, whilst A. S. Schultz and L. Atkin[7] confirmed the need of other yeasts for aneurine. Additional species for which aneurine was found to be essential were [8] *Saccharomyces hanseniaspora valbyensis* and *S. galactosus.* For the latter, aneurine could be replaced by a mixture of the thiazole and pyrimidine halves, but the former required the intact vitamin.

Pyruvic acid was formed in a medium inoculated with a yeast deprived of aneurine and incubated for twenty-five hours. On addition of aneurine, the pyruvic acid disappeared.[9]

Most yeasts—those grown commercially at all events—synthesise aneurine, especially if the thiazole moiety is added to the culture fluid. For instance, the aneurine content of bakers' yeast was increased from 20 or 30 to 200 μg. per g. of dry weight by addition of the thiazole compound to a wort agar.[10] The factors affecting the accumulation of aneurine in the cells of various kinds of yeast were studied by H. Fink and F. Just and their colleagues.[11] They found that the normal metabolism of brewers' yeast, growing in a medium containing aneurine, was disturbed by aeration, resulting in a lower aneurine content. A large proportion of the aneurine present in the yeast cells was in the form of cocarboxylase. Thus about 75 % of aneurine added to a press-yeast fermenting molasses was converted into cocarboxylase ; only 6 to 8 % remained in solution and 15 to 30 % of the total vitamin in the washed cells was free aneurine. After two hours, the amount of aneurine in the yeast (on a dry solids basis) was 152 μg. per g. of glucose fermented ; the maximum amount, 306 μg., was formed after eight hours. Increasing amounts of aneurine were obtained as the temperature was increased to 30° C. Galactose and maltose, but not lactose or xylose, stimulated the synthesis of aneurine.

Torula utilis, like brewers' yeast, converts aneurine into the pyrophosphate ; the yield was lower when the culture was aerated. The pyrimidine and thiazole halves of aneurine (5-hydroxyethyl-4-methyl-thiazole and 4-amino-5-hydroxymethyl-2-methyl-pyrimidine) were quantitatively utilised and converted into cocarboxylase. With only one component present, little or no synthesis of aneurine occurred. Bakers' yeast, *Oidium lactis*, *Endomyces vernalis* and *Aspergillus oryzae* also synthesise aneurine from its components. *T. utilis*, bakers' yeast, and top and bottom brewers' yeast did not produce aneurine from 5-hydroxyethyl-4-methyl-thiazole when 4-hydroxy-2-methyl-pyrimidine-5-acetic ester, 4-chloro-2-methyl-pyrimidine-5-acetic ester, 4-amino-2-methyl-pyrimidine-5-acetamide or 4-amino-5-cyano-2-methyl-pyrimidine were used as the pyrimidine component. Bottom yeast failed to synthesise aneurine from 4-amino-5-aminomethyl-pyrimidine or 4-amino-5-hydroxymethyl-2-methyl-pyrimidine, but bakers' yeast and top yeast, like *T. utilis*, were able to utilise both 4-amino-5-hydroxymethyl-2-methyl-pyrimidine and 4-amino-5-aminomethyl-2-methyl-pyrimidine for the synthesis of aneurine.

Similar results were reported by van Lanen *et al.*,[12] who found that yeasts grown on a medium rich in aneurine might contain up to 6 mg. per g. of the vitamin. Aneurine was synthesised from the pyrimidine and thiazole halves, the yields being 70 to 100 %. Contrary to the findings of Fink and Just, the yields were found to be increased by aeration. Resting cells synthesised some pyrimidine, but not much thiazole.

A reduced yield on aeration, however, was obtained by Sperber *et al.*[13] and by E. N. Odintzova.[14] The latter found that *Saccharomyces* spp., *T. utilis* and *Endomyces magnusii* in anaerobic culture took up to 1 mg. of aneurine per g. of dried cells from the culture liquid, but much less when grown aerobically. Sperber observed two stages in the uptake of aneurine by yeast. The first stage was rapid and appeared to coincide with the adsorption of the vitamin on the cell. It was sensitive to salts ; sodium chloride, potassium chloride, sodium thiocyanate and potassium dihydrogen phosphate had the same relatively weak effect, but sodium fluoride, potassium sulphate and magnesium chloride were more potent, and lanthanum nitrate still more potent, inhibitors of this adsorptive phase. The second stage was of longer duration and was very sensitive to pH; maximum absorption occurred at pH 3·5 to 4·0. This stage was inhibited by iodoacetate or azide and slightly by potassium cyanide or sodium fluoride. Absorption was also almost completely inhibited by 4-amino-5-aminomethyl-2-methyl-pyrimidine, which was also found to inhibit the dephosphorylation of cocarboxylase by yeast phosphatase. It is therefore suggested that phosphatase may be connected with this second phase of aneurine absorption, which probably involves phosphorylation.

Other Fungi

The aneurine requirements of other fungi exhibit the same wide variations that have been noted for the yeasts. *Phycomyces Blakesleeanus*, as already stated (page 35), fails to grow in the absence of aneurine, and the weight of the mycelium formed on a medium containing aneurine is, within limits, proportional to its concentration. The test is highly specific and only closely related analogues of aneurine (see page 122) give a response.[15] An equimolecular mixture of the pyrimidine and thiazole moieties, however, gave the same growth response as the corresponding amount of aneurine,[16] though the organisms fail to grow when only one of these fractions is present.

Phytophthora cinnamomi [17] and *P. erythroseptica* [18] also require aneurine for growth, but these fail to respond to a mixture of the two halves of the molecule. *Pythiomorpha gonapodioides* [15] will respond either to aneurine or to the pyrimidine moiety alone, and it has been suggested that by means of this organism in conjunction with *P. Blakesleeanus* and *P. erythroseptica*, an estimate might be made of the amounts of aneurine and of the thiazole and the pyrimidine halves of the molecule in a mixture of all three.

F. Kavanagh [19] observed that aneurine disappeared from cultures in which *Phycomyces Blakesleeanus*, *Phytophthora cinnamomi*, *Mucor Ramannianus* or *Sclerotium rolfori* were grown and that with *P. Blakesleeanus* the pyrimidine half of the aneurine molecule was liberated and the thiazole half destroyed; the addition of the thiazole compound, but not the pyrimidine compound, increased the growth of the mould. *P. cinnamomi* utilised aneurine without destroying either the thiazole or the pyrimidine moiety, whilst *M. Ramannianus* synthesised the pyrimidine half and grew well in the presence of the thiazole half. *S. rolfori*, when grown in solutions containing aneurine, synthesised the thiazole half. Like *M. Ramannianus, Rhodotorula rubra* cannot grow in the absence of aneurine but the two moulds together will grow and develop satisfactorily in an aneurine-free medium, because the former is able to synthesise the pyrimidine half of the molecule, which the latter cannot synthesise, whereas the latter can synthesise the thiazole half, which the former cannot synthesise. The behaviour of these two moulds is a striking example of symbiosis, and is due to the ability of each partner to supply a nutrient that the other needs. Another illustration is provided by the phenomenon, well-known to horticulturists, that orchid seeds will only germinate when a mycorrhizal fungus is present. It is now known that the latter synthesises aneurine, which the seeds require.

An increase in the amount of glucose consumed by *Melanospora destruens* or *Phycomyces nitens* occurred on addition of aneurine to the medium,[20] owing to the increased rate of respiration. *Phytophthora infestans* also required aneurine for growth and this could not be replaced by a mixture of the two halves of the molecule.[21]

Aneurine is also necessary for the growth of *Ustilago violacea*, and *U. scabiosae*, but not of other species of *Ustilago*.[22] It is also necessary for the growth of the wood-destroying fungi, *Stercum frustulosum, Hydnum erinaceus, Polyporus Spraguei* and *Fomes igniarius*,[23] of a number of other wood-destroying *Polyporiaceae*,[24] and of *Lophiodermum pinastri, Sclerotinia cinerea, Helvella infesta, Polyporus adustus, P. abietinus, Fomes pinicola, Trametes cinnabarina, T. serialis, Lenzites sepiaria* and *Tricholoma nudum*.[25]

Other moulds for which aneurine is a growth factor were reported by P. R. Burkholder and D. Moyer ;[26] of seventeen fungi tested, the following required aneurine : *Hormodendron pedrosoi, Phialophora verrucosa, Sporotrichon schencki, Trichopyton faviforme, T. sulphureum, T. violaceum, Fomes annosus, Coryne sarcoides, Cytospora* sp., and *Lenzites betulina*. W. H. Schopfer and S. Blumer [27] reported that aneurine was necessary for the growth of *Trichophyton album*, but could be replaced by an equimolecular mixture of the thiazole and pyrimidine halves ; either alone was without effect.

According to N. Fries,[28] pyridoxine is essential for several species of *Ophiostoma (Ceratostomella)*. Some of them, including *O. multiannulatum* and *O. pluriannulatum*, required aneurine in addition, whilst the growth of *O. ulmi* was stimulated by the addition of aneurine. *Ascoidea rubescens* required pyridoxine, aneurine and biotin. Aneurine was an essential growth factor for *O. coeruleum, O. quercus, O. piceae, O. stenoceras, O. pini* and for *Mitrula pusilla*. These species were apparently capable of synthesising the thiazole moiety but not the pyrimidine half of the molecule. W. Schopfer [29] also observed that *Ceratostomella ulmi* could grow without added aneurine, but not in the absence of pyridoxine. The effect of the pyridoxine was, however, enormously enhanced, within certain limits of concentration, by the presence of aneurine ; with high concentrations of pyridoxine, aneurine had an antagonistic effect. Of sixteen fungi, chiefly *Ceratostomella* spp., examined by W. J. Robbins and R. Ma,[30] four required aneurine as such and were unable to utilise its intermediates, five others grew with a mixture of the pyrimidine and thiazole halves and six grew well with aneurine, or a mixture of the pyrimidine and thiazole compounds or of the pyrimidine compound alone. None of the organisms responded to the thiazole half only. Aneurine is a supplementary, though not an essential, growth factor for *Eremothecium Ashbyii*.[31]

According to M. N. Musil,[32] cocarboxylase, aneurine, a mixture of the thiazole and pyrimidine moieties or the thiazole moiety alone produced what he terms " fermentative rearrangement " of the cells of *Endomyces magnusii*, characterised by large cell nuclei poor in thymonucleic acid. The pyrimidine moiety alone was without effect. On addition of the thiazole compound, aneurine was synthesised, and accumulated in the cells.

Aneurine or a related substance appears to be synthesised by several species of *Actinomyces*, since extracts prepared from cultures stimulated the growth of *Phycomyces Blakesleeanus*.[33]

Pyruvic acid accumulates in cultures of *Phycomyces Blakesleeanus* containing inadequate amounts of aneurine, though not in the total absence of aneurine.[34] The formation of pyruvic acid was prevented by the addition of aneurine or of cocarboxylase or of a mixture of the pyrimidine and thiazole halves of the molecule.

The growth of *Pityrosporum ovale* was also increased by aneurine, especially in the presence of asparagine.[35] The addition of oxaloacetate instead of aneurine caused an equal increase, however, and the subsequent addition of aneurine did not augment the increase further. This observation supports Kreb's hypothesis (page 96) that aneurine catalyses the formation of oxaloacetic acid, but objections have been made to this hypothesis on other grounds (page 98).

Bacteria

Comparatively few bacteria have been shown to require aneurine, in striking contrast to the widespread requirement for this factor among yeasts and moulds. Indeed, great difficulty has been experienced in devising a satisfactory assay method analogous to those now in widespread use for riboflavine, nicotinic acid and other members of the vitamin B complex. Only *Lactobacillus fermenti* appears to be sufficiently exacting in its requirements to be of value for this purpose,[36] although attempts have been made to use *Streptococcus salivarius* [37] and *Staphylococcus aureus*.[38] *Neisseria gonorrhaeae* gave good growth only in the presence of aneurine,[39] but a strain was described by C. E. Lankford and P. K. Skeggs [40] that failed to grow with aneurine, and required the whole cocarboxylase molecule although, rather surprisingly, aneurine monophosphate (see page 125) had 80 % of the activity of cocarboxylase. Aneurine itself competitively inhibited the utilisation of cocarboxylase by the organism. The cocarboxylase strain gave rise to variants capable of synthesising cocarboxylase. Aneurine was essential for *Clostridium tetani* [41] and *Cl. botulinum*.[42]

Kligler *et al.*[43] studied the effect of aneurine deficiency on a culture of *S. aureus*. They found that the particular strain failed to grow or ferment glucose in the absence of nicotinic acid, but in the absence of aneurine about 40 % of the glucose consumed was converted into pyruvic acid and 60 % into lactic acid. When both vitamins were present, 40 % was converted to acetic acid, 20 % to lactic acid and only a trace to pyruvic acid, whence they concluded that aneurine was acting as a catalyst for the oxidation of pyruvic acid and could only do this when nicotinic acid was available.

It is obvious therefore that, although most bacteria grow without the addition of aneurine to the medium, aneurine (or cocarboxylase) is necessary for the metabolism of these micro-organisms. H. McIlwain [44] calculated that *Aerobacter aerogenes* contained 2200 molecules of aneurine per cell and that the organism synthesised aneurine at the rate of one molecule per cell per second. With *Serratia marcescens, Pseudomonas fluorescens, Proteus vulgaris* and *Clostridium butylicum*, the corresponding values were : 5400, 5200, 4200 and 1900 ; 1·7, 2·8, 0·8 and 1·5 respectively. The " turnover number " of yeast carboxylase was calculated to be twenty-two molecules per molecule of enzyme per second, that is, twenty-two molecules of pyruvic acid reacted with one molecule of carboxylase per second. The rates of synthesis and inactivation of aneurine indicated that these reactions belonged to the group termed by McIlwain reactions of mμmol. order, because their speed is of the order of a few mμmols. per gram of dry weight per second ; they therefore differ from the ordinary reactions of the bacterial cell, which are of μmol. order. The significance of this distinction is discussed in the chapter on nicotinic acid (page 284).

B. paraalvei grew well in a synthetic medium containing fifteen to eighteen amino acids when aneurine was added, but only moderately well in its absence.[45] In the absence of aneurine, phenylalanine, valine, isoleucine and cystine were essential for growth, but cystine could be replaced by cysteine, glutathione, homocystine or homocysteine, though not by methionine. The thiazole portion of aneurine, though not the pyrimidine portion, was a satisfactory substitute for aneurine, and it was therefore suggested that the thiazole half was synthesised from the above four amino acids.

Other Micro-organisms. Aneurine is essential for the growth of the following flagellates : *Polytoma ocellatum*,[46] *P. caudatum*,[47] and *Chilomonas paramaecium*,[47] which utilise the thiazole half in place of aneurine ; *Polytomella caeca*,[48, 49] which requires either the intact molecule or both halves ; *Strigomonas oncopelti*,[50] *S. fasciculata* [50] and *S. culicidarum*,[51] all three of which require the intact aneurine molecule; *Chlamydomonas orbicularis*,[52] *Chlorogonium tetragamum* [52] and *Haematococcus pluvialis*.[52] The ciliate, *Glaucoma piriformis*, required the intact aneurine molecule and failed to respond to a mixture of the thiazole and pyrimidine halves.[53]

References to Section 19

1. E. Wildiers, *La Cellule*, 1901, **18**, 313.
2. W. Lash Miller, *Trans. Roy. Soc., Canada*, III, 1937, **31**, 169.
3. P. R. Burkholder, *Amer. J. Bot.*, 1943, **30**, 206.
4. P. R. Burkholder and D. Moyer, *Bull. Torrey Bot. Club*, 1943, **70**, 372.
5. P. R. Burkholder, I. McVeigh and D. Moyer, *J. Bact.*, 1944, **48**, 385.
6. W. B. Emery, N. McLeod and F. A. Robinson, *Biochem. J.*, 1946, **40**, 426.
7. A. S. Schultz and L. Atkin, *Arch. Biochem.*, 1947, **14**, 369.
8. C. Marchant, *Canad. J. Res.*, 1942, **20B**, 21.
9. E. Haag and C. Dalphin, *Arch. Sci. phys. nat.*, 1940 (v), **22**, *Suppl.*, 76.
10. E. N. Odintzova, *Compt. rend. Acad. Sci., U.R.S.S.*, 1943, **41**, 250.
11. H. Fink and F. Just, *Biochem. Z.*, 1941, **308**, 15 ; 1941, **309**, 1, 212, 219 ; 1941-2, **311**, 61, 287 ; 1942, **313**, 39 ; *Ber.*, 1942, **75B**, 2101.
12. J. M. van Lanen, H. P. Broquist, M. J. Johnson, I. L. Baldwin and W. H. Peterson, *Ind. Eng. Chem.*, 1942, **34**, 1244.
13. E. Sperber and S. Renvall, *Biochem. Z.*, 1941, **310**, 160 ; E. Sperber, *ibid.*, 1942, **313**, 62.
14. E. N. Odintzova, *Compt. rend. Acad. Sci., U.R.S.S.*, 1944, **42**, 129.
15. W. H. Schopfer, *Experientia*, 1945, **1**, 1.
16. W. H. Schopfer and A. Jung, *Compt. rend.*, 1937, **204**, 1500 ; H. M. Sinclair, *Nature*, 1937, **140**, 360 ; W. J. Robbins and F. Kavanagh, *Proc. Nat. Acad. Sci.*, 1937, **23**, 499 ; J. Bonner and J. Erikson, *Amer. J. Bot.*, 1938, **25**, 685.
17. W. J. Robbins, *Bull. Torrey Bot. Club*, 1938, **65**, 267.
18. V. G. Lilly and L. H. Leonian, *Science*, 1939, **89**, 292.
19. F. Kavanagh, *Bull. Torrey Bot. Club*, 1942, **69**, 669.
20. L. E. Hawker, *Ann. Bot.*, 1944, **8**, 79.
21. A. Payette and C. Perrault, *Canad. J. Res.*, 1944, **22C**, 127.

22. W. H. Schopfer, *Ber. deut. botan. Ges.*, 1937, **55**, 572 ; W. H. Schopfer and S. Blumer, *Compt. rend.*, 1938, **206**, 1141.
23. N. L. Noecker, *Amer. J. Bot.*, 1938, **25**, 345.
24. N. Fries, *Symbolae Botan. Upsalienses*, 1938, **3**, No. 1 ; *Rev. Applied Mycol.*, **18**, 335.
25. F. Kögl and N. Fries, *Z. physiol. Chem.*, 1937, **249**, 93.
26. P. R. Burkholder and D. Moyer, *Bull. Torrey Bot. Club*, 1943, **70**, 372.
27. W. H. Schopfer and S. Blumer, *Ber. Schweiz. Bot. Ges.*, 1943, **53**, 409.
28. N. Fries, *Symbolae Botan. Upsalienses*, 1943, **7**, No. 2.
29. W. H. Schopfer, *Arch. Julius Klaus-Stift.*, 1945, **20**, 27.
30. W. J. Robbins and R. Ma, *Bull. Torrey Bot. Club*, 1943, **70**, 190.
31. W. H. Schopfer, *Helv. Chim. Acta*, 1944, **27**, 1017.
32. M. N. Musil, *Compt. rend. Acad. Sci., U.R.S.S.*, 1943, **41**, 248.
33. J. E. Mackinnon, *Bull. Torrey Bot. Club*, 1942, **69**, 21 ; J. A. Herrick and C. J. Alexopoulos, *ibid.*, 1942, **69**, 569 ; 1943, **70**, 369.
34. E. Haag, *Arch. Sci. phys. nat.*, 1940 (v), **22**, *Suppl.*, 136.
35. R. W. Benham, *Proc. Soc. Exp. Biol. Med.*, 1945, **58**, 199.
36. H. P. Sarett and V. H. Cheldelin, *J. Biol. Chem.*, 1944, **155**, 153.
37. C. F. Niven and K. L. Smiley, *ibid.*, 1943, **150**, 1.
38. P. M. West and P. W. Wilson, *Science*, 1938, **88**, 334.
39. A. Schuetz, *Schweiz. Z. Path. Bakt.*, 1942, **5**, 238.
40. C. E. Lankford and P. K. Skeggs, *Arch. Biochem.*, 1946, **9**, 265.
41. R. E. Feeney, J. H. Mueller and P. A. Miller, *J. Bact.*, 1943, **46**, 563.
42. C. Lamanna and C. Lewis, *ibid.*, 1946, **51**, 398.
43. I. J. Kligler, H. Grossowicz and S. Bergner, *ibid.*, 1943, **46**, 399.
44. H. McIlwain, *Nature*, 1946, **158**, 898.
45. H. Katznelson, *J. Biol. Chem.*, 1947, **167**, 615.
46. A. Lwoff and H. Dusi, *Compt. rend.*, 1937, **205**, 882.
47. A. Lwoff and H. Dusi, *ibid.*, 756 ; *Compt. rend. Soc. Biol.*, 1938, **127**, 1408.
48. M. Javillier and L. Emerique-Blum, *Compt. rend.*, 1940, **211**, 374.
49. A. Lwoff and H. Dusi, *ibid.*, 1937, **205**, 630.
50. M. Lwoff, *Compt. rend. Soc. Biol.*, 1937, **126**, 771.
51. M. Lwoff, *ibid.*, 1938, **128**, 241.
52. K. Ondratschek, *Arch. Mikrobiol.*, 1940, **11**, 239.
53. A. and M. Lwoff, *Compt. rend.*, 1937, **126**, 644 ; L. Emerique-Blum and A. Lwoff, *Bull. Soc. Chim. biol.*, 1940, **22**, 179.

20. EFFECT OF ANEURINE ON HIGHER PLANTS

The pronounced stimulating effect of aneurine on micro-organisms suggested that it might be a growth factor for higher plants, and possibly even a plant hormone, biologically similar to auxin. Expectations of this type, however, have not been realised, for in no plant treated with aneurine has any convincing evidence of growth-stimulation been obtained. The addition of aneurine (o·oɪ mg. per litre) to the nutrient solution failed to affect the fresh or dry weights of plants or their times of flowering, or the size, number and colour of their flowers.[1] Aneurine had no effect on the growth of *Agrostis tenuis* or *Brassica alba*,[2] of rice,[3] or of radish or cauliflower.[4] It did not affect pollen germination or pollen tube elongation,[5] and did not promote growth in, or alter the yield of, sunflowers, maize, flax, wheat or beans.[6]

Three reports have been published, however, claiming that aneurine had a positive growth effect on certain plants. The first is a statement [7] that the growth of aster seedlings was increased by aneurine, although it had no effect on the growth of the roots ; the authors suggested that aneurine might be an activator of indolyl butyric acid.

The second report claimed [8] that aneurine stimulated the growth of cosmos seedlings at 20° C. but not at 26·6° C. A temperature favouring luxuriant growth did not favour stimulation by aneurine. The third records [9] that aneurine could not replace indolylacetic acid for promoting the growth of carrot tissue, though root cultures could be maintained in presence of aneurine.

A little work has been carried out on the changes that take place in the distribution of aneurine as plants develop. In cereals, beans and peas, no increase in the aneurine content took place during germination or, in oat seedlings, during the first five days after germination, although the riboflavine, nicotinic acid and pyridoxine contents increased.[10] Half the aneurine present was found in the embryo, although this represented only 6·5 % of the dry weight of the seed. No increase occurred in the amount of aneurine in the coleoptile, although the riboflavine and nicotinic acid contents increased. All three substances appeared to be synthesised in the leaves. In tomato leaves, the maximum concentration was found in newly developed leaves, the concentration decreasing progressively towards the roots.[11] It would seem that aneurine is synthesised in the mature leaves and translocated to the actively growing tissues, in which it accumulates.

The aneurine content of forty-one genera of herbs and medicinal plants was ɪ·25 to 28·8 µg. per g. of dry weight.[12] The amounts of aneurine in a variety of foodstuffs have been listed on pages 43 to 45.

Although aneurine does not appear to be a growth hormone, it is present in soil and natural manures,[13] from which it is presumably taken up by plants, since its concentration in pasture was increased by manuring with farmyard manure.

References to Section 20

1. C. L. Hamner, *Bot. Gaz.*, 1940, **102,** 156.
2. D. G. Clark, *Plant Physiol.*, 1942, **17,** 137.
3. C. E. Minarick, *ibid.*, 141.
4. E. C. Minnum, *Bot. Gaz.*, 1941, **103,** 397.
5. P. F. Smith, *Amer. J. Bot.*, 1942, **29,** 56.
6. L. Gisiger, *Mitt. Lebensm. Hyg.*, 1943, **34,** 315.
7. A. E. Hitchcock and P. W. Zimmerman, *Contrib. Boyce Thompson Inst.*, 1941, **12,** 143.
8. J. Bonner, *Bot. Gaz.*, 1942, **104,** 475.
9. P. Nobécourt, *Compt. rend.*, 1943, **216,** 902.
10. P. R. Burkholder and I. McVeigh, *Proc. Nat. Acad. Sci.*, 1942, **28,** 440 ; I. McVeigh, *Bull. Torrey Bot. Club*, 1944, **71,** 438.
11. J. Bonner, *Amer. J. Bot.*, 1942, **29,** 136.
12. A. S. Chaikelis, *J. Amer. Pharm. Assoc.*, 1946, **35,** 343.
13. M. A. Roulet, *Experientia*, 1948, **4,** 149.

21. ANEURINE REQUIREMENTS OF INSECTS

Insects require in their diet several members of the vitamin B complex if they are to develop normally, and aneurine has been shown to be essential for the growth of the fruit-fly, *Drosophila melanogaster*,[1] of various species of mosquito,[2] of the beetles, *Tenebrio molitor*,[3] *Tribolium confusum*,[4,5] and *Ptinus tectus*[5] and the moth, *Ephestia elutella*.[5] The beetles, *Silvanus surinamensis, Sitodrepa panicea* and *Lasioderma serricorne* did not apparently require either aneurine or most other members of the vitamin B complex,[5] and this was shown to be due to the presence in these last three insect of intracellular symbiotic micro-organisms capable of synthesising some of the vitamins ; on sterilising the larvae, no growth occurred in the absence of aneurine. This observation affords a striking parallel to the phenomenon of intestinal synthesis in animals. A number of early workers considered that the function of these intracellular symbionts might be the provision of accessory food substances,[6] and their predictions have been amply fulfilled.

Aneurine, together with other members of the vitamin B complex, was necessary for the growth of sterile larvae of the mosquito, *Aedes aegypti*, to the fourth instar.[7]

An attempt has been made to utilise insect larvae, for which aneurine is an essential nutrient, as a test organism in vitamin B_1 assays. Thus, Sarma *et al.*[8] found that the pyruvic acid content of the larvae of the rice moth (*Corcyra cephalonica*) increased from about 20 to 164 mg. per 100 g. of dry weight when maintained on a vitamin B_1-deficient diet for thirty-five days, and that this decreased to half within sixty-six hours of adding aneurine. The growth of larvae fed a vitamin B_1-deficient diet, supplemented by graded doses of aneurine, was proportional to the amount of aneurine. This method of assay has not been adopted by other workers, however.

References to Section 21

1. E. G. van t'Hoog, *Z. Vitaminforsch.*, 1935, **4**, 300 ; 1936, **5**, 118 ; E. L. Tatum, *Proc. Nat. Acad. Sci.*, 1939, **25**, 490 ; 1941, **27**, 193.
2. W. Trager and Y. SubbaRow, *Biol. Bull. Woods Hole*, 1938, **75**, 75 ; Y. SubbaRow and W. Trager, *J. Gen. Physiol.*, 1940, **23**, 561.
3. H. E. Martin and L. Hare, *Biol. Bull. Woods Hole*, 1942, **83**, 428.
4. G. Fröbrich, *Z. vergl. Physiol.*, 1939, **27**, 335 ; K. Offhaus, *ibid.*, 384.
5. G. Fraenkel and M. Blewett, *Nature*, 1943, **151**, 703; 1943, **152**, 506; *Biochem. J.*, 1943, **37**, 686 ; *Proc. Roy. Soc. B.*, 1944, **132**, 212.
6. V. B. Wigglesworth, *Parasitology*, 1929, **21**, 288 ; P. Buchner, *Tiere und Pflanzen Symbiose*, Berlin, 1930 ; M. Aschner, *Z. Morph. Ökol. Tiere*, 1931, **20**, 368 ; A. Koch, *Biol. Zbl.*, 1933, **53**, 199 ; *Verh. dtsch. Zool. Ges.*, 1933, **35**, 143.
7. L. Golberg, B. de Meillon and M. Lavoipierre, *J. Exp. Biol.*, 1945, **21**, 84, 90.
8. P. S. Sarma and K. Bhagvat, *Current Sci.*, 1942, **11**, 331 ; P. S. Sarma, G. B. L. Swami and M. Sreenivasaya, *ibid.*, 332 ; P. S. Sarma, *Indian J. Med. Res.*, 1943, **31**, 173.

22. ANALOGUES OF ANEURINE

Thiazole and Pyrimidine Compounds

In the course of the researches that led to the synthesis of aneurine, a number of compounds closely related to the vitamin were prepared, and their biological activities were determined. Subsequently, deliberate attempts were made to modify the aneurine molecule with a view to ascertaining the effect of such changes on the biological activity.

As already mentioned above, Todd *et al.*[1] prepared a substituted 3-pyrimidyl-thiazolium salt (see page 17) isomeric with aneurine, but differing from it in the absence of a methylene group joining the two rings, and in the orientation of the groups on the pyrimidine ring ; it was inactive when tested on vitamin B_1-deficient rats. It also failed to yield thiochrome on oxidation with potassium ferricyanide, but it gave a positive formaldehyde-azo test.

In a later paper, A. R. Todd and F. Bergel[2] described the preparation of several compounds differing from aneurine only in the nature of the substituents on the two rings. None of these analogues possessed vitamin B_1 activity. Their constitution is represented by the following formula :

$$
\begin{array}{c}
\text{N}=\text{C}\,.\,\text{R}_1 \qquad\qquad \text{CH}_3 \\
\mid\quad\mid \qquad\qquad\qquad \overset{\cdot}{\text{C}}=\text{C}\,.\,\text{R}_3 \\
\text{CH}_3\,.\,\text{C}\quad\text{C}-\text{CH}_2-\text{N}\Big\langle\qquad\mid \\
\parallel\quad\parallel \qquad\qquad\quad \text{C}-\text{S} \\
\text{N}-\text{CH}\quad\text{Cl}\quad\ \ \underset{\text{R}_2}{\cdot}\qquad\qquad .\,\text{HCl}
\end{array}
$$

in which R_1, R_2 and R_3 were :

	R_1	R_2	R_3	Azo Test	Thiochrome Test
Compound 1	NH$_2$	H	H	—	+
,, 2	OH	H	H	—	—
,, 3	OH	H	CH$_2$. CH$_2$OH	+	—
,, 4	NH$_2$	CH$_3$	CH$_2$. CH$_2$OH	—	—
Aneurine .	NH$_2$	H	CH$_2$. CH$_2$OH	+	+

The first of these compounds differed from aneurine only in the absence of the hydroxyethyl group, which is therefore essential for biological activity, as might be expected, since the hydroxyl group is the point of attachment of the pyrophosphate radicle in cocarboxylase. Compound 3 differed from aneurine only in the replacement of the amino group by a hydroxyl group ; evidently the presence of the amino group is also essential. The most surprising result of the series is the inactivity of compound 4, which merely contains an additional methyl group in the thiazole ring. The loss of activity would be understandable if Williams and Zima's hypothesis (page 101) were true and cleavage of the thiazole ring were essential for aneurine to exercise its function, but this idea has not received support.

H. Andersag and K. Westphal,[3] in the course of their synthesis of the vitamin, prepared an isomer of aneurine, 3-(4'-amino-6'-methyl-pyrimidyl-5'-methyl)-5-β-hydroxyethyl-4-methyl-thiazolium chloride, which they stated to be active, although they did not record its activity relative to that of aneurine ; F. Schultz[4] found it to be only slightly active, however. It gave a positive thiochrome reaction.

B. C. J. G. Knight and H. McIlwain[5] tested a number of aneurine analogues and pyrimidine and thiazole derivatives by means of a strain of *Staphylococcus aureus* that would not grow on a synthetic medium unless either aneurine or both the pyrimidine and thiazole moieties were present. They found that 3-(4'-amino-2'-methyl-5'-pyrimidyl-methyl)-5-α-hydroxyethyl-4-methyl-thiazolium chloride, which differs from aneurine only in the position of the hydroxyl group in the hydroxyethyl side-chain, and 3-(4'-amino-2'-chloro-6'-methyl-5'-pyrimidyl-methyl)-5-β-hydroxyethyl-4-methyl-thiazolium chloride had only slight growth-promoting activity, whilst the 2-methyl analogue of aneurine and the compound derived from aneurine by loss of the hydroxyethyl group were inactive.

The bromide corresponding to the α-hydroxyethyl compound prepared by Knight and McIlwain was prepared by Baumgarten *et al.*,[6] who found it to have no antineuritic activity.

Knight and McIlwain also tested the effect of various pyrimidine derivatives in place of 4-amino-5-aminomethyl-2-methyl-pyrimidine, the thiazole moiety being present in each instance. Substitution of aminomethyl group by the hydroxymethyl or thioformamidomethyl group resulted in active compounds, but all other changes in the molecule resulted in loss of activity. Similarly, the effect of changing the substituents attached to the thiazole ring was studied. Activity was retained when the β-hydroxyethyl group was replaced by the β-acetoxyethyl group and, to a less extent, by a β- or γ-hydroxypropyl group. The introduction of an α-hydroxyethyl group into the molecule and most other structural changes resulted in loss of activity. 4-Methyl-5-vinyl-thiazole, however, had a slight and delayed activity possibly due to hydration to the hydroxyethyl derivative.

A micro-organism that can utilise the two halves of the aneurine molecule is the flagellate, *Polytomella caeca* (see page 112). The effect on the response of this organism of changing the nature of the substituent at carbon atom 5 in the pyrimidine moiety was examined by M. Javillier and L. Emerique-Blum.[7] They showed that when the substituent was a hydroxymethyl, formyl, aminomethyl or cyano group, growth was stimulated, whereas the compounds containing a carboxyl, amido or methyl group on carbon atom 5 did not permit growth. It is easy to see how the compounds in the first series could readily be converted into aneurine, and how the compounds in the second group could be converted with great difficulty, if at all.

A micro-organism that responds to the presence of either component of the aneurine molecule is *Rhizopus suinus*. Alcoholic fermentation by means of this organism was increased [8] by the addition of 4-amino-5-aminomethyl-2-methyl-pyrimidine or the corresponding 5-thioformamidomethyl- or 5-hydroxymethyl-derivatives, but reduced by the addition of 4-amino-5-aminomethyl-2-ethyl-pyrimidine, 4-amino-2 : 5-dimethyl-pyrimidine, 4-hydroxy-2 : 5-dimethyl-pyrimidine, 4-amino-5-carbethoxy-2-methyl-pyrimidine, 4-amino-6-hydroxy-2-methyl-pyrimidine or uracil. The structure of the thiazole moiety was less critical, and could be varied within wide limits without adversely affecting the fermentation, which was increased in the presence of the following compounds : 5-β-hydroxyethyl-4-methyl-thiazole,

5-β-hydroxyethyl-4-methyl-3-[4'-(5'-methyl-imidazolyl)]-thiazolium chloride, 3-benzyl-5-β-hydroxyethyl-4-methyl-thiazolium chloride, 4-methyl-thiazole, 4 : 5-dimethyl-thiazole, 5-β-acetoxyethyl-4-methyl-2-thiol-thiazole, 2-amino-4-methyl-thiazole and 4 : 5-dimethyl-2-thiol-thiazole. It is difficult to see how some of these compounds could act as precursors of aneurine, especially those compounds in which the β-hydroxyethyl group is lacking. It is more consistent with current views concerning the biosynthesis of aneurine to regard these thiazole compounds as having a general stimulating effect, rather than a specific action due to their conversion into aneurine.

5-β-Hydroxyethyl-4-methyl-imidazole failed to support the growth of pea-roots or of *Phycomyces* [9] so that the imidazole ring is apparently not a substitute for the thiazole ring.

The growth-promoting effects of a mixture of the thiazole and pyrimidine portions of aneurine, observed with such micro-organisms as *Staphylococcus aureus*, *Polytomella caeca* and *Phycomyces Blakesleeanus* (see page 108), were shown by E. and R. Abderhalden [10] to occur also with pigeons, vitamin B_1-deficient birds showing a similar response to that produced by aneurine ; the effect was more marked after oral administration than after intramuscular injection. No aneurine was synthesised from the two halves of the molecule by pigeon tissues *in vitro.*

The physiological activity of other pyrimidines and thiazoles was tested by S. Morii,[11] who found that 4-amino-5-hydroxymethyl-2-methyl-pyrimidine and the corresponding chloro- and bromomethyl compounds produced convulsions in vitamin B_1-deficient pigeons, whereas 4-amino-5-aminomethyl-2-methyl-pyrimidine, 4-ethyl-2-amino-pyrimidine, 4-amino-6-ethyl-pyrimidine, uracil, thymine, and adenylic acid were inert. 5-β-Hydroxyethyl-4-methyl-thiazole exerted a marked curative action on vitamin B_1-deficient pigeons, and this was not enhanced by simultaneous administration of various pyrimidine derivatives, a result not necessarily in conflict with that recorded by E. and R. Abderhalden, who do not appear to have tested the compounds separately. No curative effect was observed on administration of N-(4'-amino-2'-methyl-5'-pyrimidyl-methyl)-5-hydroxy-3 : 4-bishydroxymethyl-6-methyl-pyridinium bromide hydrobromide or its triacetate, or with acetopropyl alcohol given together with 4-amino-2-methyl-5-thioformamidomethyl-pyrimidine or with methionol given together with 4-amino-5-aminomethyl-2-methyl-pyrimidine hydrochloride.

F. Schultz [4] prepared and tested on vitamin B_1-deficient pigeons, thirty-nine compounds closely related to aneurine. Of these, sixteen showed some activity, one actually being more, though perhaps not significantly more, active than aneurine. Assuming aneurine to have a biological activity of $2 \cdot 5$ μg. per unit, the activity of the compounds tested ranged from $2 \cdot 1$ to $11,800$ μg. per unit. The compounds are listed in the table on page 121, in order of decreasing activity. Compounds 1 to 9 have the general formula:

$$
\begin{array}{c}
N{=}C \, . \, NH_2 \qquad R_2 \\
| \qquad | \qquad\qquad C{=}\!\!=\!\!C \, . \, CH_2 \, . \, CH_2OH \\
R_1 \, . \, C \quad C{-}CH_2{-}N \\
\| \quad \| \qquad\qquad CH{-}S \\
N{-}CH \quad Cl \qquad\qquad\qquad . \, HCl
\end{array}
$$

The presence of biological activity in compounds 1 to 9 indicates that the introduction of additional methylene groups at position 2 of the pyrimidine ring and position 4 of the thiazole ring generally reduced, but did not entirely destroy, vitamin B_1 activity. The removal of the methyl groups from either of these positions was accompanied by a marked reduction in activity.

Compound 10 is of considerable interest, in that the interposition of an additional group between the two rings would at first sight be expected to alter fundamentally the spatial arrangement of the molecule, yet some biological activity was apparently retained. The addition of a methyl group to the amino group or an increase in the number of carbon atoms in the hydroxyethyl group decreased the activity very considerably, whilst appreciable loss of activity also occurred when the hydroxyethyl group was replaced by a chloroethyl, an ethoxyethyl or, according to D. Price and F. D. Pickel,[12] an aminoethyl-group. The introduction of a methyl group into the 6-position of the pyrimidine ring reduced the activity almost to vanishing point, especially if the 2-methyl group was also removed, as in compound 16.

G. A. Stein et al.[13] found the bromide corresponding to compound 16 to be inactive. These workers also prepared the bromide corresponding to Schultz's compound 1 and confirmed that it possessed vitamin B_1 activity. In addition, Stein et al. prepared the two compounds :

$$
\begin{array}{c}
N{=}C \, . \, NH_2 \\
| \qquad | \qquad\qquad CH_3 \\
R_1 \, . \, C \quad C \, . \, R_2 \qquad C{=}\!\!=\!\!C \, . \, CH_2 \, . \, CH_2OH \\
\| \quad \| \qquad\qquad\qquad | \\
N{-}C{-}CH_2{-}N \qquad CH{-}S \qquad . \, HBr \\
| \\
Br
\end{array}
$$

where $R_1 = H$ and $R_2 = CH_3$ in the one instance, and $R_1 = CH_3$ and $R_2 = H$ in the other, and found them to be inactive.

F. Schultz,[14] reviewing the results previously reported by him, concluded that the activity manifested by certain compounds was not true vitamin B_1 activity ; he recalled Funk's idea that beriberi could be cured either by administering the specific vitamin or by the

		R_1	R_2
Compound	1	C_2H_5	CH_3
Aneurine	.	CH_3	CH_3
Compound	2	CH_3	C_2H_5
,,	3	C_2H_5	C_2H_5
,,	4	$n\text{-}C_3H_7$	C_2H_5
,,	5	$iso\text{-}C_3H_7$	C_2H_5
,,	6	H	C_2H_5
,,	7	CH_3	$n\text{-}C_3H_7$
,,	8	C_2H_5	$n\text{-}C_3H_7$
,,	9	CH_3	H

,,	10	

$$\begin{array}{c} N{=}C.NH_2 \\ CH_3.C\ \ C{-}CH_2{-}CH_2{-}N \\ N{-}CH \end{array} \overset{CH_3}{\underset{\overset{|}{C}l}{\overset{\cdot}{C}}}{=}\underset{CH{-}S}{C}.CH_2.CH_2OH \qquad .HCl$$

,,	11	

$$\begin{array}{c} N{=}C.NH_2 \\ CH_3.C\ \ C{-}CH_2{-}N \\ N{-}CH\ \ \ \ Cl \end{array} \overset{CH_3}{\underset{CH{-}S}{\overset{\cdot}{C}}}{=}C.CH_2.CH_2.CH_2.CH_2OH \qquad .HCl$$

,,	12	

$$\begin{array}{c} N{=}C.NH.CH_3 \\ CH_3.C\ \ C{-}{-}CH_2{-}N \\ N{-}CH\ \ \ \ Cl \end{array} \overset{CH_3}{\underset{CH{-}S}{\overset{\cdot}{C}}}{=}C.CH_2.CH_2OH \qquad .HCl$$

,,	13	

$$\begin{array}{c} N{=}C.NH_2 \\ CH_3.C\ \ C{-}CH_2{-}N \\ N{-}CH\ \ \ Cl \end{array} \overset{CH_3}{\underset{CH{-}S}{\overset{\cdot}{C}}}{=}C.CH_2.CH_2Cl \qquad .HCl$$

,,	14	

$$\begin{array}{c} N{=}C.NH_2 \\ CH_3.C\ \ C{-}CH_2{-}N \\ N{-}CH\ \ \ \ Cl \end{array} \overset{CH_3}{\underset{CH{-}S}{\overset{\cdot}{C}}}{=}C.CH_2.CH_2OC_2H_5 \qquad \cdot HCl$$

,,	15	

$$\begin{array}{c} N{=}C.NH_2 \\ CH_3.C\ \ C{-}{-}CH_2{-}N \\ N{-}C.CH_3\ \ \ Cl \end{array} \overset{CH_3}{\underset{CH{-}S}{\overset{\cdot}{C}}}{=}C.CH_2.CH_2OH \qquad .HCl$$

,,	16	

$$\begin{array}{c} N{=}C.NH_2 \\ CH\ \ C{-}{-}CH_2{-}N \\ N{-}C.CH_3\ \ \ Cl \end{array} \overset{CH_3}{\underset{CH{-}S}{\overset{\cdot}{C}}}{=}C.CH_2.CH_2OH \qquad .HCl$$

adoption of measures that allowed sudden mobilisation of the reserve vitamins from organs and tissues. He therefore postulated that a substance with true vitamin activity should be able (*a*) to cure repeatedly beriberi spasm occurring several times in the same animal ; (*b*) to keep the animal alive after cure ; and (*c*) prevent the appearance of symptoms of vitamin B$_1$ deficiency. Tested in this way, the 2'-ethyl-4-methyl-, 2'-*n*-propyl-4-ethyl- and 4-ethyl analogues of aneurine (compounds 1, 4 and 6 above) had a true curative effect on pigeons, and moreover the substances appeared to act directly and not by conversion into aneurine.

The substances :

and

which had previously been shown to have a pseudo-antineuritic action failed to achieve a second cure.

The superior activity of compound 1 over aneurine was confirmed by W. H. Schopfer,[15] using *Phycomyces Blakesleeanus*. Other compounds tested at the same time were less active, with the sole exception of cocarboxylase.

W. Huber[16] prepared 3-(2' : 4'-diamino-5'-pyrimidyl-methyl)-5-β-hydroxyethyl-4-methyl-thiazolium chloride hydrochloride, and found it to be devoid of vitamin B$_1$ activity on rats at a level of 25 μg. This compound differs from aneurine in the presence of a second amino group in the pyrimidine ring in place of the methyl group.

Other compounds related to aneurine were prepared by E. R. Buchman and E. M. Richardson.[17] In these the β-hydroxyethyl group of aneurine hydrobromide was replaced by a hydrogen atom or an ethyl, vinyl, hydroxymethyl, α-hydroxyethyl or α-, β- or γ-hydroxy-*n*-propyl group. None of the compounds exhibited antineuritic activity when fed to rats at a level of 0·5 mg.

The 2-*n*-butylpyrimidine homologue of aneurine hydrobromide was prepared by G. A. Emerson and P. L. Southwick,[18] and found to inhibit growth and produce polyneuritis in rats fed a subnormal amount of aneurine. The effects were prevented by feeding excess aneurine, one part of which counteracted the effect of about forty parts of the homologue. The homologue also decreased the survival period of rats maintained on a diet low in aneurine.

The isomer of aneurine in which the positions of the amino and methyl groups in the pyrimidine ring were reversed had no vitamin B_1 activity.[19]

Hetero-vitamins B₁

A particularly interesting substance would be obtained by replacing the thiazole ring with a pyridine ring. J. Finkelstein and R. C. Elderfield [20] synthesised two pyridine analogues, both of which were stated to be inactive for rats at a dose of 100 μg. per rat, whilst P. Baumgarten and A. Dornow [21] claimed to have prepared " hetero-vitamin B_1 ", 1 - (4' - amino - 2' - methyl - 5' - pyrimidyl - methyl) - 3 - β - hydroxyethyl-2-methyl-pyridinium bromide hydrobromide :

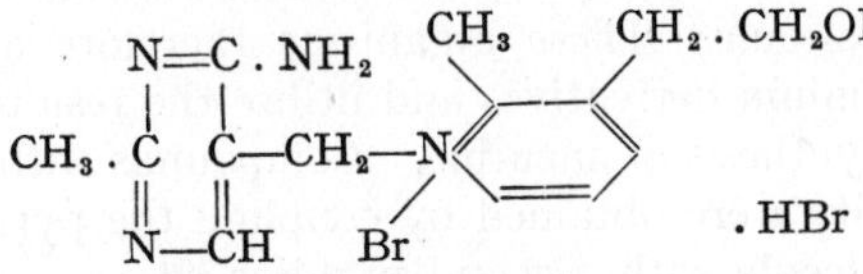

and its lower homologue, in which the methyl group was absent from the pyridine ring ; these compounds were said to possess 1/26th and 1/240th the activity of aneurine respectively. Subsequently, however, they showed [22] that the compound was the α- and not the β-hydroxy-ethyl-pyridine analogue. A. H. Tracy and R. C. Elderfield [23] then announced the synthesis of a substance which they believed to be the true pyridine analogue of aneurine, noting that the compound was different in chemical properties from that of P. Baumgarten and A. Dornow [21] and from that prepared by F. C. Smelkes,[24] which had been stated to possess some activity. The activity of this new compound, called by them pyrithiamine, was tested by W. J. Robbins [25] on three different fungi. The growth of *Phycomyces Blakesleeanus* was not stimulated unless the thiazole half of aneurine was also present, indicating that this fungus could split the pyridine analogue and utilise the pyrimidine half for synthesising aneurine from the added thiazole compound. *Pythiomorpha gonapodioides*, which grows in the absence of the thiazole half of the aneurine molecule if the pyrimidine portion is present, was able to grow in presence of the pyridine analogue only, presumably degrading it and then utilising the pyrimidine portion. *Phytophthora cinnamomi*, which normally requires intact aneurine, would not grow when this was replaced by the pyridine analogue, even in presence of the pyrimidine or the thiazole portion.

Pyrithiamine actually antagonises the growth of some micro-organisms (see page 126).

Unfortunately, pyrithiamine seems to have met a similar fate to Baumgarten and Dornow's pyridine analogue, for A. N. Wilson and S. A. Harris [25a] claim that it does not possess the above structure, assigned to it by Tracy and Elderfield. They in their turn claim to have prepared an authentic specimen of this elusive substance, and report that it has an absorption spectrum similar to that of aneurine. They have named the new substance neopyrithiamine, and suggest that pyrithiamine is a mixture of compounds having pyridine and pyrimidine moieties in the ratios $1:2$, $1:3$, $1:4$, etc. Neopyrithiamine is a more potent antagonist of aneurine than is pyrithiamine (see page 127).

W. H. Schopfer [26] tested the two compounds prepared by Baumgarten and Dornow, and found that, although they had only slight vitamin B_1 activity, they stimulated the growth of *Phycomyces Blakesleeanus* and *Ustilago violacea* in presence of the thiazole half of the aneurine molecule. These organisms therefore appear able to cleave the pyridinium derivatives and utilise the resulting pyrimidine portion for the synthesis of aneurine. Compounds with weak growth-promoting activity were obtained by coupling the pyrimidine half of the aneurine molecule with 3-acetyl pyridine.[26a]

A pyrimidine analogue of aneurine, 3-(4'-amino-2'-methyl-5'-pyrimidyl-methyl)-6-hydroxy-5-β-hydroxyethyl-4-methyl-pyrimidinium bromide hydrobromide :

$$\begin{array}{ccc}
\text{N}{=}\text{C . NH}_2 & \text{CH}_3 . \text{C}{=\!=\!=}\text{C . CH}_2 . \text{CH}_2\text{OH} \\
\text{CH}_3 . \text{C} \quad \text{C}{-\!-\!-}\text{CH}_2{-\!-}\text{N} \quad \text{C . OH} \\
\text{N}{-}\text{CH} \qquad \text{Br} \;\; \text{CH}{-}\text{N} \qquad \text{HBr}
\end{array}$$

was prepared by Y. A. Tota and R. C. Elderfield,[27] and tested by W. J. Robbins [28] on *Phycomyces Blakesleeanus, Pythiomorpha gonapodioides* and *Phytophthora cinnamomi*. It had little or no effect on any of these moulds.

Another heterocyclic analogue of aneurine was tested by W. H. Schopfer [26] on *Phycomyces Blakesleeanus* and found to have no appreciable biological activity. This was the compound, 3-[4'-(5'-methyl-imidazolyl)]-5-β-hydroxyethyl-4-methyl-thiazolium chloride in which the pyrimidine ring was replaced by an imidazole ring :

$$\begin{array}{cc}
\text{CH}_3 & \text{CH}_3 \\
\text{N}{-}\text{C} \qquad \text{C}{=\!=}\text{C . CH}_2 . \text{CH}_2\text{OH} \\
\text{N}{-}\text{CH} \quad \text{C}{-}\text{N} \quad \text{CH}{-}\text{S} \\
\text{Cl}
\end{array}$$

3-Benzyl-5-β-hydroxyethyl-4-methyl-thiazolium chloride was like-wise inactive. As might be expected, however, both compounds stimulated the growth of *Phycomyces* when the pyrimidine half of the aneurine molecule was present in the culture fluid.

Erlenmeyer *et al.*[28a] prepared two other analogues of aneurine, in which the thiazole ring is replaced by an iminazole ring. They were obtained by coupling the pyrimidine half of the aneurine molecule with 5-hydroxymethyl- and 5-β-hydroxyethyl-4-methyl-iminazole.

Simple Derivatives of Aneurine

Of the simple derivatives of aneurine, all the halogen salts are active. It has been claimed [29] that aneurine iodide hydriodide, m.p. 230 to 231° C., is actually more potent than aneurine chloride hydrochloride, but no suggestion has been put forward as to the reason for this.

The preparation of several water-insoluble salts of aneurine for use in the enrichment of cereals was described by Huber *et al.*[30] Water-soluble salts such as the chloride, when used for this purpose, are washed off in the rinsing preparatory to cooking, with consequent loss of the vitamin. The 2-ethylhexyl sulphate, the methylene-bis-(2-hydroxy-3-naphthoate) and cholestenone-6-sulphonate of aneurine were prepared and found to be sparingly soluble in water, the last two being practically insoluble. All three were biologically active. Salts of other alkyl sulphuric acids could only be obtained as oils, as also could the salts of isopropyl-naphthalene-sulphonic acid and di-octylsulphosuccinic acid. The aneurine salt of dibutylsulphosuccinic acid was found to be water soluble.

The only other simple derivatives of aneurine to be prepared are the esters. F. Schultz,[4] found that the pyrophosphate (cocarboxylase), the monophosphate, acetate, benzoate, and chaulmoograte had a more prolonged action than aneurine, whilst the phenylurethane, though active, did not produce 100 % cures in vitamin B_1-deficient rats. The preparation of the orthophosphoric and pyrophosphoric esters of aneurine was described by J. Weijlard.[31] The latter was prepared not only by direct esterification of aneurine, but also by condensation of 4-amino-5-bromomethyl-2-methyl-pyrimidine hydro-bromide with 5-β-hydroxyethyl-4-methyl-thiazole pyrophosphate on the one hand and with 5-β-chloroethyl-4-methyl-thiazole in presence of silver pyrophosphate on the other. Weijlard also prepared aneurine sulphate but did not record its activity. 5-β-Hydroxyethyl-4-methyl-thiazole pyrophosphate could not replace cocarboxylase in the enzy-matic decarboxylation of pyruvic acid.[32] On the contrary, it in-hibited cocarboxylase activity, presumably by competition with aneurine pyrophosphate for the specific enzyme, carboxylase.

Compounds related to Folic Acid

According to Busnel *et al.*,[33] the growth of vitamin B_1-deficient pigeons is accelerated by several substances related to folic acid (see page 513), namely, isoxanthopterin, 2 : 6-dihydroxy-8 : 9-dimethylpteridine, 2-amino-6-hydroxy-8 : 9-dimethylpteridine and desiminoisoxanthopterin-carboxylic acid ; these had approximately one-tenth the activity of aneurine. Fluorescyanine, from carp-scales, had a similar action to aneurine, although much weaker, in Peter's catatorulin test (page 28). All the above substances and, in addition, xanthopterin-carboxylic acid and isoxanthopterin-carboxylic acid maintained normal growth and chronaxia in young rats deprived of aneurine. None of them, however, stimulated the growth of *Polytomella caeca* deprived of aneurine. So far, these results remain unconfirmed but, in view of the observations with *P. caeca*, it is unlikely that the effect is due to the presence of true vitamin B_1 activity in the folic acid analogues.

Pyrithiamine

Pyrithiamine, the pyridine analogue of aneurine prepared by A. H. Tracy and R. C. Elderfield,[23] was without growth-promoting properties, as has already been noted (see page 123). Nevertheless it is a most interesting substance, as it inhibits the growth of several micro-organisms for which aneurine is an essential growth factor. Thus O. Wyss [34] showed that it interfered competitively with the utilisation of aneurine by *Staphylococcus aureus*, the addition of aneurine counteracting the inhibition due to pyrithiamine. This is an instance of competition between a growth factor and a growth inhibitor of analogous chemical structure, of which the vitamin B complex provides many other examples (see pages 292, 345, 397, 546).

To neutralise the growth-stimulating effect of one molecule of aneurine on *S. aureus*, 666 to 750 molecules of pyrithiamine were required, a value similar to that observed for sulphapyridine and *p*-aminobenzoic acid. For *E. coli*, the ratio between the amounts of growth inhibitor and growth factor that just counterbalanced one another was 20,000. Pyrithiamine is therefore a much less efficient antagonist towards aneurine for *E. coli* than for *S. aureus*. Similar variations with different organisms have been noted with other pairs of growth factors and inhibitors.

D. W. Woolley and A. G. C. White [35] correlated this difference in the response of different organisms with their requirements for aneurine. Organisms that required the intact aneurine molecule were inhibited by smaller amounts of pyrithiamine than organisms that could utilise the pyrimidine and thiazole portions of the aneurine molecule. In other words, the more exacting the organism, the more sensitive it is to the effect of pyrithiamine—a phenomenon also observed with other growth inhibitors.

Pyrithiamine and certain derivatives of 6-aminopyrimidine inhibited the utilisation by *Lactobacillus fermenti* of aneurine pyrophosphate more readily than the utilisation of free aneurine.[36] Iodoacetate, malonate, dinitrophenol, fluoride and cyanide also inhibited growth and acid production by this organism in presence of aneurine or its mono- or pyrophosphate. H. P. Sarett and V. H. Cheldelin [36] suggested that, when aneurine combines with the protein of the enzyme before being phosphorylated, a more stable form of cocarboxylase results than when combination takes place after phosphorylation.

Drug-fastness has been observed with pyrithiamine, as with most other antibacterial substances. This is a well-known phenomenon in chemotherapy, and means the development of resistance to the inhibitory effect of an antibacterial substance. A strain of *Endomyces vernalis* resistant to pyrithiamine was developed by D. W. Woolley [37] by conditioning it to gradually increasing concentrations of inhibitor. This strain was able to tolerate twenty-five times the concentration that inhibited the parent strain. The pyrithiamine-fast strain required either aneurine or the pyrimidine half for growth, but in presence of small amounts of pyrithiamine and in absence of aneurine, it converted a portion of the pyrithiamine into the pyrimidine half.

Not only did pyrithiamine inhibit the growth of several species of bacteria, but it also produced symptoms of vitamin B_1 deficiency in mice.[38] The effect was cumulative and delayed, and could be cured by the administration of aneurine at a level equal to 1/40th that of the pyrithiamine.

Neopyrithiamine and Oxythiamine

Neopyrithiamine hydrobromide (page 124) proved to be at least four times as active as pyrithiamine as an antagonist of aneurine hydrochloride in the growth of rats.[25a] The index of inhibition was about 10 : 1. It produced polyneuritic symptoms in mice, the animals developing complete paralysis of the hind legs.[39] It protected aneurine from destruction by carp thiaminase (page 25), being preferentially attacked by the enzyme.[40]

A somewhat less potent antagonist of aneurine is 3-(4'-hydroxy-2'-methyl-pyrimidyl-5'-methyl)-5-β-hydroxyethyl-4-methyl-thiazolium chloride, first prepared by Todd and Bergel,[2] and given the name oxythiamine by M. Soodak and L. R. Cerecedo,[41] who obtained it by treatment of aneurine with nitrous acid. Oxythiamine had little or no vitamin B_1 activity, but was toxic to mice and rats, causing a decline in weight and a drop in food intake ; unlike neopyrithiamine, it did not produce polyneuritic symptoms in rats.[39] It was a potent antagonist of aneurine, however, and increased the levels of pyruvic and lactic acids in the blood of rats and the pyruvate : lactate ratio.[42] It increased the urinary excretion of aneurine, presumably because it displaced aneurine from the tissues,[42] and it inhibited the action of thiaminase on aneurine.[41] It produced typical symptoms of vitamin B_1 deficiency in chicks.[43] Because of its anti-vitamin B_1 activity, it was tested in poliomyelitis (see page 51), but was found to protect mice less effectively than did a vitamin B_1-free diet.[44]

Other Antagonists

Von Euler *et al.*[45] claimed that salicylic acid and certain other acids inhibited the action of some enzyme systems, including the " aetiozymase " system, that is, the decarboxylation of pyruvic acid in presence of added cocarboxylase. The effect was said to be enhanced by acetaldehyde, which is itself an inhibitor. The extent of the inhibition by salicylic acid did not increase in proportion to the reduction in the cocarboxylase concentration. The evidence, it was suggested, indicated that salicylic acid and other inhibitors acted by displacing coenzymes from attachment to the apoenzyme molecule or by attaching themselves to a group in the apoenzyme molecule not already occupied by the coenzyme. This suggestion is actually another way of enunciating the Woods-Fildes hypothesis (see page 546), which satisfactorily explains the behaviour of pairs of inhibitors and growth factors, such as sulphanilamide and p-aminobenzoic acid, pantoyltaurine and pantothenic acid, pyridine-β-sulphonic acid and nicotinic acid, pyrithiamine and aneurine.

The Woods-Fildes hypothesis demands a high degree of specificity between these pairs of substances, based on analogous chemical structure, and it is irrational to apply the hypothesis to a heterogeneous group of inhibitors such as that listed by von Euler *et al.* If the effect noted really exists it can hardly be due to a competition between inhibitor and coenzyme in the sense in which Woods and Fildes used this conception, but rather to a non-specific type of poisoning.

The only true analogue of aneurine other than pyrithiamine, neo-pyrithiamine and oxythiamine that appears to antagonise completely the growth-promoting action of the vitamin is the n-butyl homologue, which was shown [18] to produce aneurine deficiency in rats maintained on a suboptimal intake of aneurine ; the symptoms were relieved by administration of aneurine.

Attempts to find simple derivatives of thiazole that would inhibit the growth of bacteria by competition with aneurine led to the discovery [46] that several thiol derivatives of thiazole were bacteriostatic, but the inhibition was not reversed on addition of aneurine. In fact, the bacteriostatic activity appeared to be a function of the thiol group rather than of the thiazole ring, and quite unconnected with aneurine requirements.

General Conclusions

The data summarised above on the vitamin B_1 activity of compounds related to aneurine has an obvious bearing on the question of enzyme specificity. The first generalisation that can be made—and this will be evident also from the discussion of the functions of other members of the vitamin B complex—is that specificity is not absolute ; there is generally a group of compounds, the activity of which increases to a maximum with one particular member. As it happens, maximum vitamin B_1 activity is not exhibited by the compound that Nature chose to use for this purpose, but by the next higher homologue. This is admittedly unusual. The second generalisation is that activity is confined to the compounds comprising a thiazole ring and a pyrimidine ring linked together at specific points by a chain of one or two carbon atoms. Compounds that are linked directly are inactive, suggesting that a certain freedom of movement of the molecule is essential. The third generalisation is that the presence of a hydroxyl group in the side-chain attached to the thiazole ring is essential for activity, obviously because without it no pyrophosphate could be formed. This must be a primary alcohol group, but the side-chain can apparently contain three carbon atoms, although optimal activity is obtained with two. Fourthly, one amino group in the pyrimidine ring, and only one, is essential, and this is preferably a primary group. A quaternary nitrogen atom in the thiazole ring is also essential. Fifthly, the nature of the alkyl groups attached to both rings is important ; optimal activity was exhibited by compounds in which these together amounted to two or three carbon atoms, and fell progressively as the number increased.

The antagonistic action of pyrithiamine, neopyrithiamine and oxythiamine are highly significant, as, although they have no vitamin B_1 activity, they appear to be capable of displacing aneurine from attachment to the protein of the enzyme molecule. It has been customary to picture the attachment of a molecule at the surface of an enzyme as taking place at a particular point, but the theory advanced by Linus Pauling to explain the formation of anti-bodies suggests that contact is more probably over a particular area rather than at a point.

ANEURINE (THIAMINE)

The anti-aneurine properties of these three compounds probably
depend on the fact that they bear a close structural similarity to
aneurine, and are thereby able to attach themselves to that portion
of the apoenzyme surface normally occupied by the aneurine molecule.
The antagonist-apoenzyme complex so formed is, however, incapable
of effecting the chemical changes characteristic of the aneurine-
apoenzyme complex, and pyruvic acid decarboxylation, for example,
therefore ceases, and the organism—whether bacteria or animal—
suffers in consequence from vitamin B_1 deficiency and cannot develop
normally.

References to Section 22

1. A. R. Todd, F. Bergel and Karimullah, *J. Chem. Soc.*, 1936, 1559.
2. A. R. Todd and F. Bergel, *ibid.*, 1937, 1504.
3. H. Andersag and K. Westphal, *Ber.*, 1937, **70**, 2035.
4. F. Schultz, *Z. physiol. Chem.*, 1940, **265**, 113.
5. B. C. J. G. Knight and H. McIlwain, *Biochem. J.*, 1938, **32**, 1241.
6. P. Baumgarten, A. Dornow, K. Gutschmidt and H. Krehl, *Ber.*, 1942, **75**, 442.
7. M. Javillier and L. Emerique-Blum, *Compt. rend.*, 1940, **211**, 374.
8. W. H. Schopfer, *Helv. Physiol. Pharm. Acta*, 1943, **1**, 83.
9. S. W. Fox, H. Sargent and E. R. Buchman, *J. Amer. Chem. Soc.*, 1945, **67**, 496.
10. E. and R. Abderhalden, *Pflügers Archiv.*, 1938, **240**, 746.
11. S. Morii, *J. Oriental Med.*, 1941, **55**, 9; *Biochem. Z.*, 1941, **309**, 354.
12. D. Price and F. D. Pickel, *J. Amer. Chem. Soc.*, 1941, **63**, 1067.
13. G. A. Stein, W. L. Sampson, J. K. Cline and J. R. Stevens, *ibid.*, 2059.
14. F. Schultz, *Z. physiol. Chem.*, 1941, **272**, 29.
15. W. H. Schopfer, *Arch. Sci. phys. nat.*, 1941, [V], **23**, *Suppl.*, 58.
16. W. Huber, *J. Amer. Chem. Soc.*, 1943, **65**, 2222.
17. E. R. Buchman and E. M. Richardson, *ibid.*, 1945, **67**, 395.
18. G. A. Emerson and P. L. Southwick, *J. Biol. Chem.*, 1945, **160**, 169.
19. C. C. Price, N. J. Leonard and R. H. Reitsema, *J. Amer. Chem. Soc.*, 1946, **68**, 766.
20. J. Finkelstein and R. C. Elderfield, *J. Org. Chem.*, 1939, **4**, 365.
21. P. Baumgarten and A. Dornow, *Ber.*, 1940, **73**, 44, 156.
22. P. Baumgarten and A. Dornow, *ibid.*, 353.
23. A. H. Tracy and R. C. Elderfield, *Science*, 1940, **92**, 180; *J. Org. Chem.*, 1941, **6**, 54.
24. F. C. Smelkes, *Science*, 1939, **90**, 113; *J. Amer. Chem. Soc.*, 1939, **61**, 2562.
25. W. J. Robbins, *Proc. Nat. Acad. Sci.*, 1941, **27**, 419.
25a. A. N. Wilson and S. A. Harris, *J. Amer. Chem. Soc.*, 1949, **71**, 2231.
26. W. H. Schopfer, *Arch. Sci. phys. nat.*, 1941, [V], **23**, *Suppl.*, 64.

26a. A. Dornow and M. Machens, *Chem. Ber.*, 1947, **80**, 502.

27. Y. A. Tota and R. C. Elderfield, *J. Org. Chem.*, 1942, **7**, 309.

28. W. J. Robbins, *Proc. Nat. Acad. Sci.*, 1942, **28**, 352.

28a. H. Erlenmeyer, D. Waldi and E. Sorkin, *Helv. Chim. Acta*, 1948, **31**, 32.

29. J. G. Tolpin, J. R. Foy and L. R. Cerecedo, *J. Amer. Chem. Soc.*, 1941, **63**, 2848.

30. W. Huber, W. Boehme and S. C. Laskowski, *ibid.*, 1946, **68**, 187 ; Merck & Co., U.S.P. 2437504.

31. J. Weijlard, *J. Amer. Chem. Soc.*, 1942, **64**, 2279.

32. E. R. Buchman, E. Heegaard and J. Bonner, *Proc. Nat. Acad. Sci.*, 1940, **26**, 561.

33. R. G. Busnel, P. Chaucard, H. Mazoué, M. Pesson, R. Vieillefosse and M. Polanovski, *Compt. rend. Soc. Biol.*, 1944, **138**, 171 ; R. G. Busnel, P. Chaucard, H. Mazoué, A. Pelou and M. Polonovski, *ibid.*, 366.

34. C. Wyss, *J. Bact.*, 1943, **46**, 483.

35. D. W. Woolley and A. G. C. White, *J. Exp. Med.*, 1943, **78**, 489.

36. H. P. Sarett and V. H. Cheldelin, *J. Biol. Chem.*, 1944, **156**, 91.

37. D. W. Woolley, *Proc. Soc. Exp. Biol. Med.*, 1944, **55**, 179.

38. D. W. Woolley and A. G. C. White, *J. Biol. Chem.*, 1943, **189**, 285.

39. A. J. Eusebi and L. R. Cerecedo, *Science*, 1949, **110**, 162.

40. R. R. Sealock and H. S. White, *J. Biol. Chem.*, 1949, **181**, 393.

41. M. Soodak and L. R. Cerecedo, *J. Amer. Chem. Soc.*, 1944, **66**, 1988 ; 1949, **71**, 3566 ; *Fed. Proc.*, 1947, **6**, 293.

42. C. E. Frohman and H. G. Day, *J. Biol. Chem.*, 1949, **180**, 93.

43. L. J. Daniel and L. C. Norris, *Proc. Soc. Exp. Biol. Med.*, 1949, **72**, 165.

44. J. H. Jones, C. Foster and W. Henle, *ibid.*, 1948, **69**, 454.

45. H. von Euler, L. Ahlstrom, I. Patterson and S. Tingstam, *Arkiv Kemi. Min. Geol.*, 1943, **17**A, No. 8.

46. E. M. Gibbs and F. A. Robinson, *J. Chem. Soc.*, 1945, 925.

CHAPTER III

RIBOFLAVINE

1. INTRODUCTION

In the course of an investigation into the nature of pellagra, J. Goldberger and R. D. Lillie [1] produced a deficiency disease in rats, characterised by ophthalmic and bilaterally symmetrical denuded areas. The factor that prevented these lesions was heat-stable, in contrast to vitamin B_1, which is heat-labile. It was termed by Goldberger, the P.P. (pellagra-preventive) factor, but was subsequently designated vitamin B_2 in Britain and vitamin G in the U.S.A. [2]

The symptoms reported by other workers as characteristic of vitamin B_2 deficiency varied considerably, however, and frequently differed markedly from those observed by Goldberger and Lillie. In particular, some workers reported only an absence of growth, whilst others noted the appearance of dermatitis in some of the experimental animals. It was shown by means of improved technique [3] that failure to grow and the onset of dermatitis were due to a deficiency of two different factors, and either symptom could be produced at will by omitting one factor or the other. The second factor was termed vitamin H in the U.S.A. [4] and vitamin B_6 in Europe. Unfortunately, however, the term vitamin H has also been used to describe the factor now known as biotin (see page 404). Absence of vitamin B_2 was responsible for the failure of the experimental animals to grow, whilst absence of vitamin B_6 was responsible for the dermatitis—the so-called rat " pellagra ".

Thus, initially, the term vitamin B_2 was intended to describe the factor that cures pellagra, now known to be identical with nicotinic acid, but subsequently it came to be used to denote the rat growth factor, riboflavine.

The situation was further complicated by the production in dogs [5] of a deficiency disease known as canine blacktongue, so-called from one of its characteristic manifestations ; the diets used were similar to those required to produce rat " pellagra ". Up to the end of 1934 it appeared probable that this condition, like rat " pellagra ", was due to a deficiency of riboflavine, but in 1935-36 several workers [6] showed that this was not so, whilst Birch *et al.*[7] differentiated the anti-black-tongue and the " P.P." factors from riboflavine and vitamin B_6. In 1937, Sebrell *et al.*[8] confirmed the fact that riboflavine did not cure canine blacktongue, whilst W. J. Dann[9] reported that it did not cure human pellagra, and Fouts *et al.*[10] successfully treated two pellagrins with an extract from which the riboflavine had been removed. Thus it was clearly demonstrated that riboflavine had no connection with pellagra, except perhaps by way of complicating the condition.

In spite of the recognition that riboflavine was different from vitamin B_6 on the one hand and from the anti-blacktongue and P.P. factors on the other, the situation remained obscure. Three groups of workers[11] produced " pellagra " in chicks by feeding them on diets that had been heated. The responsible factor was called the filtrate factor to distinguish it from the eluate factor, as vitamin B_6 was sometimes called, the latter but not the former being adsorbed on fuller's earth. The filtrate factor was shown by C. A. Elvehjem and C. J. Koehn[12] to be different from riboflavine, but, on the other hand, a filtrate factor concentrate was found by Fouts *et al.*[10] to cure human pellagra and by C. J. Koehn and C. A. Elvehjem[13] to cure canine blacktongue. The human antipellagra factor was ultimately distinguished from the filtrate factor by W. J. Dann and Y. SubbaRow,[14] who showed that, whilst nicotinic acid cured human pellagra, it did not cure chick pellagra.

References to Section 1

1. J. Goldberger and R. D. Lillie, *U.S. Publ. Health Rep.*, 1926, **41,** 1025.
2. B. Sure, *J. Amer. Med. Assoc.*, 1932, **99,** 26.
3. A. G. Hogan and L. R. Richardson, *J. Nutrition*, 1934, **8,** 385.
4. L. E. Booher, *J. Biol. Chem.*, 1937, **119,** 223.
5. J. Goldberger and G. A. Wheeler, *U.S. Publ. Health Rep.*, 1928, **43,** 172.
6. C. P. Rhoads and D. K. Miller, *Science*, 1935, **81,** 159 ; C. J. Koehn and C. A. Elvehjem, *J. Nutrition*, 1936, **11,** 67.
7. T. W. Birch, P. György and L. J. Harris, *Biochem. J.*, 1935, **29,** 2830.
8. W. H. Sebrell, D. J. Hunt and R. H. Onstatt, *U.S. Publ. Health Rep.*, 1937, **52,** 235 ; W. H. Sebrell, R. H. Onstatt and D. J. Hunt, *ibid.*, 427.
9. W. J. Dann, *J. Nutrition*, 1936, **11,** 451.
10. P. J. Fouts, S. Lepkovsky, O. M. Helmer and T. H. Jukes, *Proc. Soc. Exp. Biol. Med.*, 1936, **35,** 245.
11. O. L. Kline, J. A. Keenan, C. A. Elvehjem and E. B. Hart, *J. Biol. Chem.*, 1932, **99,** 295 ; S. Lepkovsky and T. H. Jukes, *ibid.*,

1935, **111**, 119 ; S. Ansbacher, G. C. Supplee and R. C. Bender, *J. Nutrition*, 1936, **11**, 529.

12. C. A. Elvehjem and C. J. Koehn, *J. Biol. Chem.*, 1935, **108**, 709.
13. C. J. Koehn and C. A. Elvehjem, *J. Nutrition*, 1936, **11**, 67.
14. W. J. Dann and Y. SubbaRow, *ibid.*, 1938, **16**, 183.

2. ISOLATION OF RIBOFLAVINE

The first step towards an understanding of the nature of vitamin B_2 was taken by R. Kuhn, P. György and T. Wagner-Jauregg,[1] who isolated from egg-white a compound with a strong yellowish-green fluorescence. They called this substance " ovoflavine ", and showed that it stimulated the growth of rats, 100 μg. a day producing an increase in weight of about 10 g. per week. In the issue of the *Berichte* containing the paper by Kuhn *et al.*, P. Ellinger and W. Koschara [2] reported the presence of similar fluorescent substances in milk, liver, kidney, urine, muscle, yeast and certain plant materials, and described the isolation of a crystalline fluorescent substance from whey. They proposed the name " lyochrome " for the group to which all these substances belonged, and both Kuhn and Koschara suggested that the pigments might be related to the " yellow enzyme " discovered in yeast by O. Warburg and W. Christian [3] in the preceding year. Kuhn showed, in fact, that one and the same substance, lumiflavine, was produced by irradiation of the yellow enzyme and of ovoflavine. Shortly after the publication of these papers, L. E. Booher [4] reported the preparation of a concentrate from whey powder that showed a strong yellow fluorescence and had growth-promoting properties for the rat.

The isolation of fluorescent pigments from milk, liver, kidney, urine, malt, dandelion flowers, lucerne, egg-yolk and the retinae of fishes was reported by Kuhn *et al.*,[5] by Karrer *et al.*,[6] by W. Koschara,[7] and by H. von Euler and E. Adler,[8] and by Itter *et al.*[9]

At first these pigments were given specific names according to their origin, *e.g.* ovoflavine, lactoflavine, uroflavine and hepatoflavine, until it was realised that they were probably identical with one another. This was confirmed by a direct comparison of some of the compounds, but several were isolated in such small amounts that a rigid proof of identity was not possible. The substance was generally referred to as lactoflavine, until its constitution had been determined, when the name was altered to riboflavine. Shortly afterwards, the terminal " e " was dropped to avoid confusion with acriflavine and its analogues, which have an entirely different type of structure. Recently, however, there has been a tendency to revert to the original spelling, to conform with the recognised convention that the names of organic bases should end in " ine ", and " Riboflavine " is now its official name in the British Pharmacopœia. Accordingly, riboflavine is the spelling adopted in this book.

The method of isolation varied somewhat in different laboratories and with the raw materials employed, but nearly all the workers used adsorption on fuller's earth (or in some instances lead sulphide), from a slightly acid aqueous or aqueous-alcoholic extract. The resulting adsorbate was eluted with pyridine, or pyridine-methanol-water mixture or dilute ammonia, and the eluate, after being concentrated, was treated with a heavy metal, such as silver or thallium, to precipitate the flavine in the form of a salt. The free flavine was recovered from the precipitate by suitable treatment and recrystallised from water, dilute alcohol or dilute acetic acid. One of the most recent methods is that due to R. D. Greene and A. Black.[10]

The recovery of riboflavine from fermented liquors is discussed on page 152.

References to Section 2

1. R. Kuhn, P. György and T. Wagner-Jauregg, *Ber.*, 1933, **66**, 317, 576 ; *Naturwiss.*, 1933, **21**, 560.
2. P. Ellinger and W. Koschara, *Ber.*, 1933, **66**, 315.
3. O. Warburg and W. Christian, *Biochem. Z.*, 1932, **254**, 438 ; 1933, **266**, 377.
4. L. E. Booher, *J. Biol. Chem.*, 1933, **102**, 39 ; 1934, **107**, 591.
5. R. Kuhn, H. Rudy and T. Wagner-Jauregg, *Ber.*, 1933, **66**, 1950 ; R. Kuhn and H. Kaltschmitt, *ibid.*, 1935, **68**, 128.
6. P. Karrer and K. Schöpp, *Helv. Chim. Acta*, 1934, **17**, 735, 771 ; 1936, **19**, E33.
7. W. Koschara, *Ber.*, 1934, **67**, 761.
8. H. von Euler and E. Adler, *Z. physiol. Chem.*, 1934, **223**, 105.
9. S. Itter, E. R. Orent and E. V. McCollum, *J. Biol. Chem.*, 1935, **108**, 579.
10. R. D. Greene and A. Black, *J. Amer. Chem. Soc.*, 1937, **59**, 1820.

3. CHEMICAL CONSTITUTION OF RIBOFLAVINE

Riboflavine has the empirical formula, $C_{17}H_{20}N_4O_6$. It was found to be reversibly reduced by sodium dithionite solution, by zinc in acid solution, by hydrogen in presence of a catalyst, by titanous chloride or by hydrogen sulphide in alkaline solution to a leuco-compound, which was re-oxidised to riboflavine on shaking with air.[1] It was stable to most oxidising agents, but chromic acid decomposed it with formation of ammonia, carbon dioxide and a nitrogen-free compound, not identified. On acetylation it yielded a tetra-acetate, indicating the presence of four hydroxyl groups ; [2,3] since oxidation with lead tetra-acetate yielded formaldehyde,[3] it followed that a primary hydroxyl group was present in the α-position to a secondary hydroxyl group. Confirmation of this was subsequently obtained by the formation of a diacetone compound.[4] Riboflavine gave a positive murexide test,[1] indicating the presence of a purine group, whilst alkaline hydrolysis gave urea.[2]

Lumiflavine

On irradiation in alkaline solution, riboflavine yielded lumiflavine,[3,5] with the empirical formula, $C_{13}H_{12}N_4O_2$. Thus, photolysis removed from riboflavine the elements $C_4H_8O_4$ and, since lumiflavine was incapable of acetylation and failed to give formaldehyde on treatment with lead tetra-acetate, it was concluded that a hydroxylated side-chain, $\cdot CHOH$—$CHOH$—$CHOH$—CH_2OH, had been removed.

Lumiflavine was sparingly soluble in water, but soluble in chloroform and, like the parent substance, it yielded urea on alkaline hydrolysis, together with an acidic substance, $C_{12}H_{12}N_2O_3$, which lost CO_2 on heating to give a substance, $C_{11}H_{12}N_2O$.[2,6] Since two moles of water were taken up during the alkaline hydrolysis, R. Kuhn and H. Rudy [6] concluded that the latter must arise, not from a ureido or guanidino group, which would require only one mole of water, but from a ring. This must, therefore, contain two carbonyl groups, one forming urea and the other being hydrolysed to a carboxyl group. These changes can be represented as follows :—

The decarboxylated compound, $C_{11}H_{12}N_2O$, which had the properties of a lactam, yielded 4-amino-1 : 2-dimethyl-5-methylamino-benzene (I) [7] when heated with sodium hydroxide, so that lumiflavine must be an alloxazine derivative (II).

(I)   (II)

Since the methylimino group was not present in riboflavine the hydroxylated side-chain must be attached to the methylene group. This was supported by the observation of R. Kuhn and F. Bär[8] that the photolysis of riboflavine was closely simulated by the behaviour of 2-tetrahydroxybutyl-quinoxaline, which on irradiation lost its hydroxylated side-chain. Just as lumiflavine had the same absorption spectrum as riboflavine so the product, quinoxaline, had the same absorption spectrum as its tetrahydroxybutyl derivative.

Isoalloxazines

Next, Kuhn and Weygand[9] synthesised 9-methyl-isoalloxazine, m.p. 392° C. by boiling N-methyl-o-phenylene diamine with alloxan in hydrochloric acid solution ; it had properties closely resembling those of lumiflavine. Thus, with sodium dithionite, it yielded a leuco-derivative that was reconverted to a fluorescent substance on exposure to air. Its absorption spectrum was similar to that of riboflavine and it gave urea when boiled with baryta solution ; the product was 1-methyl-2-keto-1 : 2-dihydroquinoxaline-3-carboxylic acid. In their next papers, Kuhn et al. described the preparation of 3 : 9-dimethyl-isoalloxazine from N-methyl-o-phenylene diamine and methyl alloxan,[10] and the synthesis of lumiflavine itself, m.p. 330° C., from 2-methyl-amino-4 : 5-dimethylaniline and alloxan,[11] thereby proving it to be 6 : 7 : 9-trimethyl-isoalloxazine (II).

The complete synthesis was described in a subsequent paper by R. Kuhn and K. Reinemund[12] and is similar to that used for riboflavine (see page 140).

R. Kuhn and H. Rudy[13] isolated another degradation product of riboflavine resulting from the treatment of lumiflavine with alkali, and identified it as 6 : 7-dimethyl-alloxazine, which they synthesised from 3 : 4-dimethyl-o-phenylene diamine and alloxan. Both the synthetic substance and the product from riboflavine yielded 1 : 3 : 6 : 7-tetramethyl-alloxazine on treatment with diazomethane.

A photolytic product was also obtained by Karrer et al.,[14] by exposure of a flavine solution to sunlight with access of air. Lumi-chrome, as they called the substance, had a characteristic absorption spectrum, gave a yellowish-green fluorescence in alkaline solution and a sky-blue fluorescence in aqueous or alcoholic solution, and was identified as 6 : 7-dimethyl-alloxazine. Karrer et al. also obtained lumiflavine, and showed that it was the 9-methyl derivative of lumi-chrome. They postulated that riboflavine was an N-tetrahydroxy-amyl-isoalloxazine, since the side-chain split off in the formation of lumichrome gave a strong positive pentose reaction.

R. Kuhn and F. Weygand [15] condensed L-arabinamine and D-xylamine with halogeno-*o*-nitrobenzene and halogeno-*o*-nitroxylene. The compounds obtained on reducing the products with stannous chloride in presence of alloxan had properties similar to those of riboflavine. In a later paper [16] they described synthetic 6 : 7-dimethyl-9-tetraacetyl-L-arabityl-isoalloxazine, m.p. 298° C., as resembling the tetraacetyl derivative of riboflavine in absorption spectrum, colour intensity, the effect of *p*H on the fluorescence and in optical rotation. The activity of this substance as a substitute for Warburg's yellow enzyme could not be tested, as it could not be adsorbed on the colloidal carrier.

Karrer *et al.*[17] obtained the same substance by a slightly different route, in which arabinose was reductively condensed with N-mono-acyl- or N-monocarbethoxy-*o*-phenylene diamine giving, after hydrolysis, N-(*o*-aminophenyl)-arabinamine ; other sugars gave analogous compounds. These were all converted to the corresponding isoalloxazines by condensation with alloxan. Karrer *et al.* also noted the close resemblance of the arabityl compound to riboflavine, but found slight differences in m.p. and optical rotation. P. Karrer, K. Schöpp and F. Benz [18] then synthesised the D-xylityl and D-ribityl compounds and found that the latter was identical with riboflavine.

Riboflavine therefore has the structure :

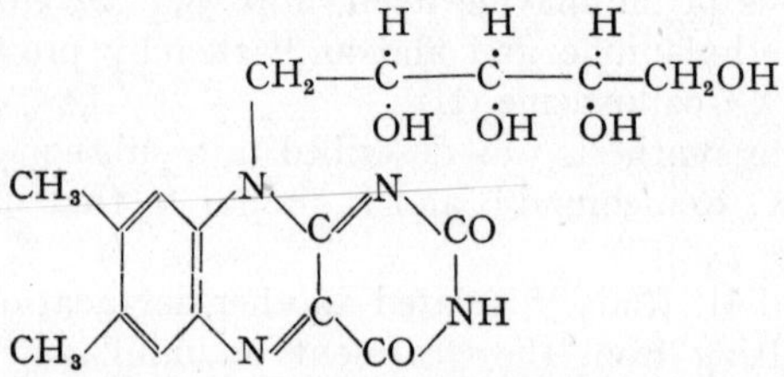

This paper is therefore the first to describe the synthesis of riboflavine, although a patent [19] based on this method was ante-dated by a patent covering the general reaction, filed earlier by the I.G. (see page 142). R. Kuhn [20] announced the successful synthesis five weeks after Karrer and his colleagues.

The identity of the synthetic and natural substances was confirmed by von Euler *et al.*,[21] who reported the results of growth tests with synthetic riboflavine and other homologues prepared from different sugars. The D-ribityl compound was fully active, the L-arabityl compound was slightly active, whilst the other derivatives tested were inactive. These and other compounds subsequently prepared are discussed in more detail on page 206.

A better method of condensing alloxan with pentitylamino

xylidines was introduced by R. Kuhn and F. Weygand.[22] Whereas they experienced no difficulty in obtaining quantitative yields of lumiflavine, the yields of riboflavine, araboflavine, etc., were only 5 to 10 % of the theoretical. This they attributed to the presence, not of the sugar residue, but of the methyl groups. O. Kühling and O. Kaselitz,[23] in attempting to prepare alloxazines, had obtained pale yellow substances containing one molecule of water more than the alloxazines when the condensation was effected in neutral solution. When the condensation was carried out in strongly acid solution, however, good yields of alloxazines were obtained. When this method was applied to the synthesis of riboflavine, with perchloric acid as the condensing agent, it met with little or no success, but the use of boric acid increased the yield to 95 % of the theoretical.

References to Section 3

1. P. Ellinger and W. Koschara, *Ber.*, 1933, **66**, 1411.
2. R. Kuhn and T. Wagner-Jauregg, *ibid.*, 1577.
3. R. Kuhn, H. Rudy and T. Wagner-Jauregg, *ibid.*, 1950.
4. R. Kuhn, H. Rudy and F. Weygand, *ibid.*, 1935, **68**, 625.
5. O. Warburg and W. Christian, *Biochem. Z.*, 1933, **266**, 377.
6. R. Kuhn and H. Rudy, *Ber.*, 1934, **67**, 892.
7. R. Kuhn and H. Rudy, *ibid.*, 1298.
8. R. Kuhn and F. Bär, *ibid.*, 898.
9. R. Kuhn and F. Weygand, *ibid.*, 1409.
10. R. Kuhn and F. Weygand, *ibid.*, 1459.
11. R. Kuhn, K. Reinemund and F. Weygand, *ibid.*, 1460.
12. R. Kuhn and K. Reinemund, *ibid.*, 1932.
13. R. Kuhn and H. Rudy, *ibid.*, 1936. 1826.
14. P. Karrer, H. Salomon, K. Schöpp, E. Schlitter and H. Fritzsche, *Helv. Chim. Acta*, 1934, **17**, 1010.
15. R. Kuhn and F. Weygand, *Ber.*, 1934, **67**, 1939.
16. R. Kuhn and F. Weygand, *ibid.*, 1935, **68**, 166.
17. P. Karrer, K. Schöpp, F. Benz and K. Pfaehler, *Helv. Chim. Acta*, 1935, **18**, 69 ; *Ber.*, 1935, **68**, 216.
18. P. Karrer, K. Schöpp and F. Benz, *Helv. Chim. Acta*, 1935, **18**, 426.
19. Hoffmann-la Roche, B.P. 457984.
20. R. Kuhn, *Naturwiss.*, 1935, **23**, 260.
21. H. von Euler, P. Karrer, M. Malmberg, K. Schöpp, F. Benz and P. Frei, *Helv. Chim. Acta*, 1935, **18**, 522 ; *Svensk. Kem. Tids.*, 1935, **47**, 99.
22. R. Kuhn and F. Weygand, *Ber.*, 1935, **68**, 1282.
23. O. Kühling and O. Kaselitz, *ibid.*, 1906, **39**, 1324.

4. SYNTHESIS OF RIBOFLAVINE

In the synthetic method used by R. Kuhn et al.,[1, 2] calcium D-gluconate was converted into D-arabinose by oxidation with ferric acetate and hydrogen peroxide (cf. R. C. Hockett and C. S. Hudson [3]), and the D-arabinose was converted into D-ribose by way of acetobromo-D-arabinose, diacetyl-D-arabinal, and D-arabinal, the overall yield being about 10 %. The oxime of D-ribose was reduced to D-ribamine and this was condensed with 1 : 2-dimethyl-4 : 5-dinitrobenzene by heating in 80 % alcohol for six hours at 130° C., giving 1 : 2-dimethyl-4-nitro-5-(D-1'-ribitylamino-)-benzene. This was reduced to the corresponding amino derivative by catalytic hydrogenation in presence of platinum oxide, and the product was condensed with alloxan tetrahydrate in acetic acid solution containing boric acid. A 70 % yield of riboflavine, m.p. 291 to 292° C., was obtained.

Kuhn et al. also prepared 4-amino-1 : 2-dimethyl-5(D-1'-ribityl-amino)-benzene in two other ways. In the first method, 1 : 2-dimethyl-4 : 5-dinitrobenzene was converted by treatment with ammonia into 5-amino-1 : 2-dimethyl-4-nitro-benzene, which with phosgene yielded 4 : 5-dimethyl-2-nitro-phenylisocyanate. On treatment with alcohol this gave the corresponding carbethoxyamino compound, which on catalytic reduction gave 6-amino-1-carbethoxyamino-3 : 4-dimethyl-benzene. On reductive condensation with ribose followed by hydrolysis, 4-amino-1 : 2-dimethyl-5-(D-1'-ribitylamino)-benzene was obtained.

In the second method, which was used for the preparation of the corresponding arabityl compound, 5-amino-1 : 2-dimethyl-4-nitro-benzene was heated with D-arabinose and the product was hydrogenated. These three methods of synthesis are summarised in the scheme shown on the opposite page.

The method used by the Swiss workers [4] differed somewhat from that of Kuhn et al. They nitrated o-xylene to give 3 : 4-dimethyl-1-nitrobenzene, which they reduced catalytically to 3 : 4-dimethyl-aniline, the overall yield being less than 20 %. The dimethyl-aniline was then converted into 3 : 4-dimethyl-1-carbethoxyaminobenzene by treatment with chloroformic ester, and this was nitrated to give 1-carbethoxyamino-3 : 4-dimethyl-6-nitro-benzene, which was then reduced catalytically to the corresponding amino compound. This was treated with ribose, obtained by the same route as in Kuhn's method, in the presence of hydrogen under pressure and a nickel catalyst, yielding 2-carbethoxyamino-4 : 5-dimethyl-phenyl-D-ribamine. This was hydrolysed and decarboxylated, and the resulting 2-amino-4 : 5-dimethyl-phenyl-D-ribamine was condensed with alloxan in presence of boric acid.

COOH   H OH   H Br

H——OH

HO——H

H——OH

H——OH

CH₂OH

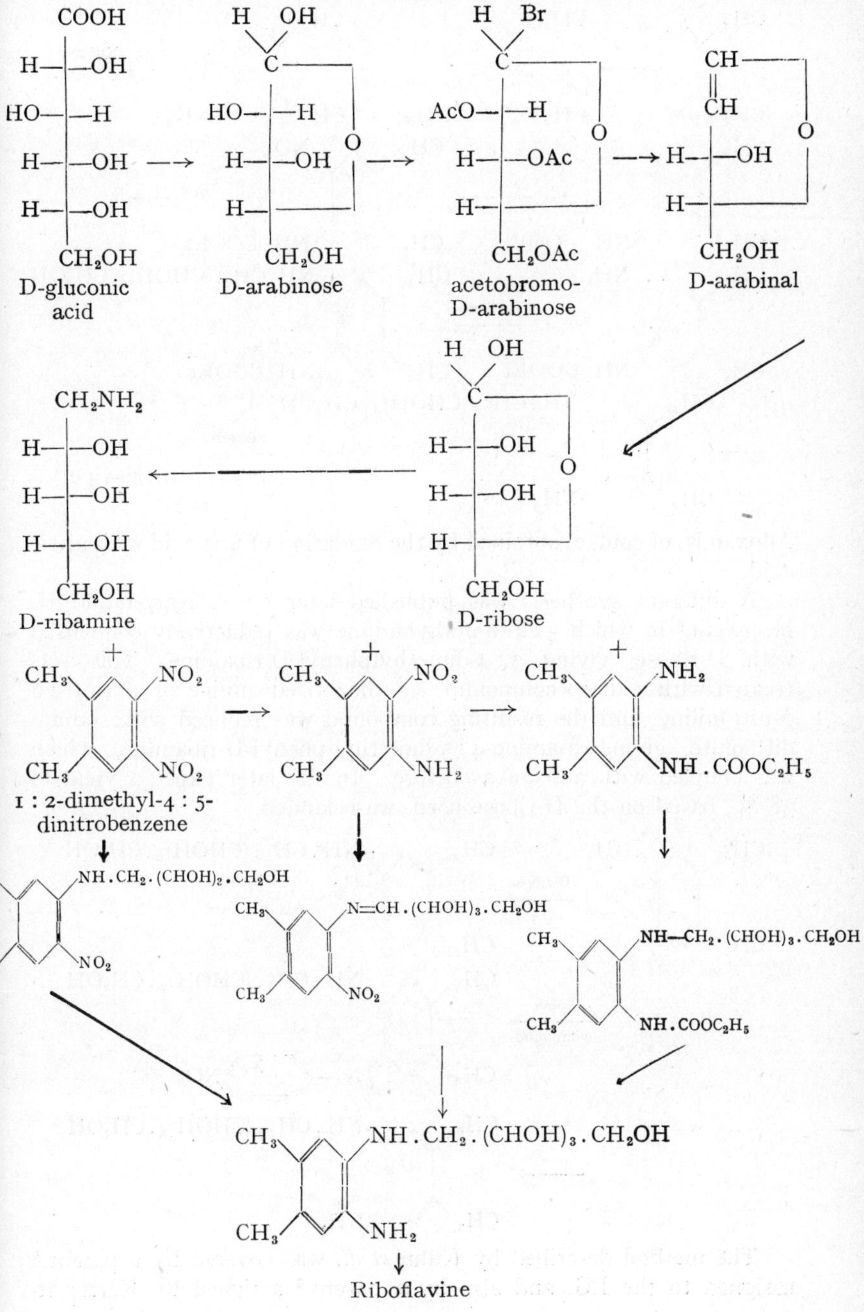

D-gluconic
acid

D-arabinose

acetobromo-
D-arabinose

D-arabinal

CH₂NH₂

H——OH

H——OH

H——OH

CH₂OH

D-ribamine

D-ribose

CH₃ NO₂

CH₃ NO₂

1 : 2-dimethyl-4 : 5-
dinitrobenzene

NH.CH₂.(CHOH)₂.CH₂OH

NO₂

N=CH.(CHOH)₃.CH₂OH

NO₂

NH—CH₂.(CHOH)₃.CH₂OH

NH.COOC₂H₅

CH₃   NH.CH₂.(CHOH)₃.CH₂OH

CH₃   NH₂

Riboflavine

141

Alloxan is, of course, obtained by the oxidation of uric acid with nitric acid.

A different synthesis was published later by P. Karrer and H. Meerwein,[5] in which 3 : 4-dimethylaniline was reductively condensed with D-ribose, giving 3 : 4-dimethylphenyl-D-ribamine. This was treated with a diazo compound, e.g. diazotised aniline or diazotised p-nitraniline, and the resulting compound was reduced with sodium dithionite, giving 2-amino-4 : 5-dimethyl-phenyl-D-ribamine, which was coupled with alloxan as before. In the later paper a yield of 38 %, based on the D-ribose used, was claimed.

The method described by Kuhn et al. was covered by a patent [6] assigned to the I.G. and also by a patent [7] assigned by Karrer to

Hoffmann-la Roche. The two patents were very similar, differing only in one or two minor details, but the I.G. patent was filed first and therefore has priority. It covers the condensation of " N-mono-substituted aromatic o-diamines " with " alloxan, its monosubstitution products or its derivatives " and so includes the preparation of riboflavine from 4-amino-1 : 2-dimethyl-5-(D-1'-ribitylamino)-benzene by Kuhn's first and second methods and by Karrer's first method, although the Swiss workers used a different method for preparing the carbethoxyamino compound. Karrer's second method is also implicitly covered. Hoffmann-La Roche patented the condensation of N-substituted aromatic o-diamines with alloxan in presence of equimolecular proportions of alloxantin.[7a]

The I.G. filed a second patent [8] covering Kuhn's third method, that is, condensation of ribose with 5-amino-1 : 2-dimethyl-4-nitro-benzene and reduction of the resulting Schiff's base to 1 : 2-dimethyl-4-nitro-5-(D-1'-ribitylamino)-benzene. This was condensed with alloxan under reducing conditions to give riboflavine.

A variant of the above methods was used later by R. Kuhn and R. Ströbele.[9] 3 : 4-Dimethyl-6-nitro-aniline was condensed with ribose and the resulting Schiff's base was catalytically reduced to the diamine, which with alloxan gave a 16 % yield of riboflavine. The Schiff's base was also partially reduced to the o-phenylene-diamine glycoside, which was acetylated and the product condensed with alloxan to give the corresponding acetylated flavine glycoside. This, on hydrolysis, yielded the free glycoside.

Preparation of Ribose

The outstanding difficulty in the synthesis of riboflavine lies in the preparation of ribose. The method used by Karrer was identical with that used by Kuhn et al. (page 140), 1 kg. of calcium gluconate yielding about 24 g. of ribose, which had to be separated from arabinose by fractional crystallisation of the bromophenylhydrazones.

A somewhat better method (p. 143) was that of T. Reichstein and M. Steiger;[10] this gave about 36 g. of ribose from 1 kg. of calcium gluconate.

The mixture of ribonic acid and unchanged arabonic acid was freed from the latter by conversion to the calcium salt, and the ribonic acid was then isolated as the cadmium salt and converted to ribose by reduction with sodium amalgam.

Ribose can also be made in one stage from calcium altronate by oxidation with hydrogen peroxide in presence of ferric acetate[11] but, unfortunately, altronic acid is not readily available, although it can be made from cellobiose acetate:

Cellobiose octaacetate $\longrightarrow$ Acetochloro-celtrobiose

($+$acetochloro-cellobiose) $\longrightarrow$ celtrobiose $\xrightarrow{Br_2}$ altronic acid

or from sedoheptulose, a seven-carbon sugar occurring in *Sedum spectabile*.[12]

$$
\begin{array}{ccc}
\underset{|}{CH_2OH} & & \\
\underset{|}{CO} & COOH & \\
HO-\!\!-H & HO-\!\!-H & CHO \\
H-\!\!-OH \xrightarrow{} & H-\!\!-OH \xrightarrow{H_2O_2} & H-\!\!-OH \\
H-\!\!-OH & H-\!\!-OH & H-\!\!-OH \\
H-\!\!-OH & H-\!\!-OH & H-\!\!-OH \\
CH_2OH & CH_2OH & CH_2OH \\
\text{Sedoheptulose} & \text{Altronic} & \text{Ribose} \\
& \text{acid} &
\end{array}
$$

Methods of Synthesis not involving Ribose

A method that avoided the use of D-ribose was discovered by F. Weygand,[13] who showed that the Amadori rearrangement was not limited to glucose, as had been previously supposed. He prepared, *inter alia*, 3 : 4-dimethylaniline-D-arabinoside by condensing D-arabinose with *o*-4-xylidine, and converted it into the D-isoarabinosamine by heating at 75° C. This yielded 3 : 4-dimethyl phenyl-D-ribamine on hydrogenation in alkaline solution. The product obtained by coupling with a diazo compound was reduced to the corresponding amine by the method of Karrer and Meerwein.[5]   (*See opposite page*) Incidentally Weygand suggested that the vitamin B_2 activity of araboflavine (see page 206) might be due to contamination with riboflavine formed by an Amadori rearrangement.

A variant of Weygand's method was patented by the Miles Labs. Inc.[14] *o*-4-Xylidine was condensed with D-arabinose under conditions

$$CH_3 \diagdown \text{—N}{=}CH\text{—}\underset{H}{\overset{OH}{C}}\text{—}\underset{OH}{\overset{H}{C}}\text{—}\underset{OH}{\overset{H}{C}}\text{—}CH_2OH \longrightarrow$$

$$CH_3 \diagdown \text{—NH—}CH_2\text{—}CO\text{—}\underset{OH}{\overset{H}{C}}\text{—}\underset{OH}{\overset{H}{C}}\text{—}CH_2OH \quad \xrightarrow{H_2}$$

$$CH_3 \diagdown \text{—NH—}CH_2\text{—}\underset{OH}{\overset{H}{C}}\text{—}\underset{OH}{\overset{H}{C}}\text{—}\underset{OH}{\overset{H}{C}}\text{—}CH_2OH \longrightarrow$$

$$CH_3 \diagdown \underset{N_2R}{\text{—NH—}CH_2\text{—}}\underset{OH}{\overset{H}{C}}\text{—}\underset{OH}{\overset{H}{C}}\text{—}\underset{OH}{\overset{H}{C}}\text{—}CH_2OH \longrightarrow$$

$$CH_3 \diagdown \underset{NH_2}{\text{—NH—}CH_2\text{—}}\underset{OH}{\overset{H}{C}}\text{—}\underset{OH}{\overset{H}{C}}\text{—}\underset{OH}{\overset{H}{C}}\text{—}CH_2OH$$

that brought about an Amadori rearrangement, with formation of 3 : 4-dimethylphenyl-D-isoarabinosamine. This was coupled in the usual way with a diazonium salt, and the product was hydrogenated to reduce the carbonyl to a carbinol group and the azo to an amino group. The resulting compound was coupled with alloxan, dialuric acid, isodialuric acid or alloxantin.

Pfizer & Co.[15] used a different method for avoiding ribose, namely, acetylation of D-ribonamide, conversion of the product into tetra-acetyl-ribonic acid by treatment with nitrous acid, and then reaction with phosphorus pentachloride to form the acid chloride. This was reduced catalytically in presence of palladium supported on barium sulphate, giving tetraacetyl-D-ribose. This compound, which is claimed to exist in the aldehydo form, was hydrogenated in presence of o-4-xylidine, using Raney nickel or platinum as catalyst, giving tetraacetyl-D-ribityl-o-4-xylidine. This was coupled with a phenyl diazonium salt. In a similar method, due to Merck,[16] tetrabutyryl-D-ribonamide was converted into tetrabutyrylribonic acid by the action of oxides of nitrogen, and the acid was converted *via* the acid halide into tetrabutyryl ribose, as in Pfizer's method.

A somewhat different method of preparing N-(D-ribityl)-3 : 4-dimethylaniline, again without the use of D-ribose, was described by Tishler *et al*.[17] D-Arabonic acid was converted into D-ribonic acid, from which D-ribonolactone was prepared.   This was reacted with 3 : 4-dimethylaniline and the product acetylated to give 3 : 4-dimethyl (tetraacetyl-D-ribonyl)-aniline.   This with phosphorus pentachloride gave the chloroimine, which was reduced catalytically to the amine and then deacetylated :

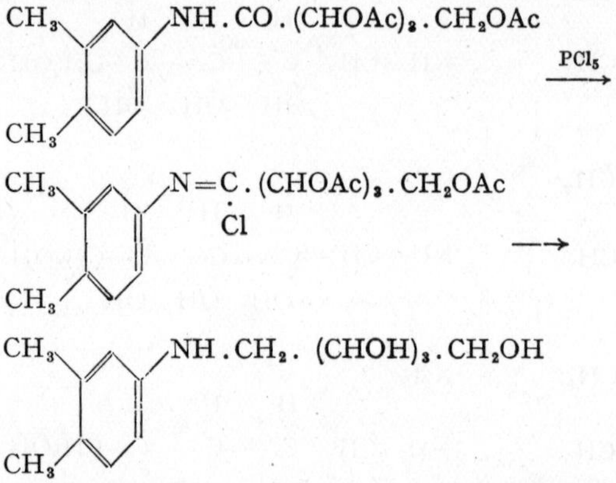

Another method not involving ribose was described by M. Tishler and J. W. Wellman.[18] 3 : 4-Dimethylaniline was reductively condensed with tetraacetyl-D-ribononitrile, which was prepared from ribonic acid *via* the amide.   The resulting N-tetraacetyl-D-ribityl-3 : 4-dimethylaniline was then coupled with *p*-nitrophenyl diazonium chloride and the product reduced to 5-tetraacetyl-ribitylamino-4-amino-1 : 2-dimethylbenzene.   This was hydrolysed and the product coupled, not with alloxan as in the methods previously described, but with 5 : 5-dichlorobarbituric acid ; for, contrary to the report of R. Kuhn and A. H. Cook [19] that alloxazines could not be prepared by the interaction of *o*-phenylene diamine and 5-bromo-barbituric acid, Tishler *et al*.[20] found that under certain conditions 5-chloro- and 5 : 5-dichloro-barbituric acids reacted with alkylated *o*-phenylene diamines to give alloxazines, *e.g.* 4 : 5-dimethyl-*o*-phenylene diamine and 5 : 5-dichloro-barbituric acid gave 6 : 7-dimethylalloxazine :

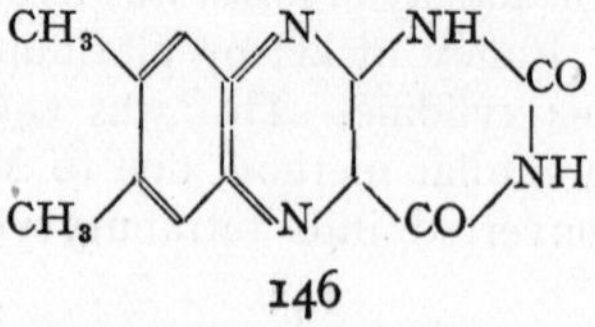

The condensation was best carried out in pyridine. Similarly, 5-amino-N-ribityl-o-4-xylidine and 5 : 5-dichlorobarbituric acid gave an excellent yield of riboflavine.

Subsequently, Tishler et al.[21] found that o-aminoazo compounds reacted with barbituric acid to give riboflavine.

A similar method had been used previously by Bergel et al.[22] N-D-Ribityl-o-4-xylidine was converted into riboflavine by coupling with diazotised aniline and shaking the azo compound so obtained with excess alloxantin or dialuric acid in an atmosphere of nitrogen and finally oxidising any leuco-riboflavine by shaking in air :

$\longrightarrow$ Riboflavine

References to Section 4

1. R. Kuhn and F. Weygand, Ber., 1935, **68**, 1001.
2. R. Kuhn, K. Reinemund, F. Weygand and R. Ströbele, ibid., 1765.
3. R. C. Hockett and C. S. Hudson, J. Amer. Chem. Soc., 1934, **56**, 1632.
4. P. Karrer, B. Becker, F. Benz, P. Frei, H. Salomon and K. Schöpp, Helv. Chim. Acta, 1935, **18**, 1435.
5. P. Karrer and H. Meerwein, ibid., 1935, **18**, 1130 ; 1936, **19**, 264.
6. I.G., B.P. 441692.
7. Hoffmann-la Roche, B.P. 457984.
7a. Hoffmann-la Roche, B.P. 628410.
8. I.G., B.P. 461245.
9. R. Kuhn and R. Ströbele, Ber., 1937, **70**, 747, 773.
10. T. Reichstein and M. Steiger, Helv. Chim. Acta, 1936, **19**, 189.
11. C. S. Hudson, U.S.P. 2162721.
12. F. B. La Forge and C. S. Hudson, J. Biol. Chem., 1917, **30**, 132 ; C. S. Hudson, J. Amer. Chem. Soc., 1939, **61**, 343.
13. F. Weygand, Ber., 1940, **73**, 1259.
14. Miles Laboratories, Inc., B.P. 594949.
15. Pfizer & Co., Inc., B.P. 545360, 551491, 585212.
16. Merck & Co., U.S.P. 2424341.
17. M. Tishler, N. L. Wendler, K. Ladenburg and J. W. Wellman, J. Amer. Chem. Soc., 1944, **66**, 1328 ; Merck & Co., U.S.P. 2420210.
18. M. Tishler and J. W. Wellman, U.S.P. 2261608.
19. R. Kuhn and A. H. Cook, Ber., 1937, **70**, 761.

20. M. Tishler, J. W. Wellman and K. Ladenburg, *J. Amer. Chem. Soc.*, 1945, **67**, 2165.
21. M. Tishler, K. Pfister, R. D. Babson, K. Ladenburg and A. J. Fleming, *ibid.*, 1947, **69**, 1487.
22. F. Bergel, A. Cohen and J. W. Haworth, *J. Chem. Soc.*, 1945, 165 ; B.P. 550169 ; 550836.

5. MICROBIOLOGICAL PRODUCTION OF RIBOFLAVINE

It is unusual for a synthetic method of producing a commercially important chemical to be displaced by a method based on its isolation from natural sources ; generally, the tendency is in the reverse direction. Yet the production of riboflavine can now be effected more cheaply by fermentation than by chemical synthesis.

Patents were filed as early as 1937 for the production of " vitamin B_2 " concentrates by fermenting whey or other milk by-products with lactose-fermenting yeasts, especially *Saccharomyces fragilis*, or with *Clostridium butylicum*, several species of *Lactobacilli* or with moulds,[1] or by fermenting molasses or other carbohydrate mashes with various strains of butanol-producing *Clostridia*,[2] especially *Cl. acetobutylicum*. The vitamin was recovered from the fermented liquors by adsorption and elution. This process often gave low yields, which were subsequently shown [3] to be due to the presence of certain metals, particularly iron. The use of a mash prepared from cereals containing only traces of these metals was said to give much higher yields—up to 2 mg. of riboflavine per gram of dry matter. Fermentation of brown rice was also said to give good yields, especially in admixture with maize.[4]

Fermentation with Clostridia

The first report in the scientific literature that a fluorescent pigment resembling riboflavine was produced by *Cl. acetobutylicum* was made by I. Yamasaki and W. Yositome.[5] They used a sterilised starchy medium prepared from cereals, and stated that the addition of calcium carbonate was necessary for the formation of optimal amounts. The riboflavine was recovered by adsorption on fuller's earth, elution of the adsorbate with aqueous pyridine-methanol and precipitation with acetone. The process was protected by a patent filed in 1938.[6] The pigment was subsequently identified as riboflavine,[7] and a detailed investigation was made [8] of the effect on the yield of varying the composition of the medium. It was found that iron had a markedly toxic effect, 36 to 70 p.p.m. suppressing riboflavine production entirely. The deleterious effect of iron was confirmed by other workers.[9] The addition of sufficient $\alpha\alpha'$-dipyridyl, to inactivate all but a small amount of iron, increased the yield of riboflavine,[10] so that, for instance, in the fermentation of corn-mash, a yield of 2 to 13 mg. of riboflavine per litre was obtained in presence of 1·5 mg. of iron per litre. The addition of sodium sulphite was claimed [11] to result in consistently high yields, although the maximum amount produced (2 mg. per g. of dry solids) was not appreciably affected. The production of ribo-flavine by fermentation of whey or skimmed milk with *Cl. aceto-butylicum* was also protected by patents.[12] Again, the concentration of iron in the mash was found to be very critical, and it was stated that, to obtain the best results, this should lie between 1 and 3 p.p.m. Yields of 0·24 to 2·2 mg. per gram of dried material were claimed. The sensitivity of the fermentation to iron was confirmed by A. Leviton,[13] who found that less than 0·2 mg.-atom of ferrous (though not of ferric) iron per litre prevented the formation of riboflavine and destroyed any that was added to the fermentation liquor. Crystalline catalase counteracted the effect of the iron, provided the concentration of iron did not exceed 0·29 mg.-atom per litre, but in the presence of 0·33 mg.-atom per litre, catalase had little effect. Low concentrations of sodium dithionite minimised the effect of iron, whilst potassium iodide enhanced it. Riboflavine was destroyed by hydrogen peroxide in the presence, though not in the absence, of iron, and the addition of catalase or potassium iodide stabilised the riboflavine, although it speeded up the destruction of the hydrogen peroxide.

A. Leviton suggested that the synthesis and decomposition of ribo-flavine during fermentation were intracellular processes involving the formation of hydrogen peroxide. When iron was present, the hydrogen peroxide destroyed the riboflavine inside the cells, so that catalase had no effect. When less iron was present, hydrogen peroxide and riboflavine accumulated in the cell and then diffused into the culture fluid, where catalase destroyed the hydrogen peroxide and thus pro-tected the riboflavine from destruction.

The production of riboflavine by butyl alcohol-producing bacteria has also been patented.[14]

Fermentation with Candida

A large number of different strains of yeast also produced ribo-flavine, although mostly in moderate amounts only.[15] Certain strains, however, were found to produce 10 to 60 mg. per litre of fermented liquor.[16] In particular, most species and varieties of *Candida* produced substantial amounts of riboflavine, though only when glucose was used as the carbon source.[17] The highest yields were obtained from *C. guillermondia* and *C. tropicalis* var. *Rhagii*.[18]

The use of *C. guillermondia* has been covered by a patent,[19] yields of 50 to 60 mg. per litre being claimed. Good yields have also been obtained with *C. flareri*.[20]

C. guillermondia produced riboflavine on a medium in which either ammonium sulphate or urea was the sole source of nitrogen, and *C. flareri* with only urea as the nitrogen source ; the iron content must not exceed about 50 μg. per litre. Under comparable conditions, the two species yielded 175 and 567 mg. per litre respectively in shake flasks and 118 and 325 mg. per litre in stirred, aerated tanks. *C. flareri* yielded a preparation containing 97 mg. of riboflavine per gram of solids.[20a]

An investigation into the effect of varying the constituents of the medium for *C. guillermondia* showed [21] that the processes involved in growth were different from those involved in the production of riboflavine. Good growth was obtained with arabinose, galactose, inulin, maltose, mannitol, sorbose or xylose as the carbohydrate, but yields of riboflavine were low. With glucose, mannose, fructose or sucrose on the other hand, both growth and riboflavine production were good. Asparagine and glycine were good sources of nitrogen for riboflavine production.

Fermentation with Moulds

High yields have also been recorded in fermentations with the mould, *Eremothecium Ashbyii*.[22] Thus A. Raffy and M. Fontaine, using a meat broth-peptone-glucose agar, obtained a yield of 86 mg. per litre of medium on the nineteenth day after inoculation, though on a liquid peptone-glucose medium, in which growth was much slower, a yield of only 27 mg. per litre was obtained after fifty-two days. The flavine was isolated by adsorption on frankonite and elution of the adsorbate. Considerably lower yields of riboflavine were obtained by fermentation under anaerobic conditions.[23]

W. H. Schopfer [24] studied the influence of various nutrients on riboflavine production ; fermentation was conducted in the dark at 28° C. in small flasks. Good growth was obtained on liquid media containing a variety of vegetable or animal extracts. With yeast extract, a yield of 30 mg. per litre was obtained in seven days. Higher yields—up to 128 mg. per litre—were claimed by J. Renaud and M. Lachaux [25] after twenty-four days fermentation on a peptone-glucose medium. Leucine and arginine were said [26] to be capable of replacing peptone for riboflavine production. The formation of riboflavine was inhibited by sulphaguanidine and other sulphonamides,[27] and the inhibition was reversed by peptone, but this effect was not related to the *p*-aminobenzoic acid present.

Better yields were obtained by Moore *et al.*[28] in shake cultures. With a yeast extract-glucose-peptone broth, a concentration of 198 mg. per litre of liquor or 4 mg. per g. of solid was obtained in seventy-two hours and with distiller's thin stillage 124 mg. per litre or 4·6 mg. per g. of solids. When supplemented with molasses or corn oil, the yield was increased to 356 mg. per litre. Cultures kept at low temperature produced less riboflavine, whilst lyophilised cultures lost the ability altogether. Maintenance of stock cultures on maltose broth at room temperature is advocated.

W. Ritter[29] separated *E. Ashbyii* into two strains, one white and one yellow, and found that the former synthesised only a fraction of the riboflavine produced by the latter. The higher yields obtained by the yellow variant were produced on wort agar, which gave up to 80 mg. per litre. Biotin was essential for growth of the organism.

The most efficient method for the production of riboflavine by fermentation with *E. Ashbyii*, appears to be submerged growth with continuous aeration and agitation. Patents covering this process were filed by Société des Usines chimiques Rhône-Poulenc,[29a] Commercial Solvents Corporation,[30] Pfizer & Co.,[31] Merck & Co.,[32] Lederle Labs. Inc.,[33] and Roche Products Ltd.[33a] In every instance, the recommended medium comprised a carbohydrate source, such as glucose or molasses, together with a source of nitrogen, such as peptone, animal tissue, yeast extract, corn steep liquor or skimmed milk. One patent[30] advocated as an additional supplement a metabolisable lipid, such as corn-, olive- or peanut-oil, or cocoa-butter ; with alcohol fermentation residues and corn steep water, yields of 436 mg. per litre were obtained in four days, whilst a medium containing animal tissues[33] gave up to 400 mg. per litre in a similar time, and a yeast extract-molasses medium 468 mg. per litre.

Another micro-organism that appears to be of potential value in the microbiological production of riboflavine is *Ashbya gossypii*. Small yields were obtained by Guillermond *et al.*[34] but considerably larger amounts were obtained by Wickerham *et al.*,[35] who used an orange-yellow variant ; with an aerated cerelose-yeast extract medium at 26° to 28° C., up to 380 mg. per litre were produced after eight days. The highest recorded yields of riboflavine, using *Ashbya gossypii*, were obtained in shake cultures on a medium containing 4 % glucose, 0·5 % peptone and 0·5 % corn steep liquor solids ;[36] titres of 500 to 600 mg. per litre were obtained, equivalent to more than 10 mg. of riboflavine per g. of solid.

Riboflavine was also obtained by fermentation with *Mycobacterium smegmatis*, yields varying according to the speed of growth and the nature of the medium.[37] The best yields were obtained in the absence of organic nitrogen. Fructose was the best source of carbon for growth and riboflavine production, but xylose gave the highest yields of riboflavine, although it resulted in poor growth. Potassium, magnesium and sulphate ions were essential for riboflavine production. V. E. Pontovich [38] claimed to have isolated 2 mg. of riboflavine per g. from the mycelium of *Aspergillus flavus*, whilst Tanner *et al.*[39] found up to 1·38 μg. per ml. in fermentation liquor from *Penicillium chrysogenum*. Of 240 moulds isolated from soil and compost, all synthesised riboflavine, especially large amounts being produced by species of *Fusarium*.[40]

Recovery

Various methods have been used to recover riboflavine from fermentation liquors. Thus it may be adsorbed on a suitable material such as fuller's earth or florisil, and eluted from the adsorbate with, for example, polyhydric alcohols.[41] It may be extracted with butanol and then precipitated from the extract by addition of petroleum ether,[42] or impurities may be precipitated from the fermentation liquors by means of acetone, and the riboflavine recovered from the concentrated filtrate by the addition of more acetone.[42a] Spray or roller drying of the metabolism solution from *E. ashbyii* gave a product containing 0·2 to 6·0 mg. of riboflavine per g. of dry matter.[43] A novel method of isolation, devised by Commercial Solvents Corporation,[44] was to add a soluble reducing agent to the fermentation liquor, such that an E_h of from — 0·05 to — 0·40 volt was produced, and filter off the precipitate that formed ; this contained most of the riboflavine. Alternatively, the E_h was reduced to at least — 0·096 volt by fermenting the metabolism solution anaerobically with such organisms as *Streptococcus faecalis*, *Escherichia coli* and *Clostridium acetobutylicum* and the precipitate that formed was centrifuged off.[45] This may contain up to 90 % of the riboflavine present in the fermentation liquor.

References to Section 5

1. Seal-test System Laboratories Ltd., U.S.P. 2128845.
2. Commercial Solvents Corporation, U.S.P. 2202161 ; B.P. 527478.
3. Commercial Solvents Corporation, U.S.P. 2326425 ; B.P. 553465.
4. Commercial Solvents Corporation, U.S.P. 2368074 ; B.P. 553903-4.
5. I. Yamasaki and W. Yositome, *Biochem. Z.*, 1938, **297**, 398.
6. I. Yamasaki, U.S.P. 2297671.
7. I. Yamasaki, *Biochem. Z.*, 1939, **300**, 160 ; *Proc. Imp. Acad. Tokyo*, 1940, **16**, 6.
8. I. Yamasaki, *Biochem. Z.*, 1941, **307**, 431.
9. A. Saunders and L. S. McClung, *J. Bact.*, 1943, **46**, 575.
10. R. J. Hickey, *Arch. Biochem.*, 1945, **8**, 439 ; R. J. Hickey and Commercial Solvents Corporation, U.S.P. 2425280.

11. Commercial Alcohol Co. Inc., U.S.P. 2370177.
12. Western Condensing Co., U.S.P. 2369680; B.P. 602029, 602031.
13. A. Leviton, *J. Amer. Chem. Soc.*, 1946, **68**, 835.
14. Commercial Solvents Corporation, U.S.P. 2425280.
15. M. Rogosa, *J. Bact.*, 1943, **45**, 459.
16. P. R. Burkholder, *Proc. Nat. Acad. Sci.*, 1943, **29**, 166.
17. W. H. Schopfer and M. Guilloud, *Compt. rend. Soc. Phys. Hist. nat. Geneve*, 1944, **61**, 232.
18. W. H. Schopfer, *ibid.*, 147 ; *Z. Vitaminforsch.*, 1945, **16**, 106.
19. P. R. Burkholder and Research Corp., U.S.P. 2363227.
20. F. W. Tanner, C. Vojnovich and J. M. van Lanen, *Science*, 1945, **101**, 180 ; F. W. Tanner and J. M. van Lanen, U.S.P. 2424003.
20a. H. Levine, J. E. Oyaas, L. Wasserman, J. C. Hoogerheide and R. M. Stern, *Ind. Eng. Chem.*, 1949, **41**, 1665.
21. P. R. Burkholder, *Arch. Biochem.*, 1943, **3**, 121.
22. A. Guillermond, M. Fontaine and A. Raffy, *Compt. rend.*, 1935, **201**, 1077 ; A. Raffy and M. Fontaine, *ibid.*, 1937, **205**, 1005 ; A. Raffy and A. Mirimanoff, *ibid.*, 1938, **206**, 1507 ; A. Mirimanoff and A. Raffy, *Helv. Chim. Acta*, 1938, **21**, 1004 ; *Bull. Soc. Chim. biol.*, 1938, **20**, 1166.
23. A. Raffy, *Compt. rend.*, 1939, **209**, 900.
24. W. H. Schopfer, *Z. Vitaminforsch.*, 1943–44, **14**, 42 ; *Helv. Chim. Acta*, 1944, **27**, 1017.
25. J. Renaud and M. Lachaux, *Compt. rend.*, 1944, **219**, 498 ; 1945, **221**, 187.
26. W. H. Schopfer and M. Guilloud, *Experientia*, 1945, **1**, 1.
27. W. H. Schopfer and M. Guilloud, *ibid.*, 333.
28. H. N. Moore, G. de Becze and E. Schraffenberger, *J. Bact.*, 1947, **53**, 502 ; H. N. Moore and G. de Becze, *ibid.*, 1947, **54**, 40.
29. W. Ritter, *Schweiz. Z. Pathol. Bakt.*, 1944, **7**, 370.
29a. Société des Usines Rhône-Poulenc, B.P. 594015.
30. Commercial Solvents Corporation, U.S.P. 2374503 ; B.P. 623082.
31. Pfizer & Co., B.P. 593953.
32. Merck & Co., B.P. 593027.
33. Lederle Labs. Inc., U.S.P. 2400710.
33a. Roche Products Ltd., B.P. 615847.
34. A. Guillermond, M. Fontaine and A. Raffy, *Compt. rend.*, 1935, **201**, 1077.
35. L. J. Wickerham, M. H. Flickinger and R. M. Johnston, *Arch. Biochem.*, 1946, **9**, 95 ; F. W. Tanner, L. J. Wickerham and J. M. van Lanen, U.S.P. 2445128.
36. F. W. Tanner and J. M. van Lanen, *J. Bact.*, 1947, **54**, 38.
37. R. L. Mayer and M. Rodbart, *Arch. Biochem.*, 1946, **11**, 49.
38. V. E. Pontovich, *Biokhimiya*, 1943, **8**, 297.
39. F. W. Tanner, S. E. Pfeiffer and J. M. van Lanen, *Arch. Biochem.*, 1945, **8**, 29.
40. G. L. Peltier and R. Borchers, *J. Bact.*, 1947, **54**, 519.
41. S. H. Rubin and E. de Ritter, *J. Biol. Chem.*, 1945, **158**, 639 ; Commercial Solvents Corporation, U.S.P. 2343254.

42. Merck & Co., U.S.P. 2355220.

42a. Merck & Co., B.P. 621401.

43. Commercial Solvents Corporation, U.S.P. 2374503.

44. Commercial Solvents Corporation, U.S.P. 2367644 ; 2367646 ;
    B.P. 621468, 621552.

45. R. J. Hickey, *Arch. Biochem.*, 1946, **11**, 259 ; Commercial Solvents
    Corporation, U.S.P. 2387023 ; B.P. 621469.

6. PROPERTIES OF RIBOFLAVINE

Riboflavine is a bright yellow powder, m.p. 292° C., and its solubility in water is 12 mg. per 100 ml. at 27·5° C., and 19 mg. per 100 ml. at 40° C. The aqueous solution has a strong yellowish-green fluorescence, which is discharged by acids or alkalis ; the fluorescence is maximal at pH 3 to 9. The solution is laevo-rotatory,[1] $[\alpha]_D^{20°}$ being − 114° in a 0·1 N sodium hydroxide solution (concentration 0·125). In neutral or acid solution, however, the rotation is very much smaller. In presence of borax the rotation is strongly dextrorotatory, $[\alpha]_D^{20°}$ being + 340° at pH 12. Riboflavine is soluble in aqueous alkali solutions.

In view of the low solubility in water, which complicates the problem of administering riboflavine, numerous methods have been suggested for preparing solutions containing a relatively high concentration of the vitamin. Thus the addition of urea or urethan,[2] sodium desoxycholate or N-methylacetamide,[3] acetamidine salts,[4] boric acid,[5] l-tyrosine amide,[5a] tryptophan[5b] or propylene glycol with or without the addition of a monohydroxymonoalkoxybenzaldehyde [5c] has been claimed to increase the solubility of riboflavine in water. Hoffmann-La Roche [6] claimed the use of 2 : 4-dihydroxybenzoic acid or its monoalkyl ethers and of gentisic acid for this purpose, whilst the Winthrop Chemical Co.[7] claimed the use of borax which, with alkali, was said to give the complex,

$$C_{17}H_{19}O_6N_4Na\text{-}Na_2B_4O_7 . 10H_2O.$$

Eli Lilly & Co.[8] used benzoic, aminobenzoic or hydrobenzoic acid and their salts, whilst M. R. Zentner [9] heated riboflavine with gallic acid in presence of a dilute mineral acid. Other methods of obtaining more concentrated solutions of riboflavine included the formation of the phthalic or succinic esters [10] and the citric, malic or tartaric esters ; [10a] and the formation of mono- and di-methylolriboflavine by reaction with formaldehyde.[10b] Riboflavine is soluble in nicotinamide solutions, the solubility increasing at pH 5 from about 0·1 % to about 2·5 % when the nicotinamide concentration was increased from 5 to 50 %.[11] Both the pyridine ring and the amide group of nicotinamide are involved.

Riboflavine is sparingly soluble in ethyl alcohol (4·5 mg. per 100 ml. at 27·5° C.), amyl alcohol, cyclohexanol, phenol or amyl acetate, but insoluble in acetone, ether, benzene or chloroform.

Riboflavine is amphoteric in nature, with an isoelectric point at pH 6.[12] The dissociation constants are :

$$K_a = 63 \times 10^{-12} \text{ and } K_b = 0·5 \times 10^{-5}.$$

On acetylation a tetraacetate, m.p. 242° C., is formed.

As already stated above (page 136), when an alkaline solution is irradiated, lumiflavine, m.p. 330° C., is produced, and this, being sparingly soluble in water, separates out from the irradiated solution.

Riboflavine is reduced to a colourless leuco-compound on treatment with sodium dithionite solution, and the colour and fluorescence are restored on exposure to air.

Riboflavine has a characteristic absorption spectrum, the peaks of the absorption bands being situated at 221, 266, 359 and 445 mμ.

Crystalline riboflavine is stable in the dark at ordinary temperatures, but slowly decomposes on exposure to light. In solution it is unstable, especially when alkaline solutions are exposed to light. It is moderately stable to heat, and no appreciable destruction occurred, for example, when milk was incubated for twenty-two hours at 31 to 37° C.,[13] or during the cooking of foods.[14] When, on the other hand, milk in bottles was exposed to sunlight, more than half the riboflavine was destroyed within two hours.[15, 16] The rate of destruction by light increased as the temperature and pH were increased.[14]

So sensitive is riboflavine to the action of light that riboflavine assays (see page 159) should be carried out in dim light and preferably in a red light ; a 150-watt lamp screened with a red cellophane filter has been recommended.[17] The light from the lamp normally employed in a Coleman spectrophotometer, however, does not cause appreciable destruction.

Riboflavine was said to be rendered more stable to light by the presence of sodium dithionite [18] or by heating with boric acid.[19] Solutions containing boric acid are recommended for injection, being said to be self-sterilising as well as photo-stable.

Riboflavine was included in the Sixth Addendum (1945) to the British Pharmacopoeia 1932, which laid down tests for identity and purity. The monograph was slightly modified in the British Pharmacopoeia 1948. The prophylactic and therapeutic doses are given as 1 to 4 mg. and 5 to 10 mg. daily respectively.

References to Section 6

1. R. Kuhn and H. Rudy, *Ber.*, 1935, **68,** 169 ; P. Karrer and H. Fritzsche, *Helv. Chim. Acta*, 1935, **18,** 1026.

2. S. A. Schou and B. Fretheim, *Dansk. Tidskr. Farm.*, 1940, **14**, 97 ; Merck & Co., B.P. 4966/47.

3. R. Kuhn, *Klin. Woch.*, 1938, **17**, 222.

4. A. E. Jurist, U.S.P. 2358331.

5. D. V. Frost, *J. Biol. Chem.*, 1942, **145**, 693 ; U.S.P. 2388261.

5a. Wyeth Inc., U.S.P. 2445208.

5b. R. A. Harte and J. L. Chen, *J. Amer. Pharm. Assoc. Sci. Ed.*, 1949, **38**, 568.

5c. American Cyanamid Co., U.S.P. 2449041 ; Wyeth Inc., U.S.P. 2449640.

6. Hoffmann-La Roche, B.P. 555346 ; U.S.P. 2349986, 2438880.

7. Winthrop Chemical Co., B.P. 560631 ; U.S.P. 2332548.

8. Eli Lilly & Co., U.S.P. 2395378.

9. M. R. Zentner, U.S.P. 2423074.

10. Merck & Co., U.S.P. 2358356 ; M. F. Furter, G. J. Haas and S. H. Rubin, *J. Biol. Chem.*, 1945, **160**, 293.

10a. American Cyanamid Co., U.S.P. 2449003.

10b. K. Schoen and S. M. Gordon, *Arch. Biochem.*, 1949, **22**, 149.

11. D. V. Frost, *J. Amer. Chem. Soc.*, 1947, **69**, 1064 ; U.S.P. 2407412.

12. R. Kuhn and G. Moruzzi, *Ber.*, 1934, **67**, 888.

13. B. Sure and Z. W. Ford, *Proc. Soc. Exp. Biol. Med.*, 1943, **54**, 83.

14. R. R. Williams and V. H. Cheldelin, *Science*, 1942, **96**, 22.

15. W. J. Peterson, F. M. Haig and A. O. Shaw, *J. Amer. Chem. Soc.*, 1944, **66**, 662.

16. J. A. Ziegler, *ibid.*, 1039.

17. L. J. De Merre and W. S. Brown, *Arch. Biochem.*, 1944, **5**, 181.

18. C. M. O'Malley and C. W. Sievert, *Ind. Eng. Chem.*, 1942, **34**, 1117.

19. D. V. Frost, *J. Biol. Chem.*, 1942, **145**, 693 ; Abbott Labs., U.S.P. 2388261.

7. ESTIMATION OF RIBOFLAVINE

Biological Assays

Riboflavine is generally regarded as the component of the vitamin B_2 group responsible for increasing the growth rate of rats and chicks, but it is not unique in this respect, and other factors contribute materially to the growth of animals on a synthetic diet. Consequently the problem of developing a good biological method of assay resolves itself mainly into the problem of providing adequate amounts of the other members of the group in the diet, without at the same time introducing small amounts of riboflavine. Care must also be taken to prevent coprophagy, since riboflavine is synthesised by micro-organisms present in the contents of the gut (see page 183).

H. von Euler and M. Malmberg [1] and El Sadr *et al.*[2] used rats, the latter group of workers introducing the vitamin B_2 group into the diet in the form of an aqueous extract of whole liver from which the riboflavine had been removed by adsorption on norite at pH 5. Satisfactory assays of riboflavine in milk were obtained by this method. A fraction prepared from liver extract was used by Wagner *et al.*,[3] whilst others have used rice polishings [4] and rice bran,[5] both of which were claimed to be more reliable sources of the vitamin B complex than whole wheat or yeast.

Chicks were used for riboflavine assays by T. H. Jukes,[6] but these appear to give less satisfactory results than rats.

Microbiological Assays

The biological method of assay has now been completely superseded by the microbiological method, introduced by E. E. Snell and F. M. Strong.[7] They used a lactic acid-producing organism, *Lactobacillus casei* ε, now generally referred to in this country as *L. helveticus ;* this will not grow in the absence, *inter alia*, of riboflavine. Using a suitable basal medium, the amount of lactic acid produced is proportional to the concentration of added riboflavine. This method and its modifications have been extensively used in the assay of foodstuffs. The original medium employed by Snell and Strong consisted of alkali-treated peptone, cystine, yeast supplement, glucose and inorganic salts, but various modifications were made by later workers in order to improve the specificity of the medium and the growth response.

E. C. Barton-Wright,[8] for example, advocated the addition of xylose, asparagine, nicotinic acid and pantothenic acid to Snell and Strong's medium, whilst R. D. Greene and A. Black,[9] on the other hand, supplemented the original medium with ammonium sulphate, sodium acetate and photolysed yeast ; with this modified medium, they obtained results in good agreement with those given by the rat growth method. M. Landy and D. M. Dicken [10] evolved a completely new medium, which they used for the assay, not only of riboflavine, but also of pantothenic acid, nicotinic acid, folic acid, pyridoxine and biotin. It was a complex medium, containing casein hydrolysate, sodium acetate, glucose, asparagine, tryptophan, cystine, inorganic salts, guanine, adenine, xanthine and uracil, aneurine, biotin, folic acid, calcium pantothenate, nicotinic acid and pyridoxine. For the assay of other vitamins, riboflavine was included and the particular vitamin being assayed was omitted.

Other workers showed that various substances might interfere with the microbiological estimation of riboflavine, and suggested methods of overcoming the interference. Urea, for instance, inhibits the growth-promoting action of riboflavine,[11] so that to obtain satisfactory assays of urine a correction must be applied for the urea present. Again, starch contains material that stimulates the growth of *L. helveticus*, leading to high results ; to eliminate errors from this cause, preliminary treatment with takadiastase is recommended.[12] E. C. Barton-Wright,[13] however, stated that digestion with acid or ptyalin was preferable to digestion with takadiastase. Another stimulatory substance encountered in extracts of rice bran, wheat bran and whole wheat flour,[14] was not destroyed by takadiastase or papain, and no satisfactory method of eliminating it was discovered. Yet other growth-stimulating substances were reported by Bauernfeind *et al.*[15] in certain foodstuffs ; to eliminate these, the use of clarified aqueous extracts of the solvent-extracted material was recommended. It has also been suggested that a photolysed extract of the product to be assayed might be added to the assay medium, in order to compensate for the additional growth produced by the presence of such impurities. Another stimulatory substance was obtained when certain types of foodstuff were autoclaved at 15 lb. pressure with $0\cdot1$ N hydrochloric acid for 15 minutes ; it was eliminated by adjusting to pH $4\cdot5$ and filtering off the precipitate that formed.[16]

The amount of acid produced by *L. helveticus* was said to be altered by variations in the concentrations of metal ions.[17] Small amounts of certain fatty acids also exerted an inhibitory effect on the organism,[18, 19] whilst other fatty acids had a stimulatory effect.[24] To prevent interference from this source, all materials should be extracted with ether, chloroform or other suitable solvent after hydrolysis. Solvent extraction was also employed in assaying buttermilk.[20] In addition, the casein in the basal medium was replaced by 4 % gelatine plus $0\cdot2$ % of cystine.

An important practical point in carrying out riboflavine assays is that great care must be taken to maintain the temperature of incubation constant; [21] a variation of 4 to 5° C. may cause marked differences in the growth response. The temperature inside some types of bacteriological incubators varies considerably at different points, and these variations may be sufficiently great to give erroneous results with *L. helveticus* and, indeed, with other micro-organisms.

Although the customary method of measuring the growth response of *L. helveticus* is to titrate the lactic acid produced, a method has been proposed in which changes in the pH of the culture were measured and compared with those produced by the addition of known amounts of riboflavine.[22] Another modification of the method utilises the Heatley technique for assaying antibiotics ; the test solution is put in holes cut in an agar plate seeded with *L. helveticus*, and the diameters of the zones of stimulation are measured after incubation of the plates.[23]

In the face of this multiplicity of methods it is difficult to select, with any degree of confidence, the most reliable. E. C. Barton-

Wright [24] recommended the general procedure of Snell and Strong with either of two modified media. For routine work he advocated a relatively simple medium, containing photolysed peptone, cystine, glucose, xylose, riboflavine-free yeast, nicotinic acid, calcium pantothenate and inorganic salts. The second medium, which was claimed to give a steeper standard curve and a slight extension of the assay range, was more complicated, and contained, in addition to the constituents listed above, tryptophan, adenine, guanine, uracil, xanthine, pyridoxine, and p-aminobenzoic acid. In both instances, the growth response was measured by titration of the lactic acid produced.

The use of *Leuconostoc mesenteroides* was advocated by Kornberg *et al.* ; [25] it was said to be sensitive to 0·0001 μg. per ml. of riboflavine as against 0·02 μg. per ml. for *L. helveticus*.

Chemical Assays

Unlike other members of the vitamin B complex, riboflavine solutions are strongly fluorescent, and the intensity of the fluorescence is proportional to the concentration of riboflavine. Assays based on measurement of the fluorescence have been widely used, perhaps more widely than the microbiological method, which is of more recent date. The fluorimetric method appears to have been first used by M. van Eekelen and A. Emmerie,[26] who eliminated interfering substances by oxidation with potassium permanganate (excess of which was removed with hydrogen peroxide), which is without effect on riboflavine. The intensity of the fluorescence of the purified solution was measured in a step-photometer. They found that the riboflavine could be adsorbed on lead sulphide and eluted with pyridine-acetic acid without loss, and in later work this was introduced as an additional purification stage. The fluorometric method was also used by Supplee *et al.*,[27] S. M. Weisberg and I. Levin [28] and A. Z. Hodson and L. C. Norris.[29] The last-named workers reduced all the pigments with sodium dithionite and stannous chloride and then reoxidised the riboflavine by shaking with air ; this procedure did not reoxidise the interfering pigments. The fluorescence of the resulting solution was then measured in a fluorimeter (reading A). A second reading (B) was taken after the addition of a known amount of riboflavine, and a third reading (C) after reduction of the test solution with sodium dithionite. Finally, the reading (D) of a pure solution containing the same amount of riboflavine as that added to the test solution was recorded. The true riboflavine content of the unknown solution was calculated from the expression $(A - C) \times \dfrac{D}{B - A}$.

W. S. Jones and W. Christiansen [30] used a similar method, in which, however, the reduction and re-oxidation steps were omitted ; they employed a fluorophotometer for measuring the fluorescence.

G. E. Shaw [31] used another modification of the fluorimetric method. The alkaline riboflavine solution was irradiated and extracted with chloroform, and the fluorescence of the chloroform extract, which contained the lumiflavine, was then compared with that of a standard solution. A similar method had previously been used, though not very successfully, by Warburg and Christian. A. R. Kemmerer [32] found that the fluorimetric method of Hodson and Norris and the microbiological method of Snell and Strong gave more reliable results than a colorimetric method in which a methanolic solution containing acetic acid was treated with potassium permanganate and then with hydrogen peroxide.

A. E. Schumacher and G. F. Heuser [33] adopted a modification of the Hodson and Norris method, in which the fluorescence was measured after reduction with sodium dithionite solution and again after re-oxidation by air ; the increase in the intensity of the fluorescence was proportional to the riboflavine concentration. The results were in good agreement with those obtained by biological assay, using chicks or rats. Other workers [34, 35, 36] also reported good agreement between the two types of assay, although the fluorimetric method gave unsatisfactory results with skeletal muscle, a blue fluorescent substance being obtained in the digest together with the riboflavine.

A somewhat different modification was used by Rubin et al.[37] In this method, the material was extracted in a Waring blendor, digested with clarase at pH 4·5, treated with potassium permanganate solution at the same pH and then twice reduced with sodium dithionite at pH 4·5, instead of at pH 7·0 to 7·5, and re-oxidised. Good agreement with the microbiological method of assay was obtained.

The fluorimetric method was applied to urine by V. A. Najjar,[38] whose method has been adopted, with minor modifications, by other workers. The urine was acidified with acetic acid and saturated with sodium sulphate. The riboflavine was then extracted with pyridine-butanol, and interfering substances were destroyed by oxidation with potassium permanganate. After decomposing the excess of the latter by treatment with hydrogen peroxide, the fluorescence was measured, and the riboflavine content calculated from a standard curve. Urines low in riboflavine were first treated with lead sulphide to adsorb the riboflavine, which was subsequently eluted with a mixture of water, pyridine and acetic acid.

E. C. Barton-Wright and R. G. Booth [39] adopted Najjar's method for the assay of cereals, but found Super-filtrol to be more satisfactory than lead sulphide for adsorption of the vitamin. M. Swaminathan [40] eliminated interfering substances by precipitation with lead acetate, and then recovered the riboflavine by adsorption on fuller's earth and elution with aqueous alcoholic alkali. The fluorescence was measured after treatment with potassium permanganate solution, and again after destruction of the riboflavine by treatment with hot $0 \cdot 1$ N sodium hydroxide. The value thus obtained was subtracted from the first value, the difference being proportional to the riboflavine concentration.

M. Fujiwara and H. Shimizu [40a] removed fluorescent impurities with a higher adsorption affinity than riboflavine on a column of pyridine-treated zeolite and then adsorbed riboflavine and impurities with the same adsorption affinity on a column of a phenolsulphonic acid resin, KH9, from which the riboflavine was eluted with a mixture of pyridine and acetic acid.

Some inorganic ions were said [41] to have a quenching effect on the fluorescence of riboflavine ; the fluorescence was found to be maximal within the pH range $5 \cdot 9$ to $7 \cdot 7$. E. C. Slater and D. B. Morell [42] modified Najjar's method by introducing an " internal standard " to correct for the quenching of the fluorescence by other constituents of biological extracts and also to check the specificity of the method by exposing test solutions for short controlled periods to sunlight. The rate of photochemical decomposition was dependent on the concentration of unidentified degradation products. Values obtained for urine by this method were in agreement with those obtained by biological assay. The addition of known amounts of riboflavine to test solutions was also used by Scott et al.,[43] who also corrected for the presence of stable fluorescent substances by reducing riboflavine with dithionite, a procedure which Slater and Morell claimed to give high results.

The treatment of biological materials preparatory to fluorimetric assay generally comprises some form of hydrolysis. Meat samples may be digested with clarase [44] or with papain or taka-diastase,[45] and cereals and other starchy foods with acid or taka-diastase.

J. S. Andrews [46] published results obtained in collaborative assays of different flours, including flours fortified with riboflavine. A wide spread was noted in the results reported from different laboratories with both the fluorimetric and microbiological methods of assay. Good recoveries were obtained in both methods, but the absolute values obtained by the microbiological method were higher than those obtained by the fluorimetric method. With enriched flours, direct readings of the fluorescence of the extracts gave results as satisfactory as those obtained when potassium permanganate or Florisil were employed for the removal of impurities.

Riboflavine nucleotides (page 191) can also be estimated fluorimetrically. At high salt concentrations, the dinucleotide has 15 % of the fluorescence of a corresponding amount of free riboflavine, but after hydrolysis in 10 % trichloroacetic acid solution it is converted into the monophosphate which has the same fluorescence as riboflavine.[46a]

Physical Methods

J. J. Lingane and O. L. Davis [47] described a method of assaying riboflavine polarographically. Riboflavine is reduced very readily at the dropping mercury electrode, the optimal pH being 7·2. The potential at the dropping electrode is − 0·47 volt and the diffusion current is proportional to the concentration of riboflavine over the range 2 to 50 p.p.m. Aneurine and nicotinic acid can also be estimated polarographically and, in fact, the three substances can be estimated simultaneously in the same solution, the resulting polarogram exhibiting separate and well-defined waves for each substance. Such a simultaneous assay is best carried out in unbuffered potassium chloride solution as the base solution ; the potential of riboflavine is then − 0·35 volt.

The oxidation-reduction potential of riboflavine was first measured by R. Kuhn and G. Moruzzi.[48] The shape of the titration curve depended on the pH and, according to K. G. Stern,[49] the slope of the curve at pH values between 6·0 and 12·4 corresponded to a two-electron system, and between 4·0 and 1·0 to a one-electron system whilst at 0·4, two maxima appeared, indicating a two-stage process. R. Kuhn and R. Ströbele [50] isolated three coloured intermediates—verdo-, chloro-, and rhodo-flavine—in the conversion of riboflavine to leucoriboflavine (see page 199).

References to Section 7

1. H. von Euler and M. Malmberg, *Z. physiol. Chem.*, 1937, **250**, 158.
2. M. M. El Sadr, T. F. Macrae and C. E. Work, *Biochem. J.*, 1940, **34**, 601.
3. J. R. Wagner, A. E. Axelrod, M. A. Lipton and C. A. Elvehjem, *J. Biol. Chem.*, 1940, **136**, 357.
4. M. F. Clarke, M. Lechycka and C. A. Cook, *J. Nutrition*, 1940, **20**, 133.
5. H. R. Street, *ibid.*, 1941, **22**, 399.
6. T. H. Jukes, *ibid.*, 1937, **14**, 223.
7. E. E. Snell and F. M. Strong, *Ind. Eng. Chem., Anal. Ed.*, 1939, **11**, 346.
8. E. C. Barton-Wright, *Nature*, 1942, **149**, 696 ; E. C. Barton-Wright and R. G. Booth, *Biochem. J.*, 1943, **37**, 25.
9. R. D. Greene and A. Black, *J. Amer. Pharm. Assoc.*, 1943, **32**, 217.
10. M. Landy and D. M. Dicken, *J. Lab. Clin. Med.*, 1942, **27**, 1086.

11. H. Isbell, J. G. Wooley and H. F. Fraser, *U.S. Publ. Health Rep.*, 1941, **56**, 282.
12. M. L. Scott, F. E. Randall and F. H. Hessell, *J. Biol. Chem.*, 1941, **141**, 325.
13. E. C. Barton-Wright, *Nature*, 1942, **149**, 696.
14. M. I. Wegner, A. R. Kemmerer and G. S. Fraps, *J. Biol. Chem.*, 1942, **144**, 731.
15. J. C. Bauernfeind, A. L. Sotier and C. S. Boruff, *Ind. Eng. Chem. Anal. Ed.*, 1942, **14**, 666.
16. M. I. Wegner, A. R. Kemmerer and G. S. Fraps *J. Biol. Chem.*, 1942, **146**, 547.
17. F. W. Chattaway, F. C. Happold and M. Sandford, *Biochem. J.*, 1943, **37**, 298.
18. F. M. Strong and L. E. Carpenter, *Ind. Eng. Chem., Anal. Ed.*, 1942, **14**, 909.
19. E. Kodicek and A. N. Worden, *Biochem. J.*, 1945, **39**, 79.
20. R. A. Sullivan, A. Beatty, E. Bloom and E. Reeves, *Arch. Biochem.*, 1943, **2**, 333.
21. S. A. Price and H. C. H. Graves, *Nature*, 1944, **153**, 461.
22. R. H. Silber and C. W. Mushett, *J. Biol. Chem.*, 1942, **146**, 271.
23. S. A. Price, *Nature*, 1948, **161**, 19.
24. E. C. Barton-Wright, *Analyst*, 1945, **70**, 285 ; *Practical Methods for the Microbiological Assay of the Vitamin B Complex and Essential Amino Acids*, Ashe Laboratories Ltd., London.
25. H. A. Kornberg, R. S. Langdon and V. H. Cheldelin, *Anal. Chem.*, 1948, **20**, 81.
26. M. van Eekelen and A. Emmerie, *Acta Brevia Neerland.*, 1935, **5**, 77 ; 1936, **6**, 136.
27. G. C. Supplee, S. Ansbacher, G. E. Flanigan and Z. M. Hanford, *J. Dairy Sci.*, 1936, **19**, 215.
28. S. M. Weisberg and I. Levin, *Ind. Eng. Chem., Anal. Ed.*, 1937, **9**, 523.
29. A. Z. Hodson and L. C. Norris, *J. Biol. Chem.*, 1939, **131**, 621.
30. W. S. Jones and W. Christiansen, *J. Amer. Pharm. Assoc.*, 1941, **30**, 270.
31. G. E. Shaw, *Pharm. J.*, 1939, **143**, 222.
32. A. R. Kemmerer, *J. Assoc. Off. Agric. Chem.*, 1941, **24**, 413.
33. A. E. Schumacher and G. F. Heuser, *Ind. Eng. Chem., Anal. Ed.*, 1940, **12**, 203.
34. K. M. Henry, J. Houston and S. K. Kon, *Biochem. J.*, 1940, **34**, 601.
35. F. O. Van Duyne, *J. Biol. Chem.*, 1941, **139**, 207.
36. A. D. Emmett, O. D. Bird, R. A. Brown, G. Peacock and J. M. Vandenbelt, *Ind. Eng. Chem., Anal. Ed.*, 1941, **13**, 219.
37. S. H. Rubin, E. de Ritter, R. L. Schuman and J. C. Bauernfeind, *ibid.*, 1945, **17**, 136.
38. V. A. Najjar, *J. Biol. Chem.*, 1941, **141**, 355.
39. E. C. Barton-Wright and R. G. Booth, *Biochem. J.*, 1943, **37**, 25.
40. M. Swaminathan, *Indian J. Med. Res.*, 1942, **30**, 37.

40a. M. Fujiwara and H. Shimizu, *Anal. Chem.*, 1949, **21**, 1009.

41. P. Ellinger and M. Holden, *Biochem. J.*, 1944, **38**, 147.

42. E. C. Slater and D. B. Morell, *ibid.*, 1946, **40**, 644.

43. M. L. Scott, F. W. Hill, L. C. Norris and G. F. Heuser, *J. Biol. Chem.*, 1946, **165**, 65.

44. W. J. Peterson, D. E. Brady and A. O. Shaw, *Ind. Eng. Chem., Anal. Ed.*, 1943, **15**, 634.

45. B. A. McLaren, S. Cover and P. B. Pearson, *Arch. Biochem.*, 1944, **4**, 1.

46. J. S. Andrews, *Cereal Chem.*, 1943, **20**, 613 ; 1944, **21**, 398.

46a. O. A. Bessey, O. H. Lowry and R. H. Love, *J. Biol. Chem.*, 1949, **180**, 755.

47. J. J. Lingane and O. L. Davis, *J. Biol. Chem.*, 1941, **137**, 567.

48. R. Kuhn and G. Moruzzi, *Ber.*, 1934, **67**, 1220.

49. K. G. Stern, *Biochem. J.*, 1934, **28**, 949.

50. R. Kuhn and R. Ströbele, *Ber.*, 1937, **70**, 753.

8. OCCURRENCE OF RIBOFLAVINE IN FOODSTUFFS

The riboflavine contents of a large variety of foodstuffs were listed by M. A. Boas-Fixsen and M. H. Roscoe,[1] and most of the results recorded here are taken from their paper. Wheat (whole) contained 0·02 to 0·17,[2] and wheat germ 0·033 mg. per 100 g. ; barley (unsprouted), 0·01 ; barley (sprouted), 0·10 to 0·22 ; oats, 0·02 ; maize, 0·036 to 0·3 ; rice, 0·04 to 0·05 and sorghum,[3] 0·12 to 0·21 mg. per 100 g. White bread contained 0·03 to 0·076 mg. per 100 g., and bread from 98 % extraction flour, 0·25 mg. per 100 g.[4]

The riboflavine content of flour increased three-fold when the extraction was increased from the value of 73 %, corresponding to white flour, to 85 %, corresponding to National wheat-meal flour.[5] Wheat germ contained more than three times and bran twice as much riboflavine as did wholemeal. Riboflavine was present throughout the embryo, the aleurone layer and the bran of the wheat berry.[6]

Fruits contained the following amounts of riboflavine : apple, 0·005 to 0·03 ; banana, 0·0075 to 0·048 ; date, 0·03 ; fig, 0·052 ; grape, 0·005 ; grape-fruit, 0·024 ; orange (juice), 0·007 to 0·059 ; peach, 0·007 ; pear, 0·007 to 0·03 ; pineapple, 0·013 to 0·13 ; and plum, 0·025 mg. per 100 g.

Cocoanut contained 0·10 ; pecan, 0·1 to 0·3 ; cashew, 0·19 and peanut, 0·17 to 0·75 mg. per 100 g.[7]

The following values were reported for a variety of vegetables : French bean, 0·03 to 0·566 ; soya bean, 0·16 to 0·32 ; beetroot, 0·085 ; cabbage, 0·03 to 0·215 ; carrot, 0·02 ; cauliflower, 0·08 ; chicory, 0·02 to 0·03 ; cucumber, 0·004 ; lentil, 0·068 ; lettuce, 0·03 to 0·116 ;

onion, 0·005 to 0·015 ; pea (fresh), 0·01 to 0·28 ; potato, 0·0075 to 0·2 ; radish, 0·02 ; spinach, 0·057 to 0·089 ; tomato, 0·05 to 0·236 ; and turnip, 0·04 mg. per 100 g.

The effect of storage and cooking on the riboflavine content of vegetables was studied with spinach and asparagus.[8] The amounts present in the fresh materials were 0·21 and 0·32 mg. per 100 g. respectively. On storage for twenty-four hours at 18·8 to 25·5° C., the loss of potency was only 5 and 22 % respectively and, on storage for one week at 0 to 4·4° C., only 17 and 27 %. The losses on freezing, however, were 40 and 42 % respectively. From 52 to 91 % of the riboflavine was retained on cooking. Cabbage lost little of its riboflavine content on dehydration with or without sulphiting, and the loss on cooking was 20 to 40 % ; a similar loss occurred on cooking potatoes.[9]

Cow's milk contained 0·027 to 0·3 mg. per 100 ml., most recorded values being between 0·1 and 0·15 ; colostrum contained 0·6 mg. per 100 ml.[10] A decrease in the riboflavine content of milk from 0·18 to 0·13 mg. per 100 ml. occurred when cows were transferred from pasture to artificial feeds.[11] Pasteurising at 143 to 145° F. for thirty minutes scarcely affected the riboflavine content of milk.[12] Dried whole milk contained somewhat larger amounts of riboflavine when prepared by spray drying (1·54 mg. per 100 g.) than when prepared by roller-drying (1·48 mg. per 100 g.).[13] A similar relationship existed between the two types of dried skim milk, which contained 1·98 and 1·88 mg. per 100 g. respectively.

Ewe's colostrum and milk contained 2·0 and 0·44 mg. per 100 ml. respectively.[10]

Butter contained 0·008 and cheese 0·12 to 0·8 mg. per 100 g.[14] The older values recorded for eggs were : yolk, 0·5 to 0·6 and white, 0·4 to 0·5 mg. per 100 g., whereas lower values were obtained more recently,[15] namely : yolk, 0·24 to 0·4 and white, 0·19 to 0·29 mg. per 100 g.

Fish muscle contained relatively large amounts of riboflavine, ranging from 0·046 to 0·31 for cod ; 0·1 to 0·4 for herring ; and averaging 0·2 for flounder ; 0·165 for haddock ; 0·185 for halibut ; and 0·66 mg. per 100 g. for mackerel. Hard roe was much richer in riboflavine than was muscle from the same species of fish, with one exception, the following values being recorded : cod, 0·7 to 1·13 ; flounder, 0·48 to 0·57 ; haddock, 1·42 ; and mackerel, 1·14 mg. per 100 g. Herring roe, however, contained only 0·385 mg. per 100 g. Soft roe was generally a poorer source of riboflavine than hard roe.

Some crustaceans were found to contain relatively enormous amounts of riboflavine, and some of the tissues from certain crabs are among the richest known sources.[16] The antennary glands of certain melanin-containing crabs, for example, contained 1·4 to 27·5 mg. per 100 g., and the dorsal subcutaneous tissue 2·4 to 3·05 mg. per 100 g. The eye, on the other hand, which, from the association between ariboflavinosis and eye lesions in mammals, might have been expected to be a particularly good source of the vitamin, contained only 0·1 to 0·7 mg. per 100 g.

There appears to be a close connection between the occurrence in tissues of melanin and riboflavine, the above high values being observed only with crustaceans that were heavily pigmented. Species containing no melanin generally contained no riboflavine ; riboflavine was also found to be absent from the skin of albino animals. In the lower vertebrates, on the other hand, the melanocyte was very rich in riboflavine, reaching a value of 10 mg. per 100 g. in tissue from batrachians. Among higher vertebrates, however, including man, the riboflavine content of the melanocyte was very low, not exceeding 0·2 mg. per 100 g. of tissue.

The following values were recorded for different kinds of meat : beef, 0·04 to 0·35 ; pork,[17] 0·09 to 0·35 ; rabbit, 0·06 to 1·2 ; mutton, 0·27 ; and chicken,[18] 0·05 to 0·35 mg. per 100 g. Ox kidney contained 0·8 to 2·0 ; ox liver, 0·1 to 3·0 ; pig liver,[17] 4·4 ; and sheep's liver, 1·7 mg. per 100 g.

In general, the liver and kidney of the pig, ox, calf and lamb were richer than other organs and tissues [19] in riboflavine. The liver, heart and gizzard of the chicken were likewise richer than the leg or heart muscle.[20]

Beef extracts contained the bulk of the riboflavine originally present in the fresh meat, five commercial samples containing 1·5 to 2·6 mg. per 100 g., so that a breakfast-cup made with a teaspoonful of extract would supply up to 0·25 mg. of riboflavine. Corned beef was correspondingly poorer in this factor, containing 0·07 to 0·18 mg. per 100 g., that is, about one-fifth of the quantity present in roast beef.[21]

Dried yeast is, next to crustacean tissue, the richest known edible source of riboflavine, values up to 12·4 mg. per 100 g. being recorded. Brewers' yeast was richer than bakers' yeast, and *Torula* richer than brewers' yeast, which generally contained about 5 mg. per 100 g.[22] The riboflavine in live yeast was not available, however, for animal or human nutrition and only partial absorption of riboflavine took place from two dried yeasts containing living cells.[23] Heating rendered the riboflavine available.

Many other fungi were relatively rich in riboflavine,[24] containing up to 0·69 mg. per 100 g. *Eremothecium Ashbyii* (see page 150) contained considerably more than any other micro-organism tested, values up to 264 mg. per 100 g. of the moist material being recorded ; [25] it is probably the richest of all known sources.

Tea contained about 0·9 mg. of riboflavine per 100 g. and the whole of this passed into the infusion as ordinarily prepared.[26] Maté leaves contained a similar amount.[27] Beers contained 0·5 to 1·45 µg. of riboflavine per 100 ml. per degree of original gravity, the actual value depending on the type of beer.[28] A substantial proportion of the riboflavine present in the malt was extracted during the mashing process, and this was augmented during fermentation by the transfer of riboflavine from the yeast, which synthesises it, into the beer.

Honey, pollen and royal jelly contained 0·026, 1·7 and 2·8 mg. of riboflavine per 100 g. respectively.[29]

References to Section 8

1. M. A. Boas-Fixsen and M. H. Roscoe, *Nutr. Absts.*, 1937-38, **7**, 843 ; 1939-40, **9**, 820.
2. R. A. McCance, E. M. Widdowson, T. Moran, W. J. S. Pringle and T. F. Macrae, *Biochem. J.*, 1945, **30**, 13.
3. G. Knox, V. G. Heller and J. B. Sieglinger, *Food Res.*, 1944, **9**, 89.
4. R. R. Sealock and A. H. Livermore, *J. Nutrition*, 1943, **25**, 265.
5. A. M. Copping, *Biochem. J.*, 1943, **37**, 12.
6. G. F. Somers, M. H. Coolidge and K. C. Hamner, *Cereal Chem.*, 1945, **26**, 333.
7. R. Melville, *Chem. and Ind.*, 1947, 304.
8. E. Gleim, D. K. Tressler and F. Fenton, *Food Res.*, 1944, **9**, 471.
9. E. Gleim, M. Albury, J. R. McCartney, K. Visnyei and F. Fenton, *ibid.*, 1946, **11**, 461 ; F. Fenton, E. Gleim, M. Albury, J. R. McCartney and K. Visnyei, *ibid.*, 468 ; F. Fenton, E. Gleim, A. Arnason, J. F. Thompson, M. Albury and M. Phillips, *ibid.*, 475.
10. P. B. Pearson and A. L. Darnell, *J. Nutrition*, 1946, **31**, 51.
11. P. Johnson, L. A. Maynard and J. K. Loosli, *J. Dairy Sci.*, 1941, **24**, 57.
12. A. D. Holmes, C. P. Jones, A. W. Wertz and J. W. Kuzmeski, *J. Nutrition*, 1943, **26**, 337.
13. L. J. Daniel and L. C. Norris, *Food Res.*, 1944, **9**, 312.
14. R. A. Sullivan, E. Bloom and J. Jarmol, *J. Nutrition*, 1943, **25**, 463.
15. L. C. Norris and J. C. Bauernfeind, *Food Res.*, 1940, **5**, 521 ; W. J. Peterson, R. S. Dearslyne, R. E. Comstock and V. Weldon, *Ind. Eng. Chem., Anal. Ed.*, 1945, **17**, 370.
16. R. G. Busnel, *Compt. rend.*, 1942, **214**, 189 ; 1943, **216**, 85, 162.
17. R. C. Miller, J. W. Pence, R. A. Dutcher, P. T. Ziegler and M. A. McCarty, *J. Nutrition*, 1943, **26**, 261.
18. E. E. Rice, E. J. Strandine, E. M. Squires and B. Lyddon, *Arch. Biochem.*, 1946, **10**, 251.
19. O. Mickelsen, H. A. Waisman and C. A. Elvehjem, *J. Nutrition*, 1939, **18**, 517.
20. A. Z. Hodson, *ibid.*, 1940, **20**, 377.

21. R. G. Booth and E. C. Barton-Wright, *Lancet*, 1944, **1**, 585.
22. M. Swaminathan, *Indian J. Med. Res.*, 1942, **30**, 409.
23. E. L. Price, M. M. Marquette and H. T. Parsons, *J. Nutrition*, 1947, **34**, 311.
24. H. Willstaedt, *Svensk. Kem. Tidskr.*, 1941, **53**, 23.
25. M. Kasahara and I. Gammo, *Klin. Woch.*, 1942, **21**, 348.
26. E. A. M. Bradford and E. B. Hughes, *Analyst*, 1945, **70**, 2.
27. J. M. Chaves, *Rev. Alimenta*, 1944, **8**, 173.
28. R. H. Hopkins and S. Wiener, *J. Inst. Brew.*, 1945, **51**, 34 ; J. W. Tullo and W. J. Stringer, *ibid.*, 86.
29. G. Kitzes, H. A. Schuette and C. A. Elvehjem, *J. Nutrition*, 1943, **26**, 241.

9. EFFECT OF RIBOFLAVINE DEFICIENCY IN ANIMALS

Attention has already been drawn to the confusion that existed, prior to its recognition as a complex, concerning the effect of vitamin B deficiency on different species of animals. Rats, for example, showed two well-defined deficiency symptoms—failure to grow and a form of dermatitis—and it was not immediately realised that each of these was due in the main to a different vitamin. Then, too, the factor that cured these symptoms in rats was at first assumed to be identical with the substance that cured blacktongue in dogs, on the one hand, and a form of dermatitis in chickens on the other. Not until pure riboflavine became available was it possible to describe the symptoms attributable solely to a deficiency of riboflavine.

Effect in Rats

The most complete information is available in respect of the rat. The most obvious effect, and the one long used for assaying riboflavine, is failure of the animals to grow. According to B. Sure,[1] riboflavine-deficient rats showed a gain in weight of only 6 g. in 125 days, compared with a gain of 61 g. in similar animals receiving 20 μg. of riboflavine per day. Unlike aneurine-deficient rats, riboflavine-deficient rats did not develop anorexia. The second symptom characteristic of riboflavine deficiency was an effect on the skin, animals exhibiting rough hair or loss of hair (alopecia), together with dermatitis in the denuded areas of the skin.[1,2] A third result of riboflavine deficiency in rats was a syndrome comprising conjunctivitis, blepharitis, diffuse corneal opacity and vascularisation of the cornea followed, as the deficiency progressed, by corneal infiltration and corneal ulcers ;[1] all these symptoms disappeared on treatment with pure riboflavine. Formerly it was believed that cataract was also a result of riboflavine deficiency, but this condition was not cured by pure riboflavine, and, moreover, rats on a diet completely free from riboflavine, and containing other members of the vitamin B complex, did not develop cataract.[3] Only when rats were fed on a diet containing suboptimal amounts of riboflavine, such as the Bourquin-Sherman diet, which supplies an average of 0·5 μg. of riboflavine per day, did they exhibit a high incidence of cataract. Thus, whereas corneal opacity and vascularisation [4] invariably resulted from a complete absence of the vitamin, cataract formation only occurred with diets containing small amounts of riboflavine.

Changes in riboflavine intake were promptly reflected by changes in its concentration in the cornea.[5] Intense visible or ultra-violet light had no effect on the riboflavine concentration, and it was suggested that this rather unexpected insensitivity to light might be due to a combination of the flavine with an acceptor.

Other symptoms associated with a severe deficiency of riboflavine were a partial paralysis of the legs due to myelin degeneration of the muscle sheaths, atrophy of the testes, early involution of the thymus gland and structural alterations in the thyroid and adrenal glands.[6]

Prolonged deficiency of riboflavine also led [4] to neurological abnormalities, such as loss of reflexes, myelin degeneration of peripheral nerves and the posterior column of the spinal cord.

Leucopenia, with both a relative and an absolute decrease in the number of lymphocytes, appeared to be an early sign of ariboflavinosis, and, in rats, occurred prior to changes in the lens and cornea of the eye.[7] Granulocytopenia was also observed [8] in rats maintained on a purified diet deficient in riboflavine, but it was cured by folic acid (see page 489) and not by riboflavine. An anaemia observed in some of the animals was partially relieved by riboflavine but was not affected by folic acid.

At low oxygen tensions, the liver glycogen of riboflavine-deficient rats was not increased to the same degree as in normal rats, and the deficient animals had a lower blood-sugar when fasted at sea-level than had normal animals ; the riboflavine content of the liver depended on the riboflavine intake.[9] L-Cystine, DL-tryptophan, L-tyrosine, L-histidine, glycine and D-glutamic acid were more toxic to riboflavine-deficient rats than to adequately nourished animals.[10]

Effect in other Mammals

The effects of riboflavine deficiency in mice were very similar to the effects in rats, and were characterised by dermatitis, myelin degeneration and keratitis.[11] Pigs on a riboflavine-deficient diet failed to grow at the normal rate,[12, 13] the hair became rough, dry and thin, whilst mottled erythematous eruptions developed on the skin, accompanied by scaling and ulceration. The lens of the eye became opaque, and cataracts were frequently formed. The animals developed hypoglycaemia and a normocytic anaemia, and acquired an abnormal gait. At autopsy, changes in the corneal epithelium were observed, together with microscopic haemorrhages in the adrenals, and lipoid degeneration of the proximal tubules.

A similar picture was observed in riboflavine-deficient dogs, which lost weight, developed dermatitis, conjunctivitis, vascularisation and opacity of the cornea, and muscular weakness in the hind quarters.[14] Some of the dogs exhibited fatty liver, a condition more generally associated with choline deficiency (see page 590), and tachycardia. They also developed a microcytic, hypochromic anaemia.

Riboflavine has also been shown to be essential for foxes,[15] in which the deficiency symptoms resemble those in the dog, and for horses [16] and monkeys.[17] Rhesus monkeys on a riboflavine-deficient diet developed a dermatitis on the face, hands, legs and groin, together with a hypochromic, normocytic anaemia ; in addition, they exhibited muscular inco-ordination. Some of the monkeys also developed fatty livers, and these were not due to inanition. Riboflavine was also shown to be essential for the cow, although adequate amounts are generally provided by bacterial synthesis in the rumen or intestine (see page 183). Symptoms of riboflavine deficiency have, however, been observed in the calf ; [18] these included hyperaemia of the buccal mucosa, lesions of the cornea, of the mouth along the edges of the lips, and around the navel; loss of appetite, poor growth, scours, excess salivation and lachrymation, and loss of hair. No vascularisation of the cornea or opacity of the lens was observed.

Effect in Birds and Fish

Little has been reported concerning the effect of riboflavine deficiency in birds. Riboflavine is known to be necessary for the growth of chickens,[19] ducklings [20] and turkey poults ; [21] in its absence, chickens developed " curled-toe paralysis ", whilst young turkeys grew slowly and developed dermatitis. The hatchability of hen eggs appeared to depend on the amount of riboflavine present in the diet, eggs laid by riboflavine-deficient hens showing a high embryo mortality.[22]

On a riboflavine-deficient diet, young rainbow trout (*Salmo gairdnerii irideus*) developed haemorrhagic eyes, livers, nose and operculum, together with an anaemia, which was partially cured by riboflavine, pyridoxine and choline and completely cured by whole liver.[23]

Riboflavine and Cancer

Cancer tissue contained amounts of riboflavine similar to those present in brain, lung, spleen and muscle.[24] The absence of riboflavine from the diet of C_3H mice reduced the growth rate of spontaneous mammary tumours as well as the growth rate of the animal whilst the addition of riboflavine to the diet increased the average number of tumours per mouse.[25] Complete regression of lymphosarcoma implants followed the temporary induction of riboflavine deficiency in mice.[25a]

When certain carcinogenic dyes were added to the diet of rats, the riboflavine content of the liver decreased, the decrease being approximately proportional to the carcinogenicity.[26] *m'*-Methyl-*p*-dimethylaminoazobenzene was the most effective of the compounds tested. More riboflavine was stored in the liver when the basal diet contained 24 % of casein than with 12 %, but the relative effects of the carcinogens was the same on either diet. Although the food intake was reduced when the azo dyes were fed, this was not responsible for the change in vitamin storage. Limitation of the riboflavine intake reduced the ability of rat liver slices to destroy NN-dimethyl-*p*-aminoazobenzene.[26a]

Effect on Infected Animals

The effect of riboflavine deficiency on the resistance of experimental animals to infection varied according to the nature of the invading organisms. For example, mice fed a diet deficient in riboflavine were said to be more susceptible then normal mice to *Pneumococcus* Type I.[27] A similar result was obtained with aneurine-deficient animals, and the effect was shown not to be due to the restricted food-intake. On the other hand, treatment with riboflavine or aneurine at the time of infection did not appear to affect the mortality rate.

Riboflavine-deficient mice were also said to be more susceptible than normal mice to a spontaneous *Salmonella* infection,[28] whereas they were apparently less susceptible than normal mice to the Lansing strain of the influenza virus.[29] Similarly, riboflavine-deficient chicks exhibited less severe symptoms when infected with *Plasmodium lophurae* than did normal chicks, and the severity of the disease appeared to increase on administration of riboflavine.[30] Finally a deficiency of riboflavine (or aneurine) reduced the resistance of rats to infection by the worm, *Nippostrongylus muris*, and plasma from riboflavine- (or aneurine-) deficient animals was less effective than immune sera from normal animals in combating the infection.[31]

The absence of any clear-cut connection between the susceptibility of animals to infection and the vitamin B content of the diet may be disappointing, but is hardly surprising. As will be seen subsequently (see page 203) riboflavine, like aneurine, is a growth factor for micro-organisms as well as for animals, and it is to be expected, therefore, that ingested riboflavine would stimulate the growth of the invading organisms to a similar or even greater extent than it benefits the host. It might well be imagined, for example, that, where either the invading organism does not require the particular growth factor or this is not available to it, administration of a vitamin or mixture of vitamins might help the host to resist infection, whereas in other instances the beneficial effect on the host might be counter-balanced by the stimulatory effect of the supplement on the micro-organism. This, it is suggested, is the explanation of the variable effect of aneurine and riboflavine on animals infected with different parasites.

References to Section 9

1. B. Sure, *J. Nutrition*, 1941, **22**, 295.
2. H. Chick, T. F. Macrae and A. N. Worden, *Biochem. J.*, 1940, **34**, 580.
3. H. M. Baum, J. F. Michaelree and E. B. Brown, *Science*, 1942, **95**, 24.
4. H. R. Street, G. R. Cowgill and H. M. Zimmerman, *J. Nutrition*, 1941, **22**, 7.
5. O. A. Bessey and O. H. Lowry, *J. Biol. Chem.*, 1944, **155**, 635.
6. J. H. Shaw and P. H. Phillips, *J. Nutrition*, 1941, **22**, 345.
7. C. F. Shukers and P. L. Day, *ibid.*, 1943, **25**, 511.
8. A. Kornberg, F. S. Daft and W. H. Sebrell, *Arch. Biochem.*, 1945, **8**, 431.
9. M. E. Wickson and A. F. Morgan, *J. Biol. Chem.*, 1946, **162**, 209.
10. G. J. Martin, *Proc. Soc. Exp. Biol. Med.*, 1946, **62**, 528.
11. S. W. Lippincott and H. P. Morris, *J. Nat. Cancer Inst.*, 1942, **2**, 601.
12. A. J. Patek, J. Post and J. Victor, *Amer. J. Physiol.*, 1941, **133**, 47.
13. M. M. Wintrobe, W. H. Buschke, R. H. Follis and S. Humphreys, *Johns Hopkins Hosp. Bull.*, 1944, **25**, 102.
14. R. L. Potter, A. E. Axelrod and C. A. Elvehjem, *J. Nutrition*, 1942, **24**, 449; H. Spector, A. R. Maass, L. Michaud, C. A. Elvehjem and E. B. Hart, *J. Biol. Chem.*, 1943, **150**, 75.
15. A. E. Schaefer, C. K. Whitehair and C. A. Elvehjem, *J. Nutrition*, 1947, **34**, 131.
16. P. B. Pearson, M. K. Sheybani and H. Schmidt, *Arch. Biochem.*, 1944, **3**, 467.
17. H. A. Waisman, *Proc. Soc. Exp. Biol. Med.*, 1944, **55**, 69; J. M. Cooperman, H. A. Waisman, K. B. McCall and C. A. Elvehjem, *J. Nutrition*, 1945, **30**, 45.
18. A. C. Wiese, B. C. Johnson, H. H. Mitchell and W. B. Nevens, *ibid.*, 1947, **33**, 263.

19. W. Bolton, *J. Agric. Sci.*, 1944, **34**, 198.

20. J. C. Fritz, W. Archer and D. Barker, *Poultry Sci.*, 1939, **18**, 449.

21. T. H. Jukes, E. L. R. Stokstad and M. Belt, *J. Nutrition*, 1947, **33**, 1.

22. C. H. Hunt, A. R. Winter and R. M. Bethke, *Poultry Sci.*, 1939, **18**, 330 ; A. E. Schumacher and G. F. Heuser, *ibid.*, 369 ; A. L. Romanoff and J. C. Bauernfeind, *Anat. Rec.*, 1942, **82**, 11.

23. B. A. McLaren, E. F. Herman and C. A. Elvehjem, *Arch. Biochem.*, 1946, **10**, 453 ; B. A. McLaren, E. Keller, D. J. O'Donnell and C. A. Elvehjem, *ibid.*, 1947, **15**, 169.

24. M. A. Pollack, A. Taylor, J. Taylor and R. J. Williams, *Cancer Res.*, 1942, **2**, 739.

25. H. P. Morris and W. van B. Robertson, *J. Nat. Cancer Inst.*, 1943, **3**, 479.

25a. H. C. Stoerk and G. A. Emerson, *Proc. Soc. Exp. Biol. Med.*, 1949, **70**, 703.

26. A. C. Griffin and C. A. Baumann, *Arch. Biochem.*, 1946, **11**, 467.

26a. C. J. Kensler, *J. Biol. Chem.*, 1949, **179**, 1079.

27. J. G. Wooley and W. H. Sebrell, *U.S. Publ. Health Rep.*, 1942, **57**, 149.

28. I. J. Kligler, K. Guggenheim and E. Buechler, *Proc. Soc. Exp. Biol. Med.*, 1944, **57**, 132.

29. A. F. Rasmussen, H. A. Waisman and H. C. Lichstein, *ibid.*, 92.

30. A. O. Seeler and W. H. Ott, *J. Infect. Dis.*, 1944, **75**, 175.

31. J. Y. C. Watt, *J. Hygiene*, 1944, **39**, 145.

10. EFFECT OF RIBOFLAVINE DEFICIENCY IN MAN

The results of riboflavine deficiency in man conform to the general pattern observed with experimental animals, and the most characteristic symptoms are eye lesions and skin lesions. There is, however, no unanimity amongst clinical workers as to which of the several individual lesions are due to the absence of riboflavine or of other members of the vitamin B complex. Indeed the clinical manifestations of riboflavine deficiency are less clearly defined than those associated with a deficiency of aneurine or of nicotinic acid, and appear to overlap to some extent with other deficiency symptoms, particularly with those of nicotinic acid deficiency.

Whilst it is possible that a pure riboflavine deficiency, uncomplicated by other vitamin deficiencies, may exist, it is more probable that it generally occurs as part of a multiple vitamin B deficiency, which can only be treated successfully with a mixture of factors, including riboflavine. Thus, for example, Vilter *et al.*[1] obtained beneficial effects by treatment with riboflavine of pellagrins whose skin lesions had been cured by nicotinic acid but who still had vague symptoms of ill-health.

Skin Lesions

W. H. Sebrell and R. E. Butler [2] appear to have been the first to study artificial riboflavine deficiency in man ; they found that ten out of eighteen women developed lesions in the angles of the mouth, described as cheilosis, whilst the mucosa of the lips became red and shiny and seborrhoeic accumulations appeared on the face. The symptoms were cured by riboflavine but not by nicotinamide. Volunteers maintained for nine to seventeen months on a diet which supplied only 0·55 mg. of riboflavine per 2200 cals. developed angular stomatitis, seborrhoeic dermatitis, scrotal skin lesions and also diminished ability to perceive flicker.[2a] V. P. Sydenstricker et al.[3] relieved cheilosis in five patients by treatment with riboflavine, nicotinic acid being ineffective.

V. P. Sydenstricker,[4] in fact, regarded cheilosis and glossitis as diagnostic of riboflavine deficiency, although these symptoms were often preceded or followed by seborrhoeic lesions of the ear, nose and forehead. The skin lesions, as well as the eye lesions, might yield *Staphylococcus aureus* or *Streptococcus haemolyticus* on culture, but the organisms disappeared after administration of riboflavine.[5] Cheilosis and seborrhoeic filiform excrescences on the face were observed in badly-nourished Chinese and cleared up on treatment with riboflavine.[6] Cheilosis was also noted as a usual symptom of riboflavine deficiency in infants and children in districts of Alabama, U.S.A.[7] The children of mothers given riboflavine during pregnancy and lactation showed no symptoms of riboflavine deficiency.

T. E. Machella,[8] on the other hand, claimed that cheilosis was not an essential manifestation of riboflavine deficiency, for he observed a number of cases of apparent ariboflavinosis, with lesions of the lips, cornea and tongue, in which the cheilosis failed to respond to treatment with riboflavine. Some of the cases responded to pyridoxine and nicotinic acid, and others to ascorbic acid. One of the few conditions that can be ascribed mainly to riboflavine deficiency is kwashiorkor,[9] which occurs in West Africa. The clinical response to riboflavine administration in this condition was, however, confined to the healing of epithelial lesions of the tongue, lips and external genitalia, the mortality being unaffected. The condition is regarded as due to riboflavine deficiency complicated by intercurrent disease and general inanition.

Ocular Lesions

According to V. P. Sydenstricker,[10] lesions of the eye due to riboflavine deficiency in man may take the form of photophobia and dimness of vision at a distance or in poor light with, as one of the earliest symptoms, a superficial vascularisation of the cornea progressing to severe interstitial keratitis. Rosacea keratitis was said to be improved by treatment with riboflavine. Similar ocular lesions were reported by H. C. Hou,[11] by Spies et al.[7, 12] and by K. W. Cosgrove and P. L. Day.[13] Spies et al.[12] treated patients who developed ocular disease on diets deficient in riboflavine with intravenous injections of ribo-flavine. Within forty-eight hours, there was subjective improvement in all cases, with a decrease in the ocular vasodilatation, the photo-phobia, and the corneal ulceration. The number of haemolytic staphylococci, streptococci and xerosis bacilli in the exudate from the eyes decreased. Although many of the patients had irreparable eye damage, pain was relieved and vision was improved.

According to M. K. Gregory,[14] riboflavine deficiency was characterised by superficial invasion of the cornea by fine capillaries arising from the apices of the marginal loops, whilst I. Mann [15] observed that an early sign of ariboflavinosis was the budding of new capillaries from the apices of limbal loops with extensions on to the true cornea. These were generally present around the whole circumference of the cornea in both eyes, and should disappear after giving riboflavine.

There appears to be considerable doubt as to the value of corneal vascularisation as a diagnostic criterion of ariboflavinosis. H. R. Sandstead [16] and L. Lehrfeld,[17] for example, remarked that not all types of corneal vascularisation could be cured by riboflavine, whilst H. Scarborough [18] showed that riboflavine had no effect on circum-corneal injection, which is therefore not diagnostic of ariboflavinosis. W. M. Fish [19] showed that the corneal vascularisation in acne rosacea was different from that in riboflavine deficiency and did not respond to riboflavine. Tisdall et al.,[20] however, observed that the incidence of corneal vascularisation in Royal Canadian Air Force personnel was high, and varied with the riboflavine content of the diet ; moreover, a proportion of the cases responded with decreased vascularisation on administration of large doses of riboflavine. On the other hand, no change in corneal vascularisation occurred with different levels of riboflavine in the diet. Similar results were obtained with Royal Air Force personnel,[21] many of whom had corneal vascularisation in spite of receiving a satisfactory diet, nor was the condition always improved by giving additional riboflavine. Similarly, corneal vascularisation was observed in a high proportion of patients,[22] but only in a small number of the cases did the condition appear to be due to riboflavine deficiency and not all of these were cured by riboflavine. It therefore appears that corneal vascularisation is often, but by no means always, associated with riboflavine deficiency, and may sometimes be improved by riboflavine, although it frequently requires an additional factor.

Vernal conjunctivitis is the name given to a form of conjunctivitis associated with the hot season in the tropics ; it was benefited by administration of riboflavine. L. Castellanos [23] suggested that the condition was due to riboflavine deficiency caused by the more rapid destruction of the vitamin by ultra-violet light or by the greater demand for the vitamin in the hot season.

Other Conditions

Riboflavine deficiency often accompanies sprue and steatorrhoea ; on giving riboflavine, the steatorrhoea disappeared and riboflavine was excreted in the urine.[24] Riboflavine deficiency can also be caused by a lack of balance in the vitamin intake, even when the riboflavine intake is relatively high.[25] It may also be produced by an excessive metabolic demand, as in pregnancy. Of 900 pregnant women examined in Palestine, for instance, 190 had glossitis and heartburn during the last trimester, the symptoms clearing up, without treatment, after delivery.[26]

References to Section 10

1. R. W. Vilter, S. P. Vilter and T. D. Spies, *J. Amer. Med. Assoc.*, 1939, **112,** 420.
2. W. H. Sebrell and R. E. Butler, *U.S. Publ. Health Rep.*, 1938, **53,** 2282.
2a. M. K. Horwitt, O. W. Hills, C. C. Harvey, E. Liebert and D. L. Steinberg, *J. Nutrition*, 1949, **39,** 357.
3. V. P. Sydenstricker, L. E. Geeslin, C. M. Templeton and J. W. Weaver, *J. Amer. Med. Assoc.*, 1939, **113,** 1697.
4. V. P. Sydenstricker, *Ann. Int. Med.*, 1941, **14,** 1499 ; *Amer. J. Publ. Health*, 1941, **31,** 344.
5. J. W. Riddle, T. D. Spies and N. P. Hudson, *Proc. Soc. Exp. Biol. Med.*, 1940, **45,** 361.
6. H. C. Hou, *Chinese Med. J.*, 1941, **59,** 324.
7. T. D. Spies, W. B. Bean, R. W. Vilter and N. E. Huff, *Amer. J. Med. Sci.*, 1941, **200,** 697.
8. T. E. Machella, *ibid.*, 1942, **203,** 114 ; T. E. Machella and P. R. McDonald, *ibid.*, 1943, **205,** 214.
9. W. Hughes, *Trans. Roy. Soc. Trop. Med.*, 1946, **39,** 437.
10. V. P. Sydenstricker, *Amer. J. Publ. Health*, 1941, **31,** 344 ; V. P. Sydenstricker, W. H. Sebrell, R. M. Cleckley and H. D. Kruse, *J. Amer. Med. Assoc.*, 1940, **114,** 2437 ; H. D. Kruse, V. P. Sydenstricker, W. H. Sebrell and H. M. Cleckley, *U.S. Publ. Health Rep.*, 1940, **55,** 157.
11. H. C. Hou, *Chinese Med. J.*, 1940, **58,** 616.
12. T. D. Spies, D. J. Perry, R. C. Gogswell and W. B. Frommeyer, *J. Lab. Clin. Med.*, 1945, **30,** 751.

13. K. W. Cosgrove and P. L. Day, *Amer. J. Ophthal.*, 1942, **25**, 544.
14. M. K. Gregory, *Brit. Med. J.*, 1943, **2**, 134.
15. I. Mann, *Amer. J. Ophthal.*, 1945, **28**, 243.
16. H. R. Sandstead, *U.S. Publ. Health Rep.*, 1942, **57**, 1821.
17. L. Lehrfeld, *Arch. Ophthal.*, 1944, **31**, 557.
18. H. Scarborough, *Brit. Med. J.*, 1942, **2**, 601.
19. W. M. Fish, *Brit. J. Ophthal.*, 1943, **27**, 107 ; *Amer. J. Ophthal.*, 1944, **27**, 354.
20. F. F. Tisdall, J. F. McCreary and H. Pearce, *Canad. Med. Assoc. J.*, 1943, **49**, 5 ; J. F. McCreary, J. V. V. Nicholls and F. F. Tisdall, *ibid.*, 1944, **51**, 206.
21. T. K. Lyle, T. F. Macrae and P. A. Gardiner, *Lancet*, 1944, **1**, 393.
22. W. J. Wellwood-Ferguson, *ibid.*, 431.
23. L. Castellanos, *Arch. Ophthal.*, 1944, **31**, 214.
24. R. Antognini, *Schweiz. med. Woch.*, 1941, **71**, 510.
25. I. J. Boerer, C. E. Stanford and E. Ryan, *Amer. J. Med. Sci.*, 1943, **205**, 544.
26. K. Braun, Y. M. Bromberg and A. Brzezinski, *J. Obstet. Gynec.*, 1945, **52**, 43.

11. METABOLISM OF RIBOFLAVINE

Concentration of Riboflavine in Blood

The blood of man, the rat and the calf were reported [1] to contain 0·5 μg. of riboflavine per ml., and that of the dog and pig 1·0 μg. per ml. The microbiological assay method of Snell and Strong was used. No attempt appears to have been made to use blood concentrations for assessing the nutritional status of animals or human subjects with respect to riboflavine such as were made with aneurine. Indeed, it has been said that there is no relation between blood concentration and dietary intake in the horse.[2]

Urinary Excretion of Riboflavine

Riboflavine-deficient dogs and rats excreted less riboflavine in the urine than did animals fed a normal diet.[3] The fall in excretion was observed before the other symptoms of riboflavine deficiency appeared. Riboflavine can be estimated in urine either by the microbiological method, using *L. helveticus*,[3] or fluorimetrically [4] (see page 157). When the former method is used, a correction must be applied to compensate for the effect of urea, the presence of which tends to suppress the growth of the organism.[5]

A relationship has been shown to exist between the urinary excretion and the dietary intake of riboflavine in many species of animals, including man, but the relationship does not appear to be as simple as with some other members of the vitamin B complex. A group of rats on an adequate diet excreted 24·6 μg. per day in the urine,[6] whilst other rats on a poor diet excreted only about 2μg. per day.[7] A horse excreted 1·5 mg. per day,[6] but this value fell to less than 30 μg. per day on a restricted dietary intake of riboflavine. Following the oral administration of large amounts of riboflavine a very large apparent increase was observed in the amount excreted by goats and sheep, when the fluorimetric method of assay was used, whereas an increase of only about 20 % was observed when microbiological assays were employed.[8] With rats and humans on the other hand, good agreement was obtained between the microbiological and fluorimetric values.

Women on an adequate diet excreted 357 μg. of riboflavine per day in the urine, and this value fell to 77 μg. per day on a diet containing only 0·5 mg. of riboflavine per 2400 cals.[9] Other values recorded for the urinary excretion of humans on adequate diets were 320 to 360 μg. per day,[7] and 500 to 800 μg. per day.[1] In the last group of subjects the excretion fell rapidly to 50 to 150 μg. per day when the intake dropped to 1 to 2 mg. per day, and rose again on increasing the intake to 2 to 5 mg. per day. In another experiment,[10] the average daily urinary excretions on diets containing 0·28, 0·49, 0·66 and 7·1 mg. per 1000 cals. were 119, 107, 150 and 263 μg. respectively, and increased to 325 μg. after two weeks on a diet supplying 9·63 mg. per 1000 cals. Still higher values were recorded by Brewer et al,[11] daily excretions of 70, 160, 130, 320, 1180 and 1310 μg. being obtained on daily intakes of 0·79, 1·04, 1·26, 1·62, 2·23 and 2·72 mg. per day. Infants excreted 35 to 50 μg. per day on a diet deficient in riboflavine.[11a]

On self-selected diets supplying 1·25 to 2·47 mg. of riboflavine per day, young women excreted [11b] 36 to 50 % in the urine and 27 to 54 % in the faeces ; following a 5-mg. supplement, between 24 and 44 % was eliminated in the urine. In no instance did the urinary and faecal excretion together exceed the intake. Oldham et al.[12] observed a correlation between riboflavine excretion and nitrogen balance ; on a diet providing 1 mg. of riboflavine daily for ten days, 1·2 to 1·4 mg. daily for a further ten days and 1 mg. daily for a further ten-day period with nitrogen intakes of 5, 19, and 5 g. daily in each ten-day period respectively, 40 to 60 % of the riboflavine was excreted in the first and third periods, when the subjects were in negative nitrogen balance, and 7 % when the subjects were in positive nitrogen balance. The urinary excretion of riboflavine increased in protein deficiency, and fell during recovery.[13]

Assessment of Nutritional Status

The daily output of riboflavine is an unreliable method of assessing riboflavine deficiency,[14] since it only reflects the immediate dietary intake. A more satisfactory method of assessing nutritional status is to measure the response to a test dose of pure riboflavine, the method being similar in principle to that used in nutritional surveys relating to aneurine (see page 63).

V. A. Najjar and L. E. Holt,[14] for example, employed intravenous injection of 1 mg. of riboflavine and found that the amount of ribo-flavine excreted in the urine at half-hourly intervals was related to the degree of riboflavine deficiency. M. Swaminathan [7] administered test doses of 1 to 10 mg. orally to adequately nourished subjects and found that 80 to 85 % was excreted within twenty-four hours, whereas Keys et al.,[15] who administered a 1-mg. test dose to young men on a diet supplying slightly sub-optimal amounts (0·31 mg. per 1000 cals.) of riboflavine obtained only a 12 % recovery in the urine. Similarly, R. D. Williams et al.[16] observed a progressive decrease in the urinary excretion of a 2-mg. test dose administered to a subject maintained on a diet providing 0·35 mg. of riboflavine per 1000 cals.

Axelrod et al.,[17] however, claimed that even the test dose method was unsatisfactory for assessing nutritional status. They gave doses of 200 and 400 μg. of pure riboflavine per kg. of bodyweight to several subjects, and failed to find any correlation between the percentage of the test dose retained and the amount excreted in the urine.

The volume of work carried out on the assessment of riboflavine deficiency by measuring the urinary excretion with or without ad-ministration of a test dose is considerably less than that undertaken in the case of aneurine (see page 63) or of nicotinic acid (see page 252), and it is therefore impossible to reach any definite conclusion about the merits of the saturation test.

In spite of this, however, many attempts have been made to lay down criteria for diagnosing riboflavine deficiency. According to Feder et al.,[18] an excretion of less than 0·3 μg. of riboflavine per ml. of urine is indicative of riboflavine deficiency, whilst the concentration of riboflavine in a sample of fasting morning urine was claimed to be as valuable as a saturation test for estimating the degree of riboflavine deficiency. Oldham et al.[19] also reported a close relationship between the excretion rate and the response to a test dose, and suggested that the elimination of 1 μg. of riboflavine per hour by a fasting subject or the elimination of 20 % of a test dose within four hours of its adminis-tration was indicative of an adequate level of nutrition.

Hagedorn et al.[20] reported that an adult male, receiving 0·5 mg. of riboflavine daily for five years, showed no signs of ribofl .vine deficiency and excreted between 50 and 120 μg. of riboflavine daily. A similar result was obtained by Keys *et al.*,[15] who maintained a number of young men on a diet containing 0·31 mg. of riboflavine per 1000 cals., that is, between 0·78 and 0·93 mg. per day. They reported that 12 % of the intake, that is 94 to 112 μg., was excreted daily, and that approximately the same proportion of a 1-mg. test dose was recovered.

Subjects maintained on a synthetic diet and a natural diet which supplied 1·09 and 1·33 mg. respectively of riboflavine daily excreted 152 to 165 and 174 to 229 μg. per day respectively. The one-hour fasting urinary excretion ranged from 3·7 to 10·9 μg.[21] A number of women who received a daily intake of 0·79, 1·04, 1·26, 1·62, 2·23 and 2·72 mg. of riboflavine excreted 70, 160, 130, 320, 1180 and 1310 μg. daily. Following a 3-mg. test dose, 22, 30, 27, 31, 55 and 56 % respectively was excreted in the following twenty-four hours.[11] The response to a test dose, like the daily riboflavine excretion, varied inversely with the nitrogen balance.[12]

From the above evidence, therefore, it would appear that an adequate intake of riboflavine results in the excretion in the urine of not less than about 200 μg. per day and in the elimination of not less than 20 % of a test dose within twenty-four hours.

An observation which does not appear to have been adequately explained was made by B. Sure and Z. W. Ford,[22] who found that when rats, maintained on a synthetic diet supplemented by five pure vitamins, were given subcutaneous injections of thyroxine (0·5 to 1 mg. daily), the rate of excretion of riboflavine, though not of aneurine, was greatly increased. At the same time, a large loss of bodyweight was produced and a large loss of riboflavine from many of the organs.

Faecal Excretion

The faecal excretion of riboflavine varied considerably in different individuals, but was less dependent than the urinary excretion on changes in the riboflavine content of the diet, being in fact remarkably constant in any one individual [10] (see page 185). Unlike the urinary excretion, the faecal excretion bore no relationship to the nitrogen balance.[12]

Riboflavine in other Body Fluids and Tissues

The hourly excretion of riboflavine in the sweat was 10 μg., and this value was not increased on administration of riboflavine.[23]

Injection of riboflavine into the blood stream caused an immediate increase in the concentration in the liver ; [24] and this was also increased during digestion and assimilation, even after a prolonged deficiency of riboflavine. This mobilisation was prevented by a deficiency of aneurine or pantothenic acid. The amount of riboflavine stored in the liver also increased when the amount of protein (casein) in the diet was increased ; about one-third of the increase could be accounted for by ingestion of increased amounts of methionine and none by ingestion of cystine.[25] In confirmation of this result, A. V. Trufanov [13] found that, although the free riboflavine in the livers of rats remained unchanged in protein deficiency, the bound riboflavine fell ; at the same time, the urinary excretion increased. Liver and muscle tissue from protein-deficient rats was incapable of synthesising flavine-adenine dinucleotide.

The changes that took place in the riboflavine content of different tissues with increasing age were studied by Murray et al.[26] In thirty-day old rats, the muscle riboflavine was fairly constant at 4·13 to 4·28 μg. per g., but at sixty days lower values were obtained and at 360 to 500 days still lower values. Values for liver were more variable, and at thirty days were about six, and at sixty days, about nine times as high as in muscle. Blood values were still more variable, ranging from 0·1 to 0·2 μg. per g.

Intravenously administered riboflavine was rapidly excreted into the small intestine of bilaterally nephrectomised rats ; [27] excretion through the bile was relatively unimportant. Riboflavine was rapidly destroyed in the isolated large intestine, but only slowly in the isolated loop of the duodenum. Intravenously injected ribo-flavine was not destroyed or eliminated by rats without an intestinal canal and both kidneys. Appreciable destruction occurred on incubation with liver, lung, heart, stomach and intestinal preparations.[28]

Riboflavine in Pregnancy and Lactation

Pregnant women excreted less riboflavine in the urine than did non-pregnant women,[29] even when large doses (5 mg.) were injected intravenously. After parturition, the excretion remained at a low level, but increased, sometimes to the normal level, on administration of a 5-mg. dose. The riboflavine content of the placenta was not increased by the intravenous injection of 5 to 25 mg. of riboflavine a few days or hours before parturition.

The human placenta contained 1·68 to 3·14 μg. of riboflavine per 100 g., and of this 40 to 55 % was present in the free state.[30] The arterial and venous blood of the mother and the umbilical cord blood contained about 60 μg. per 100 ml., the value being increased to 150 μg. per 100 ml. two to three minutes after the intravenous injection into the mother of 30 to 50 mg. of the vitamin. The value fell to

normal in twenty to sixty minutes. The injection increased the riboflavine content of the infant's urine but did not increase that of the
placenta.

The concentration of riboflavine in human milk averaged $17\cdot3$ μg.
per 100 ml.,[29] equivalent to $68\cdot8$ μg. per day and, in the early stages
of lactation, was not affected by administration of riboflavine. During
the later stages, however, the amount secreted in the milk could be
substantially increased in this way. More recently, an average value
of 60 μg. per 100 ml. has been reported.[30a]

According to Roderuck et al.,[31] the riboflavine content of human
milk increased in the first ten days after parturition from $0\cdot01$ to $0\cdot45$
mg. per day when the daily intake was $3\cdot1$ mg. The output in the
milk at this stage accounted for 3 to 32 % of the intake and the
urinary excretion for 12 to 82 %. The output in the mature milk
amounted to 3 to 15 % of the intake and the corresponding urinary
excretion to 26 to 61 %. The free riboflavine in the milk varied
from 43 to 86 % of the total.

In France, the average riboflavine content of breast milk was found
to be $32\cdot4$ μg. per 100 ml. in summer 1940 and $27\cdot5$ μg. per 100 ml.
in the winter ; in 1942, the corresponding values were $23\cdot3$ and $20\cdot1$
μg. per 100 ml., corresponding to a decrease in the riboflavine intake.[32]

References to Section 11

1. F. M. Strong, R. E. Feeney, B. Moore and H. T. Parsons, *J. Biol. Chem.*, 1941, **137**, 363.
2. P. B. Pearson, M. K. Sheybani and H. Schmidt, *Arch. Biochem.*, 1944, **3**, 467.
3. H. F. Fraser, N. H. Topping and H. Isbell, *U.S. Publ. Health Rep.*, 1940, **55**, 280.
4. J. W. Ferrebee, *J. Clin. Invest.*, 1940, **19**, 251.
5. H. Isbell, J. G. Wooley and H. F. Fraser, *U.S. Publ. Health Rep.*, 1941, **56**, 282.
6. L. Laszt and L. D. Torre, *Z. Vitaminforsch.*, 1943, **13**, 77.
7. M. Swaminathan, *Indian J. Med. Res.*, 1942, **30**, 37.
8. P. B. Pearson and B. S. Schweigert, *J. Nutrition*, 1947, **34**, 443.
9. W. H. Sebrell, R. E. Butler, J. G. Wooley and H. Isbell, *U.S. Publ. Health Rep.*, 1941, **56**, 510.
10. M. V. Davis, H. G. Oldham and L. J. Roberts, *J. Nutrition*, 1946, **32**, 143.
11. W. Brewer, T. Porter, B. Ingalls and M. A. Ohlson, *ibid.*, 583.
11a. S. E. Snyderman, K. C. Ketron, H. B. Burch, O. H. Lowry, O. A. Bessey, L. P. Guy and L. E. Holt, *ibid.*, 1949, **39**, 219.
11b. J. N. Harris and F. I. Scoular, *ibid.*, 1949, **38**, 435.
12. H. Oldham, E. Lounds and T. Porter, *ibid.*, 1947, **34**, 69.
13. A. V. Trufanov, *Biochimia*, 1946, **11**, 33.

14. V. A. Najjar and L. E. Holt, *Johns Hopkins Hosp. Bull.*, 1941, **69**, 479.
15. A. Keys, A. F. Henschel, O. Mickelsen, J. Brozek and J. H. Crawford, *J. Nutrition*, 1944, **27**, 165.
16. R. D. Williams, H. L. Mason, P. L. Cusick and R. M. Wilder, *ibid.*, 1943, **25**, 361.
17. A. E. Axelrod, T. D. Spies, C. A. Elvehjem and V. Axelrod, *J. Clin. Invest.*, 1941, **20**, 229.
18. V. H. Feder, G. T. Lewis and H. S. Alden, *J. Nutrition*, 1944, **27**, 347.
19. H. Oldham, F. Johnston, S. C. Kleiger and H. H. Arismendi, *ibid.*, 435.
20. D. R. Hagedorn, E. D. Kyhos, O. A. Germek and E. L. Sevringhaus, *ibid.*, 1945, **29**, 179.
21. M. L. Hathaway and D. E. Lobb, *ibid.*, 1946, **32**, 9.
22. B. Sure and Z. W. Ford, *Endocrin.*, 1943, **32**, 433.
23. D. M. Tennant and R. H. Silber, *J. Biol. Chem.*, 1943, **148**, 359.
24. G. C. Supplee, O. G. Jensen, R. C. Bender and O. J. Kahlenberg, *ibid.*, 1942, **144**, 79.
25. W. H. Riesen, B. S. Schweigert and C. A. Elvehjem, *Arch. Biochem.*, 1946, **10**, 387.
26. A. Z. Murray, L. M. Greenstein and H. C. Sherman, *J. Biol. Chem.*, 1946, **165**, 91.
27. H. Selye, *J. Nutrition*, 1943, **25**, 137.
28. B. Sure and Z. W. Ford, *ibid.*, 1943, **26**, 659.
29. V. Dubrauszky and S. Blazso, *Z. Vitaminforsch.*, 1943, **14**, 2, 13.
30. W. Neuweiler and Esterman, *ibid.*, 1946, **18**, 74.
30a. J. Sos, *Z. Vit. Horm. Fermentf.*, 1947, **1**, 369.
31. C. E. Roderuck, M. N. Coryell, H. H. Williams and I. G. Macy, *Amer. J. Dis. Child.*, 1945, **70**, 171 ; *J. Nutrition*, 1946, **32**, 267.
32. L. Randoin and A. Raffy, *Bull. acad. méd.*, 1943, **127**, 12 ; *Compt. rend. Soc. Biol.*, 1942, **136**, 743.

12. INTESTINAL SYNTHESIS OF RIBOFLAVINE

Normal rats were reported [1] to excrete 55·6 μg. of riboflavine daily in the faeces, compared with 24·6 μg. in the urine. Adrenalectomised rats excreted somewhat more by both routes. However, it is generally agreed that the values obtained for faecal riboflavine excretion cannot be used to assess nutritional status as they are determined solely by the extent of intestinal synthesis and not by the dietary intake. Thus, the amount of riboflavine excreted in the faeces was approximately the same with an intake of 0, 10 and 40 μg. per day.[2, 3]

The nature of the diet affected the amount of riboflavine synthesised in the gut, and rats excreted larger amounts in the faeces on diets rich in dextrin or maize starch than on diets containing sucrose, cellulose, lactose or lard.[4] Riboflavine-deficient rats survived for a shorter time when fed on a high fat diet than on a high carbohydrate diet, and they developed a severe spastic paralysis of the hind quarters not observed in rats fed the high carbohydrate diet. Intestinal synthesis was also stimulated by feeding dried liver or a vitamin concentrate prepared from liver,[5] and animals given this supplement excreted more riboflavine both in the urine and in the faeces. Similarly, rats fed on fresh or dried milk excreted more riboflavine in the urine and faeces than did rats fed the same amount of riboflavine in the pure state. The larger faecal excretions were considerably reduced when succinyl sulphathiazole was added to the diet.[6] On the other hand, the riboflavine content of liver and muscle tissue was not affected when sulphonamide was added to the diet,[7] suggesting that the riboflavine reserves were not dependent to any appreciable extent on the vitamin produced by intestinal synthesis.

There is some evidence, however, that part of the riboflavine originating in this way may be utilised by animals, for caecectomised rats previously fed on sucrose showed an increased growth rate and increased riboflavine excretion when this was replaced by lactose, which favoured bacterial synthesis in the intestine.[8] The caecum in rats was presumably an important site of bacterial synthesis, since normal rats synthesised more riboflavine than caecectomised rats when lactose was the carbohydrate supplied ; with sucrose, however, there was little difference between normal and caecectomised rats.

The phenomenon of refection has already been discussed (see page 75). Refected rats were found to be particularly useful for testing the effect of sulphonamides on the intestinal flora of rats. Addition of several sulphonamides to such animals reduced the amount of riboflavine excreted ; this was restored to normal by administration of p-aminobenzoic acid.[9]

The first report of intestinal synthesis in humans was made by Najjar et al.[10] Twelve young men were maintained on a diet that provided 60 to 90 μg. of riboflavine per day. They remained perfectly healthy, without any signs of ariboflavinosis throughout the twelve-week period of the experiment. After a preliminary fall, the urinary excretion remained constant at 150 to 250 μg. per day, that is, at about twice the intake, whilst the faecal excretion amounted to 200 to 600 μg. per day, that is, up to six times the dietary intake. The ability of the large intestine to absorb riboflavine was demonstrated by giving a retention enema. An attempt to inhibit bacterial synthesis of riboflavine by administration of succinyl sulphathiazole for four weeks was, rather surprisingly, unsuccessful. Partial confirmation of these results was obtained by M. L. Hathaway and D. E. Lobb,[11] who found that the faecal excretion of riboflavine was 3·7 to 3·8 times as great on a natural as on a synthetic diet, and actually exceeded the dietary intake in many instances.

Slightly different results were obtained by Denko *et al.*,[12] to whose work reference has already been made (see page 77). They found that the combined faecal and urinary excretion of riboflavine by seven healthy young men on a normal diet was just about equal to the dietary intake of riboflavine ; the amount excreted in the faeces (1·03 mg. per day) was nearly twice that excreted in the urine (0·68 mg. per day). Moreover, the faecal excretion remained the same on a vitamin-deficient diet and was unaffected by vitamin supplementation, whereas the urinary excretion of riboflavine dropped markedly on a restricted diet, but returned to its original value on supplementation.[13] Similar results were obtained with infants.[13a] Obviously these experimental subjects behaved in a different manner from those of Najjar *et al.*, who appear to have obtained somewhat unusual conditions. What the conditions are that will induce bacterial synthesis of riboflavine in man and so prevent the appearance of deficiency symptoms, are not yet known, but it is obviously of great scientific interest to determine them. The application of such knowledge to nutrition is also of considerable practical importance, since it provides a possible alternative to treatment of riboflavine deficiency by administration of pure riboflavine or of concentrates.

Riboflavine, like aneurine, is synthesised [14] by the intestinal organisms, *Bacillus proteus vulgaris*, *B. lactis aerogenes*, *B. mesentericus*, *B. vulgatus*, *B. faecalis alcaligenes* and *Escherichia coli*.

Synthesis of Riboflavine in Ruminants

A general outline of the work leading to the recognition that " vitamin B " was synthesised by the bacterial flora of the rumen of cattle and other ruminants has already been given (see page 79). Evidence for the synthesis of riboflavine was presented by L. W. McElroy and H. Goss,[15] who found that the rumen of sheep receiving a ration containing less than 0·3 μg. of riboflavine per g. contained 33 μg. per g., whilst the rumen of cows fed a similar ration contained 25 μg. of riboflavine per g. The milk from these cows, after removal of the cream, contained 20 μg. of riboflavine per g. Whereas the dietary intake was 1·8 mg. per day, the amount secreted in the milk alone was 16 to 18 mg. per day. Thus bacterial synthesis may largely be responsible for one of the main sources—milk—of riboflavine in the human dietary. These results were confirmed by Hunt *et al.*,[16] who showed that bacterial synthesis in the rumen of cattle was enhanced when the diet contained a large proportion of carbohydrate. On a ration of maize, lucerne and a protein supplement, the amount of riboflavine in the rumen exceeded that in the diet, but when the maize was omitted the rumen contained less than the diet.

References to Section 12

1. L. Laszt and L. D. Torre, *Z. Vitaminforsch.*, 1943, **13,** 77.
2. B. Sure and Z. W. Ford, *J. Nutrition*, 1943, **26,** 659.
3. H. G. Obermeyer, E. Wurtz and G. A. Emerson, *Proc. Soc. Exp. Biol. Med.*, 1945, **59,** 300.
4. G. J. Mannering, D. Orsini and C. A. Elvehjem, *J. Nutrition*, 1944, **28,** 141.
5. B. Sure, *ibid.*, 1945, **29,** 283.
6. B. Sure, *Arch. Biochem.*, 1947, **12,** 389.
7. B. S. Schweigert, L. J. Teply, I. T. Greenhut and C. A. Elvehjem, *Amer. J. Physiol.*, 1945, **144,** 74.
8. B. S. Schweigert, J. M. McIntire, L. M. Henderson and C. A. Elvehjem, *Arch. Biochem.*, 1945, **6,** 403.
9. M. E. Coates, R. M. Henry, P. M. Kon, S. K. Kon, E. H. Mawson, J. E. Stanier and S. Y. Thompson, *Nature*, 1946, **157,** 262.
10. V. A. Najjar, G. A. Johns, G. C. Medairy, G. Fleischmann and L. E. Holt, *J. Amer. Med. Assoc.*, 1944, **126,** 357.
11. M. L. Hathaway and D. E. Lobb, *J. Nutrition*, 1946, **32,** 9.
12. C. W. Denko, W. E. Grundy, J. W. Porter, G. H. Berryman, T. E. Friedemann and J. B. Youmans, *Arch. Biochem.*, 1946, **10,** 33.
13. C. W. Denko, W. E. Grundy, N. C. Wheeler, C. R. Henderson, G. H. Berryman, T. E. Friedemann and J. B. Youmans, *ibid.*, 1946, **11,** 109.
13a. S. E. Snyderman, K. C. Ketron, H. B. Burch, O. H. Lowry, O. A. Bessey, L. P. Guy and L. E. Holt, *J. Nutrition*, 1949, **39,** 219.
14. R. C. Thompson, *Univ. Texas Publ.*, 1942, No. 4237, p. 87 ; P. R. Burkholder and I. McVeigh, *Proc. Nat. Acad. Sci.*, 1942, **28,** 285.
15. L. W. McElroy and H. Goss, *J. Nutrition*, 1940, **20,** 527.
16. C. H. Hunt, C. H. Kirk, E. W. Burroughs, R. M. Bethke, A. F. Schalk and P. Gerlaugh, *ibid.*, 1941, **21,** 85 ; C. H. Hunt, E. W. Burroughs, R. M. Bethke, A. F. Schalk and P. Gerlaugh, *ibid.*, 1943, **25,** 207.

13. ANIMAL AND HUMAN REQUIREMENTS OF RIBOFLAVINE

Attempts to assess human and animal requirements of riboflavine are complicated by the phenomenon of intestinal synthesis and, in ruminants, synthesis in the rumen. Human requirements can be calculated with a fair degree of certainty, however, as intestinal synthesis does not appear to be a usual source of riboflavine in man.

Human Requirements

There is general agreement that the minimum intake requisite to maintain normal health lies between 0·5 and 3 mg. per day, although admittedly this is a somewhat wide range. Sebrell et al.,[1] as a result of excretion studies, suggested that a minimum intake of 3 mg. per day was necessary, whilst Williams et al.[2] maintained a subject for 288 days on a diet that provided 0·35 mg. of riboflavine per 1000 cals., that is, about 1 mg. per day, and found that, although the percentage excretion of a 2-g. test dose fell progressively, no clinical symptoms developed. They suggested that the minimum daily requirement was 0·5 mg. per 1000 cals., or about 1·25 mg. per day. Brewer et al.[3] calculated the requirement of women to be 1·3 to 1·5 mg. per day on a diet supplying 2100 to 2300 cals. per day, whilst Horwitt et al.,[3a] from excretion studies over a prolonged period, suggested that the daily requirement of an adult was between 1·1 and 1·6 mg.

Macrae et al.,[4] using biological and microbiological methods of assay, which incidentally gave results in excellent agreement with one another, estimated the riboflavine contents of meals served in Royal Air Force messes, and found that on the average these yielded 2 mg. of riboflavine per day. As there were no signs of riboflavine deficiency on these diets, they concluded that an intake of 2 mg. per day was in excess of the minimum requirement. Oldham et al.[5] and Hagedorn et al.[6] stipulated a substantially lower figure for the minimum daily intake. The former observed a steady excretion with an intake of 0·5 mg. per day, whilst the latter failed to find any physical signs of riboflavine deficiency in an adult male maintained for five years on a diet also supplying 0·5 mg. daily. Perhaps these lower values should be accepted with reserve until more is known about the possibility of intestinal synthesis supplying appreciable amounts of riboflavine.

The minimum riboflavine requirement of infants is 0·4 mg. per day ; this maintained the urinary excretion above a " safe " level of 50 μg. per day and the serum concentration above a minimum of 0·5 μg. per 100 ml., and prevented symptoms of riboflavine deficiency.[6a] The most satisfactory criterion of nutritional status with respect to riboflavine is said to be the amount in the red blood cells, which should not be less than 2·5 μg. per 100 cells.

There has been a recent tendency to reduce the official figures for the riboflavine requirements of man and, whereas the U.S. National Research Council's estimate in 1941 was 3·3 mg. per day for a very active man, 2·2 mg. for a sedentary man, 2·7 mg. for a very active woman, and 1·8 mg. for a sedentary woman, in 1945 these values were reduced to 2·6, 1·6, 2·0 and 1·5 mg. per day respectively. Rations in Great Britain during the war of 1939-45 were based on 70 % of the 1941 estimates,[7] whereas the actual consumption of riboflavine was 1·6 mg. per day during 1939 to 1941, followed by a steady rise during the next two or three years to a maximum of 2·0 mg. in 1944, then by a slight fall in 1945 and another rise in 1946 to 2·0 mg. per day.[8]

Requirements of Rats

A diet containing 3 μg. of riboflavine per g. of air-dried food was adequate to support normal activity in adult rats and enabled them to live for a normal life-span.[9] It was inadequate to produce the normal growth rate in young rats, however, and for this purpose, the riboflavine content had to be increased to 10 μg. per g. G. J. Mannering and C. A. Elvehjem [10] found that the food requirement of rats varied with the riboflavine intake. As the latter increased, less and less food was required in order to produce the same increment of growth, whilst rats receiving adequate amounts of riboflavine were able to grow at the same rate as rats on a diet partially deficient in riboflavine, when the food intake of the former group was much lower than that of the latter. This suggests that food was utilised more efficiently when adequate amounts of riboflavine were available. However, the riboflavine-deficient rats fed on a more liberal diet were much more active than the rats with a limited food intake and receiving adequate riboflavine. Riboflavine deficiency in rats led to an increased deposition of body-fat.[11]

Rats on high protein and high fat diets required at least twice as much riboflavine as did rats on a normal diet in order to maintain an equal level of riboflavine in the organs and urine.[12] On a low fat diet, the animals required only about half the normal amount of riboflavine, which was calculated to be about 7·5 μg. per day. It was assumed that the different amounts required were due to differences in the amounts of riboflavine synthesised in the intestine in a form available to the organism.

Requirements of Other Species of Mammals

The amount of riboflavine required by mice varied according to the strain.[13] The C57 strain gave maximal growth with 0·4 mg. per 100 g. of bodyweight and the A strain with 0·6 mg. per 100 g. At a level of 0·2 mg. per 100 g., the C57 mice had a reduced red blood-cell count and a lower muscle and liver riboflavine, whereas the A strain suffered no change.

Dogs required 15 to 100 μg. of riboflavine per kg. of bodyweight per day to maintain normal health,[14] young growing pigs 40 to 66 μg.

per kg. of bodyweight per day,[15] and a horse 44 μg. per kg. of bodyweight per day.[16] In mild cases, the symptoms of riboflavine deficiency in rhesus monkeys were relieved by the administration of 50 μg. of riboflavine per day for two to three weeks, but severe cases required 100 to 500 μg. daily.[17] The minimum daily intake necessary to maintain normal health was estimated to be 25 to 30 μg. per kg. of bodyweight. Thus, the requirements of all species of mammals for which data are available, including man, are of the same order when calculated per kg. of bodyweight.

Requirements of Birds and Fish

To prevent the development of " curled-toe paralysis " in chickens, the diet should contain 3·6 μg. of riboflavine per g.[18] Ducklings required a similar amount for proper development.[19] For satisfactory egg production, the diet of hens should contain at least 2 μg. of riboflavine per g. With a diet containing 2·7 μg. per g., hens kept in pens laid eggs containing 24 % of the ingested riboflavine, whilst hens kept in batteries and fed a diet containing 3·3 μg. per g. laid eggs containing 30 % of the ingested riboflavine.[20]

Young rainbow trout required 5 to 15 μg. of riboflavine per g. of diet.[21]

References to Section 13

1. W. H. Sebrell, R. E. Butler, J. G. Wooley and H. Isbell, *U.S. Publ. Health Rep.*, 1941, **56**, 510.
2. R. D. Williams, H. L. Mason, P. L. Cusick and R. M. Wilder, *J. Nutrition*, 1943, **25**, 361.
3. W. Brewer, T. Porter, B. Ingalls and M. A. Ohlson, *ibid.*, 1946, **32**, 583.
3a. M. K. Horwitt, O. W. Hills, C. C. Harvey, E. Liebert and D. L. Steinberg, *ibid.*, 1949, **39**, 357.
4. T. F. Macrae, E. C. Barton-Wright and A. M. Copping, *Biochem. J.*, 1944, **38**, 132.
5. H. Oldham, F. Johnston, S. C. Kleiger and H. H. Arismendi, *J. Nutrition*, 1944, **27**, 435.
6. D. R. Hagedorn, E. D. Kyhos, O. A. Germek and E. L. Sevringhaus, *ibid.*, 1945, **29**, 179.
6a. S. E. Snyderman, K. C. Ketron, H. B. Burch, O. H. Lowry, O. A. Bessey, L. P. Guy and L. E. Holt, *ibid.*, 1949, **39**, 219.
7. J. C. Drummond, " Nutritional Requirements of Man in the Light of Wartime Experience ", Royal Institute of Chemistry, 1948.
8. " Food Consumption Levels in the United Kingdom ", Cmd. 7203, H.M.S.O., 1947.
9. L. N. Ellis, A. Zmachinsky and H. C. Sherman, *J. Nutrition*, 1943, **25**, 153.
10. G. J. Mannering and C. A. Elvehjem, *ibid.*, 1944, **28**, 157.
11. Le R. Voris and H. P. Moore, *ibid.*, 1943, **25**, 7.

12. J. W. Czaczkes and K. Guggenheim, *J. Biol. Chem.*, 1946, **162,** 267.

13. P. F. Fenton and G. R. Cowgill, *J. Nutrition*, 1947, **34,** 273.

14. R. L. Potter, A. E. Axelrod and C. A. Elvehjem, *ibid.*, 1942, **24,** 449 ; H. Spector, A. R. Maass, L. Michaud, C. A. Elvehjem and E. B. Hart, *J. Biol. Chem.*, 1943, **150,** 75.

15. E. H. Hughes, *J. Nutrition*, 1940, **20,** 233.

16. P. B. Pearson, M. K. Sheybani and H. Schmidt, *Arch. Biochem.*, 1944, **3,** 467.

17. H. A. Waisman, *Proc. Soc. Exp. Biol. Med.*, 1944, **55,** 69 ; J. M. Cooperman, H. A. Waisman, K. B. McCall and C. A. Elvehjem, *J. Nutrition*, 1945, **30,** 45.

18. W. Bolton, *J. Agric. Sci.*, 1944, **34,** 198.

19. J. C. Fritz, W. Archer and D. Barker, *Poultry Sci.*, 1939, **18,** 449 ; D. M. Hegsted and R. L. Perry, *J. Nutrition*, 1948, **35,** 411.

20. S. H. Jackson, T. G. H. Drake, S. J. Slinger, E. V. Evans and R. Pocock, *J. Nutrition*, 1946, **32,** 567.

21. B. A. McLaren, E. Keller, D. J. O'Donnell and C. A. Elvehjem, *Arch. Biochem.*, 1947, **15,** 169.

14. PHARMACOLOGICAL ACTION OF RIBOFLAVINE

The toxicity and pharmacology of riboflavine were investigated by K. Unna and J. G. Greslin,[1] who found that the value of LD_{50} when the vitamin was given intra-peritoneally into rats was 560 mg. per kg. Death occurred in two to five days with anuria and azotemia, due to obstruction of the kidneys by concretions. No toxic effects were encountered with rats given 10 g. per kg. orally or with dogs given 2 g. per kg. orally. The daily oral administration of 10 mg. to rats or of 25 mg. per kg. to dogs for four months gave rise to no toxic symptoms. The metabolic, circulatory and respiratory systems and isolated smooth muscles were not affected by riboflavine.

R. Kuhn and P. Boulanger [2] recorded the toxicity of riboflavine to mice by intraperitoneal injection as 340 mg. per kg.

References to Section 14

1. K. Unna and J. G. Greslin, *J. Pharmacol.*, 1942, **76,** 75.
2. R. Kuhn and P. Boulanger, *Z. physiol. Chem.*, 1936, **241,** 233.

15. FUNCTION OF RIBOFLAVINE

Presence in Enzymes

Information concerning the function of riboflavine was available long before anything was known as to its chemical nature, for in 1931

O. Warburg and W. Christian [1] had shown that the " yellow enzyme ", of which riboflavine was later shown to be the prosthetic group, was an essential link in the metabolism of carbohydrates. The series of transformations whereby oxygen is transferred from a substrate undergoing dehydrogenation to atmospheric oxygen, is discussed in the chapter on nicotinic acid (see page 277), where it is stated that the yellow enzyme, diaphorase, oxidises reduced coenzyme (di- or tri-phosphopyridine nucleotide) and is itself re-oxidised (with one exception) by cytochrome.

Actually the picture is complicated by the fact that riboflavine is a constituent of two different coenzymes, the second of which can catalyse several important transformations. The first of these co-enzymes, known as riboflavine mononucleotide, was isolated from Warburg and Christian's yellow enzyme by H. Theorell,[2] who purified the enzyme from yeast by cataphoresis, and split it by dialysis into the apoenzyme (the protein carrier) and the coenzyme.

Weygand et al.[3] improved the isolation of the enzyme by adsorption on " ortho aluminium hydroxide γ " and elution with ammonium sulphate at pH 5·2, followed by precipitation at pH 6 by 70 % saturation with ammonium sulphate and then dialysis.[4]

The molecular weight of the enzyme was estimated to be 74,000.[5, 6]

The nature of the coenzyme was established by R. Kuhn and H. Rudy,[7] who showed that " cytoflav ", a golden-yellow pigment isolated from heart-muscle by I. Banga and A. Szent-Györgyi [8] four years before, was riboflavine-5'-phosphoric ester. They prepared this compound synthetically by treating riboflavine with phosphorus oxy-chloride, and showed that the product had the same activity as natural cytoflav. Moreover, it had the same growth-promoting activity on rats, mole for mole, as riboflavine. The flavine-phosphoric ester prepared from yeast by Theorell had similar properties. H. Rudy [9] prepared riboflavine-phosphoric ester from riboflavine by digestion with intestinal phosphatase. An improved method of synthesis was described by Kuhn et al.[10]; 5'-trityl-riboflavine was acetylated, giving 2' : 3' : 4'-triacetyl-5'-trityl-riboflavine, and the trityl group was then removed and the product phosphorylated and de-acetylated. R. Kuhn and H. Rudy [11] completed their work by preparing a " synthetic " enzyme ; sodium riboflavine-5'-phosphate was adsorbed on the colloidal carrier of the yellow enzyme, giving a non-fluorescent, non-dialysable chromoprotein, which decolorised methylene blue at the same rate as the natural enzyme. They suggested that the protein was probably linked to the riboflavine-phosphoric ester at the phosphoric acid radical and the 3-imido group as in the formula :

$$CH_2 . (CHOH)_3 . CH_2O . PO(OH)_2$$

[chemical structure diagram of riboflavine with Protein]

since flavines substituted in the 3-position did not form enzyme systems [12] and were devoid of vitamin activity.

According to L. Laszt and F. Verzár,[13] the formation of riboflavine-phosphoric ester was promoted by the hormones of the adrenal cortex and was inhibited by iodoacetic acid. They suggested that this accounted for the toxicity of iodoacetic acid, and claimed that the symptoms could be cured by administration of riboflavine-phosphoric ester. H. Rudy,[14] however, found that riboflavine was just as effective as riboflavine-phosphoric ester in restoring the growth of rats poisoned with iodoacetic acid, whilst J. W. Ferrebee [15] found that riboflavine was phosphorylated as efficiently in adrenalectomised rats as in normal rats.

The second coenzyme, riboflavine-adenine-dinucleotide, is present in the enzymes known collectively as diaphorases. These are widely distributed in animal tissues and micro-organisms and also occur in plants. The dinucleotide has been isolated from liver, kidney, heart, muscle tissue, Jensen rat sarcoma and yeast.[16] To accomplish this the apoenzyme was denatured by heat, the mixture was extracted with phenol and the dinucleotide was recovered from the phenol extract by addition of water and ether, and then precipitated from the aqueous solution as the silver salt. This was converted to the barium salt which was recrystallised from water. The dinucleotide was split by hydrolysis with enzyme [17] or acid [18] into riboflavine-5'-phosphoric acid and adenosine-5'-monophosphoric acid (adenylic acid), but how the two moieties are linked together has not been definitely established, nor is it known how they are linked to the apoenzyme.

A possible structure for the nucleotide is the following :

[chemical structure diagram]

When rats were maintained on a riboflavine-deficient diet, the heart and liver were found to contain less flavine adenine dinucleotide than the corresponding organs from normal rats.[19] The dinucleotide was synthesised from riboflavine *in vitro* by human red blood cells when incubated at 30 to 34° C. with a solution of riboflavine, or *in vivo* by red blood cells on ingestion of a suspension of riboflavine.[20]

Riboflavine monophosphate and riboflavine adenine dinucleotide account for practically all the riboflavine present in rat kidney, and the dinucleotide accounts for 70 to 90 % of the total riboflavine in all tissues.[20a]

Flavine Mononucleotide : Cytochrome *c* Reductase

The first flavine enzyme to be recognised was the enzyme system that oxidised hexose-monophosphoric acid to phosphohexonic acid. It was first isolated by O. Warburg and W. Christian [21] and is now known as " old " yellow enzyme.   They postulated that the oxidation was effected by the following chain-reaction :

(1) Hexose-monophosphate + triphosphopyridine nucleotide-protein → dihydro-triphosphopyridine nucleotide-protein + phosphohexonic acid ;

(2) Dihydro-triphosphopyridine nucleotide-protein + flavoprotein → triphosphopyridine nucleotide-protein + dihydro-flavoprotein ;

(3) Dihydro-flavoprotein + O_2 → flavoprotein + H_2O_2.

H. Theorell [22] pointed out, however, that the rate of oxidation of this dihydro-flavoprotein at the oxygen tension of the organism was too small for dehydrogenation to occur by this route, and he suggested that cytochrome *c* was responsible for the reoxidation, though the rate of reaction of the " old " yellow enzyme with cytochrome *c* was also too small to account adequately for the facts.   Support was given to the suggestion, however, by the observation of E. S. G. Barron [23] that the oxidation of hexose-monophosphate by certain bacteria was completely inhibited by hydrogen cyanide, which is known to inhibit the action of cytochrome *c*.   Final proof of Theorell's hypothesis was afforded by Haas *et al.*,[24] who isolated from yeast a new flavoprotein, which reacted very rapidly with both oxidised cytochrome *c* and reduced triphosphopyridine nucleotide.   The prosthetic group of the new enzyme, which they called cytochrome *c* reductase, was shown to be alloxazine mononucleotide.

The new enzyme, unlike the " old " yellow enzyme, reacted specifically with cytochrome *c*, but the prosthetic groups of cytochrome *c* reductase, the " old " yellow enzyme and amino acid oxidase proved to be interchangeable.[25]   The enzyme was shown to be very unstable, thus accounting for its failure to escape detection.   It would appear that the " old " yellow enzyme was an artefact resulting from degradation of the true enzyme during the isolation procedure.

Cytochrome c reductase had a molecular weight of 75,000.   The affinity of the flavine for the protein was much greater than that of flavine-adenine-dinucleotide for the protein of amino acid oxidase, the respective dissociation constants being 1×10^{-9} and 250×10^{-9} mole per litre ; the two yellow enzymes had intermediate values.

A still purer preparation of the enzyme was obtained by Haas et al.[26]

Flavine Adenine Dinucleotide : Diaphorases

Although flavine mononucleotide appears to be present in only one enzyme, riboflavine adenine-dinucleotide occurs in several.   The first of these, diaphorase I, was shown to be present in heart muscle, and to dehydrogenate dihydro-coenzyme I ; the second, diaphorase II was present in yeast and adrenal gland, and it dehydrogenated dihydro-coenzyme II.[27]   Reduced diaphorase I was dehydrogenated by cytochrome b [28] and possibly by cytochrome a.   Haas' " new " yellow enzyme [25] may be identical with diaphorase I.

The Schardinger Enzyme

Another enzyme now known to belong to the group of flavine enzymes is the Schardinger enzyme [29] which catalyses the oxidation of aldehydes to carboxylic acids.   It occurs in raw milk and is heat-labile ; failure to detect its presence in milk is taken to indicate that the milk has been heated.   The aldehyde oxidase from milk also acts as a xanthine oxidase and as an oxidase of dihydro-coenzyme I.   Liver also contains an aldehyde oxidase,[30] which appears to be distinct from liver xanthine oxidase.

Xanthine Oxidase

Xanthine oxidase is the name given to the enzyme that dehydrogenates xanthine and hypoxanthine to uric acid.[31, 32]   The conversion of both hypoxanthine and xanthine to uric acid is effected by means of the same enzyme.   It can also bring about the dismutation of xanthine, giving hypoxanthine and uric acid.[33]   Xanthine oxidase occurs in milk and in liver, and appears to contain besides riboflavine, a red pigment of unknown constitution.   Green et al.[34] isolated another brownish-red enzyme from top yeast, but, although it contained flavine-adenine-dinucleotide, it was inactive towards all the substrates tried ; it contained o·86 % of flavine phosphate.

A. E. Axelrod and C. A. Elvehjem [35] found that the xanthine oxidase content of rat liver was markedly reduced in rats fed a riboflavine-deficient diet ; addition of the prosthetic group to the liver homogenate failed to increase the activity, so that the reduction in activity would appear to be due to a deficiency of the protein part of the enzyme. Addition of riboflavine to the diet, however, resulted in rapid restoration of the liver xanthine oxidase to normal.

D-Amino Acid Oxidase

The oxidation of amino acids to keto acids *via* imino acids is also brought about by an enzyme containing riboflavine-adenine-dinucleotide,[36-39] and Axelrod et al.[40] showed that a deficiency of riboflavine in the diet of rats reduced the D-amino acid oxidase content of liver and kidney ; administration of riboflavine restored the enzyme activity to normal.

This observation presumably explains why rats on a diet providing less than 2·5 μg. of riboflavine per day did not utilise protein as efficiently as rats fed 5 μg. or more per day.[40a]

Krahl et al.[41] claimed that the oxidation of α-alanine by D-amino acid oxidase was inhibited by certain phenols containing nitro or halogen groups, e.g. dinitrophenol, at relatively high concentrations, but Haas et al.[26] showed that the pyridine-catalysed dehydrogenation of hexose-6-phosphate was even more strongly inhibited than the flavine enzyme.

Hoagland et al.[42] obtained a flavine-containing compound from the elementary bodies of vaccinia, 100 g. of virus containing 1·1 to 1·5 mg. of riboflavine. The substance functioned as a coenzyme for D-amino acid oxidase, and was probably a flavine adenine dinucleotide.

The specificity of D-amino acid oxidase has been the subject of controversy, but most workers agree that D-glutamic acid and D-lysine are not attacked by the isolated enzyme system. Handler et al.[43] found that the N-methyl derivatives of DL-methionine, DL-alanine and DL-leucine were oxidised by D-amino acid oxidase preparations. J. R. Klein and H. Kamin [44] found that the enzyme was inhibited by benzoic acid.

The D-amino acid oxidase of *Neurospora* [45] deaminated some nineteen D-amino acids with optimal activity at pH 8·0 to 8·5. Unlike the enzyme from animal tissues, it is not inhibited by benzoic acid.

A. Neuberger and F. Sanger [46] found that, although D-lysine was not deaminated by the enzyme, ϵ-acetyl- and ϵ-benzoyl-lysine were oxidised at a moderate rate ; ϵ-methyl lysine, however, was not attacked. They suggested that the free basic group in the ε-position might inhibit the enzyme by repelling another basic group in the oxidising enzyme.

The activity of D-amino acid oxidase was inhibited by mepacrine.[47] The oxidation of glucose, lactate, pyruvate, malate and citrate by rat tissues was also inhibited by the drug, whilst E. Haas [48] found that it also inhibited cytochrome reductase, glucose-6-phosphate dehydrogenase and, to a slight extent, cytochrome oxidase. The addition of 1 μg. of riboflavine phosphate counteracted the inhibition of cytochrome reductase by 500 μg. of mepacrine.

L-Amino Acid Oxidase.

An enzyme that oxidised L-amino acids was isolated from rat kidney and shown to be a flavoprotein.[49]

Glycine Oxidase

Glycine oxidase is another flavoprotein ; its existence was first recognised by Ratner *et al.*[50] It occurs in liver and kidney, and catalyses the oxidation of glycine to glyoxylic acid and ammonia, and of sarcosine to glyoxylic acid and methylamine. As isolated from lamb, cat and human kidneys, glycine oxidase showed no tendency to dissociate except in acid solution, but the enzyme from pig kidney was very unstable, and this was shown to be due to a factor in pig kidney, possibly enzymic in nature. Exactly the same behaviour was observed with D-amino acid oxidase from pig kidney and kidneys from other species. Unfortunately the early work on amino acid oxidase was done with preparations from pig kidney and the report that it was completely dissociated at neutral *p*H values must, therefore, be accepted with reserve.

Diamino Oxidase

Di- and poly-amines, such as histamine, cadaverine and spermine, are converted into amino aldehydes by an enzyme similar to, but apparently not identical with, amino acid oxidase.[51] The enzyme was purified by M. Laskowski.[52] Histaminase contains flavine adenine dinucleotide.[52a]

Quinine Oxidase

Riboflavine was also present in an enzyme from rabbit liver that oxidised quinine and other quinoline derivatives to their carbostyrils. Isoquinolines, some pyridine derivatives and N^1-methylnicotinamide were also oxidised.[53]

Notatin

The oxidation of glucose to gluconic acid by micro-organisms is effected by another flavine enzyme.[54, 55] A preparation of this enzyme was isolated by Coulthard *et al.*[56] from the metabolism solution of *Penicillium notatum*, and was given the name notatin. Other workers [57-59] isolated it from similar sources and called it penatin. Notatin proved to be inhibitory in extremely high dilution to many bacteria in presence of glucose. On investigation it was shown to effect the oxidation of glucose to gluconic acid with the production of hydrogen peroxide ; the hydrogen peroxide was responsible for the antibacterial activity. The reduced form of the enzyme was oxidised by molecular oxygen. That the antibacterial action was in fact due to the formation of hydrogen peroxide, was confirmed by the demonstration that other flavoproteins were equally effective. F. Lipmann and C. R. Owen [60] and D. E. Green and R. Pauli [61] showed that milk xanthine oxidase had similar properties, but other flavoproteins were more difficult to test, as it was impossible to free them from catalase that destroyed the hydrogen peroxide as it was formed.

Fumaric Hydrogenase

Fumaric acid is reduced to succinic acid by an enzyme system which contains riboflavine adenine dinucleotide.[62] This enzyme was also shown to reduce maleic acid, crotyl alcohol, phenyl crotyl alcohol and geraniol, but the rate of reduction of these compounds was only a fraction of the rate at which fumaric acid was reduced. The identity of fumaric hydrogenase with eight other flavoproteins was excluded by subsequent work carried out by Fischer *et al.*,[63] but it may be identical with the xanthine oxidase-like enzyme isolated by Green *et al.*[34]

Lactic and Pyruvic Acid Oxidases

Two other enzymes containing flavine-adenine-dinucleotide are pyruvic acid oxidase,[64] and an enzyme isolated from *Mycobacterium phlei* that was specific for the oxidation of lactic acid to pyruvic acid under anaerobic, and to acetic acid under aerobic, conditions.[65]

Luciferin

F. H. Johnson and H. Eyring [66] showed that the substrate, luciferin, of the luminescent system of *Cypridina* consists of a pyridine nucleotide and a flavoprotein.

The former acted as reductant, whilst the latter comprised the component capable of being excited by oxidation. Some of these excited molecules emitted radiations without being destroyed, whilst others were destroyed by the energy absorbed. It is this latter phenomenon that is responsible for the degradation of riboflavine on exposure to light. The authors conclude : " Thus, in luminous bacteria, light emission presumably occurs when flavoprotein, reduced by hydrogen from suitable substrates (*e.g.* glucose) *via* the dehydrogenase-coenzyme system, is oxidised directly by oxygen ".

Oxidation of Flavoproteins

The flavoprotein dinucleotides can be oxidised by molecular oxygen, but in the organism they are, like the mononucleotide, oxidised by cytochrome *c* and this explains why the oxidation of D-amino acids and of pyruvic acid by bacteria possessing cytochromes is completely inhibited by hydrogen cyanide.[67, 68] When cytochrome is absent, as in some bacteria and protozoa, oxidation may be effected by molecular oxygen. The effect of cyanide on oxygen consumption and luminescence, respectively, indicates that most of the hydrogen proceeds stepwise, by electron transfer through the cytochrome-haeme system, to oxygen. If chlorophyll were substituted for the related haeme molecule, the same system of catalysts operating in the reverse direction would lead to photosynthesis. In luminescence two hydrogen atoms were oxidised for each quantum emitted, whilst in photosynthesis single hydrogen atoms were made available.

To bring about this transfer of hydrogen in these enzymic reactions, the riboflavine within the coenzyme undergoes alternate reduction and oxidation. The reduction product is dihydro- or leuco-riboflavine and, as already stated, it readily undergoes re-oxidation on shaking with air.

According to R. Kuhn and R. Ströbele [69] the mechanism of the reduction is not just simple addition of hydrogen across the centre ring, but proceeds *via* three intermediate compounds, the bronze-green verdoflavine, the grass-green chloroflavine and the carmine-red rhodoflavine. These changes are represented by the formulæ on the opposite page (where R = ribityl-).

Other Functions of Riboflavine : Riboflavine in the Eye

The occurrence of flavines in the retinae of fishes has long been known and the possible importance of riboflavine for vision in dim light was confirmed by observations made by P. Karrer and H. Fritzsche [70] on the fluorescence curves of riboflavine and its analogues. They found that maximum fluorescence occurred at a concentration similar to that in which the flavines occur in the eyes

Oxygen
consumption

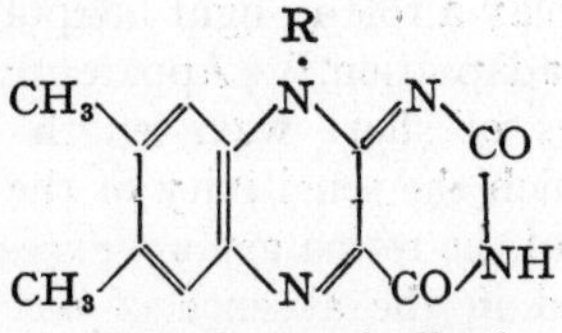

Riboflavine (yellow)

0

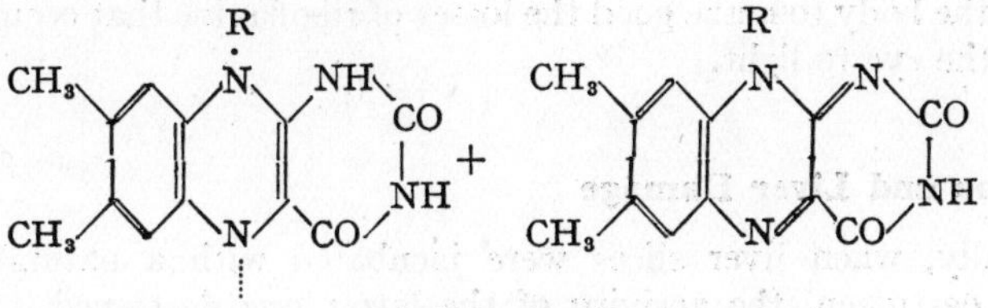

Verdoflavine (bronze-green)

0·25

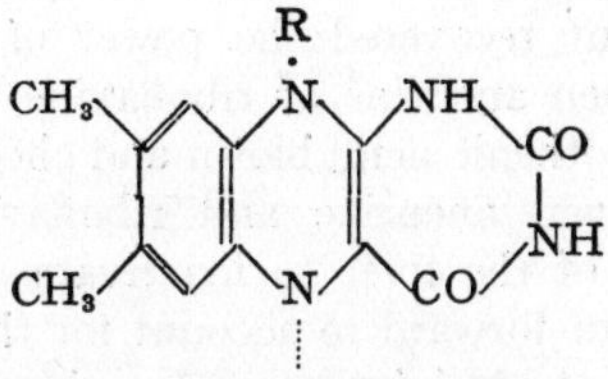

Chloroflavine (grass-green)

0·50

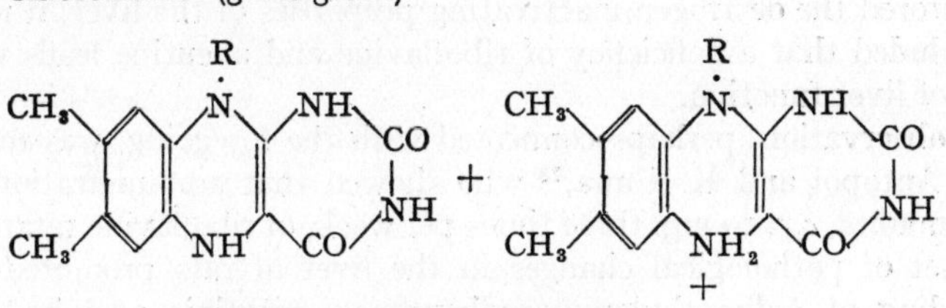

Rhodoflavine (carmoisine red)

0·75

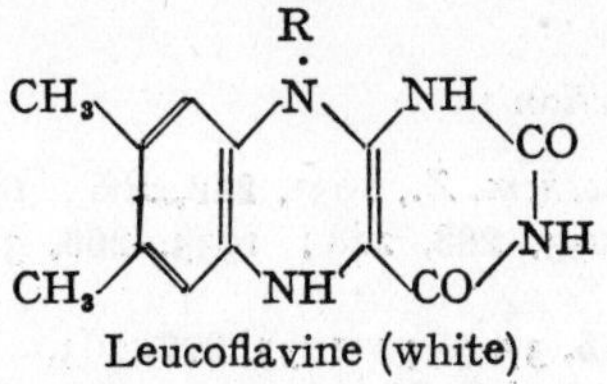

Leucoflavine (white)

1·00

of fishes. This observation seems of particular significance in view of the clinical data (see page 174) associating the presence of opaque cornea and impaired vision in dim light with ariboflavinosis. It was suggested that photolysis of riboflavine with precipitation of the sparingly soluble lumiflavine may be a factor in the mechanism.

Riboflavine has also been shown to be present in the retinal pigment of the human eye, where it appears to play a rôle in light adaptation similar to that of rhodopsin in dark adaptation.[71] Apparently, it has the property of transforming rays of short wave-length into yellowish-green fluorescent light, for which the sensitivity of the eye is maximal. It also protects the cones of the retina against excessive light. Riboflavine is not re-synthesised in the absence of oxygen, and the ocular manifestations of ariboflavinosis are due to the inability of the body to make good the losses of riboflavine that occur on exposing the eye to light.

Riboflavine and Liver Damage

Normally, when liver slices were incubated with a natural or synthetic oestrogen, the activity of the latter was destroyed. The livers of rats reared on a vitamin B-deficient diet, however, were unable to effect this inactivation, but recovered the power of inactivating oestrone and oestradiol when aneurine or riboflavine was added to the diet ; [72] pyridoxine, pantothenic acid, biotin and choline were ineffective in this respect. Even aneurine and riboflavine, however, did not restore the ability of the liver to inactivate stilboestrol. No explanation has been put forward to account for these observations, although, from the fact that administration of methionine also restored the oestrogen-inactivating properties of the liver, it may be concluded that a deficiency of riboflavine and aneurine leads to a failure of liver function.

An observation, perhaps connected with the foregoing, was made by W. Antopol and K. Unna,[73] who showed that administration of large amounts, e.g. 10 mg. three times per week, of riboflavine retarded the onset of pathological changes in the liver of rats promoted by the feeding of p-dimethylaminoazobenzene ; nicotinic acid had no effect.

References to Section 15

1. O. Warburg and W. Christian, *Biochem. Z.*, 1931, **242,** 206 ; 1932, **254,** 438 ; 1933, **257,** 492 ; 1933, **263,** 228 ; 1933, **266,** 377 ; *Naturwiss.*, 1932, **20,** 688, 980.
2. H. Theorell, *Biochem. Z.*, 1934, **275,** 37, 344 ; 1935, **278,** 263.
3. F. Weygand and H. Stocher, *Z. physiol. Chem.*, 1937, **247,** 167.
4. F. Weygand and L. Birkofer, *ibid.*, 1939, **261,** 172.
5. H. Theorell, *Biochem. Z.*, 1935, **278,** 279.
6. R. A. Kekwick and K. O. Pederson, *Biochem. J.*, 1936, **30,** 2201.

7. R. Kuhn and H. Rudy, *Z. physiol. Chem.*, 1936, **239**, 47 ; *Ber.*, 1936, **69**, 1974, 2034.

8. I. Banga, A. Szent-Györgyi and L. Vargha, *Biochem. Z.*, 1932, **246**, 203 ; *Z. physiol. Chem.*, 1932, **210**, 228.

9. H. Rudy, *Naturwiss.*, 1935, **23**, 286.

10. R. Kuhn, H. Rudy and F. Weygand, *Ber.*, 1936, **69**, 1543.

11. R. Kuhn and H. Rudy, *ibid.*, 1074.

12. R. Kuhn and H. Rudy, *ibid.*, 2557.

13. L. Laszt and F. Verzár, *Arch. ges., Physiol.*, 1935, **236**, 693.

14. H. Rudy, *Z. angew. Chem.*, 1936, **49**, 323.

15. J. W. Ferrebee, *J. Biol. Chem.*, 1940, **136**, 719.

16. P. Karrer, P. Frei and H. Meerwein, *Helv. Chim. Acta*, 1937, **20**, 79 ; P. Karrer, P. Frei, B. H. Ringier and H. Bendas, *ibid.*, 1938, **21**, 826 ; O. Warburg, W. Christian and A. Griese, *Biochem. Z.*, 1938, **295**, 261 ; 1938, **297**, 417 ; 1938, **298**, 150.

17. O. Warburg and W. Christian, *ibid.*, 1938, **298**, 150, 368.

18. E. P. Abraham, *Biochem. J.*, 1939, **33**, 543.

19. S. Ochoa and R. J. Possiter, *Nature*, 1939, **144**, 787.

20. J. R. Klein and H. I. Kohn, *J. Biol. Chem.*, 1940, **136**, 177.

20a. O. A. Bessey, O. H. Lowry and R. H. Love, *ibid.*, 1949, **180**, 755.

21. O. Warburg and W. Christian, *Biochem. Z.*, 1932, **254**, 438 ; 1933, **266**, 377.

22. H. Theorell, *ibid.*, 1936, **288**, 317 ; *Nature*, 1936, **138**, 687.

23. E. S. G. Barron, *Cold Spring Harbour Symposia Quant. Biol.*, 1939, **7**, 154.

24. E. Haas, B. L. Horecker and T. R. Hogness, *J. Biol. Chem.*, 1940, **136**, 747.

25. E. Haas, *Biochem. Z.*, 1938, **298**, 378.

26. E. Haas, C. J. Harrer and T. R. Hogness, *J. Biol. Chem.*, 1942, **143**, 341.

27. E. Adler, H. von Euler, G. Günther and E. D. Plass, *Skand. Arch. Physiol.*, 1939, **82**, 61 ; E. Adler, H. von Euler and G. Günther, *Nature*, 1939, **143**, 641 ; E. P. Abraham and E. Adler, *Biochem. J.*, 1940, **34**, 119.

28. K. Okunuki and E. Yakusizi, *Proc. Imp. Acad. Tokyo*, 1940, **16**, 144.

29. F. Schardinger, *Z. Untersuch. Nahr. Genussm.*, 1902, **5**, 1113.

30. V. Subrahmanyan, D. E. Green and A. H. Gordon, *Nature*, 1939, **144**, 1016 ; A. H. Gordon, D. E. Green and V. Subrahmanyan, *Biochem. J.*, 1940, **34**, 764.

31. E. G. Ball, *Science*, 1938, **88**, 131 ; *Angew. Chem.*, 1938, **51**, 738 ; *J. Biol. Chem.*, 1939, **128**, 51.

32. H. S. Corran and D. E. Green, *Biochem. J.*, 1938, **32**, 2231 ; D. E. Green and H. S. Corran, *Angew. Chem.*, 1938, **51**, 738 ; H. S. Corran, J. G. Dewan, A. H. Gordon and D. E. Green, *Biochem. J.*, 1939, **34**, 1694.

33. D. E. Green, *ibid.*, 1934, **28**, 1550.

34. D. E. Green, W. E. Knox and P. K. Stumpf, *J. Biol. Chem.*, 1941, **138**, 775.

35. A. E. Axelrod and C. A. Elvehjem, *J. Biol. Chem.*, 1941, **140**, 725.
36. O. Warburg and W. Christian, *Biochem. Z.*, 1938, **295**, 261 ; 1938, **298**, 150.
37. E. Negelein and H. Brömel, *ibid.*, 1939, **300**, 225.
38. F. B. Straub, *Nature*, 1938, **141**, 603.
39. H. A. Krebs, *Z. physiol. Chem.*, 1933, **217**, 191 ; 1933, **218**, 157 ; *Biochem. J.*, 1935, **29**, 1620.
40. A. E. Axelrod, H. A. Sober and C. A. Elvehjem, *Nature*, 1939, **144**, 670.
40a. H. L. Mayfield and M. T. Hedrick, *J. Nutrition*, 1949, **37**, 475.
41. M. E. Krahl, A. K. Keltch and G. H. A. Clowes, *J. Biol. Chem.*, 1940, **136**, 563.
42. C. L. Hoagland, S. M. Ward, J. E. Smadel and T. M. Rivers, *J. Exp. Med.*, 1941, **74**, 133.
43. P. Handler, F. Bernheim and J. R. Klein, *J. Biol. Chem.*, 1941, **138**, 203.
44. J. R. Klein and H. Kamin, *ibid.*, 507.
45. N. H. Horowitz, *ibid.*, 1944, **154**, 141.
46. A. Neuberger and F. Sanger, *Biochem. J.*, 1944, **38**, 119.
47. C. L. Wright and S. C. Sabine, *J. Biol. Chem.*, 1944, **155**, 315.
48. E. Haas, *ibid.*, 321.
49. M. Blanchard, D. E. Green, V. Nocito and S. Ratner, *ibid.*, 1945, **161**, 583.
50. S. Ratner, V. Nocito and D. E. Green, *ibid.*, 1944, **152**, 49.
51. E. A. Zeller, R. Stern and N. Wenk, *Helv. Chim. Acta*, 1940, **23**, 1.
52. M. Laskowski, *J. Biol. Chem.*, 1942, **145**, 457.
52a. R. Kapeller-Adler, *Biochem. J.*, 1949, **44**, 70.
53. W. E. Knox, *J. Biol. Chem.*, 1946, **163**, 699.
54. W. Franke and M. Deffner, *Annalen*, 1937, **532**, 1 ; 1939, **541**, 117.
55. D. Mueller, *Biochem. Z.*, 1928, **199**, 136 ; 1929, **205**, 111 ; 1929, **213**, 211 ; 1931, **232**, 423.
56. C. E. Coulthard, R. Michaelis, W. F. Short, G. Sykes, G. E. H. Skrimshire, A. F. B. Standfast, J. H. Birkinshaw and H. Raistrick, *Nature*, 1942, **150**, 634 ; *Biochem. J.*, 1945, **39**, 24.
57. J. R. Van Bruggen, F. J. Reithel, C. K. Cain, P. A. Katzman, E. A. Doisy, R. D. Muir, E. C. Roberts, W. L. Gaby, D. M. Homan and L. R. Jones, *J. Biol. Chem.*, 1943, **148**, 365.
58. W. Kocholaty, *Arch. Biochem.*, 1943, **2**, 73.
59. O. Schales, *ibid.*, 487.
60. F. Lipmann and C. R. Owen, *Science*, 1943, **98**, 246.
61. D. E. Green and R. Pauli, *Proc. Soc. Exp. Biol. Med.*, 1943, **54**, 148.
62. F. G. Fischer, A. Roedig and K. Rauch, *Naturwiss.*, 1939, **27**, 197 ; F. G. Fischer and H. Eysenbach, *Annalen*, 1937, **529**, 87 ; 1937, **530**, 99.
63. F. G. Fischer, A. Roedig and K. Rauch, *ibid.*, 1942, **552**, 203.
64. F. Lipmann, *Nature*, 1939, **143**, 436.

65. N. L. Edson, *Biochem. J.*, 1947, **41**, 145.

66. F. H. Johnson and H. Eyring, *J. Amer. Chem. Soc.*, 1944, **66**, 848.

67. E. S. G. Barron and T. E. Friedemann, *J. Biol. Chem.*, 1941, **137**, 593.

68. F. Bernheim, M. L. C. Bernheim and M. D. Webster, *ibid.*, 1935, **110**, 165.

69. R. Kuhn and R. Ströbele, *Ber.*, 1937, **70**, 753.

70. P. Karrer and H. Fritzsche, *Helv. Chim. Acta*, 1935, **18**, 911.

71. M. Heiman, *Arch. Ophthal.*, 1942, **28**, 493.

72. A. Segaloff and A. Segaloff, *Endocrin*, 1944, **34**, 346; K. Unna, H. O. Singher, C. J. Kensler, H. C. Taylor and C. P. Rhoads, *Proc. Soc. Exp. Biol. Med.*, 1944, **55**, 254; H. O. Singher, C. J. Kensler, H. C. Taylor, C. P. Rhoads and K. Unna, *J. Biol. Chem.*, 1944, **154**, 79.

73. W. Antopol and K. Unna, *Cancer Res.*, 1942, **2**, 694.

16. RIBOFLAVINE IN THE NUTRITION OF MICRO-ORGANISMS

Yeasts and Other Fungi

No yeast has been reported for which riboflavine is an essential growth factor [1, 2, 3] and, of seventeen moulds also examined, none required riboflavine. Riboflavine is not, in fact, a constituent of " bios " (see page 105).

Yeasts and moulds appear to be capable of synthesising riboflavine, some in astonishingly large amounts (see page 148).

Bacteria

Bacteria vary greatly in their requirements for riboflavine. Some, such as *Bacillus proteus vulgaris*, *B. lactis aerogenes*, *B. mesentericus*, *B. vulgatus*, *B. faecalis alcaligenes* and *Escherichia coli*, are capable of synthesising it,[4] and the significance of this synthesis in the animal economy has already been discussed (see page 185). The tuberculosis bacterium does not require riboflavine.[4a] Some bacteria, on the other hand, are incapable of growth in the absence of riboflavine, but these are very few in number. *Lactobacillus helveticus* (*L. casei* ε) is the best known of these and is the organism most commonly employed for the microbiological assay of riboflavine (see page 157) ; the closely related organism, *L. arabinosus*, does not require riboflavine. Other bacteria for which riboflavine is essential are : *Streptococcus mastiditis*, *S. faecium*, *Bacterium bifidum*, and *Streptobacterium plantarum* ; [5] *Bacillus Delbrückii*, *Streptobacterium casei*, *Leuconostoc Gayoni* and

B. lactis acidi ; [6] *Clostridium tetani* ; [7] *Erysipelothrix rhusiopathiae* and *Listerella monocytogenes* ; [8] *Leuconostoc mesenteroides* P. 60 [9] and *Streptococcus faecalis* R (*S. lactis* R).[10] *L. helveticus* utilises riboflavine-phosphate and flavine adenine dinucleotide for growth and acid production equally as well as riboflavine.

Riboflavine is utilised by micro-organisms whether they are able to synthesise it or whether they require an exogenous source of the vitamin. H. McIlwain [11] estimated that in the five bacteria, *Aerobacter aerogenes*, *Serratia marcescens*, *Pseudomonas fluorescens*, *Proteus vulgaris* and *Clostridium butylicum* between 7200 and 11,000 molecules of ribo-flavine are present in each cell, and that the rate of synthesis ranges from 2·4 to 11 molecules per cell per second. The " turnover numbers " for fumaric hydrogenase, D-amino acid oxidase and diaphorase, for each of which flavine-adenine-dinucleotide is the coenzyme, were 22, 40 to 50 and 33 molecules per molecule of enzyme per second, that is, between 22 and 50 molecules of substrate react with each molecule of the enzyme per second. The rates of synthesis and inactivation of riboflavine indicate that these reactions are reactions of mμ mol. order in contrast to the ordinary reactions of the bacterial cell, which are of μml. order. This matter is further discussed on page 284.

Riboflavine is associated with a possible explanation of the pheno-menon of drug-resistance, that is the ability of certain micro-organisms on repeated exposure to sub-lethal concentrations of a drug to acquire resistance to it. It has been suggested [12] that the flavoproteins of resistant cells may have become more easily dissociated, due pre-sumably to some alteration in the protein component. It was ob-served, for instance, that *Pneumococci* which had become resistant to acriflavine or mepacrine readily lost dehydrogenase activity on dilu-tion or warming, and that the activity was restored on addition of riboflavine ; susceptible cells did not exhibit this behaviour. Simi-larly, an extract from resistant cells showed reduced activity when compared with a similar extract from susceptible cells. Riboflavine increased the activity of the former, although the riboflavine contents of both types of cells were approximately the same.

References to Section 16

1. P. R. Burkholder, *Amer. J. Bot.*, 1943, **30**, 206.
2. P. R. Burkholder and I. McVeigh, *Bull. Torrey Bot. Club*, 1943, **70**, 372.
3. P. R. Burkholder, I. McVeigh and D. Moyer, *J. Bact.*, 1944, **48**, 385.
4. R. C. Thompson, *Univ. Texas Publ.*, 1942, No. 4237, p. 87 ; P. R. Burkholder and I. McVeigh, *Proc. Nat. Acad. Sci.*, 1942, **28**, 285.
4a. H. C. Hou, *Proc. Soc. Exp. Biol. Med.*, 1949, **70**, 582.
5. S. Orla-Jensen, N. C. Otte and A. Snog-Kjaer, *Danske Videnskab. Selskabs. Skrifter*, 1936, **6**, No. 5.

6. E. E. Snell and F. M. Strong, *Ind. Eng. Chem., Anal. Ed.*, 1939, **11**, 346.

7. R. E. Feeney, J. H. Mueller and P. A. Miller, *J. Bact.*, 1943, **46**, 563.

8. S. H. Hutner, *ibid.*, 1942, **43**, 629.

9. M. S. Dunn, N. N. Camien, S. Shankman, W. Frankl and L. B. Rockland, *J. Biol. Chem.*, 1944, **156**, 703.

10. J. L. Stokes, M. Gunness, I. M. Dwyer and M. C. Caswell, *ibid.*, 1945, **160**, 35.

11. H. McIlwain, *Nature*, 1946, **158**, 898.

12. M. G. Sevag and J. S. Gots, *J. Bact.*, 1948, **56**, 723.

17. EFFECT OF RIBOFLAVINE ON HIGHER PLANTS

Riboflavine appears to have no stimulatory effect on the growth of higher plants and, indeed, it is said to be synthesised during the germination of oats, wheat, barley and maize,[1] and in the root-tips of various plant species.[2]   The riboflavine content of cereals, peas and beans increased considerably during germination—from 0·6–2·0 to 2·0–12·4 μg. per g. of dry matter.

References to Section 17

1. P. R. Burkholder, *Science*, 1943, **97**, 562.
2. J. Bonner, *Bot. Gaz.*, 1942, **103**, 581.

18. RIBOFLAVINE REQUIREMENTS OF INSECTS

Riboflavine is essential for the normal development of the beetles, *Ptinus tectus*, *Tribolium confusum* and *Silvanus surinamensis* and of the moth, *Ephestia elutella*, but not of the beetles, *Sitodrepa panicea* and *Lasioderma serricorne*.[1]   The difference in the requirements of the two groups of beetles was shown to be due, as with aneurine (see page 115), to the presence in the last two insects of intracellular symbiotic micro-organisms capable of synthesising riboflavine, which then became available to supply the metabolic needs of the host. Neither *Lasioderma* nor *Sitodrepa* grew in the absence of riboflavine when reared from sterilised eggs.

Riboflavine was also necessary for the development of the larvae of the mosquito, *Aedes aegypti*,[2] of *Tenebrio molitor*,[3] of the fruit fly, *Drosophila melanogaster*,[4] and of the larvae of the rice-moth, *Corcyra cephalonica*.[5]

In two species of insects, namely the American cockroach,[6] *Periplaneta americana*, and *Tineola bisselliella*,[7] riboflavine accumulated in the Malpighian tubes, even when the diet contained little or no riboflavine. In the cockroach, the contents of the tubes were forty times as rich in riboflavine as is ox-liver.

References to Section 18

1. G. Fraenkel and M. Blewett, *Nature*, 1941, **147**, 716 ; 1943, **151**, 703 ; 1943, **152**, 506 ; *Biochem. J.*, 1943, **37**, 686 ; *Proc. Roy. Soc. B.*, 1944, **132**, 212.
2. L. Golberg, B. de Meillon and M. Lavoipierre, *J. Exp. Biol.*, 1945, **21**, 84, 90.
3. H. E. Martin and L. Hare, *Biol. Bull. Woods Hole*, 1942, **83**, 428.
4. E. L. Tatum, *Proc. Nat. Acad. Sci.*, 1941, **27**, 193.
5. P. S. Sarma, *Indian J. Med. Res.*, 1943, **31**, 165.
6. R. L. Metcalf and R. L. Patton, *J. Cell. Comp. Physiol.*, 1942, **19**, 373.
7. R. G. Busnel and A. Drilhon, *Compt. rend.*, 1943, **216**, 213.

19. ANALOGUES OF RIBOFLAVINE

Growth Stimulators

The first analogue of riboflavine to be prepared was 6 : 7-dimethyl-9-(L-1'-arabityl)-isoalloxazine, which R. Kuhn and F. Weygand [1] synthesised before it was known that riboflavine was derived from ribose. It was found to possess vitamin B_2 activity, though to a smaller degree than the D-ribityl compound prepared subsequently. Other compounds with biological activity were synthesised later, mainly by Karrer and his collaborators. In general, these bore a close resemblence to riboflavine and it was evident that the molecule could not be greatly modified without loss of activity. Karrer *et al.*[2] found that even the L-ribityl compound, the optical isomer of ribo-flavine, was inactive in rats in a dose of 20 μg. per day. The following compounds were prepared and found to be active in rats :

6 : 7-dimethyl-9-(L-1'-arabityl)-isoalloxazine (araboflavine) [1, 3]
7-methyl-9-(D-1'-ribityl)-isoalloxazine [2, 4]
6-methyl-9-(D-1'-ribityl)-isoalloxazine [4, 5]
6-ethyl-7-methyl-9-(D-1'-ribityl)-isoalloxazine [6]

Their activity was approximately half that of riboflavine. F. Weygand [8] suggested, however, that the apparent activity of arabo-flavine might be due to the presence, as a contaminant, of riboflavine formed by an Amadori rearrangement (see page 144).

These analogues, with the possible exception of the arabityl derivatives, were also shown to stimulate the growth of *Strepto-bacterium casei* and *B. lactis acidi*.[7]

The following compounds were found to have no appreciable activity in rats :

6 : 7-dimethyl-9-(D-1'-xylityl)-isoalloxazine [3]
     ,,   -9-(L-1'-rhamnityl)-   ,,   [3]
     ,,   -9-(D-1'-arabityl)-   ,,   [2]
   7-methyl-9-(D-1'-dulcityl)-   ,,   [3]
     ,,   -9-(L-1'-arabityl)-   ,,   [3]
     ,,   -9-(D-1'-sorbityl)-   ,,   [3]
     ,,   -9-(D-1'-mannityl)-   ,,   [3]
6 : 7-dimethyl-9-(L-1'-ribityl)-   ,,   [2]
     ,,   -9-(D-1'-lyxityl)-   ,,   [2]
     ,,   -9-(D-1'-desoxyribityl)- ,,   [9]
   7-ethyl-9-(D-1'-ribityl)-   ,,   [6]
6-ethyl-7-methyl-9-(L-1'-arabityl)-   ,,   [6]
5 : 6-benzo-9-(D-1'-ribityl)-   ,,   [6]
     ,,   -9-(L-1'-arabityl)-   ,,   [6]
6 : 7-dimethyl-9-(D-ribosido)-   ,,   [10]
     ,,   -9-(L-arabinosido)-   ,,   [10]
6 : 8-dimethyl-9-(D-1'-ribityl)-   ,,   [11]
     ,,   -9-(L-1-'arabityl)-   ,,   [11]
5 : 7-dimethyl-9-(D-1'-ribityl)-   ,,   [11]
     ,,   -9-(L-1'-arabityl)-   ,,   [11]

Several of these compounds were also tested on *S. casei* and *L. lactis acidi,* and were likewise found to be inactive.[7]

6 : 7-Dimethyl-9-(D-1'-lyxityl)-isoalloxazine (lyxoflavine) has been isolated from the human myocardium, 5 mg. being obtained from 10 kg.[12a]

The preparation of compounds related to lumiflavine was described by H. Lettré and M. E. Fernholz.[12] These were a series of 9-alkyl-5 : 6-benzoflavines, made by condensing alloxan with 9-substituted naphthalene-*o*-diamines. The substituents ranged from the methyl to the cetyl group, and all the compounds were sparingly soluble in water. When injected subcutaneously, a water-soluble flavine of unknown constitution appeared in the urine within one hour of the injection. None of the compounds was active.

Isoriboflavine (5 : 6-dimethyl-9-D-r'-ribityl-isoalloxazine) (I) and 2-amino-4 : 5-dimethyl-1-ribitylamino-benzene (II) :

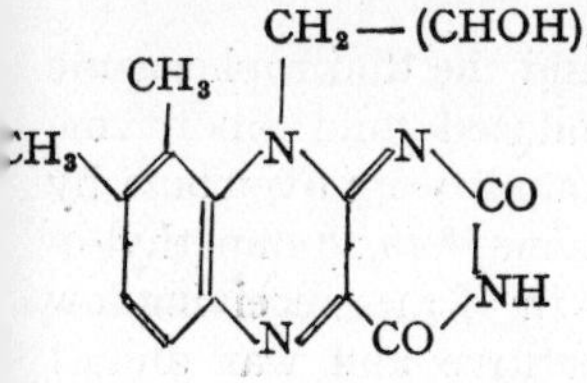

    I. 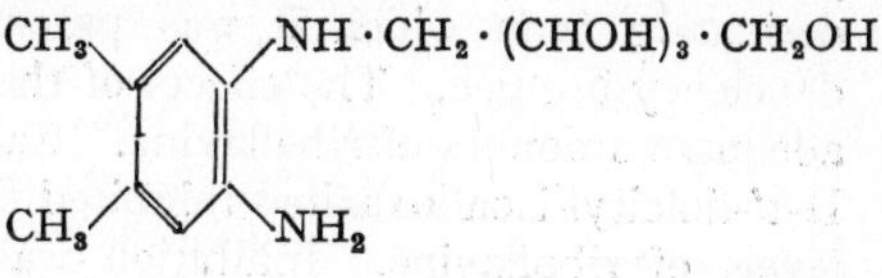   II.

had little growth-stimulating effect on *Lactobacillus helveticus*, but were able to enhance the effect of traces of riboflavine or flavine adenine dinucleotide on this organism.[13] In the presence of alloxan, however, the ribitylamino compound (II) was a potent stimulator of *L. helveticus*. Both riboflavine phosphate and flavine adenine diphosphate were as effective as riboflavine for growth and acid production in *L. helveticus*.

Fluorescyanine, in 50-μg. doses, accelerated the growth of rats maintained on a riboflavine-deficient diet, and abolished the nervous symptoms from which the animals suffered.[14]

Growth Inhibitors

Not all the analogues of riboflavine that fail to stimulate the growth of organisms for which riboflavine is essential are merely inert to the organisms, for some inhibit their growth. Thus, 6 : 7-dichloro-9-D-1'-ribityl-isoalloxazine, which failed to stimulate the growth of two strains of *B. lactis acidi* that were unable to grow without riboflavine, and yeast, *Staph. aureus* and *Streptobacterium plantarum*, for which riboflavine was not essential, inhibited the growth of all these organisms with the exception of the yeast.[15] Inhibition was competitive, being overcome by the addition of riboflavine. The oxidation-reduction potential of the antagonist was − 0·095 v. compared with − 0·185 v. for riboflavine ; possibly the dichloro-compound is unable to replace riboflavine because its dihydro-derivative is not sufficiently negative to hydrogenate oxygen. Isoriboflavine[16] (5 : 6-dimethyl-9-D-1'-ribityl-isoalloxazine) counteracted the growth-promoting action of riboflavine in rats, whilst the phenazine analogue of riboflavine[17] (2 : 4-diamino-7 : 8-dimethyl-10-ribityl-5 : 10-dihydrophenazine)

$$CH_2 \cdot (CHOH)_3 \cdot CH_2OH$$

produced riboflavine deficiency in bacteria, and the dinitrophenazine derivative from which it was prepared produced mild riboflavine deficiency in mice. The effects of the compounds were overcome by adequate amounts of riboflavine. Galactoflavine[18] (6 : 7-dimethyl-9-D-1'-dulcityl-isoalloxazine) inhibited the growth of rats receiving low levels of riboflavine. Inhibition was competitive and was almost completely counteracted by a daily intake of 200 μg. of riboflavine. A similar, though less marked, effect was observed with D-arabo-flavine[19] in rats, but L-araboflavine had no such antagonistic effect.

The antagonism of the D-isomer was not due to mechanical displacement of riboflavine from an enzyme system.

Lumiflavine, the photolysis product of riboflavine, inhibited or stimulated the utilisation of riboflavine or flavine adenine dinucleotide by *L. helveticus*, according to the relative amounts present.[13] Inhibition by lumiflavine was much greater with flavine adenine dinucleotide than with riboflavine, suggesting that riboflavine may be attached to the apo-enzyme before conversion to riboflavine phosphate or flavine adenine dinucleotide.

Riboflavine was oxidised stoichiometrically to lumiflavine by *Pseudomonas riboflavina*, and this organism also attacked the ribityl group of analogues of riboflavine. The oxidation was inhibited by phenyl-4 : 5-dimethyl-isoalloxazine,[20] but the inhibition was not competitive, since it was not reversed by high concentrations of riboflavine. Moreover, this compound had no antiriboflavine activity in rats.

Many substances that exhibited antimalarial activity were found to inhibit the growth-promoting effect of riboflavine on *L. helveticus*.[21] These included mepacrine, 2-*p*-chloroanilino-, 2-(6'-bromonaphthyl-2'-amino)-, and 2-*p*-chlorophenylguanidino-4-diethylaminoethylamino-6-methylpyrimidine. This type of approach led to the elaboration of a number of new antimalarials, but rather paradoxically the best of these, proguanil, did not antagonise riboflavine. Isoalloxazines containing a basic side-chain, *e.g.* 6 : 7-dimethyl-9-γ-amino-β-hydroxypropyl-isoalloxazine

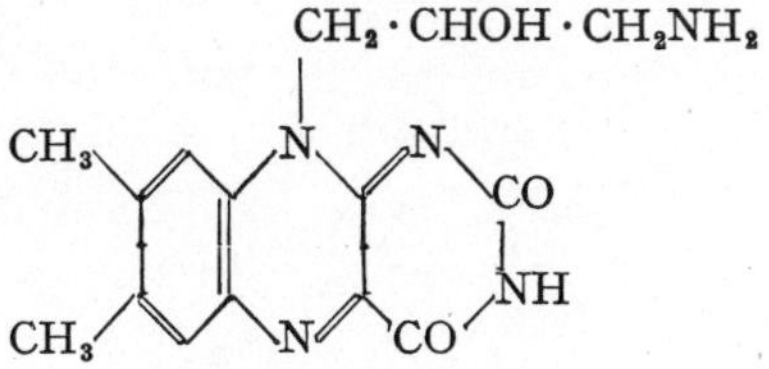

$$CH_2 \cdot CHOH \cdot CH_2NH_2$$

had no antimalarial or bacteriostatic activity, and did not antagonise the growth-promoting effect of riboflavine on *L. helveticus* or *E. coli*.[22]

References to Section 19

1. R. Kuhn and F. Weygand, *Ber.*, 1934, **67**, 2084.
2. P. Karrer, H. Salomon, K. Schöpp, F. Benz and B. Becker, *Helv. Chim. Acta*, 1935, **18**, 908.
3. H. von Euler, P. Karrer, M. Malmberg, K. Schöpp, F. Benz, B. Becker and P. Frei, *ibid.*, 522.
4. P. Karrer, H. von Euler, M. Malmberg and K. Schöpp, *Svensk. Kem. Tids.*, 1935, **47**, 153.
5. P. Karrer and F. M. Strong, *Helv. Chim. Acta*, 1935, **18**, 1343.
6. P. Karrer and T. H. Quibell, *ibid.*, 1936, **19**, 1034.

7. E. F. Möller, *Angew. Chem.*, 1940, **53**, 204.
8. F. Weygand, *Ber.*, 1940, **73**, 1259.
9. P. Karrer, H. Salomon, K. Schöpp and F. Benz, *Helv. Chim. Acta*, 1935, **18**, 1143.
10. R. Kuhn and R. Ströbele, *Ber.*, 1937, **70**, 747.
11. R. Kuhn, P. Desnuelle and F. Weygand, *ibid.*, 1293.
12. H. Lettré and M. E. Fernholz, *ibid.*, 1940, **73**, 436.
12a. E. S. Pallares and H. M. Garza, *Arch. Biochem.*, 1949, **22**, 63.
13. H. P. Sarett, *Fed. Proc.*, 1945, **4**, 101 ; *J. Biol. Chem.*, 1946, **162**, 87.
14. R. G. Busnel, P. Chaucard, H. Mazoué, M. Pesson and M. Polonovski, *Compt. rend.*, 1943, **217**, 185.
15. R. Kuhn, F. Weygand and E. F. Möller, *Ber.*, 1943, **76**, 1044.
16. G. A. Emerson and M. Tishler, *Proc. Soc. Exp. Biol. Med.*, 1944, **55**, 184.
17. D. W. Woolley, *J. Biol. Chem.*, 1944, **154**, 31.
18. G. A. Emerson, E. Wurtz and O. H. Johnson, *ibid.*, 1945, **160**, 165.
19. H. von Euler and P. Karrer, *Helv. Chim. Acta*, 1946, **29**, 353.
20. J. W. Foster, *J. Bact.*, 1944, **47**, 27 ; 1944, **48**, 97.
21. J. Madinaveitia, *Biochem. J.*, 1946, **40**, 373.
22. R. R. Adams, C. A. Weisel and H. S. Mosher, *J. Amer. Chem. Soc.*, 1946, **68**, 883.

CHAPTER IV

NICOTINIC ACID (NIACIN)

1. INTRODUCTION

THE term "pellagra" was originally used rather loosely to describe a condition characterised by a bilaterally symmetrical eruption. As far back as 1918, J. Goldberger, G. A. Wheeler and V. P. Sydenstricker,[1] claimed that pellagra, as thus defined, included at least two aetiologically distinct syndromes, and suggested that two dietary factors might be involved. Seven years later, J. Goldberger and W. F. Tanner [2] announced that pellagra could be cured by yeast and called the responsible factor the PP (pellagra preventative) factor.

Pellagra is largely a disease of warm climates, and has always been associated with the use of maize as the staple cereal, though oats and rye may also produce pellagra if used as the sole cereal. Pellagra assumes a variety of forms, mainly because other members of the vitamin B complex besides the pellagra preventative factor are invariably deficient in or missing from the pellagra-producing diet.

The use of experimental animals in the investigation of pellagra did not meet with immediate success ; indeed, the use of the three species, rats, chicks and dogs, only led to bewildering and often contradictory results, which at the time were extremely difficult to interpret. Thus a dermatitis similar to pellagra was produced artificially in rats by J. Goldberger and R. D. Lillie,[3] using a ration to which adequate amounts of an antineuritic concentrate had been added ; the rats were cured by administration of autoclaved yeast, and it was hoped that a satisfactory animal test for the new factor had been discovered, thus facilitating research on its isolation and identification. These hopes were not realised, however, for it was found difficult to use the onset of dermatitis as the basis of a quantitative method of assaying the PP-factor content of foodstuffs. It therefore became customary to assay these by the growth produced in rats. W. R. Ackroyd, however, found that maize, the pellagra-producing cereal *par excellence* (see page 240), produced good growth in rats, and it became evident that the rat-growth method was not assaying the PP-factor at all, but another factor, later shown to be riboflavine. Much of the old literature in which this method is used is, therefore, misleading. As will be seen later (page 296), the so-called " pellagra-like " dermatitis of rats is produced by yet another factor called by P. György,[4] vitamin B_6.

An attempt to find an animal the response of which to the PP-factor was more specific than that of the rat was made by C. A. Elvehjem and C. J. Koehn,[5] who found that chicks, when fed on a pellagra-producing diet, also developed a form of dermatitis ; for a time, protection against chick " pellagra " and the production of normal growth were taken to be a measure of PP-factor activity. Liver and a commercial extract of liver were found to be highly active, whereas riboflavine was inactive. By fractionation of the liver extract a much richer concentrate of the chick dermatitis factor was obtained which also cured blacktongue in dogs,[6] and it seemed as though the production of dermatitis in chickens was in fact a valid test of PP-factor deficiency. Subsequently, however, it was found that the factor responsible for chick dermatitis (the so-called filtrate factor) was not the PP-factor at all but the substance now known as pantothenic acid (see page 348).

In the ultimate, therefore, experiments with rats and chicks were unsuccessful, and progress in the elucidation of the nature of the pellagra-preventative factor came to depend on clinical tests supplemented by experiments with dogs. In a series of papers published between 1926 and 1934, Goldberger and his colleagues [7] reported the examination of a large number of foodstuffs by the addition of known quantities of the food to a pellagra-producing diet and noting the incidence of pellagra in a group of patients.

Goldberger and his colleagues also carried out parallel tests with dogs,[8] and this work eventually demonstrated that the foodstuffs that cured pellagra in human beings also cured blacktongue in dogs, whence it was concluded that the same dietary factor was responsible for both conditions.

Yeast was introduced in the treatment of pellagra by J. Goldberger and W. F. Tanner,[9] but large amounts had to be administered to make this form of treatment successful. Liver extracts gave better results, and in 1937 Elvehjem et al.,[10] by fractionating a liver extract having marked anti-blacktongue activity and subjecting the active fraction to high vacuum distillation, isolated nicotinamide and showed that it and nicotinic acid were highly effective in curing canine blacktongue. H. R. Street and G. R. Cowgill [11] also obtained good results with nicotinic acid in blacktongue, and Chick et al.[12] in a corresponding condition in pigs (see page 238).

The beneficial effects of nicotinic acid on pellagrins was reported by Spies et al.,[13] by L. J. Harris,[14] and by Smith et al.[15]

Actually nicotinic acid had been isolated in 1912 from yeast by

C. Funk [16] and from rice bran by Suzuki *et al.*[17] during attempts to isolate the anti-beriberi factor. They observed that it had no beneficial effect in beriberi, and did not apparently suspect that they had actually isolated a vitamin capable of curing a different deficiency disease.

Nicotinic acid is known in the U.S.A. as niacin, this name having been coined to make the distinction between the vitamin and the alkaloid, nicotine, quite clear to the lay public.

References to Section 1

1. J. Goldberger, G. A. Wheeler and V. P. Sydenstricker, *J. Amer. Med. Assoc.*, 1918, **71**, 944.
2. J. Goldberger and W. F. Tanner, *U.S. Pub. Health Rep.*, 1925, **40**, 58.
3. J. Goldberger and R. D. Lillie, *ibid.*, 1926, **41**, 201.
4. P. György, *Nature*, 1934, **133**, 498.
5. C. A. Elvehjem and C. J. Koehn, *J. Biol. Chem.*, 1935, **108**, 709.
6. C. A. Elvehjem and C. J. Koehn, *J. Nutrition*, 1936, **11**, 67.
7. J. Goldberger, G. A. Wheeler, R. D. Lillie and L. M. Rogers, *U.S. Publ. Health Rep.*, 1926, **41**, 297 ; J. Goldberger and G. A. Wheeler, *ibid.*, 1927, **42**, 1299, 2383 ; 1929, **44**, 2769 ; G. A. Wheeler, *ibid.*, 1931, **46**, 2663 ; 1933, **48**, 67 ; G. A. Wheeler and D. J. Hunt, *ibid.*, 1933, **48**, 754 ; 1934, **49**, 732 ; 1926, **41**, 201.
8. J. Goldberger and G. A. Wheeler, *ibid.*, 1928, **43**, 172 ; J. Goldberger, G. A. Wheeler, R. D. Lillie and L. M. Rogers, *ibid.*, 1928, **43**, 657, 1385 ; J. Goldberger, G. A. Wheeler, L. M. Rogers and W. H. Sebrell, *ibid.*, 1930, **45**, 273, 1297 ; W. H. Sebrell, G. A. Wheeler and D. J. Hunt, *ibid.*, 1935, **50**, 1333 ; G. A. Wheeler and W. H. Sebrell, *U.S. Nat. Inst., Health Bull.*, 1933, 162.
9. J. Goldberger and W. F. Tanner, *U.S. Publ. Health Rep.*, 1925, **40**, 54.
10. C. A. Elvehjem, R. J. Madden, F. M. Strong and D. W. Woolley, *J. Amer. Chem. Soc.*, 1937, **59**, 1767.
11. H. R. Street and G. R. Cowgill, *Proc. Soc. Exp. Biol. Med.*, 1937, **37**, 547.
12. H. Chick, T. F. Macrae, A. J. P. Martin and C. J. Martin, *Biochem. J.*, 1938, **32**, 10.
13. T. D. Spies, C. Cooper and M. A. Blankenhorn, *J. Amer. Med. Assoc.*, 1938, **110**, 622 ; T. D. Spies, *Lancet*, 1938, **1**, 252.
14. L. J. Harris, *Chem. and Ind.*, 1937, **56**, 1134.
15. D. T. Smith, J. M. Ruffin and S. G. Smith, *J. Amer. Med. Assoc.*, 1937, **109**, 2054.
16. C. Funk, *J. State Med.*, 1912, **20**, 341 ; *J. Physiol.*, 1913, **46**, 173 ; *Brit. Med. J.*, 1913, **1**, 814.
17. U. Suzuki and S. Matsunaga, *J. Agr. Tokyo Imp. Univ.*, 1912, **5**, 59 ; U. Suzuki, T. Shamimura and S. Okade, *Biochem. Z.*, 1912, **43**, 89, 99.

2. ISOLATION OF NICOTINIC ACID

As already noted, the identity of the PP-factor with nicotinamide and nicotinic acid was first established by Elvehjem *et al.*,[1] who isolated nicotinamide from a liver extract (Eli Lilly) by molecular distillation.

Nicotinic acid can readily be isolated from natural sources by extraction of the acidified hydrolysed material with organic solvents. The nicotinic acid can be separated from the extract as such, or in the form of its esters or copper salt. The free acid is obtained from the copper salt by decomposition with hydrogen sulphide.

Nicotinamide can be isolated from natural sources by aqueous extraction, followed by partial hydrolysis with acid to liberate it from the combined form in which it exists, and then extraction with butanol or chloroform. The extract is fractionated by molecular distillation, nicotinamide distilling at 150 to 160° C. at 5×10^{-4} mm.

Reference to Section 2

1. C. A. Elvehjem, R. J. Madden, F. M. Strong and D. W. Woolley, *J. Amer. Chem. Soc.*, 1937, **59**, 1767 ; *J. Biol. Chem.*, 1938, **123**, 137.

3. PREPARATION OF NICOTINIC ACID

Synthesis of Nicotinic Acid

Nicotinic acid was first prepared in 1867 by C. Huber[1] by the oxidation of the alkaloid, nicotine, and this method is still in use for the commercial preparation of nicotinic acid. Nicotine is obtained from waste tobacco, and is widely employed as an insecticide. H. Weidel,[2] A. Pictet and G. Sussdorff,[3] E. Winterstein and A. B. Weinhagen,[4] and S. M. McElvain and R. Adams[5] used nitric acid for the oxidation, whilst R. Laiblin[6] used potassium permanganate solution which gave a particularly good yield, and Huber *et al.*[7] used chromic acid. Most of the nicotinic acid crystallises out from the acidified oxidation product, and the remainder (about 1 %) can be recovered from the filtrate as the sparingly soluble zinc salt.[7a]

H. Weidel[8] also prepared nicotinic acid by the oxidation of picoline (a mixture of the β and γ isomers, b.p. 132 to 140° C., was used) with boiling potassium permanganate solution. He obtained a mixture of nicotinic and picolinic acids, which were separated by conversion to the copper salts ; the copper salt of picolinic acid was less soluble and immediately separated out, whilst the copper salt of nicotinic acid was recovered subsequently from the filtrate. The two copper salts were decomposed with sulphuric acid, yielding free picolinic and nicotinic acids respectively. Technical picoline was also used as the starting material by K. Hess and F. Leibbrandt,[9] but the mixed acids obtained on oxidation were separated by extraction with absolute alcohol, in which nicotinic acid was sparingly soluble. 3-Ethyl-pyridine,[10] 3-phenyl-pyridine [11] and 3 : 3'-dipyridyl [12] have also been used as starting materials for the preparation of nicotinic acid.

The preparation of nicotinic acid by the oxidation of picoline is, like the oxidation of nicotine, a method now used commercially. It is more economical to purify the β-picoline prior to oxidation than to separate nicotinic acid from the oxidation products of the other isomers. Purification can be effected by refluxing the technical picoline with phthalic anhydride, acetic anhydride, acetyl chloride, chlorosulphonic acid or sulphur dioxide, with which the γ-picoline and 2 : 6-lutidine react ; [13] by preferentially oxidising these substances in the vapour phase with air in presence of a vanadium and iron catalyst ; [14] or by removing the lutidine with urea and the γ-picoline by heating with benzaldehyde or furfural.[15] The most attractive technical method of producing nicotinic acid from β-picoline is one due to the Reilly Tar & Chemical Corp.,[16] in which the picoline is oxidised in the vapour phase with air, using vanadium and iron oxides as catalyst. β-Picoline can also be oxidised by means of sulphuric acid in presence of a selenium compound.[17]

Yet a third method of preparation was used by Huber *et al.*[7] In this, quinoline was oxidised by means of boiling alkaline potassium permanganate solution to quinolinic acid, which slowly lost carbon dioxide on heating at 120° C., and more readily at 150° C., giving a moderate yield of nicotinic acid. Quinoline, alkyl quinolines and isoquinoline can be similarly oxidised by other oxidising agents, such as nitric acid with or without the addition of a catalyst.[18] Sulphuric acid in presence of a selenium compound, such as selenium oxychloride, can also be used for the oxidation of quinoline.[17]

The oxidation of unsubstituted quinoline does not give good yields, however, because both the pyridine ring and the benzene ring are oxidised. Derivatives of quinoline substituted in the benzene ring are more suitable, and the oxidation of 8-quinoline-sulphonic acid, 8-quinolinol and alizarine indigo blue, for example, gave better yields of nicotinic acid than did the oxidation of quinoline itself. Quino-linol, however, is not recommended, as the oxidation is strongly exothermic and an explosion may result. 5 : 7-Dinitro-8-quinolinol, prepared by nitration of 8-quinolinol, is to be preferred ; this gave a good yield of nicotinic acid on oxidation with nitric acid.[19]

The oxidation of nicotine, β-picoline and quinoline to nicotinic acid by means of sulphuric acid in presence of various catalysts was studied by Woodward *et al.*[20] With nicotine, the best yields were obtained with selenium ; β-picoline gave lower yields than either nicotine or quinoline.

Other methods are available for the preparation of nicotinic acid. Thus O. Fischer [21] obtained it from pyridine *via* pyridine-sulphonic acid and cyano-pyridine but the overall yield was not good, and a better route was suggested by S. M. McElvain and M. A. Goese,[22] in which pyridine was treated with bromine and hydrobromic acid to yield a dark red perbromide ; this, when heated at 300° C., yielded β-bromopyridine, which, when heated with cuprous cyanide at about 170° C., was converted into 3-cyanopyridine. This can be hydrolysed as in Fischer's method with acid, or by means of alcoholic sodium hydroxide solution to nicotinic acid.

Synthesis of Nicotinamide

Nicotinamide was first prepared in 1894 by reacting ethyl nicotinate with concentrated ammonia ; [23] details of a more recent modification of this method were given by F. B. LaForge.[24] It can also be made by treating the acid chloride with ammonia ; by passing ammonia gas into nicotinic acid at 230°C.,[25] or spraying molten ammonium nicotinate into ammonia gas at 140–200° C.[26] ; by the action of ammonium polysulphide on 3-acetylpyridine [27] ; or by reacting nicotinic acid with urea,[28] preferably in presence of a molybenum catalyst.[29] A useful technical process is based on the partial hydrolysis of 3-cyanopyridine with mineral acid [30] or with dilute sodium hydroxide solution, sodium carbonate solution or triethylamine in presence of hydrogen peroxide.[31] 3-Cyanopyridine can also be converted into nicotinamide by boiling an aqueous solution with the quaternary ammonium hydroxide resin, IRA — 400 ; an 86 to 90 % yield is claimed.[31a] Nicotinamide was produced in low yield when asparagine was heated with glutamic acid and perhaps with other acids.[32]

References to Section 3

1. C. Huber, *Annalon*, 1867, **141**, 271 ; *Ber.*, 1870, **3**, 849.
2. H. Weidel, *Annalen*, 1873, **165**, 331, 346.
3. A. Pictet and G. Sussdorff, *Arch. sci. phys. nat.* (4), 1898, **5**, 113.
4. E. Winterstein and A. B. Weinhagen, *Helv. Chim. Acta*, 1917, **100**, 181.
5. S. M. McElvain and R. Adams, *J. Amer. Chem. Soc.*, 1923, **45**, 2738.
6. R. Laiblin, *Annalen.*, 1879, **196**, 135.
7. C. Huber, S. Hoogewerff and W. A. van Dorp, *Rec. Trav. Chim. Pays-Bas*, 1882, **1**, 121.
7a. American Cyanamid Co., U.S.P. 2447234.
8. H. Weidel, *Ber.*, 1879, **12**, 1992, 2004.
9. K. Hess and F. Leibbrandt, *ibid.*, 1917, **50**, 385.

10. H. Weidel and K. Hazura, *Monatsh.*, 1882, **3**, 783.
11. Z. H. Skraup and A. Cobenzl, *ibid.*, 1883, **4**, 458.
12. Z. H. Skraup and G. Vortmann, *ibid.*, 594.
13. Reilly Tar & Chemical Corp., B.P. 561722, 561723.
14. Reilly Tar & Chemical Corp., B.P. 563273.
15. Pittsburgh Coke & Iron Co., B.P. 570427.
16. Reilly Tar & Chemical Corp., B.P. 563274.
17. Allied Chemical & Dye Corp., U.S.P. 2436660.
18. Reilly Tar & Chemical Corp., B.P. 568889.
19. A. Zimmerli, U.S.P. 2394650.
20. C. F. Woodward, C. O. Badgett and J. G. Kaufman, *Ind. Eng. Chem.*, 1944, **36**, 544.
21. O. Fischer, *Ber.*, 1882, **15**, 63.
22. S. M. McElvain and M. A. Goese, *J. Amer. Chem. Soc.*, 1941, **63**, 2283.
23. C. Engler, *Ber.*, 1894, **27**, 1787 ; F. Pollak, *Monatsh.*, 1895, **16**, 53.
24. F. B. LaForge, *J. Amer. Chem. Soc.*, 1928, **50**, 2477.
25. S. Keimatsu, K. Yokata and I. Satoda, *J. Pharm. Soc., Japan*, 1933, **53**, 994.
26. P. W. Garbo, U.S.P. 2427400.
27. Ciba Ltd., B.P. 558774.
28. Ciba Ltd., B.P. 561019.
29. P. W. Garbo, U.S.P. 2419831.
30. Geigy Colour Co. Ltd., I. E. Balaban and F. Manchester, B.P. 575119.
31. Pyridium Corp., B.P. 563184.
31a. A. Galat, *J. Amer. Chem. Soc.*, 1948, **70**, 3945.
32. J. R. Bovarnick, *J. Biol. Chem.*, 1943, **149**, 301 ; 1943, **151**, 467; 1944, **153**, 1.

4. PROPERTIES OF NICOTINIC ACID

Nicotinic Acid

Nicotinic acid forms white needles, m.p. 235·5 to 236·5° C. It is sparingly soluble in cold water, but soluble in hot water and alcohol ; it is sparingly soluble in ether. It sublimes without decomposition on heating. It behaves as a base, forming a crystalline hydrochloride, m.p. 274° C., and other salts, and also as an acid, forming salts with metals, and esters with alcohol. The methyl ester is a solid, m.p. 38° C., and the ethyl ester a liquid, b.p. 223 to 224° C. Nicotinic acid forms an acid chloride, amide, hydrazide, etc.

Nicotinic acid sold in Great Britain for pharmaceutical purposes must conform to certain standards laid down in the Fourth Addendum to the British Pharmacopoeia, 1932, and modified in the 1948 edition. Nicotinic acid tablets were included in the Seventh Addendum. The dosage is now given as 15 to 30 mg. daily for prophylaxis, and 50 to 250 mg. daily for therapeutic use and the substance is normally dispensed in 50-mg. tablets.

Nicotinamide

Nicotinamide is a white substance crystallising from benzene in needles, m.p. 131° C. It is very soluble in water (1 in 1) and in 95 % alcohol (1 in 1·5), soluble in glycerol (1 in 10), but only slightly soluble in ether. On distillation with phosphorus pentoxide it yields 3-cyano-pyridine and on hydrolysis with acid or alkali it yields nicotinic acid. On heating in a dry tube, pyridine is evolved.

Nicotinamide sold in Great Britain for pharmaceutical purposes must conform to certain standards laid down in the Sixth Addendum of the British Pharmacopoeia, 1932, and modified in the 1948 edition. Nicotinamide tablets were included in the Seventh Addendum. The therapeutic dose is the same as for the acid, and the substance is normally dispensed in 50-mg. tablets.

Several N-alkyl derivatives of nicotinamide are known, of which N-diethyl-nicotinamide is the well-known heart stimulant, Nikethamide (Coramine).

5. ESTIMATION OF NICOTINIC ACID

It will already be evident from what has been said in the introduction that there is no satisfactory biological method of assaying the pellagra-preventative factor. Rats and chickens fail to respond specifically, whilst the prevention of blacktongue in dogs, although specific, does not constitute a convenient method of assay.

In spite of this, dogs were used for assaying foodstuffs by Waisman et al.,[1] whilst Schaefer et al.[2] described a diet consisting of casein and sucrose supplemented by aneurine, riboflavine, pantothenic acid and choline, which was said to produce an uncomplicated nicotinic acid deficiency in dogs, suitable for assay purposes.

Fortunately, nicotinic acid and nicotinamide can readily be estimated chemically or microbiologically, and the absence of a satisfactory biological method of assay is not a serious disadvantage.

Chemical Methods based on the Vongerichten Reaction

One of the first chemical tests proposed was a modification of Vongerichten's reaction for pyridine compounds.[3] P. Karrer and H. Keller [4] used the reaction to estimate the amount of nicotinic acid and nicotinamide in animal tissues. These were digested with water, the aqueous extract was neutralised with potassium hydroxide solution to liberate the nicotinic acid, the resulting solution was evaporated to dryness and the residue extracted with benzene. The extract was freed from benzene, the residue was fused with 2 : 4-dinitro-1-chloro-benzene and the melt dissolved in ether and the solution extracted with water. The intensity of the colour formed on adding one or two drops of potassium hydroxide solution was found to be proportional to the nicotinic acid content. Substantially the same method was used by Vilter *et al.*[5] for the estimation of nicotinic acid and nicotin-amide in urine. Urine contains other pyridine compounds in addition to these two substances, however, and, although trigonelline does not give a colour with dinitrochlorobenzene, nicotinuric acid, the con-jugated compound of nicotinic acid with glycine interferes with the estimation, giving high results.

Chemical Methods based on the König Reaction

The Vongerichten reaction proved to be rather inconvenient for analytical purposes, and the majority of workers have made use of the König reaction,[6] in which the pyridine compound is warmed with cyanogen bromide solution, and an organic base is then added ; a yellow colour is formed, the intensity of which is proportional to the amount of pyridine compound present. The method was first applied to the estimation of nicotinic acid in foodstuffs by M. Swaminathan,[7] who used aniline as the base ; this was also used by H. Kringstad and T. Naess.[8] E. Bandier and J. Hald[9] used metol (*p*-methylamino-phenol sulphate) as the organic base in place of aniline, and found that nicotinamide gave a stronger colour than nicotinic acid, so that it was necessary to hydrolyse the amide to the acid before applying the reaction. E. Bandier[10] also used the method for the estimation of nicotinic acid in urine but, like Vilter *et al.*,[5] encountered difficulties due to the presence of other pyridine compounds (page 252). These were overcome by hydrolysis with alkali in order to convert all the derivatives of nicotinic acid into the free acid, the values thus obtained being a measure of the total (free and combined) nicotinic acid in the urine.

Von Euler *et al.*[11] used β-naphthylamine as the base, whilst L. J. Harris and W. D. Raymond[12] worked out a method of estimating nicotinic acid in urine, using *p*-aminoacetophenone. This method was modified by E. Kodicek,[13] who stressed the importance of adhering rigidly to the detailed conditions laid down, if satisfactory results were to be obtained. Like Bandier, Kodicek used alkaline hydrolysis of biological materials to convert nicotinamide and other derivatives into nicotinic acid ; impurities were then removed by precipitation with alcohol. W. S. Jones[14] used substantially the same method in conjunction with a fluorophotometer.

Hydrolysis with alkali, however, did not completely eliminate the errors of the method, and D. Melnick and H. Field [15] found that hydrolysates sometimes contained substances that reacted with aniline or p-aminoacetophenone to give colours indistinguishable from the nicotinic acid colour, but that, in presence of cyanogen bromide, these interfering side-reactions did not occur. They therefore recommended that the base should not be included in the blank. Further slight modifications were introduced by H. A. Waisman and C. A. Elvehjem [16] and by W. J. Dann and P. Handler.[17] The latter workers stated that metol was preferable to other bases, as the colour produced was more stable, but this preference for metol is not shared by other workers. According to M. Swaminathan,[18] for example, aniline and β-naphthylamine give stronger colours than either metol or p-amino-acetophenone. He found that heating the test solution with cyanogen bromide in alcohol gave colours two or three times as intense as those obtained in aqueous solution. Alcoholic extracts of urine, however, gave interfering red colours.

Another base used in conjunction with cyanogen bromide is p-aminophenol, which was said to be less affected by light and pH than p-aminoacetophenone.[19] m-Phenylene diamine,[20] orthoform,[21] procaine [22] and p-aminopropiophenone [22a] have also been used. Aniline would appear to be the base most generally used, with p-amino-acetophenone as a second favourite. The choice of base is, perhaps, of less importance than other considerations, such as the procedures used for preparing the nicotinic acid extract and for eliminating the errors due to the existence of several forms of nicotinic acid, some biologically active and others inactive.

Metabolites of Nicotinic Acid and Nicotinamide

One of these substances is the alkaloid, trigonelline, which occurs in the seeds of *Trigonella foenugraecum*, *Pisum sativum*, *Cannabis sativa* and *Strophanthus* spp. It is the betaine of nicotinic acid :

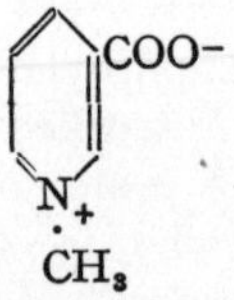

and may be present in human urine in relatively large amounts, especially after the consumption of materials rich in trigonelline, such as coffee. In addition, however, it is formed from nicotinic acid in the human and animal organism and eliminated in the urine. It has no anti-pellagra activity, so that methods of estimating nicotinic acid in vegetable materials should be capable of distinguishing it from biologically active nicotinic acid derivatives. On the other hand, in studying the metabolism of nicotinic acid (see page 252), it is essential to estimate the urinary trigonelline derived from dietary nicotinic acid, whilst at the same time making due allowance for the trigonelline originally present as such in the diet—a problem to which no simple solution exists !

Fortunately, comparatively few foods contain sufficiently large amounts of trigonelline to interfere seriously with the estimation of the other metabolites ; such foods should be avoided by subjects about to take part in metabolic experiments.

Another nicotinic acid derivative present in urine is nicotinuric acid (page 252). This does not exist in foodstuffs, but is formed from nicotinic acid *in vivo* by conjugation with glycine ; its estimation in urine is essential in studying the metabolism of nicotinic acid.

Another pyridine compound formed *in vivo* from nicotinamide is N^1-methylnicotinamide, the amide corresponding to trigonelline (page 254). It forms a strongly fluorescent compound (" F_2 ") on treatment with alkali, so that its separate estimation, where necessary, presents no great difficulty. Conversion to N^1-methylnicotinamide can actually be used for the estimation of nicotinamide. This is brought about by leaving a dilute methanolic solution of nicotinamide overnight with excess methyl iodide and evaporating. On treatment with alkali and isobutanol a fluorescence develops, the intensity of which is proportional to the nicotinamide concentration.[23] Alternatively, nicotinamide is treated with cyanogen bromide and alkali, and the fluorescent product extracted with isobutanol. The second procedure gives a more intense fluorescence than the first (see also page 226).

The latter method was modified by Huff et al.,[51] who used acetone in a single phase at an alkaline pH instead of extracting into isobutanol. E. Kodicek used methyl ethyl ketone instead of acetone, but subsequently found that the use of a solvent was unnecessary.[24]

N^1-Methylnicotinamide is not the end-product of nicotinamide metabolism, an oxidation product of the former, N^1-methyl-6-pyridone-3-carboxylamide, being excreted at the same time (see page 255).[24a]

Preparation of Extracts

A variety of methods have been employed for the preparation of extracts suitable for the estimation of nicotinic acid by means of the König reaction. Many workers followed the principle employed by E. Bandier [10] and by Vilter et al.,[5] and used hydrolysis to convert nicotinamide and other nicotinic acid derivatives into free nicotinic acid, whilst V. H. Cheldelin and R. R. Williams [25] found that many materials yielded nicotinic acid quantitatively on digestion with taka-diastase or papain. Whereas meat and milk gave the same values whether an enzyme, acid or alkali was used for hydrolysis, cereals gave higher results after treatment with acid or alkali than after enzymic digestion. Hale *et al.*[26] recommended extraction of the material with water at 100° C. for forty-five minutes and subsequent hydrolysis with sodium hydroxide solution in the case of seeds and roots or with hydrochloric acid in the case of substances containing chlorophyll ; interfering substances were then precipitated with alcohol.

Several workers have used adsorption to remove interfering pigments. This does not always give satisfactory results, however, as nicotinic acid and nicotinamide are readily adsorbed by some adsorbents. K. V. Giri and B. Naganna [27] followed an initial extraction and hydrolysis by adsorption on charcoal at pH 6·0 to 6·5, and elution with 0·2 N alcoholic sodium hydroxide, and claimed to have obtained satisfactory assays of foodstuffs by this method. Other workers, however, obtained erroneous results. Thus, W. J. Dann and P. Handler [17] found that the use of charcoal for decolorisation resulted in large losses of nicotinic acid, and that it was impossible to compensate for the presence of the interfering substances in coloured extracts by an extrapolation method. They recommended adsorption of the nicotinic acid on fuller's earth, followed by elution with sodium hydroxide solution, precipitation of impurities by addition of lead nitrate and removal of excess lead from the filtrate by means of phosphate. This gave much lower results with some biological materials than did earlier methods. Corn meal, for instance, gave a value of 0·6 to 1 mg. per 100 g. compared with the value of 10·7 mg. per 100 g. reported earlier by Waisman and Elvehjem. The method gave quantitative recoveries of nicotinic acid added to liver tissues.

K. Taufel and F. Dahle [28] confirmed Dann and Handler's results, using a variety of fuller's earth known as " Clarit Standard A " to adsorb both the colour and the nicotinic acid ; the nicotinic acid was then eluted from the adsorbate by means of barium hydroxide solution. As an alternative procedure they recommended evaporation of the original solution to dryness and extraction of the residue with benzene or a mixture of chloroform and isopropanol.

Y. L. Wang and E. Kodicek [29] eliminated interfering pigments in urine by treatment with permanganate (see page 223), but when this method was applied to cereals and cereal products,[30] the values obtained averaged only 75 % of those obtained by the microbiological method ; the results also varied widely. More consistent results were obtained by standardising the amount of permanganate by keeping the temperature constant and by using Melnick's solution blank.[31] The method was still farther improved by adsorbing the nicotinic acid on Lloyd's reagent and eluting with dilute alkali as in the method of Dann and Handler ; the values thus obtained were in very close agreement with microbiological assay results obtained using *L. arabinosus*.[32]

Estimation of Nicotinic Acid in Blood

The König reaction was used for the estimation of nicotinic acid in blood by E. Kodicek,[13] by Klein *et al.*[33] and by M. J. C. Allenson.[34] The last-named used an enzyme from certain soil bacteria to eliminate interference from other chromogens, the difference between the colours produced with cyanogen bromide and metol before and after incubation with the enzyme preparation being assumed to be proportional to the nicotinic acid content of the blood. B. D. Kochhar [35] deproteinised the blood with trichloroacetic acid and hydrolysed the filtrate with hydrochloric acid.

Estimation of Nicotinic Acid in Urine

The estimation of nicotinic acid in urine is complicated for two reasons. In the first place, urine contains pigments and chromogens that interfere with the measurement of the coloured compound produced from nicotinic acid. The problem of eliminating interference from this source was solved by Y. L. Wang and E. Kodicek,[29] who extracted the urine with isobutanol, after digestion with acid, and then treated the extract with potassium permanganate solution to oxidise residual impurities. Kodicek's original method [13] was found to be unsatisfactory for the assay of urine, but almost theoretical recoveries of nicotinic acid added to urine were obtained when a lower temperature was used, together with a shorter time for the reaction between cyanogen bromide and nicotinic acid, and larger amounts of *p*-aminoacetophenone.

The other reason why nicotinic acid assays of urine are complicated is that, as already stated (page 220), several forms of nicotinic acid exist in urine, most, but not all, of which are derived from ingested nicotinic acid or nicotinamide.

Urine assays are usually carried out with the object of assessing nutritional status (see page 259), that is, the extent to which ingested nicotinic acid is utilised by the body. In this event, not only must the amount of nicotinic acid and nicotinamide in the urine be estimated, but also the nicotinuric acid, trigonelline, N^1-methylnicotinamide, N^1-methyl-6-pyridone-3-carboxylamide and other metabolites into which they may have been converted during their passage through the body. The simplest procedure is one in which all these substances are converted into free nicotinic acid, but errors will then be introduced if substantial amounts of the trigonelline present have been derived from the diet.

Early attempts to estimate nicotinic acid in urine by this method are those of E. Bandier [10] and L. J. Harris and W. D. Raymond,[12] already referred to. J. C. Roggen [36] heated the sample of urine with nitric acid to hydrolyse nicotinamide and nicotinuric acid to nicotinic acid and then added saturated potassium permanganate solution, which does not attack nicotinic acid, in order to oxidise interfering substances. The resulting solution was adsorbed on frankonite and the adsorbate was eluted with barium hydroxide solution. The colour was developed in the usual way with cyanogen bromide and aniline.

More satisfactory methods of estimating nicotinic acid in urine, capable of giving information of greater value in metabolic studies than a mere knowledge of the total free and combined nicotinic acid, are those in which nicotinic acid and each of its metabolites are separately estimated. Melnick and his colleagues [15, 37, 38] worked out a method of estimating total nicotinic acid, nicotinuric acid and trigonelline based on the fact that nicotinamide is hydrolysed when the urine is heated with 4N acid for half an hour, whereas nicotinuric acid is more stable and requires heating for five hours with 4N acid whilst trigonelline can only be hydrolysed to nicotinic acid by treatment with alkali. They used this method to study the fate of nicotinic acid in the organism (see page 253). F. W. Lamb [39] noted that the maximum extinction coefficient of the colour, and the time required for its development, varied for nicotinic acid, nicotinamide, pyridine and β-picoline, and was characteristic for each substance. D. Melnick and B. L. Oser [40] devised a method of differentiating between nicotinamide and nicotinic acid, based on the observation that, when cyanogen bromide and aniline were added in quick succession, the two substances gave colours of different intensity. By evaluating the colour before and after acid hydrolysis, it was possible to obtain an approximate idea of the relative amounts of the two substances present in the mixture.

Perlzweig et al.[41] devised a method of estimating total nicotinic acid and trigonelline separately in urine. Total nicotinic acid (excluding trigonelline) was estimated by boiling the urine with hydrochloric acid to hydrolyse all the nicotinic acid derivatives, with the exception of trigonelline, to nicotinic acid. This was then adsorbed on Lloyd's reagent, eluted with alkali and the colour developed as in Bandier and Hald's method. Trigonelline was estimated by treating with urea and alkali, which convert it into a substance giving a colour identical with the nicotinic acid colour in a yield equivalent to 70 % of the theoretical conversion. The solution was treated with Lloyd's reagent as before and the colour evaluated. The value obtained in the second estimation was equivalent to the amount of nicotinic acid derivatives measured in the first estimation plus 70 % of the trigonelline.

Högberg et al.[42] observed that the colour produced by nicotinamide was more intense and more stable in butanol solution than that produced by nicotinic acid, so that if the coloured derivatives were extracted into butanol and the extract left for ten minutes the residual colour was due solely to nicotinamide. To estimate bound nicotinic acid and nicotinamide, the material was heated with $0 \cdot 1$ N hydrochloric acid in a sealed tube at $100°$ C. and the estimation repeated.

Other Chemical and Physical Methods of Assay

Atkin et al.[43] made use of the Hoffman reaction with bromine and potassium hydroxide to destroy nicotinamide, in order to improve the accuracy of the microbiological method of assay (page 227). The same reaction was used by J. M. Goodyear and H. W. Murphy [44] as a method of estimation, the 3-aminopyridine into which nicotinamide was converted by this treatment being diazotised and coupled with N-1-naphthylethylenediamine. The intensity of the red dye thus produced was proportional to the amount of nicotinamide originally present.

J. J. Lingane and O. L. Davis [45] developed a polarographic method of estimating nicotinic acid, which gives a characteristic wave, the position of which varies with the base solution used. The best results were obtained with a tetramethylammonium borate buffer solution of pH 9; nicotinic acid then had a half-wave potential of $- 1 \cdot 6$ volts, but an unbuffered potassium chloride solution gave quite satisfactory results. The method has the advantage that aneurine, riboflavine and nicotinic acid can be estimated simultaneously in the same solution.

Nicotinamide is also reduced at the dropping mercury electrode [46] in alkaline solutions giving a well-defined wave at $- 1 \cdot 6$ to $- 1 \cdot 7$ volts, the height of which is proportional to the concentration of amide. The mechanism of the reaction is not known. N^1-Methylnicotinamide was reduced in two steps; the first, at $- 1 \cdot 025$ volts, is possibly due to the formation of a dimer, and the second, at $- 1 \cdot 6$ to $- 1 \cdot 8$ volts, to the formation of a dihydro-derivative. Trigonelline gave a single step at $- 1 \cdot 35$ volts due to the formation of a dimer.

Estimation of N¹-Methylnicotinamide

As already stated, ingested nicotinamide is partially converted into N¹-methylnicotinamide, which can be estimated by conversion into a fluorescent substance by treatment with alkali.

J. W. Huff and W. A. Perlzweig [47] used adsorption on Permutit at pH 4 to separate the substance from impurities, and eluted it from the adsorbate by means of potassium chloride solution. It was then extracted into butanol, aqueous alkali was added and the fluorescence evaluated. In estimating N¹-methylnicotinamide in urine, the preliminary adsorption on zeolite was unnecessary. Coulson *et al.*[48] adsorbed on Decalso, eluted with potassium chloride solution and then extracted the eluate with *sec.* butanol after making alkaline. V. A. Najjar [49] treated the solution with active charcoal, adsorbed the N¹-methylnicotinamide on Permutit and eluted with potassium chloride solution ; as in the foregoing method, the eluate was then made alkaline, extracted with butanol, and the fluorescence of the solution was evaluated in a fluorimeter. M. Hochberg *et al.*[50] also adsorbed on a zeolite.

Huff *et al.*[51] improved the method by treating an aqueous alkaline solution with acetone instead of extracting into isobutanol. This produced a greenish-blue fluorescence, the intensity of which was proportional to the concentration of N¹-methylnicotinamide. E. Kodicek [24] used methyl ethyl ketone in place of acetone, but subsequently found that satisfactory results were obtained in the absence of a solvent.

Estimation of N¹-Methyl-6-pyridone-3-carboxylamide

The amount of N¹-methyl-6-pyridone-3-carboxylamide in urine was estimated by clarifying the urine with lead acetate, saturating the filtrate with potassium carbonate and extracting with ether, evaporating the extract to dryness, dissolving the residue in acetone and measuring the fluorescence produced on addition of a small amount of concentrated potassium hydroxide solution. Alternatively the pyridone was estimated spectrophotometrically in an aqueous solution of the residue left after evaporation of the ethereal extract.[51a] A third method was to adsorb the pyridone on Lloyd's reagent, elute with chloroform, nitrate and measure the coloured product in alkaline solution.[51b]

Microbiological Methods of Assay

An entirely different principle, depending on the response of micro-organisms to nicotinic acid, has been used by a number of workers who claim that such methods are more expeditious and accurate than chemical methods. E. E. Snell and L. D. Wright [52] measured the amount of lactic acid produced by *Lactobacillus arabinosus* 17-5 on a synthetic medium, containing all known growth factors except nicotinic acid and to which the test solution had been added, and compared it with the amount produced on the basal medium containing known amounts of added nicotinic acid. The nicotinic acid contents of blood, milk, urine, plant and animal extracts were estimated in this way with a fair degree of accuracy ; as little as 0·05 μg. of nicotinic acid could be measured.

The method of Snell and Wright failed to give a linear standard curve with concentrations in excess of 0·2 μg. per 10 ml., but this objection was overcome by Krehl *et al.*[53] who, in addition to other modifications, increased the concentration of glucose and buffer (sodium acetate) in the basal medium, whilst H. Isbell [54] advocated the addition of p-aminobenzoic acid to the medium. The medium was still further modified by E. C. Barton-Wright,[55] whose method has been adopted as a standard procedure by most workers in this country. The medium consists of acid-hydrolysed casein, the preparation of which must be carefully carried out if satisfactory results are to be obtained, DL-tryptophan and L-cystine, glucose, sodium acetate and xylose, calcium pantothenate, pyridoxine, riboflavine, p-aminobenzoic acid and biotin, adenine, guanine, uracil and xanthine, and the usual inorganic salts. Barton-Wright recommends that extracts be prepared in the same way as for riboflavine assays (page 158), although the growth of *L. arabinosus* is not stimulated by starch or free fatty acids ; hydrolysis is effected by autoclaving with N-hydrochloric acid at 15 lb. pressure for fifteen to twenty minutes. A similar method was made official in the U.S.A.[56]

Sarett *et al.*[57] proposed to use for the assay of nicotinic acid with *L. arabinosus* a basal medium consisting of yeast extract, peptone, and liver extract treated with Lloyd's reagent to remove nicotinic acid.

A method for the microbiological estimation of nicotinamide in presence of nicotinic acid by means of *L. arabinosus* was devised by Atkin *et al.*,[43] who carried out two assays, one before and one after the conversion of nicotinamide, by treatment with bromine and potassium hydroxide, into 3-aminopyridine which has no growth-stimulating activity. The difference in the amount of lactic acid produced in the two tests was proportional to the amount of nicotinamide present.

Assay methods based on the response of *L. arabinosus* have been most commonly employed, but other organisms have been used. P. Fildes [58] found that *Proteus vulgaris* required nicotinic acid, and A. Lwoff and A. Querido [59] used it for the estimation of nicotinic acid and nicotinamide. H. Grossowicz and E. Sherstinsky [60] used " *Proteus* HX 19 ". Dorfman *et al.*[61] used *Shigella dysenteriae,* and Fraser *et al.*[62] and Isbell *et al.*[63] used *Shigella paradysenteriae.* Although these methods have the advantage of requiring less complex media than the Snell and Wright method, they involve a turbidimetric estimation of the amount of growth produced ; this is less convenient and less accurate than a titration of lactic acid. Moreover, one of the organisms, *Proteus vulgaris,* responds to coenzymes I and II as well as to nicotinamide.

In fact, the only possible rival to *L. arabinosus* is *Lactobacillus casei (helveticus)* used by M. Landy and D. M. Dicken [64] for the assay of six B vitamins with one and the same medium. This contains casein hydrolysate and glucose, vitamins and pyrimidines, and is similar in composition to that used by Snell and Wright, though the proportions of the constituents are different. The growth response is not linear, however, and the method gives inferior results to the *L. arabinosus* method.

Leuconostoc mesenteroides was used by B. C. Johnson [65] in conjunction with *L. arabinosus* to estimate nicotinic acid, nicotinamide and nicotinuric acid in a mixture of the three ; *L. mesenteroides* is unaffected by nicotinamide or nicotinuric acid, and the increase in the response following hydrolysis with acid is proportional to the nicotinamide and nicotinuric acid present. Nicotinuric acid is estimated by measuring the difference in the response of *L. arabinosus* (the growth of which is stimulated by both nicotinic acid and nicotinamide) before and after hydrolysis, and the amount of nicotinamide present is calculated by subtracting the value so obtained from the previous result.

A yeast, *Torula cremoris,* was used by W. L. Williams,[66] the growth of the organism being measured turbidimetrically. Differential assays of nicotinic acid, trigonelline and N^1-methylnicotinamide were carried out with this organism by measuring the response before and after acid and alkaline hydrolysis.

A modification of the Heatley method of assaying antibiotics [67] has been tried out for the assay of growth factors, including nicotinic acid.[68] An agar plate was seeded with *L. arabinosus* and holes were cut in the agar or, alternatively, little porcelain cups were placed on the surface of the agar. Into the holes or the cups, a little of the test solutions and standards were poured, the plates were incubated and the diameters of the zone of " exhibition " (analogous to the zones of inhibition produced by antibiotics) were plotted against the logarithms of the concentrations. Although this gave a straight line, the method suffered from the same disadvantages as the conventional microbiological assay together with the added disadvantage that the edges of the zones tended to be diffuse.

Kynurenine and 3-hydroxyanthranilic acid, two intermediates in the conversion of tryptophan into nicotinic acid (page 250), did not stimulate the growth of *L. arabinosus*, *L. mesenteroides*, *S. faecalis*, *Pr. vulgaris* or *Torula cremoris*, and therefore do not interfere with the estimation of nicotinic acid by any of these organisms.[68a]

Estimation of Coenzymes I and II

Several methods are available for the estimation of coenzymes I and II, di- and triphospho-pyridine nucleotides (see page 274). O. Warburg and W. Christian [69] estimated codehydrogenase II by measuring the amount of carbon dioxide evolved by the action on sodium bicarbonate of glycerophosphoric acid produced enzymatically with hexose monophosphate (Robison ester) as substrate ; in addition to the coenzyme, the specific apoenzyme and the yellow ferment must also be present. Jandorf *et al.*[70] adopted the same method in principle, but used the more readily accessible hexose diphosphate as substrate. D. E. Green and J. Brasteaux [71] used oxidation of lactic acid by animal tissues as a method of estimation.

Haemophilus parainfluenzae, which cannot synthesise codehydrogenase I or II from its constituents and cannot grow without one or the other, can be used to estimate " factor V ", the coenzyme-like substance in blood or yeast.[72, 73] This is presumably a mixture of the two coenzymes. Vilter *et al.*[74] used *Bacillus influenzae* to estimate the factor V content of blood, whilst K. Myrbäck [75] and A. E. Axelrod and C. A. Elvehjem [76] used a yeast-growth method, which estimates coenzyme I, but not coenzyme II. It is not certain whether these two methods of estimating factor V give comparable results.

A rapid method for the estimation of pyridine nucleotides in blood was developed by Levitas *et al.*[77] In this method, the nucleotide was converted into N^1-methylnicotinamide by treatment with alkali, and this was then condensed with acetone to give the fluorescent compound referred to above (page 226). When attempts were made to apply this method to tissues, low values were obtained.[78] The losses were due to the action of nucleotidases (page 279) and were avoided by the addition of nicotinamide, which is a specific inhibitor of nucleotidase. This modification gave results in excellent agreement with those obtained by the microbiological method using *Haemophilus parainfluenzae*. When the values thus obtained for pyridine nucleotides were compared with the total nicotinic acid content of tissues, as determined microbiologically with the aid of *L. arabinosus*, it was found that all the nicotinic acid in rat tissues was in the form of pyridine nucleotide.

References to Section 5

1. H. A. Waisman, O. Mickelsen, J. M. McKibbin and C. A. Elvehjem, *J. Nutrition*, 1940, **19**, 483 ; J. M. McKibbin, H. A. Waisman, O. Mickelsen and C. A. Elvehjem, *Wisconsin Agric. Exp. Sta. Bull.*, No. 446.
2. A. E. Schaefer, J. M. McKibbin and C. A. Elvehjem, *J. Biol. Chem.*, 1942, **144**, 679.
3. E. Vongerichten, *Ber.*, 1899, **32**, 2571.
4. P. Karrer and H. Keller, *Helv. Chim. Acta*, 1938, **21**, 463, 1170 ; 1939, **22**, 1292.
5. S. P. Vilter, T. D. Spies and A. P. Mathews, *J. Biol. Chem.*, 1938, **125**, 85 ; *J. Amer. Chem. Soc.*, 1938, **60**, 731.
6. W. König, *J. prakt. Chem.*, 1904, **69**, 105 ; 1904, **70**, 19.
7. M. Swaminathan, *Nature*, 1938, **141**, 830.
8. H. Kringstad and T. Naess, *Z. physiol. Chem.*, 1939, **260**, 108.
9. E. Bandier and J. Hald, *Biochem. J.*, 1939, **33**, 264.
10. E. Bandier, *ibid.*, 1787.
11. H. von Euler, F. Schlenk, H. Heiwinke and B. Högberg, *Z. physiol. Chem.*, 1938, **256**, 208.
12. L. J. Harris and W. D. Raymond, *Biochem. J.*, 1939, **33**, 2037.
13. E. Kodicek, *ibid.*, 1940, **34**, 712, 724.
14. W. S. Jones, *J. Amer. Pharm. Assoc.*, 1941, **30**, 272.
15. D. Melnick and H. Field, *J. Biol. Chem.*, 1940, **135**, 53.
16. H. A. Waisman and C. A. Elvehjem, *Ind. Eng. Chem. Anal. Ed.*, 1941, **13**, 221.
17. W. J. Dann and P. Handler, *J. Biol. Chem.*, 1941, **140**, 201.
18. M. Swaminathan, *Indian J. Med. Res.*, 1941, **29**, 325.
19. E. Stotz, *J. Lab. Clin. Med.*, 1941, **26**, 1042.
20. A. E. Teeri and S. R. Shimer, *J. Biol. Chem.*, 1944, **153**, 307.
21. R. G. Martinek, E. R. Kirch and G. L. Webster, *ibid.*, 1943, **149**, 245.
22. E. C. Barton-Wright and R. G. Booth, *Lancet*, 1944, **1**, 565 ; P. O. Dennis and H. G. Rees, *Analyst*, 1949, **74**, 481.
22a. C. Klatzkin, F. W. Norris and F. Wokes, *ibid.*, 447.
23. J. V. Scudi, *Science*, 1946, **103**, 567.
24. E. Kodicek, *Analyst*, 1947, **72**, 385 ; D. K. Chaudhuri and E. Kodicek, *Biochem. J.*, 1949, **44**, 343.
24a. W. E. Knox and W. I. Grossman, *J. Biol. Chem.*, 1946, **166**, 391 ; 1947, **168**, 363.
25. V. H. Cheldelin and R. R. Williams, *Ind. Eng. Chem.*, *Anal. Ed.*, 1942, **14**, 671.
26. E. B. Hale, G. K. Davis and H. R. Baldwin, *J. Biol. Chem.*, 1942, **146**, 553.
27. K. V. Giri and B. Naganna, *Indian J. Med. Res.*, 1941, **29**, 125.
28. K. Taufel and F. Dahle, *Z. Unters. Lebensm.*, 1943, **85**, 414.
29. Y. L. Wang and E. Kodicek, *Biochem. J.*, 1943, **37**, 530.
30. E. M. James, F. W. Norris and F. Wokes, *Analyst*, 1947, **72**, 327.
31. D. Melnick, *Cereal Chem.*, 1942, **19**, 553.

32. Analytical Methods Committee, *Analyst*, 1946, **71**, 397.

33. J. R. Klein, W. A. Perlzweig and D. Handler, *J. Biol. Chem.*, 1942, **145**, 27.

34. M. J. C. Allenson, *ibid.*, 1943, **147**, 785.

35. B. D. Kochhar, *Indian J. Med. Res.*, 1940, **28**, 385.

36. J. C. Roggen, *Rec. trav. chim.*, 1943, **62**, 137.

37. D. Melnick and H. Field, *J. Biol. Chem.*, 1940, **134**, 1.

38. D. Melnick, W. D. Robinson and H. Field, *ibid.*, 1940, **136**, 131, 145.

39. F. W. Lamb, *Ind. Eng. Chem.*, *Anal. Ed.*, 1943, **15**, 352.

40. D. Melnick and B. L. Oser, *ibid.*, 355.

41. W. A. Perlzweig, E. D. Levy and H. P. Sarett, *J. Biol. Chem.*, 1940, **136**, 729.

42. B. Högberg, F. Schlenk and H. von Euler, *Arkiv Kemi, Min., Geol.*, 1942, **15A**, No. 18.

43. L. Atkin, A. S. Schultz, W. L. Williams and C. N. Frey, *J. Amer. Chem. Soc.*, 1943, **65**, 992.

44. J. M. Goodyear and H. W. Murphy, *J. Amer. Pharm. Assoc.*, 1944, **33**, 129.

45. J. J. Lingane and O. L. Davis, *J. Biol. Chem.*, 1941, **137**, 567.

46. P. C. Tompkins and C. L. A. Schmidt, *Univ. California Publ. Physiol.*, 1943, **8**, 221.

47. J. W. Huff and W. A. Perlzweig, *J. Biol. Chem.*, 1943, **150**, 395, 483.

48. R. A. Coulson, P. Ellinger and M. Holden, *Biochem. J.*, 1944, **38**, 150.

49. V. A. Najjar, *Johns Hopkins Hosp. Bull.*, 1944, **74**, 92.

50. M. Hochberg, D. Melnick and B. L. Oser, *J. Biol. Chem.*, 1945, **158**, 265.

51. J. W. Huff, W. A. Perlzweig and M. Tilden, *Fed. Proc.*, 1945, **4**, 92.

51a. F. Rosen, W. A. Perlzweig and I. G. Leder, *J. Biol. Chem.*, 1949, **179**, 157.

51b. W. I. M. Holman and D. J. de Lange, *Biochem. J.*, 1949, **45**, 559.

52. E. E. Snell and L. D. Wright, *J. Biol. Chem.*, 1941, **139**, 675.

53. W. A. Krehl, F. M. Strong and C. A. Elvehjem, *Ind. Eng. Chem.*, *Anal. Ed.*, 1943, **15**, 471.

54. H. Isbell, *J. Biol. Chem.*, 1942, **144**, 567.

55. E. C. Barton-Wright, *Biochem. J.*, 1944, **38**, 314.

56. *J. Assoc. Off. Agric. Chem.*, 1947, **30**, 44, 82, 398 ; *Cf.* E. Kodicek and C. R. Pepper, *J. Gen. Microbiol.*, 1948, **2**, 292.

57. H. P. Sarett, R. L. Pederson and V. H. Cheldelin, *Arch. Biochem.*, 1945, **7**, 77.

58. P. Fildes, *Brit. J. Exp. Path.*, 1938, **29**, 239.

59. A. Lwoff and A. Querido, *Compt. rend. Soc. Biol.*, 1938, **129**, 1039 ; 1938, **130**, 1569.

60. H. Grossowicz and E. Sherstinsky, *J. Biol. Chem.*, 1947, **167**, 101.

61. A. Dorfman, S. A. Koser, M. Horwitt, S. Berkman and F. Saunders, *Proc. Soc. Exp. Biol. Med.*, 1940, **43**, 434.

62. H. F. Fraser, N. H. Topping and W. H. Sebrell, *U.S. Publ. Health Rep.*, 1938, **53**, 1836.
63. H. Isbell, J. G. Wooley, R. E. Butler and W. H. Sebrell, *J. Biol. Chem.*, 1941, **139**, 499.
64. M. Landy and D. M. Dicken, *J. Lab. Clin. Med.*, 1942, **27**, 1086.
65. B. C. Johnson, *J. Biol. Chem.*, 1945, **159**, 227.
66. W. L. Williams, *ibid.*, 1946, **166**, 397.
67. N. G. Heatley, *Biochem. J.*, 1944, **38**, 61.
68. S. A. Price, *Nature*, 1948, **161**, 20.
68a. B. E. Volcani and E. E. Snell, *Proc. Soc. Exp. Biol. Med.*, 1948, **67**, 511.
69. O. Warburg and W. Christian, *Biochem. Z.*, 1936, **287**, 291.
70. B. J. Jandorf, F. W. Klemperer and A. B. Hastings, *J. Biol. Chem.*, 1941, **138**, 311.
71. D. E. Green and J. Brosteaux, *Biochem. J.*, 1936, **30**, 1489.
72. A. Lwoff and M. Lwoff, *Proc. Roy. Soc. B.*, 1937, **122**, 352, 360 ; *Compt. rend.*, 1936, **203**, 520.
73. H. I. Kohn, *Biochem. J.*, 1938, **32**, 2075.
74. R. W. Vilter, S. P. Vilter and T. D. Spies, *J. Amer. Med. Assoc.*, 1939, **112**, 420.
75. K. Myrbäck, *Z. physiol. Chem.*, 1928, **177**, 158.
76. A. E. Axelrod and C. A. Elvehjem, *J. Biol. Chem.*, 1939, **131**, 77.
77. N. Levitas, J. Robinson, F. Rosen, J. W. Huff and W. A. Perlzweig, *ibid.*, 1947, **167**, 169.
78. J. Robinson, N. Levitas, F. Rosen and W. A. Perlzweig, *ibid.*, 1947, **170**, 653.

6. OCCURRENCE OF NICOTINIC ACID IN FOODSTUFFS

Nicotinic acid is widely distributed in foodstuffs and the values obtained by various workers have been tabulated by A. L. Bacharach [1] and R. W. McVicar and G. H. Berryman.[2] The following summary is based on these tables but is supplemented by more recent information. The earlier references given in these two reviews have been omitted. In many instances, the higher and lower values recorded have been obtained by different methods of assay, some of which might not now be regarded as satisfactory.

Wheat bread (brown) contains 1·2 ; wheat flour (wholemeal), 3·1 to 5·7 ; [3] and wheat flour (white), 0·9 to 1·1 mg. per 100 g.

Barley contains 2·5 to 3·0 ; maize (white), 0·7 to 1·5 ; maize (yellow), 1·2 to 3·0 ; [4] millet, 0·6 to 3·1 ; [5] oats, 1·0 to 1·1 ; rice (unpolished), 6·0 ; rice (milled), 1·6 to 3·2 ; rice (parboiled), 2·8 to 4·0 ; rice polishings, 8·8 to 28 ; [5] rye (whole), 1·3 ; wheat (whole), 4·0 to 5·3 ; wheat germ, 2·7 to 9·1 ; wheat bran, 5·0 ; sorghum, 2·0 to 7·9 mg. per 100 g.

It is worth noting that nicotinic acid is found in the germ and pericarp in rice (as well as in wheat), and that parboiling prevents its removal in the milling process, although it may subsequently be lost in washing and cooking.[6] Another point of very great nutritional significance is that maize contains only slightly less nicotinic acid than milled rice, and the association between pellagra and a maize diet cannot therefore be attributed solely to the low nicotinic acid content of maize. This point will be referred to later (see page 240).

Fruits are relatively deficient in nicotinic acid, as they are in most other members of the vitamin B complex. Apples, pears and tomatoes contain less than 0·5 mg. per 100 g., whilst bananas, fresh figs, grapes, plums and peaches contain between 0·5 and 1·0 mg. per 100 g. Cranberries contain 1·29 and dates 2·18 mg. per 100 g.

Nuts are somewhat richer, raw peanuts containing 5·9 to 13, almonds 1·82 and chestnuts 1·17 mg. per 100 mg. Coconut, however, contains only 0·4 mg. per 100 g.

The nicotinic acid content of vegetables varies. Potatoes contain 1·0 to 2·0 ; cabbage 0·3 ; carrots, 0·5 to 1·5 ; spinach, 0·7 to 1·7 ; broccoli, 1·0 to 1·5 ; lettuce, 0·5 ; cauliflower, 0·6 ; cucumber, 0·3 ; onion, 0·1 ; and beets, 0·3 to 0·6 mg. per 100 g. Legumes contain more nicotinic acid than do other vegetables. Peas (fresh) contain 1·0 to 2·0 ; peas (dry) 1·0 ; broad beans, 2·1 ; soya beans, 1·2 to 4·8 ; lentils, 3·1 ; gram (Bengal), 4·7 ; and gram (red), 5·3 mg. per 100 g.

Cow's milk contains 0·1 to 0·5 and human milk less than 0·1 mg. per 100 ml. The nicotinic acid content of cow's colostrum is about the same as that of the milk.[7] The nicotinic acid content of cow's milk is less in the winter and early spring than in summer and early autumn. It also decreases regularly during the period of lactation.[8] Dried milk contains 5 to 15 mg. per 100 g. and fresh cheese 0·03 to 1·6 mg. per 100 g.[9] When cheese is ripened, the nicotinic acid content is doubled or trebled. Ewe's colostrum and milk contain 0·2 and 0·4 mg. per 100 ml.[8]

Hen's eggs contain less than 0·5 mg. per 100 g. in the white and about 1 mg. per 100 g. in the yolk.

Fish, on the whole, is a good source of nicotinic acid. The muscle of cod contains 1·7 to 3·0 ; of herring, 2·9 to 4·0 ; and of salmon, 8·4 mg. per 100 g. Roe, rather surprisingly, contains less than the muscle from the same fish, cod roe containing 1·4 to 1·5 ; herring roe, 2·1 and turbot roe, 2·3 mg. per 100 g. Cod liver contains 1·6 mg. per 100 g. Halibut contains 3·0 to 6·0 ;[10] mackerel, 5·5 to 7·2 ; mullet, 2·9 ; haddock, 0·9 ; crab, 2·6 to 2·8 ; oyster 1·3 ; and scallop, 1·4 mg. per 100 g. Prawn and crab contain 2 to 4 mg. per 100 g. of fresh tissue.[11]

Salt-water fish on the whole constitutes a richer source of nicotinic acid than fresh-water fish,[12] the highest value observed in eight
varieties of salt-water fish purchased in Calcutta market being 3·1, and
in thirteen varieties of fresh-water fish, 1·77 mg. per 100 g. Trout,
however, contains 3·5 and perch 1·7 mg. of nicotinic acid per 100 g.[10]

Fish from Lake Michigan contained : [13] lake herring, 2·3 to 5·5 ;
common suckers, 1·1 to 1·3 ; carp, 1·5 ; burbot, 1·6 ; carp roe, 1·3 ;
and herring roe, 0·6 mg. of nicotinic acid per 100 g. Wide individual
and seasonal variations were observed. No significant loss occurred on
freezing and subsequent storage for two to three months or on baking ;
smoked fish retained 66 to 72 % of the nicotinic acid originally present.

Meat is another rich source of nicotinic acid, richer even than
fish, and the following values are recorded for muscle tissue : [10] ox,
3·8 to 10·2 ; calf, 4·9 to 18·0 ; horse, 4·7 ; pig, 3·3 to 13·0 ; rabbit,
6·5 to 13·0 ; chicken, leg, 6·1 to 8·0 ; breast, 11·0 to 18·1 ; grouse,
6·5 ; and lamb, 5·4 to 10·2 mg. per 100 g. The amount of nicotinic
acid in chicken muscle appeared to vary inversely with the aneurine
content, dark muscle containing three times as much aneurine as pale
muscle, but only one-half to one-third of the nicotinic acid.[14]

In general, kidneys are richer than the corresponding muscle
tissue,[10] ox containing 6·5 to 19·4 ; pig, 4·1 to 15·5 ; calf, 8·3 to 10·0 ;
rabbit, 3·8 to 16·2 ; sheep, 7·5 to 9·6 mg. per 100 g., whilst liver is
richer still, that of ox containing 7·6 to 27·5 ; calf, 11·5 to 22·5 ;
horse, 16·0 ; sheep, 12·5 to 20·0 ; lamb, 39·2 to 46·0 ; pig, 9·7 to 27·5 ;
rabbit, 7·85 to 22·0 ; and chicken, 11·4 to 17·8 mg. per 100 g. Ox
tongue contains 6·1 to 12·8 mg. per 100 g.

Other " offal " is a poorer source of nicotinic acid than kidney and
liver, the following values being recorded : adrenal, ox, 5·0 to 6·0 ;
adrenal, sheep, 13·5 ; brain, ox, 3·0 to 7·5 ; brain, rabbit, 1·2 ; heart,
ox, 4·9 to 5·9 ; heart, pig, 5·3 to 8·0 ; heart, rabbit, 3·4 ; heart, sheep,
6·0 ; lung, ox, 4·3 to 8·3 ; lung, rabbit, 0·9 ; ovary, pig, 3·8 ; pancreas,
ox, 2·7 to 5·0 ; pancreas, sheep, 4·0 ; spleen, ox, 4·4 to 8·3 ; spleen,
pig, 4·0 ; and testis, pig, 4·4 mg. per 100 g.

In animal tissues, nicotinic acid exists mainly in the form of nicotinamide or,[15] more probably, pyridine nucleotide,[16] whereas plant
tissues contain a smaller, often a very much smaller, proportion of
nicotinamide.

The richest readily available source of nicotinic acid, as of other
members of the vitamin B complex, is yeast. Bakers' yeast contains
7·4 to 12·0 mg. per 100 g., compressed yeast 25·7 mg. per 100 g. of
dry matter and dry yeast 25 to 50 mg. per 100 g. Dried brewer's
yeast contains 34 to 93 and moist brewer's yeast 9·1 to 10·2 mg. per
100 g. *Torula utilis* contains 20 to 38 mg. per 100 g.[17, 18] The yeast
extract, " Marmite ", contains 65·5 mg. per 100 g.[19]

Beers and pale ales contain 0·45 to 0·82, strong ales 1·35 to 2·7, and stouts 0·62 to 1·1 mg. per 100 ml.,[20] so that each pint provides approximately 5 mg. The daily requirement of nicotinic acid can therefore be provided by about two pints of beer.

Seven samples of tea, examined by the method of Wang *et al.* were found [21] to contain 5·6 to 9·4 mg. of nicotinic acid per 100 g., and most of this dissolved in boiling water when the tea was infused. Assuming that twenty-four cups can be prepared from ¼ lb. of tea, the daily requirement would be supplied by about twenty-four cups.

Raw coffee beans contain 1·6 to 4·4 mg. of nicotinic acid per 100 g. and roast coffee 9·5 to 26 mg. per 100 g., dark roast coffee containing more than light roast.[22] The increase is explained by decomposition of trigonelline during roasting. Almost the whole of the nicotinic acid is extracted in making a cup of coffee and an average cup of white coffee contains 1 to 2 mg., that is, one-tenth to one-fifth of the amount required per day. An attempt to assay coffee biologically by means of chicks was unsuccessful, owing to the presence of toxic substances, whilst the feeding of a charcoal eluate of coffee extract to blacktongue dogs produced symptoms of biotin deficiency.[23] On addition of biotin, the dogs responded normally to nicotinic acid.

Honey, pollen and royal jelly contain 0·11, 10 and 11 mg. of nicotinic acid per 100 g. respectively.[24]

Effect of Processing Food on Nicotinic Acid Content

Less work has been carried out on the effect of cooking and storage on the nicotinic acid contents of food than with other members of the vitamin B complex, possibly because it is considerably more stable to heat than aneurine and more stable to light than riboflavine. Nevertheless, in calculating the dietary intake of nicotinic acid, the losses caused by extraction of the vitamin into the water used in cooking fruit and vegetables must be taken into consideration. This may be up to 30 % of the amount present in the food.[25] Cooking water was found to contain 2 to 40 % and the liquid in canned vegetables 30 to 40 % of the total nicotinic acid. As already mentioned above, roast coffee may contain several times the amount of nicotinic acid present in the raw bean, owing to decomposition of trigonelline. Raw milled rice lost 60 % of its nicotinic acid on washing and cooking, whereas parboiled milled rice, that is, rice steamed in the husk, lost only 12 %.[26]

Roast beef retained nearly all the nicotinic acid present in the raw meat.[19] Beef extract is a rich source of nicotinic acid,[19] as well as of riboflavine (see page 166), and seven samples of commercial meat extracts and meat juices contained 34·5 to 102·5 mg. of nicotinic acid per 100 g. A breakfast-cup, made with a teaspoonful of such an extract may supply up to 10 mg. of nicotinic acid, that is, a day's requirement. The nicotinic acid content of corned beef was correspondingly low, values ranging from 0·85 to 3·3 mg. per 100 g. being obtained, compared with values of 4·5 to 8·5 mg. per 100 g. for fresh beef. On an average, four-fifths of the original content was lost in the pickling process by extraction, but hardly any by destruction, even when nitrite was used.

References to Section 6

1. A. L. Bacharach, *Nutr. Abs.*, 1940-41, **10**, 459.
2. R. W. McVicar and G. H. Berryman, *J. Nutrition*, 1942, **24**, 235.
3. S. Josem, *Anal. Assoc. Quim. Argentina*, 1944, **32**, 185.
4. K. Mather and E. C. Barton-Wright, *Nature*, 1946, **157**, 109.
5. M. Swaminathan, *Indian J. Med. Res.*, 1941, **29**, 325.
6. W. R. Aykroyd and M. Swaminathan, *ibid.*, 1940, **27**, 666.
7. P. B. Pearson and A. L. Darnell, *J. Nutrition*, 1946, **31**, 51.
8. J. M. Lawrence, B. L. Herrington and L. A. Maynard, *ibid.*, 1946, **32**, 73.
9. R. A. Sullivan, E. Bloom and J. Jarmol, *ibid.*, 1943, **25**, 463.
10. W. J. Dann and P. Handler, *ibid.*, 1942, **24**, 153.
11. M. L. Khorana, M. L. Sarma and K. V. Giri, *Indian J. Med. Res.*, 1942, **30**, 315.
12. B. de M. Braganea, *Ann. Biochem. Exp. Med.*, 1944, **4**, 41.
13. J. F. Klocke, T. Porter, P. I. Tack, E. Laffler, N. S. Henry and R. Nitchals, *Food Res.*, 1946, **11**, 179.
14. E. E. Rice, E. J. Strandine, E. M. Squires and B. Lyddon, *Arch. Biochem.*, 1946, **10**, 251.
15. W. A. Krehl, J. de la Huerga, C. A. Elvehjem and E. B. Hart, *J. Biol. Chem.*, 1940, **166**, 53.
16. J. Robinson, N. Levitas, F. Rosen and W. A. Perlzweig, *ibid.*, 1947, **170**, 653.
17. H. Fink and F. Just, *Biochem. Z.*, 1940, **303**, 404.
18. M. Swaminathan, *Indian J. Med. Res.*, 1942, **30**, 403.
19. R. G. Booth and E. C. Barton-Wright, *Lancet*, 1944, **1**, 565.
20. F. W. Norris, *J. Inst. Brew.*, 1945, **51**, 177.
21. E. B. Hughes and F. L. Parkinson, *Analyst*, 1945, **70**, 86.
22. E. B. Hughes and R. F. Smith, *J. Soc. Chem. Ind.*, 1946, 284.
23. L. J. Teply, W. A. Krehl and C. A. Elvehjem, *Arch. Biochem.*, 1945, **6**, 139.
24. G. Kitzes, H. A. Schuette and C. A. Elvehjem, *J. Nutrition*, 1943, **26**, 241.
25. W. C. Russell, M. W. Taylor and J. F. Benk, *ibid.*, 1943, **25**, 275; E. Gleim, M. Albury, J. R. McCartney, K. Visnyei and F. Fenton, *Food Res.*, 1946, **11**, 461; F. Fenton, E. Gleim, M. Albury, J. R. McCartney and K. Visnyei, *ibid.*, 468.
26. M. Swaminathan, *Indian J. Med. Res.*, 1941, **29**, 83.

7. EFFECT OF NICOTINIC ACID DEFICIENCY IN ANIMALS

It has already been stated (page 211) that, in the original experiments on the cause of pellagra, rats and chickens did not respond with characteristic deficiency symptoms when maintained on a nicotinic acid-deficient diet ; the symptoms observed were in fact due to a deficiency of other vitamins. The diets used in these early experiments presumably contained tryptophan and, as is now known, rats do not require nicotinic acid if tryptophan is available, being able to convert it into nicotinic acid (page 241). Moreover, in some animals nicotinic acid may be provided by intestinal bacteria,[1] although rats were not rendered nicotinic acid-deficient by administration of sulphaguanidine ;[2] in these experiments, however, tryptophan was probably present in the diet.

Rats

Nicotinic acid deficiency can be induced in rats by feeding a diet substantially free from both nicotinic acid and tryptophan.[3] Growth is suppressed and the nicotinic acid content of the tissues is diminished. Under normal circumstances nicotinamide does not promote growth in the rat, but actually inhibits it.[4] This adverse effect is attributed to the conversion of nicotinamide into N^1-methylnicotinamide by methylation. This results in a smaller number of methyl groups than usual being available for essential metabolic processes. The administration of methionine or of choline plus homocystine prevented the inhibition of growth by nicotinamide, but choline, betaine, homocystine or cystine alone had no effect. Nicotinic acid behaved differently from nicotinamide ; it had no adverse effect on growth but caused fatty livers. These were prevented by methionine, choline or betaine, but were aggravated by cystine or homocystine. The apparent trigonelline excretion was greater after feeding nicotinamide than after feeding nicotinic acid, and was increased by administration of methionine or choline.

Horses[5] and cows,[6] like rats, were able to synthesise all the nicotinic acid they required.

Dogs

The dog is the animal that most clearly demonstrates the effects of nicotinic acid deficiency. The most striking symptom is the appearance of the tongue, which becomes very dark in colour ; hence the name applied to this condition—canine blacktongue. It was the onset of this symptom that Goldberger and his colleagues used as a test in their pioneer work on pellagra (see page 212). Dogs suffering from blacktongue exhibited dehydration and electrolyte imbalance ; [7] these symptoms were alleviated and life was prolonged by feeding sodium chloride, but nicotinic acid deficiency eventually supervened. This was characterised by a lowered content of glucose and chloride in the blood and by a low carbon dioxide-combining capacity of the blood. The plasma protein and non-protein nitrogen were high. These changes were reversed on administration of nicotinic acid. Nicotinic acid deficiency also resulted in the appearance of a severe macrocytic anaemia, which was not alleviated by iron, protein, glucose, haemoglobin, xanthopterin, the anti-pernicious anaemia factor or cobalt.[8] The reticulocyte count rapidly increased on ad-ministration of nicotinic acid or nicotinamide, unless the deficiency was severe ; in this event, folic acid relieved the symptoms.[9] Folic acid prevented the development of symptoms of blacktongue, suggest-ing that some connection exists between folic acid and nicotinic acid.

Other Animals

Nicotinic acid is also essential for pigs,[10] monkeys [11] and rabbits.[12] On a high protein diet, pigs failed to exhibit symptoms of nicotinic acid deficiency, but on a diet low in protein, impaired growth, rough coats, diarrhoea, poor appetite and severe anaemia were observed in the absence of nicotinic acid.[13] The protective effect of protein was presumably due to its tryptophan content (see page 242). Nicotinic acid-deficient pigs responded to tryptophan equally as well as to nicotinic acid.[14]

Monkeys fed a purified diet low in nicotinic acid developed a deficiency syndrome characterised by loss in weight, anorexia and low haemoglobin.[15] The animals also failed to grow on a diet containing 40 % of corn grits ; the haemoglobin was again suboptimal and a reversed neutrophil-lymphocyte count occurred. In neither instance were the symptoms cured by nicotinamide, but whole liver effected a complete cure.

Rabbits on a nicotinic acid-deficient diet lost weight and developed anorexia and diarrhoea,[12] but the diarrhoea was probably due to inanition, rather than to the absence of nicotinic acid *per se*. After eight weeks on a deficient diet the haemoglobin and cellular com-ponents of the blood were reduced, and after twelve weeks the nico-tinic acid content of the tissues was markedly reduced.[16] The symptoms were cured by administration of either 400 mg. of DL-tryptophan or 10 mg. of nicotinic acid per kg. of bodyweight, the response to each being approximately equal. The only difference be-tween the two was that the nicotinic acid content of the muscles was increased when nicotinic acid, but not tryptophan, was administered.

Birds and Fish

As already noted (page 212), in the early days of research on the PP-factor, chickens on a nicotinic acid-deficient diet were observed to lose weight and develop a form of dermatitis,[17] but subsequent investigations showed that the factor mainly responsible for these symptoms was pantothenic acid, not nicotinic acid. Nevertheless, chickens do suffer from deficiency symptoms when nicotinic acid is absent from their diet ; the growth rate decreased, feather formation was defective, and sometimes perosis and dermatitis developed.[18] Chickens appear able to synthesise about one-sixth of their nicotinic acid requirements.

The growth of chicks was reduced by adding 10 % of gelatine to the diet, the inhibitory effect being neutralised by the addition of 5 mg. of nicotinic acid or 200 mg. of DL-tryptophan per 100 g. of diet. These supplements prevented blacktongue, which occurred on the gelatine diet.[19]

Nicotinic acid deficiency in ducklings was characterised by lack of growth, diarrhoea and general weakness.[20] It was produced by feeding either purified diets low in nicotinic acid or diets containing large amounts of maize.

Turkeys on a highly purified diet, deficient only in nicotinic acid, exhibited poor growth and feathering, inflammation of the mouth, low food consumption, diarrhoea and perosis.[21, 22] All the symptoms were prevented by the addition of 50 mg. of nicotinic acid per kg. of ration.

In chicks, *Plasmodium lophurae* infection was aggravated by nicotinic acid deficiency,[23] whereas this did not affect the symptoms in infected ducks, these presumably being more susceptible to the infection than chicks.

Nicotinic acid was also essential for the growth of young rainbow trout (*Salmo gairdneri irideus*).[24] In the absence of this vitamin the fish developed swollen gills ; these were prevented by the addition of 0·1 to 0·5 mg. of nicotinic acid per 100 g. of diet.

References to Section 7

1. W. A. Krehl, P. S. Sarma, L. J. Teply and C. A. Elvehjem, *J. Nutrition*, 1946, **31**, 85.
2. W. J. Dann, *J. Biol. Chem.*, 1941, **141**, 803.
3. J. M. Hundley, *J. Nutrition*, 1947, **34**, 253.
4. P. Handler and W. J. Dann, *J. Biol. Chem.*, 1942, **146**, 357 ; P. P. Foâ, N. L. Foâ and H. Field, *Arch. Biochem.*, 1945, **6**, 215.
5. P. B. Pearson and R. W. Luecke, *ibid.*, 63.
6. B. C. Johnson, A. C. Wiese, H. H. Mitchell and W. B. Nevens, *J. Biol. Chem.*, 1947, **167**, 729.

7. P. Handler and W. J. Dann, *J. Biol. Chem.*, 1942, **145**, 145.
8. P. Handler and W. P. Featherston, *ibid.*, 1943, **151**, 395.
9. W. A. Krehl and C. A. Elvehjem, *ibid.*, 1945, **158**, 173.
10. H. Chick, T. F. Macrae, A. J. P. Martin and C. J. Martin, *Biochem. J.*, 1938, **32**, 10 ; E. H. Hughes, *J. Animal Sci.*, 1943, **2**, 23.
11. M. Swaminathan, *Indian J. Med. Res.*, 1940, **28**, 91.
12. J. G. Wooley and W. H. Sebrell, *J. Nutrition*, 1945, **29**, 191.
13. M. M. Wintrobe, H. J. Stein, R. H. Follis and S. Humphreys, *ibid.*, 1945, **30**, 395 ; G. E. Cartwright, B. Tatting and M. M. Wintrobe, *Arch. Biochem.*, 1948, **19**, 109.
14. R. Braude, S. K. Kon and E. G. White, *Biochem. J.*, 1946, **40**, 843.
15. J. M. Cooperman, K. B. McCall, W. R. Ruegamer and C. A. Elvehjem, *J. Nutrition*, 1946, **32**, 37.
16. J. G. Wooley, *Proc. Soc. Exp. Biol. Med.*, 1947, **65**, 315.
17. C. A. Elvehjem and C. J. Koehn, *J. Biol. Chem.*, 1935, **108**, 709.
18. G. M. Briggs, T. D. Luckey, L. J. Teply, C. A. Elvehjem and E. B. Hart, *ibid.*, 1943, **148**, 517.
19. G. M. Briggs, *ibid.*, 1945, **161**, 749.
20. D. M. Hegsted, *J. Nutrition*, 1946, **32**, 467.
21. G. M. Briggs, *ibid.*, 1946, **31**, 79.
22. T. H. Jukes, E. L. R. Stokstad and M. Belt, *ibid.*, 1947, **33**, 1.
23. A. Ross, D. M. Hegsted and F. J. Stare, *ibid.*, 1946, **32**, 473.
24. B. A. McLaren, E. Keller, D. J. O'Donnell and C. A. Elvehjem, *Arch. Biochem.*, 1947, **15**, 169.

8. EFFECT OF NICOTINIC ACID DEFICIENCY IN MAN

Pellagra

The classical disease associated with nicotinic acid deficiency is pellagra. " True " pellagra manifests itself in what Goldberger *et al.*[1] described as a " definite bilaterally symmetrical eruption ", associated with mental and gastro-intestinal disturbances and other less characteristic symptoms. The dermatitis is generally worse on exposure to sunlight, but this is apparently not the only factor capable of producing the characteristic pigmentation ; for heat, pressure and irritation may do the same. The disease is common in tropical and sub-tropical countries, and appears to be especially rife where maize is the staple article of diet.

Pellagra and Maize

The association between pellagra and the consumption of maize has puzzled a good many workers in the past. It is not due solely to the low nicotinic acid content of maize, for rice and wheat contain approximately the same amounts (page 233), yet pellagra is far more frequent amongst maize-eating than among rice-eating or wheat-eating communities.[2]   Moreover, nicotinic acid is no less available in maize than in rice, since monkeys fed on a whole maize diet accumulated larger amounts of nicotinic acid in the liver, muscle and brain than monkeys fed on milled rice ; [3] and whole wheat resulted in a higher nicotinic acid content than either maize or rice.

P. Handler [4] suggested that maize may be responsible for the dehydration and haemo-concentration generally present in black-tongue and pellagra.   It has also been suggested [5] that maize does not favour the growth of intestinal bacteria capable of synthesising nicotinic acid (page 268), whereas other cereals and pellagra-preventive foodstuffs such as milk, which are very deficient in nicotinic acid, are able to stimulate the growth of the right type of intestinal flora, leading to the formation of nicotinic acid in the intestine.

A different hypothesis was suggested by D. W. Woolley, [6] who was able to produce symptoms of pellagra in rats and mice by feeding a chloroform extract of maize ; the condition was prevented or cured by administration of nicotinamide. He therefore postulated that maize contained a toxic factor responsible for its pellagragenic activity. This hypothesis was supported by Kodicek et al.,[7] who found that indole-3-acetic acid, which is present in maize in substantial amounts, depressed the growth of rats fed a diet poor in protein, although Woolley [6] considered that the toxic factor in maize was a basic substance.   Kodicek et al.,[8] however, showed that maize, after extraction with aqueous acetone to remove indole-3-acetic acid, promoted a growth rate significantly higher than that obtained with the un-extracted maize but that when indole-3-acetic acid was added to the extracted maize diet, it did not cause any retardation of growth.   It therefore appeared unlikely that indole-3-acetic acid was responsible, as had been suggested, for the pellagragenic activity of maize.   The variable results obtained in these experiments with rats was attributed to synthesis or destruction of nicotinic acid by the intestinal flora, the activity of which was affected by indole-3-acetic acid.

The true explanation of the pellagragenic effect of maize was discovered by Krehl et al.,[9] who found that the reduced growth rate of rats induced by the addition of corn or corn grits to a diet low in nicotinic acid could be brought back to normal by the addition of either 1 mg. of nicotinic acid or 50 mg. of L-tryptophan per 100 g. of diet.   Other cereals which contained substantial amounts of tryptophan did not produce nicotinic acid deficiency in rats, so that the pellagragenic activity of maize must be due to its low content of tryptophan.   The effect of maize could in fact be simulated by adding a tryptophan-free protein or an acid-hydrolysed protein to the diet.

This observation explained the curious paradox, which had puzzled clinicians for years, that milk and milk products, which are notoriously poor in nicotinic acid, are, nevertheless, amongst the most valuable of pellagra-preventive foodstuffs. Casein, the protein of milk, is a very good source of tryptophan and it is this that prevents nicotinic acid deficiency.

The observation that tryptophan increased the growth rate of rats fed on a diet containing corn grits was confirmed by H. Spector and H. H. Mitchell.[10] Subsequent work indicated [11] that administration of tryptophan led to the synthesis of nicotinic acid, which in turn led to an improved utilisation of nicotinic acid. Moreover, Krehl *et al.*[12] found that the growth of rats was not inhibited by indole-3-acetic acid or by cyanopyridine, indole or anthranilic acid, although pyridine-3-sulphonic acid (see page 291) suppressed growth. From this it would seem that the absence of both nicotinic acid and tryptophan from maize is a satisfactory explanation of its pellagragenic effect, and that it is unnecessary to postulate the existence of a toxic factor in maize ; nor is the evidence for the existence of such a factor particularly strong. Symptoms of nicotinic acid deficiency were produced in pigs fed a diet containing a large proportion of maize,[13] and the symptoms were cured by the addition of tryptophan to the diet, or by replacing the maize by oats.

It has been demonstrated [14-16] that the pig, horse, cotton-rat, chick, chick embryo and turkey, as well as the rat, are able to convert dietary tryptophan into nicotinic acid, which is excreted either as the free acid or as N^1-methylnicotinamide (page 261). The mechanism of the transformation in animals is discussed below (page 249).

Symptoms of Pellagra

The symptoms exhibited in pellagra and in " pseudo-pellagrous conditions " (page 244) depend on whether or not the nicotinic acid deficiency is accompanied by a deficiency of other members of the vitamin B complex, and on the speed with which the body reserves are depleted. A chronic partial deficiency produces functional and anatomical changes quite different from those produced by an acute or total depletion of the vitamin reserves.[17] A partial deficiency, for instance, may produce mild biochemical disturbances, which in course of time may lead to irreversible anatomical changes, whereas a gross deficiency may cause severe functional disturbances, sometimes fatal, often without any gross anatomical lesions developing.

In classical pellagra, alcoholic pellagra and other pseudo-pellagrous states, psychic disturbances generally precede other manifestations by weeks or months. The usual symptoms are lassitude, slight mental retardation, loss of memory for recent events, apprehension and a tendency to confabulation ; depression and mild delusional states may also develop. Similar symptoms were observed by Williams *et al.*[18] in artificially induced aneurine deficiency, but the psychic manifestations in pellagra cannot be cured by administration of aneurine. After several relapses the mild psychoses are replaced by marked disorientation, hysterical and confusional episodes and sometimes by maniacal states. Advanced cases fail to respond to nicotinic acid, presumably because the cerebral neurones are actually destroyed, whereas earlier cases respond dramatically to nicotinic acid or nicotinamide.

These psychic disturbances are followed, after a variable interval of time, by characteristic dermatitis, stomatitis (desquamation of the tongue) and glossitis, with ulceration of the angles of the mouth, a condition now known as cheilosis, and probably due to riboflavine deficiency (see page 174). P. Manson-Bahr and O. N. Ransford[19] believe that the skin lesions of pellagra do not develop in temperate climates, but that the condition then manifests itself as stomatitis and chronic diarrhoea ; they describe a case of this type that was rapidly cured by nicotinic acid. I. Katzenellenbogen,[20] in Palestine, also described the successful treatment with nicotinic acid of cases of stomato-glossitis, in which there were no signs of pellagra except soreness of the tongue, of the angles of the mouth, and of the throat. J. V. Landor,[21] on the other hand, described cases in the hospital at Singapore similar to pellagra in certain respects but different in others. Eczema of the scrotum and stomatitis were the most constant symptoms noted, and the disease was not curable by nicotinic acid, although the symptoms cleared up on the administration of yeast or " marmite " ; this condition was, therefore, caused by a deficiency of other factors. Aykroyd *et al.*[22] described twenty-four cases of stomatitis occurring among a rice-eating population in India. These were treated with nicotinic acid and only nine showed rapid improvement, whilst seven showed some improvement and eight none. The authors concluded that the stomatitis in question was not true pellagra but arose from a multiple vitamin deficiency.

Pellagra assumed epidemic proportions in the war of 1939-45 among American prisoners of war in the Philippines after six months on a diet made up largely of carbohydrates and deficient in animal proteins, fresh fruit, vegetables and calories.[23] The condition was remedied by a crude yeast culture, and with less satisfactory results, by pure vitamin preparations. As might be expected, the symptoms were due to a multiple vitamin deficiency rather than to a deficiency of any one vitamin.

Nicotinic acid and nicotinamide generally have a beneficial effect in pellagra and " pseudo-pellagrous conditions ", and are specific in the treatment of what may be termed " classical " pellagra ; 50 to 500 mg. of nicotinic acid a day cured the dermatitis in the acute form of the disease and 150 to 500 mg. a day in the chronic form. Doses up to 500 mg. controlled the diarrhoea, but not the neuritis or mental symptoms.[24] Nicotinamide in 50-mg. doses effected prompt improvement in patients with atrophy of the tongue, fissures of the tongue or atrophy of the papillae.[25]

Excretion of Pigment

Pellagrins excrete a red pigment in the urine. According to C. J. Watson,[26] this was not porphyrin, but urorosein,[27] derived from its chromogen, indolylacetic acid,[28] by the action of other substances, e.g. nitrites, present in the urine of pellagrins ;[29] indirubin or a closely related substance was also present.[30] These pigments were not observed in normal urine, although indolylacetic acid is ordinarily present, being excreted by subjects who exhibit no clinical symptoms of nicotinic acid deficiency.[29] There appears to be no correlation between the presence of the chromogen and nicotinic acid deficiency or its disappearance on administration of nicotinic acid, but the conversion to urorosein appears to take place spontaneously only in association with the disease. Urorosein was not present in urine from dogs with blacktongue, nor was there any increase in the coproporphyrin excretion in canine blacktongue.[31]

The excessive coproporphyrinuria, frequently reported in alcoholic pellagrins (see page 245), is believed by C. Rimington and Z. A. Leitner [32] to be due to liver damage by the alcohol or by the dietary deficiency. Out of fifteen proved cases of pellagra, only two showed excessive porphyrinuria, and these were explicable on other grounds. It was concluded that porphyrinuria is not an essential feature of pellagra.

" Pseudo-pellagrous Conditions "

Although " classical " pellagra is due to a deficiency of nicotinic acid, related conditions are known in which a deficiency of other members of the vitamin B complex co-exists with a nicotinic acid deficiency and, in this event, the clinical picture is atypical. Again, other examples of nicotinic acid deficiency occur, in which the causes are different from those leading to true pellagra. For convenience, these various forms of nicotinic acid deficiency have been referred to as " pseudo-pellagrous conditions ".

All such cases are benefited by nicotinic acid or nicotinamide, and in some a complete cure may result. In others, however, additional members of the vitamin B complex have to be given, together with the nicotinic acid, in order to obtain a complete cure. Cures invariably result following administration of yeast or liver.

Such cases are not examples of true pellagra but of a multiple vitamin B deficiency due to the absence of several members of the vitamin B complex, and several of the cases described in the literature as pellagra are more properly regarded as of this type. According to V. P. Sydenstricker,[33] the paraesthesias, neuritic pains, diminished tendon reflexes, oedema and tachycardia, often seen in so-called pellagra, are relieved by aneurine, whilst the anorexia, flatulence and constipation sometimes disappear at the same time. On the other hand, the psychic manifestations only disappear on administration of nicotinic acid, which also controls the nausea and diarrhoea. At the same time, the typical red tongue, due to distended capillaries, becomes blanched, and the stomatitis and other lesions heal rapidly. Certain of the patients who respond in this way, however, retain some of the lesions, or acquire others, probably as the result of riboflavine deficiency, for example, seborrhoeic dermatitis of the face (" shark skin ") and fissures of the lip. In some patients, the tongue acquires a purplish-red colour and becomes pebbly in appearance. W. H. Sebrell and R. E. Butler [34] reported similar symptoms in subjects fed a riboflavine-deficient diet (see page 174), thus confirming the association of riboflavine and nicotinic acid deficiencies in " pseudo-pellagrous conditions ".

Symptoms of multiple vitamin deficiency were observed in pellagra in infants by T. Gillman and J. Gillman.[35] In addition to dermatitis and stomatitis, presumably due to nicotinic acid deficiency, greying of hair with alopecia, steatorrhoea and large fatty livers were noted ; these symptoms are generally regarded as indicating a deficiency of pantothenic acid, p-aminobenzoic acid or inositol.

A different type of " pseudo-pellagrous condition ", which benefits by administration of nicotinic acid, is " alcoholic pellagra ".[33] This is the result of an excessive consumption of spirits, and is due to the fact that the metabolism of alcohol and glucose involves the same coenzyme system, so that the two sources of energy are in competition with one another for the available nicotinic acid which is essential for their oxidation. At the same time, the loss of nicotinic acid is not made good, a high proportion of the calorie intake being derived from the spirit, which, being a distillate, does not contain any of the vitamin B complex, although fermented liquors contain considerable amounts (see page 235). F. Mainzer and M. Krause [36] described a case in which a chronic whisky addict, suffering from delirium tremens associated with severe gastro-intestinal manifestations and acute stomatitis, responded dramatically twelve hours after oral administration of nicotinic acid.

Another example of a pseudo-pellagrous state is the toxic psychosis or exhaustion delirium sometimes seen after surgical operation or delivery.[17] Such cases have no previous history of deficiency disease, but may have been maintained in hospital on a restricted diet for the treatment of gastro-intestinal disease, or their metabolic demands may have been increased by fever. In these cases, the onset of delirium hallucinations or mania is frequently abrupt, but physical signs are absent. In rare instances there may be acute stomatitis and glossitis with an abundance of Vincent's organisms. Response to nicotinic acid or nicotinamide is rapid.

Another condition, due at least in part to nicotinic acid deficiency, is Wernicke's syndrome,[37] characterised by clouding of the consciousness, cogwheel rigidities and uncontrollable grasping and sucking reflexes ; many such patients have involvement of the mid-brain and some peripheral neuropathy. About half of the patients examined had clinical evidence of pellagra, and all were alcoholic. The mortality rate was very high, but fell considerably when nicotinic acid treatment was introduced. This condition is believed to represent the extreme picture of nicotinic acid deficiency.

Another form of vitamin B deficiency results when diabetics are maintained on a high carbohydrate diet with insulin injections. In this instance, energy is derived from carbohydrate in excess of the vitamin reserves, which are gradually depleted and not replaced. Such cases respond well to nicotinic acid and riboflavine. Another type of case where similar treatment is successful is the elderly or senile stuporous condition generally given glucose to combat dehydration ; [38] nicotinic acid treatment reduced the mortality rate dramatically in such cases. It has been suggested that this result may be due in part to the vasodilator effect of nicotinic acid increasing the supply of blood to the brain (see page 274) ; nicotinamide and nikethamide, however, which have no vasodilator effect, produce cures in cases of stupor and encephalopathy as rapidly as does nicotinic acid.

Other factors that may precipitate symptoms of nicotinic acid deficiency are hard manual work and infection, both of which lead to a heightened metabolism and therefore to an increased consumption of coenzymes I and II ; snake venom, which is known to inactivate coenzyme I ; and cyanogenetic glycosides, which may also inactivate coenzyme I by the liberation of hydrogen cyanide.

Other Conditions affected by Nicotinic Acid

Other conditions besides pellagra and " pseudo pellagra " may benefit by nicotinic acid treatment. Thus, J. D. King [39] found that nicotinic acid cured Vincent's angina, an ulcerative infection of the mouth and throat, known as "trench mouth" among the troops during the war of 1914-18. Large numbers of fusiform bacilli and spirochetes invade the tonsils in this condition, and similar organisms have been reported in patients suffering from pellagrous stomatitis and glossitis, in the mouths of dogs with blacktongue, and in pellagrous pigs and monkeys. King concluded that a pre-pellagrous condition, due to nicotinic acid deficiency, was one of the predisposing factors in Vincent's angina.

V. P. Sydenstricker and R. M. Cleckley [40] used nicotinic acid for the treatment of psychiatric disorders unconnected with pellagra. Twenty-nine patients with no sign of pellagra were treated, and the psychic manifestations, which included maniac excitement, delusions, hallucinations, disorientation and delirium tremens, disappeared promptly, often dramatically. In other cases treated, the underlying cause may have been a vitamin deficiency.

F. J. Neuwahl,[41] following a similar line of reasoning, tried nicotinic acid in angina pectoris, where the mental symptoms are similar to those in pellagrous psychosis. Administration of the drug by mouth produced a decrease in the number and severity of attacks in some cases, but in others the effect was transient. Better results were obtained by drip infusion of a nicotinic acid solution. The mechanism of this effect is still obscure but may be connected with the vasodilator action of nicotinic acid (see page 274).

The paroxysms in sixteen out of nineteen asthmatical subjects were relieved when nicotinic acid was injected intravenously, and the frequency and severity of the attacks were reduced in sixteen out of thirty patients by oral doses taken between attacks.[42] This effect is also probably associated with the vasodilator action of nicotinic acid. Again, over a hundred patients with idiopathic Meniere syndrome showed improvement on treatment with nicotinic acid,[43] though nicotinamide had no effect. In such cases nicotinic acid owes its value to its vasodilator properties.

Nicotinic acid has been stated [44] to benefit intestinal irregularities in patients, a claim that is consistent with the existence of excessive gut movement in dogs maintained on a blacktongue-producing diet.

Nicotinic acid has been used with success in so-called radiation sickness, the vomiting produced by X-ray therapy.[45]

Several cases of lupus erythematosus were reported [46] to have responded rapidly to oral or parenteral administration of nicotinamide.

References to Section 8

1. J. Goldberger, G. A. Wheeler and V. P. Sydenstricker, *J. Amer. Med. Assoc.*, 1918, **71**, 1944.

2. W. R. Aykroyd and M. Swaminathan, *Indian J. Med. Res.*, 1940, **27,** 666.

3. M. Swaminathan, *ibid.*, 1940, **28,** 91.

4. P. Handler, *Proc. Soc. Exp. Biol. Med.*, 1943, **52,** 263.

5. P. Ellinger, R. A. Coulson and R. Benesch, *Nature*, 1944, **154,** 270.

6. D. W. Woolley, *J. Biol. Chem.*, 1946, **163,** 773.

7. E. Kodicek, K. J. Carpenter and L. J. Harris, *Lancet*, 1946, **2,** 491.

8. E. Kodicek, K. J. Carpenter and L. J. Harris, *ibid.*, 1946, **2,** 716; 1947, **2,** 616.

9. W. A. Krehl, P. S. Sarma, L. J. Teply and C. A. Elvehjem, *Science*, 1945, **101,** 489; *J. Nutrition*, 1946, **31,** 85; W. A. Krehl, P. S. Sarma and C. A. Elvehjem, *J. Biol. Chem.*, 1946, **162,** 403.

10. H. Spector and H. H. Mitchell, *ibid.*, 1946, **165,** 37.

11. W. A. Krehl, J. de la Huerga and C. A. Elvehjem, *ibid.*, 1946, **164,** 551.

12. W. A. Krehl, L. M. Henderson, J. de la Huerga and C. A. Elvehjem, *ibid.*, 1946, **166,** 531; F. Rosen and W. A. Perlzweig, *Arch. Biochem.*, 1947, **15,** 111.

13. R. W. Luecke, W. N. McMillen, F. Thorp and C. Tull, *J. Nutrition*, 1947, **33,** 251.

14. F. Rosen, J. W. Huff and W. A. Perlzweig, *J. Biol. Chem.*, 1946, **163,** 343; R. W. Luecke, W. N. McMillen, F. Thorp and C. Tull, *J. Animal Sci.*, 1946, **5,** 408; B. S. Schweigert, P. B. Pearson and M. C. Wilkening, *Arch. Biochem.*, 1947, **12,** 139.

15. S. A. Singal, A. P. Briggs, V. P. Sydenstricker and J. M. Littlejohn, *J. Biol. Chem.*, 1946, **166,** 573; G. M. Briggs, A. C. Groschke and R. J. Lillie, *J. Nutrition*, 1946, **32,** 659; C. Furman, E. E. Snell and W. W. Cravens, *Poultry Sci.*, 1947, **26,** 307.

16. B. S. Schweigert, H. L. German and M. J. Garber, *J. Biol. Chem.*, 1948, **174,** 383.

17. V. P. Sydenstricker, *Proc. Roy. Soc. Med.*, 1943, **36,** 169.

18. R. D. Williams, H. L. Mason, R. M. Wilder and B. F. Smith, *Arch. intern. Med.*, 1940, **66,** 785.

19. P. Manson-Bahr and O. N. Ransford, *Lancet*, 1938, **2,** 426.

20. I. Katzenellenbogen, *ibid.*, 1939, **1,** 1260.

21. J. V. Landor, *ibid.*, 1939, **1,** 1368.

22. W. R. Aykroyd, B. G. Krishnan and R. Passmore, *ibid.*, 1939, **2,** 825.

23. C. F. Lewis and M. M. Musselman, *J. Nutrition*, 1946, **32,** 549.

24. V. H. Musick, *Amer. J. Digest. Dis. Nutr.*, 1939, **5,** 807.

25. E. L. Sevringhaus and E. D. Kyhos, *Arch. intern. Med.*, 1945, **76,** 31.

26. C. J. Watson, *Proc. Soc. Exp. Biol. Med.*, 1939, **41,** 591.

27. M. Nencki and M. Sieber, *J. prakt. Chem.*, 1882, **26,** 333.

28. C. A. Herter, *J. Biol. Chem.*, 1908, **4,** 253.

29. C. J. Watson and J. A. Layne, *Ann. intern. Med.*, 1943, **19,** 183.

30. S. Schwartz, J. F. Marvin, J. A. Layne and C. J. Watson, *ibid.*, 206.

31. C. J. Watson and J. A. Layne, *ibid.*, 200.
32. C. Rimington and Z. A. Leitner, *Lancet*, 1945, **2**, 494.
33. V. P. Sydenstricker, *Ann. intern. Med.*, 1941. **14**, 1499.
34. W. H. Sebrell and R. E. Butler, *U.S. Publ. Health Rep.*, 1938, **53**, 2282.
35. T. Gillman and J. Gillman, *Arch. intern. Med.*, 1945, **76**, 63.
36. F. Mainzer and M. Krause, *Brit. Med. J.*, 1939, **2**, 331.
37. N. Jolliffe, K. M. Bowman, L. A. Rosenblum and H. D. Fein, *J. Amer. Med. Assoc.*, 1940, **114**, 307.
38. R. M. Cleckley, V. P. Sydenstricker and L. E. Geeslin, *ibid.*, 1939, **112**, 2107.
39. J. D. King, *Lancet*, 1940, **2**, 32 ; *Brit. Dental J.*, 1943, **74**, 113, 141, 169.
40. V. P. Sydenstricker and R. M. Cleckley, *Amer. J. Psychiat.*, 1941, **98**, 83.
41. F. J. Neuwahl, *Lancet*, 1942, **2**, 419.
42. G. Melton, *Brit. Med. J.*, 1943, **1**, 600.
43. M. Atkinson, *Arch. Otolaryngol.*, 1944, **40**, 101.
44. L. A. Crandall, F. F. Chesley, D. Hansen and J. Dunbar, *Proc. Soc. Exp. Biol. Med.*, 1939, **41**, 472.
45. J. W. Graham, *J. Amer. Med. Assoc.*, 1939, **113**, 664.
46. W. W. Kühnau, *Klin. Woch.*, 1939, **18**, 1117.

9. BIOSYNTHESIS OF NICOTINIC ACID

Two contrasting views have been advanced to account for the interchangeability of nicotinic acid and tryptophan. It is maintained on the one hand that tryptophan is directly converted into nicotinic acid in the tissues of animals, and on the other that tryptophan acts as a catalyst for the synthesis of nicotinamide by intestinal bacteria.

The evidence supporting the first hypothesis is as follows. Symptoms of nicotinic acid deficiency in the pig,[1] the dog,[2] and in humans [3] were relieved by the administration of L-tryptophan, and the reserves of nicotinic acid and the urinary excretion of nicotinic acid metabolites were thereby increased. Administration of sulphasuxidine did not impair the action of tryptophan in relieving symptoms of pellagra in humans, although such a result could be anticipated if the intestinal flora were involved. Moreover, the *intravenous* administration of L-tryptophan to infants gave a prompt and large increase in the urinary output of N^1-methylnicotinamide.[4] The synthesis of nicotinic acid by rats was apparently not affected by elimination of the bacterial flora [5] or by enterectomy ; [6] and nicotinic acid was synthesised from tryptophan by rat liver slices.[7] Indirect evidence in support of the view that tryptophan is converted directly into nicotinic acid is that the presence of pyridoxine is essential for nicotinic acid synthesis, none being formed when vitamin B_6-deficient rats were given tryptophan.[8] It is known that pyridoxine-like compounds are involved in amino acid metabolism (page 330).

Further evidence has been obtained by C. Heidelberger and his colleagues [9] from a study of the metabolism of tryptophan containing isotopic carbon, C^{14}, at various positions in the molecule. When DL-tryptophan-β-C^{14} (I) was fed to rabbits, dogs and rats, kynurenine (II) and kynurenic acid (III) containing C^{14} were isolated together with nicotinic acid from which C^{14} was absent. On the other hand, when DL-tryptophan-3-C^{14} (IV) was fed to the animals, kynurenine, 3-hydroxyanthranilic acid (V) and nicotinic acid, all containing C^{14}, were isolated from the urine ; in the last two compounds, the C^{14} was in the carboxyl groups. These changes can be represented as follows :

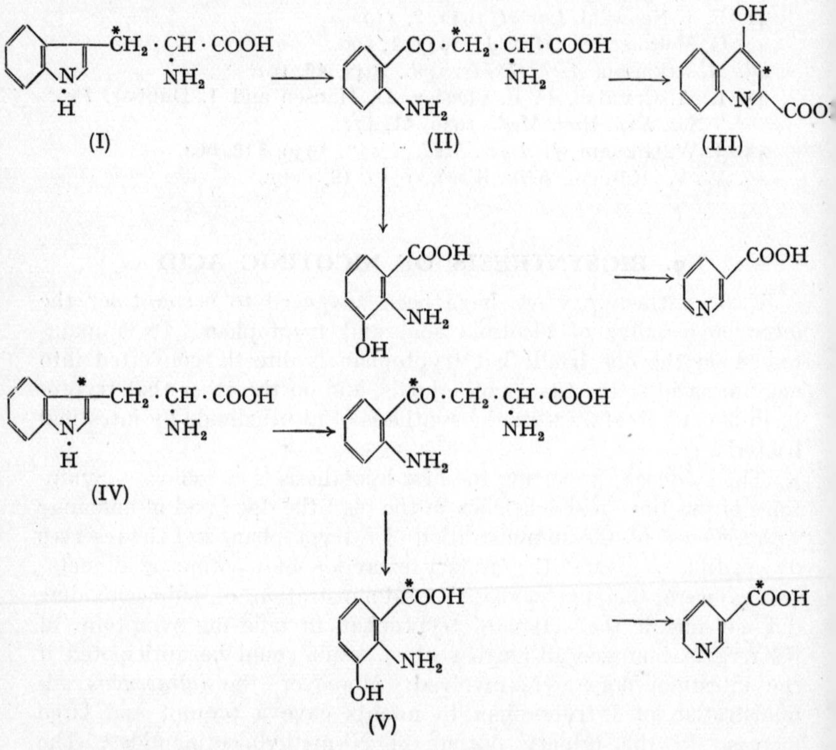

When DL-tryptophan containing C^{13} in the carboxyl group was administered to rats,[10] the N^1-methylnicotinamide excreted in the urine did not contain C^{13}.

That 3-hydroxyanthranilic acid is indeed an intermediate in the conversion of tryptophan into nicotinic acid is confirmed by the fact that it can replace tryptophan in promoting the growth of rats [11] and that it is converted into nicotinic acid and quinolinic acid by rat liver slices.[12] Quinolinic acid was excreted by rats following intraperitoneal injection of 3-hydroxyanthranilic acid or L-tryptophan.[13] An analogous series of transformations to the foregoing has been shown to take place with certain micro-organisms (see page 281). That L-kynurenine, but not kynurenic acid, is an intermediate in the synthesis of nicotinic acid is confirmed by the observation that the former, but not the latter, increased the N^1-methylnicotinamide excretion in rats.[14]

The supporters of the contrary view, that tryptophan merely stimulates the synthesis of nicotinic acid by intestinal bacteria, are P. Ellinger and M. M. Abdel Kader.[15] They observed that, although a mixed culture from rats' caecum was apparently able to produce nicotinamide from tryptophan, *Escherichia coli* was not able to effect this transformation in the absence of lactate, whereas ornithine and, to a smaller extent, glutamine and arginine were readily converted into nicotinamide. The synthesis was completely inhibited by 2-, 4-, 5- and 7-methyltryptophan. Since more N^1-methylnicotinamide was excreted when tryptophan was given to rats orally than when given parenterally, and since less was excreted when the animals were given sulphasuxidine, it was concluded that the nicotinamide was synthesised by the intestinal flora and that the precursor was ornithine, not tryptophan; it is suggested that the latter is a catalyst stimulating the formation of ornithine.

These two views are not irreconcilable and, in any event, none of the evidence advanced in support of the intestinal synthesis hypothesis is opposed to the view that tryptophan can be converted into nicotinic acid directly in the tissues of animals.

The recognition of L-tryptophan as a precursor of nicotinic acid makes it necessary to assume that pellagra can only occur where there is deficiency of both nicotinic acid and typtophan in the diet. By feeding two normal adults on a diet of known nicotinic acid content and estimating the urinary output of N^1-methyl-6-pyridone-3-carboxylamide (page 255) and other nicotinic acid metabolites, W. I. M. Holman and D. J. de Lange [16] found that the ingestion of 12 g. of L-tryptophan over the test period increased the nicotinic acid output by 145 and 181 mg. in the two individuals. This implies that the tryptophan in the diet, normally equal to about 1·1 g. per day, may be of great importance in the prevention of pellagra.

References to Section 9

1. R. W. Luecke, W. N. McMillen, F. Thorp and C. Tull, *J. Nutrition*, 1948, **36**, 417 ; F. Rosen and W. A. Perlzweig, *J. Biol. Chem.*, 1949, **177**, 163.

2. S. A. Singal, V. P. Sydenstricker and J. M. Littlejohn, *J. Biol. Chem.*, 1948, **176**, 1051, 1063.

3. V. A. Najjar, L. E. Holt, G. A. Johns, G. C. Medairy and G. Fleischmann, *Proc. Soc. Exp. Biol. Med.*, 1946, **61**, 371 ; H. P. Sarett and G. A. Goldsmith, *J. Biol. Chem.*, 1949, **177**, 461 ; R. W. Vilter, J. F. Mueller and W. B. Bean, *J. Lab. Clin. Med.*, 1949, **34**, 409.

4. S. E. Snyderman, K. C. Ketron, R. Carretero and L. E. Holt, *Proc. Soc. Exp. Biol. Med.*, 1949, **70**, 569.

5. J. M. Hundley, *ibid.*, 592.

6. L. M. Henderson and L. V. Hankes, *ibid.*, 26.

7. W. W. Hurt, B. T. Scheer and H. J. Deuel, *Arch. Biochem.*, 1949, **21**, 37.

8. B. S. Schweigert and P. B. Pearson, *J. Biol. Chem.*, 1947, **168**, 555 ; G. H. Bell, B. T. Scheer and H. J. Deuel, *J. Nutrition*, 1948, **35**, 239.

9. C. Heidelberger, M. E. Gullberg, A. F. Morgan and S. Lepkovsky, *J. Biol. Chem.*, 1948, **175**, 471 ; C. Heidelberger, E. P. Abraham and S. Lepkovsky, *ibid.*, 1949, **176**, 1461 ; C. Heidelberger, *ibid.*, 1949, **179**, 139 ; C. Heidelberger, M. E. Gullberg, A. F. Morgan and S. Lepkovsky, *ibid.*, 143 ; C. Heidelberger, E. P. Abraham and S. Lepkovsky, *ibid.*, 151.

10. J. M. Hundley and H. W. Bond, *Arch. Biochem.*, 1949, **21**, 313.

11. H. K. Mitchell, J. F. Nyc and R. D. Owen, *J. Biol. Chem.*, 1948, **175**, 433 ; P. W. Albert, B. T. Scheer and H. J. Deuel, *ibid.*, 479.

12. B. S. Schweigert, *ibid.*, 1949, **178**, 707 ; B. S. Schweigert and M. M. Marquette, *ibid.*, 1949, **181**, 199.

13. L. M. Henderson, *ibid.*, 1949, **178**, 1005.

14. R. E. Kallio and C. P. Berg, *ibid.*, 1949, **181**, 333.

15. P. Ellinger and M. M. Abdel Kader, *Nature*, 1947, **160**, 675 ; 1949, **163**, 799 ; *Biochem. J.*, 1949, **44**, 285, 506 ; 1949, **45**, 276.

16. W. I. M. Holman and D. J. de Lange, *Nature*, 1950, **165**, 112.

10. METABOLISM OF NICOTINIC ACID

Fate of Ingested Nicotinic Acid and Nicotinamide

The earliest attempts to study the fate of nicotinic acid in the body were confined to the estimation of the urinary excretion of free nicotinic acid and its amide. Normal subjects were said to excrete up to 30 mg. per day,[1, 2] whereas in pellagrins the amount excreted was extremely low.[3]

It was soon recognised, however, that ingested nicotinic acid was excreted in other forms, and the first derivatives of nicotinic acid to be recognised as metabolites were nicotinuric acid and trigonelline.

Melnick and his colleagues [2], [4] worked out a method of estimating nicotinic acid, nicotinamide, nicotinuric acid and trigonelline separately in urine (see page 224), and used the method to study the fate of ingested nicotinic acid. They found that the total free and combined nicotinic acid in the urine increased when additional nicotinic acid was given. Most of the increase (over 50 %) was apparently due to trigonelline, a substantial proportion (36 %) to nicotinuric acid and only 13 % to nicotinic acid and nicotinamide. The ingestion of nicotinamide was followed by a slower excretion of nicotinic acid compounds, 80 to 90 % of which apparently consisted of trigonelline. The excretion of trigonelline was also increased by heavy smoking or by drinking coffee, so that both these sources of interference must be eliminated in metabolic studies on nicotinic acid.

These and other results obtained prior to 1943, do not, however, take into account the excretion of part of the ingested nicotinic acid as N^1-methylnicotinamide and N^1-methyl-6-pyridone-3-carboxylamide, which were discovered subsequently ; the values reported for the urinary trigonelline probably included the N^1-methylnicotinamide and the pyridone.

Rats were said to convert a substantial proportion of ingested nicotinic acid into trigonelline and nicotinuric acid, only a small amount being excreted unchanged.[5] Nicotinamide was apparently excreted mainly as trigonelline (but see below).

Somewhat similar results were obtained with dogs,[6] which apparently excreted trigonelline and nicotinuric acid as the principal end-products of nicotinic acid metabolism. On a blacktongue-producing diet, the amount of (apparent) trigonelline excreted fell to 0·1 mg. per day and several 25-mg. doses of nicotinic acid were required to increase the output to normal levels. On a diet containing 1·1 mg. of nicotinic acid per kg., 50 % was excreted in the urine, 90 % of it in the form of (apparent) trigonelline. After saturation with nicotinic acid, 100-mg. doses of nicotinamide were completely excreted as (apparent) trigonelline (75 to 94 %) and nicotinuric acid (6 to 25 %). Neither trigonelline nor nicotinuric acid was utilised by the dog.

Rabbits excreted 1·54 mg. of nicotinic acid per day or 0·77 mg. per kg. of bodyweight per day in the urine when maintained on a normal diet, but less than half that amount on a pellagra-producing diet ; the urinary excretion increased on administration of nicotinic acid.[7] According to M. Swaminathan,[8] rabbits on a diet low in nicotinic acid (0·7 mg. per kg.) excreted 0·15 mg. of nicotinic acid and 0·086 mg. of (apparent) trigonelline in the urine daily, and almost similar amounts in the faeces. When given extra nicotinic acid, 15 to 20 % of it was excreted in the urine.

N^1-Methylnicotinamide

The excretion of another metabolite of nicotinic acid was first noted by Najjar and his co-workers.[9] They observed that pellagrins excreted in the urine a fluorescent substance designated F_1, which disappeared when the patients were treated with nicotinic acid, and was replaced by another fluorescent substance known as F_2; this was not present in the urine of pellagrins. The administration of nicotinic acid to a normal individual led to a marked increase in the excretion of this second fluorescent substance, and it was suggested that F_1 was a precursor of F_2, into which it was converted under the influence of nicotinic acid. They found that in addition to nicotinic acid, nicotinamide and coramine were able to bring about this transformation, but not trigonelline, quinolinic acid or pyrazine-carboxylic acids; there was a close parallelism between the ability of substances to cure pellagra and their effect on the fluorescent excretion products.

The excretion of F_1 was also observed in dogs with canine black-tongue; it was replaced by F_2 when the dogs were given nicotinic acid.[10] Large doses of F_2 were excreted by all animals capable of methylating nicotinamide, and in rats, which synthesise nicotinic acid from tryptophan, the excretion of F_2 ran parallel with that of trigonelline when a nicotinic acid-free diet was administered. In rabbits, on the other hand, which do not convert nicotinic acid into trigonelline, the administration of nicotinamide was not followed by excretion of F_2.[11] F_2 was isolated and shown to be N^1-methylnicotinamide, which was synthesised by the method of Karrer *et al*.[12]

Both formed a picrate, m.p. 189·5° C.[11, 13] The substance is sometimes referred to as nicotinamide methochloride. It obviously bears the same relationship to nicotinamide that trigonelline does to nicotinic acid.

Nicotinamide was converted into N^1-methylnicotinamide by incubation with rat-liver slices, and the extent of the transformation was increased by the addition of methionine.[14] The *in vivo* conversion of nicotinic acid into trigonelline is also brought about by methionine, and these reactions compete with others that depend on the availability of methionine or choline (see page 601). Thus, nicotinic acid, although it had no adverse effect on the growth of rats, resulted in the formation of fatty livers, which were prevented by methionine, choline or betaine and aggravated by cystine or homocystine. Nicotinamide actually inhibited the growth of rats when added at a level of 1 % to a diet containing 10 % of casein.[15] The effect was probably due to a deprivation of methyl groups, for the administration of methionine or of choline together with homocystine prevented the inhibition of growth by nicotinamide. Choline, betaine, homocystine or cystine alone had no effect. Presumably the increased severity of the symptoms caused by nicotinamide is due to the greater facility with which nicotinamide is methylated as compared with the acid. Interference with growth on administration of nicotinamide was only observed with rats ; rabbits and guinea-pigs continued to grow normally, and there was no increase in the excretion of N^1-methyl-nicotinamide.[16]

P. Ellinger [17] confirmed these results, and showed that kidney and muscle did not methylate nicotinamide, the enzyme being present only in liver. Moreover, the enzyme was specific for nicotinamide, and did not methylate nicotinic acid. Liver tissue from rats with a low N^1-methylnicotinamide elimination was only able to convert small amounts of nicotinamide into N^1-methylnicotinamide ; the addition of methionine increased the amount formed. The only tissues capable of converting the acid into the amide were kidney and brain ; the specificity of the amidase was not tested, but the same tissues converted glutamic acid into glutamine. When glutamine was added to liver, N^1-methylnicotinamide was formed from nicotinic acid.

Other Metabolites

The presence of another fluorescent substance in urine was reported by Y. Raoul.[18] Its constitution is unknown, but it was stated to be an oxidation product of indole-3-acetic acid. It may be related to the pigment, urorosein, the presence of which in the urine of pellagrins has already been noted (page 244). Another substance apparently connected with the metabolism of nicotinic acid is " pseudo-nicotinic acid ", formed from trigonelline by the action of alkali ; [19] this has similar properties to pyridine-3-acetic acid, with which it may be identical. It is likely that " pseudo-nicotinic acid " is an artefact, however, rather than a true metabolite.

Another metabolite of nicotinic acid was isolated from urine by W. E. Knox and W. L. Grossman,[20] and identified as N^1-methyl-6-pyridone-3-carboxylamide :

It was prepared from N^1-methylnicotinamide by the quinine-oxidising enzyme of rabbit liver,[20] and synthesised by treatment of N^1-methyl-3-carboxy-6-pyridone (prepared by oxidising trigonelline with alkaline ferricyanide or by ring closure of coumalic acid with methylamine) with thionyl chloride and ammonia.[21]   Methylation and oxidation of nicotinamide gave the isomer, N^1-methyl-2-pyridone-3-carboxylamide.[21a]

Another metabolite was isolated from dried chick droppings by W. J. Dann and J. W. Huff [22] and identified as dinicotinyl ornithine :

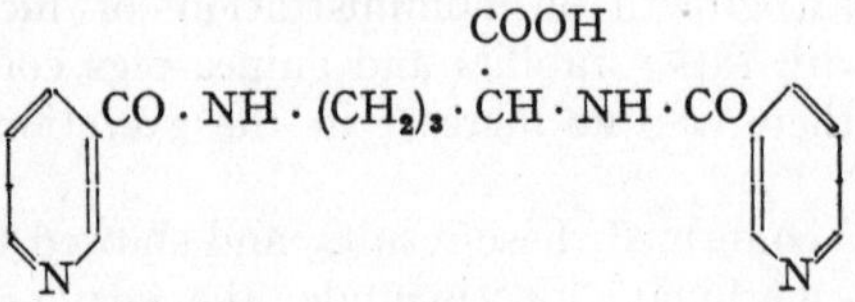

Thus the metabolism of nicotinic acid and nicotinamide is extremely complex, and the early results reported in the literature may be misleading, as they do not take into account all the substances into which nicotinic acid may be converted.

Excretion of Nicotinic Acid and its Metabolities in Urine

A true picture of the fate of nicotinic acid in the body was only obtained when the excretion of N^1-methylnicotinamide was taken into account.   The method used for estimating trigonelline, involving hydrolysis to nicotinic acid with strong alkali, also converts N^1-methylnicotinamide into nicotinic acid, so that any F_2 present would, in the earlier studies, have been included in the values reported for trigonelline.[23]   When 200 mg. of N^1-methylnicotinamide were given orally to a normal adult, 55 mg. of F_2 and 85 mg. of trigonelline were excreted within forty-eight hours, so that the organism is evidently capable of effecting the transformation of the amide into the betaine.

Hochberg et al.[24] found that the urinary output of N^1-methylnicotinamide on a diet yielding 23 mg. of nicotinic acid per day was 3 to 8 mg. daily, and that when this was supplemented with 50 to 200 mg. of nicotinamide, the excretion increased by an amount equivalent to about 20 % of the test dose over a twenty-four hour period ; one-third of this was eliminated in the first four hours.   On the other hand, O. Mickelsen and L. L. Erickson [25] found that the amounts of N^1-methylnicotinamide excreted by normal subjects differed but little with diets providing from 0·12 to 22·4 mg. of nicotinic acid daily, so that merely measuring the excretion of N^1-methylnicotinamide resulting from an unsupplemented diet could give no useful information as to the state of nicotinic acid nutrition.   Johnson et al.[26] however, found that 94 % of the nicotinic acid derivatives excreted in human urine consisted of N^1-methylnicotinamide and that only 1 to 1·5 % was excreted in the form of the free acid and 3·5 to 4·5 % as nicotinamide. Thus, opinions vary greatly as to the amounts of N^1-methylnicotinamide excreted at different levels of nicotinic acid intake. A possible reason for these discordant results was suggested by W. A. Perlzweig and J. W. Huff,[27] who found that when nicotinamide was administered orally to man, 10 to 20 % was excreted in the form of N^1-methylnicotinamide, and that a similar amount was excreted when N^1-methylnicotinamide itself was administered orally. When trigonelline was injected, no appreciable conversion into N^1-methylnicotinamide occurred, whilst when N^1-methylnicotinamide was injected intravenously, 67 % was recovered unchanged in the urine. Perlzweig and Huff therefore suggested that the amount of N^1-methyl-nicotinamide excreted is the resultant of at least two processes, one the conversion of nicotinic acid into N^1-methylnicotinamide and the other the conversion of N^1-methylnicotinamide into other substances. This was confirmed by subsequent work. Thus when rats were fed large amounts of nicotinic acid containing C^{13} in the carboxyl group, almost all of the isotopic carbon was recovered in the N^1-methylnicotinamide excreted in the urine,[27a] although in the mouse about 15 % of a dose of nicotinic acid or amide was lost by decarboxylation ; for on feeding nicotinic acid containing C^{14} in the carboxyl group, or the corresponding amide, 15 % of the C^{14} appeared as exhaled carbon dioxide.[27b] In man, the urinary excretion of N^1-methyl-6-pyridone-3-carboxylamide accounted for about 50 % of a dose of nicotinamide and, when N^1-methylnicotinamide was administered, 20 % was excreted in the urine unchanged and 19 % as the pyridone.[27c] Relatively less pyridone and more N^1-methylnicotinamide was excreted by infants than by adults.[27d]

The most complete data on the urinary excretion of nicotinic acid and its metabolites are those of P. Ellinger and M. M. Abdel Kader.[28] They found, contrary to the claims made by many earlier workers, that no trigonelline or nicotinuric acid was excreted by man or by the rat, cat, guinea-pig or rabbit on a normal diet. The following values were obtained for the excretion of other metabolites (mg. per day) :

	Nicotinamide	Nicotinic acid	N^1-methyl-nicotinamide
Man . . .	0·6-4·0	0·25-1·26	3·2-12·6
Rat . . .	0·004-0·16	0	0·03-2·0
Cat . . .	0	0	0·07-0·4
Guinea-pig . .	0	0	0
Rabbit . . .	0	0·5-1·5	0

Somewhat different results were obtained following the injection of nicotinic acid, nicotinamide and nikethamide (diethylnicotinamide). The values (μg.) found were:

	Compound (μg.)	Excretion			
		Nicotin-amide	Nicotinic acid	Methyl-nicotin-amide	Trigonelline
Man .	Nicotin-amide 100	1·8	0	25·0	0
	Nicotinic acid 100	2·5	0·9	21·2	0
	Niketh-amide 100	6·3	0	15·6	0
Rat .	Nicotin-amide 20	15-24	0	9-30	0
	Nicotinic acid 20	24·0	27·0	2-16	0
	Niketh-amide 20	36·8	0	10-33	0
Cat .	Nicotin-amide 40	34·8	0	28·5	0
	Nicotinic acid 40	12·8	9·8	24·2	0
	Niketh-amide 40	18·9	0	16·1	0
Guinea-pig	Nicotin-amide 200	0	24·2	0	0
	Nicotinic acid 200	0	82·2	0	0
	Niketh-amide 50	19·2	40·8	0	0
Rabbit	Nicotin-amide 200	7-12	13-15	0	6-9
	Nicotinic acid 200	0	50-63	0	29-33
	Niketh-amide 200	4·8	9·9	0	6·9

Thus all the species examined, except the guinea-pig, were able to methylate either nicotinamide or nicotinic acid, but methionine appeared to have no constant effect on the metabolism. Nicotinic acid was aminated in man and in dogs, cats and rats, but not in rabbits and guinea-pigs, whilst rabbits and guinea-pigs, but not the other four species, deaminated nicotinamide. When rabbits were given a meat-bread diet in place of a diet of cabbage or oats, the methylating mechanism was suppressed completely and the deaminating mechanism partially.

Following oral or subcutaneous administration of 2 g. of nicotinamide daily for three days, goats, sheep and calves excreted slightly more N^1-methylnicotinamide than usual ; goats and sheep also excreted slightly more N^1-methyl-6-pyridone-3-carboxylamide, but no measurable amount was excreted by calves.[28a]

Assessment of Nutritional Status

It has been pointed out above (page 257) that the excretion of N^1-methylnicotinamide by subjects given an unsupplemented diet cannot be used to measure nutritional status. More promising results were obtained when the increased excretion of N^1-methylnicotinamide and other metabolites of nicotinic acid was estimated, following the administration of a test dose of nicotinic acid or nicotinamide. G. A. Goldsmith [29] found that normal subjects given a 300-mg. dose of nicotinamide by mouth excreted twice as much trigonelline (this would also have included any N^1-methylnicotinamide) as hospital patients given the same treatment, whilst patients with pellagra or vitamin B complex deficiency excreted still less. He suggested that measurement of the nicotinic acid derivatives excreted within six hours of administering a 300-mg. test dose of nicotinamide orally was a useful indication of nutritional status.

Perlzweig et al.[30] found that excretion of both trigonelline and nicotinic acid was increased after intravenous injection of a 500-mg. dose of nicotinamide. " Normal " subjects, however, showed a lower excretion than did hospital patients, presumably because in this instance the latter were the more saturated with respect to nicotinic acid. The urinary excretion of nicotinic acid after a test dose was much less in pellagrins than in controls,[31] and the response to a test dose was said to be a better criterion of nicotinic acid deficiency than a low blood level.

According to P. Ellinger and R. A. Coulson,[32] from 2 to 8 mg. of N^1-methylnicotinamide are eliminated daily in the urine, and this is increased by the ingestion of additional nicotinamide or nicotinic acid, though significant amounts are stored in the body. They found that the elimination curve was constant for different individuals but that the height of the curve depended on the dietary intake and on the efficiency of the methylation mechanism of the body. They suggested that N^1-methylnicotinamide was not the final metabolite, but that this was converted into other products not yet identified.

(One of these is presumably N^1-methyl-6-pyridone-3-carboxylamide, page 255). This view is also supported by the findings of W. A. Perlzweig and J. W. Huff [27] referred to above.

Similar saturation tests were used by several other workers ;[33-36] in these the amount of N^1-methylnicotinamide excreted in the urine in response to nicotinamide orally administered was measured. Substantially lower excretions were observed in pellagrins than in healthy subjects,[33, 35, 36, 37] e.g. deficient subjects excreted up to 5 % only of the test dose compared with 8 to 25 % excreted by controls. The excretion of acid-hydrolysable nicotinic acid derivatives in normal subjects is remarkably constant and no significant difference was observed in the output of non-pregnant women and women in early pregnancy.[39a] In the last trimester of pregnancy, however, the amount excreted increased significantly and so did the proportion of a 50-mg. test dose that was eliminated, suggesting that the maternal organism requires additional coenzymes I and II in the last three months of pregnancy and that during this period there is a greater turnover of coenzymes.

Not only may the extent to which N^1-methylnicotinamide is eliminated be influenced by the efficiency of the methylating mechanism, but it will also depend on the efficiency of absorption from the intestine.[37, 38] This second factor affects the response in pellagrins but not in healthy persons. A third factor that may influence nicotinamide saturation tests is the presence of bacteria in the intestine that either synthesise,[37, 39, 40, 42] or destroy,[41, 42] nicotinamide.

A critical study of the effect of methionine on the nicotinamide saturation test was undertaken by P. Ellinger and S. W. Hardwick,[43] who demonstrated that the test previously proposed by them [36] might be affected by exhaustion of the methyl donators of the body and therefore not provide a true picture of nicotinamide status. It was found, for instance, that methionine gave a greater response after ingestion of 500 mg. of nicotinamide than after ingestion of 100 mg. Accordingly the test was modified, the amount of N^1-methylnicotinamide excreted in the urine being estimated each day for eighteen days ; immediately after the third, sixth, ninth and twelfth collections, 100 mg. of nicotinamide were administered, subcutaneously on the first and last, orally on the second and rectally on the third occasion. The percentage recovery of ingested nicotinamide was calculated for a twenty-four-hour and a seventy-two-hour period. Three pellagrins gave a response of 3·28 mg. and 5·35 mg. after twenty-four and seventy-two hours, whilst healthy subjects gave 8·18 and 9·96 mg. respectively. It was impossible to account for all the nicotinamide administered.

N^1-Methylnicotinamide was excreted by newborn and premature infants following the administration of nicotinamide, nicotinic acid or diethylnicotinamide, but in this instance methionine appeared to have no effect on the methylation.[44]

Conversion of Tryptophan into Nicotinic Acid and its Metabolites

Another important factor that has to be borne in mind in attempting to assess the nicotinic acid status of any individual is the possibility that the administration of other substances besides nicotinic acid may result in an increased excretion of N^1-methylnicotinamide. Tryptophan is of particular importance in this respect for, as already stated (page 241), the rat, pig, horse, cotton-rat, chick and turkey are able to convert dietary tryptophan into nicotinic acid.[45-48] Clearly therefore, different N^1-methylnicotinamide excretions would be expected to occur on diets that differ markedly in the amount of tryptophan present.

Such variations were in fact found by Rosen et al.,[45] who showed that the amount of nicotinic acid excreted by rats dropped immediately when the casein in the diet was replaced by gelatine, which contains much less tryptophan. The addition of tryptophan led to a large increase in the excretion of nicotinic acid and N^1-methylnicotinamide; the amount of nicotinic acid was so large, in fact, that it exceeded the capacity of the animals to methylate it. Similarly, P. Ellinger[49] observed a fall in the urinary N^1-methylnicotinamide when rats were fed on a maize diet instead of a diet containing wheat and oats. As already mentioned, wheat and oats contain much more tryptophan than does maize. When nicotinamide was given to the animals, followed by the injection of a mixture of chloroform and carbon tetrachloride, which causes liver damage, the excretion of N^1-methylnicotinamide first increased and then fell markedly.

Similar observations were made by H. P. Sarett and G. A. Goldsmith[50] and Perlzweig et al.[51] with human subjects, the urinary excretion of N^1-methylnicotinamide increasing on administration of L- or DL-tryptophan.

Horses behave rather differently from other animals in that on a normal diet they excrete only small amounts of N^1-methylnicotinamide although, rather paradoxically, on a diet containing only 0·1 mg. of nicotinic acid per kg., they excreted N^1-methylnicotinamide and no nicotinamide, nicotinuric acid or glycuronide.[52] However, the oral ingestion of 2 g. of nicotinic acid daily led to the excretion of 18 to 54 % of unchanged acid together with a little nicotinuric acid, and the oral administration or subcutaneous injection of nicotinamide resulted in the excretion of 5 % of unchanged amide, the remainder being unaccounted for. No increase in the excretion of trigonelline or N^1-methylnicotinamide resulted from administration of either nicotinic acid or the amide.

Similarly when 6 g. of DL-tryptophan were fed to horses, the amount of free nicotinic acid excreted increased two- to four-fold, whereas the N^1-methylnicotinamide remained unchanged.[47] This was in marked contrast to the behaviour of cotton-rats, which excreted large amounts of N^1-methylnicotinamide after ingestion of nicotinic acid or tryptophan.

The amount of nicotinic acid formed from dietary tryptophan was increased when pyridoxine was added to the diet of rats or mice, a result to be anticipated from the fact that administration of trypto-phan accentuated pyridoxine deficiency in the rat and mouse (see page 331). Thus, when 100 mg. of DL-tryptophan were added to the basal ration, rats fed pyridoxine excreted 810 to 2190 μg. of N^1-methylnicotinamide per day, whilst deficient animals excreted 180 to 485 μg. per day.[53] With the basal diet only, the excretions were 95 to 185 and 45 to 140 μg. per day respectively. The corresponding values for excreted nicotinic acid were 95 to 430 ; 16 to 35 ; 23 to 50 ; and 10 to 24 μg. per day.

Conversely, when pyridoxine was omitted from the diet of rats the amount of excreted nicotinic acid and metabolites fell. A similar result was obtained when aneurine or riboflavine, but not pantothenic acid or pteroylglutamic acid, were omitted. When sulphasuxidine was added to a pteroylglutamic acid-deficient diet, however, nicotinic acid excretion was depressed, although administration of sulphasuxi-dine when the diet contained pteroylglutamic acid did not affect the excretion.[53a]

Nicotinic Acid in Blood and Cerebrospinal Fluid

Some of the difficulties inherent in the estimation of nicotinic acid in urine apply to its estimation in blood.

Factor V

The earliest values for the nicotinic acid content of blood relate to its coenzyme, or as it was first called, " factor V ", content (see page 229). According to H. von Euler and F. Schlenk,[54] normal blood contained 4 to 8 mg. of factor V per 100 ml., and 150 μg. of nicotinamide per 100 ml.

The effect of nicotinic acid deficiency on the amount of coenzyme present in various tissues of the dog was studied by Kohn et al.[55] and by M. Pittman and H. F. Fraser,[56] who used Haemophilus para-influenzae as the test organism. They observed a decrease in the factor V content of the liver and muscle in blacktongue, whilst Axelrod et al.,[57] using a yeast fermentation method, found a similar decrease in the coenzyme I content of the liver and muscle of nicotinic acid-deficient dogs and pigs. H. I. Kohn [58] and Vilter et al.[59] observed that the factor V content of the blood of pellagrins increased after administration of nicotinic acid, whilst H. I. Kohn and J. R. Klein [60] and Vilter et al.[61] showed that incubation of defibrinated blood with nicotinic acid increased its factor V content. Ingestion of large amounts of nicotinic acid increased the coenzyme I content of the erythrocytes.[62]

Using *Bacillus influenzae*, Vilter et al.[59, 63] found that the factor V content of the blood decreased in pellagra, but H. I. Kohn and F. Bernheim,[64] using *H. parainfluenzae*, failed to find any significant difference in the amount of factor V present in erythrocytes from pellagrins, compared with controls. This was confirmed by Axelrod et al.,[65] using the yeast fermentation method ; [66] they found that the coenzyme I content of erythrocytes averaged 85 μg. per ml. in controls, 77 and 69 μg. per ml. in sub-clinical and mild pellagra respectively and from 70 to 90 μg. per ml. in severe cases. The amount in muscle, on the other hand, decreased from 382 in controls to 317, 258 and 214 μg. per g. in sub-clinical, mild and severe pellagra respectively.

Nicotinic Acid in Blood

B. D. Kochhar,[67] using acid hydrolysis followed by colour development as in Swaminathan's method, found that the nicotinic acid content of blood varied from 230 to 650 μg. per 100 ml. with an average value of 367 μg. per 100 ml. These values presumably included the free nicotinic acid, nicotinamide, nicotinuric acid and coenzymes I and II, but not trigonelline or N^1-methylnicotinamide. Most of the nicotinic acid was present in the corpuscles, the value for serum being 62 to 170, with an average of 92 μg. per 100 ml. Cerebrospinal fluid was found to contain 56 to 120 with an average of 92 μg. per 100 ml. of acid-hydrolysable nicotinic acid derivatives.

Most of the nicotinic acid in dogs' blood was present in the red cells,[68] the actual values found being 77 % in the erythrocytes, 12 % in the leucocytes and 11 % in the plasma. Oral administration of nicotinic acid increased the plasma nicotinic acid to a greater extent than the erythrocyte nicotinic acid. Oral administration of 200-mg. doses of nicotinic acid daily to humans slightly increased the blood level up to a maximum value which was maintained as long as the additional nicotinic acid was given.[69] Oral administration of a single dose temporarily increased the blood level, a peak being reached after thirty minutes.

Nicotinic acid was taken up quantitatively by red blood cells *in vitro* and fixed in the cells in a non-diffusible form, presumably as coenzyme. Nicotinamide was also taken up, but nearly all in a form that could be removed from the cells by repeated washings.[69a]

The nicotinic acid content of blood or plasma in pellagra was very little different from that of controls,[70] nor did the coenzyme I content of erythrocytes vary significantly in different stages of pellagra,[65] normal cells containing 85 μg. per ml. and cells from pellagrins 70 to 90 μg. per ml. This remarkable constancy in the amounts of nicotinic acid and its derivatives in blood, and the transitory nature of the increase resulting from the administration of nicotinic acid or the amide make the estimation of blood levels of no value in assessing nutritional status, and it is generally agreed that the only satisfactory method is one based on the excretion of nicotinic acid derivatives in response to a test dose of the acid or amide (page 259).

Nicotinic Acid Content of Other Body Fluids and Tissues

Human milk is a poor source of nicotinic acid and contains less than cow's milk (see page 233). According to A. Lwoff and his collaborators, human milk contained only 0·07 μg. of the amide per 100 ml. (estimated microbiologically by means of *Proteus*) in the first three to eight days after delivery, but after the third week this rose to 0·16 mg. per 100 ml.[71] At this stage, the requirements of the baby, assumed to be 0·78 mg. per day, were satisfied by the ingestion of 500 ml. of milk per day, but subsequently the demands increased to a level that could not be met solely by the amount present in the milk. The amount of nicotinamide present in early milk could be increased many-fold by giving a 600-mg. dose of the amide forty-eight hours before delivery ; [72] for instance, when 600-mg. doses were given daily for one month prior to delivery, the nicotinamide content of the milk was increased to 0·07 mg. per 100 ml.[73] This would appear to be an observation of considerable importance, as the human foetus has been said to have no store of nicotinamide ; [74] this assertion must be accepted with reserve, however, for it has been shown that blood from the umbilical cord contains as much nicotinic acid as the maternal blood.[75]

Coryell et al.[76] found that the amount of nicotinic acid secreted in the milk during twenty-four hours increased from 0·04 mg. on the first day *post partum* to 2·94 mg. on the tenth day, the intake being 16·5 mg. per day. The amount secreted in the mature milk varied from 0·52 to 2·02 mg. per day. Earlier results, in which the nicotinic acid content was expressed in mg. per 100 ml., were 0·245 for the amount secreted on the tenth day and 0·176 to 0·196 mg. per 100 ml. for the mature milk. Of the ingested nicotinic acid, 7 % appeared in the milk and 3 % in the urine.

Only traces of nicotinamide and no nicotinic acid were excreted in the sweat.[77]

The amounts of nicotinic acid and its derivatives in certain tissues showed considerable variation according to the degree of nicotinic acid deficiency. Thus in the rat, dog and pig, the amount of total nicotinic acid and coenzyme I in the liver and muscles decreased progressively when the animals were maintained on a pellagra-producing diet, but the amounts in the brain and kidney cortex, as well as in the blood, showed little change.[57, 78] Similarly, the coenzyme I content of striated muscle was higher in normal human tissue (382 μg. per g.) than in tissue from pellagrins (214 μg. per g.[65]) and the administration of nicotinic acid led to a marked increase in the coenzyme I content.

In normal dogs 50 % of the nicotinic acid in the liver and 25 % of that in the muscle was present in the free state ; all the nicotinic acid in the kidney cortex, on the other hand, was combined.[78]

The decrease in the tissue nicotinic acid of dogs with blacktongue was almost entirely due to a fall in the bound nicotinic acid. Rabbits also suffered a decrease in the amount of nicotinic acid present in the voluntary muscles when fed for three months on a nicotinic acid-deficient diet.[79]

Rats behaved differently from other species of animals. They showed no increase in the coenzyme I content of the muscle tissues when fed large amounts of nicotinic acid ;[57] and the coenzyme I contents of the liver, kidney and thigh muscle fell by only 10 % when rats were maintained on a diet that produced blacktongue in dogs.[80] This is due to the fact that rats synthesise nicotinic acid, and are therefore independent of an external source of supply, provided adequate tryptophan is present in the diet (page 241). All the nicotinic acid in the muscle and kidneys of rats was present as coenzyme, but only 58 % of that in the liver was in the combined form.[81]

Eggs contained 80 μg. of nicotinic acid, a value that remained unchanged for eleven days, but increased to 470 μg. after sixteen days and to 820 μg. on hatching.[82] Most of the nicotinic acid was present as diphosphopyridine nucleotide.[83]

References to Section 10

1. H. von Euler and F. Schlenk, *Klin. Woch.*, 1939, **18**, 1109.
2. D. Melnick, W. D. Robinson and H. Field, *J. Biol. Chem.*, 1940, **136**, 131, 145.
3. W. W. Kühnau, *Klin. Woch.*, 1939, **18**, 1333.
4. D. Melnick and H. Field, *J. Biol. Chem.*, 1940, **134**, 1 ; 1940, **135**, 53.
5. J. W. Huff and W. A. Perlzweig, *J. Biol. Chem.*, 1941, **142**, 401.

6. H. P. Sarett, *J. Nutrition*, 1942, **23,** 35.
7. P. B. Pearson and A. H. Winegar, *Z. Vitaminforsch*, 1940, **10,** 238.
8. M. Swaminathan, *Indian J. Med. Res.*, 1942, **30,** 537.
9. V. A. Najjar and L. E. Holt, *Proc. Soc. Exp. Biol. Med.*, 1940, **44,** 386 ; 1941, **48,** 413 ; *Science*, 1941, **93,** 20.
10. V. A. Najjar, H. J. Stein, L. E. Holt and C. V. Kabler, *J. Clin. Invest.*, 1942, **21,** 26.
11. J. W. Huff and W. A. Perlzweig, *J. Biol. Chem.*, 1943, **150,** 395.
12. P. Karrer, G. Schwartzenbach, F. Benz and U. V. Solmssen, *Helv. Chim. Acta*, 1936, **19,** 826.
13. V. A. Najjar, D. B. M. Scott and L. E. Holt, *Science*, 1943, **97,** 537.
14. W. A. Perlzweig, M. L. C. Bernheim and F. Bernheim, *J. Biol. Chem.*, 1943, **150,** 401.
15. P. Handler and W. J. Dann, *ibid.*, 1942, **146,** 357.
16. P. Handler, *ibid.*, 1944, **154,** 203.
17. P. Ellinger, *Biochem. J.*, 1946, **40,** *Proc.*, xxxi ; 1948, **42,** 175.
18. Y. Raoul, *Bull. Soc. Chim. biol.*, 1943, **25,** 266, 271.
19. J. C. Roggen, *Rec. trav. chim.*, 1943, **62,** 137.
20. W. E. Knox and W. L. Grossman, *J. Biol. Chem.*, 1946, **166,** 391 ; 1947, **168,** 363.
21. J. W. Huff, *ibid.*, 1947, **171,** 639.
21*a*. W. I. M. Holman and C. Wiegand, *Nature*, 1948, **162,** 659 ; *Biochem J.*, 1948, **43,** 423.
22. W. J. Dann and J. W. Huff, *J. Biol. Chem.*, 1947, **168,** 121.
23. J. W. Huff and W. A. Perlzweig, *Science*, 1943, **97,** 538.
24. M. Hochberg, D. Melnick and B. L. Oser, *J. Biol. Chem.*, 1945, **158,** 265.
25. O. Mickelsen and L. L. Erickson, *Proc. Soc. Exp. Biol. Med.*, 1945, **58,** 33.
26. B. C. Johnson, T. S. Hamilton and H. H. Mitchell, *J. Biol. Chem.*, 1945, **159,** 231.
27. W. A. Perlzweig and J. W. Huff, *ibid.*, 1945, **161,** 417.
27*a*. J. M. Hundley and H. W. Bond, *ibid.*, 1948, **173,** 513.
27*b*. L. J. Roth, E. Leifer, J. R. Hogness and W. H. Langham, *ibid.*, 1948, **176,** 249.
27*c*. W. I. M. Holman and D. J. de Lange, *Nature*, 1949, **164,** 845 ; *Biochem J.*, 1949, **45,** 559.
27*d*. R. F. A. Dean and W. I. M. Holman, *Nature*, 1949, **163,** 97.
28. P. Ellinger and M. M. Abdel Kader, *Biochem. J.*, 1948, **42,** *Proc.*, xxxiii ; 1949, **44,** 77, 627.
28*a*. P. B. Pearson, W. A. Perlzweig and F. Rosen, *Arch. Biochem.*, 1949, **22,** 191.
29. G. A. Goldsmith, *Proc. Soc. Exp. Biol. Med.*, 1942, **51,** 42 ; *Arch. intern. Med.*, 1944, **73,** 410.
30. W. A. Perlzweig, H. P. Sarett, L. H. Margolis, H. Stenhouse and F. Spilman, *J. Amer. Med. Assoc.*, 1942, **118,** 28.
31. B. D. Kochhar, *Ann. Biochem. Exp. Med.*, 1943, **3,** 85.
32. P. Ellinger and R. A. Coulson, *Biochem. J.*, 1944, **38,** 265.
33. L. E. Holt and V. A. Najjar, *J.—Lancet*, 1943, **63,** 366.

34. J. M. Ruffin, D. Cayer and W. A. Perlzweig, *Gastro-enterology*, 1944, **3,** 340.

35. D. W. Roberts and V. A. Najjar, *Johns Hopkins Hosp. Bull.*, 1944, **74,** 400.

36. R. A. Coulson, P. Ellinger and G. A. Smart, *Brit. Med. J.*, 1945, **1,** 6; P. Ellinger, R. Benesch and S. W. Hardwick, *Lancet*, 1945, **2,** 197.

37. P. Ellinger, R. Benesch and W. W. Kay, *ibid.*, 1945, **1,** 432.

38. P. Ellinger, A. Hassan and M. M. Taha, *ibid.*, 1937, **2,** 755.

39. P. Ellinger, R. A. Coulson and R. Benesch, *Nature*, 1944, **154,** 270.

39*a*. E. I. Frazier, T. Porter and M. J. Humphrey, *J. Nutrition*, 1949, **37,** 393.

40. V. A. Najjar, L. E. Holt, G. A. Johns, G. C. Medairy and G. Fleischmann, *Proc. Soc. Exp. Biol. Med.*, 1946, **61,** 371.

41. S. A. Koser and G. R. Baird, *J. infect. Dis.*, 1944, **75,** 250.

42. R. Benesch, *Lancet*, 1945, **1,** 718.

43. P. Ellinger and S. W. Hardwick, *Brit. Med. J.*, 1947, **1,** 672.

44. R. A. Coulson and C. A. Stewart, *Proc. Soc. Exp. Biol. Med.*, 1946, **61,** 364.

45. F. Rosen, J. W. Huff and W. A. Perlzweig, *J. Biol. Chem.*, 1946, **163,** 343.

46. R. W. Luecke, W. N. McMillen, F. Thorp and C. Tull, *J. Animal Sci.*, 1946, **5,** 408.

47. B. S. Schweigert, P. B. Pearson and M. C. Wilkening, *Arch. Biochem.*, 1947, **12,** 139.

48. S. A. Singal, A. P. Briggs, V. P. Sydenstricker and J. M. Littlejohn, *J. Biol. Chem.*, 1946, **166,** 573.

49. P. Ellinger, *Biochem. J.*, 1946, **40,** *Proc.*, xxxiii; 1947, **41,** 308.

50. H. P. Sarett and G. A. Goldsmith, *J. Biol. Chem.*, 1947, **167,** 293.

51. W. A. Perlzweig, F. Rosen, N. Levitas and J. Robinson, *ibid.*, 511.

52. J. W. Huff, P. B. Pearson and W. A. Perlzweig, *Arch. Biochem.*, 1946, **9,** 99.

53. B. S. Schweigert and P. B. Pearson, *J. Biol. Chem.*, 1947, **168,** 555.

53*a*. P. B. Junqueira and B. S. Schweigert, *ibid.*, 1948, **175,** 535.

54. H. von Euler and F. Schlenk, *Klin. Woch.*, 1939, **18,** 1109.

55. H. I. Kohn, J. R. Klein and W. J. Dann, *Biochem. J.*, 1939, **33,** 1432.

56. M. Pittman and H. F. Fraser, *U.S. Publ. Health Rep.*, 1940, **55,** 915.

57. A. E. Axelrod, R. J. Madden and C. A. Elvehjem, *J. Biol. Chem.*, 1939, **131,** 85.

58. H. I. Kohn, *Biochem. J.*, 1938, **32,** 2075.

59. R. W. Vilter, S. P. Vilter and T. D. Spies, *J. Amer. Med. Assoc.*, 1939, **112,** 420.

60. H. I. Kohn and J. R. Klein, *J. Biol. Chem.*, 1939, **130,** 1.

61. R. W. Vilter, S. P. Vilter and T. D. Spies, *Nature*, 1939, **144,** 943.

62. A. E. Axelrod, E. S. Gordon and C. A. Elvehjem, *Amer. J. Med. Sci.*, 1940, **199,** 697.

63. S. P. Vilter, M. B. Koch and T. D. Spies, *J. Lab. Clin. Med.*, 1940, **26**, 31.

64. H. I. Kohn and F. Bernheim, *J. Clin. Invest.*, 1939, **18**, 585.

65. A. E. Axelrod, T. D. Spies and C. A. Elvehjem, *J. Biol. Chem.*, 1941, **138**, 667.

66. A. E. Axelrod and C. A. Elvehjem, *ibid.*, 1939, **131**, 77.

67. B. D. Kochhar, *Indian J. Med. Res.*, 1940, **28**, 385.

68. B. D. Kochhar, *ibid.*, 1941, **29**, 133 ; *Ann. Biochem. Exp. Med.*, 1941, **1**, 285.

69. B. D. Kochhar, *ibid.*, 341.

69a. E. Leifer, J. R. Hogness, L. J. Roth and W. Langham, *J. Amer. Chem. Soc.*, 1948, **70**, 2908.

70. H. Field, D. Melnick, W. D. Robinson and C. F. Wilkinson, *J. Clin. Invest.*, 1941, **20**, 379.

71. A. Lwoff, M. Morel and M. Bilhaud, *Compt. rend.*, 1942, **214**, 244.

72. A. Lwoff, L. Digonnet and H. Dusi, *ibid.*, 39.

73. A. Lwoff, M. Morel and L. Digonnet, *ibid.*, 1941, **213**, 811.

74. A. Lwoff, M. Morel and L. Digonnet, *ibid.*, 1030.

75. R. F. A. Dean and W. I. M. Holman, *Nature*, 1948, **161**, 439.

76. M. N. Coryell, M. E. Harris, S. Miller, H. H. Williams and I. G. Macy, *Amer. J. Dis. Child.*, 1945, **70**, 150 ; M. N. Coryell, C. E. Roderuck, M. E. Harris, S. Miller, M. M. Rutledge, H. H. Williams and I. G. Macy, *J. Nutrition*, 1947, **34**, 219.

77. B. C. Johnson, T. S. Hamilton and H. H. Mitchell, *J. Biol. Chem.*, 1945, **159**, 231.

78. W. J. Dann and P. Handler, *J. Nutrition*, 1941, **22**, 409 ; S. A. Singal, V. P. Sydenstricker and J. M. Littlejohn, *J. Biol. Chem.*, 1948, **176**, 1069.

79. J. G. Wooley and W. H. Sebrell, *J. Nutrition*, 1945, **29**, 191.

80. W. J. Dann and H. I. Kohn, *J. Biol. Chem.*, 1940, **136**, 435.

81. P. Handler and W. J. Dann, *ibid.*, 1941, **140**, 739.

82. W. J. Dann and P. Handler, *ibid.*, 935.

83. M. Levy and N. F. Young, *ibid.*, 1948, **176**, 185.

ii. INTESTINAL SYNTHESIS OF NICOTINIC ACID

Intestinal Synthesis in Man

The first suggestion that nicotinamide might be synthesised in the human gut and made available to the human body was advanced by P. Ellinger, R. A. Coulson and R. Benesch,[1] who observed a discrepancy between the nicotinamide intake and the N^1-methylnicotinamide output. They were able to show that this was due to the production of nicotinamide by the intestinal flora, since the urinary excretion of N^1-methylnicotinamide was reduced when either sulphaguanidine or succinyl sulphathiazole was administered. Both these sulphonamides, being poorly absorbed from the gut, act as intestinal antiseptics. Ellinger *et al.* suggested that the pellagra-preventive action of milk, which contains only a small amount of nicotinic acid, may be due to its favourable effect on the intestinal flora, but the pellagragenic action of milk is now attributed to its tryptophan content (page 242). In a further paper, Ellinger *et al.*[2] reported that succinyl sulphathiazole, administered to five subjects, resulted in a 60 % decrease in the urinary output of N^1-methylnicotinamide, whereas little reduction in output resulted in three other subjects who were given sulphathiazole, which, being more readily absorbed from the gut than its succinyl derivative, does not appreciably affect the bacterial population of the intestine. Succinyl sulphathiazole did not bring about inhibition of nicotinamide methylation *in vivo*, which might have been responsible for the fall in N^1-methylnicotinamide output. Ellinger *et al.* suggested that pellagra may be due to decreased absorption of nicotinamide from the intestinal tract. Subsequently, however, R. Benesch[3] showed that bacteria isolated from faeces at caecostomy were able to synthesise considerable amounts of nicotinic acid under aerobic conditions but that under anaerobic conditions these bacteria actually destroyed nicotinic acid. He suggested that in the normal caecum an equilibrium exists between the two groups of organisms and that disturbance of this equilibrium may lead to nicotinic acid deficiency.

P. Ellinger and A. Emmanuelowa[4] used another antibacterial agent to study the phenomenon of intestinal synthesis. This was *p*-aminomethylbenzene sulphonamide (marfanil, ambamide), which inhibits the growth of anaerobes, but not of aerobes. They hoped in this way to prevent the growth of organisms that destroyed nicotinic acid without affecting the growth of those that synthesised it. They did in fact find that the output of N^1-methylnicotinamide increased, whilst the proportion of anaerobes and coliform organisms decreased and increased respectively. In rats given ambamide, the nicotinamide excretion decreased and then increased.

The conclusions reached by Ellinger and his colleagues that intestinal synthesis may provide part of the nicotinic acid requirements of man received support from the observations of Briggs *et al.*[5] on two subjects who showed symptoms of mild nicotinic acid deficiency. Although maintained on a diet low in trigonelline and providing only 3 mg. of nicotinic acid daily, no symptoms of pellagra developed. In one case, nicotinic acid excretion continued low, whilst in the other it was normal ; the trigonelline output was low in both cases and tests for urinary N^1-methylnicotinamide were negative.

According to Denko *et al.*[6] the faecal excretion of nicotinic acid on a normal diet was higher than the urinary excretion, whilst the combined faecal and urinary output was less than the dietary intake. In this respect, nicotinic acid resembled aneurine, riboflavine and pyridoxine, but differed from *p*-aminobenzoic acid, folic acid, biotin and pantothenic acid. Thus, intestinal synthesis is normally of less importance in the first group, to which nicotinic acid belongs, than in the second. On a restricted diet, the faecal excretion of nicotinic acid was as high as on the normal diet and was unaffected by supplementation with the vitamin, whereas the urinary excretion was reduced, and increased on supplementation though not to the normal value.[7] On the restricted diet the combined urinary and faecal output exceeded the intake.

In none of these experiments does the intake of tryptophan appear to have been controlled, so that variations in the output of N^1-methylnicotinamide and other metabolites may have been due to variations in the amount of tryptophan in the diet. This factor alone, however, would scarcely explain the effect of succinyl sulphathiazole on the *urinary* excretion of N^1-methylnicotinamide, and there appears to be little doubt that nicotinic acid is synthesised by the intestinal flora and can be utilised under certain conditions. It is to be hoped that further investigations will indicate what these conditions are.

S. W. Hardwick [8] noted that an acute nicotinic acid deficiency was produced in a psychotic patient given sulphaguanidine for the treatment of dysentery, thus providing further confirmation of the above conclusions.

A. C. Frazer,[8a] however, rejects the views held by Ellinger *et al.* that in man nicotinic acid (and other vitamins) synthesised by intestinal bacteria are normally absorbed. He suggests that in sprue, with which a deficiency of nicotinic acid and other B vitamins is frequently associated, bacterial synthesis is greatly enhanced, the intestinal contents often being richer in certain vitamins than the diet. He believes that the bacteria may invade areas of the small intestine that are normally absorbing, and that here they compete with the host for essential nutrients, thus giving rise to symptoms of vitamin deficiency.

Intestinal Synthesis in Animals

It is probable that in other species of animals, nicotinic acid is synthesised by the intestinal flora, but evidence that nicotinic acid produced in this way is utilised by animals is not conclusive. Thus, lambs fed from the age of three to eight months on a diet producing blacktongue in dogs, continued to excrete normal amounts of nicotinic acid,[9] but it was not certain whether this was synthesised from tryptophan in the tissues or derived from micro-organisms in the rumen. Chicks appear to be capable of synthesising about one-sixth of their nicotinic acid requirements.[10]

Rats could not be rendered deficient in nicotinic acid by feeding sulphaguanidine when the diet contained tryptophan,[11] but the synthesis of nicotinic acid by the intestinal flora in rats was demonstrated in other ways. Thus, on a protein-free diet providing only 7 μg. of nicotinic acid per day, rats excreted 25 to 75 μg. per day in the urine and 40 to 90 μg. per day in the faeces. The urinary, but not the faecal, excretion was increased by adding casein, amino acids or choline to the diet. When nicotinic acid was added, 62 % of the additional amount was excreted in the urine and only a negligible proportion in the faeces.[12]

Again, Krehl et al.[13] showed that nicotinic acid deficiency induced in rats by the addition of corn or corn grits to the diet, could be corrected by feeding carbohydrates that favoured the development of a satisfactory intestinal flora, as well as by feeding tryptophan or materials rich in tryptophan (page 242). Glucose, dextrin and lactose counteracted the growth-depressant effect of maize, but sucrose was without effect.

The peculiar effect of maize in reducing the growth rate of rats maintained on a low protein diet is due primarily to its low tryptophan content (page 240), but Krehl et al.[14] suggested that it was also due in part to amino acid imbalance. They therefore investigated the growth-suppressing effects of other proteins and amino acids, and found [15] that the addition of glycine or acid-hydrolysed casein suppressed the growth of rats receiving a casein-sucrose diet free from nicotinic acid. The growth-suppressing effect of glycine was not observed when dextrin was used as carbohydrate. Although evidence for the mechanism of this effect is lacking, it is suggested that free dietary amino acids may affect the type, quantity or location of intestinal micro-organisms and therefore the amount of nicotinic acid synthesised and its availability to the host.

Rabbits lost weight when fed a nicotinic acid-deficient diet, although large amounts of nicotinic acid were synthesised in the digestive tract, and excreted partly in the faeces, partly in the urine.[16]

References to Section 11

1. P. Ellinger, R. A. Coulson and R. Benesch, *Nature*, 1944, **154**, 270.
2. P. Ellinger, R. Benesch and W. W. Kay, *Lancet*, 1945, **1**, 432.
3. R. Benesch, *ibid.*, 718.
4. P. Ellinger and A. Emmanuelowa, *ibid.*, 1946, **2**, 716.
5. A. P. Briggs, S. A. Singal and V. P. Sydenstricker, *J. Nutrition*, 1945, **29**, 331.
6. C. W. Denko, W. E. Grundy, J. W. Porter, G. H. Berryman, T. E. Friedemann and J. B. Youmans, *Arch. Biochem.*, 1946, **10**, 33.

7. C. W. Denko, W. E. Grundy, N. C. Wheeler, C. R. Henderson, G. H. Berryman, T. E. Friedemann and J. B. Youmans, *Arch. Biochem.*, 1946, **11**, 109.

8. S. W. Hardwick, *Lancet*, 1946, **1**, 267.

8a. A. C. Frazer, *Brit. Med. J.*, 1949, **2**, 731.

9. A. H. Winegar, P. B. Pearson and H. Schmidt, *Science*, 1940, **91**, 508 ; *J. Nutrition*, 1940, **20**, 551.

10. G. M. Briggs, T. D. Luckey, L. J. Teply, C. A. Elvehjem and E. B. Hart, *J. Biol. Chem.*, 1943, **148**, 517.

11. W. J. Dann, *ibid.*, 1941, **141**, 803.

12. J. W. Huff and W. A. Perlzweig, *ibid.*, 1941, **142**, 401.

13. W. A. Krehl, P. S. Sarma, L. J. Teply and C. A. Elvehjem, *J. Nutrition*, 1946, **31**, 85.

14. W. A. Krehl, L. M. Henderson, J. de la Huerga and C. A. Elvehjem, *J. Biol. Chem.*, 1946, **166**, 531.

15. L. M. Henderson, T. Deodhar, W. A. Krehl and C. A. Elvehjem, *ibid.*, 1947, **170**, 261.

16. O. Olcese, P. B. Pearson and P. Sparks, *J. Nutrition*, 1949, **39**, 93.

12. ANIMAL AND HUMAN REQUIREMENTS OF NICOTINIC ACID

Estimates of the nicotinic acid requirements of animals and man must necessarily be provisional until more data are available concerning the conditions necessary for intestinal synthesis and the proportion of the total requirements that can be provided from this source.

Human requirements have been estimated to be 8 to 10 mg. per day [1] or about 110 to 140 μg. per kg. of bodyweight. Adult dogs and puppies required 200 to 225 and 250 to 365 μg. per kg. of bodyweight per day respectively,[2] and protection against blacktongue was secured by the presence in the diet of 2 mg. per kg.[3] Growing chicks were protected from blacktongue by a diet containing 18 mg. of nicotinic acid per kg.[4] Young growing pigs required 100 to 200 μg. per kg. of bodyweight per day,[5] whilst young rabbits were said to require 10 mg. per kg. of bodyweight per day,[6] a considerably larger amount than is required by any other species of animal.

As already stated, rats and horses synthesise nicotinic acid and can thrive on a nicotinic acid-free diet, provided tryptophan is present.

The National Research Council (U.S.A.) in 1941 estimated the nicotinic acid requirements of a very active man, a sedentary man, a very active woman and a sedentary woman at 23, 15, 18 and 12 mg. per day respectively. Amounts equal to 70 % of these values were used as the basis of the rationing system adopted in this country during the 1939-45 war, with satisfactory results. In 1945 the N.R.C.

reduced its estimates to 20, 12, 15 and 11 mg. per day.[7]   In Japanese prisoner of war camps nicotinic acid deficiency was common with diets supplying 4 to 6 mg. per day.   A marginal intake of 7 to 9 mg. per day was usual in the liberated towns of Western Europe in 1944-45.[7]

The actual intake of nicotinic acid in the United Kingdom during the war years increased steadily from 13·5 in 1939 to 15·5 in 1944 followed by a fall and then a rise to 16·7 mg. per day in 1947.[8]

References to Section 12

1. E. Kodicek, *Lancet*, 1942, **1**, 380.
2. A. E. Schaefer, J. M. McKibbin and C. A. Elvehjem, *J. Biol. Chem.*, 1942, **144**, 679.
3. S. G. Smith, R. Curry and H. Hawfield, *J. Nutrition*, 1943, **25**, 341.
4. G. M. Briggs, R. C. Mills, C. A. Elvehjem and E. B. Hart, *Proc. Soc. Exp. Biol. Med.*, 1942, **51**, 59.
5. E. H. Hughes, *J. Animal Sci.*, 1943, **2**, 23 ; R. W. Luecke, W. N. McMillen, F. Thorp and C. Tull, *J. Nutrition*, 1948, **36**, 417.
6. J. G. Wooley and W. H. Sebrell, *J. Nutrition*, 1945, **29**, 191.
7. J. C. Drummond, " Nutritional Requirements of Man in the Light of Wartime Experience ", Royal Institute of Chemistry, 1948.
8. " Food Consumption Levels in the United Kingdom ", Cmd. 7203. H.M.S.O., 1947.

13. PHARMACOLOGICAL ACTION OF NICOTINIC ACID

The toxicity (LD50) of nicotinic acid for rats has been variously reported as 3·5,[1] 4·0 to 7·0,[2] 5·0 [3] and 3·75 mg.[4] per kg. ; for mice, the corresponding values are 4·5,[1] 4·0 to 7·0 [2] and 4·5 mg. per kg.[4] The toxicity of nicotinamide was higher, the value of LD50 for rats being 1·68 [3] or 1·50,[4] and the value for mice 1·75 mg. per kg.

Both compounds had a stimulant action on the central nervous system, and mice developed " morphia tail " and jumped like kangaroos ; lethal doses caused convulsions.[4] Nicotinamide did not increase the work output of the perfused frog gastrocnemius muscle,[5] and nicotinic acid had no effect on the isolated normal heart.[6] In the case of failure of the myocardium, however, nicotinic acid brought about a marked increase in the amplitude of the cardiac excursion, reversed the abnormal rhythms and at times increased the coronary flow considerably.[6] It was suggested that the observed disturbances of myocardial action were due to inactivation or depletion of pyridine nucleotides by the anoxia, and that the addition of nicotinic acid to the perfusion fluid remedied the deficiency. Rats treated with nicotinic acid or amide survived a reduction of atmospheric pressure equivalent to a height of 53,800 feet ; untreated rats succumbed at a pressure equivalent to 49,275 feet. The increase in respiratory rate at low pressures was much less in treated than in untreated rats.

Nicotinic acid, but not the amide, has a pronounced, though transient, vasodilator action. This is the reason for the flushing and tingling of the skin and rise in the cutaneous temperature when nicotinic acid is taken orally. The effect may be somewhat alarming for patients who have not been warned to expect it, but it soon passes off. Nicotinamide does not have this effect.[7] The vasodilator action of nicotinic acid is of value in conditions where it is desirable to increase the peripheral blood flow, such as gangrene of the mouth and indolent ulcers. It also accounts for the ability of nicotinic acid to relieve severe idiopathic headache and migraine.[8] Nicotinic acid, but not nicotinamide, increased the intracranial blood flow in human subjects, the effect running parallel with the flushing of the skin.[9]

Nicotinamide was without effect on the blood sugar levels in normal subjects and in diabetic patients.[10] Nicotinic acid and nicotinamide stimulated bile secretion, and the former also increased the serum bilirubin and the excretion of urobilin.[11]

References to Section 13

1. K. K. Chen, C. L. Rose and E. B. Robbins, *Proc. Soc. Exp. Biol. Med.*, 1938, **38**, 241.
2. K. Unna, *J. Pharmacol.*, 1939, **65**, 95.
3. F. G. Brazda and R. A. Coulson, *Proc. Soc. Exp. Biol. Med.*, 1946, **62**, 19.
4. P. Ellinger, G. Fraenkel and M. M. Abdel Kader, *Biochem. J.*, 1947, **41**, 559.
5. N. W. Shock and W. H. Sebrell, *Amer. J. Physiol.*, 1946, **146**, 52.
6. R. M. Calder, *Proc. Soc. Exp. Biol. Med.*, 1947, **65**, 76; 1948, **68**, 642.
7. H. Field and W. D. Robinson, *Amer. J. Med. Sci.*, 1940, **199**, 275.
8. J. W. Goldzierer and G. L. Popkin, *J. Amer. Med. Assoc.*, 1946, **131**, 103.
9. C. D. Aring, H. W. Ryder, E. Roseman, M. Rosenbaum and E. B. Ferris, *Arch. Neurol., Psychiat.*, 1941, **46**, 649.
10. J. N. Cumings, *Brit. Med. J.*, 1947, **2**, 613.
11. M. Stefanini, *J. Lab. Clin. Med.*, 1949, **34**, 1039.

14. FUNCTION OF NICOTINIC ACID

Coenzymes I and II

By an unusual inversion of the customary course of events, the biological significance of nicotinic acid was understood before its importance in human nutrition was appreciated, for in 1935 O. Warburg and W. Christian [1] showed that the coenzyme, codehydrogenase II, which is widely distributed in animal tissue, contained nicotinamide, and Albus *et al.*[2] showed that it was a constituent of another co-enzyme, codehydrogenase I or cozymase, which occurs in yeast and acts as a catalyst in alcoholic fermentation. Both coenzymes are com-pounds of adenine, nicotinamide, ribose and phosphoric acid, and were given the formulae:

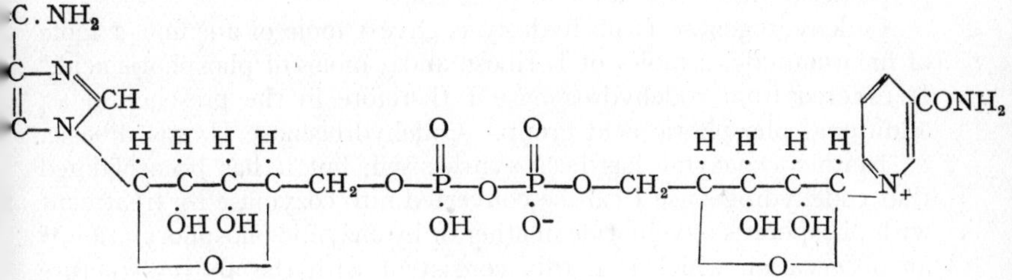

Coenzyme I

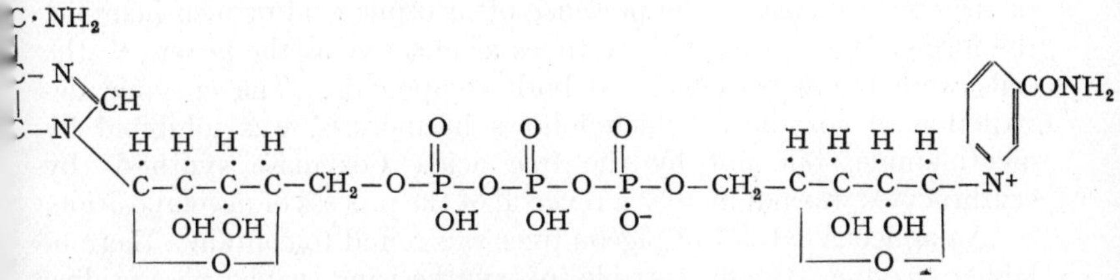

Coenzyme II

Coenzymes I and II are usually referred to as diphosphopyridine nucleotide and triphosphopyridine nucleotide respectively. They are essential links in a series of transformations the effect of which is to transfer hydrogen from a substrate, which is thereby oxidised, to molecular oxygen with the formation of water.

A method for the isolation of coenzyme I from bakers' yeast was described by S. Williamson and D. E. Green,[3] who obtained 500 mg. of material with a purity of 65 % from 3·2 kg. A method of purifying the enzyme was described by F. Schlenk.[4]

An improved method for the isolation of diphosphopyridine nucleotide was published by G. A. Le Page,[5] who obtained, from 1 lb. of bakers' yeast, 50 to 70 mg. of a preparation with a purity of about 63 %.

The constitution of coenzyme I or codehydrogenase I was estab-lished as follows. On hydrolysis it yielded adenine, nicotinamide and 2 moles of D-ribose-phosphoric acid. The phosphoric acid was attached to the ribose in the 5-position, because periodic acid failed to liberate formaldehyde.[6] Alkaline hydrolysis yielded adenosine-di-phosphoric acid,[7] indicating the presence of a pyrophosphoric acid group. It was assumed that one of the phosphoric acid groups in cozymase (but not in dihydro-cozymase) was neutralised by the nitrogen atom of the pyridine ring. That ribose is attached directly to the nicotinamide was established by the isolation of nicotinamide riboside from yeast codehydrogenase I, following hydrolysis with an enzyme preparation made from almond press-cake.[8]

Codehydrogenase II on hydrolysis gave 1 mole of adenine, 1 mole of nicotinamide, 2 moles of D-ribose and 3 moles of phosphoric acid.[9] It differed from codehydrogenase I therefore in the presence of an additional phosphoric acid group. Codehydrogenase II was dibasic.

Neither coenzyme has been synthesised, but it has been claimed that codehydrogenase I can be converted into cozymase by treatment with phosphorus oxychloride in ether or by enzymic phosphorylation,[10] an observation which is hardly consistent with the above structure for triphosphopyridine nucleotide.

The synthesis of cozymase by red blood cells was enhanced both *in vitro* and *in vivo* by the presence of nicotinic acid or nicotinamide, the former being at least three times as effective as the latter ; [11] the cells were freely permeable to both compounds. The enzymic destruction of cozymase, which follows haemolysis, was inhibited by nicotinamide, but not by the free acid. Cozymase synthesis by erythrocytes was not merely a reversal of the process of decomposition.

An aqueous extract of pigeon liver was found to contain a thermolabile enzyme system capable of synthesising triphosphopyridine nucleotide from ribose, nicotinamide and adenosine triphosphate.[12]

Function of Coenzyme I

It appears probable that the two coenzymes combine with a variety of protein carriers, the apoenzymes, each of which is specific for a particular reaction ; they are thus enabled to effect the dehydrogenation of a large number of substrates. Coenzyme I effects the conversion of β-hydroxybutyric acid into acetoacetic acid,[13] formic acid into carbon dioxide and water,[14] lactic acid into pyruvic acid,[15] malic acid into oxaloacetic acid,[15] alcohol into acetaldehyde,[16] glucose into gluconic acid,[17] glutamic acid into α-ketoglutaric acid,[18] α-glycerophosphoric acid into phosphoglyceric acid,[19] and phosphoglyceric aldehyde into diphosphoglyceric acid.[20] It also effects the dismutation of aldehyde into alcohol and acid,[21] and the conversion of retinene into vitamin A.[21a] It is also said to be involved in the metabolism of testosterone by the liver.[21b]

Codehydrogenase I (coenzyme I or cozymase) occurs in all animal and plant cells in which carbohydrates are metabolised. Fresh yeast contains about 0·5 g. per kg. and the heart muscle of man and the rabbit 0·4 g. per kg. It also occurs in micro-organisms (see page 282).

Function of Coenzyme II

Coenzyme II also brings about the conversion of glucose into gluconic acid [22] and of glutamic acid into α-ketoglutaric acid,[23] but it also effects certain changes not brought about by coenzyme I. Thus glucose-6-phosphoric acid is converted into 6-phosphogluconic acid,[24] 6-phosphogluconic acid into phosphoketohexonic acid, and citric acid into D-ketoglutaric acid.[25] Coenzyme II also catalysed the decarboxylation of oxaloacetic acid by oxaloacetic carboxylase from pigeon liver, but not the exchange reaction between $C^{14}O_2$ and the β-carbonyl carbon atom of oxaloacetic acid.[26]

Codehydrogenase II (or coenzyme II) appears to occur in all cells in association with codehydrogenase I, but the ratio of the two coenzymes varies greatly in different tissues, *e.g.* yeast contains very little codehydrogenase II, whereas animal tissues may contain 40 to 80 μg. per g.[27]

In effecting these transformations, the codehydrogenases are reduced to the dihydro-forms, which are themselves dehydrogenated by flavine enzymes. As already explained in the chapter on riboflavine (page 191) the nucleotides are reduced in the process to dihydro-compounds, which are re-oxidised by the cytochrome-cytochrome oxidase system. This is re-oxidised in turn by molecular oxygen with the ultimate formation of water as the end-product. The transfer of hydrogen from the substrate at one end of the scale to oxygen at the other can be represented schematically as follows :

Substrate	$\longrightarrow$	Oxidised substrate
	H_2	
Codehydrogenase	$\rightleftharpoons$	Dihydro-codehydrogenase
	H_2	
Flavoprotein	$\rightleftharpoons$	Dihydro-flavoprotein
	H_2	
Cytochrome *b*	$\rightleftharpoons$	Reduced cytochrome *b*
	H_2	
Cytochrome *c*	$\rightleftharpoons$	Reduced cytochrome *c*
	H_2	
Cytochrome *a*	$\rightleftharpoons$	Reduced cytochrome *a*
	H_2	
Cytochrome oxidase	$\rightleftharpoons$	Reduced cytochrome oxidase
	H_2	
Oxygen	$\longrightarrow$	Water

Many of the dehydrogenations effected by codehydrogenase I are reversible. For example, acetoacetic acid can be converted by dihydro-codehydrogenase I into β-hydroxybutyric acid, pyruvic acid into lactic acid, oxaloacetic acid into malic acid, acetaldehyde into alcohol, α-ketoglutaric acid (and ammonia) into glutamic acid, and diphospho-glyceric acid into phosphoglyceraldehyde. It is possible that the oxidation of dihydro-codehydrogenase I may be brought about in tissues by such coenzyme-linked reactions,[28] *e.g.* β-hydroxybutyric acid may be oxidised to acetoacetic acid and the dihydro-coenzyme thus formed may reduce an aldehyde to an alcohol.

The inter-convertibility of codehydrogenase I and II and dihydro-codehydrogenase I and II is due to the nicotinamide portion of the molecule. Karrer *et al.*[29] studied a number of nicotinamide derivatives as models for this reaction and found that only those derivatives with a pentavalent nitrogen atom in the ring, *e.g.* nicotin-amide methiodide, gave dihydro-compounds with an absorption spectrum comparable with that of the dihydro-coenzymes; these have two maxima, at 260 and 340 mμ, whereas the coenzymes them-selves have only one peak at 260 mμ. On reduction, the nitrogen atom became tervalent. By a comparison of the dihydro-coenzymes with model dihydropyridine derivatives, it was concluded that the former were 1 : 2-dihydro-derivatives, so that the reduction of the coenzymes can be represented as :

W. A. Waters [30] suggested that the prosthetic group of the de-hydrogenases provides an initial free radical :

in a reaction chain.

Nucleotidase

It is generally assumed that nicotinic acid and nicotinamide are equally effective in the treatment of pellagra and related conditions, and it seems likely that the normal body can convert the acid into the amide and so into the coenzyme. P. J. G. Mann and J. H. Quastel,[31] however, observed one difference between them. Brain extracts contain an enzyme, nucleotidase, which, by hydrolysing cozymase, inhibited the oxygen uptake of lactic acid in presence of lactic dehydrogenase and cozymase ; nicotinamide, but not nicotinic acid, inhibited the action of nucleotidase on cozymase. The exact significance of this phenomenon in therapeutics is not clear, but if nicotinamide can prevent the destruction of cozymase, it might explain why certain other substances, such as quinolinic acid, coramine and pyrazine-monocarboxylic acid (see page 288) are effective in pellagra. Otherwise it is difficult to find a satisfactory explanation, since many of these compounds cannot possibly be converted into nicotinamide, although they may well be converted into substances that inhibit nucleotidase.

Nucleotidase occurs in a large number of animal tissues, lung tissue being especially rich.[32] In the intact cell, the enzyme is kept out of contact with pyridine nucleotides. It is suggested that the release of nucleotidase on damage of the lung may play an important rôle in the action of some lung irritants.

An enzyme that liberated nicotinamide from both cozymase and coenzyme II was shown to be present in preparations from the mammalian central nervous system.[33] Competition took place between the two coenzymes, so that presumably a common enzyme is concerned ; this may be nucleotidase.

References to Section 14

1. O. Warburg and W. Christian, *Biochem. Z.*, 1935, **275,** 464.
2. H. Albus, F. Schlenk and H. von Euler, *Z. physiol. Chem.*, 1935, **237,** 1 ; *Biochem. Z.*, 1936, **286,** 140.
3. S. Williamson and D. E. Green, *J. Biol. Chem.*, 1940, **135,** 345.
4. F. Schlenk, *ibid.*, 1942, **146,** 619 ; F. Schlenk and T. Schlenk, *Arch. Biochem.*, 1947, **14,** 131.
5. G. A. Le Page, *J. Biol. Chem.*, 1947, **168,** 623.
6. H. von Euler, P. Karrer and B. Becker, *Helv. Chim. Acta*, 1936, **19,** 1060.
7. H. von Euler, F. Schlenk and R. Vestin, *Naturwiss.*, 1937, **25,** 318.
8. F. Schlenk, *Arch. Biochem.*, 1943, **3,** 93.
9. F. Schlenk, *Naturwiss.*, 1937, **25,** 668.
10. R. Vertin, *ibid.*, 667 ; H. von Euler and E. Bauer, *Ber.*, 1938, **71,** 411 ; H. von Euler and E. Adler, *Z. physiol. Chem.*, 1938, **252,** 41.

11. P. Handler and H. I. Kohn, *J. Biol. Chem.*, 1943, **150**, 447.
12. K. I. Altman and E. A. Evans, *ibid.*, 1947, **169**, 462.
13. D. E. Green, J. G. Dewan and L. F. Leloir, *Biochem. J.*, 1937, **31**, 934 ; D. E. Green and J. G. Dewan, *ibid.*, 1937, **31**, 1069, 1074.
14. E. Adler and M. Sreenivasaya, *Z. physiol. Chem.*, 1937, **240**, 24.
15. D. E. Green, D. M. Needham and J. G. Dewan, *Biochem. J.*, 1937, **31**, 2327 ; D. E. Green and J. Brosteaux, *ibid.*, 1936, **30**, 1489 ; D. E. Green, *ibid.*, 1936, **30**, 2095.
16. E. Negelein and H. J. Wulff, *Biochem. Z.*, 1937, **289**, 436 ; 1937, **293**, 351 ; O. Warburg and W. Christian, *Helv. Chem. Acta*, 1936, **19**, E79 ; H. von Euler, E. Adler and H. Hellström, *Z. physiol. Chem.*, 1936, **241**, 239 ; C. Lutwak-Mann, *Biochem. J.*, 1938, **32**, 1364.
17. D. C. Harrison, *ibid.*, 1931, **25**, 1016 ; E. Adler and H. von Euler, *Z. physiol. Chem.*, 1935, **232**, 6.
18. H. von Euler, E. Adler, G. Günther and N. B. Das, *ibid.*, 1938, **259**, 61.
19. H. von Euler, E. Adler and G. Günther, *ibid.*, 1937, **249**, 1.
20. O. Warburg and W. Christian, *Biochem. Z.*, 1939, **301**, 221 ; 1939, **303**, 40.
21. M. Dixon and C. Lutwak-Mann, *Biochem. J.*, 1937, **31**, 1347 ; E. Racker, *J. Biol. Chem.*, 1949, **177**, 883.
21a. G. Wald, *Science*, 1949, **109**, 482.
21b. M. L. Sweat and L. T. Samuels, *J. Biol. Chem.*, 1948, **175**, 1.
22. N. B. Das, *Z. physiol. Chem.*, 1936, **238**, 269.
23. H. von Euler, E. Adler, G. Günther and N. B. Das, *ibid.*, 1938, **259**, 61 ; H. von Euler, E. Adler and T. S. Eriksen, *ibid.*, 1937, **248**, 227 ; E. Adler, G. Günther and J. E. Everett, *ibid.*, 1938, **255**, 27.
24. O. Warburg and W. Christian, *Biochem. Z.*, 1931, **242**, 206 ; 1932, **254**, 438 ; E. Negelein and W. Gerischer, *ibid.*, 1936, **284**, 289.
25. F. Dickens, *Biochem. J.*, 1938, **32**, 1626 ; F. Lipmann, *Nature*, 1936, **138**, 588 ; O. Warburg and W. Christian, *Biochem. Z.*, 1936, **287**, 440 ; 1936, **292**, 287.
26. B. Vennesland, E. A. Evans and K. I. Altman, *J. Biol. Chem.*, 1947, **171**, 675.
27. E. Adler, H. von Euler, G. Günther and M. Plass, *Biochem. J.*, 1939, **33**, 1028.
28. J. G. Dewan and D. E. Green, *ibid.*, 1937, **31**, 1074.
29. P. Karrer and O. Warburg, *Biochem. Z.*, 1936, **225**, 297 ; P. Karrer, G. Schwarzenbach, F. Benz and U. V. Solmssen, *Helv. Chim. Acta*, 1936, **19**, 811 ; P. Karrer and F. Benz, *ibid.*, 1936, **19**, 1028 ; P. Karrer, B. H. Ringier, J. Büchi, H. Fritzsche and U. V. Solmssen, *ibid.*, 1937, **20**, 55 ; P. Karrer, G. Schwarzenbach and G. E. Utzinger, *ibid.*, 1937, **20**, 72.
30. W. A. Waters, *J. Chem. Soc.*, 1946, 414.
31. P. J. G. Mann and J. H. Quastel, *Nature*, 1941, **147**, 326.
32. E. S. G. Barron, Z. B. Miller and G. R. Bartlett, *J. Biol. Chem.*, 1947, **171**, 791.
33. H. McIlwain and R. Rodnight, *Biochem. J.*, 1949, **45**, 337.

15. NICOTINIC ACID IN THE NUTRITION OF MICRO-ORGANISMS

Nicotinic acid, like aneurine and riboflavine, is necessary for the growth of certain micro-organisms, and was identified as a component of " bios " by Schultz et al.[1]

Yeasts

Yeasts do not require nicotinic acid to the same extent as they require biotin, aneurine or pantothenic acid and, of seventy-one kinds of yeasts tested by P. R. Burkholder,[2] only nine required nicotinic acid. These were : Candida pseudotropicalis, Mycoderma valida, M. vini, Saccharomyces fragilis, S. macedoniensis, Saccharomycodes ludwigii, Schizosaccharomyces pombe, Torulopsis sphaerica, Zygosaccharomyces marxianus and Z. lactis. A. S. Schultz and L. Atkin [3] found that in addition Kloeckera brevis, Saccharomyces carlsbergensis and Torula cremoris also required nicotinic acid. According to M. Rogosa,[4] yeasts that ferment lactose require nicotinic acid, but yeasts that do not ferment lactose do not require nicotinic acid, but the above list contains representatives of both types.

Yeasts were found to take up nicotinic acid added to the medium on which they were grown.[5]

Other Fungi

P. R. Burkholder [2] examined a number of moulds, but none of them required nicotinic acid.

By exposing Neurospora crassa to X-rays and ultra-violet light, D. Bonner and G. W. Beadle [6] obtained five different mutants. One of these, when grown on nicotinic acid or nicotinamide, produced two substances which exhibited nicotinic acid activity for one of the other mutants. The substances formed were believed to be a hydroxy-pyridine-carboxylic acid and its methylation product.

One mutant of N. crassa was obtained which required tryptophan for growth and could not utilise indole, and another which grew with either anthranilic acid, indole or tryptophan.[6a] When the latter mutant was grown on a medium containing anthranilic acid with C^{14} in the side-chain, the nicotinic acid and tryptophan isolated from the mould tissue contained no C^{14}, most of which was lost in the carbon dioxide formed during growth (see also page 250).

Bacteria

Reference has already been made (page 226) to the use of Lactobacillus arabinosus, L. helveticus and Leuconostoc mesenteroides in the microbiological assay of nicotinic acid, but many other bacteria also fail to grow in its absence. These include *Proteus vulgaris*,[7] *Pr. morganii*,[8] *Shigella dysenteriae*[9] and *S. paradysenteriae*.[10, 11, 12] Cultures of the dysentery bacteria could be trained to grow without nicotinic acid by repeated transfer into media containing progressively smaller amounts ;[13] the variants so produced, however, grew better in the presence of optimal amounts of nicotinamide. Culture filtrates of the variants stimulated the growth of the parent strain, indicating that nicotinamide, or a substance biologically equivalent to it, must have been synthesised by the variant. Nicotinic acid was also essential for the growth of *Acetobacter suboxydans*[9,14] *Staphylococcus aureus*,[15] *Streptobacterium plantarum*[16] and *Clostridium tetani*.[17] A mutant of *Escherichia coli* that required nicotinamide was produced by Roepke *et al.*[18] Nicotinic acid enhanced the growth of *Leptospira icterohaemorrhagiae*[19] and of *Brucella abortus*, but not of *Br. melitensis*, the growth of which was actually inhibited.[20]

The cell content of *L. arabinosus*, which assimilates nicotinic acid during growth, rises to 0·7-5·0 mμ mol. per mg. of dry weight. It exists in the cell as cozymase.[20a]

High concentrations of nicotinic acid or nicotinamide, *e.g.* of the order of 10 mg. per ml., were found [21] to inhibit the growth of a number of representative bacteria in a simple medium ; but in casein hydrolysate the inhibition was much less marked and was completely nullified by the addition of yeast extract. The phenomenon is believed to be an example of nutritional imbalance.

Nicotinamide suppressed the spread of tuberculosis in mice, the effect of 0·50 to 0·75 % in the diet being equivalent to that of 1 mg. of streptomycin four times daily.[21a] It is unlikely that the effect is due to a direct antibacterial action of the nicotinamide.

Nicotinic acid is not an essential growth factor for *Bacillus paratyphosum A*, but is essential for the fermentation of carbohydrates by this organism ; it must first be converted into cozymase.[22] Some organisms, *e.g. Haemophilus parainfluenzae*, cannot utilise nicotinic acid or nicotinamide in the absence of D-ribose and adenylic acid, although they grow in presence of the mixture just as well as they do in presence of codehydrogenase I.[23] *H. parainfluenzae* was able to utilise nicotinamide nucleoside, dihydrocozymase and deaminocozymase, showing that the reaction it cannot perform is the combination of nicotinamide with ribose. The utilisation of nicotinic acid by many micro-organisms is impeded by the presence of pyridine-β-sulphonic acid or its amide, which appears to interfere with its conversion into cozymase (see page 291). Several species of *Pasteurella* were stimulated by nicotinamide, but not by nicotinic acid,[24] suggesting that these organisms are unable to convert the acid into the amide.

Bacteria that grow well without added nicotinic acid presumably synthesise sufficient for their needs. The formation of nicotinic acid on a synthetic medium was in fact demonstrated by P. R. Burkholder and I. McVeigh [25] for *E. coli, B. aerogenes, B. mesentericus* and *B. vulgatus.*

According to M. R. Bovarnick,[26] the product obtained by heating glutamic acid, methionine or certain other amino acids with asparagine or iso-asparagine at 100° C. at pH 7, could replace nicotinamide as a growth factor for *S. dysenteriae, S. aureus* and *L. arabinosus.* The culture fluid was found to contain nicotinamide. According to P. Ellinger and M. M. Abdel Kader,[27] however, ornithine was a more effective precursor of nicotinic acid. Using two strains of *E. coli,* isolated from rat faeces and known to synthesise nicotinamide when grown in an ammonium lactate medium, they showed that the amount of nicotinamide synthesised was increased $4\frac{1}{2}$-fold by ornithine and to the extent of only 50 to 70 % by glutamine and arginine. Ornithine was therefore utilised by *E. coli* for the biosynthesis of nicotinamide, a conclusion of particular significance in view of the isolation of dinicotinyl ornithine from chick faeces (page 256). It was suggested that arginine and glutamine, with δ-amino groups, were probably converted into ornithine and thus exhibit a similar, though less marked effect.

No evidence was obtained to suggest that tryptophan could be converted into ornithine, and *E. coli* could not convert tryptophan into nicotinamide. It may be, however, that other intestinal organisms can effect the first part of this transformation, for a mixed culture from rats' caecum was able to convert tryptophan into nicotinamide. On the other hand, ingestion of ornithine did not increase the output of N^1-methylnicotinamide ; perhaps the amino acid was utilised too rapidly for protein formation.

The synthesis of nicotinic acid by sulphonamide-resistant and sulphonamide-sensitive strains of *E. coli* was not diminished by sulphathiazole.[28]

Nicotinic acid was destroyed during cell proliferation by *Pseudomonas fluorescens* [29] and by a mixed culture isolated from faeces.[30] Destruction was due to enzymic oxidation, which was inhibited by inhibitors of metal enzymes, *e.g.* sodium azide, or by surface active agents.[31] Thus, unless an adequate supply of nicotinic acid is maintained or an organism is able to synthesise it as rapidly as it is used up, the organism will fail to grow.

H. McIlwain [32] has calculated the rate of production of nicotinic acid and the " turnover number " of enzymes containing it. He estimated that, making allowance for the vitamin that passed into the culture fluid, the five bacteria *Aerobacter aerogenes, Serratia marcescens, Pseudomonas fluorescens, Proteus vulgaris* and *Clostridium butylicum* produced from 30 to 180 molecules of nicotinic acid per cell per second, and that each contained from 96,000 to 120,000 molecules of nicotinic acid per cell. The "turnover number" of three different non-bacterial enzyme systems containing cozymase ranged from 300 to 450 molecules per molecule of enzyme per second, that is, between 300 and 450 molecules of substrate reacted with each molecule of enzyme per second.

The rate of inactivation of nicotinamide by *Proteus vulgaris* was estimated to be 5 molecules per cell per second, the rate of inactivation of cozymase by *H. parainfluenzae* 11 molecules per cell per second, the rate of inactivation and reactivation of cozymase by yeast 12 to 18 molecules per cell per second and the rate of interconversion of coenzymes I and II by yeast 8 to 10 molecules per cell per second ; in each instance, the rate given is for the non-proliferating organism. Thus, the reactions of synthesis, inactivation and interconversion occurred in nicotinic acid derivatives with velocities not far removed from 10 molecules per cell per second, suggesting the existence of a group of well-defined reactions of low velocity, which McIlwain terms "reactions of $m\mu$ mol-order", because their velocity is some $m\mu$ mols. per gram of dry weight of the organism per second. The ordinary reactions of the cell proceed much faster, being reactions of μ mol. order ; there is therefore a sharp distinction between the two types.

Actually the rate at which coenzyme is synthesised is not constant. *L. arabinosus*, for instance, synthesised cozymase at a rate of 24 $m\mu$ mol. per mg. of dry weight per hour in a nicotinic acid-deficient medium and at a rate of less than 3 $m\mu$ mol. per mg. per hour in presence of nicotinic acid. The rate of synthesis appears to be controlled by a mechanism that inhibits synthesis as the cells become saturated.[33]

If an enzyme that effects an $m\mu$ mol. reaction is operating with a turnover number of say 50 molecules per molecule per second, then in the twenty minutes of a bacterial generation it could have controlled the production of 6×10^4 molecules, possibly of a coenzyme capable of acting with a similar turnover number. In this event, the effect of the initial enzyme molecule would extend to 1.8×10^9 molecules ; that is, if the substrate were glucose, 5.4×10^{-13} g., or about five times the bacterial mass, would have been metabolised.

When bacteria are irradiated, the genes may be altered and the biochemical reactions of the cell modified accordingly. It has been suggested that each gene controls one biochemical reaction. Some enzymes occur in the bacterial cell in large numbers and, in such instances, one gene must influence the production of large numbers of enzyme molecules.

Other enzymes, however, occur in much smaller numbers. The

more rapid reactions of μ mol. order are almost certainly those in which large numbers of enzymes are involved, and the slower reactions, of $m\mu$ mol. order, those in which only one or a few molecules take part. It is suggested that reactions of the first type are concerned with protein formation, and reactions of the second type with the production of coenzymes or prosthetic groups. McIlwain estimates that genes constitute 0·1 to 1 % of the protein molecules in a bacterium, which is consistent with the suggested balance between μ mol. and $m\mu$ mol. reactions. The significance of the difference between these two types of reaction is that the more rapid reactions are the more likely to be closely related to the unit of inheritance. The precise relation between genes and enzymes provides a fascinating field for future research and one that may lead to an understanding of the fundamental mechanism of heredity.

Protozoa

Nicotinic acid or nicotinamide is essential for the growth of *Tetrahymena geleii*, and could not be replaced by tryptophan.[34]

References to Section 15

1. A. S. Schultz, L. Atkin and C. N. Frey, *J. Amer. Chem. Soc.*, 1938, **60,** 1514.
2. P. R. Burkholder, *Amer. J. Bot.*, 1943, **30,** 206 ; P. R. Burkholder and D. Moyer, *Bull. Torrey Bot. Club*, 1943, **70,** 372.
3. A. S. Schultz and L. Atkin, *Arch. Biochem.*, 1947, **14,** 369.
4. M. Rogosa, *J. Bact.*, 1943, **46,** 435.
5. J. M. van Lanen, *Arch. Biochem.*, 1947, **12,** 101.
6. D. Bonner and G. W. Beadle, *ibid.*, 1946, **11,** 319.
6a. H. K. Mitchell and J. Lein, *J. Biol. Chem.*, 1948, **175,** 481 ; J. F. Nyc, H. K. Mitchell, E. Leifer and W. H. Langham, *ibid.*, 1949, **179,** 783.
7. P. Fildes, *Brit. J. Exp. Path.*, 1938, **29,** 239.
8. M. J. Pelczar and J. R. Porter, *Proc. Soc. Exp. Biol. Med.*, 1940, **43,** 151.
9. A. Dorfman, S. A. Koser, M. Horwitt, S. Berkman and F. Saunders, *ibid.*, 434.
10. H. F. Fraser, N. H. Topping and W. H. Sebrell, *U.S. Publ. Health Rep.*, 1938, **53,** 1836.
11. H. Isbell, J. G. Wooley, R. E. Butler and W. H. Sebrell, *J. Biol. Chem.*, 1941, **139,** 499.
12. A. J. Weil and J. Black, *Proc. Soc. Exp. Biol. Med.*, 1944, **55,** 24.
13. S. A. Koser and M. H. Wright, *J. Bact.*, 1943, **46,** 239.
14. L. A. Underkofer, A. C. Bantz and W. H. Peterson, *ibid.*, 1943, **45,** 183.
15. B. C. J. G. Knight, *Bacterial Nutrition* ; M.R.C. London, 1936.
16. E. F. Möller, *Angew. Chem.*, 1940, **53,** 204.

17. R. E. Feeney, J. H. Mueller and P. A. Miller, *J. Bact.*, 1943, **46**, 563.
18. R. R. Roepke, R. L. Libby and M. H. Small, *ibid.*, 1944, **48**, 401.
19. T. G. Ward and E. B. Starbuch, *Proc. Soc. Exp. Biol. Med.*, 1941, **48**, 19.
20. G. P. Kerby, *J. Bact.*, 1939, **37**, 495.
20a. H. McIlwain, D. A. Stanley and D. E. Hughes, *Biochem. J.*, 1949, **44**, 153.
21. S. A. Koser and G. J. Kasai, *J. Bact.*, 1947, **53**, 743 ; 1947, **54**, 20.
21a. D. McKenzie, L. Malone, S. Kushner, J. J. Oleson and Y. Subba-Row, *J. Lab. Clin. Med.*, 1949, **33**, 1249.
22. I. J. Kligler and N. Grossowicz, *J. Bact.*, 1941, **42**, 173.
23. F. Schlenk and W. Gingrich, *J. Biol. Chem.*, 1942, **143**, 295.
24. S. A. Koser, S. Berkman and A. Dorfman, *Proc. Soc. Exp. Biol. Med.*, 1941, **41**, 504.
25. P. R. Burkholder and I. McVeigh, *Proc. Nat. Acad. Sci.*, 1942, **28**, 285.
26. M. R. Bovarnick, *J. Biol. Chem.*, 1943, **148**, 151 ; 1943, **149**, 301.
27. P. Ellinger and M. M. Abdel Kader, *Nature*, 1947, **160**, 675.
28. A. K. Miller, P. Bruno and R. M. Berglund, *J. Bact.*, 1947, **54**, 9.
29. S. A. Koser and G. R. Baird, *J. Infect. Dis.*, 1944, **75**, 250.
30. R. Benesch, *Lancet*, 1945, **1**, 718.
31. C. A. Nichol and M. Michaelis, *Proc. Soc. Exp. Biol. Med.*, 1947, **66**, 70.
32. H. McIlwain, *Nature*, 1946, **158**, 898.
33. D. E. Hughes, *Biochem. J.*, 1949, **45**, xxxvi.
34. G. W. Kidder, V. C. Dewey, M. B. Andrews and R. R. Kidder, *J. Nutrition*, 1949, **37**, 521.

16. EFFECT OF NICOTINIC ACID ON HIGHER PLANTS

Comparatively little study has been made of the nicotinic acid requirements of the higher plants. According to J. Bonner,[1] nicotinic acid is indispensable for pea seedlings, whilst orchid seeds are said [2] to require the presence of nicotinic acid or pyridoxine before germination can take place ; with pyridoxine, however, subsequent growth was poor, whereas nicotinic acid promoted normal development. Nicotinic acid may be one of the substances produced by the mycorrhizal fungus.

On the other hand, both nicotinic acid and nicotinamide markedly inhibited root growth in cress seedlings.[3] Nicotinic acid also enhanced the inhibitory effect of indole-3-acetic acid on the growth rate of asparagus stem tips in the dark, although by itself it had no effect.[4] No such effect was observed with cress seedlings.[4a]

Considerable increases in the nicotinic acid content occurred during the germination of oats, wheat, barley and maize.[5] The amount of nicotinic acid in leaf tissue was generally higher in trisomic than in disomic maize.[6] This increase is probably due to synthesis from tryptophan, which increased the nicotinic acid content of corn embryos when added to sterile cultures on which they were grown [7] and that of cabbage, broccoli and tomato leaves when supplied through the petioles.[8] Tryptophan was apparently not converted into nicotinic acid by haricot beans.[9]

References to Section 16

1. J. Bonner, *Plant Physiol.*, 1938, **13**, 865
2. G. R. Noggle and F. L. Wynd, *Bot. Gaz.*, 1942, **104**, 455 ; R. B. Bahme, *Science*, 1949, **109**, 522.
3. L. J. Andus and J. H. Quastel, *Nature*, 1947, **160**, 222.
4. A. W. Galston, *J. Biol. Chem.*, 1947, **169**, 465.
4a. L. J. Andus, *Nature*, 1948, **162**, 811.
5. P. R. Burkholder, *Science*, 1943, **97**, 562.
6. N. H. Giles, P. R. Burkholder, I. McVeigh and K. S. Wilson, *Genetics*, 1946, **31**, 216.
7. A. Nason, *Science*, 1949, **109**, 170.
8. F. G. Gustafson, *ibid.*, 1949, **110**, 279.
9. T. Terroine, *Compt. rend. Soc. biol.*, 1948, **227**, 367.

17. NICOTINIC ACID REQUIREMENTS OF INSECTS

Nicotinic acid was found to be essential for the development of the fruit fly, *Drosophila melanogaster*,[1] of the moths, *Galleria mellonella* [2] and *Ephestia elutella*,[4] and of the beetles, *Ptinus tectus*,[3] *Tribolium confusum* [3] and *Silvanus surinamensis*,[3] but not of the two beetles, *Sitodrepa panicea* and *Lasioderma serricorne*.[3] When the larvae of these last two insects were sterilised, however, normal development did not take place until several members of the vitamin B complex, including nicotinic acid, were added to the diet.[4] This indicated that the reason why certain insects do not require endogenous sources of these vitamins is that they are provided by the intracellular symbionts. The larvae of the mosquito, *Aedes aegypti*, required nicotinic acid as well as other vitamins to permit growth to the fourth instar.[5]

References to Section 17

1. E. L. Tatum, *Proc. Nat. Acad. Sci.*, 1941, **27**, 193.
2. D. L. Rubinstein and L. A. Shekun, *Nature*, 1939, **143**, 1064.
3. G. Fraenkel and M. Blewett, *ibid.*, 1943, **151**, 703.
4. G. Fraenkel and M. Blewett, *ibid.*, 1943, **152**, 506 ; *Biochem. J.*, 1943, **37**, 686 ; *Proc. Roy. Soc. B.*, 1944, **132**, 212.
5. L. Golberg, B. de Meillon and M. Lavoipierre, *J. Exp. Biol.*, 1945, **21**, 90.

18. ANALOGUES OF NICOTINIC ACID

Activity in Canine Blacktongue

The first report of the effects in pellagra and blacktongue of compounds other than nicotinic acid was that of Woolley et al.,[1] who found that only β-picoline and the ethyl ester, amide and (to a smaller extent) N-methylamide of nicotinic acid, cured blacktongue in dogs ; picolinic acid (pyridine-2-carboxylic acid), quinolinic acid (pyridine-2 : 3-dicarboxylic acid), isonicotinic acid (pyridine-4-carboxylic acid), nipecotic acid (hexahydronicotinic acid), nicotinic acid diethylamide, 6-methylnicotinic acid, trigonelline, pyridine and N[1]-methylnicotinamide were inactive. SubbaRow et al.[2] reported that β-aminopyridine was as effective as nicotinic acid in curing blacktongue in dogs, whilst Najjar et al.,[3] in contradiction to the findings of Woolley et al.,[1] reported that nicotinic acid diethylamide and N[1]-methylnicotinamide were active and that the latter prevented fatty liver formation in rats, so that its methyl group was apparently biologically active also.[4] According to Smith et al.[5] the diethylamide had 1/15th the activity of nicotinic acid, whilst L. J. Teply and C. A. Elvehjem [6] also found it to be active.

A difference of opinion also exists in respect of the activity of nicotinuric acid which, according to Najjar et al.,[3] was effective and, according to J. W. Huff and W. A. Perlzweig [7] and W. J. Dann and P. Handler,[8] ineffective. Again, Teply et al.[9] found that N[1]-methylnicotinamide was inactive, thus confirming Woolley's observation and contradicting the results obtained by Najjar et al.[3]

On the other hand, there appears to be general agreement that quinolinic acid,[1, 3, 10, 11] and trigonelline [1, 3] are inactive, and that pyrazine-monocarboxylic acid (I) and pyrazine-dicarboxylic acid (II), which obviously bear a close structural relationship to nicotinic acid :

(I)   (II)

and therefore might be expected to show some activity, are of no value in the treatment of blacktongue.[10, 11] Thiazole-5-carboxylic acid,[10] pyrimidine-4-carboxylic acid,[11] 3-aminopyridine [11] and 2-amino-nicotinic acid [11] were also inactive.

Badgett et al.[12] prepared a series of fourteen esters of nicotinic acid and fourteen substituted amides of such a type that when added to cereals, no appreciable loss of the vitamin would occur on rinsing the cereal with water. The ethyl and lauryl esters and the anilide were tested on dogs and found to possess considerable activity. Several esters of nicotinic acid also exhibited biological activity when tested on chicks ; [13] the activity varied with the nature of the esterifying group. Ethyl, propyl and butyl nicotinates were as effective as the free acid in curing blacktongue in dogs and a similar condition in chicks ; [14] their behaviour closely simulated that of a substance isolated from wheat bran.[15]

Esters of glycerol and two simple sugars were also found to cure blacktongue in dogs.[15a] When incorporated in rice they were not removed on subsequent cooking.

Activity in Pellagra

Fewer discrepancies have been reported in the activities of nicotinic acid derivatives in pellagra than in blacktongue, although in some instances there is a marked difference in the behaviour of a particular substance in the two conditions, sufficiently striking, in fact, to suggest that whilst the conditions are analogous they are possibly due to a breakdown of carbohydrate metabolism at two different points. Thus, whereas quinolinic acid was found by four different groups of workers to be inactive in blacktongue, R. W. Vilter and T. D. Spies [16] found that it produced a dramatic response in pellagrins, and confirmed the subjective improvement by demonstrating that the coenzyme I and II content of the blood also increased to normal within twenty-four hours. T. D. Spies and his colleagues [17] found that, in addition to nicotinic acid and the amide, nicotinethyl- and -diethylamide and ethyl nicotinate were active in pellagra, whilst α-picoline, trigonelline and 2-aminopyridine were inactive. Results were inconclusive with β-picoline, 2 : 6-dimethylpyridine-3 : 5-dicarboxylic acid and pyridine-3 : 5-dicarboxylic acid. Similarly, pyrazine-mono- and di-carboxylic acids, which according to two groups of workers were inactive in blacktongue, were found to cause prompt disappearance of glossitis in pellagrins, [16, 18] whilst pyrazine-monocarboxylic acid increased the coenzyme I content of erythrocytes and muscle to the same extent as did nicotinic acid.[19] According to T. D. Spies and his colleagues [16, 18] it also increased the amount of " factor V " (page 229), but this last observation was at variance with the results of W. J. Dann et al.,[11] who found, using *Haemophilus parainfluenzae* to estimate the activity, that neither pyrazine-monocarboxylic acid nor quinolinic acid could effect an *in vivo* or *in vitro* synthesis of factor V in human blood.

According to Axelrod et al.,[19] however, " the antipellagric value of a compound is not necessarily associated with its ability to affect the coenzyme I content of tissues " since they found " definite clinical improvement " in pellagrins treated with pyrazine-monocarboxylic acid and nicotinic acid diethylamide and this was not accompanied by changes in the coenzyme I content of the blood or tissue.

The behaviour of nicotinic acid diethylamide was apparently much the same in pellagra and blacktongue, and the compound had 1/14th and 1/7th the activity of nicotinic acid respectively in the two conditions ; [6, 19, 20], it had no effect on the coenzyme I content of erythrocytes.[19]

Huber et al.[21] attempted to prepare derivatives of aneurine and nicotinic acid that could be added to cereals without being lost on subsequent washing with water. Nicotinic acid and its amide, in contrast to aneurine, failed to form satisfactory salts with methylene-bis-(2-hydroxy-3-naphthoic acid) or 2-ethylhexyl-sulphuric acid, the basicity of the ring-nitrogen being apparently reduced by the presence of the carboxyl group. A series of n-alkyl esters of nicotinic acid was prepared, the properties of which agreed with those reported earlier by Badgett et al. These esters had too pronounced an odour for use in the enrichment of cereals, but they formed salts with methylene-bis-(2-hydroxy-3-naphthoic acid), and both the ethyl and butyl ester salts were sparingly soluble in water. After treatment with dilute alkali, both stimulated the growth of L. arabinosus.

N-(p-Carboxyphenyl)-nicotinamide, N-(phenylcarbamyl)-nicotinamide and N-(6-methoxy-8-quinolyl)-nicotinamide were sparingly soluble in water. The first two showed activity after standing in dilute alkali, but the last was inactive after standing in dilute sulphuric acid.

Effect on Micro-organisms

The requirements of micro-organisms for nicotinic acid are even more specific than are those of animals, and B. C. J. G. Knight and H. McIlwain [22] found that quinolinic acid, picolinic acid and isonicotinic acid, trigonelline, nicotinic acid diethylamide, nicotine, pyridine-β-sulphonic acid, 3-cyano-pyridine, β-picoline, 2 : 4-dimethyl-pyridine-3 : 5-dicarboxylic acid and 2 : 4 : 6-trimethylpyridine-3 : 5-dicarboxylic acid could not replace nicotinic acid as a growth factor for *Staphylococcus aureus*.

The requirements of *Proteus vulgaris* were just as specific, with two exceptions ; for, whereas both organisms grew in presence of nicotinic acid, and its sodium and ammonium salts, ethyl nicotinate, nicotinamide and nicotinuric acid, *Pr. vulgaris* also grew in presence of nicotinic acid mono- and diethylamides, whilst *S. aureus* did not.[23, 24] 2- and 4-Methylpyridines were also inactive for *S. aureus* [24]. According to E. F. Möller and L. Birkofer,[25] nicotinic acid and its analogues stimulated the growth of *Pr. vulgaris* in the following molar concentrations : nicotinic acid, 2×10^{-8} to 1×10^{-6} ; methyl nicotinate, $3·7 \times 10^{-9}$ to 2×10^{-6}; nicotinamide, 2×10^{-8} to 1×10^{-6} ; nicotinamide methiodide, $0·8 \times 10^{-4}$ to $0·6 \times 10^{-3}$; nicotinic acid diethylamide, $0·3 \times 10^{-4}$ to $0·4 \times 10^{-2}$; pyridine-β-sulphonic acid, 1×10^{-3} to more than $0·3 \times 10^{-1}$; pyridine-β-sulphonamide, $2·7 \times 10^{-4}$ to 1×10^{-3} ; pyridine-β-sulphonic acid diethylamide, dilution uncertain ; 6-methylnicotinamide, less than $0·6 \times 10^{-2}$ to $0·5 \times 10^{-2}$; methyl picolinate, less than $1·2 \times 10^{-3}$ to $4·4 \times 10^{-3}$; nicotine, $1·6 \times 10^{-5}$ to $0·5 \times 10^{-3}$; thiazole-5-carboxylic acid, $1·6 \times 10^{-4}$ to 2×10^{-2} ; 2 : 6-dimethylnicotinamide, greater than $3·6 \times 10^{-2}$; 2-acetylnicotinic acid, greater than $1·6 \times 10^{-2}$; pyrazine-monocarboxylic acid, greater than $1·1 \times 10^{-2}$; pyrazine-dicarboxylic acid, greater than $1·6 \times 10^{-2}$. Many of these results are at variance with those obtained by other workers, most of whom have found, for instance, that pyridine-β-sulphonic acid and its amide cannot replace nicotinic acid for micro-organisms.

Thiazole-5-carboxylic acid amide did not replace nicotinic acid in the nutrition of *Pr. vulgaris* [26] or *S. aureus*,[27] but partially neutralised the growth-stimulating effect of nicotinamide on the latter. Thiazole-5-sulphonic acid in large amounts could replace nicotinic acid or the amide for *S. aureus*.

1 : 2 : 5 : 6-Tetrahydronicotinic acid (gervacine) had a similar action to nicotinic acid both on *S. aureus* and *Pr. vulgaris*, dehydrogenation occurring very readily. Hexahydronicotinic acid was also utilised by both organisms, but its effect was not immediate, dehydrogenation apparently taking place with more difficulty than with the tetrahydro compound.[28] 1-Methyl-tetrahydronicotinic acid (arecaidine) had no growth-stimulating action. Tetrahydronicotinic acid did not increase the oxygen uptake when added to pig's kidney or liver pulp.

Most esters of nicotinic acid proved to be only slightly active when tested on *L. arabinosus*.[12] Nipecotic acid had only $0·01$ % of the activity of nicotinic acid towards this organism.[9] A substance isolated from wheat bran was as active as nicotinic acid in blacktongue and in nicotinic acid deficiency in chicks,[14] but stimulated the growth of *L. arabinosus* only after hydrolysis with dilute alkali ;[15] its properties suggested that it might be an ester.

Substances Antagonistic to Nicotinic Acid

Although according to E. F. Möller, pyridine-β-sulphonic acid and its amide may have a slight stimulating action on the growth of *Pr. vulgaris* and *S. aureus* at relatively high dilutions and in the absence of nicotinic acid or amide, other workers have found that they inhibit the growth of these organisms. In presence of nicotinic acid or amide [29] the inhibitory action was reversed owing to competition between the two substances, similar to that between p-aminobenzoic acid and sulphanilamide (page 546) or between pantothenic acid and pantoyl-taurine (page 381).

The growth of *Pr. vulgaris* was partially inhibited by pyridine-β-sulphonic acid [26] at a concentration of 4×10^{-5} mole per l. and completely at 4×10^{-3} mole per l. The inhibition was counteracted by nicotinic acid and by thiazole-5-carboxylic acid amide, a close analogue of nicotinamide ; the thiazole derivative had no inhibitory action on *Pr. vulgaris*.

Pyridine-β-sulphonic acid did not inhibit the growth of *Streptobacterium plantarum*,[30] but nicotinic acid methiodide and pyridine-3-sulphonamide methiodide were more effective than the sulphonic acid, owing to the presence of the iodide ion. Thionicotinamide had some inhibitory effect. Some suppression of growth also occurred with picolinic acid and its amide, and with quinoline-2- and -3-carboxylic acids. Thiazole-5-carboxylic acid amide had a slight inhibitory action on *S. aureus*,[27] but thiazole-5-sulphonic acid and 2-(thiazole-5'-carboxylamido-)-pyridine were inert. Thiazole-4-sulphonic acid likewise possessed no inhibitory activity.[31]

Pyridine-β-sulphonic acid inhibited the dehydrogenation of lactic acid and of glucose when the concentration of the coenzyme was kept constant and that of the sulphonic acid was increased,[32] so that the latter would appear to compete with the coenzyme for the apoenzyme. The inhibitory action decreased as the concentration of the coenzyme or of nicotinic acid or nicotinamide was increased. The affinity of cozymase for apodehydrogenase was two to three times that of pyridine-β-sulphonic acid, whilst nicotinic acid, benzoic acid and benzene sulphonic acid had about the same affinity as pyridine-β-sulphonic acid for apodehydrogenase ; pyridine-β-sulphonamide was considerably less active. The inhibition of enzyme activity by these compounds was not due solely to the carboxylic or sulphonic acid groups but was rather a function of the whole molecule.

According to P. Karrer and W. Manz,[33] the antagonistic action of pyridine-3-sulphonamide towards nicotinamide was probably not due to displacement of the latter by the former from codehydrogenase I or II. If, however, displacement actually does occur, then the altered codehydrogenase is probably capable of reversible reduction, since pyridine-3-sulphonamide methiodide and ethiodide were reduced by sodium dithionite to 1-methyl- and 1-ethyl-1 : 2-dihydropyridine-3-sulphonamide respectively.

Pyridine-β-sulphonic acid exerted an antagonistic effect on the growth-stimulation produced by tetrahydronicotinic acid to the same extent as with nicotinic acid.[28] Tetrahydronicotinic acid, but not hexahydronicotinic acid, inhibited the fermentative activity of apozymase and cozymase.[28]

Pyridine-β-sulphonic acid did not produce symptoms of nicotinic acid deficiency when fed to mice.[34]

Sulphapyridine, in common with many other sulphonamides, has a bacteriostatic action on *S. aureus*, but part of this is believed to be due to an antagonistic effect on nicotinic acid, although the addition of nicotinic acid did not counteract the effect [35] as it did with pyridine-β-sulphonic acid. Sulphapyridine inhibited the response of nicotinic acid-deficient dogs to nicotinamide.[36] Sulphapyridine, like pyridine-β-sulphonic acid, had an affinity for apodehydrogenase and was able to displace cozymase and inhibit dehydrogenation.[32]

Another substance antagonistic to nicotinic acid is 3-acetyl-pyridine, which produced symptoms of nicotinic acid deficiency when fed at a level of 2 mg. or more per day to mice maintained on a purified diet ; the effect was abolished by administration of nicotinic acid [37] or tryptophan.[38] 3-Acetyl-pyridine had only a slight inhibitory effect on the growth of bacteria, and this was not reversed by nicotinic acid.[39]

Sym.-dinicotinylhydrazine did not antagonise nicotinic acid.[40]

2- and 6-Fluoronicotinic acid [41] and 5-fluoronicotinic acid and its amide [42] have been prepared. The first two compounds did not inhibit the growth of *E. coli, S. aureus* or *S. viridans, in vitro* at a dilution of 1 in 2000. 6-Aminonicotinic acid, on the other hand, inhibited the growth of *S. aureus* at a dilution of 1 in 10^6, and the inhibition was reversed by nicotinic acid or amide.[43]

Comparison of Activities of Nicotinic Acid Analogues on Different Species of Organisms

A comprehensive survey of the biological activity of various compounds related to nicotinic acid was made by Ellinger *et al.*[44] All the compounds tested had an action on the central nervous system. In some, the exciting action predominated, as in nicotinic acid and nicotinamide (see page 273), but many compounds were predominantly narcotic, death resulting from paralysis of the respiratory centre. All the compounds tested, with the exception of trigonelline, were considerably more toxic than nicotinic acid or even the amide. All the compounds which, it is generally agreed, possess anti-blacktongue activity, namely nicotinic acid and its esters, nicotinamide and nicotinuric acid were converted into N^1-methylnicotinamide by incubation with liver or kidney slices. Many alkylated derivatives of nicotinamide and also β-picoline were similarly converted to N^1-methylnicotinamide.

Rats can utilise, besides nicotinic acid and nicotinamide, the alkyl and monoaryl derivatives, and many other compounds (see above). Insects were more exacting, and *Tribolium confusum* could utilise only the acid, its esters and the amide, although slight activity was shown by nicotinallylamide, nicotin-(4'-methoxyphenyl)-amide and nicotin-phenylamide and very slight activity by nicotin-mono- and di-ethyl-amides, nicotinbenzylamide, quinolinic acid and β-picoline. Bacteria were still more exacting. *L. arabinosus* utilised only the acid and amide, quinolinic acid, β-picoline and nicotinonitrile ; *Proteus vulgaris* showed a response with nicotinethylamide, quinolinic acid and β-picoline ; whilst *Shigella sonnei* utilised only the acid and amide and, to a very much smaller extent, quinolinic acid and β-picoline. Thus, summarising, it can be said that the rat can utilise all the compounds available to insects, and insects can utilise all the compounds that stimulate the growth of bacteria, but the converse is not true in either instance.

References to Section 18

1. D. W. Woolley, F. M. Strong, R. J. Madden and C. A. Elvehjem, *J. Biol. Chem.*, 1938, **124,** 715.
2. Y. SubbaRow, W. J. Dann and E. Meilman, *J. Amer. Chem. Soc.*, 1938, **60,** 1510 ; Y. SubbaRow and W. J. Dann, *ibid.*, 2565.
3. V. A. Najjar, M. M. Hammond, M. A. English, M. B. Wooden and C. C. Deal, *Johns Hopkins Hosp. Bull.*, 1944, **74,** 406.
4. V. A. Najjar and C. C. Deal, *J. Biol. Chem.*, 1946, **162,** 741.
5. D. T. Smith, G. Margolis and L. H. Margolis, *J. Pharmacol.*, 1940, **68,** 458.
6. L. J. Teply and C. A. Elvehjem, *Proc. Soc. Exp. Biol. Med.*, 1944, **55,** 72.
7. J. W. Huff and W. A. Perlzweig, *J. Biol. Chem.*, 1942, **142,** 401.
8. W. J. Dann and P. Handler, *Proc. Soc. Exp. Biol. Med.*, 1941, **48,** 355.
9. L. J. Teply, W. A. Krehl and C. A. Elvehjem, *ibid.*, 1945, **58,** 169.
10. H. A. Waisman, O. Mickelsen, J. M. McKibbin and C. A. Elvehjem, *J. Nutrition*, 1940, **19,** 483.
11. W. J. Dann, H. I. Kohn and P. Handler, *ibid.*, 1940, **19,** viii ; 1940, **20,** 477.
12. C. O. Badgett, R. C. Provost, C. L. Ogg and C. F. Woodward, *J. Amer. Chem. Soc.*, 1945, **67,** 1138 ; C. O. Badgett and C. F. Woodward, *ibid.*, 1947, **69,** 2907.
13. G. M. Briggs, T. D. Luckey, L. J. Teply, C. A. Elvehjem and E. B. Hart, *J. Biol. Chem.*, 1943, **148,** 517.
14. W. A. Krehl, C. A. Elvehjem and F. M. Strong, *ibid.*, 1944, **156,** 13.
15. W. A. Krehl and F. M. Strong, *ibid.*, 1.
15a. F. M. Strong, L. Lutwak and M. A. Farooque, *Arch. Biochem.*, 1948, **18,** 297.
16. R. W. Vilter and T. D. Spies, *Lancet*, 1939, **2,** 423.

17. T. D. Spies, W. B. Bean and R. E. Stone, *J. Amer. Med. Assoc.*, 1938, **111**, 584 ; T. D. Spies, H. M. Grant and N. E. Huff, *Southern Med. J.*, 1938, **31**, 901 ; S. P. Vilter, W. B. Bean and T. D. Spies, *ibid.*, 1163.

18. C. E. Bills, F. G. McDonald and T. D. Spies, *ibid.*, 1939, **32**, 793.

19. A. E. Axelrod, T. D. Spies and C. A. Elvehjem, *J. Biol. Chem.*, 1941, **138**, 667.

20. D. T. Smith, J. M. Ruffin and S. G. Smith, *J. Nutrition*, 1940, **19**, xiv.

21. W. Huber, W. Boehme and S. C. Laskowski, *J. Amer. Chem. Soc.*, 1946, **68**, 187.

22. B. C. J. G. Knight and H. McIlwain, *Biochem. J.*, 1938, **32**, 1241.

23. M. J. Pelczar and J. R. Porter, *J. Bact.*, 1940, **39**, 429.

24. M. Landy, *Proc. Soc. Exp. Biol. Med.*, 1938, **38**, 504.

25. E. F. Möller and L. Birkofer, *Ber.*, 1942, **75**, 1108.

26. H. Erlenmeyer and W. Würgler, *Helv. Chim. Acta*, 1942, **25**, 249.

27. H. Erlenmeyer, H. Bloch and H. Kiefer, *ibid.*, 1068.

28. H. von Euler, B. Högberg, P. Karrer, H. Salomon and H. Ruckstuhl, *ibid.*, 1944, **27**, 382.

29. H. McIlwain, *Brit. J. Exp. Path.*, 1940, **21**, 136.

30. E. F. Möller and L. Birkofer, *Ber.*, 1942, **75**, 1118.

31. H. Erlenmeyer and H. Kiefer, *Helv. Chim. Acta*, 1945, **28**, 985.

32. H. von Euler, *Ber.*, 1942, **75**, 1876 ; E. Adler, H. von Euler and B. Skarzynski, *Arkiv. Kemi, Min., Geol.*, 1943, **16**A, No. 9.

33. P. Karrer and W. Manz, *Helv. Chim. Acta*, 1946, **29**, 1152.

34. D. W. Woolley and A. G. C. White, *Proc. Soc. Exp. Biol. Med.*, 1943, **52**, 106.

35. R. West and A. F. Coburn, *Trans. Assoc. Amer. Physicians*, 1940, **55**, 173.

36. A. E. Schaefer, J. M. McKibbin and C. A. Elvehjem, *J. Biol. Chem.*, 1942, **144**, 679.

37. D. W. Woolley, *ibid.*, 1945, **157**, 455.

38. D. W. Woolley, *ibid.*, 1946, **162**, 179.

39. E. Auhagen, *Z. physiol. Chem.*, 1942, **274**, 48.

40. J. A. Gautier, *Compt. rend.*, 1946, **222**, 394.

41. J. T. Minor, G. F. Hawkins, C. A. Vander Werf and A. Roe, *J. Amer. Chem. Soc.*, 1949, **71**, 1125.

42. G. F. Hawkins and A. Roe, *J. Org. Chem.*, 1949, **14**, 328.

43. J. Schmidt-Thome, *Z. Naturforsch.*, 1943, **3**b, 136.

44. P. Ellinger, G. Fraenkel and M. M. Abdel Kader, *Biochem. J.*, 1947, **41**, 559.

CHAPTER V

PYRIDOXINE (ADERMIN: VITAMIN B_6)

1. HISTORICAL

IN the previous chapter, mention was made of the observation of J. Goldberger and R. D. Lillie [1] that a pellagra-like dermatitis was produced in rats fed a vitamin B_2-deficient diet (page 211). For a time it was believed that this dermatitis was analogous to human pellagra and that the condition could be used as a test for the " PP-factor ". In 1935, however, Birch et al.[2] showed that this dermatitis, which they preferred to call rat acrodynia, was cured, not by the PP-factor, but by another component of the vitamin B_2 group, previously designated vitamin B_6 by P. György,[3] who defined it as " that part of the vitamin B complex which is responsible for the cure of a specific dermatitis developed by young rats on the vitamin-free diet supplemented with vitamin B_1 and lactoflavin ". On the other hand, a highly active pellagra-preventive concentrate was found to possess little or no vitamin B_6 activity. Thus, for the first time, a clear distinction was recognised between riboflavine, the PP-factor and vitamin B_6.

At about the same time, C. A. Elvehjem and C. J. Koehn [4] were making observations on a form of dermatitis produced in chicks on a vitamin B_2 deficient diet, and they prepared a concentrate of the responsible substance from a commercial liver extract (Eli Lilly's). This concentrate, although highly effective in chick dermatitis, was inactive in rat dermatitis, and the fractions that had been discarded in the course of its preparation were therefore tested on rats. One of them, presumably containing György's vitamin B_6, was found to be very active. The chick dermatitis factor was also investigated by S. Lepkovsky and T. H. Jukes,[5] who found that, unlike the factor that cured rat dermatitis, it was not adsorbed on fuller's earth from aqueous solutions. The rat factor they called factor 1 and the chick factor, factor 2. They found that both factors were essential for puppies, and that a microcytic hypochromic anaemia developed in the absence of factor 1.

The first step toward the isolation of the new factor was taken by T. W. Birch and P. György,[6] who found that vitamin B_6 was present as an insoluble complex in fresh fish muscle and in wheat germ, and that the vitamin was adsorbed from acid solution on fuller's earth and was precipitated by phosphotungstic acid. A. M. Copping [7] was able to make further distinctions between the symptoms of vitamin B_6 and riboflavine deficiencies in rats ; the absence of vitamin B_6 produced dermatitis, with redness, swelling and oedema of the paws, ears, etc., whilst absence of riboflavine produced skin lesions, associated with loss of hair but unaccompanied by swelling or inflammation. She showed that the acrodynia was cured by an alcoholic extract of whole maize or wheat. C. E. Edgar and T. F. Macrae [8] showed that rats did not grow optimally on a vitamin B_2 free diet to which riboflavine had been added, but did so when an alcoholic extract of wheat germ or yeast was also added. Further work showed that neither the factor adsorbed on fuller's earth (" eluate factor ") nor the factor remaining in solution after fuller's earth treatment (" filtrate factor ") was effective alone, but that both were needed in order to obtain a maximal response. They stated that the " eluate factor " appeared to resemble György's vitamin B_6, whilst the " filtrate factor " was similar to Lepkovsky and Juke's factor 2.

One of the reasons for confusion concerning vitamin B_6 at this stage of its history was that different workers used different sources of the vitamin and different test animals, yet tended to assume that the corresponding fractions were equivalent. Thus, when Edgar et al. [9] came to apply their fuller's earth treatment to liver extract, they obtained fractions that behaved differently from the corresponding fractions from yeast extract, and they had to resort to other methods to secure parallel results.

A clearer picture of the syndromes associated with each factor was presented by Chick et al., [10] who found that rats deprived of riboflavine for a long time showed no increase in weight and developed an eczematous condition of the skin affecting especially the nostrils and eyes, that rats deprived of filtrate factor grew slowly and developed poor coats, with matted fur that tended to become grey on the head and shoulders, and that rats deprived of vitamin B_6 developed dermatitis and, later, epileptiform fits. These fits could be prevented and cured by administration of 10 to 15 mg. of the vitamin per day.[11] They were similar in appearance to fits observed in young pigs.

References to Section 1

1. J. Goldberger and R. D. Lillie, *U.S. Publ. Health Rep.*, 1926, **41**, 201.
2. T. W. Birch, P. György and L. J. Harris, *Biochem. J.*, 1935, **29**, 2830.
3. P. György, *Nature*, 1934, **133**, 498.
4. C. A. Elvehjem and C. J. Koehn, *J. Biol. Chem.*, 1935, **108**, 709.
5. S. Lepkovsky and T. H. Jukes, *ibid.*, 1936, **114**, 109 ; 1937, **119**, lx ; *J. Nutrition*, 1938, **16**, 197.

6. T. W. Birch and P. György, *Biochem. J.*, 1936, **30**, 304.
7. A. M. Copping, *ibid.*, 845.
8. C. E. Edgar and T. F. Macrae, *ibid.*, 1937, **31**, 879, 893.
9. C. E. Edgar, M. M. El Sadr and T. F. Macrae, *ibid.*, 1938, **32**, 2225.
10. H. Chick, T. F. Macrae and A. N. Worden, *ibid.*, 1940, **34**, 580.
11. H. Chick, M. M. El Sadr and A. N. Worden, *ibid.*, 595.

2. ISOLATION OF PYRIDOXINE

The isolation of vitamin B_6 in crystalline form was announced in 1938 from four different laboratories. P. György [1] and S. Lepkovsky [2] obtained it from rice bran and yeast respectively by eluting the fuller's earth adsorbate with baryta and precipitating the active substance from the eluate with phosphotungstic acid, after removal of inert material by precipitation with alcohol, mercuric chloride and similar methods. The precipitate was decomposed with baryta, and the filtrate crystallised on being concentrated.

J. C. Keresztesy and J. R. Stevens [3] isolated the vitamin from an adsorbate of rice extract, whilst R. Kuhn and G. Wendt [4] used yeast, in which they stated the vitamin was present as a non-dialysable protein complex with the properties of an enzyme. Pyridoxine was also isolated from rice bran in 1940 by T. Matukawa,[5] who used fractional adsorption, acetylation and extraction with ether followed by hydrolysis.

According to J. V. Scudi,[6] rice bran contained a water-soluble conjugate of low molecular weight, in addition to free pyridoxine. This was not precipitated by the usual protein precipitants, and could be adsorbed on acid clay and eluted in a similar manner to pyridoxine.

References to Section 2

1. P. György, *J. Amer. Chem. Soc.*, 1938, **60**, 983.
2. S. Lepkovsky, *Science*, 1938, **87**, 169 ; *J. Biol. Chem.*, 1938, **124**, 125.
3. J. C. Keresztesy and J. R. Stevens, *Proc. Soc. Exp. Biol. Med.*, 1938, **38**, 64 ; *J. Amer. Chem. Soc.*, 1938, **60**, 1267.
4. R. Kuhn and G. Wendt, *Ber.*, 1938, **71**, 780, 1118.
5. T. Matukawa, *J. Pharm. Soc., Japan*, 1940, **60**, 216.
6. J. V. Scudi, *J. Biol. Chem.*, 1942, **145**, 637.

3. CHEMICAL CONSTITUTION OF PYRIDOXINE

Pyridoxine

Pyridoxine hydrochloride has the empirical formula, $C_8H_{12}O_3NCl$, and its structural formula was worked out independently by R. Kuhn and his fellow-workers in Germany, and by a group of workers in the U.S.A.

R. Kuhn and G. Wendt [1] showed that, on treatment with diazo-methane, vitamin B_6 (which they called adermin) yielded a methyl ether which was converted into a diacetyl ether on acetylation. They therefore concluded that all three oxygen atoms in adermin were present in the form of hydroxyl groups, one phenolic and the other two alcoholic and that, since diacetyl adermin methyl ether contained no active hydrogen atom, the nitrogen atom was tertiary.

The position of the phenolic hydroxyl group was established [2] by the fact that vitamin B_6, like β-hydroxypyridine, gave a positive reaction with the Folin-Denis phenol reagent,[3] whereas α and γ-hydroxypyridine did not. Confirmation was obtained by the close resemblance between the absorption spectra of vitamin B_6 and β-hydroxypyridine. That the two alcoholic hydroxyl groups were not on adjacent carbon atoms was shown [2] by recovery of unchanged adermin methyl ether after treatment with lead tetraacetate.

Oxidation of the methyl ether with neutral potassium perman-ganate solution resulted in the formation of a lactone, $C_9H_9O_3N$, by removal of four hydrogen atoms, suggesting that the aliphatic hydroxyl groups were in the $1:4$ or $1:5$ positions. Oxidation with alkaline potassium permanganate solution yielded the anhydride of a di-carboxylic acid, $C_8H_5O_4N$, with loss of a molecule of carbon dioxide. Oxidation by barium permanganate [4] gave the dicarboxylic acid. By more cautious treatment with potassium permanganate, loss of carbon dioxide was avoided and a tricarboxylic acid, $C_9H_7O_7N$, was obtained. From an examination of its absorption spectrum, it was concluded that the anhydride was either

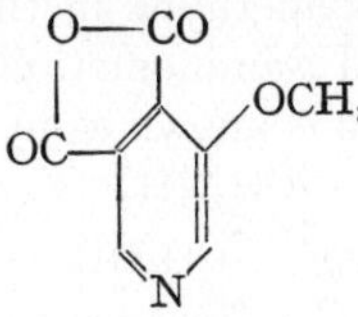

(I) or (II)

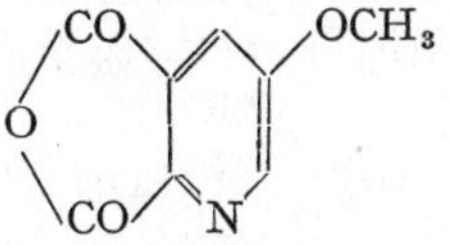

and the tricarboxylic acid therefore

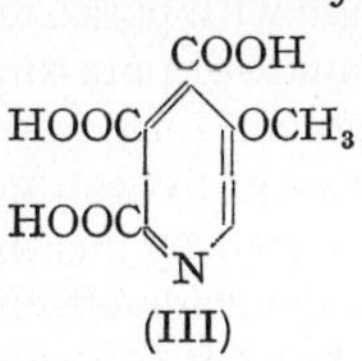

(III) or (IV) or (V)

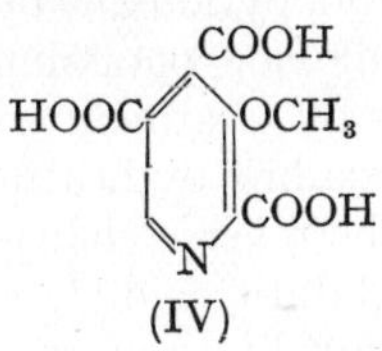

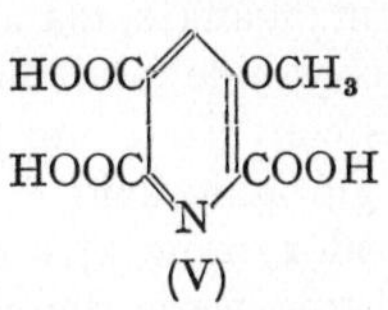

As the tricarboxylic acid gave a blood-red colour with ferrous sulphate, characteristic of pyridine-α-carboxylic acid, whereas the dicarboxylic acid gave no such colour, formula II for the anhydride, and formula

V for the tricarboxylic acid, could be excluded. Adermin must therefore be :

(VI)   or   (VII)

Kuhn *et al.*[5] synthesised the anhydride represented by formula I and found it to be identical with that from adermin, thus confirming that the latter must have structure VI or VII. They [4] also synthesised 3-methoxy-2-methyl-pyridine-4 : 5-dicarboxylic acid and showed that it was identical with the dicarboxylic acid obtained by treating adermin methyl ether with barium permanganate.

Stiller *et al.*[6] also obtained the lactone, $C_9H_9O_3N$, by treating the methyl ether of adermin with barium permanganate, together with a dibasic acid, $C_9H_9O_5N$, which they presumed to be 3-methoxy-2-methyl-pyridine-4 : 5-dicarboxylic acid, since it yielded a phthalein on fusion with resorcinol and a hydroxypicoline on being heated with calcium hydroxide. Its constitution was confirmed by synthesis, accomplished by S. A. Harris, E. T. Stiller and K. Folkers.[7]

Pyridoxal and Pyridoxamine

As a result of a study of the effect of pyridoxine on micro-organisms (see page 212), Snell *et al.*[8] discovered the existence in various natural materials of two substances closely related to pyridoxine. These were identified as 4-formyl-3-hydroxy-5-hydroxymethyl-2-methyl-pyridine, to which the name pyridoxal was given, and 4-aminomethyl-3-hydroxy-5-hydroxymethyl-2-methyl-pyridine, which is known as pyridoxamine.

The former was produced from pyridoxine by oxidation with potassium permanganate, manganese dioxide, potassium dichromate or potassium ferricyanide, and the latter by treatment with ammonia.[9] Pyridoxal was converted into pyridoxamine by heating with casein hydrolysate or glutamic acid, whilst the reverse change was effected by heating pyridoxamine with α-ketoglutaric acid.[10] Other amino acids effected the transformation of pyridoxal into pyridoxamine, but not so readily as did glutamic acid.

The structure of these two substances was established by Harris *et al.*[11] who synthesised the isomer of pyridoxamine, 5-aminomethyl-3-

hydroxy-4-hydroxymethyl-2-methylpyridine, by the following route :

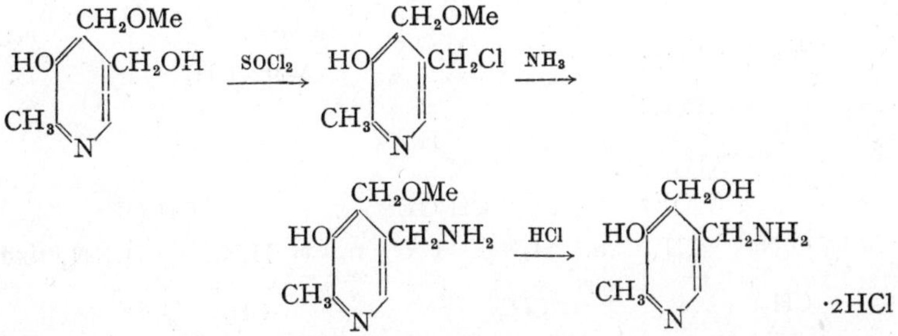

and showed that it differed from pyridoxamine in its chemical behaviour and in the absence of growth-promoting activity. They also showed that the oxime of pyridoxal yielded pyridoxamine on catalytic hydrogenation, thus establishing the fact that the formyl group was in the 4- and not the 5-position. The isomeric aldehyde, 5-formyl-3-hydroxy-4-hydroxymethyl-2-methylpyridine, was synthesised and shown to be different from pyridoxal and to have no significant growth-promoting properties.

References to Section 3

1. R. Kuhn and G. Wendt, *Ber.*, 1938, **71**, 1534.
2. R. Kuhn and G. Wendt, *ibid.*, 1939, **72**, 305.
3. O. Folin and W. Denis, *J. Biol. Chem.*, 1912, **12**, 239 ; 1915, **22**, 305.
4. R. Kuhn, G. Wendt and K. Westphal, *Ber.*, 1939, **72**, 310.
5. R. Kuhn, H. Andersag, K. Westphal and G. Wendt, *ibid.*, 309.
6. E. T. Stiller, J. C. Keresztesy and J. R. Stevens, *J. Amer. Chem. Soc.*, 1939, **61**, 1237.
7. S. A. Harris, E. T. Stiller and K. Folkers, *ibid.*, 1242.
8. E. E. Snell, B. M. Guirard and R. J. Williams, *J. Biol. Chem.*, 1942, **143**, 519.
9. E. E. Snell, *ibid.*, 1944, **154**, 313 ; *J. Amer. Chem. Soc.*, 1944 **66**, 2082 ; Research Corp. and E. E. Snell, B.P. 603289, 603290.
10. E. E. Snell, *ibid.*, 1945, **67**, 194.
11. S. A. Harris, D. Heyl, K. Folkers and E. E. Snell, *J. Biol. Chem.*, 1944, **154**, 315 ; S. A. Harris, D. Heyl and K. Folkers, *J. Amer. Chem. Soc.*, 1944, **66**, 2088.

4. SYNTHESIS OF PYRIDOXINE

Pyridoxine was synthesised independently by the two groups of workers mentioned above and, in addition, by a group of Japanese workers.

S. A. Harris and K. Folkers [1] used the method represented by the following series of transformations :

Subsequently, improved modifications of this method were devised. The synthetic material made by these workers was tested by Reedman *et al.*[2] and shown to have the same degree of vitamin B_6-activity as the natural vitamin, being fully active in rats in a dose of 100 μg.

The synthetic methods adopted by Kuhn *et al.*[3] and by A. Ichiba and K. Michi [4] were different from those used by the American workers and involved the use of 4-methoxy-3-methyl-isoquinoline as starting material. Ichiba and Michi used oxidation with alkaline potassium permanganate solution to effect the first step, whilst Kuhn *et al.* nitrated the isoquinoline, reduced the nitro compound to the corresponding amino compound and then oxidised the latter with permanganate. The remaining stages used by these two groups of workers were identical, namely :

The following method of preparing the starting material for this synthesis had been described in 1900 by S. Gabriel and J. Colman : [5]

Another method of synthesis leading to the formation of adermin monomethyl ether was described by S. Morii and K. Makino.[6] In this method, the initial step was the same as in the method of Harris and Folkers, and the subsequent stages differed only in detail.

The synthesis of pyridoxine was protected by the American workers in a series of patents, assigned to Merck & Co. These covered the following series of transformations :

(b) [8]

$$CH_3 . CO + \overset{CH_2OEt}{\underset{CH_2}{\overset{|}{CO}}} \quad \overset{CH_2CN}{\underset{NH_2}{\overset{|}{CO}}} \longrightarrow$$

[Reaction scheme showing the synthesis of pyridoxine through a series of pyridine ring intermediates, with reagents H₂O, HNO₃, PCl₅, H₂, HNO₂, and H₂.]

(c) [9] the method of S. A. Harris and K. Folkers [1] (page 301);

(d) [10] the same method using dilute hydrochloric acid under pressure instead of hydrobromic acid to hydrolyse the ethoxymethyl group; this simplifies the process by eliminating the final step, *i.e.* the conversion of the bisbromomethyl compound into pyridoxine;

(e) [11] the same method in which the amino-group is protected by acetylation prior to the chlorination.

The preparation of the dimethyl ester of 3-methoxy-2-methyl-cinchomeronic acid:

[Structure: pyridine ring with CH₃O, COOMe, COOMe, CH₃ substituents]

for use in the synthesis of pyridoxine was also patented by Merck & Co.,[12] who also protected [13] the preparation of 4 : 5-epoxydimethyl-3-hydroxy-2-methyl-pyridine by acid treatment of 4-alkoxymethyl-3-hydroxy-5-hydroxymethyl-2-methyl-pyridine, and its conversion into 4 : 5-di-(halomethyl)-3-hydroxy-2-methyl-pyridine by heating with hydrogen halide.

They also patented [14] the preparation of pyracin (see page 344) by oxidising a salt of 3-hydroxy-4 : 5-di-(hydroxymethyl)-2-methyl-pyridine with aqueous potassium permanganate solution. This can be methylated with diazomethane.

The following reactions relating to the synthesis of pyridoxine were protected by Hoffmann-La Roche :

a)[15]

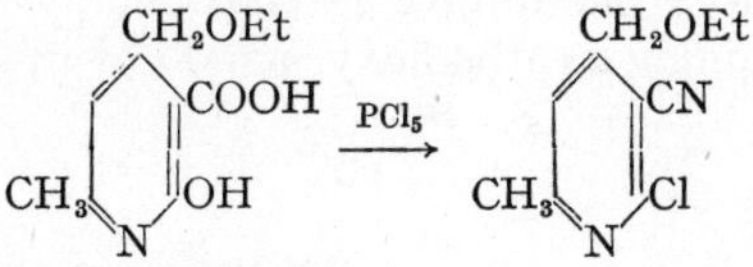

$$CH_2OEt \quad COOH \quad CH_3 \quad OH \xrightarrow{PCl_5} CH_2OEt \quad CN \quad CH_3 \quad Cl$$

b)[16]

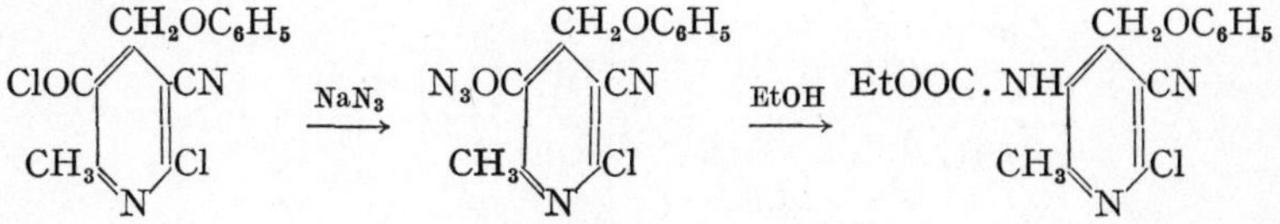

$$CH_2OC_6H_5 \quad ClOC \quad CN \quad CH_3 \quad Cl \xrightarrow{NaN_3} CH_2OC_6H_5 \quad N_3OC \quad CN \quad CH_3 \quad Cl \xrightarrow[\text{EtOH}]{} CH_2OC_6H_5 \quad EtOOC.NH \quad CN \quad CH_3 \quad Cl$$

c)[17]

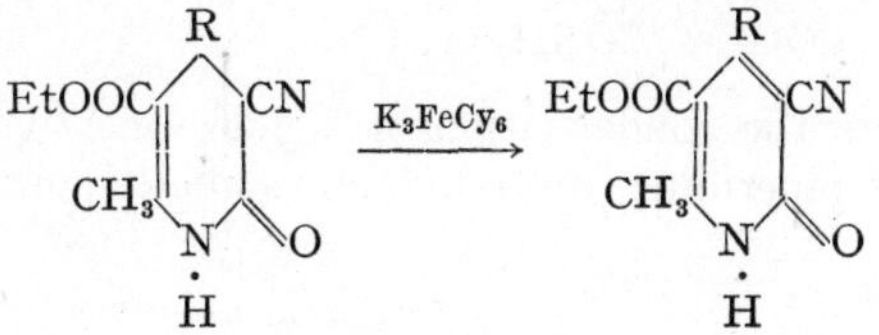

$$R \quad EtOOC \quad CN \quad CH_3 \quad N \quad O \quad H \xrightarrow{K_3FeCy_6} R \quad EtOOC \quad CN \quad CH_3 \quad N \quad O \quad H \qquad (R = \text{alkyl, aryl or aralkyl})$$

d)[18]

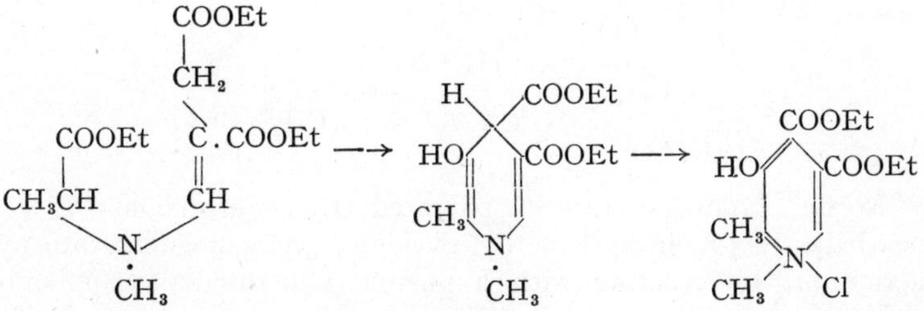

$$\begin{array}{c} COOEt \\ CH_2 \\ COOEt \quad C.COOEt \\ CH_3CH \quad CH \\ N \\ CH_3 \end{array} \longrightarrow \begin{array}{c} H \quad COOEt \\ HO \quad COOEt \\ CH_3 \quad N \\ CH_3 \end{array} \longrightarrow \begin{array}{c} COOEt \\ HO \quad COOEt \\ CH_3 \quad N \quad Cl \end{array}$$

e)[19]

$$CH_2OC_6H_5 \quad HOOC \quad CN \quad CH_3 \quad OH \xrightarrow{PCl_5} CH_2OC_6H_5 \quad ClOC \quad CN \quad CH_3 \quad Cl \xrightarrow{NH_2.NH_2} CH_2OC_6H_5 \quad NH_2.NH.CO \quad CN \quad CH_3 \quad Cl$$

$$\xrightarrow{HNO_2} CH_2OC_6H_5 \quad EtOOC.NH \quad CN \quad CH_3 \quad Cl \xrightarrow{H_2} CH_2OC_6H_5 \quad EtOOC.NH \quad CH_2NH_2 \quad CH_3 \quad N \xrightarrow{HNO_2}$$

$$CH_2OC_6H_5 \quad EtOOC.NH \quad CH_2OH \quad CH_3 \quad N \xrightarrow{HBr} CH_2OH \quad H_2N \quad CH_2OH \quad CH_3 \quad N \xrightarrow{HNO_2} CH_2OH \quad HO \quad CH_2OH \quad CH_3 \quad N$$

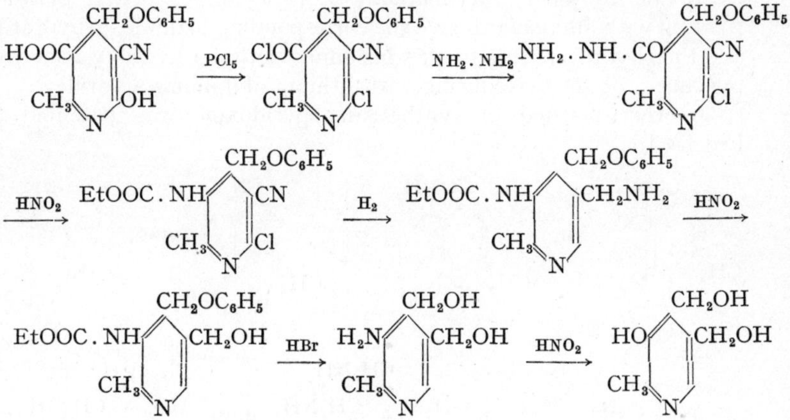

Alternatively, the final hydrolysis can be effected with hydro-chloric acid and the diazotisation with silver nitrite.[20]

Hoffmann-La Roche [21] also patented the condensation of malono-nitrile, malonic esters, malonic acid diamide or cyanacetamide with 2-amino-5-ethoxy-pent-2 : 3-en-4-one to give 4-ethoxymethyl-6-hydroxy-2-methyl-pyridines containing a carbethoxy, amido or cyano group in position 5 :

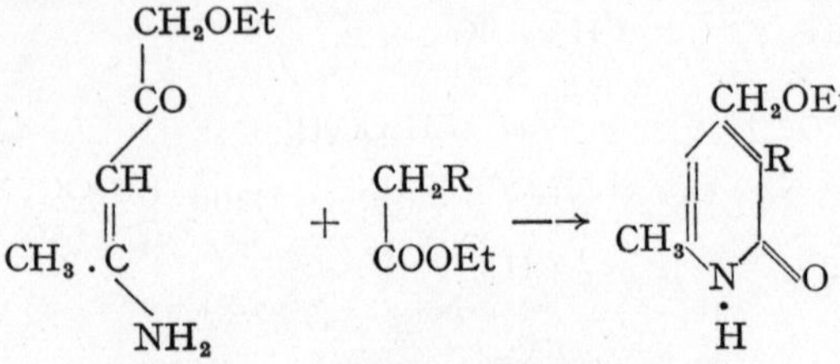

where R = . COOEt, . CONH$_2$ or . CN.

A further patent [22] covers the condensation of acylacetones with malononitrile in presence of piperidine, dimethylamine, diethylamine or dipropylamine :

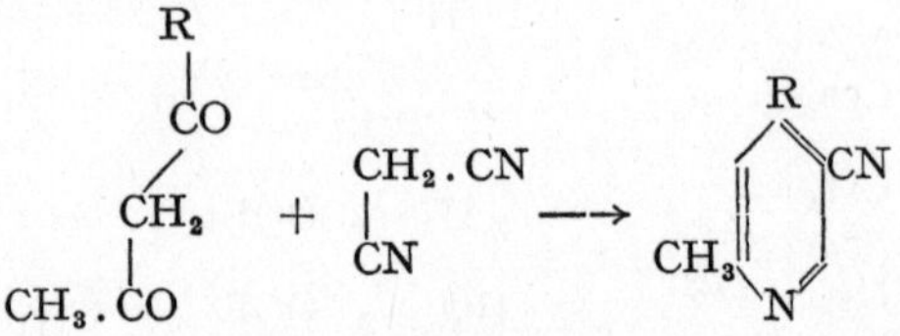

Roche Products Ltd.[22a] patented the conversion of 4 : 5-dicarbalkoxy 3-hydroxy-2-methyl-pyridines (pyracin esters) into pyridoxine (a) by reacting with a phenylarylmethyldialkylammonium hydroxide to yield 3-arylmethoxy-4 : 5-dicyano-2-methyl-pyridine, treating with ammonia to give the corresponding diamide, dehydrating and then hydrogenating to 4 : 5-bis-aminomethyl-3-hydroxy-2-methyl-pyridine ; or (b) by reducing with lithium aluminium hydride.

Another method of synthesising pyridoxine was patented by Lederle Inc.[23]

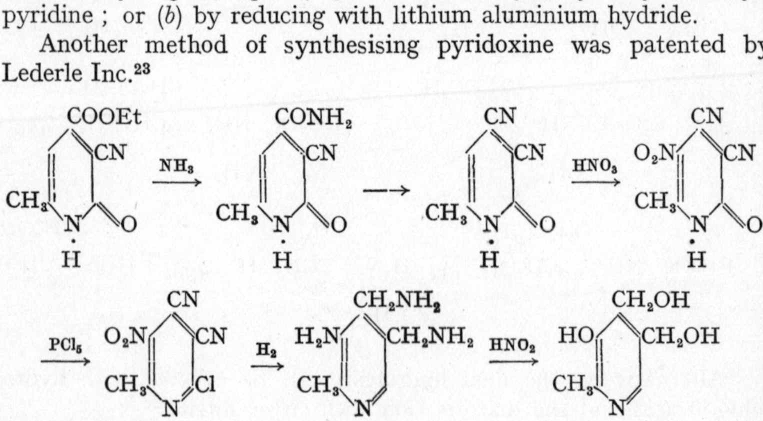

References to Section 4

1. S. A. Harris and K. Folkers, *J. Amer. Chem. Soc.*, 1939, **61**, 1245, 3307.
2. E. J. Reedman, W. L. Sampson and K. Unna, *Proc. Soc. Exp. Biol. Med.*, 1940, **43**, 112.
3. R. Kuhn, K. Westphal, G. Wendt and G. Westphal, *Naturwiss.*, 1939, **27**, 469.
4. A. Ichiba and K. Michi, *Sci. Papers Inst. Phys. Chem. Res. (Tokyo)*, 1939, **36**, 173.
5. S. Gabriel and J. Colman, *Ber.*, 1900, **33**, 988.
6. S. Morii and K. Makino, *Enzymologia*, 1939, **7**, 385.
7. Merck & Co., U.S.P. 2399347.
8. Merck & Co., B.P. 534916-7 ; U.S.P. 2422616.
9. Merck & Co., B.P. 543615 ; U.S.P. 2422617, 2422622.
10. Merck & Co., B.P. 557804 ; U.S.P. 2422619.
11. Merck & Co., B.P. 557805 ; U.S.P. 2422618, 2422620.
12. Merck & Co., B.P. 536249.
13. Merck & Co., U.S.P. 2422621.
14. Merck & Co., B.P. 603442.
15. Hoffmann-La Roche, B.P. 550889.
16. Hoffmann-La Roche, B.P. 550939.
17. Hoffmann-La Roche, B.P. 552419.
18. Hoffmann-La Roche, B.P. 556044.
19. Hoffmann-La Roche, B.P. 556136 ; U.S.P. 2410938-41.
20. Hoffmann-La Roche, B.P. 570365.
21. Hoffmann-La Roche, B.P. 552808.
22. Hoffmann-La Roche, B.P. 553097.
22a. Roche Products Ltd., B.P. 625997, 629450.
23. Lederle Inc., B.P. 567611 ; American Cyanamid Co., B.P. 626368.

5. PROPERTIES OF PYRIDOXINE

The first compound with vitamin B_6-activity to be isolated in the pure state was 3-hydroxy-4 : 5-bis-hydroxymethyl-2-methyl-pyridine

for which the name adermin was proposed by R. Kuhn, and pyridoxine by P. György and R. E. Eckardt.[1]   The latter name is to be preferred, for György and Eckardt showed that crystalline vitamin B_6 hydrochloride, unlike the crude concentrates with which the early results had been obtained, generally failed to cure rat acrodynia and, in the absence of other factors, led to secondary symptoms such as scaly skin, inflammation, alopecia and, occasionally, watery eyes.

Pyridoxine hydrochloride is readily soluble in water (1 g. in 4·5 ml.), acetone and alcohol (1 g. in 90 ml.), and slightly soluble in ether and chloroform. It melts at 204 to 206° C., with decomposition. It gives a characteristic absorption spectrum with a single maximum at 292 mμ at pH 3 and two maxima at 255 and 325 mμ at pH 7·45. Harris et al.[2] attributed this change in the absorption spectrum to a tautomeric change of the type :

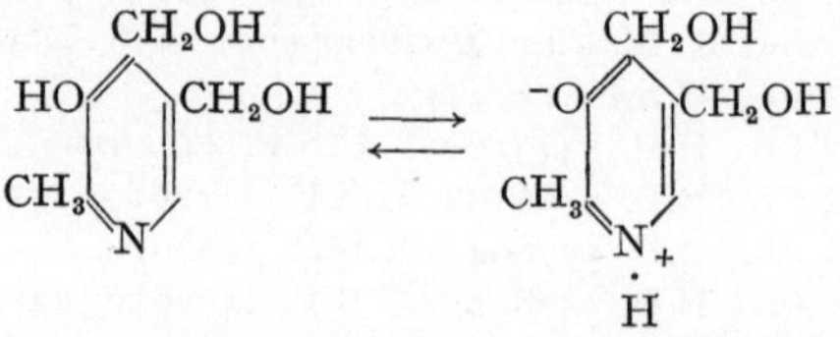

When the hydroxyl group was methylated, the single absorption band at 280 mμ remained unchanged on altering the pH. Pyridoxine is optically inactive.

Other compounds with vitamin B$_6$ activity are described on pages 312, 342–344.

References to Section 5

1. P. György and R. E. Eckardt, *Nature*, 1939, **144**, 512.
2. S. A. Harris, T. J. Webb and K. Folkers, *J. Amer. Chem. Soc.*, 1940, **62**, 3198.

6. STABILITY OF VITAMIN B$_6$

Pyridoxine hydrochloride is a remarkably stable substance in comparison with most other members of the vitamin B complex. Thus, it was not destroyed on heating with 5N acid or alkali at 100° C., by autoclaving in acid or alkaline solution, or by heating at 45° C. for 500 hours in a mixed oil preparation.[1,2] Pyridoxal and pyridoxamine (see page 312) are also stable to hot acid or alkali, although pyridoxal suffered some decomposition on being heated in alkaline solution.[2] All three substances can be autoclaved in 2N-sulphuric acid without appreciable destruction occurring.[3]

Pyridoxine was rapidly destroyed on irradiation in neutral or alkaline solution, although stable in acid solution.[1,2,4] Pyridoxal and pyridoxamine behaved similarly, except that the latter was destroyed by direct sunlight in acid solution.[2] Red light was much less destructive than blue or unfiltered light, and solutions kept better in amber bottles than in colourless bottles.[5] All three substances were destroyed by oxidising agents such as nitric acid at 100° C. or potassium permanganate or hydrogen peroxide at room temperature.[1, 2]

References to Section 6

1. M. Hochberg, D. Melnick and B. L. Oser, *J. Biol. Chem.*, 1944, **155,** 129.
2. E. Cunningham and E. E. Snell, *ibid.*, 1945, **158,** 491.
3. D. Melnick, M. Hochberg, H. W. Himes and B. L. Oser, *ibid.*, 1945, **160,** 1.
4. M. Hochberg, D. Melnick, L. Siegel and B. L. Oser, *ibid.*, 1943, **148,** 253.
5. H. C. Epley, *Amer. J. Pharm.*, 1945, **117,** 265.

7. ESTIMATION OF VITAMIN B₆

Biological Assay

The biological estimation of pyridoxine by means of rats depends largely on finding a diet complete in all the vitamins except vitamin B_6 ; and probably much of the earlier work was unsatisfactory because the diets used were not completely free from traces of the vitamin. Edgar *et al.*[1] described a method of assaying " eluate factor " (pyridoxine) and " filtrate factor " (pantothenic acid) based on the growth response of rats to graded doses of each of the factors, but they did not claim that their method was completely satisfactory, whilst R. C. Bender and G. C. Supplee [2] stated that the growth rate of rats was not sufficiently specific for use in the estimation of vitamin B_6, and used the onset of acrodynia as the basis of an assay method ; they devised a basal diet that produced acrodynia in 100 % of their animals in six to eight weeks. They reported that in order to obtain optimal growth with vitamin B_6, another factor, " factor II " (presumably pantothenic acid), had to be added to the diet, thus confirming the work of Edgar *et al.*

T. W. Conger and C. A. Elvehjem [3] used a synthetic diet consisting of sucrose and casein, supplemented by aneurine, riboflavine, nicotinic acid, choline and pantothenic acid with a fuller's earth filtrate from a butanol extract of liver to supply other members of the vitamin B complex. They claimed to obtain satisfactory results when the growth of rats was used as the criterion of response. Satisfactory results were also reported by M. F. Clarke and M. Lechycka,[4] using a similar method ; the dose-response curve obtained by plotting the logarithm of the dose against the gain in weight was linear with amounts of pyridoxine ranging from 1 to 1·8 μg. Even the best biological method, however, takes at least a month to carry out.[5]

A modified vitamin B_6-deficient diet for rats was devised by Sarma et al.[6] This was based on sucrose and blood-fibrin and, when supplemented with up to 75 μg. of pyridoxine hydrochloride per 100 g. of diet, gave a linear growth curve. Pyridoxal and pyridoxamine had the same activity as pyridoxine when given separately by mouth or when injected intraperitoneally, but both exhibited reduced activity when given with the diet. Because of this, the results obtained when the method was applied to natural materials were somewhat lower than the results obtained by the yeast growth method (page 311).

Colorimetric Methods of Estimation

R. Kuhn and I. Löw [7] were the first to describe a colour reaction for pyridoxine. They observed that diazotised sulphanilic acid coupled with the vitamin to give an orange-coloured dyestuff and that a colour was obtained by treating pyridoxine with phosphotungstomolybic acid reagent and lithium hydroxide.

M. Swaminathan [8] made use of the colour reaction with diazotised sulphanilic acid to estimate pyridoxine in foodstuffs. The material was first digested with pepsin or papain, and the protein degradation products were removed with phosphotungstic acid, and the purine and other bases by means of silver nitrate and baryta. The pyridoxine was then adsorbed from the filtrate, acidified to pH 1 to 2, on to Clarit, from which it was eluted with hot baryta solution. After neutralising the eluate, the colour was developed and compared with that of a standard. The method was used to estimate pyridoxine in urine.

This colour reaction was also used by Bina et al.,[9] though they used a somewhat different method of preparing the pyridoxine extract. The food was first hydrolysed by autoclaving with dilute sulphuric acid and was then digested with a mixture of takadiastase and papain after which proteins and other interfering substances were precipitated with sodium tungstate. The filtrate was then treated with Superfiltrol and the adsorbed pyridoxine eluted with alkaline alcohol. These workers subsequently [10] modified the method by using the ion-exchange resin, Amberlite IR-4, to purify the solution, and diazotised p-aminoacetophenone in place of diazotised sulphanilic acid to develop the colour.

Another colour reaction was discovered by J. C. Keresztesy and J. R. Stevens,[11] who observed that ferric chloride gave a reddish brown colour with vitamin B_6; R. D. Greene [12] made use of this reaction to estimate the vitamin in rich concentrates.

J. V. Scudi and his colleagues [13] made use of Gibbs' reagent,[14] 2 : 6-dichloroquinone-chloroimide, to estimate the vitamin in urine.

This produces a blue pigment, presumably the indophenol :

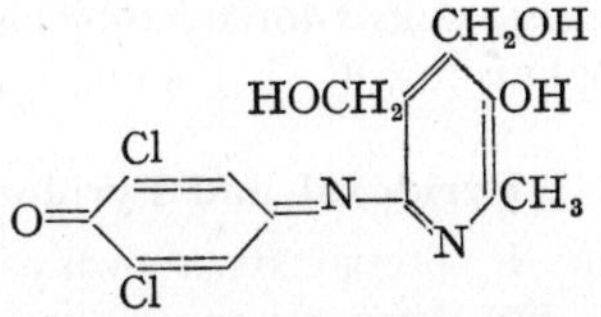

Pyridoxine did not give the reaction in presence of a borate buffer,[15] whereas 4-ethoxymethyl-3-hydroxy-5-hydroxymethyl-2-methyl-pyridine and 4:5-epoxydimethyl-3-hydroxy-2-methyl-pyridine gave colours with the reagent both in the presence and in the absence of borate, so that they could readily be distinguished from pyridoxine.[16] Unfortunately, however, it is not possible to correct for the presence of these substances in pyridoxine merely by subtracting the value found in presence of borate from that found in its absence, as the different compounds react with borate at different rates. It is preferable to remove interfering substances before colour development.

2 : 6-Dichloroquinone-chloroimide was also used by Bird *et al.*,[17] who carried out the coupling reaction in a veronal buffer solution, pH 7·8 to 8·0, and by Hochberg *et al.*,[18] who coupled in aqueous iso-propanol solution. The method was said to give results in close agreement with the biological method when applied to foodstuffs [19] and to rice bran,[20] but not to liver or yeast.[20]

Pyridoxine exhibits a characteristic half-wave potential at the dropping mercury electrode,[21] but the polarographic method does not seem to have been used for the estimation of pyridoxine.

Microbiological Assay Methods

In recent years, there has been a marked increase in the use of microbiological methods of assay for the estimation of vitamin B_6 in foodstuffs. These led incidentally to the discovery of compounds with vitamin B_6-activity other than pyridoxine.

The first microbiological method to be used was a yeast growth method due to Atkin *et al.*[22] The organism was a strain of *Saccharomyces cerevisiae* (No. 4228), which requires pyridoxine for growth. Extracts were prepared for assay by acid digestion, and the growth of the organism was measured turbidimetrically. A similar method was used by R. J. Williams *et al.*[23] and by Siegel *et al.*[24] The latter group of workers autoclaved the test material in acid suspension to liberate bound pyridoxine.

An attempt was made by Emery *et al.*[25] to develop a pyridoxine assay method using another yeast, *Kloeckera brevis*, which requires pyridoxine for growth, but the results were frequently at variance with those obtained with *Neurospora sitophila* (see below). The successful use of *S. carlsbergensis* for microbiological assays has been reported by R. H. Hopkins and R. J. Pennington.[26]

" Pseudo-pyridoxine ", Pyridoxal and Pyridoxamine

Streptococcus faecalis R, previously known as *S. lactis* R, requires pyridoxine for growth, but when attempts were made to utilise it for the assay of pyridoxine it was found [27] that the growth response was much greater, several times greater in fact, than could be accounted for by the pyridoxine content, as estimated chemically or biologically. It appeared that pyridoxine was converted, prior to its utilisation by the organism, into a more active metabolite, provisionally termed " pseudo-pyridoxine " ; this also appeared to be present in some natural products. Although it was so much more active than pyridoxine on *S. faecalis* R " pseudo-pyridoxine ", formed either by treating synthetic pyridoxine with hydrogen peroxide or by autoclaving in presence of cystine, did not stimulate the growth of rats or yeast to a greater extent than did pyridoxine.[28]

The nature of " pseudo-pyridoxine " was elucidated by E. E. Snell,[29] who showed that substances with a greater growth-promoting action on both *S. faecalis* R and *Lactobacillus helveticus* could be formed from pyridoxine by amination or by partial oxidation. Treatment with ammonia yielded a closely related amine, which he called pyridoxamine, whilst oxidation yielded an aldehyde, pyridoxal. Both compounds were more active towards *S. faecalis* and *L. helveticus* than was pyridoxine.

The constitution of pyridoxamine and pyridoxal was established by Harris *et al.*[30] (see page 300).

Whereas pyridoxamine and pyridoxal had much the same growth-promoting activity as pyridoxine for rats, some moulds and some yeasts, for many of the lactic acid bacteria their activity was several thousand-fold greater.[31] The two compounds had little or no effect on *Saccharomyces cerevisiae*, however, but stimulated the growth of *S. carlsbergensis* to the same extent as did pyridoxine.[32] Pyridoxal and pyridoxamine had 3/5th and 4/5th respectively of the growth-promoting activity of pyridoxine in chicks.[33]

Pyridoxal and pyridoxamine are more labile than pyridoxine (page 308), and readily react with other constituents of the medium ; they are also destroyed by light. By using three different organisms —*L. helveticus*, *S. faecalis* and *S. carlsbergensis*—E. E. Snell [34] was able to distinguish between pyridoxine, pyridoxal and pyridoxamine ; he found by this method that pyridoxal and pyridoxamine constituted a high proportion of the vitamin B_6-active compounds in many natural products.

Microbiological Assay of Pyridoxine in presence of Pyridoxamine and Pyridoxal

It will be clear from the foregoing that the estimation of vitamin B_6 activity by measuring the growth response of micro-organisms may give misleading results, as different organisms respond in different degrees to the three substances. The lactic acid bacteria, for example, are useless for this purpose, as they show a greater response to pyridoxamine and pyridoxal than to pyridoxine. The method of M. Landy and D. M. Dicken,[35] which utilises *L. helveticus*, is invalid for this reason. By means of a special medium *L. helveticus* can be used for the assay of pyridoxal.[35a]

Perhaps the most satisfactory method of estimating pyridoxine in presence of its two derivatives is that of Stokes *et al.*,[36] in which use is made of an X-ray induced mutant of *Neurospora sitophila* [37] that requires pyridoxine but does not respond to pyridoxamine or pyridoxal. The medium is relatively simple, consisting of sucrose, ammonium tartrate, ammonium citrate, inorganic salts and a minute amount of biotin ; it was modified slightly by E. C. Barton-Wright.[38] The response is measured by weighing the dried mycelium. The results obtained were in good agreement with those obtained by biological assays. An important point to be borne in mind when carrying out assays with *N. sitophila*, is that aneurine must be destroyed with sodium sulphite, as the organism does not respond quantitatively to pyridoxine in the presence of aneurine ; residual sulphite must be destroyed by addition of hydrogen peroxide.

L. E. Carpenter and F. M. Strong [39] confirmed the claim of Stokes *et al.* that *Neurospora* assays gave results in good agreement with those obtained by the rat growth method, but they failed to obtain consistent results and expressed a preference for the yeast growth method.

Pyridoxine, pyridoxal and pyridoxamine can be separated by partition chromatography on a strip of filter-paper and the position of the spots detected by laying the filter-paper for a few minutes on the surface of an agar plate seeded with *S. carlsbergensis* and then incubating the plate.[40] Growth of the organism is stimulated around the areas in which the three substances are concentrated ; pyridoxamine is held near the top of the paper and pyridoxine near the bottom with pyridoxal just above it.

References to Section 7

1. C. E. Edgar, M. M. El Sadr and T. F. Macrae, *Biochem. J.*, 1938, **32**, 2200.
2. R. C. Bender and G. C. Supplee, *J. Nutrition*, 1940, **20**, 109.
3. T. W. Conger and C. A. Elvehjem, *J. Biol. Chem.*, 1941, **138**, 555.

4. M. F. Clarke and M. Lechycka, *J. Nutrition*, 1943, **25**, 571.
5. A. M. Copping, *Biochem. J.*, 1943, **37**, 12.
6. P. S. Sarma, E. E. Snell and C. A. Elvehjem, *J. Biol. Chem.*, 1946, **165**, 55 ; *J. Nutrition*, 1947, **33**, 121.
7. R. Kuhn and I. Löw, *Ber.*, 1939, **72**, 1453.
8. M. Swaminathan, *Nature*, 1940, **185**, 780 ; *Indian J. Med. Res.*, 1940, **28**, 427 ; 1941, **29**, 261.
9. A. F. Bina, J. M. Thomas and E. B. Brown, *J. Biol. Chem.*, 1943, **148**, 111.
10. E. B. Brown, A. F. Bina and J. M. Thomas, *ibid.*, 1945, **158**, 455.
11. J. C. Keresztesy and J. R. Stevens, *J. Amer. Chem. Soc.*, 1938, **60**, 1267.
12. R. D. Greene, *J. Biol. Chem.*, 1939, **130**, 513.
13. J. V. Scudi, K. Unna and W. Antopol, *ibid.*, 1940, **135**, 371 ; J. V. Scudi, H. F. Koones and J. C. Keresztesy, *Proc. Soc. Exp. Biol. Med.*, 1940, **43**, 118.
14. H. D. Gibbs, *J. Biol. Chem.*, 1927, **72**, 649.
15. J. V. Scudi, *ibid.*, 1941, **139**, 707.
16. J. V. Scudi, W. A. Bastedo and T. J. Webb, *ibid.*, 1940, **136**, 399.
17. O. D. Bird, J. M. Vandenbelt and A. D. Emmett, *ibid.*, 1942, **142**, 317.
18. M. Hochberg, D. Melnick and B. L. Oser, *ibid.*, 1944, **155**, 109.
19. A. E. Bottomley, *Biochem. J.*, 1944, **38**, xxxi.
20. M. Hochberg, D. Melnick and B. L. Oser, *J. Biol. Chem.*, 1944, **155**, 119.
21. J. J. Lingane and O. L. Davis, *ibid.*, 1941, **137**, 567.
22. L. Atkin, A. S. Schultz and C. N. Frey, *J. Amer. Chem. Soc.*, 1939, **61**, 1931 ; L. Atkin, A. S. Schultz, C. N. Frey and W. L. Williams, *Ind. Eng. Chem.*, *Anal. Ed.*, 1943, **15**, 141.
23. R. J. Williams, R. E. Eakin and J. R. McMahan, *Univ. Texas Publ.*, 1941, No. 4137.
24. L. Siegel, D. Melnick and B. L. Oser, *J. Biol. Chem.*, 1943, **149**, 361.
25. W. B. Emery, N. McLeod and F. A. Robinson, *Biochem. J.*, 1946, **40**, 426.
26. R. H. Hopkins and R. J. Pennington, *ibid.*, 1947, **41**, 110.
27. E. E. Snell, B. M. Guirard and R. J. Williams, *J. Biol. Chem.*, 1942, **143**, 519.
28. L. E. Carpenter, C. A. Elvehjem and F. M. Strong, *Proc. Soc. Exp. Biol. Med.*, 1943, **54**, 123.
29. E. E. Snell, *J. Biol. Chem.*, 1944, **154**, 313 ; *J. Amer. Chem. Soc.*, 1944, **66**, 2082.
30. S. A. Harris, D. Heyl, K. Folkers and E. E. Snell, *J. Biol. Chem.*, 1944, **154**, 315 ; S. A. Harris, D. Heyl and K. Folkers, *J. Amer. Chem. Soc.*, 1944, **66**, 2088.
31. E. E. Snell and A. N. Rannefeld, *J. Biol. Chem.*, 1945, **157**, 475.

32. D. Melnick, M. Hochberg, H. W. Himes and B. L. Oser, *ibid.*, 1945, **160**, 1.

33. T. D. Luckey, G. M. Briggs, C. A. Elvehjem and E. B. Hart. *Proc. Soc. Exp. Biol. Med.*, 1945, **58**, 340.

34. E. E. Snell, *J. Biol. Chem.*, 1945, **157**, 491 ; J. C. Rabinowitz and E. E. Snell, *ibid.*, 1947, **169**, 631.

35. M. Landy and D. M. Dicken, *J. Lab. Clin. Med.*, 1942, **27**, 1086.

35a. J. C. Rabinowitz, N. I. Mondy and E. E. Snell, *J. Biol. Chem.*, 1948, **175**, 147.

36. J. L. Stokes, A. Larsen, C. R. Woodward and J. W. Foster, *J. Biol. Chem.*, 1943, **150**, 17.

37. G. W. Beadle and E. L. Tatum, *Proc. Nat. Acad. Sci.*, 1941, **27**, 499 ; 1942, **28**, 234.

38. E. C. Barton-Wright, *Biochem. J.*, 1945, **39**, x ; *Analyst*, 1945, **70**, 283.

39. L. E. Carpenter and F. M. Strong, *Arch. Biochem.*, 1944, **3**, 375.

40. W. A. Winsten and E. Eigen, *Proc. Soc. Exp. Biol. Med.*, 1948, **67**, 513.

8. OCCURRENCE OF VITAMIN B₆ IN FOODSTUFFS

Vitamin B_6 occurs in most foodstuffs in the form of complexes.[1] In addition to pyridoxine, pyridoxal and pyridoxamine are present in variable proportions.[2] This makes the estimation of the vitamin B_6 activity of a foodstuff a matter of some difficulty and this fact, coupled with the virtual absence of frank vitamin B_6 deficiency in man, probably accounts for the relative lack of information about the occurrence of vitamin B_6 in foodstuffs compared with the amount of data available for aneurine or nicotinic acid, for example.

The method of estimation open to least criticism is the rat growth method, since this estimates the biological activity of a substance directly, without requiring any assumptions to be made concerning the relative vitamin B_6 activities of the three compounds. This method was used by Schneider *et al.*,[3] by Henderson *et al.*,[4] by T. W. Conger and C. A. Elvehjem,[5] and by Teply *et al.*[6] The first group of workers expressed their results in arbitrary units, making it difficult to relate them to the results obtained by subsequent workers. They showed, however, that cereals and meat contained more vitamin B_6 than did fruit and vegetables ; the surprisingly high values reported by them for fats and vegetable oils were probably due to the absence of fat from the basal diet used in their assays.

Atkin *et al.*[7] and R. J. Williams *et al.*[8] used a yeast growth method and J. Bonner and R. Dorland [9] and E. C. Barton-Wright [10] the method based on the response of *Neurospora sitophila*. M. Swaminathan [11] made use of the colour reaction with diazotised sulphanilic acid. The results obtained by different workers have not always been consistent, especially for meats.

Cereals

Whole wheat contains 3·2 to 6·1 ; [6, 7, 10] wheat germ, 16 ; [4, 10] wheat bran, 14 ; [10] white flour, 1·2,[7] 2·2 ; [6] whole wheat bread, 4·2 ; [7] white bread, 1·0 ; [7] barley, 5 to 6 ; [10] and yellow corn, 5 μg. per g.[4] Dried grass contains 8 μg. per g.[5] There was little variation (1·2 to 3·1 μg. per g.[10]) in the vitamin B_6 contents of flours of different percentage extractions, but the germ and the weatings contained three times the amount present in wholemeal.[12] Rice polishings contained 20 μg. of vitamin B_6 per g.[11] In general, flours contain approximately half the amounts present in whole grain.[12]

Fruits and Vegetables

Lemon juice and orange juice contain 0·35 and 0·52 to 0·60 μg. of vitamin B_6 per ml. respectively.[7] Cabbage and beetroot contain 3 and 1·3 μg. per g. respectively.[11]

Meat and Fish

The following values have been reported for beef : muscle, 0·8,[8] 4·0,[13] 2·3 ; [7] liver, 0·4,[8] 7·3,[13] 7·1 ; [7] and for pork : muscle, 1·23,[8] 6·1,[13] 6·8 ; [7] liver, 1·7,[8] 3·3,[13] 5·9 [7] μg. per g. Sheep's liver and muscle contain 14 and 5 μg. per g. respectively.[11] Henderson *et al.*[4] record the following values, expressed in μg. per *g. of dry matter* for the vitamin B_6 content of beef, mutton and pork " offal " : kidney and muscle, 20 to 30 ; heart and liver, 10 to 15 ; spleen, pancreas, brain and lung, 8. Fish muscle contains 20 μg. per g. of dry matter. Fried meat exhibited the least loss of vitamin B_6 ; roasting and stewing resulted in the loss of 20 to 50 % of the original vitamin content.

Miscellaneous

Fresh milk contains 1·7,[11] 1·3 ; [4] pasteurised milk, 0·5 to 0·6 ; [7] reconstituted evaporated whole milk, 0·62 μg.[7] per ml. and dried milk, 8·2 μg. per g.[10] Yeast is the richest available source of vitamin B_6, containing up to 50 μg. per g. ; [11] brewers' yeast is several times richer than bakers' yeast.[7] Only about half the vitamin B_6 activity of yeast was present in an extract made with 2N-sulphuric acid, but the activity of the extract increased considerably on autoclaving with dilute acid or on digestion with clarase.[14] The optimal growth stimulation of *S. carlsbergensis* was obtained when extraction was effected within the pH range 1·5 to 2·0. Similarly, the full vitamin B_6 activity of liver was only released by digestion with acid. Yeast contained only small amounts of pyridoxal.[15]

According to Kitzes et al.,[16] honey, pollen and royal jelly contain 10, 900 and 1000 μg. of vitamin B_6 per 100 g. respectively, whilst M. H. Haydak and L. S. Palmer [17] reported an even higher value, 5000 μg. per g. for royal jelly, and a value of 500 μg. per g. for bee bread. Royal jelly is therefore the richest known natural source of vitamin B_6, as well as of other components of the vitamin B complex.

The following values were obtained for the vitamin B_6 content of beers : [10] a modern beer, 0·5 ; a stout brewed in 1899, 0·5 ; and an ale brewed in 1796, 1·2 μg. per ml.

References to Section 8

1. L. Siegel, D. Melnick and B. L. Oser, *J. Biol. Chem.*, 1943, **149,** 361.
2. E. E. Snell, *ibid.*, 1945, **157,** 491.
3. H. A. Schneider, J. K. Ascham, B. R. Platz and H. Steinbock, *J. Nutrition*, 1939, **18,** 99.
4. L. M. Henderson, H. A. Waisman and C. A. Elvehjem, *ibid.*, 1941, **21,** 589.
5. T. W. Conger and C. A. Elvehjem, *J. Biol. Chem.*, 1941, **138,** 555.
6. L. J. Teply, F. M. Strong and C. A. Elvehjem, *J. Nutrition*, 1942, **24,** 167.
7. L. Atkin, A. S. Schultz, W. L. Williams and C. N. Frey, *Ind. Eng. Chem., Anal. Ed.*, 1943, **15,** 141.
8. R. J. Williams, R. E. Eakin and J. R. McMahan, *Univ. Texas Publ.*, 1941, No. 4137.
9. J. Bonner and R. Dorland, *Arch. Biochem.*, 1943, **2,** 451.
10. E. C. Barton-Wright, *Biochem. J.*, 1945, **39,** x.
11. M. Swaminathan, *Indian J. Med. Res.*, 1940, **28,** 427 ; *Nature*, 1940, **145,** 780.
12. A. M. Copping, *Biochem. J.*, 1943, **37,** 12.
13. H. A. Waisman and C. A. Elvehjem, *Vitamin Content of Meat*, 1941.
14. S. H. Rubin and J. Scheiner, *J. Biol. Chem.*, 1946, **162,** 389.
15. S. H. Rubin, J. Scheiner and E. Hirschberg, *ibid.*, 1947, **167,** 599.
16. G. Kitzes, H. A. Schuette and C. A. Elvehjem, *J. Nutrition*, 1943, **26,** 241.
17. M. H. Haydak and L. S. Palmer, *J. Econ. Entomol*, 1942, **35,** 310.

9. EFFECT OF VITAMIN B₆ DEFICIENCY IN ANIMALS

Although György originally defined vitamin B_6 as the fraction of the vitamin B complex that cured dermatitis in rats, György and Eckardt subsequently found that the purified vitamin did not in fact cure rat acrodynia, but only modified its symptoms (page 307). This was confirmed by W. Antopol and K. Unna,[1] who claimed that hyper-keratosis and acanthosis of the ears, paws and snout and an oedema of the corium were characteristic of vitamin B_6 deficiency, and were cured by pyridoxine. Fouts et al.[2] were able to show that crystalline pyridoxine hydrochloride, like the crude concentrates previously used, cured a microcytic hypochromic anaemia in dogs, and this was confirmed by H. J. Borson and R. S. Mettier [3] and by Street et al.[4] The onset of anaemia is now regarded as a characteristic feature of vitamin B_6 deficiency, more characteristic indeed than dermatitis. Remission of the anaemia in dogs brought about by pyridoxine was only partial, however.[5] Nervous symptoms constitute another char-acteristic feature of vitamin B_6 deficiency ; in chicks, these take the form of various convulsive movements [6, 7] and, in rats and pigs, epileptiform fits.[8] Anaemia and nervous symptoms do not always occur together, however, turkeys for instance exhibiting hyper-excitability and convulsions, but not anaemia,[9] and young ducklings, severe anaemia, but not convulsions or paralysis [10] (see also page 320).

Rats. In rats, anaemia is not a regular symptom of vitamin B_6 deficiency although latent erythropoiesis may be demonstrated by the impaired regeneration of the red blood cells after haemorrhage.[11] The total body iron and copper were significantly increased in pyri-doxine-deficient rats.[11a]

Convulsions are more characteristic of vitamin B_6 deficiency in this species and, when young rats were suckled by mothers maintained since parturition on a vitamin B_6 deficient diet, spontaneous convul-sive seizures developed towards the end of lactation.[12] These were alleviated by 10 μg. of pyridoxine per day, but even 50 μg. per day did not protect the animals against artificially induced seizures. No spontaneous seizures were observed when the mothers received between 25 and 150 μg. per day, but a high incidence of artificially induced seizures occurred ; at higher levels of pyridoxine these were delayed and were less severe.

In pyridoxine deficiency, the basal metabolic rate of rats was depressed,[13] and the administration of pyridoxine to vitamin B_6 deficient rats caused a marked acceleration in the growth rate.[14] Vitamin B_6 deficiency increased the amount of protein and water in the body, more so in male than in female rats.[15]

A further illustration of the close connection between pyridoxine and protein metabolism, which is more fully discussed on page 330, is provided by the observation that acrodynia was more severe in pyridoxine-deficient rats fed a casein-rich diet than in rats fed a low casein diet.[16] According to E. C. Sheppard and E. W. McHenry,[17] the amount of pyridoxine in the liver, kidney and leg muscles of rats fed a vitamin B_6-deficient diet for twenty-one days was independent of the protein content of the diet, but with a constant protein intake the amount of pyridoxine in the tissues increased to a maximum with increasing amounts of dietary pyridoxine up to 200 μg. per day. Storage was directly proportional to protein intake, and maximum values were obtained with a pyridoxine intake of 25 μg. per day. On the other hand, Schweigert et al.[18] found that the protein content of the diet did not affect the storage or depletion of pyridoxine.

Further evidence that a disturbance of normal protein metabolism occurs in vitamin B_6 deficiency is provided by the findings of Hawkins et al.[19] that, on a high protein diet, the fasting blood levels of urea and non-protein nitrogen increased when rats were deprived of vitamin B_6, and by the observation of G. J. Martin [20] that L-tyrosine was less toxic to pyridoxine-deficient rats than to normal rats.

Mice. The association between pyridoxine and protein metabolism noted in rats was confirmed in experiments on mice. The reserves of pyridoxine in the tissues of mice fed on a vitamin B_6-deficient diet decreased much more rapidly when the diet contained 50 % of casein than when it contained only 10 %,[18] whilst the mice on the high protein diet lost more weight and had a higher mortality than those on the low protein diet. The effects were not due to variations in calorie intake, in the urinary excretion of pyridoxine or in the tryptophan content of the diet. The pyridoxine content of the tissues increased as the pyridoxine content of the diet increased. At low levels of pyridoxine intake, less pyridoxine was stored on the high protein than on the low protein diet but at high levels the high protein diet gave the higher pyridoxine storage. In young vitamin B_6-deficient mice cartilage growth and bone formation were inhibited, the effect being accentuated on a high protein diet.[21]

Hamsters. When Syrian hamsters were fed on a vitamin B_6-deficient diet, growth stopped in two or three weeks and food and water intake diminished. Muscular weakness developed, changes in the fur occurred and increased amounts of xanthurenic acid were excreted in the urine. Deficient animals died after twelve or thirteen weeks, and autopsy revealed a loss of fat tissue and atrophy of lymphoid tissues, notably the thymus. Animals recovered after about nine weeks when given daily injections of 50 μg. of pyridoxine.[21a]

Dogs. In addition to anaemia, deficient dogs also developed cardiac embarrassment, dyspepsia, tachycardia, dilation and hypertrophy of the right ventricle and right auricle, accumulation of serous fluid in the thorax and chronic passive congestion of the liver ; degenerative changes were also found in the myelin sheaths of the peripheral nerves and spinal cord.[5]

Dogs exhibited an increased urinary output of urea, ammonia, uric acid and creatinine when maintained on a vitamin B_6-deficient diet.[19]

Pigs. The omission of pyridoxine and pantothenic acid from the diet of pigs led to the development of an abnormal gait and degenerative changes in the peripheral nerves, posterior root ganglia and the posterior roots and posterior funiculi of the spinal cord.[22] The omission of pyridoxine alone caused epileptiform convulsions of both grand mal and petit mal type, together with a severe microcytic anaemia. The administration of pyridoxine resulted in a sharp reticulocyte response and rapid regeneration of the blood, iron being mobilised from the tissues.[23] The anaemia was due to failure to synthesise protoporphyrin.[24]

The gait of vitamin B_6-deficient pigs differed from that of pantothenic acid-deficient pigs, the former exhibiting swaying and twisting of the legs and the latter a " goose-step " type of gait.[25] Degeneration of the peripheral process of the sensory neurone was the initial and most prominent feature in vitamin B_6 deficiency, whereas chromatolysis was the first evidence of damage in the afferent neurone in pantothenic acid deficiency. The rate of haemolysis in phenylhydrazine anaemia in pigs was not increased in vitamin B_6 deficiency.[26]

Monkeys. Symptoms of pyridoxine deficiency in young monkeys included lack of growth, ataxia, hypochromic microcytic anaemia, mild leucopenia, polychromatophilia and the appearance of nucleated red blood cells.[27]

Birds and Fish. The symptoms of vitamin B_6 deficiency in chicks included decreased clotting time, hyperthrombinaemia, small spleens and anaemia,[28] in addition to convulsive symptoms,[6, 7] already referred to (page 318). Turkeys exhibited convulsions, but not anaemia,[9] and young ducklings severe anaemia, but not convulsions.[10] Older ducklings, on the other hand, developed a chronic deficiency characterised by failure to grow, paralysis, convulsions, severe macrocytic anaemia and poor feather development.[10]

The anaemia of chicks was cured by a combination of α- or β-pyracin (page 344) and folic acid. When only folic acid was added, the anaemia became normocytic and hypochromic, whilst with β-pyracin only, it became macrocytic and normochromic.[29]

In the absence of vitamin B_6, young rainbow trout suffered from nervous disorders, and developed pale spots on the liver.[30] The symptoms were prevented by the addition to the diet of 0·1 to 1·0 mg. of pyridoxine per 100 g.

Vitamin B₆ and Immunity

Axelrod *et al.*[31] reported severe impairment of antibody response in pyridoxine-deficient rats, and this was confirmed by L. R. C. Agnew and R. Cook,[31a] whilst H. C. Stoerk and H. N. Eisen [32] observed that pyridoxine-deficients rats, immunised against sheep red cells, had much lower agglutinin and haemolysin titres than normal controls and controls of equal bodyweight caused by underfeeding. Pyridoxine had no effect, however, on the susceptibility of Swiss mice to experimental poliomyelitis.[33]

Pyridoxine and Cancer

The implantation of Flexner-Jobling carcinoma in rats partially depleted of vitamin B_6 resulted in fewer " takes " than in normal rats, the number of regressions were higher and the tumours were smaller.[34] Similar results were obtained with Yale carcinoma and fibrosarcoma, whilst the production of tumours by painting with methylcholanthrene was retarded in animals fed a vitamin B_6-deficient diet. Vitamin B_6 deficiency had less effect, however, on the production of sarcomas by subcutaneous injection of methylcholanthrene.

References to Section 9

1. W. Antopol and K. Unna, *Proc. Soc. Exp. Biol. Med.*, 1939, **42,** 126 ; *Arch. Path.*, 1942, **33**, 241.
2. P. J. Fouts, O. M. Helmer and S. Lepkovsky, *Proc. Soc. Exp. Biol. Med.*, 1939, **40,** 4.
3. H. J. Borson and R. S. Mettier, *ibid.*, 1940, **43,** 429.
4. H. R. Street, G. R. Cowgill and H. M. Zimmerman, *J. Nutrition*, 1941, **21,** 275.
5. J. M. McKibbin, A. E. Schaefer, D. V. Frost and C. A. Elvehjem, *J. Biol. Chem.*, 1942, **142,** 77.
6. T. H. Jukes, *Proc. Soc. Exp. Biol. Med.*, 1939, **42,** 180.
7. S. Lepkovsky and F. H. Kratzer, *J. Nutrition*, 1942, **24,** 515.
8. H. Chick, T. F. Macrae and A. N. Worden, *Biochem. J.*, 1940, **34,** 580 ; H. Chick, M. M. El Sadr and A. N. Worden, *ibid.*, 1940, **34,** 595 ; S. Lepkovsky, M. E. Krause and M. K. Dimick, *Science*, 1942, **95,** 331.
9. F. H. Bird, F. H. Kratzer, V. S. Asmundson and S. Lepkovsky, *Proc. Soc. Exp. Biol. Med.*, 1943, **52,** 44.
10. D. M. Hegsted and M. N. Rao, *J. Nutrition*, 1945, **30,** 367.
11. A. Kornberg, H. Tabor and W. H. Sebrell, *Amer. J. Physiol.*, 1945, **143,** 434.
11a. C. J. Gubler, G. E. Cartwright and M. M. Wintrobe, *J. Biol. Chem.*, 1949, **178,** 989.
12. R. A. Patton, H. W. Karn and H. E. Longenecker, *J. Biol. Chem.*, 1944, **152,** 181.
13. D. Orsini, H. A. Waisman and C. A. Elvehjem, *Proc. Soc. Exp. Biol. Med.*, 1942, **51,** 99.
14. L. R. Cerecedo and J. R. Foy, *J. Nutrition*, 1942, **24,** 93.
15. Le R. Voris and H. P. Moore, *ibid.*, 1943, **25,** 7.

16. L. R. Cerecedo and J. R. Foy, *Arch. Biochem.*, 1944, **5**, 207.

17. E. C. Sheppard and E. W. McHenry, *J. Biol. Chem.*, 1946, **165**, 649.

18. B. S. Schweigert, H. E. Sauberlich, C. A. Elvehjem and C. A. Baumann, *ibid.*, 187.

19. W. W. Hawkins, M. L. MacFarland and E. W. McHenry, *ibid.*, 1946, **166**, 223.

20. G. J. Martin, *ibid.*, 389.

21. R. Silberberg and B. M. Levy, *Proc. Soc. Exp. Biol. Med.*, 1948, **67**, 259.

21a. G. Schwartzman and L. Strauss, *J. Nutrition*, 1949, **38**, 131.

22. M. M. Wintrobe, M. H. Miller, R. H. Follis, H. J. Stein, C. Mushatt and S. Humphreys, *J. Nutrition*, 1942, **24**, 345.

23. M. M. Wintrobe, R. H. Follis, M. H. Miller, H. J. Stein, R. Alcayaga, S. Humphreys and G. E. Cartwright, *Johns Hopkins Hosp. Bull.*, 1943, **72**, 1.

24. G. E. Cartwright and M. M. Wintrobe, *J. Biol. Chem.*, 1948, **172**, 557.

25. R. H. Follis and M. M. Wintrobe, *J. Exp. Med.*, 1945, **81**, 539.

26. G. E. Cartwright, M. M. Wintrobe and S. Humphreys, *J. Biol. Chem.*, 1944, **153**, 171.

27. K. B. McCall, H. A. Waisman, C. A. Elvehjem and E. S. Jones, *J. Nutrition*, 1946, **31**, 685.

28. T. D. Luckey, G. M. Briggs, C. A. Elvehjem and E. B. Hart, *Proc. Soc. Exp. Biol. Med.*, 1945, **58**, 340.

29. M. L. Scott, L. C. Norris, G. F. Heuser and W. F. Bruce, *J. Biol. Chem.*, 1945, **158**, 291.

30. B. A. McLaren, E. Keller, D. J. O'Donnell and C. A. Elvehjem, *Arch. Biochem.*, 1947, **15**, 169.

31. A. E. Axelrod, B. B. Carter, R. H. McCoy and R. Geisinger, *Proc. Soc. Exp. Biol. Med.*, 1947, **66**, 137.

31a. L. R. C. Agnew and R. Cook, *Brit. J. Nutrition*, 1949, **2**, 321.

32. H. C. Stoerk and H. N. Eisen, *Proc. Soc. Exp. Biol. Med.*, 1946, **62**, 88.

33. H. C. Lichstein, H. A. Waisman, K. B. McCall, C. A. Elvehjem and P. F. Clark, *ibid.*, 1945, **60**, 279.

34. B. E. Kline, R. R. Rusch, C. A. Baumann and P. S. Lavik, *Cancer Res.*, 1943, **3**, 825.

10. EFFECT OF VITAMIN B₆ DEFICIENCY IN MAN

There is no clear-cut deficiency disease, analogous to beriberi or pellagra, attributable to the absence of vitamin B_6 from the diet, and an uncomplicated vitamin B_6 deficiency has probably not been observed in humans except when deliberately induced. Even then, human volunteers maintained for a period of two months on a vitamin B_6-deficient diet failed to show symptoms that could be attributed specifically to lack of this factor, although mental symptoms and white blood-cell changes were observed.[1] Not unnaturally, therefore, attention has mainly been directed to the effect of pyridoxine on different forms of anaemia and nervous symptoms, that is, on conditions associated with vitamin B_6 deficiency in animals.

Anaemia

Spies *et al.*[1a] claimed that the administration of 50 mg. of pyridoxine relieved within four hours certain symptoms remaining after treatment of undernourished patients with nicotinic acid, aneurine and riboflavine. These symptoms included extreme nervousness, insomnia, irritability, abdominal pain, weakness and difficulty in walking. Subsequently, Vilter *et al.*[2] reported that pellagrins with macrocytic anaemia, and patients with pernicious anaemia, experienced a sense of well-being following the daily injection for ten days of 50 to 100 mg. of pyridoxine. Only a slight reticulocytosis occurred, however, though the white cell count increased in a striking manner (see page 324). Pyridoxine was shown to be different from the antipernicious anaemia factor, and, since it failed to give an increased reticulocyte response after incubation with human gastric juice, from Castle's extrinsic factor (page 498).

Kark *et al.*[3] showed that pyridoxine was without effect in idiopathic hypochromic anaemia and in nutritional macrocytic anaemia ; it failed to improve cases of alcoholic pellagra and endemic pellagra. There is no evidence, therefore, that pyridoxine will cure the more usual types of human anaemia.

Nervous Disorders

Nor is there convincing evidence of its value in the treatment of nervous disorders, although numerous workers have claimed that it has a beneficial effect in muscular dystrophy and related conditions, especially in association with tocopherol. Thus, W. Antopol and C. E. Schotland [4] reported considerable improvement in six cases of pseudo-hypertrophic muscular dystrophy, whereas H. M. Keith [5] reported no increase in muscle strength after the intramuscular injection of 100 to 200 mg. weekly for two to eight months. Rosenbaum *et al.*,[6] however, claimed to have obtained an increase in muscle strength by the intravenous injection of pyridoxine in neurasthenic hyperthyroidism and ulcerative colitis, but not in myasthenia gravis, whilst A. B. Baker [7] obtained some slight improvement in a small proportion of cases of idiopathic and arteriosclerotic parkinsonism, and Vilter *et al.*[8] an increase in strength in cases of peripheral neuritis due to arsenic ; the simultaneous administration of pyridoxine and tocopherol was said to give the best results. Some improvement was also reported by C. L. Miller [9] in cases of postencephalitic and idiopathic paralysis agitans after treatment with pyridoxine, but in neither condition was there a return to normal. It had no beneficial effect in epilepsy.[10]

Miscellaneous

One of the few conditions in which pyridoxine has been successfully employed is in the treatment of nausea. Complete or considerable relief was obtained in nausea and vomiting of pregnancy,[11] using a dose of 10 to 20 mg. three or four times daily, and in radiation sickness or nausea following exposure to X-rays ; [12] this was checked by single or repeated intravenous injection of 25 mg. of pyridoxine at twenty-four to seventy-two-hourly intervals.

Pyridoxine has been claimed to be of value in certain forms of dermatitis, for example, in cheilosis [13] and in post-adolescent acne vulgaris.[14]

Pyridoxine was claimed to be effective in agranulocytic angina,[15] and was said to increase the white cell count and granulocytes in patients with toxic granulocytopenia. It was suggested that pyridoxine might be the factor involved in the maturation of the polymorphonuclear leucocytes and the stimulation of granulocytopoiesis. Intravenous injections of pyridoxine (200 mg. per day) caused a rapid increase in the leucocytes of patients who developed granulocytopenia as the result of treatment with thiouracil.[16]

References to Section 10

1. W. W. Hawkins and J. Barsky, *Science*, 1948, **108**, 284.
1a. T. D. Spies, W. B. Bean and W. F. Ashe, *J. Amer. Med. Assoc.*, 1939, **112**, 2414.
2. R. W. Vilter, H. S. Schiro and T. D. Spies, *Nature*, 1940, **145**, 388.
3. R. Kark, E. L. Lozner and A. P. Meiklejohn, *Proc. Soc. Exp. Biol. Med.*, 1940, **43**, 97.
4. W. Antopol and C. E. Schotland, *J. Amer. Med. Assoc.*, 1940, **114**, 1058.
5. H. M. Keith, *J. Pediat.*, 1942, **20**, 200.
6. E. E. Rosenbaum, S. Portis and S. Soskin, *J. Lab. Clin. Med.*, 1942, **27**, 763.
7. A. B. Baker, *J. Amer. Med. Assoc.*, 1941, **116**, 2484.
8. R. W. Vilter, C. D. Aring and T. D. Spies, *ibid.*, 1940, **115**, 209.
9. C. L. Miller, *Minnesota Med.*, 1942, **25**, 22.
10. J. T. Fox and G. M. Tullidge, *Lancet*, 1946, **2**, 343.
11. H. B. Weinstein, Z. Wohl, G. J. Mitchell and G. F. Sustendal, *Amer. J. Obstet. Gynec.*, 1944, **47**, 389.

12. J. R. Maxfield, A. J. McIlwain and J. E. Robertson, *Radiology*, 1943, **41**, 383.
13. S. G. Smith and D. W. Martin, *Proc. Soc. Exp. Biol. Med.*, 1940, **43**, 660.
14. N. Jolliffe, L. A. Rosenbaum and J. Sawhill, *J. Invest. Derm.*, 1942, **5**, 143.
15. M. M. Cantor and J. W. Scott, *Canad. Med. Assoc. J.*, 1945, **52**, 368 ; *Fed. Proc.*, 1945, **4**, 85.
16. E. H. Fishberg and J. Forzimer, *Proc. Soc. Exp. Biol. Med.*, 1945, **60**, 181.

11. METABOLISM OF PYRIDOXINE

The metabolism of pyridoxine was first studied by Scudi and his co-workers. Using the reaction with 2 : 6-dichloroquinone chloroimide, they showed [1] that at levels of 10 mg. per kg. or over, normal or vitamin B_6-deficient rats excreted 50 to 70 % of a test dose but, at lower levels, normal rats excreted a higher proportion of the test dose than did vitamin B_6-deficient animals. Dogs excreted only 20 % of a 25- to 500-mg. dose of pyridoxine within one to six hours of oral administration, and humans only 8·7 % of a 50-mg. test dose given intravenously one hour previously, or 7·6 % of a 100-mg. dose given orally four hours previously.[2]

In humans, the excretion of pyridoxine apparently varied with the age of the subject,[3] most patients under fifty years of age excreting 8·4 % of a 50-mg. test dose and most patients over fifty excreting 7·2 % and a few as little as 2·3 % ; these were mostly chronic renal cases. Patients from five to fifteen years of age excreted an average of 21·3 %. The excretion of 8·0 % and 8·4 % of a test dose by adults was regarded by Spies et al.[4] and by J. Flexner and M. R. Chassin [3] respectively as indicating a normal level of nutrition.

M. Swaminathan [5] stated that the daily excretion of pyridoxine in man was 400 to 560 μg. and that about 5 % of a 50-mg. test dose was excreted by normal (Indian) adults. He also reported that [6] rats receiving 0·9 μg. of pyridoxine per day excreted 1·0 μg. per day in excess of the intake, whereas rats receiving 10 μg. per day excreted 3·7 μg. The vitamin B_6 content of the liver and muscle was lower on the unsupplemented than on the supplemented diet and the excess vitamin may have been derived from these tissues.

Unfortunately, the inferences drawn from these early results on the excretion of pyridoxine by animals and humans were vitiated by the subsequent discovery that pyridoxine was converted *in vivo* into other substances, which were excreted in the urine along with unchanged pyridoxine. These metabolites represented a large proportion of the ingested pyridoxine and must therefore be taken into account in studies on the metabolism of pyridoxine.

Scudi *et al.*,[7] for example, found that man and the dog excreted a conjugated form of pyridoxine, possibly a glycuronate or ethereal sulphate formed by attachment of the conjugating group to the 3-hydroxyl group ; this substance was not present in the urine of the rat. A second conjugated compound, apparently derived from 4-pyridoxic acid was isolated from the urine of humans and dogs. 4-Pyridoxic acid (2-methyl-3-hydroxy-5-hydroxymethylpyridine-4-carboxylic acid, page 344) was identified as a constituent of human urine by J. W. Huff and W. A. Perlzweig.[8]

These new facts were taken into consideration by Johnson *et al.*[9] in studying the effect of tropical conditions on the excretion of pyridoxine. Young men were maintained for eight hours a day at a temperature of $37.8°$ C. and a relative humidity of 70 %. Of the vitamin B_6 excreted, 85 % was in the form of 4-pyridoxic acid, 4.0 to 4.5 % was pyridoxine and 7 to 8 % was " pseudo-pyridoxine ". The amount excreted in the sweat was one-fifth of that in the urine, and the proportion of the different forms was approximately the same. When the diet was supplemented by 8 mg. of pyridoxine per day, 50 % of the supplement was recovered unchanged and 50 % as the metabolite. The amount excreted in the urine was eight times that excreted in the sweat.

The metabolism of the three forms of vitamin B_6 in humans was studied by J. C. Rabinowitz and E. E. Snell.[9a] Pyridoxal, pyridoxamine and pyridoxine were estimated in the urine microbiologically (page 313), and pyridoxic acid fluorimetrically.[8] The predominant metabolite when any of the three substances was fed was pyridoxic acid. Next in amount were the unchanged substances when either pyridoxine or pyridoxal were fed, but pyridoxamine yielded pyridoxal and pyridoxamine in approximately equal amounts. The highest recovery with a 70 to 80 mg. test-dose was 70 % with pyridoxal ; pyridoxine gave a 45 % and pyridoxamine a 31 % recovery. Normal urine contains no pyridoxine and variable amounts of the other compounds, at least 90 % being pyridoxic acid.

Vitamin B_6-deficient rats excreted a substance that gave a green pigment with iron ; and the excretion of this substance ceased within a few hours after administering pyridoxine.[10] Vitamin B_6-deficient dogs excreted a similar chromogen.[11] The nature of these excretion products is discussed further on pages 330, 336.

No attempt appears to have been made to estimate vitamin B_6 levels in human blood, but assays with *S. carlsbergensis* have been carried out on the blood of monkeys.[12] After two weeks on a vitamin B_6-deficient diet, the blood level fell to 2 to 3 μg. per 100 ml. Controls that received 1 mg. of pyridoxine hydrochloride per day gave values of 5 to 20·8 (average 11·2) μg. per 100 ml.

References to Section 11

1. J. V. Scudi, H. F. Koones and J. C. Keresztesy, *Proc. Soc. Exp. Biol. Med.*, 1940, **43**, 118.
2. J. V. Scudi, K. Unna and W. Antopol, *J. Biol. Chem.*, 1940, **135**, 371.
3. J. Flexner and M. R. Chassin, *J. Clin. Invest.*, 1941, **20**, 313.
4. T. D. Spies, R. K. Ladisch and W. B. Bean, *J. Amer. Med. Assoc.*, 1940, **115**, 839.
5. M. Swaminathan, *Indian J. Med. Res.*, 1941, **29**, 561.
6. M. Swaminathan, *ibid.*, 557.
7. J. V. Scudi, R. P. Buhs and D. B. Herd, *J. Biol. Chem.*, 1942, **142**, 323.
8. J. W. Huff and W. A. Perlzweig, *ibid.*, 1944, **155**, 345.
9. B. C. Johnson, T. S. Hamilton and H. H. Mitchell, *ibid.*, 1945, **158**, 619.
9a. J. C. Rabinowitz and E. E. Snell, *Proc. Soc. Exp. Biol. Med.*, 1949, **70**, 235.
10. S. Lepkovsky and E. Nielsen, *J. Biol. Chem.*, 1942, **144**, 135.
11. P. J. Fouts and S. Lepkovsky, *Proc. Soc. Exp. Biol. Med.*, 1942, **50**, 221.
12. L. D. Greenberg and J. F. Rinehart, *ibid.*, 1949, **70**, 20.

12. INTESTINAL SYNTHESIS OF VITAMIN B_6

The first hint that pyridoxine might be synthesised in animals by intestinal bacteria was given by Chick *et al.*,[1] who found that the addition of cereal starches to the diet reduced the incidence of dermatitis and epileptiform fits in rats maintained on a vitamin B_6 deficient diet ; they suggested that the starch favoured the growth of bacteria capable of synthesising pyridoxine or other substances with vitamin B_6 activity.

Further evidence in support of this view was obtained by Sarma *et al.*,[2] who found that rats, when maintained on a sucrose-blood fibrin diet, failed to grow, but that when dextrin was substituted for sucrose, growth was resumed and the excretion of 4-pyridoxic acid (page 326) increased. Sulphathalidine prevented growth, whilst pyridoxine increased it, whence it was concluded that dextrin favoured the intestinal synthesis of pyridoxine, which was then utilised by the rat. Rats on a vitamin B_6-deficient diet grew slowly and, if given sulphasuxidine, died.[2a] The deficiency was cured by pyridoxine.

The existence of intestinal synthesis in man was demonstrated by

Denko *et al.*,[3] who reported that the faecal excretion was as high on a restricted intake of pyridoxine as on a normal diet. Furthermore, the faecal excretion was unaffected when the diet was supplemented by additional pyridoxine. The urinary excretion, on the other hand, fell moderately on the restricted diet, and returned to normal on supplementation. On all diets, the amount of pyridoxine excreted in the urine was greater than the amount excreted in the faeces, and the total excretion was less than the dietary intake. Thus, there is clear evidence that pyridoxine is synthesised in the intestine, but not that it is utilised in man. In this respect, pyridoxine falls into the group of B vitamins that includes aneurine, riboflavine and nicotinic acid, rather than into the group that includes biotin and folic acid, where there is a strong presumption that both synthesis and utilisation occur.

Pyridoxine is undoubtedly synthesised by ruminants, and L. W. McElroy and H. Goss [4] found that dried sheep rumen and reticulum contained 10 μg. of pyridoxine per g. and the rumen contents of a fistulated cow 8 μg. per g. In each instance, the ration contained only 1 to 1·5 μg. of pyridoxine per g. The cow supplied milk with the normal pyridoxine content in spite of the fistula.

References to Section 12

1. H. Chick, T. F. Macrae and A. N. Worden, *Biochem. J.*, 1940, **34**, 580.
2. P. S. Sarma, E. E. Snell and C. A. Elvehjem, *J. Biol. Chem.*, 1946, **165**, 55.
2a. K. J. Carpenter, L. J. Harris and E. Kodicek, *Brit. J. Nutrition*, 1948, **2**, vii.
3. C. W. Denko, W. A. Grundy, J. W. Porter, G. H. Berryman, T. E. Friedemann and J. B. Youmans, *Arch. Biochem.*, 1946, **10**, 33 ; C. W. Denko, W. E. Grundy, N. C. Wheeler, C. R. Henderson, G. H. Berryman, T. E. Friedemann and J. B. Youmans, *ibid.* 1946, **11**, 109.
4. L. W. McElroy and H. Goss, *J. Nutrition*, 1940, **20**, 527.

13. ANIMAL AND HUMAN REQUIREMENTS OF PYRIDOXINE

Considerable uncertainty exists concerning the requirements of animals and man for pyridoxine, not so much because of the possibility that pyridoxine may be synthesised by intestinal bacteria, but rather because vitamin B_6 has a three-fold function (page 330), one of which may conceivably be more readily put out of action than the others by a sub-optimal intake of pyridoxine. In that event the level of pyridoxine necessary to enable one type of function to be carried on would be higher than the level necessary for another function to be maintained. Then, too, in attempting to assess human requirements there is the added difficulty that pyridoxine deficiency does not result in the development of characteristic symptoms that can be used as a criterion of response.

The quantity of pyridoxine required to produce normal growth in the rat was found to be 10 μg. per day ; up to 100 μg. were required to cure symptoms of vitamin B_6 deficiency.[1] When maintained at a temperature of 91° F., rats required twice the amount of pyridoxine found to be necessary at 68° F., whilst chicks maintained at 91° F. required four times the amount necessary at 70° F.[2] Lactating rats required at least 50 μg. of pyridoxine per day to ensure that their offspring did not suffer from spontaneous seizures and at least 150 μg. per day to afford protection against artificially induced seizures.

Symptoms of vitamin B_6 deficiency in young turkeys[3] and ducklings[4] were prevented by 3·0 and 2·5 mg. of pyridoxine per kg. of diet respectively.

References to Section 13

1. E. J. Reedman, W. L. Sampson and K. Unna, *Proc. Soc. Exp. Biol. Med.*, 1940, **43,** 112.
2. C. A. Mills, *Arch. Biochem.*, 1942, **1,** 73.
3. F. H. Bird, F. H. Kratzer, V. S. Asmundson and S. Lepkovsky, *Proc. Soc. Exp. Biol. Med.*, 1943, **52,** 44.
4. D. M. Hegsted and M. N. Rao, *J. Nutrition*, 1945, **30,** 367.

14. PHARMACOLOGY OF PYRIDOXINE

According to K. Unna and W. Antopol,[1] the toxicities (LD50) of pyridoxine and its hydrochloride are 3·1 and 3·7 g. per kg. of body-weight respectively when given subcutaneously to rats, and 4 and 6 g. per kg. when given orally. According to Weigand *et al.*,[2] the LD50 of pyridoxine by the intravenous route was 18·3 mg. per kg. for rats and 42·9 mg. per kg. for mice ; 200 mg. were non-toxic in man.

Dogs given 20 mg. per kg. orally for seventy-five days, and monkeys given 10 mg. per kg. orally for thirty-nine days and subcutaneously for 101 days, suffered no ill-effects.[1]

A solution containing one part of pyridoxine hydrochloride in 8000 caused only a brief inhibition of the movements of the isolated rabbit's gut, but caused a lasting contraction of the guinea-pig uterus.[2] In a concentration of 0·0005 millimoles per litre, pyridoxine hydrochloride significantly increased the work output of perfused frog's muscle,[3] and the improvement was maintained when the concentration was increased ten-fold. Above this level, however, no further improvement occurred.

References to Section 14

1. K. Unna and W. Antopol, *Proc. Soc. Exp. Biol. Med.*, 1940, **43**, 116.
2. C. G. Weigand, C. R. Echler and K. K. Chen, *ibid.*, 147.
3. N. W. Shock and W. H. Sebrell, *Amer. J. Physiol.*, 1946, **146**, 399.

15. FUNCTION OF PYRIDOXINE AND RELATED COMPOUNDS

Pyridoxine, pyridoxal and pyridoxamine are now known to be concerned with the decarboxylation of amino acids, and with the transamination mechanism. All three compounds are apparently equally effective for both systems in rats, moulds and some yeasts, and are probably inter-convertible in these organisms. For many lactic acid bacteria, on the other hand, pyridoxal and pyridoxamine ("pseudo-pyridoxine") are up to 1000 times as effective as pyridoxine ;[1] such organisms presumably are very inefficient in converting pyridoxine into the biologically active derivative. A third system for which a compound related to pyridoxine is essential is one that controls red blood cell formation. Each of these three functions will be considered in turn.

Protein Metabolism

Reference has already been made (page 318) to the fact that vitamin B_6 deficiency results in an increase in the body protein, that the protein content of the diet affects the severity of the symptoms of pyridoxine deficiency and that nitrogen metabolism is upset in pyridoxine-deficient rats, mice and dogs. Subsequently, a connection was established between vitamin B_6 and tryptophan. Lepkovsky *et al.*[2] noted that tryptophan metabolism differed in the dog and the rat and that the difference was paralleled by a difference in the symptoms of vitamin B_6 deficiency in the two species ; the dog developed a severe anaemia and excreted little xanthurenic acid, whereas the rat developed only a mild anaemia and excreted large amounts of xanthurenic acid.

Vitamin B_6-deficient mice also excreted xanthurenic acid, and the amount varied with the quantity of casein or tryptophan in the diet.[3] Moreover, the more casein was added to the diet, the sooner did the animals die. The amount of chromogen excreted was reduced by administration of pyridoxine, but the amount needed to restore the level of excretion to normal was three times as much with 60 % as with 20 % of casein.

Furthermore, administration of L-tryptophan reduced the survival time of vitamin B_6-deficient mice, but to a smaller extent than did casein containing the same amount of tryptophan, suggesting that other amino acids contributed to the phenomenon. Tyrosine and histidine, however, were without effect ; so was phenylalanine, although it gave rise to a urinary chromogen the excretion of which was unaffected by pyridoxine. Cystine and methionine reduced the survival time of vitamin B_6-deficient rats.[3a]

The amount of xanthurenic acid excreted by pigs was also increased when the animals were fed on a vitamin B_6-deficient diet,[4] and high xanthurenic acid excretion was generally associated with faulty tryptophan metabolism. Again, pigs maintained on a diet in which nitrogen was supplied in the form of an acid hydrolysate of casein or as zein, neither of which contains tryptophan, failed to grow and developed a normocytic or microcytic normochromic anaemia, similar to that observed in vitamin B_6-deficient pigs.[5]

Decarboxylation of Amino Acids

A further advance was made when I. C. Gunsalus and W. D. Bellamy [6] observed that tyrosine decarboxylase (prepared from *Streptococcus faecalis* R) was stimulated by yeast extract, by pyridoxal (but not pyridoxamine) and by solutions of pyridoxine treated with cystine or hydrogen peroxide. The activity of each preparation was proportional to its " pseudo-pyridoxine " content, as determined microbiologically.

Pyridoxal, however, only became an effective coenzyme in presence of adenosine triphosphate,[7] and the actual coenzyme was therefore presumed to be a phosphorylated pyridoxal, possibly :

$$(HO)_2OP \cdot O \underset{CH_3 \quad N}{\overset{CHO}{\bigcirc}} CH_2OH$$

A phosphate was synthesised by treating pyridoxal with thionyl chloride and reacting the product with silver dihydrogen phosphate, or by treating pyridoxal in the cold with phosphoric acid.

Cell-free tyrosine decarboxylase was prepared from *S. faecalis* R and resolved into its apoenzyme and coenzyme. The latter was identified as a derivative of pyridoxal.[8] W. W. Umbreit and I. C. Gunsalus [9] then showed that arginine and glutamic acid decarboxylases, prepared from *Escherichia coli*, could be activated by the same coenzyme that activated lysine and tyrosine decarboxylases, and that the "synthetic" codecarboxylase prepared from pyridoxal functioned as a coenzyme for all four amino acid decarboxylases.

Pyridoxine, pyridoxal and pyridoxamine were all converted into codecarboxylase by micro-organisms that utilised them as a source of vitamin B_6; it was shown that with *S. faecalis* R the conversion of pyridoxamine into codecarboxylase required the presence of a keto-acid (see page 300). Organisms that grew in the absence of vitamin B_6 were able to synthesise codecarboxylase, whilst the codecarboxylase content of rat tissue was dependent on the pyridoxine intake.[10]

The properties of synthetic codecarboxylase were described by Gunsalus *et al.*[11]

J. Baddiley and E. F. Gale[12] prepared several cell-free amino acid decarboxylases and resolved those responsible for the decarboxylation of L-lysine, L-tyrosine, L-arginine and L-ornithine into specific apoenzymes and a common coenzyme, a concentrate of which was also prepared from yeast. The decarboxylases for L-histidine and L-glut-amic acid did not appear to contain the coenzyme. Pyridoxal phos-phate was found to act as a coenzyme for the decarboxylases of L-lysine, L-tyrosine, L-arginine and L-ornithine. Lichstein *et al.*[13] confirmed the observation that pyridoxal phosphate functioned as a coenzyme for L-ornithine decarboxylase and showed that it was also the coenzyme of L-dihydroxyphenylalanine decarboxylase.

P. Karrer and M. Viscontini[14] suggested that the preparations of pyridoxal phosphate used by other workers were impure and that their biological activity was due to some other constituent. They therefore synthesised pyridoxal-3-phosphate acetal :

$$CH(OC_2H_5)_2$$
$$(HO)_2OP \cdot O \diagdown \diagup CH_2OH$$
$$CH_3 \diagdown N \diagup$$

and pyridoxal-3-phosphate and claimed that both served as coenzymes for L-tyrosine decarboxylase prepared from *S. faecalis*, and for L-lysine, L-arginine and D-glutamic acid decarboxylases prepared from three strains of *Escherichia coli*. According to I. C. Gunsalus and W. W. Umbreit,[15] however, synthetic pyridoxal-3-phosphate acetal does not catalyse the decarboxylation of tyrosine, and pyridoxal-3-phosphate has only $1/2000$th to $1/3000$th of the activity of the natural coenzyme, the apparent codecarboxylase activity of Karrer and Viscontini's compounds being due to faulty testing technique. Synthetic pyri-doxal-5-phosphate, on the other hand, catalysed both the decarboxyla-tion of tyrosine and, at a higher concentration, the glutamic-aspartic transamination (page 333). Using acetone-dried vitamin B_6-free cells of *S. faecalis* R as a source of tyrosine apodecarboxylase, G. H. Sloane-Stanley [15a] confirmed that pyridoxal acetal-3-phosphate had no codecarboxylase activity, whereas pyridoxal-5-phosphate in the form of its calcium salt was as active as the natural coenzyme, and could be used as a standard in assays of codecarboxylase in animal tissues.

Pyridoxine may also function as a catalyst for the synthesis of amino acids by a reaction which is the reverse of that just discussed. For, when pyridoxine was added to a culture of *L. arabinosus* or *S. faecalis* R deficient in phenylalanine, tyrosine, arginine or aspartic acid, the growth of the organisms was impaired in the absence of carbon dioxide ; growth was restored when this was passed into the culture.[16] It appears, therefore, that carbon dioxide is necessary for specific amino acid synthesis and that pyridoxine is involved in the enzyme system that carries out the synthesis.

Transamination

The second biological reaction for which pyridoxine and its derivatives appear to be essential is the transfer of an amino group from an amino acid to a keto acid, forming a different amino acid, a reaction which is reversible, for example :

$$HOOC.CH_2.CH_2.CH.COOH + HOOC.CH_2.CO.COOH \rightleftharpoons$$
$$\overset{|}{NH_2}$$

glutamic acid   oxaloacetic acid

$$HOOC.CH_2.CH_2.CO.COOH + HOOC.CH_2.CH.COOH$$
$$\overset{|}{NH_2}$$

α-ketoglutaric acid   aspartic acid

F. Schlenk and E. E. Snell [17] observed that muscle extract prepared from normal rats had a greater transaminase activity than a similar muscle preparation from vitamin B_6-deficient animals and they therefore suggested that a derivative of pyridoxine was an essential component of the transaminase system. This seemed a particularly attractive hypothesis in view of the transformation of pyridoxal to pyridoxamine by heating with an amino acid (see page 300).

P. P. Cohen and H. C. Lichstein,[18] however, found that suspensions of *Streptococcus faecalis* R were able to catalyse the transamination reaction, whether the organism was grown on a medium with a high or a low pyridoxine content, whereas the ability of the cells to catalyse the decarboxylation of tyrosine was markedly greater when the medium contained pyridoxine than when pyridoxine was absent.

On the other hand, evidence was obtained that a phosphate of pyridoxal was the prosthetic group in transaminase preparations obtained from pig heart ; these effected the transfer of the amino group from glutamic acid to oxaloacetic acid, the reverse transfer from aspartic acid to α-ketoglutaric acid,[13, 19] the transfer from glutamic acid to succinic acid and from alanine to α-ketoglutaric acid.[19] The precise structure of the phosphate is not known, but pyridoxal-3-phosphate acetal had no coenzyme activity.

That a phosphate of pyridoxal is the coenzyme of at least two transaminases was also demonstrated by M. G. Kritzmann and O. Samarina,[20] who found that pyridoxal phosphate would partially re-activate glutamic acid-alanine transaminase from pig heart, and by D. E. O'Kane and I. C. Gunsalus,[21] who prepared a very pure specimen of the transaminase apoenzyme, and showed that a pyridoxal phosphate of uncertain constitution functioned as its coenzyme. According to F. Schlenk and A. Fisher,[22] some transaminase preparations contain pyridoxamine as well as pyridoxal derivatives, whilst J. C. Rabinowitz and E. E. Snell [23] isolated a substance that appeared to be pyridox-amine phosphate from yeast, liver and dried grass, and found that when pyridoxal phosphate was heated with glutamic acid, quantitative conversion to pyridoxamine phosphate occurred. The product stim-ulated the glutamic acid-aspartic acid transaminase of dried *S. faecalis* but not the corresponding (purified) apoenzyme from pig heart or tyrosine decarboxylase, both of which are activated by pyridoxal phosphate.[23a]

The transaminase activities of heart and kidney tissues from vitamin B_6-deficient rats fell to 40 % of their original value, and were restored to normal by the addition of pyridoxal phosphate or pyridoxamine phosphate. Pyridoxal and pyridoxamine, however, had no effect even in presence of adenosine triphosphate.[24]

Transaminases have been shown to be present in seeds. Wheat germ, for example, contained enzymes that catalysed both the glut-amic acid-aspartic acid and glutamic acid-alanine transformations.[25] The enzymes were present in the leaves, stems, roots, fruit and nodular tissue.

Aminopherase Activity

Closely related to the transaminases is another enzyme system, known as aspartic acid aminopherase, or aspartic acid-alanine trans-aminase. According to M. G. Kritzmann,[26] this catalyses the trans-amination reaction between L-aspartic acid and pyruvic acid, in presence of a dialysable coenzyme, to give alanine. Concentrates of the coenzyme, co-aminopherase, were prepared from pig heart and shown to be labile to acid.[27] The close relationship between this coenzyme and other co-transaminases suggested that it might contain pyridoxal and, to test this, A. E. Braunstein and M. G. Kritzmann [28] studied the effect of different factors on the reaction :

L-aspartic acid + pyruvic acid $\longrightarrow$ L-alanine + oxaloacetic acid.

They found that co-aminopherase and natural codecarboxylase (prepared by E. F. Gale) were active, but that pyridoxal phosphate, a co-aspartic acid aminopherase concentrate purified by a method used successfully for the purification of codecarboxylase,[29] and boiled glutamic acid aminopherase were inactive. Thus the coenzyme system of mammalian aspartic acid aminopherase appeared to be different from, or more complex than, pyridoxal phosphate. This was confirmed by E. F. Gale and H. M. R. Tomlinson,[30] who tested the activity of various factors as tyrosine codecarboxylases and found that, whereas pyridoxal phosphate and codecarboxylase were active, three co-aspartic acid aminopherases prepared by Braunstein and Kritzmann were inactive. On the other hand, two glutamic acid aminopherases prepared by the Russian workers were markedly active.

It was then shown by M. G. Kritzmann and O. Samarina [20] that glutamic acid aminopherase, after inactivation by acid or alkali, could be reactivated to the extent of 20 to 70 % by the addition of boiled muscle or liver extract, or of small amounts of pyridoxal phosphate, although larger amounts proved to be inhibitory. Green *et al.*[19] then suggested that aspartic acid-aminopherase activity might be due to a combination of glutamic acid-aspartic acid and glutamic acid-alanine transaminases, with glutamic acid or α-ketoglutaric acid as the links joining the two systems ; D. E. O'Kane and I. C. Gunsalus [21] actually reproduced the activity of aminopherase by means of a mixture of the two transaminases, together with pyridoxal phosphate and glutamic acid. Thus the so-called aminopherase is really a transaminase of which the prosthetic group is, once again, pyridoxal phosphate.

Tryptophan Synthesis

The third enzyme system with which pyridoxine is associated is one responsible for the synthesis of tryptophan, for pyridoxal phosphate was shown [31] to be the prosthetic group of an enzyme present in *Neurospora* that converted indole and serine into tryptophan :

$$\text{indole} \quad + \quad HOCH_2 . CH . COOH \quad \longrightarrow \quad \text{indole} - CH_2 . CH . COOH$$
$$NH_2 \qquad\qquad\qquad\qquad NH_2$$

The enzyme was resolved into its apoenzyme and coenzyme, and pyridoxal phosphate was shown to be capable of replacing the coenzyme in restoring the activity of the apoenzyme. This finding may explain the increased excretion of xanthurenic acid by rats and pigs fed a vitamin B_6-deficient diet (page 330), since any indole not utilised in the above reaction, by reason of the absence of pyridoxal phosphate, would presumably be excreted as xanthurenic acid or kynurenine. This hypothesis is supported by work with a pyridoxine antagonist, desoxypyridoxine (see page 345) ; normal rats given desoxypyridoxine together with tryptophan excreted more xanthurenic acid and kynurenine than animals receiving tryptophan alone.[32] The effect was still more noticeable with rats partially deficient in pyridoxine. The addition of pyridoxine to the diet counteracted the effect of the desoxypyridoxine.

Pyridoxine was also shown to be essential for the metabolic conversion of indole or anthranilic acid into tryptophan by *L. arabinosus*.[33] Pyridoxal and pyridoxamine were much more active, and tryptophan synthesis was increased by the addition of serine and acetate.

Pyridoxal phosphate was also shown [34] to be the prosthetic group of an enzyme, tryptophanase, present in *E. coli*. This enzyme catalyses the breakdown of tryptophan into indole, pyruvic acid and ammonia and not, as might be expected by analogy with the *Neurospora* enzyme, into indole and serine.

Pyridoxine facilitates the conversion of tryptophan into nicotinic acid. For example, when 100 mg. of DL-tryptophan were added to the diet, more nicotinic acid and N^1-methylnicotinamide were excreted by rats fed pyridoxine than by rats maintained on a vitamin B_6-deficient diet.[35] Pyridoxal and pyridoxamine were equally effective. The increase in xanthurenic acid production in vitamin B_6 deficiency was not responsible for the decreased conversion of tryptophan into nicotinic acid.[36]

Whereas the pyridine nucleotide level of the erythrocytes of vitamin B_6-deficient rats was not affected when L-tryptophan was injected intravenously, an immediate increase was observed when the injection was preceded by a subcutaneous injection of pyridoxine.[37]

Antianaemic Activity

As already mentioned, the onset of anaemia is one of the most constant results of vitamin B_6 deficiency in several species of animals, but attempts to establish a connection between pyridoxine and the anti-pernicious anaemia factor on the one hand and Castle's extrinsic factor on the other (page 323), were unsuccessful. Investigation showed, however, that pyridoxine did not itself possess antianaemic properties, but that the lactones of the corresponding acids, known as α- and β-pyracin (see page 344), were the effective agents. Either of these, together with the " *L. casei* factor ", prevented the development of a macrocytic hypochromic anaemia in chicks, β-pyracin being slightly more effective than α-pyracin.[38]   A deficiency of β-pyracin alone resulted in the appearance of a normocytic, hypochromic anaemia.

References to Section 15

1. E. E. Snell and A. N. Rannefeld, *J. Biol. Chem.*, 1945, **157**, 475.
2. S. Lepkovsky, E. Roboz and A. J. Haagen-Smit, *ibid.*, 1943, **149**, 195.
3. E. C. Miller and C. A. Baumann, *ibid.*, 1945, **157**, 551.
3a. L. R. Cerecedo, J. R. Foy and E. C. De Renzo, *Arch. Biochem.*, 1948, **17**, 397.
4. G. E. Cartwright, M. M. Wintrobe, P. Jones, M. Lauritsen and S. Humphreys, *Johns Hopkins Hosp. Bull.*, 1944, **75**, 35.
5. G. E. Cartwright, M. M. Wintrobe, W. H. Buschke, R. H. Follis, A. Suksta and S. Humphreys, *J. Clin. Invest.*, 1945, **25**, 268.
6. I. C. Gunsalus and W. D. Bellamy, *J. Biol. Chem.*, 1944, **155**, 357, 557.
7. I. C. Gunsalus, W. D. Bellamy and W. W. Umbreit, *ibid.*, 685.
8. W. W. Umbreit, W. D. Bellamy and I. G. Gunsalus, *Arch. Biochem.*, 1945, **7**, 185 ; W. D. Bellamy and I. C. Gunsalus, *J. Bact.*, 1945, **50**, 95.
9. W. W. Umbreit and I. C. Gunsalus, *J. Biol. Chem.*, 1945, **159**, 333.
10. W. D. Bellamy, W. W. Umbreit and I. C. Gunsalus, *ibid.*, 1945, **160**, 461.
11. I. C. Gunsalus, W. W. Umbreit, W. D. Bellamy and C. E. Foust, *ibid.*, 1945, **161**, 743.
12. J. Baddiley and E. F. Gale, *Nature*, 1945, **155**, 727.
13. H. C. Lichstein, I. C. Gunsalus and W. W. Umbreit, *J. Biol. Chem.*, 1945, **161**, 311.
14. P. Karrer and M. Viscontini, *Helv. Chim. Acta*, 1947, **30**, 52, 524 ; P. Karrer, M. Viscontini and O. Forster, *ibid.*, 1948, **31**, 1004.
15. I. C. Gunsalus and W. W. Umbreit, *J. Biol. Chem.*, 1947, **170**, 415 ; 1949, **179**, 279.
15a. G. H. Sloane-Stanley, *Biochem. J.*, 1949, **44**, 567.
16. C. M. Lyman, O. Moseley, S. Wood, B. Butler and F. Hale, *J. Biol. Chem.*, 1946, **162**, 173.
17. F. Schlenk and E. E. Snell, *ibid.*, 1945, **157**, 425.
18. P. P. Cohen and H. C. Lichstein, *ibid.*, 1945, **159**, 367.
19. D. E. Green, L. F. Leloir and V. Nocito, *ibid.*, 1945, **161**, 559.
20. M. G. Kritzmann and O. Samarina, *Nature*, 1946, **158**, 104.
21. D. E. O'Kane and I. C. Gunsalus, *J. Biol. Chem.*, 1947, **170**, 425.
22. F. Schlenk and A. Fisher, *Arch. Biochem.*, 1947, **12**, 69.
23. J. C. Rabinowitz and E. E. Snell. *J. Biol. Chem.*, 1947, **169**, 643.
23a. W. W. Umbreit, D. J. O'Kane and I. C. Gunsalus, *ibid.*, 1948, **176**, 629.
24. S. R. Ames, P. S. Sarma and C. A. Elvehjem, *ibid.*, 1947, **167**, 135.

25. M. J. K. Leonard and R. H. Burris, *J. Biol. Chem.*, 1947, **170**, 701.
26. M. G. Kritzmann, *Nature*, 1939, **143**, 603 ; *Biochimia*, 1939, **4**, 691.
27. A. E. Braunstein and M. G. Kritzmann, *ibid.*, 1943, **8**, 1.
28. A. E. Braunstein and M. G. Kritzmann, *Nature*, 1946, **158**, 102.
29. E. F. Gale and H. M. R. Epps, *Biochem. J.*, 1944, **38**, 235.
30. E. F. Gale and H. M. R. Tomlinson, *Nature*, 1946, **158**, 103.
31. W. W. Umbreit, W. A. Wood and I. C. Gunsalus, *J. Biol. Chem.*, 1946, **165**, 731.
32. C. C. Porter, I. Clark and R. H. Silber, *ibid.*, 1947, **167**, 573.
33. B. S. Schweigert, *ibid.*, 1947, **168**, 283.
34. W. A. Wood, I. C. Gunsalus and W. W. Umbreit, *ibid.*, 1947, **170**, 313.
35. B. S. Schweigert and P. B. Pearson, *ibid.*, 1947, **168**, 555 ; P. B. Junqueira and B. S. Schweigert, *ibid.*, 1948, **174**, 605.
36. F. Rosen, J. W. Huff and W. A. Perlzweig, *J. Nutrition*, 1947, **33**, 561.
37. C.-T. Ling, D. M. Hegsted and F. J. Stare, *J. Biol. Chem.*, 1948, **174**, 803.
38. M. L. Scott, L. C. Norris, G. F. Heuser and W. F. Bruce, *J. Biol. Chem.*, 1945, **158**, 291.

16. PYRIDOXINE IN THE NUTRITION OF MICRO-ORGANISMS

The requirements of micro-organisms for pyridoxine are as varied as are their requirements for other members of the vitamin B complex. Pyridoxine has been identified as " Bios VII ", one of the constituents of " bios ", the hypothetical substance alleged to be necessary for the growth of certain yeasts (page 404).

Yeasts

Pyridoxine was shown to stimulate the growth of the yeast,[1, 2] *Saccharomyces cerevisiae* and, according to P. R. Burkholder,[3] of the following additional species : *Mycoderma valida*, *Saccharomyces carlsbergensis* var. *mandshuricus*, *S. chodati*, *S. oviformis*, *Saccharomycodes ludwigii*, *Torulopsis dattila*, *T. uvae*, *Brettanomyces bruxellensis* and *Pichia kluyveri*. It is also necessary for the growth of *Saccharomyces hanseniaspora valbyensis*[4] and *Kloeckera brevis*.[1]

Moulds

Pyridoxine also stimulated the growth of several different kinds of moulds. One of these was *Ceratostomella (Ophiostoma) ulmi*, which is responsible for Dutch elm disease.[5-8] This fungus required both aneurine and pyridoxine, but, whereas the latter was essential for growth, aneurine appeared to be only a supplementary growth factor.[7]

Attempts to use *C. ulmi* for assaying pyridoxine were unsuccessful, however, the growth-response curves being too irregular.[9] Both aneurine and pyridoxine were essential growth factors for the closely-related micro-organisms, *C. multiannulata*, *C. fagi*, *C. piliferum*, *C. pluriannulatum* and *Ascoidea rubescens*,[7, 8] and for *Ophiostoma catonianum*.[5]

Another mould that required pyridoxine was a mutant of *Neurospora sitophila*, produced by irradiating the normal strain with X-rays.[10] It is generally referred to as the *pyridoxineless* mutant as it will not grow on a medium containing ammonium tartrate as the source of of nitrogen unless pyridoxine is added. Growth does occur, however, when other sources of nitrogen are used. Also, pyridoxine can largely be replaced by aneurine, so that when this organism is used for the estimation of pyridoxine (see page 313) care must be taken to eliminate aneurine from the test solutions.

Another mould that responded to pyridoxine was *Penicillium digitatum*.[11] *P. chrysogenum*, however, synthesised pyridoxine, twice as much being present in the culture fluid as in the basal medium.[12]

Bacteria

Incidental reference has already been made (page 312) to several bacteria for which pyridoxine is an essential growth factor ; some of these have been used in assaying pyridoxine and its derivatives. M. Landy and D. M. Dicken[13] suggested *Lactobacillus helveticus* as a test organism for the assay of pyridoxine, but it proved to be less satisfactory for this purpose than the *pyridoxineless* mutant of *N. sitophila*. It was found that the addition of DL-alanine to the medium of Landy and Dicken greatly increased the response of *L. helveticus* to pyridoxine,[14] and that the organism could grow without pyridoxine if DL-alanine and an enzymic hydrolysate of vitamin-free casein were added to the medium.[15] Similarly, *S. faecalis* R could grow without pyridoxine when DL-alanine was added. In both instances the effect of DL-alanine was due to the D-isomer, but in the presence of pyridoxine, the L-isomer also had a growth-promoting effect, which was actually greater than that of D-alanine. This phenomenon has not yet received an adequate explanation, but it seems unlikely that alanine is a precursor of pyridoxine, as suggested by E. E. Snell and B. M. Guirard,[16] since a possible intermediate, α-formiminopropionic acid :

$$
\begin{array}{ccc}
& & \underset{\substack{| \\ \text{C}}}{\text{CH}_2 . \text{NH}_2} \\
\underset{\substack{| \\ \text{CH}_3 . \text{CH}}}{\overset{\overset{\text{O}}{\diagup\!\!\diagup}}{\text{HO} . \text{C}}} & \underset{\substack{| \\ \text{CH}_3 . \text{C}}}{\overset{\overset{\text{O}}{\diagup\!\!\diagup}}{\text{HO} \cdot \text{C}} \quad \overset{\text{O}}{\diagdown}} & \underset{\substack{| \\ \text{CH}_3 . \text{C}}}{\overset{\overset{\text{C}}{\diagup\!\!\diagup} \diagdown}{\text{HO} \cdot \text{C}} \quad \text{C} . \text{CH}_2\text{OH}}
\end{array}
$$

$$ \text{NH}_2 \longrightarrow \text{N} \longrightarrow \text{N} $$

was found less effective than DL-alanine as a substitute for pyridoxine.[17] This is confirmed by the fact that pyridoxine was present in negligible amounts in *Lactobacilli* grown on a pyridoxine-free medium containing D-alanine.[17a] It was, in fact, found that both *L. helveticus* and *S. faecalis* accumulated D-alanine when grown on media containing either D-alanine or pyridoxine, and it seems more likely therefore that pyridoxine is necessary for the synthesis of D-alanine, as might be expected from other evidence (page 333). Not all species of lactic acid bacteria require pyridoxine, some being able to synthesise it.[18] Pyridoxine was essential for the growth of *Bacterium acetylcholini*[19] and *Streptobacterium plantarum*,[20] however, and also for *Clostridium tetani*.[21]

The amounts of pyridoxine in the cells of the five bacteria, *Aerobacter aerogenes*, *Serratia marcescens*, *Pseudomonas fluorescens*, *Proteus vulgaris* and *Clostridium butylicum* were estimated by H. McIlwain[22] to be equivalent to between 2100 and 6600 molecules per cell and the rates of synthesis at between 1 and 5 molecules per cell per second.

Protozoa

Tetrahymena geleii required 0·45 μg. per ml. of pyridoxine when the medium was sterilised by filtration or 0·25 μg. per ml. when sterilised by autoclaving, the activity of the pyridoxine being increased when heated with amino acids.[23] Pyridoxal and pyridoxamine were 100 to 500 times more effective.

References to Section 16

1. A. S. Schultz, L. Atkin and C. N. Frey, *J. Amer. Chem. Soc.*, 1939, **61**, 1931 ; A. S. Schultz and L. Atkin, *Arch. Biochem.*, 1947, **14**, 369.
2. R. E. Eakin and R. J. Williams, *J. Amer. Chem. Soc.*, 1939, **61**, 1932.
3. P. R. Burkholder, *Amer. J. Bot.*, 1943, **30**, 206 ; P. R. Burkholder and D. Moyer, *Bull. Torrey Bot. Club*, 1943, **70**, 372 ; *J. Bact.*, 1944, **48**, 385.
4. C. Marchant, *Canad. J. Res.*, 1942, **20B**, 21.
5. W. J. Robbins and R. Ma, *Bull. Torrey Bot. Club*, 1942, **69**, 342; *Proc. Nat. Acad. Sci.*, 1943, **29**, 172.
6. P. R. Burkholder and I. McVeigh, *Science*, 1942, **95**, 127.
7. W. H. Schopfer, *Arch. Julius Klaus-Stiftung*, 1945, **20**, 27.
8. N. Fries, *Naturwiss.*, 1942, **30**, 685 ; *Symbolae Botan. Upsaliensis*, 1943, **7**, No. 2.
9. W. H. Schopfer, *Experientia*, 1945, **1**, 183.
10. J. L. Stokes, J. W. Foster and C. R. Woodward, *Arch. Biochem.*, 1943, **2**, 235.
11. R. C. Wooster and V. H. Cheldelin, *ibid.*, 1945, **8**, 311.

12. F. W. Tanner, S. E. Pfeiffer and J. M. van Lanen, *ibid.*, 29.
13. M. Landy and D. M. Dicken, *J. Lab. Clin. Med.*, 1942, **27**, 1086.
14. E. E. Snell, *Proc. Soc. Exp. Biol. Med.*, 1944, **55**, 36.
15. E. E. Snell, *J. Biol. Chem.*, 1945, **158**, 497.
16. E. E. Snell and B. M. Guirard, *Proc. Nat. Acad. Sci.*, 1943, **29**, 66.
17. W. Shive and G. W. Shive, *J. Amer. Chem. Soc.*, 1946, **68**, 117.
17a. J. T. Holden, C. Furman and E. E. Snell, *J. Biol. Chem.*, 1949, **178**, 789 ; J. T. Holden and E. E. Snell, *ibid.*, 799.
18. N. Bohonos, B. L. Hutchings and W. H. Peterson, *J. Bact.*, 1942, **44**, 479.
19. E. F. Möller, *Z. physiol. Chem.*, 1939, **260**, 246.
20. E. F. Möller, *Angew. Chem.*, 1940, **53**, 204.
21. R. E. Feeney, J. H. Mueller and P. A. Miller, *J. Bact.*, 1943, **46**, 563.
22. H. McIlwain, *Nature*, 1946, **158**, 898.
23. G. W. Kidder and V. C. Dewey, *Arch. Biochem.*, 1949, **21**, 58.

17. EFFECT OF PYRIDOXINE ON HIGHER PLANTS

Little attention appears to have been paid to the rôle of pyridoxine in the economy of plants, and the only reported observation of this type is that pyridoxine and a few of its derivatives stimulated the growth of excised tomato roots.[1]

It has been shown that the amounts of pyridoxine, like that of several other members of the vitamin B complex, increased during the germination of oats, wheat, barley and maize.[2] The distribution of pyridoxine in tomato plants was similar to that of aneurine, ribo-flavine and pantothenic acid ; a concentration gradient was found to exist from the apex of the plant to the base, with the highest concentrations in the young leaves and tops of the stems.[3]

Pyridoxine is present in soil and natural manures.[4]

References to Section 17

1. W. J. Robbins, *Amer. J. Bot.*, 1942, **29**, 241.
2. P. R. Burkholder, *Science*, 1943, **97**, 562.
3. J. Bonner and R. Dorland, *Arch. Biochem.*, 1943, **2**, 451.
4. M. A. Roulet, *Experientia*, 1948, **4**, 149.

18. PYRIDOXINE REQUIREMENTS OF INSECTS

Pyridoxine is an essential vitamin for several insects, including *Drosophila melanogaster*,[1] the mosquito *Aedes aegypti*,[2-4] the beetles, *Tenebrio molitor*,[5] *Tribolium confusum*,[6] and *Ptinus tectus*[6] and the moth *Ephestia elutella*.[6] The beetles, *Sitodrepa panicea*, *Lasioderma serricorne* and *Silvanus surinamensis*, on the other hand, grew well on a diet not containing pyridoxine.[6]   The difference in the behaviour of the two groups of beetles was shown to be due to the presence in this second group of intracellular symbiotic micro-organisms, capable of supplying, *inter alia*, pyridoxine ; [6-8] for sterilised larvae failed to grow on a purified diet, whereas the unsterilised larvae developed normally.

Pyridoxine was essential for the growth of the larvae of the rice moth, *Corcyra cephalonica*.[9]   On a vitamin B_6-deficient diet containing tryptophan, these larvae excreted a yellow compound similar to, but apparently not identical with, xanthurenic acid,[9] an observation recalling the excretion of xanthurenic acid by vitamin B_6-deficient dogs.

References to Section 18

1. E. L. Tatum, *Proc. Nat. Acad. Sci.*, 1939, **25**, 490 ;   1941, **27**, 193.
2. W. Trager and Y. SubbaRow, *Biol. Bull. Woods Hole*, 1938, **75**, 75.
3. Y. SubbaRow and W. Trager, *J. Gen. Physiol.*, 1940, **23**, 561.
4. L. Golberg, B. de Meillon and M. Lavoipierre, *J. Exp. Biol.*, 1945, **21**, 90.
5. H. E. Martin and L. Hare, *Biol. Bull. Woods Hole*, 1942, **83**, 428.
6. G. Fraenkel and M. Blewett, *Nature*, 1943, **151**, 703 ; *Biochem. J.*, 1943, **37**, 686.
7. G. Fraenkel and M. Blewett, *Nature*, 1943, **152**, 506.
8. M. Blewett and G. Fraenkel, *Proc. Roy. Soc.*, B. 1944 **132**, 212.
9. P. S. Sarma, *Indian J. Med. Res.*, 1943, **31**, 165 ; *Proc. Soc. Exp. Biol. Med.*, 1945, **58**, 140.

19. ANALOGUES OF PYRIDOXINE

Pyridoxine Derivatives

The anti-dermatitic effect on rats of a series of pyridoxine derivatives was investigated by K. Unna,[1] whose results are summarised in the following table :

Compound	Dose (mg.)						
	0·05	0·1	0·25	0·5	1·0	2·0	2·5
Pyridoxine . . .	+	+					
,, 4 : 5-diacetate .	+	+					
,, triacetate . .	+	+					
3-Methyl-pyridoxine . .				o	(+)		+
4- ,, ,, . .		(+)	(+)	+			
4-Ethyl- ,, . .		(+)	(+)	+			
4 : 5-Epoxy ,, . .		o	o	o			(+)

where + indicates a cure in 75 % of the animals after fourteen days and (+) indicates a partial cure.

Thus, acetylated pyridoxine was fully active on rats, as it also was on the mould, *Ceratostomella ulma*,[2] the bacteria, *S. faecalis*,[2] *L. helveticus* [2] and *Streptobacterium plantarum*,[3] on the yeast, *Saccharomyces oviformis* [4] and on excised tomato roots.[5] The 3-methyl, 4-methyl and 4-ethyl ethers had only about 10 % of the activity of pyridoxine for rats,[1] and little or no activity on tomato roots, bacteria [2, 3] or yeast.[4] The 4-methyl ether had anti-vitamin properties (page 345).

Replacement of the 4-hydroxy group of pyridoxine by a hydrogen atom to give 3-hydroxy-5-hydroxymethyl-2 : 4-dimethyl-pyridine, completely destroyed the activity for rats,[1, 6] for *Streptobacterium plantarum* [3] and for yeast.[4] The product, known as desoxypyridoxine, had anti-vitamin properties (page 345). Replacement of both alcoholic hydroxy groups to give 3-hydroxy-2 : 4 : 5-trimethyl-pyridine also destroyed the activity for rats [1, 6] and *S. plantarum*.[3]

3-Amino-5-aminomethyl-4-hydroxymethyl-pyridine was inactive for rats,[1] whilst 3-amino-5-aminomethyl-4-methoxymethyl-2-methyl-pyridine and 3-hydroxy-2-methyl-4 : 5-methylenedioxymethylpyridine were inactive for micro-organisms.[2] The methiodide of pyridoxine, and N-methylpyridoxine betaine :

CH₂OH (as drawn)

were inactive for rats,[7] bacteria and yeasts.[2]

The complex formed between pyridoxine and boric acid was said to be as active for rats as the vitamin itself.[8]

Isomers and Homologues

" Isopyridoxine ", 2 : 5-bis-hydroxymethyl-3-hydroxy-4-methyl-pyridine was inactive for rats and only slightly active for *S. plantarum*.[3]

By a series of reactions analogous to that used in the synthesis of pyridoxine, S. A. Harris and A. N. Wilson [9] prepared the pyridoxine homologue, 2-ethyl-3-hydroxy-4 : 5-bis-hydroxymethylpyridine hydrochloride and found that it had only 1/200th of the activity of pyridoxine in vitamin B_6-deficient rats. The compound was as active as pyridoxine on tomato roots, however.[5]

Pyridoxal and Pyridoxamine

As already stated (page 312), pyridoxal and pyridoxamine have a greater growth-promoting activity than pyridoxine on the bacteria,

S. faecalis R and *L. helveticus*,[10] whilst for other micro-organisms, such as *Saccharomyces carlsbergensis*,[11] the three compounds were about equally effective. A few micro-organisms, including *Saccharomyces cerevisiae* [2] and *pyridoxineless Neurospora sitophila*,[12] did not respond at all to pyridoxamine or pyridoxal.

Rats responded equally well to pyridoxine, pyridoxal and pyridoxamine, whilst for chicks,[13] pyridoxal and pyridoxamine had three-fifths and four-fourths respectively of the activity of pyridoxine.

The biological activity of pyridoxal phosphate for rats was equivalent to its pyridoxal content.[14]

Heyl *et al.*[15] found that the following derivatives of pyridoxamine had 50 to 100 % of the activity of pyridoxine on rats : pyridoxyl-β-phenyl ethylamine, pyridoxyl-tyramine, pyridoxyl-tryptamine, pyridoxyl-benzylamine, pyridoxyl-histamine and pyridoxyl-isobutylamine. They had little or no microbiological activity.[15a]

Pyridoxic Acids and Lactones

Two pyridoxic acids exist, formed by the oxidation of one or other of the hydroxymethyl groups to a carboxyl group. These give rise to lactones, known as pyracins (page 336) :

4-Pyridoxic acid   β-Pyracin   5-Pyridoxic acid   α-Pyracin

4-Pyridoxic acid did not stimulate the growth of micro-organisms,[16] but the corresponding lactone, β-pyracin, had one-quarter the activity of pyridoxine for *S. lactis*, 1/50th for *L. helveticus* and 1/4000th for yeast. α-Pyracin was also without appreciable growth-promoting properties on yeast.[17] According to Luckey *et al.*,[13] α-pyracin had no vitamin B_6 activity in chicks, but Scott *et al.*[18] found that it promoted growth in chicks and significantly increased the haemoglobin content of the blood, as well as stimulated the growth of *L. helveticus*. β-Pyracin was more effective than α-pyracin in promoting growth, but only slightly more effective in preventing anaemia.[19] In the absence of α- or β-pyracin, but in presence of folic acid (page 485), a normocytic, hypochromic anaemia developed. Another closely related substance that prevented anaemia in chicks was 3-carboxy-4-hydroxymethyl-6-methyl-2-pyridone :[20]

$$CH_2OH$$
$$COOH$$
$$CH_3$$
$$N \quad O$$

Growth Inhibitors

The first substance related to pyridoxine which was found to have inhibitory properties was 3-hydroxy-5-hydroxymethyl-2 : 4-dimethyl-pyridine, generally referred to as desoxypyridoxine (page 343)

$$CH_3$$
$$HO \quad CH_2OH$$
$$CH_3 \quad N$$

W. H. Ott [21] showed that two moles of this substance antagonised the effect of one mole of pyridoxine in chicks, producing symptoms of vitamin B_6 deficiency. Normal rats receiving desoxypyridoxine along with tryptophan excreted more xanthurenic acid and kynurenine (page 336) than animals receiving tryptophan alone, whilst vitamin B_6-deficient rats excreted even larger amounts of xanthurenic acid and kynurenine in presence of the anti-vitamin.[22] The administration of pyridoxine reduced the excretion of these two substances to normal levels. It was suggested that desoxypyridoxine interfered with some phase of tryptophan metabolism. Other symptoms consistent with pyridoxine deficiency were observed in chicks, dogs and monkeys to which desoxypyridoxine was administered.[23] Desoxypyridoxine administered to female rats ten to twenty days prior to mating interfered with reproduction, the effect being counteracted by pyridoxine given on the day of mating.[23a] Desoxypyridoxine (1 mg.) injected into eggs just prior to incubation resulted in 100 % mortality; this was prevented by simultaneous injection of any of the three forms of vitamin B_6.[23b]

Desoxypyridoxine did not inhibit the action of tyrosine decarboxylase, but phosphorylated desoxypyridoxine displaced pyridoxal phosphate in the tyrosine decarboxylase system.[24] Administration of desoxypyridoxine produced marked regression of lymphosarcoma implants in mice, but not when pyridoxine was added to the diet.[25] Tumour implants failed to develop in animals deprived of pyridoxine prior to the implantation. Desoxypyridoxine inhibited the multiplication of T_2r^+ E. coli bacteriophage and the inhibition was reversed by pyridoxine.[25a]

Another substance with anti-pyridoxine activity is 3-hydroxy-5-hydroxymethyl-4-methoxymethyl-2-methyl-pyridine often, though erroneously, referred to as "methoxy-pyridoxine". Four moles of this substance antagonised the growth-promoting effect of one mole of pyridoxine in chicks.[26] Unlike desoxypyridoxine, however, it actually reduced the amount of xanthurenic acid and kynurenine excreted by rats when given together with tryptophan,[22] whilst the excretion of 4-pyridoxic acid was increased. Thus although "methoxypyridoxine" has anti-vitamin activity for the chick it has vitamin B_6 activity for the rat,[1] being apparently demethylated in this animal to pyridoxine. "Methoxypyridoxine" produced symptoms of vitamin B_6 deficiency in chicks and dogs, although in dogs the symptoms were less severe than with desoxypyridoxine, due presumably to partial cleavage to pyridoxine.[23]

3-Hydroxy-4-hydroxymethyl-2-methyl-pyridine, 3-amino-5-aminomethyl-4-ethoxymethyl-2-ethyl-pyridine and 3-hydroxy-2 : 4 : 5-trimethyl-pyridine ("didesoxypyridoxine") were weak antagonists of pyridoxine.[26a]

Irradiation of pyridoxine, pyridoxal and pyridoxamine gave products that inhibited the growth of Gram-negative aerobic bacteria and, to a lesser extent, two strains of Gram-positive cocci.[27] The anti-bacterial activity was antagonised by certain amino acids, but nothing is known about the chemical constitution of the inhibitory substance.

Pyridoxine was claimed to inhibit the activity of quinine and mepacrine against *Plasmodium lophurae* infections in ducklings when given in amounts several times greater than those required for the nutrition of the ducklings.[28] This led McCasland *et al.*[29] to attempt the preparation of analogues of pyridoxine that might antagonise the pyridoxine required by the parasites. Various pyrimidines were synthesised, but 4-hydroxy-2-hydroxymethyl-5-methyl-2 : 6-bis-pyrimidine had no pyridoxine or anti-pyridoxine activity for *S. cerevisiae*.

References to Section 19

1. K. Unna, *Proc. Soc. Exp. Biol. Med.*, 1940, **43**, 122.
2. E. E. Snell, *J. Amer. Chem. Soc.*, 1944, **66**, 2082.
3. E. F. Möller, *Z. physiol. Chem.*, 1939, **260**, 246 ; E. F. Möller, O. Frina, F. Jung and T. Moll, *Naturwiss.*, 1939, **27**, 228 ; E. F. Möller, *Angew. Chem.*, 1940, **53**, 204.
4. P. R. Burkholder, *Amer. J. Bot.*, 1943, **30**, 206.
5. W. J. Robbins, *ibid.*, 1942, **29**, 241.
6. S. A. Harris, *J. Amer. Chem. Soc.*, 1940, **62**, 3203.
7. S. A. Harris, T. J. Webb, and K. Folkers, *ibid.*, 3198.
8. J. V. Scudi, W. A. Bastedo and T. J. Webb, *Proc. Soc. Exp. Biol. Med.*, 1940, **43**, 122 ; *J. Biol. Chem.*, 1940, **136**, 399.
9. S. A. Harris and A. N. Wilson, *J. Amer. Chem. Soc.*, 1941, **63**, 2526.

10. E. E. Snell, *J. Biol. Chem.*, 1944, **154**, 313.
11. D. Melnick, M. Hochberg, H. W. Himes and B. L. Oser, *ibid.*, 1945, **160**, 1.
12. G. W. Beadle and E. L. Tatum, *Proc. Nat. Acad. Sci.*, 1941, **27**, 499 ; 1942, **28**, 234.
13. T. D. Luckey, G. M. Briggs, C. A. Elvehjem and E. B. Hart, *Proc. Soc. Exp. Biol. Med.*, 1945, **58**, 340.
14. P. S. Sarma, E. E. Snell and C. A. Elvehjem, *J. Biol. Chem.*, 1946, **165**, 55.
15. D. Heyl, E. Luz, S. A. Harris and K. Folkers, *J. Amer. Chem. Soc.*, 1948, **70**, 1670, 3429, 3669.
15a. E. E. Snell and J. C. Rabinowitz, *ibid.*, 3432.
16. J. W. Huff and W. A. Perlzweig, *J. Biol. Chem.*, 1944, **155**, 345.
17. P. R. Burkholder, *Amer. J. Bot.*, 1943, **30**, 206.
18. M. L. Scott, L. C. Norris, G. F. Heuser, W. F. Bruce, H. W. Coover, W. D. Bellamy and I. C. Gunsalus, *J. Biol. Chem.*, 1944, **154**, 713.
19. M. L. Scott, L. C. Norris, G. F. Heuser and W. F. Bruce, *ibid.*, 1945, **158**, 291 ; *J. Amer. Chem. Soc.*, 1945, **67**, 157.
20. W. F. Bruce and H. W. Coover, *ibid.*, 1944, **66**, 2092.
21. W. H. Ott, *Proc. Soc. Exp. Biol. Med.*, 1946, **61**, 125.
22. C. C. Porter, I. Clark and R. H. Silber, *J. Biol. Chem.*, 1947, **167**, 573.
23. C. W. Mushett, R. B. Stebbins and M. N. Barton, *Trans. N.Y. Acad. Sci.*, 1947, **9**, 291.
23a. M. M. Nelson and H. M. Evans, *Proc. Soc. Exp. Biol. Med.*, 1948, **68**, 274.
23b. W. W. Cravens and E. E. Snell, *ibid.*, 1949, **71**, 73.
24. J. M. Beiler and G. J. Martin, *J. Biol. Chem.*, 1947, **169**, 345 ; W. W. Umbreit and J. G. Waddell, *Proc. Soc. Exp. Biol. Med.*, 1949, **70**, 293.
25. H. C. Stoerk, *J. Biol. Chem.*, 1947, **171**, 438.
25a. J. G. Wooley and M. K. Murphy, *ibid.*, 1949, **178**, 869.
26. W. H. Ott, *Proc. Soc. Exp. Biol. Med.*, 1947, **66**, 215.
26a. G. J. Martin, S. Avakian and J. Moss, *J. Biol. Chem.*, 1948, **174**, 495 ; R. P. Mariella and J. L. Leech, *J. Amer. Chem. Soc.*, 1949, **71**, 331.
27. G. Schwartzman and A. Fisher, *J. Biol. Chem.*, 1947, **167**, 345.
28. A. O. Seeler, *Proc. Soc. Exp. Biol. Med.*, 1944, **57**, 113.
29. G. E. McCasland, D. S. Tarbell, R. B. Carlin and N. Shakespeare, *J. Amer. Chem. Soc.*, 1946, **68**, 2390 ; G. E. McCasland and D. S. Tarbell, *ibid.*, 2393.

Chapter VI

PANTOTHENIC ACID

1. HISTORICAL

THE story of pantothenic acid is closely bound up with that of pyridoxine. Both factors occur together in yeast and liver, and were separated from one another by treatment with fuller's earth; pyridoxine (the " eluate factor ") was retained on the adsorbent, whilst pantothenic acid (the " filtrate factor ") remained in the filtrate. The first concentrate of pantothenic acid substantially free from other factors was prepared from liver by C. A. Elvehjem and C. J. Koehn,[1] and by S. Lepkovsky and T. H. Jukes.[2] As the factor was found to be effective in preventing and curing dermatitis in chicks, but not in rats, it became known as the " chick antidermatitis factor ", and chicks were used for assaying it.

Edgar *et al.*[3] prepared a yeast concentrate with properties similar to those of Lepkovsky and Jukes' " factor 2 ", and showed that it stimulated the growth of rats ; a method of assaying the factor was devised, based on this property.

Progress in the purification of the new vitamin was slow, partly because it did not readily give rise to derivatives of a type that might facilitate its isolation and characterisation, and partly because it was present in admixture with other substances difficult to separate from it. The concentrates prepared by S. Lepkovsky and T. H. Jukes [2] and by C. E. Edgar and T. F. Macrae [3] resembled one another in most respects ; [4] thus, the active fraction could be extracted from acid aqueous solutions by ether, butyl alcohol or amyl alcohol, it could be precipitated from alcoholic solution by barium hydroxide and it could be adsorbed on norit. Woolley *et al.*[5] prepared the barium salt, and purified it by extraction with absolute alcohol, most of the activity passing into the soluble fraction. They also made an inactive acetyl derivative, from which the activity was regenerated by hydrolysis. This acetyl compound could be purified by high-vacuum distillation. From this evidence it was concluded that the factor was an acid containing one or more hydroxyl groups. G. H. Hitchings and Y. SubbaRow [6] also prepared a concentrate of the substance and showed that it was a growth factor for rats.

A year later, Woolley et al.[7] reported that the chick antidermatitis factor was destroyed by alkali and that β-alanine could be isolated from the product. They reactivated the acidic portion of the alkali-inactivated concentrate by acetylation, conversion of the product into an acid chloride by treatment with thionyl chloride and reaction with β-alanine ethyl ester in pyridine solution, followed by hydrolysis with cold sodium hydroxide solution. The substance thus obtained was effective in curing chick dermatitis.

The authors noted a resemblance between the chick factor and pantothenic acid, a substance that R. J. Williams [8] had shown many years before to be one of the components of " bios ", the hypothetical factor essential for the growth of yeast. The name is derived from the Greek meaning " from everywhere ", on account of its widespread occurrence. Its chemical constitution was not known, but R. J. Williams [9] had described a method of preparing a concentrate of pantothenic acid from sheep's liver and had listed some of its properties. Shortly after the publication of the paper by Woolley et al., T. H. Jukes [10] tested the calcium salt of Williams' pantothenic acid on chicks and found that it was markedly active in curing chick dermatitis when administered in a dose of 10 mg.

Weinstock et al.[11] then reported the isolation of β-alanine from alkali-inactivated pantothenic acid and showed that β-alanine could replace pantothenic acid for some micro-organisms, though not for others. This strengthened the presumption that the chick anti-dermatitis factor was identical with pantothenic acid, and further support was given by the fact that a " varnish-like " calcium salt prepared from liver extract [12] by a procedure similar to that used by Williams in preparing calcium pantothenate gave good growth when fed to rats maintained on a synthetic diet and behaved like panto-thenic acid in stimulating the growth of Streptococcus haemolyticus and the diphtheria bacillus.

The identity of the liver " filtrate factor " with pantothenic acid was confirmed by Lythgoe et al.,[13] who isolated β-alanine from the hydrolysate and re-combined it with the lactone half of the molecule. Lythgoe et al. also presented evidence that the " filtrate factor " was not a single entity, but comprised at least three factors : (a) factor α, identical with pantothenic acid ; (b) factor β which, unlike factor α, was not extractable from acid solutions by amyl alcohol ; and (c) factor γ.

Similar results were obtained by Black et al.[14] and J. J. Oleson and S. Black,[15] who reported that rats required both pantothenic acid and a factor termed by D. V. Frost and C. A. Elvehjem [16] the alcohol-ether precipitate factor or factor W, and that these together were not so active as a crude liver extract, which therefore contained at least one other factor. Factor W, like pantothenic acid, was not adsorbed on fuller's earth, but differed in not being extracted from aqueous solutions by ether, and in its stability to alkali. D. V. Frost and C. A. Elvehjem noted a close resemblance between factor W and Macrae's filtrate factor. D. W. Woolley [17] found that an alcohol-soluble fraction from an aqueous liver extract gave increased growth in rats over and above that obtained with pantothenic acid ; biotin was inactive.

H. Kringstad and G. Lunde [18] obtained a growth factor, to which they gave the name factor B_w, which resembled factor W in many respects. It differed from the eluate factor, however, in not being precipitated by phosphotungstic acid and from the filtrate factor in not being extracted by ether at pH 1.

The first real clue to the structure of the non-alanine portion of pantothenic acid was provided by Y. SubbaRow and L. Rane,[19] who coupled the acid chloride of acetylated $\alpha\delta$-dihydroxyvaleric acid (prepared by deamination of ornithine) with β-alanine ethyl ester and found that, whilst the product stimulated the growth of a strain of haemolytic streptococcus, it was required in larger amounts than was calcium pantothenate or the calcium salt isolated from liver. It was inferred from this that pantothenic acid was related to, but not identical with, $\alpha\delta$-dihydroxyvaleryl-β-alanine.

G. H. Hitchings and D. W. Woolley [20] found that pantothenic acid could be replaced by a dihydroxycaproyl-β-alanine in the growth of a strain of haemolytic streptococcus. The nature of the substituted caproic acid used was not disclosed, but in the following year R. J. Williams and R. T. Major [21] announced the preparation from crude barium pantothenate of a pure lactone, mp. 91 to 92° C., identified as α-hydroxy-$\beta\beta$-dimethyl-γ-butyrolactone. This, when coupled with β-alanine, yielded racemic pantothenic acid :

$$\underset{\underset{\displaystyle \overline{}\quad O}{|\quad CH_3 \qquad |}}{CH_2.C.CHOH.CO} + NH_2.CH_2.CH_2.COOH$$

$$\longrightarrow CH_2OH.\overset{CH_3}{\underset{CH_3}{C}}.CHOH.CO.NH.CH_2.CH_2.COOH$$

α-Hydroxy-$\beta\beta$-dimethyl-γ-butyrolactone is now commonly referred to as pantolactone and the corresponding acid as pantoic acid.

References to Section 1

1. C. A. Elvehjem and C. J. Koehn, *Nature*, 1934, **134**, 1007 ; *J. Biol. Chem.*, 1935, **108**, 709.

2. S. Lepkovsky and T. H. Jukes, *ibid.*, 1936, **114**, 109.
3. C. E. Edgar, T. F. Macrae and F. Vivanco, *Biochem. J.*, 1937, **31**, 879 ; C. E. Edgar and T. F. Macrae, *ibid.*, 893.
4. T. F. Macrae, A. R. Todd, B. Lythgoe, C. E. Work, H. G. Hind and M. M. El Sadr, *ibid.*, 1939, **33**, 1681.
5. D. W. Woolley, H. A. Waisman, O. Mickelsen and C. A. Elvehjem, *J. Biol. Chem.*, 1938, **125**, 715.
6. G. H. Hitchings and Y. SubbaRow, *J. Nutrition*, 1939, **18**, 265.
7. D. W. Woolley, H. A. Waisman and C. A. Elvehjem, *J. Amer. Chem. Soc.*, 1939, **61**, 977.
8. R. J. Williams, *ibid.*, 1933, **55**, 2912.
9. R. J. Williams, *ibid.*, 1938, **60**, 2719.
10. T. H. Jukes, *ibid.*, 1939, **61**, 975.
11. H. H. Weinstock, H. K. Mitchell, E. F. Pratt and R. J. Williams, *ibid.*, 1421.
12. Y. SubbaRow and G. H. Hitchings, *ibid.*, 1615.
13. B. Lythgoe, T. F. Macrae, R. H. Stanley, A. R. Work and C. E. Work, *Biochem. J.*, 1940, **34**, 1335.
14. S. Black, D. V. Frost and C. A. Elvehjem, *J. Biol. Chem.*, 1940, **132**, 65.
15. J. J. Oleson and S. Black, *ibid.*, 1940, **133**, lxxiii.
16. D. V. Frost and C. A. Elvehjem, *ibid.*, 1937, **119**, xxxiv.
17. D. W. Woolley, *Proc. Soc. Exp. Biol. Med.*, 1940, **43**, 352.
18. H. Kringstad and G. Lunde, *Z. physiol. Chem.*, 1939, **261**, 110.
19. Y. SubbaRow and L. Rane, *J. Amer. Chem. Soc.*, 1939, **61**, 1616.
20. G. H. Hitchings and D. W. Woolley, *Science*, 1939, **90**, 41.
21. R. J. Williams and R. T. Major, *ibid.*, 1940, **91**, 246.

2. ISOLATION OF PANTOTHENIC ACID

The method used by R. J. Williams *et al.*[1] in the isolation of pantothenic acid from liver was as follows : the liver was allowed to autolyse and then heated to coagulate proteins and filtered. Alternatively, the minced liver was extracted with alcohol. In either instance, the aqueous extract was shaken with fuller's earth to remove readily adsorbed impurities and then with norit at pH 3·6 to adsorb pantothenic acid. The adsorbate was eluted with dilute ammonia or with pyridine-methanol. The eluate was neutralised with oxalic acid, and brucine was added to form the brucine salts of pantothenic acid and other acids. These were extracted with chloroform and fractionated by partitioning between chloroform and water. The purified brucine salt was decomposed by lime and the brucine removed by filtration and extraction with chloroform. The calcium pantothenate was purified by precipitation with alcohol, removal of impurities by precipitation with mercuric chloride, and fractional precipitation with isopropyl ether and with acetone from pyridine solution. About 3 g. of crude (40 %) calcium salt was obtained from 250 kg. of liver.

In an improved process the charcoal eluate was heated with barium hydroxide to pH 8 and the precipitate containing the barium pantothenate was dissolved in absolute alcohol and filtered. The filtrate was concentrated, and acetone was added, giving a precipitate containing barium pantothenate. The free acids were liberated by the addition of sulphuric acid, giving a concentrate containing 20 to 25 % of pantothenic acid.

Y. SubbaRow and G. H. Hitchings [2] also used liver as starting material. This was freed from fat by extraction with solvent, the aqueous extract was then treated with mercuric acetate to remove impurities, the filtrate treated with charcoal and the adsorbate eluted with pyridine-methanol-water. Impurities were removed from the eluate by precipitation with phosphotungstic acid, and uridine (uracil-D-riboside) was removed by crystallising the concentrated filtrate from methanol. Pantothenic acid was then precipitated from the methanol solution by means of barium hydroxide, and impurities were removed from the precipitate by repeated treatment with phosphotungstic acid. Finally, the pantothenic acid was adsorbed on acid-activated alumina, and recovered by elution.

The isolation of pantothenic acid from molasses and rice bran was described by Mohammad et al. [3]

References to Section 2

1. R. J. Williams, J. H. Truesdail, H. H. Weinstock, E. Rohrmann, C. M. Lyman and C. H. McBurney, *J. Amer. Chem. Soc.*, 1938, **60**, 2719; H. K. Mitchell, H. H. Weinstock, E. E. Snell, S. R. Stanbery and R. J. Williams, *ibid.*, 1940, **62**, 1776.
2. Y. SubbaRow and G. H. Hitchings, *ibid.*, 1939, **61**, 1615.
3. A. Mohammad, O. H. Emerson, G. A. Emerson and H. M. Evans, *J. Biol. Chem.*, 1940, **133**, 17.

3. CHEMICAL CONSTITUTION AND SYNTHESIS OF PANTOTHENIC ACID

The presence of a carboxyl group in pantothenic acid was proved by esterification,[1] whilst the presence of two hydroxyl groups was indicated by a determination of active hydrogen.[2] The observation that pantothenic acid condensed with acetaldehyde, acetone or benzaldehyde indicated the presence of an $\alpha\beta$-, $\alpha\gamma$- or $\alpha\delta$-glycol.

The details of the degradation experiments that finally established the constitution of pantothenic acid were given in two papers by

Mitchell *et al.*[3] and by Stiller *et al.*[4] In the first of these papers, the non-β-alanine fraction of the pantothenic acid molecule was shown to contain an α-hydroxyl group, since it yielded formic acid on hydrolysis with sulphuric acid, and carbon monoxide on dehydration with sulphuric acid at 140° C. Since the acid lactonised spontaneously, it probably contained a γ-hydroxyl group as well, and the absence of a β-hydroxyl group was presumed from the formation of an unsaturated derivative of the type R . CH : CH . COOH on dehydration, and the fact that oxidation with lead tetra-acetate, periodic acid or hypoiodite did not destroy the activity, as it would have done had the substance been an αβ-glycol. Accordingly, the following α-hydroxy-γ-lactones were synthesised and coupled with β-alanine : α-hydroxy-γ-valerolactone, α-hydroxy-β-methyl-γ-butyrolactone and α-hydroxy-α-methyl-γ-butyrolactone. The products showed definite, but slight, physiological activity when tested on *Streptococcus lactis* (which is unaffected by excess β-alanine).

In the second of the papers, the lactone obtained on acid hydrolysis was purified by molecular sublimation and obtained pure, m.p. 92 to 93° C., $[\alpha]_D^{26°} = 49\cdot8$. It had the empirical formula, $C_6H_{10}O_3$. It was, therefore, a derivative not of valeric acid as had been assumed previously but of caproic acid. It contained one active hydrogen atom and yielded an acetate, dinitrobenzoate and *p*-nitrobenzoate. A Kuhn-Roth determination gave a result equivalent to 26 % of C-methyl group, indicating the presence of a *gem*-dimethyl group. This was confirmed by the formation of acetone on treatment with barium permanganate. The conclusion that the lactone was α-hydroxy-ββ-dimethyl-γ-butyrolactone was established by the following series of degradations :

$$\text{CH}_3 \qquad\qquad\qquad\qquad \text{CH}_3$$
$$\text{I}_2 . \overset{|}{\underset{|}{\text{C}}} . \text{CHOH} . \text{CO} \xrightarrow{\text{C}_6\text{H}_5\text{MgBr}} \text{CH}_2\text{OH} . \overset{|}{\underset{|}{\text{C}}} . \text{CHOH} . \text{C(OH)(C}_6\text{H}_5)_2 \longrightarrow \text{CO(C}_6\text{H}_5)_2$$
$$\text{CH}_3 \qquad\qquad\qquad\qquad \text{CH}_3$$
$$\underline{\qquad\qquad\qquad} \text{O}$$

$$\downarrow \text{CH}_3\text{MgI}$$

$$\text{CH}_3 \qquad\qquad\qquad\qquad \text{CH}_3 \qquad\qquad\qquad \text{CH}_3$$
$$_2\text{OH} . \overset{|}{\underset{|}{\text{C}}} . \text{CHOH} . \text{C(OH)(CH}_3)_2 \longrightarrow \text{CH}_2\text{OH} . \overset{|}{\underset{|}{\text{C}}} . \text{CHO} \longrightarrow \text{CH}_2\text{OH} . \overset{|}{\underset{|}{\text{C}}} . \text{COOH}$$
$$\text{CH}_3 \qquad\qquad\qquad\qquad \text{CH}_3 \qquad\qquad\qquad \text{CH}_3$$

Natural pantolactone is laevorotatory, whereas pantoic acid is dextrorotatory.

The partial synthesis of pantothenic acid from this lactone and β-alanine ethyl ester or, better since this avoided hydrolysis of the pantothenic ester, by heating the lactone with the sodium salt of β-alanine, was described by R. J. Williams *et al.*[5] and by S. H. Babcock

23   353

and T. H. Jukes.[6] The complete synthesis, described by Stiller *et al.*,[7] was as follows :

$$H.CHO + (CH_3)_2CH.CHO \xrightarrow{K_2CO_3} CH_2OH.\overset{\overset{\displaystyle CH_3}{|}}{\underset{\underset{\displaystyle CH_3}{|}}{C}}.CHO \xrightarrow{KCN + \atop NaHSO_3}$$

$$CH_2OH.\overset{\overset{\displaystyle CH_3}{|}}{\underset{\underset{\displaystyle CH_3}{|}}{C}}.CHOH.CN \xrightarrow{HCl} \underbrace{CH_2.\overset{\overset{\displaystyle CH_3}{|}}{\underset{\underset{\displaystyle CH_3}{|}}{C}}.CHOH.CO}_{O} \xrightarrow{\beta\text{-alanine}} \text{Pantothenic acid.}$$

Synthetic pantothenic acid proved to have only half the growth-promoting action of the natural acid on *Lactobacillus helveticus*, but Stiller *et al.*[7] resolved the sodium salt of pantoic acid into its optically active isomers by treatment with quinine hydrochloride, and then reacted each separately with β-alanine ester, obtaining in this way ,D- and L-pantothenic acid. The former was active on micro-organisms, rats and chicks, whilst the latter was inactive.

A different synthesis was later described by D. W. Woolley.[8] The sodium salt of pantoic acid was converted *via* the acetyl derivative into the acid chloride, which was coupled with β-alanine in aqueous solution in the presence of alkali.

The synthesis of racemic pantothenic acid was also described by T. Reichstein and A. Grüssner,[9] who used a similar method to that of Williams *et al.* They resolved pantolactone with quinine and, in a later paper,[10] described the resolution of pantothenic acid with quinine or cinchonidine methydroxide and noted the biological activity of the optically active pantothenic acids, confirming the results obtained by Williams and his co-workers. M. Gätzi-Fichter *et al.*[11] prepared the crystalline sodium salt of pantothenic acid by hydrolysis of the ester with baryta and decomposition of the barium salt.

R. T. Major and J. Finkelstein[12] resolved pantolactone by means of the methydroxides of quinine, quinidine and cinchonine, whilst E. T. Stiller and P. F. Wiley[13] used quinine methydroxide for resolving racemic pantothenic acid itself. They stated that the alkaloids were not sufficiently strong bases to give stable salts of pantothenic acid, whereas the methydroxides, being more strongly basic, gave salts sufficiently stable to enable the pure D- and L-salts to be separated ; these yielded D- and L-pantothenic acid respectively on decomposition. Pantolactone has also been resolved with the aid of brucine and of diacetyl-D-tartaric anhydride.[14]

R. Kuhn and T. Wieland[15] described the preparation of a concentrate from fish liver of a factor which stimulated the growth of *Streptobacterium plantarum*. This concentrate yielded on hydrolysis β-alanine,

L-leucine, α-hydroxy-ββ-dimethyl-γ-butyrolactone and a homologous lactone, $C_{17}H_{12}O_3$, which gave an inactive substance when coupled with β-alanine. Although pantothenic acid was not actually isolated, there is little doubt that it was the active constituent of the concentrate.

Kuhn and Wieland [16] synthesised pantothenic acid by condensing pantolactone with β-alanine benzyl ester and catalytically hydrogenating the product to remove the benzyl group. The racemic pantothenic acid so obtained was resolved by means of quinine or cinchonidine. The latter was preferred, as the cinchonidine salt of D-pantothenic acid was less soluble than that of the L-isomer, enabling it to be isolated in good yield, whereas quinine D-pantothenate was more soluble than the salt of the L-isomer and therefore more difficult to isolate.

Other variants of the general method for the preparation of pantothenic acid were described by H. C. Parke and E. J. Lawson.[17] Fusion at 150° C. of the sodium salt of DL- and D-pantoic acid with β-alanine gave a 90 and 60 % yield respectively of sodium DL-pantothenate and sodium D-pantothenate. A novel method of preparing sodium DL-pantothenate was fusion at 100° C. of DL-pantamide with the sodium salt of β-alanine ; this gave a 70 % yield. Finally, sodium D-pantothenate was prepared in 90 % yield by heating pantolactone with the sodium salt of β-alanine in isopropanol.

Patents covering these different methods of preparation were filed by various commercial firms. Merck & Co., for example, protected the preparation of pantothenic acid by reacting β-alanine, its salts or esters, with an α-keto- or α-hydroxy-acid capable of lactonising ; [18] by fusing β-alanine or a salt with pantolactone ; [19] or by reacting pantolactone with β-alanine and an ester of β-alanine in presence of an alkali metal or alkaline earth metal hydroxide or alcoholate at 0° C. in an alcoholic or aqueous medium.[20] DL-Pantothenic acid was resolved by means of quinine, quinine methydroxide, cinchonidine, brucine, strychnine or ephedrine.[21] Alternatively, pantoic acid was resolved by fractional crystallisation of an alkaloidal salt,[22] and D- or L-pantothenic acid was prepared from the appropriate lactone by reaction with β-alanine.[23] The condensation of D-pantolactone with β-alanine was also patented by F. Hoffmann-La Roche & Co.[24]

A number of novel methods were patented by F. Hoffmann-La Roche & Co., and Roche Products Ltd. Thus esters of pantothenic acid were prepared by catalytic hydrogenation of β-nitropropionic esters in presence of pantolactone.[25] The reaction of pantolactone with β-alanine in alcoholic or aqueous alcoholic solution was also protected.[26] A third method of preparation was to react pantolactone with the acetal of β-aminopropionaldehyde and convert the resulting pantothenic aldehyde acetal to calcium pantothenate by oxidation with oxalic acid and hydrogen peroxide and neutralisation with calcium carbonate.[27]   Yet another method of preparation comprised the oxidation of N-D-pantoyl-3'-hydroxypropylamine [28] or N-D-pantoyl-3' : 4'-dihydroxybutylamine [29] or their derivatives first with barium or potassium permanganate to give the aldehyde and then with silver oxide to give pantothenic acid ; the N-D-pantoyl hydroxyalkylamines were prepared by condensing pantolactone with alkanolamines.[30]   Resolution of DL-pantothenic acid was effected through the quinine salt,[31] and pure calcium D-pantothenate was prepared either by acidifying the sodium salt, neutralising with calcium carbonate and crystallising from alcohol [32] or by adding calcium chloride to a solution of the sodium salt in alcohol.[33]

National Oil Products Co. protected the preparation of pantothenic acid by acylation of a salt of pantoic acid, conversion to the acid chloride by treatment with thionyl chloride, reaction with a β-alanine alkyl ester, followed by hydrolysis of the resulting pantothenic ester.[34] Calcium pantothenate was prepared by reacting the calcium salt of β-alanine with pantolactone in anhydrous methanol or ethanol.[35] Lederle Labs., Inc. prepared the calcium salt by the action of metallic calcium on a mixture of β-alanine and pantolactone ; [36] by reacting pantolactone in anhydrous alcohol with the calcium salt of β-alanine, prepared *in situ* from β-alanine and calcium hydride, calcium amide, calcium carbide, calcium hydroxide or cyanamide, but not metallic calcium ; [37] or by the interaction of the calcium salt of β-alanine and pantoic acid amide in methanol.[38]   Parke, Davis & Co. protected the preparation of sodium D-pantothenate, first, by heating β-alanine and sodium D-pantoate at 170 to 180° C. for fifteen minutes [39] and, secondly, by heating the sodium salt of β-alanine with D-pantolactone in anhydrous ethanol or isopropanol.[40]

Preparation of Pantolactone

Since most of the methods of preparing pantothenic acid involve the condensation of pantolactone with β-alanine, considerable attention has been devoted to the preparation of these two substances.

The method used by Stiller *et al.* (page 354) is the one in general use, but minor modifications have been described in the patent literature.   F. Hoffmann-La Roche & Co.,[41] for example, prepared pantolactone by the action of sodium cyanide on formylisobutyraldol bisulphite compound and hydrolysis of the resulting cyanhydrin, whilst Roche Products Ltd.[42] prepared the optically active D-pantolactone from the racemic compound by treatment with chlorosulphonic acid and pyridine to give pantolactone hydrogen sulphuric acid, fractional crystallisation of the strychnine salt of this acid and hydrolysis of the strychnine D-lactone sulphate to the optically active lactone. Merck & Co.[42a] used brucine for resolving pantolactone.

Parke, Davis & Co.,[43] patented the preparation of pantolactone by the interaction of formaldehyde, isobutyraldehyde, sodium cyanide and sodium bisulphite, giving β-hydroxy-$\alpha\alpha$-dimethylpropionaldehyde cyanhydrin, which yielded pantolactone on acid hydrolysis.

Preparation of β-Alanine and its Esters

A large number of methods have been described for the preparation of β-alanine and its esters. F. Weygand [44] prepared β-alanine ethyl ester by hydrogenation of ethyl cyanacetate in presence of platinum oxide, whilst Lederle Labs., Inc. prepared β-alanine itself by hydrogenating cyanacetic acid in presence of platinum oxide or palladium,[45] or by hydrogenating cyanacetamide and hydrolysing the resulting β-alanine amide.[46] National Oil Products Co.[47] hydrogenated methyl or ethyl cyanacetate in presence of sulphuric acid, whilst F. Hoffmann-La Roche & Co.[48] hydrogenated potassium cyanacetate in ammoniacal solution, using a nickel catalyst. Lederle Labs., Inc. prepared β-alanine by the addition of ammonia to acrylonitrile at 150° C.[49] or to a salt of acrylic acid.[50] It has also been prepared by the action of ammonia on bis-β-cyanoethylamine,[51] on thiodihydroacrylonitrile,[52] on ethylene cyanhydrin [53] and on β-alkoxypropionitriles.[54]

A. Galat [55] prepared β-alanine by the addition of phthalimide to acrylonitrile, followed by acid hydrolysis of the β-phthalimidopropionitrile. β-Alanine hydrochloride was converted into β-alanine by the use of lithium hydroxide. A variant of this method is to fuse phthalic acid or anhydride with an ester of $\beta\beta'$-imino-dipropionic acid capable of forming a volatile acrylic ester and hydrolysing the phthalimido-propionic ester so formed.[56] Finally, esters of β-alanine can be prepared by reduction of nitropropionic esters.[57]

References to Section 3

1. R. J. Williams, H. H. Weinstock, E. Rohrmann, J. H. Truesdail, H. K. Mitchell and C. E. Meyer, *J. Amer. Chem. Soc.*, 1939, **61**, 454.
2. R. J. Williams and R. Moser, *ibid.*, 1934, **56**, 169.
3. H. K. Mitchell, H. H. Weinstock, E. E. Snell, S. R. Stanbery and R. J. Williams, *ibid.*, 1940, **62**, 1776.
4. E. T. Stiller, J. C. Keresztesy and J. Finkelstein, *ibid.*, 1779.
5. R. J. Williams, H. K. Mitchell, H. H. Weinstock and E. E. Snell, *ibid.*, 1784.
6. S. H. Babcock and T. H. Jukes, *ibid.*, 1628.
7. E. T. Stiller, S. A. Harris, J. Finkelstein, J. C. Keresztesy and K. Folkers, *ibid.*, 1785.

8. D. W. Woolley, *J. Amer. Chem. Soc.*, 1940, **62**, 2251.
9. T. Reichstein and A. Grüssner, *Helv. Chim. Acta*, 1940, **23**, 650.
10. A. Grüssner, H. Gätzi-Fichter and T. Reichstein, *ibid.*, 1276.
11. M. Gätzi-Fichter, M. Reich and T. Reichstein, *ibid.*, 1941, **24**, 185.
12. R. T. Major and J. Finkelstein, *J. Amer. Chem. Soc.*, 1941, **63**, 1368.
13. E. T. Stiller and P. F. Wiley, *ibid.*, 1237.
14. R. Bental and M. Tishler, *ibid.*, 1946, **68**, 1463.
15. R. Kuhn and T. Wieland, *Ber.*, 1940, **73**, 962, 971.
16. R. Kuhn and T. Wieland, *ibid.*, 1941, **74**, 218.
17. H. C. Parke and E. J. Lawson, *J. Amer. Chem. Soc.*, 1941, **63**, 2869.
18. Merck and Co., B.P. 535988 ; U.S.P. 2396477.
19. Merck and Co., B.P. 551883.
20. Merck and Co., B.P. 553317.
21. Merck and Co., B.P. 552365, 554558.
22. Merck and Co., B.P. 552705.
23. Merck and Co., B.P. 554407, 551990.
24. F. Hoffmann-La Roche & Co., B.P. 552036.
25. F. Hoffmann-La Roche & Co., B.P. 551990.
26. F. Hoffmann-La Roche & Co., B.P. 552581.
27. Roche Products Ltd., B.P. 552713.
28. F. Hoffmann-La Roche & Co., B.P. 569083.
29. F. Hoffmann-La Roche & Co., B.P. 580509.
30. F. Hoffmann-La Roche & Co., B.P. 568355.
31. F. Hoffmann-La Roche & Co., B.P. 550593.
32. Roche Products Ltd., B.P. 559893.
33. F. Hoffmann-La Roche, B.P. 562267.
34. National Oil Products Co., B.P. 552326.
35. National Oil Products Co., B.P. 557761.
36. Lederle Labs., Inc., B.P. 561877.
37. Lederle Labs., Inc., B.P. 571915.
38. Lederle Labs., Inc., B.P. 566858.
39. Parke, Davis & Co., B.P. 564996.
40. Parke, Davis & Co., B.P. 565976.
41. F. Hoffmann-La Roche & Co., B.P. 547923.
42. Roche Products Ltd., B.P. 570341.
42a. Merck & Co., B.P. 626498.
43. Parke, Davis & Co., U.S.P. 2399362.
44. F. Weygand, *Ber.*, 1941, **74**, 256.
45. Lederle Labs., Inc., B.P. 557849 ; U.S.P. 2401547.
46. Lederle Labs., Inc., B.P. 657850.
47. National Oil Products Co., B.P. 558494.
48. F. Hoffmann-La Roche & Co., B.P. 561574.
49. Lederle Labs., Inc., B.P. 558682.
50. Lederle Labs., Inc., B.P. 561013.
51. American Cyanamid Co., U.S.P. 2334163.
52. American Cyanamid Co., U.S.P. 2335653.
53. American Cyanamid Co., Can. P. 417165.

54. American Cyanamid Co., U.S.P. 2335605 ; Lederle Labs., Inc., U.S.P. 2336067.
55. A. Galat, *J. Amer. Chem. Soc.*, 1945, **67**, 1414.
56. Nopco Chemical Co., B.P. 627816.
57. F. Hoffmann-La Roche & Co., B.P. 551990.

4. PROPERTIES OF PANTOTHENIC ACID

D-Pantothenic acid has not been obtained in the free state, and is usually supplied in the form of its sodium or calcium salt. The sodium salt is a white, very hygroscopic solid, crystallising in colourless needles, m.p. 122 to 124° C., with a specific rotation of $[\alpha]_D^{13°} = +29°$ or $[\alpha]_D^{25°} = +27°$ in water, the concentration of the solution being 1·9. According to H. C. Parke and E. J. Lawson,[1] it is much less hygroscopic after crystallisation from absolute ethyl or isopropyl alcohol. The calcium salt is a white powder, less hygroscopic than the sodium salt. It was obtained crystalline by Levy *et al.*,[2] and by J. H. Ford,[3] who recorded a m.p. of 170 to 172° C.

Quinine D-pantothenate has m.p. 136° C. and optical rotation $[\alpha]_D^{19°} = -95°$, whilst quinine L-pantothenate has m.p. 183·5° C. and optical rotation $[\alpha]_D^{18°} = -121°$, both rotations being measured in water.[4] Cinchonidine D-pantothenate has m.p. 178 to 179° C. and optical rotation $[\alpha]_D^{18°} = -62·8°$ in water.[5]

Ethyl D-pantothenate is a colourless oil with an optical rotation of $[\alpha]_D^{19°} = +36·8°$ in absolute alcohol.

References to Section 4

1. H. C. Parke and E. J. Lawson, *J. Amer. Chem. Soc.*, 1941, **63**, 2869.
2. H. Levy, J. Weijlard and E. T. Stiller, *ibid.*, 2846.
3. J. H. Ford, *ibid.*, 1946, **68**, 1666.
4. A. Grüssner, H. Gätzi-Fichter and T. Reichstein, *Helv. Chim. Acta*, 1940, **23**, 1276.
5. R. Kuhn and T. Wieland, *Ber.*, 1941, **74**, 218.

5. STABILITY OF PANTOTHENIC ACID

Pantothenic acid is one of the more heat-stable members of the vitamin B complex, but the pH of its solutions must be kept approximately neutral, as it is readily hydrolysed under acidic or alkaline conditions. The substance has maximum stability over the pH range 5·5 to 7·0.[1]

Reference to Section 5

1. D. V. Frost, *Ind. Eng. Chem., Anal. Ed.*, 1943, **15**, 306.

6. ESTIMATION OF PANTOTHENIC ACID

Attention has already been directed (page 348) to early attempts to estimate the " filtrate factor " by its effect on the growth of rats and chicks, but it is doubtful if such methods are sufficiently specific to do more than give very approximate results, although T. H. Jukes [1] used chicks to measure the pantothenic acid contents of a variety of foodstuffs, and J. D. S. Bacon and G. N. Jenkins [2] described an apparently satisfactory method of assay, using rats.

Up to the present no chemical method of estimation has been proposed, although J. J. Lingane and O. L. Davis [3] found that pantothenic acid was reduced at the dropping mercury electrode. Its polarogram was not sufficiently well defined, however, for the polarographic method to be used for its estimation.

Microbiological Methods of Assay

The only satisfactory methods of assay so far published have been microbiological methods, and these have been extensively used. Among the first micro-organisms to be tested for this purpose were *Streptococcus lactis*, *Bacillus brassicae* and *Propionibacterium pentosaceum*,[4] but these failed to give satisfactory results. The first successful method was devised by Pennington *et al.*,[5] who used *Lactobacillus helveticus*, the organism introduced by Snell and Strong for the estimation of riboflavine (page 157). The turbidity of cultures grown on a suitable medium or the amount of lactic acid produced was proportional to the amount of pantothenic acid added. Strong *et al.*[6] described a similar method, using the same organism, whilst H. R. Skeggs and L. D. Wright [7] developed an analogous method with *L. arabinosus* as test organism. M. J. Pelczar and J. R. Porter [8] used *Proteus morganii*, the growth of which on a suitable medium was proportional to the amount of pantothenic acid present. The amount of growth was measured by determining the bacterial nitrogen or by measuring the change in pH or the increase in turbidity. The method was claimed to be highly specific, but the organism also responded to pantoic acid. *L. helveticus* was the organism used by M. Landy and D. M. Dicken [9] in the method developed by them for the assay of six members of the vitamin B complex using the same basal medium. Modifications to the medium of Pennington *et al.* were suggested by J. L. Stokes and B. B. Martin [10] who found that merely increasing the amounts of glucose and sodium acetate increased the production of acid, and by A. E. Light and M. F. Clarke.[11] Good agreement was reported by Hoag *et al.*[12] for results obtained with *L. helveticus* and *L. arabinosus*, but the response was greater and more rapid with the latter ; growth was measured either turbidimetrically after fourteen hours or by titration after twenty-four to thirty hours. Other bacteria that have been used for the assay of pantothenic acid are *Streptobacterium plantarum* [13, 14] and *Lactobacillus bulgaricus*.[15]

Yeast was used by Atkin *et al.*,[16] with a medium containing ammonium sulphate as the source of nitrogen, together with sufficient asparagine to prevent interference by β-alanine, which also stimulates the growth of yeast. *Saccharomyces cerevisiae* var. *ellipsoideus* was found to be suitable for the assay of pantothenic acid by Emery *et al.*,[17] who also obtained promising results with another yeast, *Kloeckera brevis*.

A possible complication in the microbiological assay of pantothenic acid is that the two products formed by the hydrolysis of pantothenic acid, namely β-alanine and pantoic acid, may stimulate the growth of the micro-organism used. For this reason, only organisms that respond specifically to pantothenic acid should be used, or else some method must be introduced of suppressing the effect of the degradation products. An example of this is the use of asparagine to suppress the response of yeast to β-alanine.

Microbiological Response to β-Alanine and Pantoic Acid

β-Alanine can be estimated by measuring first the growth response of yeast, which is stimulated by pantothenic acid and β-alanine, and then that of *Streptobacterium plantarum*, which responds to pantothenic acid only and subtracting the second result from the first.[14] *Corynebacterium diphtheriae*, like yeast, also responds to both β-alanine and pantothenic acid.[18] *Acetobacter suboxydans*, on the other hand, responds to pantoic acid but not to β-alanine,[19] and can therefore be used for the assay of pantolactone. As already noted, *Proteus morganii* responds to both pantothenic acid and pantolactone.

Preparation of Solutions for Assay

It is particularly important to prevent hydrolysis of pantothenic acid during its liberation from foodstuffs, in which it generally occurs in the bound state. In their original method, Pennington *et al.*[5] autoclaved the material with or without previous autolysis under benzene, whilst other authors have used enzymes, such as clarase or " mylase P ", to liberate pantothenic acid.[6, 16, 20, 21, 22] A mixture of chicken liver enzyme and intestinal phosphatase is said to be even more effective.[23] With some sources of pantothenic acid, such as malt products, treatment with cold dilute alkali solution prior to digestion with papain and takadiastase increased the extraction 2- to 4-fold.[24]

A further difficulty encountered in the assay of foodstuffs with

L. helveticus was interference by other growth stimulants, subsequently shown to be fatty acids ; this phenomenon was first encountered in the assay of riboflavine (page 158) and interference from this source was overcome by extraction of the medium and test solution with solvent, as in the assay of riboflavine.[25]

References to Section 6

1. T. H. Jukes, *J. Nutrition*, 1941, **21**, 193.
2. J. D. S. Bacon and G. N. Jenkins, *Biochem. J.*, 1943, **37**, 492.
3. J. J. Lingane and O. L. Davis, *J. Biol. Chem.*, 1941, **137**, 567.
4. H. K. Mitchell, H. H. Weinstock, E. E. Snell, S. R. Stanbery and R. J. Williams, *J. Amer. Chem. Soc.*, 1940, **62**, 1776, 1779, 1785, 1791.
5. D. Pennington, E. E. Snell and R. J. Williams, *J. Biol. Chem.*, 1940, **135**, 213 ; D. Pennington, E. E. Snell, H. K. Mitchell, J. R. McMahan and R. J. Williams, *Univ. Texas Pub.*, 1941, No. 4137, 14.
6. F. M. Strong, R. E. Feeney and A. Earle, *Ind. Eng. Chem.*, *Anal. Ed.*, 1941, **13**, 566.
7. H. R. Skeggs and L. D. Wright, *J. Biol. Chem.*, 1944, **156**, 21.
8. M. J. Pelczar and J. R. Porter, *Proc. Soc. Exp. Biol. Med.*, 1940, **43**, 151 ; *J. Biol. Chem.*, 1941, **139**, 111.
9. M. Landy and D. M. Dicken, *J. Lab. Clin. Med.*, 1942, **27**, 1086.
10. J. L. Stokes and B. B. Martin, *J. Biol. Chem.*, 1943, **147**, 483.
11. A. E. Light and M. F. Clarke, *ibid.*, 739.
12. E. H. Hoag, H. P. Sarett and V. H. Cheldelin, *Ind. Eng. Chem.*, *Anal. Ed.*, 1945, **17**, 60.
13. R. Kuhn and T. Wieland, *Ber.*, 1940, **73**, 962.
14. N. Nielsen, V. Hartelius and G. Johansen, *Naturwiss.*, 1943, **31**, 550.
15. K. Bhagvat, *Current Sci.*, 1944, **13**, 75.
16. L. Atkin, W. L. Williams, A. S. Schultz and C. N. Frey, *Ind. Eng. Chem.*, *Anal. Ed.*, 1944, **16**, 67.
17. W. B. Emery, N. McLeod and F. A. Robinson, *Biochem. J.*, 1946, **40**, 426.
18. J. H. Mueller and A. W. Klotz, *J. Amer. Chem. Soc.*, 1938, **60**, 3086.
19. H. P. Sarett and V. H. Cheldelin, *J. Biol. Chem.*, 1945, **159**, 311.
20. H. A. Waisman, L. M. Henderson, J. M. McIntire and C. A. Elvehjem, *J. Nutrition*, 1942, **23**, 239.
21. A. H. Buskirk and R. A. Delor, *J. Biol. Chem.*, 1942, **145**, 707.
22. E. Willerton and W. H. Cromwell, *Ind. Eng. Chem.*, *Anal. Ed.*, 1942, **14**, 603.
23. J. B. Neilands and F. M. Strong, *Arch. Biochem.*, 1948, **19**, 287.
24. J. S. Harrison, *Nature*, 1949, **163**, 798 ; *Analyst*, 1949, **74**, 597.
25. F. M. Strong and L. E. Carpenter, *ibid.*, 909.

7. OCCURRENCE OF PANTOTHENIC ACID IN FOODSTUFFS

W. H. Peterson and C. A. Elvehjem [1] showed that the " chick anti-dermatitis factor " was present in yeast, whilst Waisman et al.[2] estimated the minimal protective levels for chicks of certain animal tissues, and reported that liver and kidney were the richest sources of pantothenic acid, which was also present in heart, spleen, brain, pancreas, tongue and lung ; muscle was but a poor source. Most of the early values recorded for the pantothenic acid content of foodstuffs are due to T. H. Jukes,[3] who also used the chick assay method. He found yeast to be the richest source, with 140 to 350 μg. per g. of dry weight. Other rich sources were liver, containing 25 to 60 ; egg, 8 to 48 ; egg yolk, 50 to 100 ; and broccoli, 46 μg. per g.

The following were moderately good sources : whole milk, 1·3 to 4·2 ; skim milk, 2·1 to 4·3 ; buttermilk, 3·5 to 5·6 ; whey, 2·4 to 5·7 ; lean beef, 10 ; canned salmon, 7 ; wheat, 11 ; wheat bran, 24 ; wheat germ, 7 ; barley, 10 ; yellow corn, 8 ; polished rice, 4 ; potatoes, 6·5 ; split peas, 20 to 22 ; carrots, 2 ; tomatoes, 1 ; spinach, 1·2 ; kale, 2·3 to 3·6 ; onion, 1·2 ; orange, 0·7 ; banana, 0·7 ; and walnuts, 8 μg. per g.

The following foodstuffs were poor sources, containing less than 1 μg. per g. : canned beans, canned peas, turnips, beets, egg white, prunes, raisins, canned peaches, apples and almonds.

According to Teply et al.[4] the pantothenic acid content of wheat averaged about 13 μg. per g., ranging from 9 to 17 μg. per g. according to the variety. Patent flour contained 5·7 ; first clear flour, 9·6 ; second clear flour, 12·8 ; and wheat germ, 15·3 μg. per g. Wholemeal flour was richer in pantothenic acid than 85 % extraction flour and this, in turn, was richer than white (73 % extraction) flour ; wheat germ contained twice as much as wholemeal.[5]

Cow's colostrum contained less pantothenic acid than cow's milk, namely 2·2 compared with 3·7 μg. per ml., and ewe's colostrum less than ewe's milk, namely, 2·6 against 3·7 μg. per ml.[6] The pantothenic acid content of cow's milk rose to 4 μg. per ml. during the first nine days of lactation and then fell to the normal level of 3·5 μg. per ml.[7]

Waisman et al.[8] assayed different animal tissues by the micro-biological method after digestion with an enzyme preparation ; pantothenic acid was liberated fairly completely by pancreatin and to a more limited extent by other enzymes with a lower proteolytic activity. They found that beef, pork, lamb and chicken tissues were good sources of pantothenic acid. In general, liver and kidney were the richest sources, containing 44 to 88 and 32 to 49 μg. per g. respectively. Striated muscle contained 7 to 21, heart 12 to 25, brain about 36 and spleen 13 μg. of pantothenic acid per g. Cooking and commercial processing destroyed 20 to 40 % of the pantothenic acid present in the raw meat.

Fresh cheese contained 1·3 to 9·6 μg. of pantothenic acid per g.[9] and the amount increased 2- to 3-fold on ripening. Sorghum contained 10·3 to 15·9 μg. per g.[10]

According to P. B. Pearson and C. J. Burgin [11] the richest known source of pantothenic acid is royal jelly, the special food given to those bee larvae that are destined to become queens. Many attempts have been made to determine the factor or factors in royal jelly responsible for this astonishing transformation, for queen and worker bees are produced from identical larvae, the difference in development being due solely to the nature of the food which each receives. It has frequently been suggested that the activity of royal jelly may be due to the presence of vitamins, especially the fertility vitamin E, or of hormones, especially the gonadotrophic hormone, but the amounts of these factors present are not sufficiently high to account for this remarkable effect of royal jelly. Pearson and Burgin, using the microbiological method of assay, found that royal jelly contained an average of 183 μg. per g. of fresh weight or 511 μg. per g. of dry weight, as compared with 200 and 180 μg. per g. of dry weight respectively for yeast and liver, the next richest sources. Kitzes et al.[12] confirmed the high pantothenic acid content of royal jelly, obtaining a value of 320 μg. per g., but they also showed that it contained an exceptionally large amount of biotin (page 424). A satisfactory explanation of the curious effect of royal jelly does not yet appear to have been found, as pantothenic acid alone will not bring about the transformation of bee larvae into queens (see page 390). Pollen contained about 30 μg. of pantothenic acid per g.[12, 13] and honey only 0·55 μg. per g.[12]

Tea contains about 30 μg. of pantothenic acid per g.[14]

References to Section 7

1. W. H. Peterson and C. A. Elvehjem, *J. Nutrition*, 1939, **18**, 181.
2. H. A. Waisman, O. Mickelsen and C. A. Elvehjem, *ibid.*, 247.
3. T. H. Jukes, *ibid.*, 1942, **21**, 193.
4. L. J. Teply, F. M. Strong and C. A. Elvehjem, *ibid.*, 1942, **24**, 167.
5. A. M. Copping, *Biochem. J.*, 1943, **37**, 12.
6. P. B. Pearson and A. L. Darnell, *J. Nutrition*, 1946, **31**, 51.
7. J. M. Lawrence, B. L. Herrington and L. A. Maynard, *ibid.*, 1946, **32**, 73.
8. H. A. Waisman, L. M. Henderson, J. M. McIntire and C. A. Elvehjem, *ibid.*, 1942, **23**, 239.
9. R. A. Sullivan, E. Bloom and J. Jarmol, *ibid.*, 1943, **25**, 463.
10. G. Knox, V. G. Heller and J. B. Sieglinger, *Food Res.*, 1944, **9**, 89.
11. P. B. Pearson and C. J. Burgin, *Proc. Soc. Exp. Biol. Med.*, 1941, **48**, 415.

12. G. Kitzes, H. A. Schuette and C. A. Elvehjem, *J. Nutrition*, 1943, **26**, 241.
13. P. B. Pearson, *Proc. Soc. Exp. Biol. Med.*, 1942, **51**, 291.
14. E. A. M. Bradford and E. B. Hughes, *Analyst*, 1945, **70**, 2.

8. EFFECT OF PANTOTHENIC ACID DEFICIENCY IN ANIMALS

Effect on Skin and Hair of Rats

Although the first symptom to be associated with pantothenic acid deficiency was the development of dermatitis in chicks,[1, 2] a connection between pantothenic acid deficiency and pigment formation in the hair of black or piebald rats was recognised even before the structure of the " filtrate factor " was known. Thus Oleson *et al.*,[3] Mohammad *et al.*[4] and Chick *et al.*[5] observed that a " filtrate factor " concentrate prevented the greying of hair (achromotrichia) induced in rats by feeding a purified diet, whilst G. Lunde and H. Kringstad[6] showed that grey hair in foxes could similarly be prevented by administration of a concentrate containing an alkali-labile factor, which they called vitamin B_x.

This ability to prevent grey hair in rats was also possessed by a preparation containing 40 to 50 % of pantothenic acid[7, 8] and by pure pantothenic acid.[9, 10] The growth rate of the animals was also increased by the addition of the vitamin to the diet. György *et al.*[7, 8] stated that pantothenic acid was not the only member of the vitamin B complex that could cure achromotrichia, and suggested that biotin might have a similar effect. As will be seen subsequently *p*-aminobenzoic acid (page 551), folic acid (page 487) and inositol (page 572) are also capable under certain conditions of preventing grey hair in rats.

According to G. A. Emerson and H. M. Evans,[11] and to P. L. Pavcek and H. M. Baum,[12] pantothenic acid did not restore the fur of rats to its original state, but resulted in stippling. Inositol did not improve the condition further,[11] but administration of cystine[12] resulted in complete recovery. According to R. R. Williams,[13] pantothenic acid did not cure achromotrichia, but this extreme view does not appear to have received support from other workers. Rustiness could be produced in the fur of albino rats by the omission of pantothenic acid and choline from the diet, and the condition was prevented by giving pantothenic acid with choline, an observation of considerable significance in the light of more recent work on the function of pantothenic acid (see page 391).

D. W. Woolley[14] observed that pantothenic acid cured hairlessness (alopecia) in mice, induced by feeding certain purified diets ; this, like achromotrichia, is a condition associated with other members of the vitamin B complex. Alopecia has also been observed in piebald rats fed a purified diet deficient in pantothenic acid, and was accompanied by mild generalised scaling of the paws and tail and pattern-greying.[15] The dermatitis and pattern-greying, but not the scaliness of the paws and tail, were cured by pantothenic acid. According to L. R. Richardson and A. G. Hogan,[16] the dermatitis was cured by pyridoxine and pantothenic acid together but not by either separately.

Haemorrhages and Degeneration of the Adrenal Glands in Rats

Another symptom observed in pantothenic acid-deficient rats, and possibly specifically associated with this deficiency, is "blood-caked whiskers".[9, 17] This was accompanied by haemorrhages under the skin and in the adrenal cortex. A condition analogous to blood-caked whiskers, due to the secretion of porphyrin from the lachrymal glands was induced in rats by restricting the water intake to 25 to 50 % of normal.[18] Since the adrenal cortex is known to regulate water metabolism, it seems likely that blood-caked whiskers may be a secondary symptom due to degeneration of the adrenals, which was observed in pantothenic acid-deficient rats by Daft et al.,[19] in addition to epistaxis, ocular exudates, "spectacled eyes" and loss of hair. According to L. L. Ashburn[20] the adrenals in such cases showed congestion, haemorrhage, atrophy, necrosis, fibrosis and cortical fat depletion. The spleen and pancreas were normal, however, though testicular function was impaired and the upper epiphyseal cartilage showed hypoplasia. These symptoms disappeared or decreased in severity on administration of pantothenic acid, whereas untreated controls grew worse.

The occurrence of adrenal haemorrhage and necrosis in pantothenic acid-deficient rats was confirmed by W. D. Salmon and R. W. Engel,[21] by Supplee et al.[22] and by Ugami et al.[23] However, the addition of adrenal cortex extract, desoxycorticosterone acetate, thyroid or anterior pituitary extract failed to cure the symptoms of pantothenic acid deficiency.[24] Pantothenic acid-deficient rats, unlike animals maintained on an adequate diet, did not exhibit lymphopenia two hours after either swimming or the administration of adrenocorticotropic hormone, indicating that changes in the adrenal cortex are brought about by pantothenic acid deficiency.[24a]

Other Symptoms in Rats

S. W. Lippincott and H. P. Morris[25] reported that the adrenals of pantothenic acid-deficient rats were normal, but noted myelin degeneration of the sciatic nerve and spinal cord. This supported the earlier claim of P. H. Phillips and R. W. Engel[26] that pantothenic acid was necessary for the maintenance of the normal intact structure of the spinal cord in chicks (page 368).

H. W. Deane and J. M. McKibbin [27] suggested that a deficiency of pantothenic acid acted as an " alarming stimulus on the pituitary ", causing hypertrophy and over-production of corticosterone-like steroids from the zona fasciculata.

Pantothenic acid deficiency has been said to stimulate the production of body fat.[28] It may also result in inflammatory changes in the respiratory tract of rats, leading to bronchitis and bronchopneumonia, and lobular hepatitis and fatty infiltration of the liver ; [29] at the same time, the erythrocytes and haemoglobin increased and leucocytosis occurred. Carter et al.,[30] however, found that pantothenic acid-deficient rats developed a severe hypochromic anaemia, with a fall in haemoglobin, erythrocytes and polymorphonuclear leucocytes, accompanied by splenomegaly, myeloid transformation, hyperplasia of the bone marrow and failure of the erythropoietic and leucopoietic cells to mature. Administration of pantothenic acid restored the blood picture to normal. Like Lippincott and Morris, they observed no pathological changes in the adrenal cortex. It has been stated that pantothenic acid reduces the toxic effects of thyreoglobulin in rats.[31] A deficiency of pantothenic acid may aggravate the symptoms of biotin deficiency induced in rats by feeding succinylsulphathiazole.[32] Administration of biotin protected against the biotin deficiency and at the same time reduced the severity of the symptoms of pantothenic acid deficiency.

According to Taylor et al.[33] the number of young rats in a litter was increased by 25 % when 100 μg. of calcium pantothenate daily was added to the diet, although the day-old offspring had relatively smaller brains and hearts than had controls. In confirmation of this observation, M. M. Nelson and H. M. Evans [34] reported that pantothenic acid deficiency adversely affected reproduction in the rat, for, when animals were made deficient sixteen to twenty-three days before mating, or even as late as the day of mating, either no implantation occurred or the foetuses were resorbed or defective. Pantothenic acid deficiency did not affect reproduction when instituted on the thirteenth day of gestation. The effect on reproduction was not due to inanition or other dietary deficiencies.

Pantothenic acid-deficient rats also suffered changes in the cornea [34a] and developed ulcers of the tongue [34b] and duodenal ulcers.[34c]

Dogs

Some of the results of pantothenic acid deficiency in dogs resemble those in rats, but there are important differences. Thus Fouts et al.[35] observed that pantothenic acid-deficient dogs lost weight and appetite and developed anaemia, whilst Shaeffer *et al.*[36] noted the onset of fatty livers and haemorrhagic kidney degeneration. According to J. V. Scudi and M. Hamlin [37] and R. H. Silber,[38] the production of fatty livers was the most constant, if not the only, pathological change associated with a deficiency of pantothenic acid. However, other symptoms have been recorded by other workers. For example, Shaeffer *et al.*[36] observed increased respiratory and heart rate, convulsions, gastrointestinal symptoms, mottled thymus glands and gastritis or enteritis in addition to the symptoms noted above. Mottled thymus glands was a symptom also observed in " filtrate factor " deficiency in foxes.[39]

Bly *et al.*[40] also recorded gastrointestinal disturbances in dogs including a 50 % decrease in gastrointestinal motility and a 40 to 65 % decrease in the rates of digestion and absorption of protein and carbohydrate ; administration of calcium pantothenate cured the condition immediately. According to A. O. Seeler and R. H. Silber,[41] the onset of pantothenic acid deficiency in adult dogs was very slow and signs might not be observed for four and a half years.

Pigs

Pantothenic acid is also essential for the growth of young pigs, and a deficiency results in symptoms similar to those observed in rats, including a subnormal appetite, emaciation, loss of co-ordination (" goose-stepping "), loss of hair, excessive nasal secretion, diarrhoea and gastritis with involvement of the large intestine, degenerative changes in the peripheral nerves, posterior root ganglia and the posterior roots and posterior funiculi of the spinal cord.[42, 43] At autopsy, diffuse hyperemia was noted,[44] with an increase in the size of the lymphoid follicles and formation of small ulcers leading to inflammatory changes involving the large intestine. The mucosa lining cells were atrophied, with abscess formation and ulceration. The animals also suffered from a normocytic anaemia, accompanied by a fall in the serum chloride and an increase in the carbon dioxide-combining capacity of the blood.

Monkeys

In the monkey, pantothenic acid deficiency was characterised by lack of growth, ataxia, greying and thinning of the fur, anaemia, diarrhoea and cachexia.[45] Pantothenic acid brought about incomplete remission of these symptoms.

Chicks

As already noted, chicks suffering from a deficiency of pantothenic acid developed dermatitis [46, 47] and lesions of the spinal cord.[27] These included myelin and axon degeneration, but there was no degradation of the peripheral nerves.[48] Black Minorca chicks showed partial depigmentation of the feathers.[49] Some evidence exists [47] for believing that pantothenic acid is essential for reproduction in the hen.

The pantothenic acid content of eggs depended on the diet of the hens,[50] but remained remarkably constant during the embryonic development of the chick.[51] Hens fed on diets containing 3·9, 8·6 and 15·7 μg. of pantothenic acid per day produced eggs containing 4·9, 7·9 and 14·0 μg. per g. respectively ; these hatched into chicks containing 5·2, 8·3 and 13·6 μg. per g.

Fish

It has been stated [52] that pantothenic acid is an essential factor, together with riboflavine and pyridoxine, for young rainbow trout, but McLaren et al.[53] showed that the anaemia which was attributed to a deficiency of these three factors was cured by a mixture of riboflavine, pyridoxine and choline. Nevertheless, they showed [54] that pantothenic acid was necessary for trout to the extent of 1 to 2 μg. per 100 g. of diet. In its absence, the fish developed clubbed gills.

Effect on Infection

Pantothenic acid-deficient rats were found to be less susceptible than normal rats to type I pneumococcus infection [55] and pantothenic acid-deficient mice were more resistant than normal mice to Theiler's encephalomyelitis virus, though not to the Lansing strain of poliomyelitis.[56] Some impairment of antibody response was observed in pantothenic acid-, as well as in pyridoxine-deficient rats. Pantothenic acid deficiency increased the severity of *Trypanosoma lewisi* infection in rats,[58] and the supplementing of a diet with pantothenic acid caused a *T. evansi* infection to develop more slowly.[59]

References to Section 8

1. C. A. Elvehjem and C. J. Koehn, *Nature*, 1934, **134,** 1007 ; *J. Biol. Chem.*, 1935, **108,** 709.
2. S. Lepkovsky and T. H. Jukes, *ibid.*, 1936, **114,** 109.
3. J. J. Oleson, C. A. Elvehjem and E. B. Hart, *Proc. Soc. Exp. Biol. Med.*, 1939, **42,** 283.
4. A. Mohammad, O. H. Emerson, G. A. Emerson and H. M. Evans, *J. Biol. Chem.*, 1940, **133,** 17.
5. H. Chick, T. F. Macrae and A. N. Worden, *Biochem. J.*, 1940, **34,** 580.
6. G. Lunde and H. Kringstad, *Naturwiss.*, 1939, **27,** 755.
7. P. György and C. E. Poling, *Science*, 1940, **92,** 202 ; *Proc. Soc. Exp. Biol. Med.*, 1940, **48,** 773.

8. P. György, C. E. Poling and Y. SubbaRow, *J. Biol. Chem.*, 1940, **132**, 789.

9. K. Unna, G. V. Richards and W. L. Sampson, *J. Nutrition*, 1941, **22**, 553.

10. L. M. Henderson, J. M. McIntire, H. A. Waisman and C. A. Elvehjem, *ibid.*, 1942, **23**, 47.

11. G. A. Emerson and H. M. Evans, *Proc. Soc. Exp. Biol. Med.*, 1941, **46**, 655.

12. P. L. Pavcek and H. M. Baum, *ibid.*, 1941, **47**, 271.

13. R. R. Williams, *Science*, 1940, **92**, 561.

14. D. W. Woolley, *Proc. Soc. Exp. Biol. Med.*, 1941, **46**, 565.

15. M. Sullivan and J. Nicholls, *Arch. Dermat. Syphil.*, 1942, **45**, 917.

16. L. R. Richardson and A. G. Hogan, *Proc. Soc. Exp. Biol. Med.*, 1940, **44**, 583.

17. K. Unna, *J. Nutrition*, 1940, **20**, 565.

18. F. H. J. Figge and W. B. Atkinson, *Proc. Soc. Exp. Biol. Med.*, 1941, **48**, 112.

19. F. S. Daft, W. H. Sebrell, S. H. Babcock and T. H. Jukes, *U.S. Publ. Health Rep.*, 1940, **55**, 1333.

20. L. L. Ashburn, *ibid.*, 1337.

21. W. D. Salmon and R. W. Engel, *Proc. Soc. Exp. Biol. Med.*, 1940, **45**, 621.

22. G. C. Supplee, R. C. Bender and O. J. Kahlenberg, *Endocrinology*, 1942, **30**, 355.

23. S. Ugami, Y. Yamao, K. Michi, S. Funahashi, S. Emoto and A. Ichiba, *Sci. Papers Inst. Phys. Chem. Res. Tokyo*, 1941, **38**, 312.

24. C. W. Mushett and K. Unna, *J. Nutrition*, 1941, **22**, 565.

24a. M. E. Dumm, P. Ovando, P. Roth and E. P. Ralli, *Proc. Soc. Exp. Biol. Med.*, 1949, **71**, 368.

25. S. W. Lippincott and H. P. Morris, *J. Nat. Cancer Inst.*, 1941, **2**, 39.

26. P. H. Phillips and R. W. Engel, *J. Nutrition*, 1939, **18**, 227.

27. H. W. Deane and J. M. McKibbin, *Endocrinology*, 1946, **38**, 385.

28. Le R. Voris and H. P. Moore, *ibid.*, 1943, **25**, 7.

29. R. Jürgens and H. Pfaltz, *Z. Vitaminforsch.*, 1944, **14**, 243.

30. C. W. Carter, R. G. Macfarlane, J. R. O'Brien and A. H. T. Robb-Smith, *Biochem. J.*, 1945, **39**, 339.

31. J. Abelin, *Experientia*, 1945, **1**, 231.

32. G. A. Emerson and E. Wurtz, *Proc. Soc. Exp. Biol. Med.*, 1944, **57**, 47.

33. A. Taylor, D. Pennington and J. Thacker, *J. Nutrition*, 1943, **25**, 389.

34. M. M. Nelson and H. M. Evans, *ibid.*, 1946, **31**, 497.

34a. L. L. Bowles, W. K. Hall, V. P. Sydenstricker and C. W. Hock, *ibid.*, 1949, **37**, 9.

34b. D. E. Ziskin, M. Karshan, G. Stein and D. A. Dragiff, *ibid.*, 457.

34c. B. N. Berg, T. F. Zucker and L. M. Zucker, *Proc. Soc. Exp. Biol. Med.*, 1949, **71**, 374.

35. P. J. Fouts, O. M. Helmer and S. Lepkovsky, *J. Nutrition*, 1940, **19**, 393.

36. A. E. Shaeffer, J. M. McKibbin and C. A. Elvehjem, *J. Biol. Chem.*, 1942, **143**, 321.

37. J. V. Scudi and M. Hamlin, *J. Nutrition*, 1944, **27**, 425.

38. R. H. Silber, *ibid.*, 1942, **24**, 273.

39. A. F. Morgan and H. M. Simms, *ibid.*, 1940, **20**, 627.

40. C. G. Bly, F. W. Heggeness and E. S. Nasset, *ibid.*, 1943, **28**, 161.

41. A. O. Seeler and R. H. Silber, *ibid.*, 1945, **30**, 111.

42. E. H. Hughes, *J. Agric. Res.*, 1942, **64**, 185.

43. M. M. Wintrobe, M. H. Miller, R. H. Follis, H. J. Stein, C. Mushatt and S. Humphreys, *J. Nutrition*, 1942, **24**, 345.

44. M. M. Wintrobe, R. H. Follis, R. Alcayaga, M. Paulson and S. Humphreys, *Johns Hopkins Hosp. Bull.*, 1943, **73**, 313.

45. K. B. McCall, H. A. Waisman, C. A. Elvehjem and E. S. Jones, *J. Nutrition*, 1946, **31**, 685.

46. M. K. Dimick and A. Lepp, *ibid.*, 1940, **20**, 413.

47. M. B. Gillis, G. F. Heuser and L. C. Norris, *ibid.*, 1942, **23**, 153.

48. J. H. Shaw and P. H. Phillips, *ibid.*, 1945, **29**, 107.

49. T. C. Groody and M. E. Groody, *Science*, 1942, **95**, 655.

50. E. E. Snell, E. Aline, J. R. Couch and P. B. Pearson, *J. Nutrition*, 1941, **21**, 201.

51. P. B. Pearson, V. H. Melass and R. M. Sherwood, *Arch. Biochem.*, 1945, **7**, 353.

52. A. L. Durr and C. M. McKay, *N. Y. Conservation Dept. Cortland Hatchery Rep.*, 1942, No. 11.

53. B. A. McLaren, E. F. Herman and C. A. Elvehjem, *Arch. Biochem.*, 1946, **10**, 433.

54. B. A. McLaren, E. Keller, D. J. O'Donnell and C. A. Elvehjem, *ibid.*, 1947, **15**, 169.

55. H. D. West, M. J. Bent, R. E. Rivera and R. E. Tisdale, *ibid.*, 1944, **3**, 321.

56. H. C. Lichstein, H. A. Waisman, C. A. Elvehjem and P. F. Clark, *Proc. Soc. Exp. Biol. Med.*, 1944, **56**, 3.

57. A. E. Axelrod, B. B. Carter, R. H. McCoy and R. Geisinger, *ibid.*, 1947, **66**, 137 ; P. P. Ludovici, A. E. Axelrod and B. B. Carter, *ibid.*, 1949, **72**, 81.

58. E. R. Becker, J. Taylor and C. Führmeister, *Iowa State Coll. J. Sci.*, 1947, **21**, 237.

59. H. N. Ray and S. Harbans, *Nature*, 1948, **162**, 849.

9. EFFECT OF PANTOTHENIC ACID DEFICIENCY IN MAN

There is no evidence that uncomplicated pantothenic acid deficiency has ever been observed in man, nor is there any record of pantothenic acid deficiency having been produced artificially in man as, for instance, by maintaining volunteers on a synthetic diet containing sub-optimal amounts of this factor. It is therefore impossible to describe any symptoms that can be attributed solely to a deficiency of pantothenic acid, although some of the symptoms noted in various forms of vitamin B complex deficiency may well have been due to the presence of inadequate amounts of pantothenic acid in the diets responsible.

The reason for the apparent lack of interest in the effect of pantothenic acid deficiency in man is possibly due to the fact that the symptoms noted in animals do not indicate that any particularly important metabolic changes occur such as are associated with a deficiency of aneurine or nicotinic acid, or even of riboflavine. Indeed, the only symptom of deficient animals that has aroused interest among clinical investigators is achromotrichia. The fact that administration of pantothenic acid prevents grey hair in experimental animals maintained on a deficient diet suggested that the same result might be produced by its administration to elderly humans, although there is no evidence to suggest that the greying of human hair is associated with a deficiency of this or any other vitamin. Not only were hopes aroused, but claims were actually made that pantothenic acid was a cure for this particular manifestation of senility, and certain pharmaceutical houses in the U.S.A. were not slow to exploit the idea. In fact, the only clinical report that might be regarded as substantiating such a claim is a very guarded statement by Brandalcone et al.[1] that " some restoration of colour " occurred in two out of forty-nine elderly grey-haired patients when treated with 100 mg. of calcium pantothenate, together with 100 mg. of p-aminobenzoic acid and 50 g. of yeast daily for eight months. Even this modest response was not observed in subsequent experiments by the same authors [2] and by I. Kerlan and R. P. Herwick,[3] and it is reasonably safe to conclude that pantothenic acid does not cause grey hair to return to its original colour in human beings.

References to Section 9

1. H. Brandalcone, E. Main and J. M. Steele, *Proc. Soc. Exp. Biol. Med.*, 1943, **53,** 47.
2. H. Brandalcone, E. Main and J. M. Steele, *Amer. J. Med. Sci.*, 1944, **208,** 315.
3. I. Kerlan and R. P. Herwick, *J. Amer. Med. Assoc.*, 1943, **123,** 391.

10. METABOLISM OF PANTOTHENIC ACID

Blood Concentration

The concentration of pantothenic acid in normal human blood was stated by Stanbery et al.[1] to vary from 18 to 34 μg. per 100 ml., with an average of 20 μg. per 100 ml., and by M. J. Pelczar and J. R. Porter[2] to be between 3 and 9 μg. per 100 ml. H. McIlwain and F. Hawking[3] reported a value of 20 to 40 μg. per 100 ml. for whole human blood or plasma, and values of 40 to 80 μg. per 100 ml. for rat blood and 200 to 400 μg. per 100 ml. for mouse blood. The pantothenic acid concentration of chicken blood and plasma was found to be 43·6 and 51·6 μg. per 100 ml. on an adequate diet and slightly lower on a less adequate diet ;[4] about 86 % of the pantothenic acid was present in the plasma.

Following the intravenous injection of sodium or calcium pantothenate, normal human subjects immediately began to excrete pantothenic acid in the urine, and the blood concentration rose by 50 % in three hours.[5] In patients suffering from pellagra, beriberi or riboflavine deficiency, however, the concentration in the blood decreased. When pantothenic acid was injected into normal subjects the riboflavine as well as the pantothenic acid level of the blood increased and, conversely, administration of riboflavine increased the pantothenic acid, as well as the riboflavine, concentration of the blood. R. H. Silber and K. Unna[6] confirmed the rapid increase in the blood concentration that followed the intravenous injection into dogs of 4 mg. per kg. of bodyweight and noted that the value fell to normal within two hours. They were unable to find any change, however, in the blood riboflavine concentration following pantothenate injection or in the pantothenic acid concentration following injection of riboflavine. The amount of pantothenic acid in the blood of rabbits decreased 20 to 30 % after administration of 5 to 10 g. of glucose.[7] Most of the pantothenic acid in the blood was present in the combined form, the complex being thrown down by protein precipitants.[8]

Pantothenic Acid in Tissues and Body Fluids

The pantothenic acid contents of different human tissues varied considerably, the following values being recorded by Nielsen et al. :[9] muscle, 4 ; liver, 40 ; kidney, 30 ; spleen, 20 ; nerve, 3 ; pancreas, 7 ; adrenals, 5 and pylorus, 10 μg. per g. of dry matter. Free β-alanine was only found in the liver (150 μg. per g.) and pancreas (7·5 μg. per g.).

According to R. H. Silber,[10] the tissues, as well as the blood, of depleted dogs contained less pantothenic acid than the tissues of controls dosed with the vitamin but, compared with normal dogs, low levels were found only in the liver, muscle and brain. Repeated oral administration increased the tissue level above normal and delayed subsequent depletion.

Chicken muscle contained between 1 and 4 μg. of pantothenic acid per g., and the pattern of distribution followed that of aneurine and riboflavine (pages 72, 181).[11] The amount of pantothenic acid in chicken liver bore little relation to the intake, but this influenced the amount present in the leg muscle and breast tissue.[4] With very high levels of intake these three tissues contained 45, 17 and 11 μg. per g. respectively. When pantothenic acid was given to deficient chicks, deposition of the vitamin in the leg and breast tissues occurred rapidly.

A large drop in the pantothenic acid content of the liver of rats occurred when hepatoma were induced by the feeding of p-dimethyl-aminazobenzene.[12] Human and rat cancers contained approximately the same amounts of pantothenic acid as did non-cancerous spleen, lung and skeletal muscle, which are poorer in this factor than the liver, heart, kidney and brain.

Human milk contained 48 μg. of pantothenic acid per 100 ml. on the first day of parturition, and the amount increased rapidly to 245 μg. per 100 ml. by the fourth day and then more slowly to 304 μg. per 100 ml. by the tenth day. The average value of mature milk was about 250 μg. per 100 ml.[13] Cow's and ewe's milk contained similar amounts and showed similar changes.

Spector et al.[14] recorded a value of 3·8 μg. per 100 ml. for the amount of pantothenic acid excreted in the sweat under normal conditions. This amount was unaffected by the administration of 18 mg. of pantothenic acid per day. Under hot moist conditions 31 % of an 18-mg. dose was recovered in the urine, and the total urinary and dermal excretion increased by 11·6 % to 3·8 to 5·7 mg. per day.

Urinary Excretion of Pantothenic Acid

Human urine contained between 70 and 600 μg. per 100 ml. of pantothenic acid,[2, 3] and the amount excreted per day was found to be from 2·5 to 5 mg. [14, 15] D. M. Tennant and R. H. Silber [16] reported that the normal urinary excretion of 24 μg. per hour increased to 50 μg. per hour after dosage with the vitamin. Humans excreted approximately 10 % of an orally administered dose of calcium pantothenate within four hours.[17] The renal output of pantothenic acid after oral administration of 100 mg. of the vitamin was not significantly less in patients with pernicious anaemia than in normal subjects.[18]

Rat urine contained 100 to 200 μg. of pantothenic acid per 100 ml.,[2, 3] and there was a rapid increase in the rate of excretion following the injection of pantothenic acid. Pantothenic acid-deficient mice rapidly excreted pantothenic acid in which the nitrogen atom was replaced by the N^{15}-isotope when this was administered parentally.[19] The fact that N^{15} was absent from a number of tissues showed that pantothenic acid was not metabolised by mice in a manner analogous to the amino acids. Urinary pantothenic acid excretion in rats was higher on a diet containing 64 % of casein than on one containing 24 %.[20]

Dogs with a bladder fistula excreted 7·2 μg. of pantothenic acid in two hours, and there was no increased excretion two hours after oral administration of 1 mg. of pantothenic acid per kg. of bodyweight. After an oral dose of 4 mg. per kg., however, 0·9 to 5·0 % was excreted in two hours.[6] Following the intravenous injection of 1 and 4 mg. per kg., 22 to 31 % and 41 to 57 % respectively of the dose was excreted, the excretion being maximal after forty and twenty minutes, respectively. More pantothenic acid was excreted following an oral dose than after subcutaneous injection. With unlimited access to food, dogs excreted up to 50 % of the dietary pantothenic acid in the faeces but no increase in the faecal excretion occurred after intravenous administration of calcium pantothenate.[17]

It is not known what degradation products of pantothenic acid are formed *in vivo*, but it is known [21] that pantolactone is not one of the substances formed in man. The excretion of pantolactone was the same whether it was given orally or intravenously, suggesting that intestinal bacteria did not attack the lactone ring. The excretion of pantoic acid, on the other hand, was slightly less after oral than after intravenous administration, suggesting that it was partially decomposed by the intestinal flora.

The amount of pantothenic acid excreted in the faeces was slightly greater after oral administration of pantolactone, possibly owing to modified metabolism of the intestinal bacteria.

References to Section 10

1. S. R. Stanbery, E. E. Snell and T. D. Spies, *J. Biol. Chem.*, 1940, **135**, 353.
2. M. J. Pelczar and J. R. Porter, *Proc. Soc. Exp. Biol. Med.*, 1941, **47**, 3.
3. H. McIlwain and F. Hawking, *Lancet*, 1943, **1**, 449.
4. P. B. Pearson, V. H. Melass and R. M. Sherwood, *J. Nutrition*, 1946, **32**, 187.
5. T. D. Spies, S. R. Stanbery, R. J. Williams, T. H. Jukes and S. H. Babcock, *J. Amer. Med. Assoc.*, 1940, **115**, 523.
6. R. H. Silber and K. Unna, *J. Biol. Chem.*, 1942, **142**, 623.
7. L. D. Wright, *ibid.*, 445.
8. L. D. Wright, *ibid.*, 1943, **147**, 261.

9. N. Nielsen, V. Hartelius and V. Schmidt, *Naturwiss.*, 1943, **31,** 550.

10. R. H. Silber, *J. Nutrition*, 1944, **27, 425.

11. E. E. Rice, E. J. Strandine, E. M. Squires and B. Lyddon, *Arch. Biochem.*, 1946, **10,** 251.

12. A. Taylor, M. A. Pollack, M. J. Hofer and R. J. Williams, *Cancer Res.*, 1942, **2,** 752.

13. M. N. Coryell, M. E. Harris, S. Miller, H. H. Williams and I. G. Macy, *Amer. J. Dis. Child.*, 1945, **70,** 150.

14. H. Spector, T. S. Hamilton and H. H. Mitchell, *J. Biol. Chem.*, 1945, **161,** 145.

15. L. D. Wright and E. Q. Wright, *Proc. Soc. Exp. Biol. Med.*, 1942, **49,** 80.

16. D. M. Tennant and R. H. Silber, *J. Biol. Chem.*, 1943, **148,** 359.

17. R. H. Silber, *Arch. Biochem.*, 1945, **7,** 329.

18. C. E. Meyer, I. F. Burton and C. E. Sturgis, *Proc. Soc. Exp. Biol. Med.*, 1942, **49,** 363.

19. B. Lustig, A. R. Goldfarb and B. Gerstl, *Arch. Biochem.*, 1944, **5,** 59.

20. M. M. Nelson, F. van Nonhuys and H. M. Evans, *J. Nutrition*, 1947, **34,** 189.

21. H. P. Sarett, *J. Biol. Chem.*, 1945, **159,** 321.

11. INTESTINAL SYNTHESIS OF PANTOTHENIC ACID

Evidence for the synthesis of pantothenic acid by micro-organisms in the rumen of ruminants was presented by L. W. McElroy and H. Goss,[1] who observed that the dried contents of the rumen and the reticulum of sheep and cows maintained on a diet low in the vitamin B complex contained respectively twenty-five and twenty- to thirty-fold the amount of pantothenic acid present in the diet, whilst milk from these cows contained twice the amount of pantothenic acid ingested in the diet, another illustration of the possible importance of this phenomenon in human nutrition.

Only indirect evidence is available to indicate that pantothenic acid is synthesised in the intestines of animals. Thus pantothenic acid deficiency was induced in experimental animals by the feeding of sulphonamides,[2, 3] which presumably inhibited the development of the intestinal flora. L. D. Wright and A. D. Welch [3] found that administration of succinylsulphathiazole not only caused severe symptoms of pantothenic acid deficiency, but considerably reduced the pantothenic acid content of the liver ; the storage of riboflavine and nicotinic acid on the other hand was unaffected, whilst that of biotin and folic acid was increased. Neither the symptoms of pantothenic acid deficiency nor the low level in the liver was affected by increasing the daily intake of the vitamins, but yielded to treatment with biotin and a folic acid concentrate, illustrating the close association between different members of the vitamin B complex. The authors concluded that the utilisation of pantothenic acid depended on the availability of biotin and folic acid.

Pantothenic acid deficiency in the rat was accentuated by feeding purified beef blood fibrin in place of casein,[4] possibly because this source of protein was less favourable than casein for the growth of the intestinal flora.

Direct evidence that pantothenic acid is synthesised by the intestinal flora in man was obtained by Denko et al.,[5] who found that both on a normal and on a restricted diet the combined faecal and urinary excretion exceeded the dietary intake, although not to the same extent as with p-aminobenzoic acid, folic acid and biotin (see page 435). Moreover, although on the restricted diet the urinary excretion was increased by administration of pantothenic acid, the faecal excretion was virtually independent of the dietary intake. It is not certain whether or not the pantothenic acid formed by the intestinal bacteria can be utilised in man.

References to Section 11

1. L. W. McElroy and H. Goss, *J. Nutrition*, 1941, **21**, 405.
2. H. D. West, N. C. Jefferson and R. E. Rivera, *ibid.*, 1943, **25**, 471.
3. L. D. Wright and A. D. Welch, *Science*, 1943, **97**, 426 ; *J. Nutrition*, 1944, **27**, 55.
4. M. M. Nelson and H. M. Evans, *Proc. Soc. Exp. Biol. Med.*, 1947, **66**, 299.
5. C. W. Denko, W. A. Grundy, J. W. Porter, G. H. Berryman, T. E. Friedemann and J. B. Youmans, *Arch. Biochem.*, 1946, **10**, 33 ; C. W. Denko, W. E. Grundy, N. C. Wheeler, C. R. Henderson, C. H. Berryman, T. E. Friedemann and J. B. Youmans, *ibid.*, 1946, **11**, 109.

12. HUMAN AND ANIMAL REQUIREMENTS OF PANTOTHENIC ACID

There is surprising unanimity in the figures quoted by different authors for the pantothenic acid requirement of the rat, most workers agreeing that the minimal dose necessary to prevent achromotrichia and produce adequate growth lies between 50 and 100 μg. per day.[1-5] Estimates of the dose required to cure achromotrichia range from 20 to 40,[5] 50 [1] and 100 μg. per day,[6] whilst the following amounts have been suggested as being necessary to promote growth : 40,[6] 50, [3,7]

80^5 and 50 to 100 μg. per day.[8] According to K. Unna and G. V. Richards [9] the daily maintenance requirement for the rat falls from 100 μg. at three weeks of age to 25 μg. at ten weeks, but it is not related to weight or food consumption. K. Schwartz [10] stated that, after an induction period, each μg. of additional pantothenic acid produced a 62·5-mg. increase in the weight of young rats up to 20 g. but that to increase the weight further the presence of another factor, known as "factor 125" (see page 608), was necessary. The nature of this additional factor seems never to have been elucidated. The amount of pantothenic acid required to maintain the health of rats was not increased by a rise in temperature, being the same at 91° F. as at 68° F., namely, 6 mg. per kg. of bodyweight.[11]

The requirements for mice appear only to have been given in terms of the dietary intake ; they are stated to be 2 mg. per 100 g. of diet.[12]

Puppies are said [13] to require 100 μg. of calcium pantothenate per kg. of bodyweight per day—considerably less, weight for weight, than the amount accepted as being necessary for the rat. Shetland ponies required proportionately less, namely 38 μg. per kg. per day.[13a]

Black Minorca chicks on a pantothenic acid-deficient diet exhibited a partial depigmentation of the feathers (page 369), which was prevented by as little as 5 μg. per day of pantothenic acid.[14] More was required to maintain optimal reproduction and egg production, however, namely, 1200 to 1700 and 700 μg. per 100 g. of food respectively.[15] From 750 to 1000 μg. per 100 g. of diet were required to ensure that the eggs hatched and that the chickens survived and showed no signs of pantothenic acid deficiency. The minimum blood level consistent with satisfactory reproductive performance was 0·45 mg. per ml. and the minimum amount in the egg 9·5 μg. About 200 μg. per 100 g. of food was considered sufficient for maintenance, although 900 μg. per 100 g. of diet were necessary for maximum growth.[16] Ducklings required 1100 μg. per 100 g. of diet for satisfactory growth.[17]

References to Section 12

1. P. György and C. E. Poling, *Science*, 1940, **92**, 202.
2. K. Unna and W. L. Sampson, *Proc. Soc. Exp. Biol. Med.*, 1940, **45**, 309.
3. K. Unna, *J. Nutrition*, 1940, **20**, 565.
4. K. Unna, G. V. Richards and W. L. Sampson, *ibid.*, 1941, **22**, 553.
5. L. M. Henderson, J. M. McIntire, H. A. Waisman and C. A. Elvehjem, *ibid.*, 1942, **23**, 47.
6. G. A. Emerson and H. M. Evans, *Proc. Soc. Exp. Biol. Med.*, 1941, **46**, 655.
7. K. Schwartz, *Z. physiol. Chem.*, 1942, **275**, 245.
8. J. D. S. Bacon and G. N. Jenkins, *Biochem. J.*, 1943, **37**, 492.

9. K. Unna and G. V. Richards, *J. Nutrition*, 1942, **23**, 545.

10. K. Schwartz, *Z. physiol. Chem.*, 1942, **275**, 232.

11. C. A. Mills, *Arch. Biochem.*, 1942, **1**, 73.

12. D. W. Woolley, *Proc. Soc. Exp. Biol. Med.*, 1941, **46**, 565.

13. A. E. Shaefer, J. M. McKibbin and C. A. Elvehjem, *J. Biol. Chem.*, 1942, **143**, 321.

13*a*. P. B. Pearson and H. Schmidt, *J. Animal Sci.*, 1948, **7**, 78.

14. T. C. Groody and M. E. Groody, *Science*, 1942, **95**, 655.

15. M. B. Gillis, G. F. Heuser and L. C. Norris, *J. Nutrition*, 1943, **26**, 285; 1948, **35**, 351.

16. D. M. Hegsted and T. R. Riggs, *ibid.*, 1949, **37**, 361.

17. D. M. Hegsted and R. L. Perry, *ibid.*, 1948, **35**, 411.

13. PHARMACOLOGY OF PANTOTHENIC ACID

The pharmacological properties of calcium pantothenate were studied by K. Unna and J. Greslin,[1] who found that the toxic dose (LD 50) for mice was 10, 2·7 and 0·92 g. per kg. by the oral, subcutaneous and intraperitoneal routes respectively; death occurred through respiratory failure. For rats the value of LD 50 was 3·4 g. per kg. by the subcutaneous route. Rats suffered no ill-effects when given 10 g. per kg. by mouth, and five dogs and one monkey were not affected by a dose of 1 g. per kg. by mouth. Rats developed normally when given 200 mg. of calcium pantothenate daily for 190 days, and dogs given 50 mg. per kg. of bodyweight daily for six months and monkeys given 1 g. per day for six months showed no ill-effects.

The subcutaneous injection of a 1 to 10 % solution of calcium pantothenate into rabbits or the instillation of a 10 % solution into the conjunctival sac caused no irritation. The blood pressure and respiration of a cat were not influenced by the intravenous injection of 10 to 50 mg. per kg., and the heart rate was unchanged. The volume of urine excreted was not affected. No effect on the intestine or uterus of a rabbit could be detected in concentrations up to 1 part in 10,000 parts.

Spies *et al.*[2] reported that the intravenous injection of a solution containing 100 mg. of calcium or sodium pantothenate produced no change in the blood pressure, pulse, temperature or respiration of normal human subjects.

References to Section 13

1. K. Unna and J. G. Greslin, *Proc. Soc. Exp. Biol. Med.*, 1940, **45**, 311; *J. Pharmacol.*, 1941, **73**, 85.

2. T. D. Spies, S. R. Stanberry, R. J. Williams, T. H. Jukes and S. H. Babcock, *J. Amer. Med. Assoc.*, 1940, **115**, 523.

14. PANTOTHENIC ACID IN THE NUTRITION OF MICRO-ORGANISMS

Bacteria

As already stated (see page 360), pantothenic acid is essential for the growth of *Streptococcus lactis, Bacillus brassicae, Propionibacterium pentosaceum, Lactobacillus helveticus, L. arabinosus* and *Proteus morganii* ; the last three organisms have been used for the micro-biological assay of pantothenic acid. It is also essential for the growth of *Streptococcus haemolyticus* and *Diplococcus pneumoniae* ; [1] of *Clostridium tetani* ; [2] of *Clostridium welchii* ; [3] of " exacting " strains of *Corynebacterium diphtheriae* [4] (other strains do not require panto-thenic acid if β-alanine is available) ; of some species of *Pasteurella* [5] and *Brucella* ; [6] of *Streptobacterium plantarum* ; [7] of five species of *Propionibacterium* ; [8] of three strains of *Shigella paradysenteriae* ; [9] and of a number of species of lactic acid bacteria. [10] *Clostridium botulinum* required biotin, aneurine and choline, but pantothenic acid could apparently substitute for aneurine and choline. [11]

The amounts of pantothenic acid in the cells of five bacteria that did not require an extra-cellular source of pantothenic acid, namely, *Aerobacter aerogenes, Serratia marcescens, Pseudomonas fluorescens, Proteus vulgaris* and *Clostridium butylicum* were estimated by H. McIlwain [12] at 24,000 and 96,000 molecules per cell and the rate of synthesis at 5 to 40 molecules per cell per second.

Escherichia coli synthesised pantothenic acid at the rate of 50 molecules per cell per second in the absence of β-alanine and at ten times this rate when β-alanine was present. [13] *Pseudomonas aeruginosa* synthesised it at the rate of 9 and 30 molecules per cell per second in the absence and presence respectively of pantoic acid. [3]

Pantothenic acid was inactivated (see below) by *Streptococcus haemolyticus* (non-proliferating) at a rate equivalent to 23 to 41 mole-cules per cell per second, [14] and the rate was not appreciably altered when the conditions were varied. Pantothenic acid was not synthe-sised by this organism and both growth and pantothenic acid meta-bolism were inhibited to the same extent by pantoyltaurine and similar antagonists (see below). Pantothenic acid was metabolised by *Proteus morganii* at a velocity ranging from 25 to 120 molecules per cell per second.

These reactions are therefore of approximately the same order, falling into the class termed by McIlwain mμmol. order reactions. The significance of this has already been discussed (page 284).

According to G. M. Hills, [15] the oxygen uptake of a pantothenic acid-deficient culture of *Proteus morganii* was increased seven-fold by the addition of pantothenic acid. The most important substrate influenced by pantothenic acid was pyruvic acid, but some effect was observed with lactic acid and certain C_4 and C_5 dicarboxylic acids. Pantothenic acid did not, however, affect the fermentation of glucose, confirming the absence of a correlation between glycolysis and the presence of pantothenic acid noted below. Dorfman *et al.*[16] also found that pantothenic acid stimulated the oxygen uptake of *P. morganii* in presence of lactic or pyruvic acid.

Pantoyltaurine

Several of the bacteria that require preformed pantothenic acid have been used to test growth inhibitors that act by antagonising the growth promoting effect of pantothenic acid. The best known of these antagonists is pantoyltaurine, which is derived from pantothenic acid by replacement of the carboxyl group by a sulphonic acid group :

$$CH_2OH . C(CH_3)_2 . CHOH . CO . NH . CH_2 . CH_2 . COOH$$
Pantothenic acid

$$CH_2OH . C(CH_3)_2 . CHOH . CO . NH . CH_2 . CH_2 . SO_3H$$
Pantoyltaurine

This compound was prepared independently by E. E. Snell[17] in the U.S.A., by R. Kuhn, T. Wieland and E. F. Möller[18] in Germany, and by J. W. Barnett and F. A. Robinson[19] and H. McIlwain[20] in this country.

It inhibits the growth of all organisms that require preformed pantothenic acid, *e.g. L. arabinosus*,[17] *L. pentosus*,[17] *S. lactis*,[17] *Propionibacterium pentosaceum*,[17] *Leuconostoc mesenteroides*,[17] *Streptobacterium plantarum*,[18] *Streptococcus haemolyticus*,[20] *Diplococcus pneumoniae*[20] and exacting strains of *C. diphtheriae*,[20] but not of organisms that synthesise their own pantothenic acid, either completely, such as *E. coli*, or from added β-alanine, such as the non-exacting strains of *C. diphtheriae*. Where inhibition occurred, it could be completely overcome by addition of more pantothenic acid, so that inhibition is of the competitive type, of which other instances are provided by *p*-aminobenzoic acid and sulphanilamide (page 546) and nicotinic acid and pyridine-β-sulphonic acid (page 291). The amide of pantoyltaurine, pantoyltauramide,[19, 20] also inhibited the growth of many of the above organisms, but was less effective than pantoyltaurine ; it appeared to act by the same mechanism as pantoyltaurine. Other inhibitors related to pantothenic acid are discussed on page 397.

The effects of pantoyl taurine and pantoyltauramide are markedly different with different organisms, although the amount of pantothenic acid needed for optimal growth of each organism is approximately the same for a number of bacteria. H. McIlwain[20] calculated the " antibacterial indices " of the two inhibitors, that is the ratio of the molar concentration of inhibitor to that of promoter necessary to produce inhibition of growth. He obtained the following results :

	DL-Pantoyltaurine	DL-Pantoyltauramide
Streptococcus haemolyticus .	500	2000
Streptococcus lactis .	8000	—
Propionibacterium pentosaceum	8000	—
Diplococcus pneumoniae .	1000	10,000–50,000
Corynebacterium diphtheriae .		
Exacting . . .	500	2000–10,000
Less exacting . .	5000	—
Lactobacillus arabinosus .	1000–2000	—
Lactobacillus pentosus . .	133,000	—
Leuconostoc mesenteroides .	133,000	—

Pantoyltaurine was believed to act by displacing pantothenic acid from an essential enzyme system and so preventing it from functioning (see page 390), and it was hoped that a new therapeutic agent, equal in importance to the sulphonamides, might have resulted. In fact, this hope was not realised, and neither pantoyltaurine nor its many derivatives (page 397) appear to be capable of inhibiting the growth *in vivo* of organisms that it readily inhibits *in vitro*. The reason for this is that in most instances pantoyltaurine is itself antagonised by the relatively large amounts of pantothenic acid present in the blood of the host, and there is then insufficient " free " pantoyltaurine left over to inhibit the growth of the invading organism.

Only by selecting a test animal which had a relatively low concentration of pantothenic acid in the blood was a therapeutic effect observed, and it was found that, whereas mice infected with a haemolytic streptococcus died however much pantoyltaurine was administered, rats could be protected by giving frequent massive doses of the inhibitor.[21] Under these conditions the ratio of pantoyltaurine to pantothenic acid was kept above the value required for *in vitro* activity. When the blood pantothenic acid concentration was artificially increased, however, pantoyltaurine ceased to be effective.

Since human blood contains a somewhat lower concentration of pantothenic acid than rat blood, it is possible that pantoyltaurine might be effective in humans, but the response would not be likely to be dramatic and the dose would have to be very large. Pantoyltaurine had no trypanocidal or antimalarial activity in experimental animals.

In spite of the fact that pantoyltaurine is of no practical therapeutic importance, it has been responsible for throwing much new light on chemotherapy and on the phenomenon of drug resistance, and probably more is known about the mode of action of pantoyltaurine than of any other chemotherapeutic substance, thanks mainly to the work of H. McIlwain.

Pantoyltaurine Resistance

Sulphonamide-resistant streptococci are sensitive to pantoyl-taurine,[21] whilst pantoyltaurine-resistant strains, produced by repeated subculturing of the organisms in presence of the inhibitor, were as susceptible to sulphanilamide as were normal strains,[22] showing that cross-resistance does not necessarily develop to different chemothera-peutic agents. The variable resistance to pantoyltaurine of different natural and experimentally produced strains of C. *diphtheriae* was correlated with their ability to grow with β-alanine in place of panto-thenic acid. Resistant strains synthesised pantothenic acid during growth, and the ability to perform this synthesis is believed to explain their resistance.

The resistance developed by Str. *haemolyticus*, however, appeared to be due to a different mechanism, as many of the naturally resistant and all the experimentally produced resistant strains, needed panto-thenic acid during growth. The pantoyltaurine-fast streptococci and some pantoyltaurine-insensitive strains were made susceptible to pantoyltaurine by the addition of salicylic acid, suggesting that pantoyl-taurine-resistant streptococci possessed metabolic processes alternative to those affected by pantoyltaurine and inhibited by salicylic acid.

A connection between the specific antibacterial action of salicylic acid on *Staphylococcus aureus* and pantothenic acid had been estab-lished earlier by G. Ivanovics,[23] who showed that this antibacterial action could be neutralised by small amounts of pantothenic acid or pantolactone, but not by β-alanine ; the degree of inhibition was pro-portional to the pantothenic acid concentration. With *Proteus morganii*, inhibition of growth by salicylic acid was similarly neutral-ised by pantothenic acid, but in this instance the degree of inhibition was independent of the amount of pantothenic acid. *Pr. morganii*, unlike *Staph. aureus*, cannot synthesise pantothenic acid or pantoic acid. Several amino acids were able to antagonise the effect of salicylic acid, the most effective being methionine. Thus, the specific antibacterial effect of salicylic acid appears to be associated with the inhibition of an enzymic process for synthesising pantoic acid. This is supported by the observation [24] that pantoic acid was nine times as effective as pantolactone in antagonising the inhibitory action of salicylic acid on E. *coli*, which suggests moreover, that pantoic acid, rather than pantolactone, is the precursor of pantothenic acid.

It seems evident, therefore, that pantoyltaurine and salicylic acid each block a different route to pantothenic acid synthesis or utilisation.

There also appears to be a connection between the antibacterial action of sulphapyridine and pantothenic acid, for it has been observed that [25] in rats on a diet low in caseinogen, administration of sulpha-pyridine produced retardation of growth and other symptoms of panto-thenic acid deficiency, which were relieved by giving pantothenic acid. This result might, of course, have been due to an inhibitory effect of sulphapyridine on the bacterial flora which under normal circumstances may supply part of the normal pantothenic acid requirements of the animal, but West *et al.*[26] suggested that sulphapyridine antagonised pantothenic acid directly, making it unavailable, not only for the host, thereby leading to the onset of symptoms of pantothenic acid deficiency, but also for the invading bacteria. Sulphapyridine may constitute a third method of blocking one of the routes by which pantothenic acid is synthesised or utilised.

Mechanism of the Inhibitory Action of Pantoyltaurine

Haemolytic streptococci grown in presence of adequate amounts of pantothenic acid exhibited a short lag phase, then a well-marked logarithmic phase, during which growth rate was optimal and, finally, a stationary phase which was reached in three to four hours. Reduc-tion of the pantothenic acid concentration to sub-optimal levels had little effect on the duration of the lag phase or on the rate of growth, but reduced the stationary population. The addition of pantoyl-taurine had quite a different effect. In presence of excess pantothenic acid, pantoyltaurine had no effect on the stationary population, but increased the lag period and reduced the rate of growth in the first half of the logarithmic phase, though not to any considerable extent the growth rate in the second half. Thus pantothenic acid appeared to lead to the formation of substances necessary for normal growth, and the action of pantoyltaurine was to reduce the formation of these substances so that the rate of growth was limited.[27] Furthermore, pantothenic acid was found to disappear from streptococcal cultures, the disappearance being independent of the growth or viability of the organism, but associated with glycolysis, for when glycolysis was prevented, pantothenic acid metabolism ceased. Addition of pantoyl-taurine, however, inhibited pantothenic acid metabolism without a corresponding inhibition of glycolysis. These facts are understand-able if it is assumed that both glycolysis and the presence of excess pantothenic acid are necessary for the formation of a substance essential for streptococcal growth, and that pantoyltaurine interfered with the metabolism of pantothenic acid, but not with the energy-yielding process of glycolysis.[14] The nature of the substance formed by pantothenic acid is discussed in a later section (page 390).

Six other compounds (see page 398) which inhibited growth and which, like pantoyltaurine, were antagonised by pantothenic acid, were also found to inhibit pantothenic acid metabolism, whilst other related compounds did not ; some of these did not inhibit growth, whilst others, although they inhibited growth, were unaffected by pantothenic acid. Pantoyltaurine and the six other compounds that inhibited pantothenic acid metabolism showed wide variations in the concentrations necessary to produce inhibition, but in every instance their ability to inhibit metabolism paralleled their ability to inhibit growth. Similarly, the concentrations of pantoyltaurine required to inhibit growth and pantothenic acid metabolism in five different micro-organisms ran parallel. These observations lend further support to the view that inhibition of pantothenic acid metabolism is responsible for the effect of pantoyltaurine (and related compounds) on growth.[28] Although low concentrations of pantoyltaurine delayed the growth of haemolytic streptococci, even relatively high concentrations had no immediate effect when added to growing cultures ; there was a lag of an hour or more. The action of pantothenic acid in antagonising inhibition by pantoyltaurine was also a delayed one. Pantothenic acid metabolism, however, was inhibited immediately by pantoyltaurine both in streptococci and in *C. diphtheriae*, and the process started again immediately the pantoyltaurine was withdrawn. The metabolism of pantothenic acid normally took place in considerable excess of the needs of the organisms and, during the latent period, they probably utilised materials previously made in excess. This was confirmed by the observation that, when pantoyltaurine was added in a concentration sufficient to inhibit pantothenic acid metabolism but not to inhibit growth, growth ceased almost immediately on addition of further pantoyltaurine.[29]

By studying the effect of various reagents on the pantothenic acid content of two strains of β-haemolytic streptococci, H. McIlwain [30] showed that the bacterial cells normally contained 15 to 50 mμmol. of firmly bound pantothenic acid per g. of dry matter. This could only be removed by autolysis or enzymic digestion, whereas loosely combined pantothenic acid was readily removed by washing with saline at 37° C. Pantoyltaurine did not remove the firmly bound protein, and, similarly, sulphanilamide did not release firmly bound *p*-aminobenzoic acid from the cells. McIlwain therefore suggested that pantoyltaurine and sulphanilamide act as bacteriostatic agents by preventing the binding by susceptible bacteria of pantothenic acid and *p*-aminobenzoic acid respectively in a form in which they can function inside the cell.

Moulds

Pantothenic acid stimulated the growth of *Penicillium digitatum*,[31] but *P. chrysogenum* synthesised pantothenic acid, the culture fluid containing ten times as much as the basal medium.[32] *Aspergillus niger*, *Penicillium wolkmanni*, two unnamed species of *Penicillium*, *Rhizopus suinus* and *Rh. nigrans* also synthesised pantothenic acid.[33]

One strain of *Neurospora* produced considerable amounts of pantothenic acid in presence of pantolactone and β-alanine, and very little in their absence, whilst another strain, differing from it by a single gene, produced no pantothenic acid in either instance.[33a]

Yeasts

Pantothenic acid was essential for the growth of a number of yeasts, including *Candida pseudotropicalis*, *Mycoderma valida*, *Saccharomyces cerevisiae*, *S. cerevisiae* var. *ellipsoideus*, *S. chodati*, *S. fragilis*, *S. logos*, *S. macedoniensis*, *S. oviformis*, *S. tubiformis*, *Saccharomycodes ludwigii*, *Schizosaccharomyces pombe*, *Zygosaccharomyces barkeri*, *Z. mandshuricus*, *Z. nadsoni*, *Z. pastori*, *Z. priorianus*, *Z. felsineus*, *Z. marxianus*, *Z. variabilis*, *Z. japonicus*, *Torulopsis sphaerica*, *Saccharomyces chevalieri*, *S. behrensianus*, *S. anomalus belgicus*, *S. bacillaris*, *S. exiguus*, *Torula thermantitoneum*, *T. colliculosa*, *T. cremoris* and *Kloeckera brevis*.[34, 35]

The growth of a strain of *S. cerevisiae* was stimulated by an amount of pantoic acid equal to 600 times that required to combine with the β-alanine present when suboptimal amounts of the latter were employed.[36] No stimulation occurred when the acid was added after an interim period. Pantoic acid appeared to have a stimulative action of its own, which could be demonstrated in presence of pantothenic acid or of optimal amounts of β-alanine. Pantolactone had no such effect. The effect of pantoyltaurine on the Gebrüder-Mayer strain of *S. cerevisiae*, which gives good growth only in the presence of pantothenic acid or β-alanine, was tested by E. E. Snell.[17] He found, as with *L. arabinosus* and other exacting bacteria, that pantoyltaurine inhibited growth induced by pantothenic acid, and that the inhibition was reversed by additional pantothenic acid. Growth induced by β-alanine was not inhibited by pantoyltaurine, nor was it affected by taurine.

In presence of an excess of pantothenic acid, yeast cells utilise it but do not synthesise additional amounts. At lower concentrations, the amount of growth is proportional to the pantothenic acid concentration, whilst at still lower concentrations mutants capable of synthesising the vitamin are produced.[36a]

Other Micro-organisms

Addition of calcium pantothenate to a diet low in aneurine, riboflavine and pantothenic acid increased the number of oocysts eliminated by rats infected with *Eimeria nieschulzi*. The further addition of pyridoxine caused a still further increase in the number of oocysts excreted.[37]

Biosynthesis of Pantothenic Acid

Both halves of the pantothenic acid molecule function as growth factors, β-alanine for some strains of *Corynebacterium diphtheriae* [4] and pantoic acid for *Acetobacter suboxydans* [38] and *Clostridium septicum*.[39] These organisms synthesise pantothenic acid by coupling β-alanine with pantoic acid, for the culture solution stimulated the growth of *L. helveticus* which does not respond to either half of the molecule.[39] According to T. Wieland and E. F. Möller,[40] yeast frozen in liquid air and subjected to dialysis with aeration had a diminished capacity for synthesising pantothenic acid from β-alanine and pantolactone. The ammonium ion and probably the carbonate and acetate ions activated the synthesis and the ammonium ion also catalysed the synthesis of pantothenic acid from β-alanine and pantamide.

From what has been said above, it is evident that many antagonists of pantothenic acid owe their effect to interference with the synthesis of pantothenic acid from pantoic acid and β-alanine, although pantoyl-taurine acts by interfering with the utilisation of pantothenic acid to form substances essential for the growth of the bacterial cell. The nature of the substance produced by the metabolism of pantothenic acid is discussed below (page 390).

Salicylic acid owes its antibacterial action to its ability to interfere with the synthesis of pantoic acid,[22, 23, 39] whilst other antagonists, for example α- and γ-hydroxy-$\beta\beta$-dimethylbutyric acid and $\beta\gamma$-di-hydroxy-β-methylbutyric acid, apparently prevent the coupling of β-alanine with pantoic acid.[38] Another growth inhibitor, cysteic acid, acts by interfering with the formation of β-alanine by the decarboxylation of aspartic acid.[41] In *E. coli*, pantothenic acid and β-alanine completely prevented the toxic effects of cysteic acid, and the rate of synthesis of pantothenic acid was determined by the ratio of cysteic acid to aspartic acid. Glutamic acid was three times as effective as aspartic acid in preventing the toxic effects of cysteic acid, owing to its conversion by transamination into α-ketoglutaric acid, which had a " sparing action " on pantothenic acid, that is, it permitted the cells to grow at a lower rate of pantothenic acid synthesis ; citric acid and *cis*-aconitic acid had a similar effect, but oxaloacetic and pyruvic acid, the precursors of *cis*-aconitic acid, were inactive.[42] Glutaric acid also enhanced the growth of *S. cerevisiae* and *S. carlsbergensis* in presence of suboptimal amounts of pantothenic acid ; the " sparing action " in this instance is attributed to the combination of glutaric acid with pantothenic acid or β-alanine to give a substance which had greater growth-promoting activity.[43]

Pantothenic acid also prevented the toxic action of 2-chloro-4-aminobenzoic acid on *E. coli*, being even more effective than *p*-aminobenzoic acid. At high levels of the inhibitor, antagonism was more complete when methionine as well as pantothenic acid was present.[44] It is not known what stage of pantothenic acid synthesis is affected by 2-chloro-4-aminobenzoic acid.

References to Section 14

1. L. Rane and Y. SubbaRow, *J. Biol. Chem.*, 1940, **134,** 455.
2. J. H. Mueller and P. A. Miller, *ibid.*, 1941, **140,** 933.
3. J. T. Tamura, A. A. Tytell, M. J. Boyd and M. A. Logan, *J. Bact.*, 1941, **42, 1**48.
4. J. H. Mueller and A. W. Klotz, *J. Amer. Chem. Soc.*, 1938, **60,** 3086 ; W. C. Evans, W. R. C. Handley and F. C. Happold, *Brit. J. Exp. Path.*, 1939, **20,** 396.
5. S. Berkman, F. Saunders and S. A. Koser, *Proc. Soc. Exp. Biol. Med.*, 1940, **44,** 68.
6. S. A. Koser, B. B. Breslove and A. Dorfman, *J. Infect. Dis.*, 1941, **69,** 114.
7. E. F. Möller, *Angew. Chem.*, 1940, **53,** 204.
8. R. C. Thompson, *J. Bact.*, 1943, **46,** 99.
9. A. J. Weil and J. Black, *Proc. Soc. Exp. Biol. Med.*, 1944, **55,** 24.
10. V. H. Cheldelin, E. H. Hoag and H. P. Sarett, *J. Bact.*, 1945, **49,** 41.
11. C. Lamanna and C. Lewis, *ibid.*, 1946, **51,** 398.
12. H. McIlwain, *Nature*, 1946, **158,** 898.
13. H. McIlwain, *Biochem. J.*, 1946, **40,** 269.
14. H. McIlwain and D. E. Hughes, *ibid.*, 1944, **38,** 187.
15. G. M. Hills, *ibid.*, 1943, **37,** 418.
16. A. Dorfman, S. Berkman and S. A. Koser, *J. Biol. Chem.*, 1942, **144,** 393.
17. E. E. Snell, *ibid.*, 1941, **139,** 975 ; 1941, **141,** 121.
18. R. Kuhn, T. Wieland and E. F. Möller, *Ber.*, 1941, **74,** 1605.
19. J. W. Barnett and F. A. Robinson, *Biochem. J.*, 1942, **36,** 364.
20. H. McIlwain, *ibid.*, 417.
21. H. McIlwain and F. Hawking, *Lancet*, 1943, **1,** 449.
22. H. McIlwain, *Brit. J. Exp. Path.*, 1943, **24,** 203.
23. G. Ivanovics, *Z. physiol. Chem.*, 1942, **276,** 33.
24. P. G. Stansly and M. E. Schlosser, *J. Biol. Chem.*, 1945, **161,** 513.
25. H. D. West, N. C. Jefferson and R. E. Rivera, *J. Nutrition*, 1943, **25,** 471.
26. H. D. West, M. J. Bent, R. E. Rivera and R. E. Tisdale, *Arch. Biochem.*, 1944, **3,** 321.
27. H. McIlwain, *Biochem. J.*, 1944, **38,** 97.
28. H. McIlwain and D. E. Hughes, *ibid.*, 1945, **39,** 133.
29. H. McIlwain, *ibid.*, 279.
30. H. McIlwain, *ibid.*, 329.
31. R. C. Wooster and V. H. Cheldelin, *Arch. Biochem.*, 1945, **8,** 311.

32. F. W. Tanner, S. E. Pfeiffer and J. M. van Lanen, *ibid.*, 29.

33. N. Nielsen and V. Hartelius, *Compt. rend. Trav. Lab. Carlsberg, Sér. Physiol.*, 1945, **24**, 117.

33*a*. R. W. Wagner and B. M. Guirard, *Proc. Nat. Acad. Sci.*, 1948, **34**, 398.

34. P. R. Burkholder, *Amer. J. Bot.*, 1943, **30**, 206 ; P. R. Burkholder and D. Moyer, *Bull. Torrey Bot. Club*, 1943, **70**, 372 ; *J. Bact.*, 1944, **48**, 385.

35. A. S. Schultz and L. Atkin, *Arch. Biochem.*, 1947, **14**, 369.

36. V. Hartelius and G. Johansen, *Compt. rend. Trav. Lab. Carlsberg, Sér. Physiol.*, 1946, **24**, 133.

36*a*. C. C. Lindegren and C. Rant, *Ann. Missouri Bot. Gard.*, 1947, **34**, 85.

37. E. R. Becker and L. Smith, *Iowa State Coll. J. Sci.*, 1942, **16**, 443.

38. V. H. Cheldelin and C. A. Schink, *J. Amer. Chem. Soc.*, 1947, **69**, 2625.

39. F. J. Ryan, R. Ballentine, E. Stolovy, M. E. Corson and L. K. Schneider, *ibid.*, 1945, **67**, 1857 ; F. J. Ryan, L. K. Schneider and R. Ballentine, *J. Bact.*, 1947, **53**, 417.

40. T. Wieland and E. F. Möller, *Z. physiol. Chem.*, 1942, **272**, 232.

41. J. M. Ravel and W. Shive, *J. Biol. Chem.*, 1946, **166**, 407.

42. W. Shive, W. W. Ackermann, J. M. Ravel and J. E. Sutherland, *J. Amer. Chem. Soc.*, 1947, **69**, 2567.

43. T. E. King and V. H. Cheldelin, *Arch. Biochem.*, 1948, **16**, 231.

44. T. E. King, R. L. Stearman and V. H. Cheldelin, *J. Amer. Soc.*, 1948, **70**, 3969.

15. EFFECT OF PANTOTHENIC ACID ON HIGHER PLANTS

According to E. F. Pratt and R. J. Williams,[1] pantothenic acid concentrates influenced the metabolism of plant tissues. P. R. Burkholder [2] reported that the amount of pantothenic acid, as well as of other vitamins, increased during the germination of oats, wheat, barley and maize.

References to Section 15

1. E. F. Pratt and R. J. Williams, *J. Gen. Physiol.*, 1939, **22**, 637.

2. P. R. Burkholder, *Science*, 1943, **97**, 562.

16. PANTOTHENIC ACID REQUIREMENTS OF INSECTS

Pantothenic acid is an essential vitamin for the fruit fly, *Drosophila melanogaster*,[1] for the larvae of the mealworm, *Tenebrio molitor*,[2] for mosquito larvae,[3] for the beetles, *Tribolium confusum* [4] and *Ptinus tectus*,[4] and the moth, *Ephestia elutella*.[4] *Silvanus surinamensis*,

Sitodrepa panicea and *Lasioderma serricorne,* however, grew normally in the absence of the vitamin B complex,[4] but if the larvae were grown under sterile conditions the addition of vitamin B complex, including pantothenic acid, to the diet was essential for the development of the insects. It was concluded from this that intracellular symbiotic micro-organisms supplied the vitamin B complex requirements of these insects under ordinary conditions.

In common with other members of the vitamin B complex, pantothenic acid must be present in the diet of the mosquito, *Aedes aegypti,* to permit larval growth to the fourth instar.[5]

Reference has already been made (page 364) to the relatively large amounts of pantothenic acid (and biotin) in royal jelly, the food on which bee larvae destined to become queens are reared, and which is apparently the only factor that determines whether larvae are to become workers or queens. This amazing property of royal jelly is not due solely to its high content of pantothenic acid or biotin, because the addition of pantothenic acid to the normal food of the larvae did not bring about the metamorphosis effected by royal jelly.

References to Section 16

1. E. L. Tatum, *Proc. Nat. Acad. Sci.*, 1941, **27,** 193.
2. H. E. Martin and L. Hare, *Biol. Bull. Woods Hole*, 1942, **83,** 428.
3. Y. SubbaRow and W. Trager, *J. Gen. Physiol.*, 1940, **23,** 561.
4. G. Fraenkel and M. Blewett, *Nature*, 1943, **151,** 703 ; 1943, **152,** 506 ; *Biochem. J.*, 1943, **37,** 686 ; M. Blewett and G. Fraenkel, *Proc. Roy. Soc. B.*, 1944, **132,** 212.
5. L. Golberg, B. de Meillon and M. Lavoipierre, *J. Exp. Biol.*, 1945, **21,** 90.

17. FUNCTION OF PANTOTHENIC ACID

Some light was thrown on the function of pantothenic acid in bacteria by the researches on pantoyltaurine and other antagonists already referred to (page 381). The conclusion drawn by H. McIlwain from this work was that pantoyltaurine interfered with the metabolism of pantothenic acid, and thus impeded the formation of a substance or substances essential for normal growth. Glycolysis was also essential for the formation of this substance, but pantothenic acid did not play any part in this energy-yielding process. That pantothenic acid did not affect the fermentation of glucose was observed by G. M. Hills [1] and by P. C. Teague and R. J. Williams.[2] The latter workers also showed that it had no effect on the rate of phosphorylation of glucose, on the rate of decarboxylation of pyruvic acid by yeast juice or on the oxygen consumption of homogenised chick tissues during the utilisation of glucose, and they concluded that pantothenic acid was not a dissociable coenzyme for the glycolytic systems investigated.

Dorfman *et al.*[3] found that calcium pantothenate increased the oxygen uptake of *Proteus morganii* when lactic or pyruvic acid was used as substrate, and concluded that pantothenic acid played a part in the oxidation of pyruvic to acetic acid. G. M. Hills[1] made a similar observation. These results were supported by the work of Pilgrim *et al.*,[4] who found that the oxidation of pyruvic acid by liver tissue was retarded by a deficiency of pantothenic acid and biotin.

M. G. Sevag and M. N. Green[5] suggested a different rôle for pantothenic acid, for they obtained evidence that it was in some way connected with the metabolism of tryptophan. *Staphylococcus aureus* required tryptophan for growth, but this could be replaced by pantothenic acid if glucose were also present. Moreover, the growth of *S. aureus* was inhibited by sulphonamides in presence of glucose and most amino acids, whether pantothenic acid was absent or not. The inhibition was abolished, however, when tryptophan was added. They interpreted this result to mean that sulphonamides inhibited the reactions leading to the synthesis of tryptophan and that pantothenic acid played a part in these reactions. So far, this suggestion has not received support from the work of other investigators.

A more satisfactory explanation of the function of pantothenic acid is that of Lipmann *et al.*,[6] who postulated that pantothenic acid was the prosthetic group of a coenzyme necessary for acetylation. F. Lipmann[7] had previously isolated from liver a coenzyme that catalysed the acetylation of aromatic amines and had shown[8] that it also acetylated choline and was apparently identical with the activator of choline acetylation reported by W. Feldberg and T. Mann,[9] D. Nachmansohn and M. Berman,[10] and M. A. Lipton.[11] A purified preparation of this coenzyme, known as " Coenzyme A ", was found to contain about 10 % of pantothenic acid, and the activity of different preparations was found to run parallel with their pantothenic acid contents. This theory is consistent with the observation of G. M. Hills[1] and Dorfman *et al.*[3] that pantothenic acid takes part in the oxidation of pyruvic acid to acetic acid, for G. D. Novelli and F. Lipmann[12] showed that the increased oxidation of pyruvic acid that occurred when pantothenic acid was added to pantothenic acid-deficient organisms was due to the synthesis of coenzyme A. In *L. arabinosus*, 90 % of the pantothenic acid could be accounted for as coenzyme A, which was present in negligible amounts in pantothenic acid-deficient organisms. The suggestion that pantothenic acid is the prosthetic group of coenzyme A might also account for the connection between pantothenic acid and choline (page 365). Pantothenic acid increased acetylcholine formation by *Lactobacillus plantarum*.[12a]

By using two cultures of yeast, one rich and one poor in co-enzyme A, G. D. Novelli and F. Lipmann [13] demonstrated that the coenzyme was concerned with the primary attack on acetate, since this disappeared from solution twice as rapidly with the high coenzyme yeast as with the low, and when ethanol was used as substrate, acetate accumulated in the solution with the low coenzyme yeast but not with the yeast rich in coenzyme A.

A method of assaying coenzyme A, based on the observation that when pigeon liver extract undergoes autolysis it loses its ability to acetylate sulphanilamide, was used to determine the distribution of the coenzyme in nature ; reactivation of the extract was proportional to the coenzyme A concentration.[14] It was found to be a general constituent of living organisms ; liver, *Clostridium butylicum* and *Proteus morganii* were especially rich sources. Coenzyme A was as active as free pantothenic acid when given intraperitoneally to chicks, but by the oral route it had only 60 % of the activity.[15] Whereas normal rats acetylated 70 % of the p-aminobenzoic acid excreted following the injection of a 1- or 2·5-mg. dose, pantothenic acid-deficient rats excreted only 50 and 37 % respectively ; the simultaneous injection of 1 mg. of calcium pantothenate increased the acetylation to normal.[16]

Administration of pantothenic acid failed to increase the acetylation of p-aminobenzoic acid in diabetic rats, although normal values were obtained after injection of insulin, adenosine triphosphate, acetyl phosphate, diacetyl or dicarboxylic acids of the tricarboxylic acid cycle.[17] It is suggested that insulin may promote the reaction between pyruvic acid and the tricarboxylic acid cycle, a suggestion not inconsistent with the view that pantothenic acid is associated with the conversion of pyruvic acid into acetic acid.

Preparations of coenzyme A made from pigeon liver extracts acetylated acetic acid (giving acetoacetic acid) and sulphanilamide,[18] whilst pantothenic acid-deficient rats excreted much less sulphanilamide in the acetylated form than did controls.[19]

The coenzyme A content of rats maintained on a pantothenic acid-deficient diet remained normal for two to three weeks and then fell to a level 35 to 50 % that of normal. Ducklings showed a more rapid depletion, and the injection of pantothenic acid restored the value to normal.[20] Liver slices from pantothenic acid-deficient rats or ducks showed a decreased ability to utilise pyruvic acid. All the pantothenic acid can be liberated from coenzyme A and made available for microbiological assay by incubation with a mixture of intestinal phosphatase and fresh pigeon liver extract ; assays confirmed the earlier observation that most if not all the pantothenic acid in living cells is bound in the form of coenzyme A.[21] Coenzyme A stimulated the growth of *A. suboxydans*, the response being greater than that produced by an equivalent amount of pantothenic acid.[22] By incubating β-alanine or pantothenic acid with glutamic acid in presence of resting cells, a product was obtained with up to 1000 times the activity of β-alanine or pantothenic acid on yeast, but this result could not always be obtained, the product being sometimes quite inactive. A conjugate of pantothenic acid isolated from pork heart was twice as active as pantothenic acid on *A. suboxydans* but appeared to differ from coenzyme A.[23]

References to Section 17

1. G. M. Hills, *Biochem. J.*, 1943, **37**, 418.
2. P. C. Teague and R. J. Williams, *J. Gen. Physiol.*, 1942, **25**, 777.
3. A. Dorfman, S. Berkman and S. A. Koser, *J. Biol. Chem.*, 1942, **144**, 393.
4. F. J. Pilgrim, A. E. Axelrod and C. A. Elvehjem, *ibid.*, 1942, **145**, 237.
5. M. G. Sevag and M. N. Green, *ibid.*, 1944, **154**, 719; *J. Bact.*, 1944, **48**, 631; *Amer. J. Med. Sci.*, 1944, **207**, 686.
6. F. Lipmann, N. O. Kaplan, G. D. Novelli, L. C. Tuttle and B. M. Guirard, *J. Biol. Chem.*, 1947, **167**, 869.
7. F. Lipmann, *Fed. Proc.*, 1945, **4**, 97; *J. Biol. Chem.*, 1945, **160**, 173.
8. F. Lipmann and N. O. Kaplan, *ibid.*, 1946, **162**, 743.
9. W. Feldberg and T. Mann, *J. Physiol.*, 1946, **104**, 411.
10. D. Nachmansohn and M. Berman, *J. Biol. Chem.*, 1946, **165**, 551.
11. M. A. Lipton, *Fed. Proc.*, 1946, **5**, 145.
12. G. D. Novelli and F. Lipmann, *J. Bact.*, 1947, **54**, 19; *Arch. Biochem.*, 1947, **14**, 23.
12a. E. Rowett, *J. Gen. Microbiol.*, 1948, **2**, 25.
13. G. D. Novelli and F. Lipmann, *J. Biol. Chem.*, 1947, **171**, 833.
14. N. O. Kaplan and F. Lipmann, *ibid.*, 1948, **174**, 37.
15. D. M. Hegsted and F. Lipmann, *ibid.*, 89.
16. T. R. Riggs and D. M. Hegsted, *ibid.*, 1948, **172**, 539; 1949, **178**, 669.
17. F. C. Charalampous and D. M. Hegsted, *ibid.*, 1949, **180**, 623.
18. M. Soodak and F. Lipmann, *ibid.*, 1948, **175**, 999.
19. M. E. Shils, H. M. Seligman and L. J. Goldwater, *J. Nutrition*, 1949, **37**, 227.
20. R. E. Olson and N. O. Kaplan, *J. Biol. Chem.*, 1948, **175**, 515.
21. G. D. Novelli, N. O. Kaplan and F. Lipmann, *ibid.*, 1949, **177**, 97.
22. G. D. Novelli, R. M. Flynn and F. Lipmann, *ibid.*, 493.
23. T. E. King, L. M. Locher and V. H. Cheldelin, *Arch. Biochem.*, 1948, **17**, 483; T. E. King, I. G. Fels and V. H. Cheldelin, *J. Amer. Chem. Soc.*, 1949, **71**, 131.

18. PANTOTHENIC ACID ANALOGUES

Pantothenic Acid and its Derivatives

It has already been stated (page 354) that L-pantothenic acid is inactive on bacteria,[1] rats and chicks.[2] Simple derivatives of D-pantothenic acid generally exhibited activity when tested on rats, but not on micro-organisms. For example, the acetate,[3] benzoate[3] and diphosphate[4] were active on rats, but inactive on bacteria, and ethyl monoacetyl-pantothenate[5, 6] and ethyl pantothenate[5, 6] were as effective as an equivalent amount of calcium pantothenate in promoting the growth of pantothenic acid deficient rats and chicks, but stimulated the growth of *L. helveticus* only slightly. Pantothenic acid *p*-nitrobenzoate was also inactive when tested microbiologically.[6] Apparently the rat and presumably other mammals are able to convert such derivatives, which are not available to the organism *per se*, into the free vitamin.

A. L. Neal and F. M. Strong[7] found that pantothenic acid in liver, yeast, cheese and eggs was accompanied by as much as half its equivalent of an alkali-stable substance utilised by *L. helveticus* with the same degree of efficiency as pantothenic acid and by chicks four times as efficiently ; this substance has not been adequately characterised, but it is believed to be a substitution product of pantothenic acid.

β-Alanine and Related Compounds

As has already been pointed out (page 361), β-alanine can serve as a growth factor for certain species of yeast,[8, 9] certain strains of *C. diphtheriae*[10, 11] and, to a certain extent apparently, for rats.[12, 13] Micro-organisms that can thus utilise β-alanine have been shown to convert it into pantothenic acid[9, 11] (page 387).

α-Methyl-β-alanine had only 0·0006 of the activity of β-alanine towards the Gebrüder-Mayer strain of bakers' yeast, and partially antagonised the growth-promoting effect of β-alanine.[14] Isoserine and β-aminobutyric acid also antagonised the action of β-alanine on yeast.[15]

Analogues Derived from β-Alanine

Most of the analogues synthesised in the course of elucidating the structure of pantothenic acid showed less than 1 % of the activity of pantothenic acid, or none at all, when tested on micro-organisms. These compounds included αδ-dihydroxyvaleryl-β-alanine,[16, 17, 19] αγ-dihydroxyvaleryl-β-alanine,[17, 18] αγ-dihydroxybutyryl-β-alanine,[18] αγ-dihydroxy-β-methylbutyryl-β-alanine,[18] αγ-dihydroxy-α-methylbutyryl-β-alanine, αβγ-trihydroxy-butyryl-β-alanine[18] and αε-dihydroxycaproyl-β-alanine.[19]

Mitchell *et al.*[19] found only one substance, the so-called " hydroxy-pantothenic acid " (α-hydroxy - ββ - bishydroxymethyl - butyryl - β - alanine), with appreciable pantothenic acid activity ; this had 20 % of the activity of pantothenic acid when tested on *Lactobacillus helveticus*. E. Zschiesche and H. K. Mitchell [20] also observed some activity in α-hydroxy-ββ-bishydroxymethyl-butyryl-β-alanine when tested on rats.

T. Reichstein and A. Grüssner [17] reported that αγ-dihydroxyvaleryl-β-alanine and αδ-dihydroxyvaleryl-β-alanine had the same activity as β-alanine on rats, but were inactive on lactic acid bacteria. Mention has already been made (page 354) of the inactivity of the compound prepared by R. Kuhn and T. Wieland by coupling β-alanine with the lactone, $C_{17}H_{12}O_3$.

Several derivatives of β-alanine were prepared by J. W. Barnett and F. A. Robinson [21] and were shown by H. McIlwain [22] to have practically no stimulating action on the growth of *Streptococcus haemolyticus*, *Staphylococcus aureus* or *Proteus morganii*. The following had only 5×10^{-6} of the activity of pantothenic acid : γ-hydroxy-*n*-butyryl-β-alanine, βδ-dihydroxy-γγ-dimethylvaleryl-β-alanine (" homopantothenic acid "), γ-hydroxy-ββ-dimethylbutyryl-β-alanine (" desoxypantothenic acid "), δ-hydroxy-γγ-dimethyl-$\Delta^{\alpha:\beta}$-pentenoyl-β-alanine (" dehydrohomopantothenic acid ") and pantoyltauramide, whilst pantoyltaurine, homopantoyltaurine and γ-hydroxy-*n*-butyryl-β-alanine had no growth-promoting action. β-Ethyl-αγ-dihydroxy-β-methyl-butyryl-β-alanine had less effect than pantothenic acid on *S. plantarum*.[22a] These results emphasise the high degree of structural specificity of pantothenic acid.

Several of these compounds were found to inhibit the growth of bacteria for which pantothenic acid is an essential growth factor (see page 397).

The β-alanides of α- and γ-hydroxy-ββ-dimethylbutyric acid and βγ-dihydroxy-β-methylbutyric acid had a slight growth-stimulating activity on *Acetobacter suboxydans*, *L. arabinosus* and Gebrüder-Mayer yeast, possibly owing to hydrolysis with liberation of β-alanine.[23]

The ethyl ester of DL-α-amino-γ-hydroxy-ββ-dimethyl-butyryl-β-alanine had no pantothenic acid activity when tested on rats or *L. arabinosus*.[23a] It has been suggested that the corresponding amino acid, α-amino-γ-hydroxy-ββ-dimethyl-butyric acid (pantonine), is the precursor of pantoic acid in the synthesis of pantothenic acid.[23b] The keto-acid corresponding to pantothenic acid, namely γ-hydroxy-α-keto-ββ-dimethyl-butyryl-β-alanine, likewise had no biological activity.[23c]

Analogues Derived from Amino Acids other than β-Alanine

Replacement of the β-alanine portion of pantothenic acid by other amino acids invariably leads to loss of activity. Thus, Weinstock *et al.*[24] found that the pantoyl derivatives of α-alanine, β-aminobutyric acid, aspartic acid and lysine were inactive when tested microbiologically, although β-pantoylaminobutyric acid was claimed by Hoffmann-La Roche [25] to have pantothenic acid activity. The pantoyl derivatives of L-leucine [26] and of lysine, leucine, valine and taurine [27] were reported to have no growth-promoting activity.

α-Methyl-pantothenic acid (N-pantoyl-α-methyl-β-alanine) had only 0·001 to 0·0001 of the potency of pantothenic acid for stimulating growth and acid production in *L. helveticus*, *L. arabinosus* and *S. faecalis* R, and 0·002 to 0·0003 of the activity of pantothenic acid in stimulating the growth of the Gebrüder-Mayer and Fleischmann strains of bakers' yeast.[14] It had a slight antagonistic effect towards pantothenic acid. β-Methyl pantothenic acid (β-pantoylaminobutyric acid), however, inhibited the growth of *Streptobacterium plantarum* (page 399) when the ratio of methyl-pantothenic acid to pantothenic acid exceeded 200 : 1; the growth of yeast was not affected, although respiration was greatly reduced.

Several other pantoyl-amino acids have been shown to possess inhibitory activity (see pages 398-400).

Analogues Derived from Amino Alcohols and Amines

So far consideration has been given only to analogues of pantothenic acid that contain a free carboxyl group, that is, to pantoyl-amino acids and substances derived from them by changes in the pantoyl portion of the molecule. A large number of substances have been prepared and tested for pantothenic acid activity, however, that do not possess a free carboxyl group. The most important of these, pantothenyl alcohol or panthenol :

$$CH_2OH . C(CH_3)_2 . CHOH . CO . NH . CH_2 . CH_2 . CH_2OH$$

was prepared by H. Pfaltz,[28] who reported that it was as effective as pantothenic acid in preventing achromotrichia in black rats. Its methyl homologue, 3-pantoylamino-butanol-2, was only slightly active, however, whilst 2-pantoylaminoethanol and γ-pantoylbutyric acid were quite inactive. Pantothenyl alcohol did not stimulate the growth of bacteria, but was quite a strong inhibitor of bacterial growth (page 400). None of the other compounds derived from alcohols or amines stimulated bacterial growth and many had inhibitory properties.

In warm-blooded animals, panthenol was converted into pantothenic acid,[29] more of which was excreted by humans following a dose of panthenol than after administration of the same weight of pantothenic acid.[29a] Panthenol had 90 % of the activity of pantothenic acid, gram for gram, in chicks.[29b]

Pantothenic aldehyde was only slightly active as a growth stimulant for *L. helveticus*, but had one-fifth the activity of pantothenic acid for rats.[8]

Growth Inhibitors

The preparation of pantoyltaurine [21, 22, 30, 31] and its inhibitory action on the growth of micro-organisms have already been described (page 381). Pantoyltaurine is perhaps the best known of the growth inhibitors allied to pantothenic acid, from which it differs in the replacement of the carboxyl by a sulphonic acid group. It is believed to compete with pantothenic acid for an active enzyme system of which pantothenic acid is the prosthetic group, presumably coenzyme A, and the two are able to displace one another from combination with the enzyme. The ratio of the concentration of pantoyltaurine to that of pantothenic acid necessary to inhibit bacterial growth, a ratio which H. McIlwain [22] has termed the " antibacterial index ", varies from 500 for *Streptococcus haemolyticus* and exacting strains of *Corynebacterium diphtheriae* to 1000 for *Diplococcus pneumoniae* and *Lactobacillus arabinosus*, 5000 for non-exacting strains of *C. diphtheriae*, 8000 for *Streptococcus faecalis* and *Propionibacterium pentosaceum and* 133,000 for *Lactobacillus pentosus* and *Leuconostoc mesenteroides*. Pantoyltauramide was considerably less effective against these organisms,[22] its antibacterial index ranging from 2000 for *S. haemolyticus* and 2000 to 10,000 for the exacting strains of *C. diphtheriae* to 10,000 to 50,000 for *Diplococcus pneumoniae* ; it failed to inhibit the other organisms tested. The antibacterial index of homopantoyltaurine [21] ($\beta\delta$-dihydroxy-$\gamma\gamma$-dimethylvaleryltaurine) was 20,000 when tested on *S. haemolyticus*.[22]

The above data were obtained with the aid of racemic pantoyltaurine and pantoyltauramide. E. E. Snell [32] tested the isomers prepared from (+)- and (−)-pantolactone, and found that the sulphonic acid from the (−)-lactone was ten times as active as that from the (+)-lactone, in spite of the fact that partial racemisation had undoubtedly occurred during the condensation. Thus growth inhibition showed the same configurational specificity as did growth promotion by pantothenic acid.

There appears to be a divergence of opinion concerning the ability of pantoyltaurine to cause symptoms of pantothenic acid deficiency in animals. According to Snell *et al.*[33] long-continued daily oral administration at a dose level of 200 mg. per kg. of bodyweight produced such symptoms in three to four weeks, but other workers failed to produce symptoms of pantothenic acid deficiency in mice,[34] hamsters [34] and rats.[35]

Desoxypantoyltaurine (α-hydroxy-$\beta\beta$-dimethylbutyryltaurine) unlike pantoyltaurine, did not inhibit bacterial growth, nor did it stimulate the growth of *Acetobacter suboxydans*, as did pantoyltaurine which was hydrolysed, liberating pantoic acid, which the organism utilised.[23]

Although pantoyltaurine was a powerful inhibitor of bacterial growth *in vitro*, the results of *in vivo* tests were disappointing ; rats, however, were protected from the effects of haemolytic streptococci by giving frequent large doses (see page 382). As already explained, the failure of pantoyltaurine to exert a more pronounced chemotherapeutic effect was due ultimately to the antagonistic action of the pantothenic acid present in the blood of the animals, but the condition was undoubtedly aggravated by the rapid elimination of the substance in the urine ; this necessitated the giving of frequent injections in order to maintain the blood concentration at a sufficiently high level. Attempts to prepare derivatives of pantoyltaurine that might be excreted less readily, have therefore been made. J. W. Barnett [36] prepared N-pantoyl-β-aminoethylthiol, bis-(pantoyl-β-aminoethyl) monosulphide, disulphide, sulphoxide and sulphone, which were tested on *L. arabinosus* and *Strep. haemolyticus*.[37] None of the compounds was more active than pantoyltaurine, but the disulphide and the thiol were almost equally active and their effects were reversed by pantothenic acid. The antibacterial index of the disulphide and of the sulphone was 40,000 against *Strep. haemolyticus*. They had no *in vivo* activity against *Strep. haemolyticus* in rats. Three aryl substituted analogues of pantoyltaurine, namely, β-($\alpha\gamma$-dihydroxy-$\beta\beta$-dimethylbutyramido)-α-phenylethane sulphonic acid, β-($\alpha\gamma$-dihydroxy-$\beta\beta$-diphenylbutyramido)-ethane sulphonic acid and β-(α-tosyl-γ-hydroxy-$\beta\beta$-dimethylbutyramido)-ethane sulphonic acid, were prepared by Barnett *et al.*,[38] but had neither *in vitro* nor *in vivo* activity.

A further series of compounds, some of which were tested by H. McIlwain and D. E. Hughes,[37] was prepared by Madinaveitia *et al.*[39] These were pantamide, panthydrazide, N-(β-diethylaminoethyl)-pantamide, N-(5-diethylamino-2-pentyl)-pantamide, N-pantoyl-phenylalanine, N-pantoyl-hexahydroanthranilic acid, N-pantoyl-nipecotic acid, β-(N-pantoylaminoethyl)-p-tolylsulphone, β-(N-pantoylaminoethyl)-p-aminophenyl sulphone, β-(N-pantoylaminoethyl)-p-methoxyphenyl sulphone, and N-pantoyl-p-anisidine. In this series the pantoyl group was combined with other radicals associated with chemotherapeutic activity. However, the only compounds that showed striking anti-bacterial activity when tested against *L. helveticus* were panthydrazide and, to a smaller extent, pantamide. The former had no therapeutic action, however, on rats infected with *Strep. pyogenes*, but the amide derived from 4-amino-phenyl-β-aminoethyl sulphone showed slight therapeutic activity under these conditions. According to McIlwain and Hughes, panthyrazide and pantamide had antibacterial indices of 4000 and 20,000 respectively against *Strep. haemolyticus*.

As pantothenic acid is the only growth factor known to be essential for *Plasmodium*,[39a] Mead *et al.*[39b] tested the activity of *d*-pantoyltaurine and several of its derivatives in malaria ; *d*-pantoyltauramide was found to be active *in vivo*. This observation has resulted in a large member of N-substituted pantoyltauramides being made but, although pantoyltauramido-4-chlorobenzene was four to sixteen times as effective as quinine in *P. gallinaceum* infections in chicks, none of the compounds appears to have any clinical value.[39c] The antimalarial effect of pantoyltauramide was neutralised by one-quarter of its weight of pantothenic acid ; [39d] and this may explain the disappointing results obtained with antimalarials of this type.

Many sulphur-free analogues of pantothenic acid have been found to inhibit the growth of bacteria. Thus, γ-hydroxy-n-butyryl-β-alanine and γ-hydroxy-n-valeryl-β-alanine were inhibitory to *S. haemolyticus* and *C. diphtheriae*, but the effect was not reversed by pantothenic acid.[21, 22] They also inhibited the growth of *E. coli*, *Proteus vulgaris* and *Staph. aureus*, which are not inhibited by pantoyl-taurine and which are capable of synthesising pantothenic acid. With *E. coli* the inhibitory effect was not prevented by the addition of pantothenic acid, but inhibition by the hydroxybutyryl derivative was partially reversed in the case of *Pr. vulgaris*. Thus, inhibition by these particular compounds would appear to be of the non-competitive type, but associated in some way, as yet undisclosed, with pantothenic acid.

As already mentioned (see page 396), α- and β-methylpantothenic acid [14, 15] inhibited bacterial growth, as did several other pantoyl amino acids. For *Streptobacterium plantarum*, β-methylpantothenic acid (pantoyl-β-aminobutyric acid) had an anti-bacterial index of 200,[15] whilst the values for other organisms were : [40] for *Lactobacillus helveticus*, 250 ; for *L. arabinosus*, 1500 ; for *Leuconostoc mesenteroides*, 2000 ; and for *Lactobacillus fermenti*, 5000. This last-named organism is particularly resistant to pantoyltaurine and pantothenyl alcohol. Pantoyl-isoserine and pantoyl-β-amino-isobutyric acid were less effective, the corresponding antibacterial indices being : 1000 and 2500 ; 1000 and 2500 ; 1000 and 5000 ; and > 50,000 respectively. In some instances, complete inhibition was not obtained, the reason being apparently that at these high concentrations they acted as growth stimulants. A homologue of pantothenic acid, N-($\alpha\gamma$-dihydroxy-$\beta\beta$-dimethylvaleryl)-β-alanine, inhibited the growth of lactic acid bacteria and the inhibition was reversed by pantothenic acid.[41] Rather surprisingly, the taurine analogue was less active than the β-alanine derivative.[41a]

Pantothenyl alcohol, N-pantoylethanolamine, N-pantoylallylamine, N-pantoyl-*n*-propylamine, N-pantoylethylamine and N-pantoylglycine also inhibited the growth of micro-organisms for which pantothenic acid is essential, and the inhibition was competitive.[42] The antibacterial indices of pantothenyl alcohol and N-pantoyl-4-amino-2-butanol, the most potent of these inhibitors, were : [41] for *L. mesenteroides*, 700 and 600 ; for *L. helveticus*, 100,000 and 20,000 ; for *L. arabinosus*, 50,000 and 10,000 ; and for *L. fermenti*, 200,000. All compounds were tested in the racemic form, but it was shown that pantothenyl alcohol derived from the (−)-lactone was more active than the isomer from the (+)-lactone.[42] Growth inhibition by pantothenyl alcohol did not run parallel with pantoyltaurine inhibition and it is assumed that the modes of action of the two compounds are different.

Subsequently, W. Shive and E. E. Snell [43] prepared and tested other pantoyl derivatives and obtained the following antibacterial indices, using *Leuconostoc mesenteroides* as test-organism :

DL-Pantothenyl alcohol	.	. .	350
DL-N-Pantoylethylamine	.	. .	10,000
,, ,,	*n*-propylamine	. .	5000
,, ,,	*n*-butylamine	. .	750
,, ,,	*n*-amylamine	. .	1500
,, ,,	*n*-heptylamine	. .	2000
,, ,,	isopropylamine	.	25,000
,, ,,	isobutylamine	. .	2500
,, ,,	isoamylamine	. .	5000
,, ,,	sec. butylamine	.	75,000
,, ,,	β-methoxyethylamine	.	4000
,, ,,	β-phenylethylamine	.	15,000
DL-Pantothenonitrile	. .	. .	10,000
DL-Pantothenylamine	.	. .	40,000

Rather different values were obtained with *L. arabinosus* and *L. helveticus* in many instances. Pantoyltaurine and N-pantoyl-*n*-butylamine also interfered with the utilisation of pantothenic acid by *Pseudomonas* spp.[44]

D. W. Woolley and M. L. Collyer [45] prepared phenylpantothenone (N-pantoylaminoethyl phenyl ketone) and showed that it inhibited bacterial growth and that the inhibition was reversed by pantothenic acid. This compound, therefore, behaved like pantoyltaurine, inhibition being competitive. Methylpantothenone (N-pantoylaminoethyl methyl ketone) exhibited growth-inhibitory properties, but the inhibition was not reversed by pantothenic acid.

The antagonistic effect of pantothenic acid towards phenyl pantothenone was only exhibited with micro-organisms for which the vitamin was essential. With other organisms, phenylpantothenone was antagonised by amino acids ; with *S. cerevisiae* for instance, histidine was the most active, followed by glutamic acid.[46]

A number of pantothenic acid analogues were prepared by Rapport *et al.*[47] and of these N-carbobenzoxy-β-alanylamide, ($+$)-pantoyl-diethyl aspartate and sodium ($+$)-β-pantoylamino-β-4-aminophenyl propionate were tested for antimalarial activity.

Phenylpantothenone exhibited antimalarial activity, and this led Singher *et al.*[48] to test the effect of ($-$)-$\alpha\gamma$-dihydroxy-$\beta\beta$-dimethyl-N-(2-phenylmercaptoethyl)-butyramide on *Plasmodium*. This compound was also tested on *Trichomonas vaginalis*, which requires pantothenic acid for growth. It was highly effective *in vitro* against this organism and also against *T. foetus* and *T. gallinae*.[49] Other analogues were less effective, namely, ($+$)-$\alpha\gamma$-dihydroxy-$\beta\beta$-dimethyl-N-(2-phenyl-sulphenylethyl)-butyramide, ($+$)-pantoyltauryl anisidide and N-2-benzyl-ethyl-$\alpha\gamma$-dihydroxy-$\beta\beta$-dimethylbutyramide. None of these compounds was active *in vivo* in monkeys or humans.

References to Section 18

1. E. T. Stiller, S. A. Harris, J. Finkelstein, J. C. Keresztesy and K. Folkers, *J. Amer. Chem. Soc.*, 1940, **62**, 1785.
2. A. Grüssner, M. Gätzi-Fichter and T. Reichstein, *Helv. Chim. Acta*, 1940, **23**, 1276.
3. D. W. Woolley, H. A. Waisman, O. Mickelsen and C. A. Elvehjem, *J. Biol. Chem.*, 1938, **125**, 715.
4. D. W. Woolley, *ibid.*, 1940, **134**, 461.
5. K. Unna and C. W. Mushett, *Amer. J. Physiol.*, 1942, **135**, 267.
6. S. A. Harris, G. A. Boyack and K. Folkers, *J. Amer. Chem. Soc.*, 1941, **63**, 2662.
7. A. L. Neal and F. M. Strong, *ibid.*, 1943, **65**, 1659.
8. U. Schindler and D. Reichstein, *Pharm. Acta Helv.*, 1945, 79.
9. H. H. Weinstock, H. K. Mitchell, E. F. Pratt and R. J. Williams, *J. Amer. Chem. Soc.*, 1939, **61**, 1421.
10. J. H. Mueller, *Proc. Soc. Exp. Biol. Med.*, 1937, **36**, 706 ; J. H. Mueller and A. W. Klotz, *J. Amer. Chem. Soc.*, 1938, **60**, 3086.
11. W. C. Evans, W. R. C. Handley and F. C. Happold, *Brit. J. Exp. Path.*, 1939, **20**, 396.
12. M. Hoffer and T. Reichstein, *Nature*, 1939, **144**, 72.
13. M. M. El Sadr, H. G. Hind, T. F. Macrae, C. E. Work, B. Lythgoe and A. R. Todd, *ibid.*, 73.
14. M. A. Pollack, *J. Amer. Chem. Soc.*, 1943, **65**, 1335.
15. N. Nielsen and G. Johansen, *Naturwiss.*, 1943, **31**, 235.
16. Y. SubbaRow and L. Rane, *J. Amer. Chem. Soc.*, 1939, **61**, 1616.
17. T. Reichstein and A. Grüssner, *Helv. Chim. Acta*, 1940, **23**, 650.
18. H. K. Mitchell, H. H. Weinstock, E. E. Snell, S. R. Stanbery and R. J. Williams, *J. Amer. Chem. Soc.*, 1940, **62**, 1776.

19. H. K. Mitchell, E. E. Snell and R. J. Williams, *J. Amer. Chem. Soc.*, 1940, **62,** 1791.
20. E. Zschiesche and H. K. Mitchell, *Proc. Soc. Exp. Biol. Med.*, 1940, **45,** 565.
21. J. W. Barnett and F. A. Robinson, *Biochem. J.*, 1942, **36,** 357, 364.
22. H. McIlwain, *ibid.*, 417.
22a. T. Wieland and E. F. Möller, *Chem. Ber.*, 1948, **81,** 316.
23. V. H. Cheldelin and C. A. Schink, *J. Amer. Chem. Soc.*, 1947, **69,** 2625.
23a. F. W. Holly, R. A. Barnes, F. R. Koniousky and K. Folkers, *ibid.*, 1948, **70,** 3088.
23b. W. W. Ackermann and H. Kirby, *J. Biol. Chem.*, 1948, **175,** 483 ; W. W. Ackermann and W. Shive, *ibid.*, 867.
23c. T. Wieland, *Chem. Ber.*, 1948, **81,** 323 ; S. H. Lipton and F. M. Strong, *J. Amer. Chem. Soc.*, 1949, **71,** 2364.
24. H. H. Weinstock, E. L. May, A. Arnold and D. Price, *J. Biol. Chem.*, 1940, **135,** 343.
25. F. Hoffmann-La Roche and Co., B.P. 570533.
26. R. Kuhn and T. Wieland, *Ber.*, 1940, **73,** 962.
27. N. Nielsen, V. Hartelius and G. Johansen, *Naturwiss.*, 1944, **32,** 294; *Compt. rend. Trav. Lab. Carlsberg, Sér. Physiol.*, 1944, **24,** 39.
28. H. Pfaltz, *Z. Vitaminforsch.*, 1943, **13,** 236.
29. E. Burlet, *ibid.*, 1944, **14,** 318.
29a. S. H. Rubin, J. M. Cooperman, M. E. Moore and J. Scheiner, *J. Nutrition*, 1948, **35,** 499.
29b. D. M. Hegsted, *Proc. Soc. Exp. Biol. Med.*, 1948, **69,** 571.
30. E. E. Snell, *J. Biol. Chem.*, 1941, **139,** 975.
31. R. Kuhn, T. Wieland and E. F. Möller, *Ber.*, 1941, **74,** 1605.
32. E. E. Snell, *J. Biol. Chem.*, 1941, **141,** 121.
33. E. E. Snell, L. Chan, S. Spiridanoff, E. L. Way and C. D. Leake, *Science*, 1943, **97,** 168 ; *Fed. Proc.*, 1943, **2,** 92.
34. D. W. Woolley and A. G. C. White, *Proc. Soc. Exp. Biol. Med.*, 1943, **52,** 106.
35. K. Unna, *ibid.*, 1943, **54,** 55.
36. J. W. Barnett, *J. Chem. Soc.*, 1944, 5.
37. H. McIlwain and D. E. Hughes, *Biochem. J.*, 1945, **39,** 133.
38. J. W. Barnett, D. J. Dupré, B. J. Holloway and F. A. Robinson, *J. Chem. Soc.*, 1944, 94.
39. J. Madinaveitia, A. R. Martin, F. L. Rose and G. Swain, *Biochem. J.*, 1945, **39,** 85 ; B.P. 578251.
39a. W. Trager, *J. Exp. Med.*, 1943, **77,** 411.
39b. J. F. Mead, M. M. Rapport, A. E. Senear, J. T. Maynard, and J. B. Koepfli, *J. Biol. Chem.*, 1946, **163,** 465.
39c. S. Brackott, E. Waletzky and M. Baker, *J. Parasit.*, 1946, **32,** 453 ; R. Winterbottom, J. W. Clapp, W. H. Miller, J. P. English and R. O. Roblin, *J. Amer. Chem. Soc.*, 1947, **69,** 1393 ; American Cyanamid Co., U.S.P. 2459111.
39d. W. Cantrell, *J. Parasit.*, 1949, **35,** 220.
40. W. Shive and E. E. Snell, *Science*, 1945, **102,** 401.

41. W. Drell and M. S. Dunn, *J. Amer. Chem. Soc.*, 1946, **68,** 1868.
41*a*. W. Drell and M. S. Dunn, *ibid.*, 1948, **70,** 2057.
42. E. E. Snell and W. Shive, *J. Biol. Chem.*, 1945, **158,** 551.
43. W. Shive and E. E. Snell, *ibid.*, 1945, **160,** 287 ; Research Corp., U.S.P. 2446615.
44. W. I. Metzger, *J. Bact.*, 1947, **54,** 135.
45. D. W. Woolley and M. L. Collyer, *J. Biol. Chem.*, 1945, **159,** 265.
46. D. W. Woolley, *ibid.*, 1946, **163,** 481.
47. M. M. Rapport, J. F. Mead, J. T. Maynard, A. E. Senear and J. D. Koepfli, *J. Amer. Chem. Soc.*, 1947, **69,** 2561.
48. H. O. Singher, N. Millman and M. R. Bosworth, *Proc. Soc. Exp. Biol. Med.*, 1948, **67,** 388.
49. G. Johnson and A. B. Kupferberg, *ibid.*, 390.

CHAPTER VII

BIOTIN

1. INTRODUCTION

THE discovery that certain strains of yeast would not grow on a medium consisting solely of sugar and inorganic salts led E. Wildiers [1] in 1901 to postulate the existence in yeast extracts and wort of a substance necessary for the growth of certain yeasts. This hypothetical substance he called " bios ". Yeasts were found to differ greatly in their requirements for bios ; certain wild yeasts grew and developed without it, whereas others showed no signs of growth in its absence.

The complex nature of bios was first recognised in 1922 by E. I. Fulmer and V. E. Nelson,[2] who showed that it consisted of at least two substances. Shortly afterwards W. Lash Miller [3] succeeded in fractionating it into three substances all essential for growth.

The first of these, which was termed Bios I, was shown by E. V. Eastcott [4] to be meso-inositol. The second fraction, Bios IIA, was identified by W. Lash Miller [5] as β-alanine supplemented by L-leucine, and by C. Rainbow and L. R. Bishop [6] as pantothenic acid. The discrepancy is explained by the fact that some yeasts require only β-alanine, whilst others require the whole pantothenic acid molecule.

The third factor, Bios IIB, was shown to be identical with biotin, isolated by F. Kögl and B. Tönnis [7] in the form of a crystalline methyl ester from egg yolk. Other factors of the bios group were subsequently identified by Miller and his co-workers, and by Rainbow and Bishop. These include aneurine, which appears to be identical with the factor previously called Bios V,[8] pyridoxine [9] and nicotinic acid.[10]

In addition to being a growth factor for micro-organisms, biotin was also recognised to be a vitamin, that is, a factor essential for the growth of animals. In 1927, M. A. Boas-Fixsen [11] observed that the feeding of raw egg white to rats produced an eczema-like dermatitis accompanied by loss of hair. She found that the condition was cured by a " protective factor X " present in liver. What was apparently the same factor was recognised by P. György,[12] who called it vitamin H, and subsequently showed [13] that it possessed properties similar to those of biotin prepared by Kögl and Tönnis from egg-yolk.

Hegsted *et al.*[14] observed that chicks fed a purified diet containing adequate pantothenic acid developed a dermatitis which was cured by vitamin H. Biotin was also shown to be identical with coenzyme R,[13, 15] a growth and respiratory factor essential for the nitrogen-fixing *Rhizobia* present in the root-nodules of legumes.[16]

Actually the substance isolated by Kögl and Tönnis[7] from egg-yolk, though very similar in chemical and biological properties to the substance isolated by du Vigneaud and György[13] from liver, is probably not identical with it. F. Kögl and E. J. ten Ham[17] found that apparently significant differences existed between the melting points and optical rotations of the two forms, and they designated the factor from egg-yolk α-biotin and that from liver β-biotin. The methyl esters of the two substances also differed in melting point and optical rotation, whilst a mixture of α- and β-biotin methyl esters had a melting point 20 to 30° lower than that of either of the pure esters. The activity of β-biotin in the yeast test was almost twice that of α-biotin, although more recent tests against five different micro-organisms suggests that α-biotin has 90 to 96 % of the activity of β-biotin.[18]

References to Section 1

1. E. Wildiers, *La Cellule*, 1901, **18**, 313.
2. E. I. Fulmer and V. E. Nelson, *Proc. Iowa Acad. Sci.*, 1922, **29**, 371.
3. W. Lash Miller, *Science*, 1924, **58**, 197.
4. E. V. Eastcott, *J. Phys. Chem.*, 1928, **32**, 1094.
5. W. Lash Miller, *Trans. Roy. Soc. Canada*, III, 1936, **30**, 99.
6. C. Rainbow and L. R. Bishop, *J. Inst. Brewing*, 1939, **45**, 593.
7. F. Kögl and B. Tönnis, *Z. physiol. Chem.*, 1936, **242**, 43.
8. W. Lash Miller, *Trans. Roy. Soc., Canada*, III, 1937, **31**, 169.
9. A. S. Schultz, L. Atkin and C. N. Frey, *J. Amer. Chem. Soc.*, 1939, **61**, 1931.
10. A. S. Schultz, L. Atkin and C. N. Frey, *ibid.*, 1938, **60**, 1514.
11. M. A. Boas-Fixsen, *Biochem. J.*, 1927, **21**, 712.
12. P. György, *Z. örztl. Fortbild.*, 1931, **28**, 377, 417 ; *J. Biol. Chem.*, 1937, **119**, xliii ; 1939, **131**, 733.
13. P. György, D. B. Melville, D. Burk and V. du Vigneaud, *Science*, 1940, **91**, 243 ; V. du Vigneaud, D. B. Melville, P. György and C. S. Rose, *ibid.*, 1940, **92**, 62.
14. D. M. Hegsted, J. J. Oleson, R. C. Mills, C. A. Elvehjem and E. B. Hart, *J. Nutrition*, 1940, **20**, 599.
15. R. Nilsson, G. Bjälfoe and D. Burström, *Naturwiss.*, 1939, **27**, 389 ; P. M. West and P. W. Wilson, *Science*, 1939, **89**, 607.
16. F. E. Allison, S. R. Hoover and D .Burk, *ibid.*, 1933, **78**, 217.
17. F. Kögl and E. J. ten Ham, *Naturwiss.*, 1943, **31**, 208 ; *Z. physiol. Chem.*, 1943, **279**, 140.
18. K. K. Krueger and W. H. Peterson, *J. Biol. Chem.*, 1948, **173**, 497.

2. ISOLATION OF BIOTIN

α-Biotin

The procedure used by F. Kögl and B. Tönnis [1] to isolate α-biotin methyl ester from egg-yolk was as follows : The yolks of 1000 fresh eggs were treated with acetone and the filtrate was concentrated and treated with four volumes of alcohol. The active precipitate was dissolved in water and impurities were removed by precipitation with lead acetate. The filtrate was freed from lead, and phosphotungstic acid was added to precipitate the active principle. The precipitate was decomposed with baryta and the solution was shaken with charcoal. After washing the adsorbate with 50 % alcohol, an active fraction was obtained by elution with 60 % acetone containing 2·5 % of ammonia. A second precipitation with phosphotungstic acid and decomposition with baryta gave an active fraction soluble in alcohol. This was freed from impurities by precipitation with mercuric chloride and then esterified with methanolic hydrogen chloride. Further impurities were removed by precipitation with picrolonic acid and then with rufianic acid. Finally, a very potent preparation was obtained by decomposition of the reineckate, the yield being 4 mg., or 8 % of the material originally present. From a second preparation, starting with a large quantity of dried egg-yolk, the methyl ester was obtained in crystalline form by high vacuum distillation and crystallisation from a mixture of chloroform and light petroleum. The substance had a m.p. of 146 to 147° C. and was active on *Saccharomyces* in a dilution of 1 in 10,000,000,000.

An improved method of isolating biotin from egg-yolk was subsequently described by F. Kögl and L. Pons,[2] who used molecular distillation to purify the crude product ; by means of this modification, the yield was increased to 10 or 20 %. The biotin methyl ester was crystallised from mesityl oxide which gave a purer product, m.p. 161 to 165° C.

β-Biotin

György *et al.*[3] used the following method for the preparation of a " vitamin H " concentrate from liver : a residue obtained in the preparation of " Campolon " was digested with papain or autoclaved with acid, and the active factor was concentrated by a variety of operations, including adsorption on charcoal, elution with a mixture of pyridine, methanol and water, precipitation with phosphotungstic acid, and precipitation with gold chloride. Yeast autolysates were also concentrated by similar methods, but the procedure was more difficult than with liver.

V. du Vigneaud *et al.*[4] used as the starting-material a liver concentrate prepared by high pressure hydrolysis of an alcohol-insoluble fraction of beef liver. Inert material was precipitated with alcohol and acetone, and an active fraction was precipitated by means of phosphotungstic acid, and the precipitate was decomposed with barium hydroxide. Pure biotin ester was prepared from this concentrate by esterification with methanolic hydrogen chloride, followed by two chromatographic adsorptions on Brockmann alumina. The yield from 5 litres of liver concentrate was 70 mg. F. Kögl and E. J. ten Ham [5] prepared β-biotin from a liver concentrate by chromatographic adsorption on norit, elution with ammoniacal acetone, esterification, chromatographic adsorption of the ester from chloroform on alumina and elution with a mixture (9 : 1) of acetone and methanol, followed by re-adsorption on alumina from acetone, elution with a mixture of acetone and methanol and, finally, hydrolysis to the free acid.

Biotin was also prepared from milk. A concentrate was esterified with acid methanol, and the ester was chromatographed first on Decalso and then on activated alumina.[6] The crude crystalline ester obtained on elution was purified by washing with ethyl acetate, sublimation *in vacuo* and re-crystallisation from a mixture of ether and methanol. The free biotin obtained on hydrolysis was identical with the biotin from liver. A yield of 25 to 40 % was obtained.

References to Section 2

1. F. Kögl and B. Tönnis, *Z. physiol. Chem.*, 1936, **242**, 43.
2. F. Kögl and L. Pons, *ibid.*, 1941, **269**, 61.
3. P. György, R. Kuhn and E. Lederer, *J. Biol. Chem.*, 1939, **131**, 745.
4. V. du Vigneaud, K. Hofmann, D. B. Melville and P. György, *ibid.*, 1941, **140**, 643.
5. F. Kögl and E. J. ten Ham, *Z. physiol. Chem.*, 1943, **279**, 140.
6. D. B. Melville, K. Hofmann, E. Hague and V. du Vigneaud, *J. Biol. Chem.*, 1942, **142**, 615.

3. CHEMICAL CONSTITUTION OF BIOTIN

Chemical Constitution of β-Biotin

β-Biotin methyl ester, m.p. 166 to 167° C., has the empirical formula, $C_{11}H_{18}O_3N_2S$,[1] and free β-biotin, m.p. 230 to 232° C., has the formula, $C_{10}H_{16}O_3N_2S$.[2]

Biotin is a carboxylic acid and, on treatment with alkali,[3] it gave a sulphur-containing diamino-carboxylic acid, $C_9H_{18}O_2N_2S$ (II), containing one CO group less than biotin. This was interpreted as indicating the presence of a NN'-substituted cyclic urea group. On oxidation with hydrogen peroxide, it yielded a sulphone (III), suggesting that the sulphur was present as a thio-ether linkage. F. Kögl

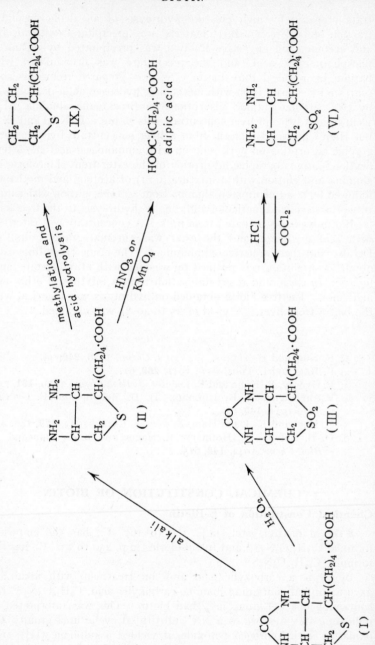

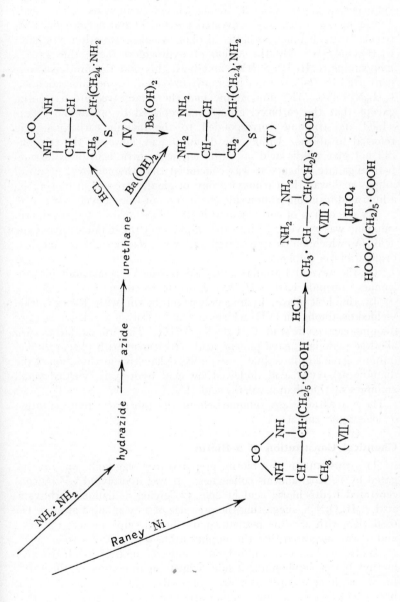

and T. J. de Man [4] suggested that the sulphur formed part of a ring. The diamino-carboxylic acid on oxidation with nitric acid or potassium permanganate yielded, amongst other compounds, adipic acid.[5] Biotin methyl ester was converted *via* the hydrazide into an azide which, with boiling absolute alcohol, yielded an ethyl urethane, $C_{12}H_{21}O_3N_3S$.[5, 6] By the action of hydrochloric acid, this gave a monoamine, $C_9H_{17}ON_3S$ (IV), and both this and the urethane were converted by the action of barium hydroxide into the same triamine, $C_8H_{19}N_3S$ (V). The monoamine had the same structure as biotin, except that the carboxyl group was replaced by an amino group, whilst the triamine corresponded to the diamino-carboxylic acid referred to above. Unlike the diamino acid, however, the triamine did not give adipic acid on oxidation with nitric acid or potassium permanganate, whence it was concluded that the carboxyl group of adipic acid was the carboxyl group originally present in biotin, the adipic acid resulting from a side-chain and not from a cyclic structure.

By the action of concentrated hydrochloric acid at 200° C., biotin sulphone was converted [7] into the sulphone of the diamino carboxylic acid (IV) which, on treatment with phosgene, was reconverted into the original biotin sulphone.

Of the several formulae proposed by du Vigneaud and his colleagues,[6] formula I (R = H) was shown to be correct.[8]

In the first place, hydrogenolysis of biotin with Raney nickel yielded desthiobiotin (VII) which on acid hydrolysis yielded a desthio-diamino-carboxylic acid, $C_9H_{20}O_2N_2$ (VIII). This, on oxidation with alkaline periodate, gave pimelic acid ; treatment with phenanthrene-quinone gave a quinoxaline. Secondly, exhaustive methylation of the diaminocarboxylic acid, followed by acid hydrolysis, yielded small amounts of thiophan-2-valeric acid (IX).[9]

These reactions are summarised in the schematic representation on pages 408 and 409.

Chemical Constitution of α-Biotin

The constitution of α-biotin, prepared from egg-yolk, was investigated by F. Kögl and his colleagues. It was hydrolysed [4, 10] by concentrated hydrochloric acid at 200° C., giving a diamino-carboxylic acid, $C_9H_{18}O_2N_2S$, suggesting the presence of a cyclic urea group. On oxidation with alkaline permanganate, biotin sulphone was obtained and it was suggested that the sulphur atom was part of a ring.

Biotin methyl ester added on 1 mole of methyl iodide to give methyl biotin sulphonium iodide, whilst on oxidation of the ester, biotin sulphone methyl ester was obtained. This on vigorous hydrolysis yielded a C_9-diamino-sulphocarboxylic acid, thus proving that the urea group and the sulphur atom were present in different rings ;

had they been present in one ring, two fragments would have resulted :

$$CO \begin{matrix} NH \\ \\ NH \end{matrix} \Big\} C_8H_{13} \begin{cases} >S \\ \\ -COOMe \end{cases} \longrightarrow CO \begin{matrix} NH \\ \\ NH \end{matrix} \Big\} C_8H_{13} \begin{cases} >SO_2 \\ \\ -COOMe \end{cases}$$

$$\longrightarrow \begin{matrix} NH_2 \\ \\ NH_2 \end{matrix} \Big\} C_8H_{14} \begin{cases} SO_3H \\ \\ COOH \end{cases}$$

To obtain information regarding the position of the carboxyl group, the diamino-carboxylic acid was oxidised with lead tetra-acetate ;[11] 2 moles were consumed, one by the sulphur atom, and one either by an α-amino acid, as in (a) or by a 1 : 2-diamine, as in (b) :

(a)
$$\begin{matrix} NH_2-C \\ \mid \\ C \end{matrix} \Big\} C_5H_{12}S \quad \xrightarrow{PbAc_4} \quad \begin{matrix} NH_2-C \\ \mid \\ C \end{matrix} \Big\} C_5H_{12}SO \quad \xrightarrow[(2\,O)]{KMnO_4} \quad \begin{matrix} NH_2-C \\ \mid \\ C \end{matrix} \Big\} C_5H_{12}SO_2$$
$$NH_2-C-COOH \qquad\qquad CHO \qquad\qquad\qquad COOH$$

(b)
$$\begin{matrix} NH_2-C \\ \mid \\ NH_2-C \end{matrix} \Big\} C_6H_{11}S\,.\,COOH \quad \xrightarrow{PbAc_4} \quad \begin{matrix} OHC \\ \\ OHC \end{matrix} \Big\} C_6H_{11}(SO)COOH$$
$$\xrightarrow[(3\,O)]{KMnO_4} \quad \begin{matrix} HOOC \\ \\ HOOC \end{matrix} \Big\} C_6H_{11}(SO_2)COOH$$

The decision between these two alternatives was made by further oxidation of the aldehydic product with permanganate ; 1·8 moles were taken up, thus favouring the first of the alternatives. This choice was supported by the observation that cold esterification of the resulting acid gave a basic ester ; this could only have been derived from reaction (a) and not from (b). Finally the intermediate aldehyde was isolated as a 2 : 4-dinitrophenylhydrazone with the expected nitrogen content. It appeared to follow from this that the urea grouping formed part of a 6- and not a 5-membered ring, and α-biotin was therefore assumed to be a derivative of 2-ketohexahydro-pyrimidine-4-carboxylic acid.

$$\begin{matrix} & NH & \\ & \diagup \quad \diagdown & \\ CO & & C \\ \mid & & \mid \\ NH & & C \\ & \diagdown \quad \diagup & \end{matrix} \Big\} C_5H_{12}S$$
$$CH$$
$$\mid$$
$$COOH$$

When the amino acid obtained by permanganate oxidation of the aldehyde was esterified in hot solution, ammonia was eliminated and an unsaturated ester was produced :

$$\underset{\text{COOH}}{\overset{\text{NH}_2\text{—C}}{\underset{\displaystyle |}{\overset{\displaystyle |}{\text{C}}}}}\Bigg\}\text{C}_5\text{H}_{12}\text{SO} \xrightarrow{\text{MeOH}} \underset{\text{COOMe}}{\overset{\text{CH—C}_5\text{H}_{10}}{\underset{\displaystyle |}{\overset{\displaystyle \|}{\text{C——SO}_2}}}} \xrightarrow{\text{KMnO}_4} \underset{\text{COOH}}{\overset{\text{COOH}}{|}} \quad \underset{\text{HO}_3\text{S}}{\overset{\text{HOOC}}{\diagup}}{>}\text{C}_5\text{H}_{10}$$

in agreement with the known behaviour of β-amino acids. On oxidation of the free acid with permanganate, 4 atoms of oxygen were utilised and the product was a sulphocarboxylic acid, isolated as the *m*-toluidine salt. To identify this sulphocarboxylic acid, it was fused with alkali,[12] model experiments indicating that β-sulphocarboxylic acids yield unsaturated carboxylic acids by this procedure. An unsaturated acid was in fact obtained and on hydrogenation, *dl*-$\alpha\beta$-dimethylbutyric acid, $(CH_3)_2 . CH . CH(CH_3) . COOH$, was isolated.

Various β- and γ-sulphonic acids derivable from this acid were synthesised, and the methyl ester anilide of β-carboxy-γ-methylbutanesulphonic acid was shown to be identical with the corresponding derivative of the sulphocarboxylic acid from biotin.

This evidence therefore leads to the structure

$$\begin{array}{c}\text{NH} \\ \diagup \;\diagdown \\ \text{CO}\quad \text{CH—CH . CH(CH}_3)_2 \\ |\qquad |\quad\; | \\ \text{NH}\;\; \text{CH}\;\; \text{CH}_2 \\ \diagdown\;\diagup\;\diagdown\;\; \diagup \\ \text{CH}\qquad\text{S} \\ | \\ \text{COOH}\end{array}$$

for the α-biotin of egg-yolk. The difference between this formula and that assigned to β-biotin would account for the fact that the diamino acid sulphone from α-biotin is so much more easily hydrolysed than the corresponding compound from β-biotin but, on the other hand, it is a little difficult to believe that two molecules differing so markedly from one another would possess the same highly specific growth-promoting properties.

Convincing as the above evidence apparently was, the formula proposed for α-biotin was withdrawn by Kögl and his colleagues when they learnt of the results obtained by the American workers on β-biotin and, on reconsideration of the evidence, they advanced the alternative formula :

$$\begin{array}{c}\text{CO} \\ \diagup\;\diagdown \\ \text{NH}\quad\text{NH} \\ |\qquad| \\ \text{CH—CH} \\ |\qquad | \\ \text{CH}_2\;\; \text{CH . CH . CH(CH}_3)_2 \\ \diagdown\;\diagup\qquad | \\ \text{S}\qquad\text{COOH}\end{array}$$

Oxidative degradation of a substance with this formula could yield β-carboxy-γ-methyl butane sulphonic acid by the following series of reactions :

$$
\begin{array}{c}
\underset{|}{NH_2} \quad \underset{|}{NH_2} \\
\underset{|}{CH}\!-\!\underset{|}{CH} \\
\underset{|}{CH_2} \quad \underset{|}{CH} . CH . CH(CH_3)_2 \\
\diagdown S \diagup \quad \underset{|}{COOH}
\end{array}
\xrightarrow[(2\,O)]{PbAc_4}
\begin{array}{c}
CHO \quad CHO \\
\underset{|}{CH_2} \quad \underset{|}{CH} . CH . CH(CH_3)_2 \\
\diagdown SO \diagup \quad \underset{|}{COOH}
\end{array}
\xrightarrow[(3\,O)]{KMnO_4}
$$

$$
\begin{array}{c}
COOH \quad COOH \\
\underset{|}{CH_2} \quad \underset{|}{CH} . CH . CH(CH_3)_2 \\
\diagdown SO_3 \diagup \quad \underset{|}{COOH}
\end{array}
\xrightarrow[(3\,O)]{KMnO_4}
\begin{array}{c}
CH_2\!-\!\underset{|}{CH}\!-\!CH(CH_3)_2 \\
\underset{|}{SO_2H} \quad \underset{|}{COOH}
\end{array}
$$

Treatment of model thio-ethers with lead tetra-acetate, however, did not confirm the course of the above oxidation, since it gave a sulphone and not a sulphoxide.

The method of degradation used by du Vigneaud and his colleagues with β-biotin, however, should be capable of distinguishing between the two possible formulae : (a) the pyrimidine formula, which should give the triamine (I) with two amino groups on one carbon atom and therefore yield an aldehyde by loss of ammonia ; and (b) the imidazoline formula which should give a stable triamine (II) :

$$
\begin{array}{c}
H_2N\!-\!CH\!-\!NH_2 \\
\underset{|}{CH}\!-\!S\!-\!CH_2 \\
H_2N\!-\!CH\!-\!\!-\!\!-\!CH . CH(CH_3)_2 \\
\text{(I)}
\end{array}
\qquad
\begin{array}{c}
H_2N\!-\!CH\!-\!CH \\
\qquad \diagdown S \\
H_2N\!-\!CH\!-\!CH_2 \diagup \\
\qquad \diagdown CH . CH(CH_3)_2 \\
\qquad NH_2 \\
\text{(II)}
\end{array}
$$

F. Kögl and W. A. J. Borg [13] therefore converted α-biotin methyl ester into the hydrazide and then via the azide into the urethane. This was hydrolysed with hydrochloric acid instead of baryta, the agent used by du Vigneaud, in order to prevent splitting off of ammonia. The product of this reaction proved to be a stable triamine, $C_8H_{19}N_3S$, identified as its picrolonate.

This result was incompatible with the formula first proposed by Kögl but consistent with his second formula, which is now generally accepted. α- and β-Biotin are therefore closely related substances, which would be expected to exhibit comparable biological properties. It would have been very surprising indeed to find such unique properties in two such unrelated molecules as those represented by du Vigneaud's formula for β-biotin and Kögl's original structure for α-biotin.

References to Section 3

1. V. du Vigneaud, K. Hofmann and D. B. Melville, *J. Biol. Chem.*, 1941, **140**, 643.
2. V. du Vigneaud, K. Hofmann, D. B. Melville and J. R. Rachele, *ibid.*, 763.
3. K. Hofmann, D. B. Melville and V. du Vigneaud, *ibid.*, 207.
4. F. Kögl and T. J. de Man, *Z. physiol. Chem.*, 1941, **269**, 81.
5. K. Hofmann, D. B. Melville and V. du Vigneaud, *J. Amer. Chem. Soc.*, 1941, **63**, 3237 ; *J. Biol. Chem.*, 1942, **144**, 513.
6. V. du Vigneaud, K. Hofmann and D. B. Melville, *J. Amer. Chem. Soc.*, 1942, **64**, 188.
7. D. B. Melville, K. Hofmann and V. du Vigneaud, *J. Biol. Chem.*, 1942, **145**, 101.
8. V. du Vigneaud, D. B. Melville, K. Folkers, D. E. Wolf, R. Mozingo, J. C. Keresztesy and S. A. Harris, *ibid.*, 1942, **146**, 475.
9. D. B. Melville, A. W. Moyer, K. Hofmann and V. du Vigneaud, *ibid.*, 487.
10. F. Kögl and L. Pons, *Z. physiol. Chem.*, 1941, **269**, 61.
11. F. Kögl, H. Erxleben and J. H. Verbeck, *ibid.*, 1942, **276**, 63.
12. F. Kögl, J. H. Verbeck, H. Erxleben and W. A. J. Borg, *ibid.*, 1943, **279**, 121.
13. F. Kögl and W. A. J. Borg, *ibid.*, 1944, **281**, 65.

4. SYNTHESIS OF BIOTIN

β-Biotin

The formula assigned to β-biotin was confirmed by synthesis. This was accomplished in 1943 by Harris et al.,[1, 2, 3] according to the following method, using L-cystine and chloroacetic acid as starting materials :

414

$$\overset{\text{Zn + HOAc}}{\underset{\text{+ Ac}_2\text{O}}{\longrightarrow}} \quad \begin{array}{l} \text{NH . CO . C}_6\text{H}_5 \\ | \\ \text{CH——C . NH . CO . CH}_3 \\ | \quad\quad \| \\ \text{CH}_2 \;\; \text{C . (CH}_2)_4 . \text{COOCH}_3 \\ \diagdown \;\; \diagup \\ \quad \text{S} \quad\quad \text{(V)} \end{array} \quad \overset{\text{Pd + H}_2}{\longrightarrow} \quad \begin{array}{l} \text{NH . CO . C}_6\text{H}_5 \\ | \\ \text{CH——CH . NH . CO . CH}_3 \\ | \quad\quad | \\ \text{CH}_2 \;\; \text{CH . (CH}_2)_4 . \text{COOCH}_3 \\ \diagdown \;\; \diagup \\ \quad \text{S} \quad\quad \text{(VI)} \end{array}$$

$$\overset{\text{Ba(OH)}_2}{\longrightarrow} \quad \begin{array}{l} \text{NH}_2 \;\; \text{NH}_2 \\ | \quad\quad | \\ \text{CH——CH} \\ | \quad\quad | \\ \text{CH}_2 \;\; \text{CH . (CH}_2)_4 . \text{COOH} \\ \diagdown \;\; \diagup \\ \quad \text{S} \quad\quad \text{(VII)} \end{array} \quad \overset{\text{COCl}_2}{\underset{\text{+ NaHCO}_3}{\longrightarrow}} \quad \begin{array}{l} \quad\quad \text{CO} \\ \quad \diagup \quad \diagdown \\ \text{NH} \quad\quad \text{NH} \\ | \quad\quad | \\ \text{CH——CH} \\ | \quad\quad | \\ \text{CH}_2 \;\; \text{CH . (CH}_2)_4 . \text{COOH} \\ \diagdown \;\; \diagup \\ \quad \text{S} \quad\quad \text{VIII)} \end{array}$$

The methyl γ-formylbutyrate used to introduce the valeric acid side-chain was prepared from glutaric acid *via* the anhydride, the monomethyl ester and γ-carbomethoxy butyryl chloride.

A method of preparing compound II *via* the di-ethyl ester of N-benzoyl-(carboxymethyl-mercapto)-alanine from N-benzoyl-serine was used as an alternative step :

$$\begin{array}{l} \text{HOCH}_2 . \text{CH . COOH} \\ \quad\quad | \\ \quad \text{NH . CO . C}_6\text{H}_5 \end{array} \longrightarrow \begin{array}{l} \text{ClCH}_2 . \text{CH . COOC}_2\text{H}_5 \\ \quad\quad | \\ \quad \text{NH . CO . C}_6\text{H}_5 \end{array}$$

$$\overset{\text{NaS . CH}_2 . \text{COOC}_2\text{H}_5}{\longrightarrow} \begin{array}{l} \text{C}_2\text{H}_5\text{OOC . CH}_2 . \text{S . CH}_2 . \text{CH . COOC}_2\text{H}_5 \\ \quad\quad\quad\quad\quad\quad\quad\quad\quad | \\ \quad\quad\quad\quad\quad\quad\quad\quad \text{NH . CO . C}_6\text{H}_5 \end{array} \longrightarrow \text{(II)}$$

Fractional crystallisation of VI yielded two racemates of methyl 3-acetamido-4-benzamidotetrahydrothiophene-2-valerate. These on hydrolysis yielded the corresponding 3 : 4-diamino-tetrahydrothio-phene-2-valeric acids (VII) as sulphates. Treatment with phosgene yielded two racemates of 2'-ketoimid-azolidino-(4' : 5' : 3 : 4) thiophan-2-valeric acid (VIII) which are distinguished as *dl*-biotin, m.p. 232° C. and *dl*-allobiotin, m.p. 194 to 196° C. The former was resolved through its esters with *l*-mandelic acid to give a compound identical with natural biotin. Subsequently,[4] the " unnatural " isomer, *l*-biotin, was obtained by esterification of racemic biotin with mandelic acid. A better method of preparing *l*-biotin was to crystallise the quinidine methydroxide salt ; this gave the *d*-isomer in poor yield and in an impure state. The best method of preparing *d*-biotin was by means of the L-arginine salt.

Subsequently the preparation of a third isomer of β-biotin from the reduction product of compound VI was described ;[5] this is termed *dl-epi*allobiotin and it decomposes without melting, commencing at 195° C. This compound on hydrogenolysis with Raney nickel gave the same desthio compound as did *dl*-allobiotin, namely, *dl*-desthioallo-biotin. It was inactive for yeast, whereas *dl*-desthiobiotin was half as active as *d*-biotin (page 449).

One or two of the known racemic pairs must therefore have the *trans*-configuration at the nitrogen atom, as in I, and the other or others the *cis*-configuration, as in II,

(I)   (II)

although it had previously been thought that compounds having two five-membered saturated heterocyclic rings fused through adjacent carbon atoms would exist only in the *cis* form.

Further investigation [6] showed that the *cis*-configuration at the nitrogen atom was present in biotin and the *trans*-configuration in allobiotin and *epi*allobiotin ; for, as already noted, biotin on hydro-genolysis with Raney nickel yielded desthiobiotin, whereas the other two isomers yielded desthioallobiotin. Moreover, allobiotin and *epi*-allobiotin were obtained when the methyl ester of 3-acetamido-4-benzamidotetrahydrothiophene-2-valeric acid was subjected to hydro-genolysis, hydrolysis and treatment with phosgene.

Formula I therefore represents *dl*-allobiotin and *dl-epi*allobiotin, whilst formula II represents *dl*-biotin.

Harris *et al.*[7] described the synthesis of *dl*-biotin, *dl*-allobiotin and *dl-epi*allobiotin by the method previously used for the synthesis of biotin (page 414). The two dehydro-esters obtained by reductive acetylation of the oximes were separately reduced with hydrogen in presence of palladium. The product from one was the *dl*-diamido ester, m.p. 152 to 153° C., which is the precursor of *dl*-biotin, whilst the other gave the *dl*-allodiamido ester, m.p. 172 to 173° C., together with the *dl-epi*allodiamido ester, m.p. 185 to 187° C., the precursors respectively of allobiotin and *epi*allobiotin.

dl-Allobiotin and *dl-epi*allobiotin are configuratively identical with one other about the asymmetric carbon atoms to which the nitrogen atoms are attached. *dl*-Biotin had 50 % of the activity of natural biotin, whilst *dl*-allobiotin and *dl-epi*allobiotin were essentially inactive towards *L. arabinosus* (see page 446).

Three of the four possible racemic β-biotins were synthesised by Grüssner *et al.*[8] from 2-δ-methoxybutyl-3-keto-4-carbethoxythiophan :

$$
\begin{array}{l}
\text{COOC}_2\text{H}_5 \\
| \\
\text{CH—CO} \\
| \qquad | \\
\text{CH}_2 \ \text{CH . (CH}_2)_3 \text{ . CH}_2\text{OCH}_3 \\
\diagdown \diagup \\
\quad \text{S}
\end{array}
$$

This was converted into the cyanhydrin, the cyano group of which was converted into the carbethoxy group and the hydroxy group removed by chlorination and hydrogenation. The two carbethoxy groups were converted into amino groups *via* the dihydrazide, diazide and diurethane, and the diamine was reacted with phosgene. The δ-methoxy group was then converted into a carboxy group *via* the bromide and cyanide. This method was patented by F. Hoffmann-La Roche & Co.[9]

From the dihydrazide, m.p. 204 to 205° C., *dl*-ψ-β-biotin, m.p. 221 to 222° C. (methyl ester, m.p. 149° C.), was obtained, whilst the non-crystalline dihydrazide fraction gave *dl*-iso-β-biotin, m.p. 182 to 183° C. (methyl ester, m.p. 166 to 167° C.) and *dl*-β-biotin, m.p. 234 to 235° C. (methyl ester, m.p. 130 to 132° C.). *dl*-Iso-β-biotin and *dl*-ψ-β-biotin were inactive towards *Saccharomyces cerevisiae* and *Lactobacillus helveticus*. It was shown subsequently[10] that *dl*-β-biotin was identical with the synthetic biotin of Harris *et al.*, but that neither " iso-β-biotin " nor " ψ-β-biotin " was a pure stereoisomer.

Another method of synthesis was described by Baker *et al.*,[11] in which a general method of synthesising the *cis* and *trans* forms of 2-alkyl-thiophan-3 : 4-dicarboxylic acids was devised and used for the synthesis of 2-(δ-carboxybutyl)-thiophan-3 : 4-*trans*-dicarboxylic acid. In one method the following series of reactions was employed :

$$\text{H}_5\text{OOC . (CH}_2)_4\text{ . COCl} \xrightarrow{\text{H}_2} \text{C}_2\text{H}_5\text{OOC . (CH}_2)_4\text{ . CHO} \xrightarrow[\text{acid}]{\text{malonic}}$$

$$\text{H}_5\text{OOC . (CH}_2)_4\text{ . CH : CH . COOH} \longrightarrow \text{CH}_3\text{OOC . (CH}_2)_4\text{ . CH : CH . COOCH}_3$$

$$\xrightarrow{\text{. CH}_2 \text{. COOCH}_3} \quad
\begin{array}{l}
\text{CH}_3\text{OOC . (CH}_2)_4\text{ . CH . CH}_2\text{ . COOCH}_3 \\
\qquad\qquad\qquad\qquad | \\
\qquad\qquad\qquad \text{S . CH}_2\text{ . COOCH}_3
\end{array}
\xrightarrow[\text{+ toluene}]{\text{NaOCH}_3}$$

$$
\begin{array}{l}
\text{—CH . COOCH}_3 \\
| \\
{}_2\ \text{CH . (CH}_2)_4\text{ . COOCH}_3 \\
\diagup \\
\text{S}
\end{array}
\xrightarrow{\text{HCN}}
\begin{array}{l}
\text{NC} \\
\quad \diagdown \\
\text{HO} \diagup \text{C——CH . COOCH}_3 \\
\qquad | \qquad\quad | \\
\qquad \text{CH}_2 \ \text{CH . (CH}_2)_4\text{ . COOCH}_3 \\
\qquad\quad \diagdown \diagup \\
\qquad\qquad \text{S}
\end{array}
$$

$$
\xrightarrow{}{}_{l_3}
\begin{array}{l}
\text{NC . C——CH . COOCH}_3 \\
\quad\ \| \qquad\quad | \\
\quad\ \text{CH} \ \text{CH . (CH}_2)_4\text{ . COOCH}_3 \\
\qquad \diagdown \diagup \\
\qquad\quad \text{S}
\end{array}
\xrightarrow[\text{NaHg}]{\text{H}_2\text{O +}}
\begin{array}{l}
\text{HOOC . CH——CH . COOH} \\
\qquad | \qquad\qquad | \\
\qquad \text{CH}_2 \ \text{CH . (CH}_2)_4\text{ . COOH} \\
\qquad\quad \diagdown \diagup \\
\qquad\qquad \text{S}
\end{array}
$$

27

A better method of synthesising this tricarboxylic acid, which gave a 23 % over-all yield from pimelic acid in seven steps, was as follows :

$$CH_3OOC.(CH_2)_5.COOCH_3 \xrightarrow{Br_2} CH_3OOC.CHBr.(CH_2)_4.COOCH_3 \longrightarrow$$

$$CH_3OOC.\underset{\underset{SH}{|}}{CH}.(CH_2)_4.COOCH_3 \xrightarrow{CH_2:CH.COOCH_3}$$

$$\begin{array}{c} COOCH_3 \\ | \\ CH_2 \quad COOCH_3 \\ | \quad \quad | \\ CH_2 \quad CH.(CH_2)_4.COOC \\ \diagdown \diagup \\ S \end{array}$$

$$\xrightarrow{NaOCH_3} \begin{array}{c} COOCH_3 \\ | \\ CH{-\!-}CO \\ | \quad \quad | \\ CH_2 \quad CH.(CH_2)_4.COOCH_3 \\ \diagdown \diagup \\ S \end{array}$$

and thence *via* the cyanhydrin as before.

The conversion of the tri-carboxylic acid into 2-(δ-carboxybutyl)-3 : 4-diaminothiophan involved the selective degradation of the two nuclear carboxyl groups without affecting the side-chain carboxyl group. This was accomplished by degrading the carboxyl groups one at a time. The *trans*-diamino-carboxylic acid thus obtained yielded *dl-epi*allobiotin on treatment with phosgene. Biotin resulted by the similar treatment of the *cis*-diamino-carboxylic acid prepared by a rather different series of reactions from a common intermediate, a *cis*-uracil with the structure :

$$\begin{array}{c} C_6H_5 \\ | \\ CO{-\!-}N \\ \diagup \quad \quad \diagdown \\ NH \quad \quad CO \\ | \quad \quad | \\ CH{-\!-}CH \\ | \quad \quad | \\ CH_2 \quad CH.(CH_2)_4.COOH \\ \diagdown \diagup \\ S \end{array}$$

This synthesis confirmed that biotin had a *cis*-configuration at the bridgehead of the two rings, whilst *epi*allobiotin and allobiotin had the *trans*-configuration.

A fourth stereoisomer of biotin, known as *epi*biotin was obtained from the *cis*-diamino-carboxylic acid that yielded biotin itself. *dl-epi*-Biotin, m.p. 190 to 191° C., was biologically inactive when assayed with

S. cerevisiae. On treatment with Raney nickel, it was converted into the biologically active *dl*-desthiobiotin.

Some of these methods have been patented by Lederle Labs. Inc.[11a]

An entirely different type of synthesis from those already described was patented by Roche Products Ltd.[12] The most striking feature of this method is that the imidazolidine ring is built up before the thiophane ring:

$$
\begin{array}{ccc}
CH . COOH & CHBr . COOH & Bz . NH . CH . COOH \\
\| & \longrightarrow & | & \longrightarrow & | & \xrightarrow{COCl_2} \\
HOOC . CH & CHBr . COOH & Bz . NH . CH . COOH
\end{array}
$$

$$
\begin{array}{ccc}
& CO & & CO & & CO \\
Bz . N \quad N . Bz & \xrightarrow{Ac_2O} & Bz . N \quad N . Bz & \xrightarrow{H_2} & Bz . N \quad N . Bz \\
| \quad\quad | & & | \quad\quad | & & \\
CH{-}CH & & CH{-}CH & & CH{-}CH \\
| \quad\quad | & & | \quad\quad | & & \\
COOH \; COOH & & CO \quad CO & & AcO . CH \quad CO \\
& & \diagdown O \diagup & & \diagdown O \diagup
\end{array}
$$

$$
\begin{array}{ccc}
& CO & & CO \\
Bz . N \quad N . Bz & & Bz . N \quad N . Bz \\
| \quad\quad | & & | \quad\quad | \\
\longrightarrow \; CH{-}CH & \longrightarrow & CH{-}CH \\
| \quad\quad | & & | \quad\quad |_{OH} \\
CH_2 \quad CO & & CH_2 \quad C \longrightarrow \\
\diagdown S \diagup & & \diagdown S \diagup \quad (CH_2)_4OCH_3
\end{array}
$$

$$
\begin{array}{cc}
CO & CO \\
Bz . N \quad N . Bz & Bz . N \quad N . Bz \\
| \quad\quad | & | \quad\quad | \\
CH{-}CH & \xrightarrow{H_2} \quad CH{-}CH \\
| \quad\quad | & | \quad\quad | \\
CH_2 \quad C{=}CH . (CH_2)_3OCH_3 & CH_2 \quad CH . (CH_2)_4 . OCH_3 \\
\diagdown S \diagup & \diagdown S \diagup
\end{array}
$$

$$
\begin{array}{c}
CO \\
NH \quad N . Bz \\
\xrightarrow[NH_3]{Na +} \quad CH{-}CH \\
| \quad\quad | \\
CH_2 \quad CH . (CH_2)_4 . OCH_3 \\
\diagdown S \diagup
\end{array}
$$

The δ-methoxy group was converted into the carboxy group *via* the bromide and cyanide, and, finally, the protective benzoyl group was removed by means of sodium and ammonia.

α-Biotin

α-Biotin has not been synthesised up to the present time. The preparation of a possible intermediate, 2-ethoxalyl-4-ethyl-3-keto-thiophan, was described by Ghosh *et al.*[13]

References to Section 4

1. S. A. Harris, D. E. Wolf, R. Mozingo and K. Folkers, *Science*, 1943, **97,** 447.
2. S. A. Harris, D. E. Wolf, R. Mozingo, R. C. Anderson, G. E. Arth, N. R. Easton, D. Heyl, A. N. Wilson and K. Folkers, *J. Amer. Chem. Soc.*, 1944, **66,** 1756.
3. S. A. Harris, N. R. Easton, D. Heyl, A. N. Wilson and K. Folkers, *ibid.*, 1757.
4. D. E. Wolf, R. Mozingo, S. A. Harris, R. C. Anderson and K. Folkers, *ibid.*, 1945, **67,** 2100.
5. S. A. Harris, R. Mozingo, D. E. Wolf, A. N. Wilson, G. E. Arth and K. Folkers, *ibid.*, 1944, **66,** 1800.
6. S. A. Harris, R. Mozingo, D. E. Wolf, A. N. Wilson and K. Folkers, *ibid.*, 1945, **67,** 2102.
7. S. A. Harris, D. E. Wolf, R. Mozingo, G. E. Arth, R. C. Anderson, N. R. Easton, and K. Folkers, *ibid.*, 2096.
8. A. Grüssner, J. P. Bourquin and O. Schnider, *Helv. Chim. Acta*, 1945, **28,** 517.
9. F. Hoffmann-La Roche and Co., B.P. 589210; U.S.P. 2417326.
10. A. Grüssner, J. P. Bourquin and O. Schnider, *Helv. Chim. Acta*, 1946, **29,** 770.
11. B. R. Baker, M. V. Querry, S. R. Safir and S. Bernstein, *J. Org. Chem.*, 1947, **12,** 138; G. B. Brown, B. R. Baker, S. Bernstein and S. R. Safir, *ibid.*, 155; G. B. Brown, M. D. Armstrong, A. W. Moyer, W. P. Anslow, B. R. Baker, M. V. Querry, S. Bernstein and S. R. Safir, *ibid.*, 160; B. R. Baker, M. V. Querry, S. Bernstein, S. R. Safir and Y. SubbaRow, *ibid.*, 167; B. R. Baker, M. V. Querry, S. R. Safir, W. L. McEwen and S. Bernstein, *ibid.*, 174; B. R. Baker, M. V. Querry, W. L. McEwen, S. Bernstein, S. R. Safir, L. Dorfman and Y. SubbaRow, *ibid.*, 186; B. R. Baker, W. L. McEwen and W. N. Kinley, *ibid.*, 322.
11a. Lederle Labs. Inc., B.P. 615798, 617435.
12. Roche Products Ltd., B.P. 628902.
13. R. Ghosh, J. F. W. McOmie and J. P. Wilson, *J. Chem. Soc.*, 1945, 705.

5. PROPERTIES OF BIOTIN

Both forms of biotin are white crystalline solids with acidic properties. α- and β-Biotin have m.ps. 220° C. and 232-233° C. respectively and $[\alpha]_D^{20°} = +51°$ and $+92°$ respectively in 0·1 N-sodium hydroxide. They form crystalline methyl esters with m.ps. 161 to 162° C. and 163 to 164° C. respectively and $[\alpha]_D^{21°} = + 47°$ and $+ 39°$ respectively in chloroform.[1] According to du Vigneaud *et al.*[2] the methyl ester of biotin isolated from liver has m.p. 166 to 167° C. and $[\alpha]_D^{21°} = + 57°$.

α- and β-Biotin methyl esters are sparingly soluble in ether and in light petroleum, somewhat more soluble in benzene or cyclohexane, and soluble to the extent of about 1 % in methanol. In general, halogenated hydrocarbons, alcohols and ketones are good solvents for the esters, mesityl oxide, phorone, methyl heptenone and allylbenzene being particularly useful for purposes of crystallisation.[3]

β-Biotin is surface-active.[4]

References to Section 5

1. F. Kögl and E. J. ten Ham, *Naturwiss.*, 1943, **31**, 208.
2. V. du Vigneaud, K. Hofmann, D. B. Melville and P. György, *J. Biol. Chem.*, 1941, **140**, 643.
3. F. Kögl and L. Pons, *Z. physiol. Chem.*, 1941, **269**, 61.
4. V. R. Williams and H. B. Williams, *J. Biol. Chem.*, 1949, **177**, 745.

6. STABILITY OF BIOTIN

Biotin is inactivated by acid and alkali and by many α-amino acid reagents, though not by ninhydrin.[1] It is not destroyed by acylating or alkylating agents or by carbonyl reagents. It is inactivated by hydrogen peroxide and by rancid oils and fats with a high peroxide content ; the rate of destruction is less in presence of α-tocopherol.[2] Since the product was active on yeast, but not on *L. helveticus* (see page 452), it is most probably biotin sulphone. Biotin is also inactivated by choline.[3]

References to Section 6

1. G. B. Brown and V. du Vigneaud, *J. Biol. Chem.*, 1941, **141**, 85.
2. P. L. Pavcek and G. M. Shull, *ibid.*, 1942, **146**, 351.
3. J. S. Harrison and E. J. Miller, *Analyst*, 1949, **74**, 463.

7. ESTIMATION OF BIOTIN

Microbiological Methods

The method first used for the estimation of biotin was a yeast growth method,[1,2] which is not applicable to the examination of turbid or highly coloured solutions, as the growth response is measured turbidimetrically. Nevertheless, the method gives good results where it can be applied.[3, 4] Turbidimetric methods have also been described using *B. radicocola* [4] and *Rhizobium trifolii* [5] as test organisms.

Biotin can be estimated more satisfactorily, however, by means of *Lactobacillus helveticus* [6] or *L. arabinosus*,[7] as the response with these organisms is measured by titrating the lactic acid produced. Improvements in the *L. helveticus* method were subsequently described,[8] including a method which was capable of assaying six members of the vitamin B complex with the same basal medium.[9] The *L. arabinosus* method, although it gives lower titres than the *L. helveticus* method, is preferred by some workers.[10] As in other assays with *Lactobacilli*, it is essential to remove fatty material from the medium and test solution, as lipoids have a stimulatory effect on the organisms.[11]

Other organisms that have been tested for use in the assay of biotin are " cholineless " *Neurospora crassa* [12] and *Candida guillermondia*.[13] Oleic acid and " Tween 80 " alone or in combination with aspartic acid gave some response with the first of these organisms in the absence of biotin.[13a]

Some of these organisms respond not only to biotin but also to certain related compounds (see pages 446-454).

The agar plate method devised by N. G. Heatley [14] for the assay of antibiotics has been used by T. I. Williams [15] for the estimation of biotin by means of *S. cerevisiae*. A slight modification of the method, in which paper discs were used in place of cups, gave good results with both *S. cerevisiae* and *L. arabinosus*.[15a]

In the earliest assays, extraction with hot water was used to prepare the test solutions,[16] but it was subsequently found that larger amounts of biotin were obtained after autolysis [2] or hydrolysis or a combination of both. According to Thompson *et al.*[17] drastic hydrolysis with 6N-sulphuric acid gives the best results, although it undoubtedly causes some destruction of biotin.

Other Methods

No chemical or physical method of estimating biotin exists at the present time.

References to Section 7

1. F. Kögl and B. Tönnis, *Z. physiol. Chem.*, 1936, **242**, 43.
2. E. E. Snell, R. E. Eakin and R. J. Williams, *J. Amer. Chem. Soc.*, 1940, **62**, 175.
3. R. Hertz, *Proc. Soc. Exp. Biol. Med.*, 1943, **52**, 15.
4. N. Nielsen and V. Hartelius, *Biochem. Z.*, 1941-42, **311**, 317.
5. P. M. West and P. W. Wilson, *Enzymologia*, 1940, **8**, 152.
6. G. M. Shull, B. L. Hutchings and W. H. Peterson, *J. Biol. Chem.*, 1942, **142**, 913.

7. L. D. Wright and H. R. Skeggs, *Proc. Soc. Exp. Biol. Med.*, 1944, **56**, 95.

8. G. M. Shull and W. H. Peterson, *J. Biol. Chem.*, 1943, **151**, 201 ; F. F. Tomlinson and W. H. Peterson, *Arch. Biochem.*, 1944, **5**, 221.

9. M. Landy and D. M. Dicken, *J. Lab. Clin. Med.*, 1942, **27**, 1086.

10. E. C. Barton-Wright, *Analyst*, 1945, **70**, 283.

11. V. R. Williams and E. A. Fieger, *Ind. Eng. Chem., Anal. Ed.*, 1945, **17**, 127 ; V. R. Williams, *J. Biol. Chem.*, 1945, **159**, 237.

12. A. Z. Hodson, *ibid.*, 1945, **157**, 383.

13. W. B. Emery, N. McLeod and F. A. Robinson, *Biochem. J.*, 1946, **40**, 426.

13*a*. A. Z. Hodson, *J. Biol. Chem.*, 1949, **179**, 49.

14. N. G. Heatley, *ibid.*, 1944, **38**, 61.

15. T. I. Williams, *Nature*, 1948, **161**, 19.

15*a*. D. S. Genghof, C. W. H. Partridge and F. H. Carpenter, *Arch. Biochem.*, 1948, **17**, 413.

16. F. Kögl and W. van Hasselt, *Z. physiol. Chem.*, 1936, **243**, 189.

17. R. C. Thompson, R. E. Eakin and R. J. Williams, *Science*, 1941, **94**, 589.

8. OCCURRENCE OF BIOTIN IN FOODSTUFFS

The materials richest in biotin are probably egg-yolk, liver and yeast, all of which have been used as sources for its isolation. It is also present in kidney and cow's milk but not in rice polishings, beef muscle or human milk.[1] Cow's milk contained 11 to 37 μg. of biotin per litre, the value rising to a maximum after the first few days and then falling.[2] It occurs in a large variety of seeds.[3] Oat seedlings contained somewhat larger amounts in the root and coleoptile tips than in other parts. Biotin was also found in the aqueous extracts of many tissues of dogs, cows, calves and hens.[4] The tissues of dogs contained on the average 0·004 μg. per g., the tissues of cows 0·007 μg. per g. and of the hen 0·02 μg. per g. The liver and kidney of all species of animals examined were particularly rich in biotin.[5] A high proportion of the biotin originally present remained in meat after cooking.[5]

Fresh cheese contained from 0·011 to 0·076 μg. per g. of biotin, and the amount increased 2- or 3-fold on ripening.[6]

In yeast and animal products, biotin appeared to exist mainly in a combined water-insoluble form, whereas in vegetable material and plants it existed predominantly as a water-soluble form. In cereals and nuts, however, a considerable proportion was present in combination with protein. To obtain satisfactory analyses of yeast and meat, therefore, hydrolysis with dilute acid or with trypsin should be used to ensure liberation of combined biotin.[7, 8]

Royal jelly was an exceptionally rich source of biotin, as it was of pantothenic acid, containing 4·1 μg. per g. ; pollen and honey contained 0·25 and 0·00066 μg. per g. respectively.[9]

Biotin was present in soil and natural manures, and the amount in pasture land was increased by farmyard manure. The soil concentration varied with the depth, but in lake deposits biotin was detected to a depth of 9 metres.[10]

References to Section 8

1. P. György, *J. Biol. Chem.*, 1939, **131**, 733.
2. J. M. Lawrence, B. L. Herrington and L. A. Maynard, *J. Nutrition*, 1946, **32**, 73.
3. F. Kögl and A. J. Haagen-Smit, *Z. physiol. Chem.*, 1936, **243**, 209.
4. F. Kögl and W. von Hasselt, *ibid.*, 189.
5. B. S. Schweigert, E. Nielsen, J. M. McIntire and C. A. Elvehjem, *J. Nutrition*, 1943, **26**, 65.
6. R. A. Sullivan, E. Nielsen and J. Jarmol, *ibid.*, 1943, **25**, 463.
7. R. C. Thompson, R. E. Eakin and R. J. Williams, *Science*, 1941, **94**, 589.
8. J. O. Lampen, G. P. Bahler and W. H. Peterson, *J. Nutrition*, 1943, **23**, 11 ; J. P. Bowden and W. H. Peterson, *J. Biol. Chem.*, 1949, **178**, 533.
9. G. Kitzes, H. A. Schuette and C. A. Elvehjem, *J. Nutrition*, 1943, **26**, 241.
10. M. A. Roulet, *Experientia*, 1948, **4**, 149.

9. EFFECT OF BIOTIN DEFICIENCY IN ANIMALS

Rats and Mice

As already mentioned above, biotin deficiency produced by feeding raw egg white to rats is characterised by an eczema-like dermatitis, paralysis or spasticity of the hind legs and the so-called " spectacle-eye " condition caused by loss of hair around the eyes. Although nutritional achromotrichia was relieved by pantothenic acid,[1] the dermatitis and other symptoms did not respond to pantothenic acid, or to riboflavine, pyridoxine or inositol, but were cured by administration of 2 μg. of biotin per day ; [2] the growth rate was also increased thereby. When biotin-deficient rats were treated with biotin (0·5 to 1·0 μg. per day), the animals recovered, but their coats became grey in a different pattern from that assumed by pantothenic acid-deficient rats.[3] Cooked white of egg did not produce biotin deficiency, the responsible factor being heat-labile (see page 427).

Biotin deficiency in rats resulted in lesions of the thymus, testes, epididymis, skin and muscles, but there was no degeneration of the spinal cord or sciatic nerves.[4] Rats required biotin for gestation and for the birth of viable young, and probably for lactation also.[5] Indeed the stress of lactation appeared to induce a mild biotin deficiency even without adding avidin or a sulphonamide to the diet.[5a] The severity and time of onset of symptoms of biotin deficiency were not modified when succinylsulphathiazole was given at the same time as raw egg white,[6] but administration of succinylsulphathiazole alone produced a combined biotin and folic acid deficiency in rats.[7]

Biotin deficiency in mice was characterised by alopecia,[8] which was more severe when sulphasuxidine was added to the diet (see page 434). The fur of black mice became rusty or grey.[8a] Biotin was essential for reproduction and lactation in mice.[8b]

Chicks

In chicks, dermatitis and perosis were the chief manifestations of biotin deficiency induced by feeding egg white,[9, 10] and it has been suggested [10] that the development and cure of these symptoms might be used for the biological assay of biotin. Injection of 0·65 μg. per day of crystalline biotin methyl ester prevented the perosis, but was insufficient to prevent the dermatitis.[11] The typical dermatitis was prevented and growth was promoted in chicks by feeding 7 to 10 μg. of biotin per 100 g. of diet.[12]

Biotin is also said to be necessary for normal embryonic development in the hen's egg ; [13] thus when hens were maintained on a biotin-deficient diet the percentage of eggs hatching was reduced by about 80 %, although egg production was not affected.

Biotin deficiency was produced in chicks on a diet of sucrose and acid-washed, alcohol-extracted casein without the administration of egg white. Although dermatitis was regularly produced, the onset of perosis was erratic. The addition of raw egg white produced perosis quickly.[14] It was prevented by feeding 1 μg. of biotin per day, but dermatitis was only cured completely by injection of 2 to 5 μg. per day. A mild biotin deficiency in chicks did not cause neurological lesions, such as were observed in pantothenic acid deficiency.[15]

Turkeys

Turkeys, like chicks, developed dermatitis and perosis when reared on a biotin-deficient diet.[16] The former symptom was cured by biotin, but the latter required, in addition, choline and a factor prepared from yeast extract by adsorption on charcoal or fuller's earth and elution by aqueous ammonia.

Monkeys

The symptoms of chronic biotin deficiency observed in monkeys were a thinning of the fur and a gradual reduction in the colour of the hair.[17] These symptoms were cured or prevented by 20 μg. of biotin per day. Acute biotin deficiency was produced by feeding egg white or by adding 3 % of succinylsulphathiazole to the diet ; both conditions were relieved by administration of 20 μg. of biotin per day.

Dogs

Puppies fed a synthetic diet deficient in the vitamin B complex, but supplemented with aneurine, riboflavine, nicotinic acid, pyridoxine, pantothenic acid, inositol, p-aminobenzoic acid and choline, developed a progressive paralysis after $7\frac{1}{2}$ to 48 weeks. A cure was effected in a few hours by administration of 100 μg. of synthetic biotin per kg. of bodyweight.[18]

Pigs

Biotin deficiency was produced in pigs by feeding 30% of desiccated egg white in the diet. It was characterised by alopecia, spasticity of the hind legs, cracks in the feet and dermatosis accompanied by dryness, roughness and a brownish exudate.

These symptoms could be prevented by intramuscular injection of 100 μg. of biotin daily into each pig.[19] The same symptoms were produced by administration of phthalylsulphathiazole, although sulphaguanidine had no effect. Biotin prevented the symptoms and inositol largely alleviated them.[20] Pigs fed a diet containing all the other members of the vitamin B complex showed no increased growth when biotin was added to the diet.

Cows

The dairy calf required an exogenous supply of biotin, otherwise paralysis of the hind quarters developed. This was curable by biotin.[21]

Fish

Biotin was found to be necessary for young rainbow trout, an anaemia developing in its absence.[22] From 0·005 to 0·025 mg. per 100 g. of diet was necessary to prevent deficiency symptoms from developing.

Avidin

The first attempt to isolate the factor in egg white responsible for producing biotin deficiency in rats and chicks was made by R. E. Eakin, E. E. Snell and R. J. Williams,[23] who showed that biotin was inactivated by egg white *in vitro* and that it was immaterial how crude the biotin preparation was. Purification of the egg-white factor, for which the name avidin was suggested,[24] was effected by precipitation with acetone and five-sixths saturation of the aqueous solution with ammonium sulphate. The biotin was not released from the complex by dialysis, but could be recovered after the complex had been steam-sterilised. This was consistent with the observation that cooked egg white did not inactivate biotin. Avidin was eventually obtained in crystalline form,[24] when it was shown to have the properties of a protein with a large carbohydrate moiety. A similar substance was isolated by D. W. Woolley and L. G. Longsworth ;[25] it had an isoelectric point at pH 10 and was homogeneous in electrophoresis and sedimentation experiments.

The discovery of the inactivation of biotin by avidin is of obvious importance in nutrition. P. György and C. S. Rose [26] showed that whole egg contained an excess of avidin, the biotin in the yolk being unable to neutralise all the avidin in the white. Thus in order to utilise the biotin in eggs, these must be cooked in order to destroy the avidin. A case of biotin deficiency resulting from a diet consisting exclusively of raw eggs has been described.[27]

P. György and C. S. Rose [28] also showed that biotin was present in egg yolk in a non-dialysable form of high molecular weight, which stimulated the growth of yeast and of rats made biotin-deficient by means of egg white. Biotin was not released from the biotin-avidin complex by incubation with pepsin, trypsin, pancreatin, papain or with liver, muscle or blood, but was liberated by oxidation with 0·45 % hydrogen peroxide at pH 3. Avidin was destroyed by light, especially in presence of riboflavine, and biotin could be liberated from the complex by irradiation.[29]

A form of biotin that will not combine with avidin has been stated to exist in normal rat urine, human urine and urine from rats fed egg white, but not in any other biological materials (see page 433).[30]

K. Meyer [31] and W. L. Laurence [32] suggested that, since biotin increased the lytic action of lysozyme and avidin, the biotin-avidin complex might be identical with lysozyme, the factor that brings about lysis of bacteria. Alderton *et al.*,[33] however, failed to confirm the stimulatory effect of biotin on the lytic action of purified crystalline lysozyme, which was in fact shown to contain only traces of biotin. Moreover, lysis by avidin preparations was not increased by biotin, and avidin did not inhibit the lytic action of lysozyme.

Avidin has been shown to occur not only in the eggs of birds and amphibia, but also in the genital tract, and avidin production can be induced experimentally in the oviduct of sexually immature chicks by the administration of oestrogen followed by progesterone. Administration of oestrogen alone increased the biotin content of the blood five-fold, and when this was followed by progesterone the amount of avidin in the oviduct increased, but the blood biotin was not affected.[33a] It is clear, therefore, that avidin as well as biotin is associated with reproduction.

Biotin and Fatty Livers

G. Gavin and E. W. McHenry [34] claimed that feeding rats with biotin on diets low in cholesterol produced fatty livers containing 0·67 to 1·25 % of cholesterol, whilst R. Okey [35] showed that the addition of biotin to the diet of guinea-pigs doubled the amount of cholesterol in the liver. According to Best et al.,[36] however, biotin produced no selective deposition of cholesterol in the liver. They found, on the contrary, that there was a constant relationship between the accumulation of cholesteryl esters in liver and the deposition of glycerides in the liver, and that biotin did not affect this relationship. They therefore suggest that the term " biotin fatty liver " should be abandoned (see page 573).

Biotin and Pantothenic Acid

There appears to be a connection between biotin deficiency and pantothenic acid,[37] since the symptoms of biotin deficiency induced in weanling rats by administration of succinylsulphathiazole were aggravated when a pantothenic acid deficiency was also present. The feeding of biotin protected the animals against these changes and, in addition, reduced the severity of the symptoms of pantothenic acid deficiency. Furthermore, L. D. Wright and A. D. Welch [38] observed signs of severe pantothenic acid deficiency, including achromotrichia, when rats receiving a highly purified diet containing all the B factors known to be required by the rat, including pantothenic acid, were treated with succinylsulphathiazole. The symptoms were accompanied by a marked reduction in the pantothenic acid content of the liver and were relieved by administration of biotin and a folic acid concentrate. Thus the utilisation of pantothenic acid appears to depend on the availability of folic acid and biotin which are not normally required by rats, being apparently synthesised in the gut by bacteria.

Biotin and Infected Animals

A deficiency of biotin increased the severity of *Plasmodium lophurae* infection in chicks,[39] but had no effect on the susceptibility of Swiss mice to experimental poliomyelitis.[40] Biotin-deficiency in rats led to a delayed or lowered production of the antibody that inhibited the reproduction of *Trypanosoma lewisi*,[41] so that the parasites multiplied unchecked.

Biotin and Cancer

Nakahara *et al.*[42] reported that rats were protected against cancer induced by butter yellow (NN-dimethyl-amino-azo-benzene) by administering liver and yeast supplements. This observation was followed up by du Vigneaud *et al.*[43] to determine whether the effect was due to biotin. They gave concentrates of biotin prepared from liver and yeast to susceptible rats, together with butter yellow, and obtained indications of a protective effect. Marked protection was also obtained with casein supplemented by riboflavine. When pure biotin was given, however, either with or without the protective casein-riboflavine supplement, the incidence of liver tumours among the mice was markedly *increased*. It would appear that not only has biotin no protective effect in cancer, but that it actually destroys the effect of the protective factor present in yeast and liver and is therefore a pro-carcinogenic substance. It was suggested that avidin, the egg white injury factor, might have a beneficial effect on cancer.

This was tested by Kensler *et al.*,[44] who fed a diet rich in egg white and avidin to mice with spontaneous mammary carcinoma, but could observe no favourable effect on the disease. Nor was the effect of high levels of egg white any more marked on mice with Flexner-Jobling carcinoma or mouse sarcoma 180. Avidin equivalent to 16 to 40 times the amount necessary to combine with the dietary biotin was fed over a period of thirty weeks to a patient with mammary carcinoma and to another with lymphatic leukemia, without any apparent improvement being observed in the patient's condition ;[45] oddly enough, no clinical signs of biotin deficiency appeared, nor was the urinary excretion of biotin reduced. The inability of avidin to affect the course of cancer was confirmed by I. I. Kaplan,[46] who gave the whites of 36 to 42 eggs daily to cancer patients maintained on a diet low in biotin without effecting a cure, although there was some improvement in certain of the cases.

Animal experiments were also carried out by Kline *et al.*[47] They fed rats 0·06 % of butter yellow in highly purified diets containing a sub-protective level of riboflavine, together with heated or unheated egg white or casein. The animals fed casein showed an incidence of liver tumours amounting to 77 to 88 %, whilst groups of rats on egg white showed an incidence of tumours ranging from 0 to 18 %. The injection of biotin did not increase the incidence of tumours, however, and, since symptoms of biotin deficiency developed on the unheated egg white diet but not on the heated diet, it was evident that the protection afforded by egg white against hepatoma formation was independent of any relation between biotin and avidin.

The biotin content of cancerous tissue ranged from 20 to 100 mμg. per g., the lowest value being 5 mμg. per g. for human ovarian adeno-carcinoma and the highest 200 mμg. per g. for rat hepatoma.[48] These values are within the range recorded for non-cancerous brain, lung, spleen and muscle tissue and much below the values accepted for liver and kidney.

References to Section 9

1. P. György and C. E. Poling, *Proc. Soc. Exp. Biol. Med.*, 1940, **45,** 773.
2. E. Nielsen and C. A. Elvehjem, *ibid.*, 1941, **48,** 349 ; *J. Biol. Chem.*, 1942, **144,** 405.
3. G. A. Emerson and J. C. Keresztesy, *Proc. Soc. Exp. Biol. Med.*, 1942, **51,** 358.
4. J. H. Shaw and P. H. Phillips, *ibid.*, 406.
5. C. Kennedy and L. S. Palmer, *Arch. Biochem.*, 1945, **7,** 9.
5a. M. M. Nelson and H. M. Evans, *ibid.*, 1948, **18,** 477.
6. G. A. Emerson and E. Wurtz, *Proc. Soc. Exp. Biol. Med.*, 1945, **59,** 297.
7. H. R. Skeggs and L. D. Wright, *J. Nutrition*, 1946, **32,** 375.
8. E. Nielsen and A. Black, *ibid.*, 1944, **28,** 203.
8a. J. W. Wilson, E. H. Leduc and D. H. Winston, *ibid.*, 1949, **38,** 73.
8b. L. Mirone and L. R. Cerecedo, *Arch. Biochem.*, 1947, **15,** 324.
9. L. W. McElroy and T. H. Jukes, *Proc. Soc. Exp. Biol. Med.*, 1940, **45,** 296.
10. S. Ansbacher and M. Landy, *ibid.*, 1941, **48,** 3.
11. T. H. Jukes and F. H. Bird, *ibid.*, 1942, **49,** 231.
12. D. M. Hegsted, R. C. Mills, G. M. Briggs, C. A. Elvehjem and E. B. Hart, *J. Nutrition*, 1942, **23,** 175.
13. W. W. Cravens, E. E. Sebesta, J. G. Halpin and E. B. Hart, *Proc. Soc. Exp. Biol. Med.*, 1942, **50,** 101 ; W. W. Cravens, W. H. McGibbon and E. E. Sebesta, *Anat. Rec.*, 1944, **90,** 55 ; J. R. Couch, W. W. Cravens, C. A. Elvehjem and J. G. Halpin, *Arch. Biochem.*, 1949, **21,** 77.
14. L. R. Richardson, A. G. Hogan and O. N. Miller, *Univ. Missouri Agr. Exp. Stat. Res. Bull.*, 1942, 343.
15. J. H. Shaw and P. H. Phillips, *J. Nutrition*, 1945, **29,** 107.
16. H. Patrick, R. V. Boucher, R. A. Dutcher and H. C. Knandel, *Proc. Soc. Exp. Biol. Med.*, 1941, **48,** 456 ; *J. Nutrition*, 1943, **26,** 197.

17. H. A. Waisman, K. B. McCall and C. A. Elvehjem, *ibid.*, 1945, **29**, 1.
18. S. G. Smith, *Amer. J. Physiol.*, 1945, **144**, 175.
19. T. J. Cunha, D. C. Lindley and M. E. Ensminger, *J. Animal Sci.*, 1946, **5**, 219.
20. D. C. Lindley and T. J. Cunha, *J. Nutrition*, 1946, **32**, 47.
21. A. C. Wiese, B. C. Johnson and W. B. Nevens, *Proc. Soc. Exp. Biol. Med.*, 1946, **62**, 521.
22. B. A. McLaren, E. Keller, D. J. O'Donnell and C. A. Elvehjem, *Arch. Biochem.*, 1947, **15**, 169.
23. R. E. Eakin, E. E. Snell and R. J. Williams, *J. Biol. Chem.*, 1940, **136**, 801.
24. D. Pennington, E. E. Snell and R. E. Eakin, *J. Amer. Chem. Soc.*, 1942, **64**, 469.
25. D. W. Woolley and L. G. Longsworth, *J. Biol. Chem.*, 1942, **142**, 285.
26. P. György and C. S. Rose, *Proc. Soc. Exp. Biol. Med.*, 1942, **49**, 294.
27. V. P. Sydenstricker, *et al.*, *Semana med. españ.*, 1943, **6**, 356.
28. P. György and C. S. Rose, *Proc. Soc. Exp. Biol. Med.*, 1943, **53**, 55.
29. P. György, C. S. Rose and R. Tomarelli, *J. Biol. Chem.*, 1942, **144**, 169.
30. E. J.-H. Chu and R. J. Williams, *J. Amer. Chem. Soc.*, 1944, **66**, 1678.
31. K. Meyer, *Science*, 1944, **99**, 391.
32. W. L. Laurence, *ibid.*, 392.
33. G. Alderton, J. C. Lewis and H. L. Fevold, *ibid.*, 1945, **101**, 151 ; G. Alderton and W. H. Ward, *J. Biol. Chem.*, 1945, **157**, 43.
33a. R. Hertz and W. H. Sebrell, *Science*, 1942, **96**, 257 ; R. M. Fraps, R. Hertz and W. H. Sebrell, *Proc. Soc. Exp. Biol. Med.*, 1943, **52**, 140, 142 ; R. Hertz, F. G. Dhyse and W. W. Tullner, *Endocrinology*, 1949, **45**, 451.
34. G. Gavin and E. W. McHenry, *J. Biol. Chem.*, 1941, **141**, 619.
35. R. Okey, *ibid.*, 1946, **165**, 383.
36. C. H. Best, C. C. Lucas, J. M. Patterson and J. H. Ridout, *Biochem. J.*, 1946, **40**, 368.
37. G. A. Emerson and E. Wurtz, *Proc. Soc. Exp. Biol. Med.*, 1944, **57**, 47.
38. L. D. Wright and A. D. Welch, *Science*, 1943, **97**, 426.
39. A. O. Seeler, W. H. Ott and M. E. Gundel, *Proc. Soc. Exp. Biol. Med.*, 1944, **55**, 107.
40. H. C. Lichstein, H. A. Waisman, K. B. McCall, C. A. Elvehjem and P. F. Clark, *ibid.*, 1945, **60**, 279.
41. F. E. Caldwell and P. György, *J. Infect. Dis.*, 1947, **81**, 197.
42. W. Nakahara, K. Mori and T. Huziwara, *Gann*, 1938, **32**, 465 ; 1939, **33**, 13, 57, 406.
43. V. du Vigneaud, J. M. Spangler, D. Burk, C. J. Kensler, K. Sugiura and C. P. Rhoads, *Science*, 1942, **95**, 174.
44. C. J. Kensler, C. Wadsworth, K. Sugiura, C. P. Rhoads, K. Dittmer and V. du Vigneaud, *Cancer Res.*, 1943, **3**, 823.

45. C. P. Rhoads and J. C. Abels, *J. Amer. Med. Assoc.*, 1943, **121**, 1261.
46. I. I. Kaplan, *Amer. J. Med. Sci.*, 1944, **207**, 733.
47. H. E. Kline, J. A. Miller and H. P. Rusch, *Cancer Res.*, 1945, **5**, 641.
48. M. A. Pollack, A. Taylor, A. Woods, R. C. Thompson and R. J. Williams, *ibid.*, 1942, **2**, 748.

10. EFFECT OF BIOTIN DEFICIENCY IN MAN

The symptoms of biotin deficiency in human beings were first reported by V. P. Sydenstricker *et al.*[1] Four volunteers were fed on a diet containing minimal amounts of biotin and 30 % of the total calorie intake in the form of egg white. During the third and fourth weeks, all developed " a fine scaly desquamation without pruritis ", which disappeared spontaneously in seven to ten days. Nothing further happened until the seventh week, when one man developed a maculosquamous dermatitis of the neck, hands, arms and legs. During the seventh and eighth weeks all showed a pronounced greyish pallor of the skin and mucous membranes, which was out of all proportion to the blood picture. No capillary engorgement occurred as in pellagra or ariboflavinosis, the tongues remaining pale. During the ninth and tenth weeks the skin became increasingly dry with marked reticulation and a return of the fine branny desquamation. After the fifth week, symptoms resembling vitamin B_1 deficiency were observed, mild depression followed by extreme lassitude, somnolence, muscle pains and hyperaesthesia. After the tenth week anorexia with occasional nausea was evident. Two patients showed definite electrocardiographic changes. The blood picture was characterised by a diminution in the haemoglobin, erythrocytes and volume of the packed red cells, together with a slight increase in the bile pigments and a large rise in the serum cholesterol. After seven to eight weeks the urinary excretion of biotin was 3·5 to 7·3 μg. per day as compared with 29 to 52 μg. per day on a normal diet. When biotin was given at a level of 75 to 300 μg. per day by injection there was prompt relief of the symptoms in three to five days and the urinary excretion at once rose to 55 μg. per day.

Three cases have been described[2] of infants with a mild skin lesion on the face which resembled that observed in artificially produced biotin deficiency. Raw egg white made the lesions worse, whilst biotin methyl ester brought about immediate improvement with complete disappearance of the lesions in three weeks. A case of biotin deficiency resulting from a diet consisting solely of raw eggs has already been referred to (page 427).

References to Section 10

1. V. P. Sydenstricker, S. A. Singal, A. P. Briggs, N. M. de Vaughn and H. Isbell, *Science,* 1942, **95,** 176 ; *J. Amer. Med. Assoc.,* 1942, **118,** 1199.
2. A. Brown, *Glasgow Med. J.,* 1948, **29,** 309.

11. METABOLISM OF BIOTIN

Sydenstricker *et al.*[1] found the amount of biotin excreted in the urine by human subjects on a normal diet to be 29 to 52 μg. per day, which fell to 3·5 to 7·3 μg. per day after seven to eight weeks on a biotin-deficient diet. After administration of 75 to 300 μg. of biotin per day the urinary excretion increased after three to five days to 55 μg. per day. T. W. Oppel[2] reported an excretion of 14 to 111 μg. per day by normal subjects on an unrestricted diet, and Gardner *et al.*[3] an excretion of 11 to 183 μg. per day. The amount increased as much as five-fold immediately following the administration of a large dose of crude biotin by mouth. The faecal excretion varied from 17 to 208 μg. per day and also increased when biotin was given by mouth.

The precise nature of the excretion product of biotin has not been determined, but it is known that some at least of the biotin in normal rat and human urine does not combine with avidin.[2, 4] D. Burk and R. J. Winzler[5] gave specific names to the different fractions, *e.g.,* the heat-labile, avidin-uncombinable fraction active for yeast but not *Rhizobium* was termed miotin, the heat-stable, avidin-combinable component was termed tiotin, and the avidin-combinable fraction inactive for yeast but active for *Rhizobium* was termed rhiotin. Miotin and tiotin were transformed into an avidin-combinable form by yeast, but they were not identical with the diamino carboxylic acid (page 407), as they were not converted into biotin by the action of phosgene.

The amount of biotin in human milk was small for the first four or five days after parturition, and then rose gradually to 0·38 μg. per 100 ml. by the tenth day. The amount in the mature milk was 0·80 to 0·82 μg. per 100 ml.[6]

References to Section 11

1. V. P. Sydenstricker, S. A. Singal, A. P. Briggs, N. M. de Vaughn and H. Isbell, *Science,* 1942, **95,** 176 ; *J. Amer. Med. Assoc.,* 1942, **118,** 1199.
2. T. W. Oppel, *Amer. J. Med. Sci.,* 1942, **204,** 886.
3. J. Gardner, H. T. Parsons and W. H. Peterson, *Arch. Biochem.,* 1945, **8,** 339 ; *Amer. J. Med. Sci.,* 1946, **211,** 198.

4. E. J.-H. Chu and R. J. Williams, *J. Amer. Chem. Soc.*, 1944, **66**, 1678.

5. D. Burk and R. J. Winzler, *Science*, 1943, **97**, 57.

6. M. N. Coryell, M. E. Harris, S. Miller, H. H. Williams and I. G. Macy, *Amer. J. Dis. Child.*, 1945, **70**, 150.

12. INTESTINAL SYNTHESIS OF BIOTIN

The synthesis of biotin by the intestinal flora of experimental animals was first demonstrated by the administration of sulphonamides, which inhibited the growth of the bacteria that produced biotin. Daft et al.,[1] for example, showed that rats given sulphaguanidine and sulphasuxidine developed dermatitis, necrosis of the heart muscle, haemorrhage into various organs and the subcutaneous tissues, and liver damage. The symptoms were prevented by administration of crystalline biotin. Similar observations were made by G. J. Martin,[2] by E. Nielsen and C. A. Elvehjem,[3] by Neumann et al.,[4] by G. A. Emerson and E. Wurtz,[5] and by A. D. Welch and L. D. Wright.[6] The symptoms of biotin deficiency in rats maintained on a diet containing 1 % of succinyl sulphathiazole were not prevented by the addition of p-aminobenzoic acid to the diet.[4] Only a small amount of biotin was synthesised by rats on a riboflavine-deficient diet [7] and by mice on a synthetic diet.[8] The amount of biotin and folic acid stored in the liver was less in rats maintained on a purified diet adequate in the vitamin B complex than in rats fed the stock diet,[9] and was further decreased when succinylsulphathiazole was added to the diet. The inference to be drawn from this observation, namely that biotin and folic acid are synthesised by the intestinal flora and then somehow utilised by the animals is supported by the results obtained by Barki et al.,[9a] who found that rats maintained on a purified diet under conditions that prevented coprophagy grew better when biotin and folic acid were added to the diet, whereas these supplements made little difference to the growth of rats kept in ordinary screen-bottom cages. The biotin and folic acid contents of the liver were also reduced, and the results suggest, therefore, that rats may obtain part of their biotin and folic acid requirements by ingesting their faeces. Direct absorption from the gut must take place to some extent, however, as the amounts of biotin and folic acid in the liver were still further depressed when succinylsulphathiazole was added to the diet. As already mentioned (page 428), pantothenic acid-deficiency due to the addition of succinyl sulphathiazole to the diet was corrected by administration of biotin and folic acid concentrates,[10] the utilisation of pantothenic acid obviously being dependent on the availability of biotin and folic acid either from the diet or from the intestinal flora.

Waisman et al.[11] drew attention to the close similarity between the symptoms of biotin deficiency caused by feeding egg white and those produced by the administration of succinylsulphathiazole, and G. A. Emerson and E. Wurtz [12] showed that the addition of succinyl-sulphathiazole to a diet containing dried egg white did not modify the severity or time of onset of biotin deficiency whether or not the diet contained liver ; in order to secure growth, the diet had to contain biotin plus liver or folic acid. It would seem from this evidence that dried egg white makes unavailable not only dietary biotin but also biotin derived from bacterial synthesis in the intestine. This was confirmed by McGregor et al.[13] who showed that biotin from a non-dietary source was eliminated in the faeces of rats fed raw egg white, the amount of biotin in the urine and faeces far exceeding that in the diet. The excess biotin was presumably derived from the intestinal bacteria and not from biotin reserves in the body.

Proof that intestinal synthesis occurs in man was obtained from metabolic experiments. Thus, T. W. Oppel [14] showed that, whereas the urinary output of biotin was roughly proportional to the intake, the daily faecal excretion greatly exceeded the intake. The total excretion on a diet supplying 30 to 40 μg. per day was in fact three to six times this amount. Incidentally faeces, unlike urine, contained no non-avidin combining fraction (page 433). These observations were confirmed by Gardner et al.[15] who found that in women, the total biotin output was nine, three and 1·5 times the intake with diets containing small, moderate and large amounts of biotin respectively.

These results were also confirmed by Denko et al.[16] (see page 377), who in addition found that on a restricted diet a moderate decrease in the urinary excretion of biotin occurred, the amount being roughly equal to the dietary intake. The faecal excretion, on the other hand, greatly exceeded the intake on the restricted diet.

Several organisms are probably responsible for the intestinal synthesis of biotin. Certainly B. proteus vulgaris can synthesise all known members of the vitamin B complex,[17, 18] whilst E. coli, B. lactis aerogenes, B. faecalis alcaligenes, B. mesentericus and B. vulgatus produce, inter alia, biotin.[18]

The effect of feeding various carbohydrates on the faecal flora and so on the intestinal synthesis of biotin in the hen was studied by Johansson et al.[19] With sucrose as carbohydrate the faeces were nearly devoid of coliform organisms, which were replaced by yeasts. The coliform count was highest in hens receiving dextrin or a mixture of sucrose and lactose. Intestinal synthesis of biotin occurred in hens fed the basal ration with added dextrin, but not with sucrose or lactose. Ground whole oats and oat groats also supported intestinal synthesis, the effect being more marked with the former. The synthesis and absorption of biotin were directly related to the level of oats in the diet.[20]

References to Section 12

1. F. S. Daft, L. L. Ashburn and W. H. Sebrell, *Science*, 1942, **96**, 321.
2. G. J. Martin, *Proc. Soc. Exp. Biol. Med.*, 1942, **51**, 353.
3. E. Nielsen and C. A. Elvehjem, *J. Biol. Chem.*, 1942, **145**, 713.
4. F. W. Neumann, M. M. Krider and H. G. Day, *Proc. Soc. Exp. Biol. Med.*, 1943, **52**, 257.
5. G. A. Emerson and E. Wurtz, *ibid.*, 1944, **57**, 47.
6. A. D. Welch and L. D. Wright, *J. Nutrition*, 1943, **25**, 555.
7. E. Nielsen, G. M. Shull and W. H. Peterson, *ibid.*, 1942, **24**, 523.
8. E. Nielsen and A. Black, *ibid.*, 1944, **28**, 203.
9. L. D. Wright and A. D. Welch, *ibid.*, 1944, **27**, 55.
9a. V. H. Barki, P. H. Derse, R. A. Collins, E. B. Hart and C. A. Elvehjem, *ibid.*, 1949, **37**, 443.
10. L. D. Wright and A. D. Welch, *Science*, 1943, **97**, 426.
11. H. A. Waisman, K. B. McCall and C. A. Elvehjem, *J. Nutrition*, 1945, **29**, 1.
12. G. A. Emerson and E. Wurtz, *Proc. Soc. Exp. Biol. Med.*, 1945, **59**, 297.
13. M. A. McGregor, H. T. Parsons and W. H. Peterson, *J. Nutrition*, 1947, **33**, 517.
14. T. W. Oppel, *Amer. J. Med. Sci.*, 1942, **204**, 886.
15. J. Gardner, H. T. Parsons and W. H. Peterson, *Arch. Biochem.*, 1945, **8**, 339 ; *Amer. J. Med. Sci.*, 1946, **211**, 198.
16. C. W. Denko, W. E. Grundy, J. W. Porter, G. H. Berryman., T. E. Friedemann and J. B. Youmans, *Arch. Biochem.*, 1946, **10**, 33 ; C. W. Denko, W. E. Grundy, N. C. Wheeler, C. R. Henderson, G. H. Berryman, T. E. Friedemann and J. B. Youmans, *ibid.*, 1946, **11**, 109.
17. R. C. Thompson, *Univ. Texas Publ.*, No. 4237, p. 87.
18. P. R. Burkholder and I. McVeigh, *Proc. Nat. Acad. Sci.*, 1942, **28**, 285.
19. K. R. Johansson, S. K. Shapiro and W. B. Sarles, *J. Bact.*, 1947, **54**, 35 ; 1948, **56**, 619 ; J. R. Couch, W. W. Cravens, C. A. Elvehjem and J. G. Halpin, *J. Nutrition*, 1948, **35**, 57.
20. J. R. Couch, M. L. Sunde, W. W. Cravens, C. A. Elvehjem and J. G. Halpin, *ibid.*, 1949, **37**, 251.

13. ANIMAL AND HUMAN REQUIREMENTS OF BIOTIN

It is obvious, from what has been said already about the metabolism of biotin and the existence of bacterial synthesis in the gut of many animal species, that it is not easy to assess the biotin requirements of animals with any degree of confidence. It is not known how much of the biotin produced by the intestinal flora is normally available to the host and whether changes in the diet, which can certainly affect the amount of biotin synthesised by them (page 435), can affect the extent to which biotin can be utilised.

Bearing in mind the possibility that present-day estimates may have to be revised in the light of future observations, the following values have been recorded for the daily requirements of different animal species : for the rat, $2^{[1]}$ and 0·5 to 1·0$^{[2]}$ μg. ; for chicks, 1$^{[3]}$ and 0·65$^{[4]}$ μg. (supplied by a diet containing 7 to 10 μg. of biotin per 100 g.$^{[5]}$) ; for turkeys, 40 " rat units "; $^{[6]}$ for monkeys, 20 μg. ; $^{[7]}$ and for pigs, 100 μg.$^{[8]}$ Chick embryos failed to develop if the yolk contained less than 50 mμg. of biotin per g., but 150 mμg. per g. supported growth.$^{[9]}$

No precise estimate of the human requirements of biotin appears to be available, but subjects made biotin-deficient quickly became normal when 75 to 300 μg. of biotin were injected per day.$^{[10]}$

References to Section 13

1. E. Nielsen and C. A. Elvehjem, *Proc. Soc. Exp. Biol. Med.*, 1941, **48,** 349.
2. G. A. Emerson and J. C. Keresztesy, *ibid.*, 1942, **51,** 358.
3. L. R. Richardson, A. G. Hogan and O. N. Miller, *Univ. Missouri Agric. Exp. Stat., Res. Bull.*, 1942, 343 ; J. H. Shaw and P. H. Phillips, *J. Nutrition*, 1945, **29,** 107.
4. T. H. Jukes and F. H. Bird, *Proc. Soc. Exp. Biol. Med.*, 1942, **49,** 231.
5. D. M. Hegsted, R. C. Mills, G. M. Briggs, C. A. Elvehjem and E. B. Hart, *J. Nutrition*, 1942, **23,** 175.
6. H. Patrick, R. V. Boucher, R. A. Dutcher and H. C. Knandel, *Proc. Soc. Exp. Biol. Med.*, 1941, **48,** 456.
7. H. A. Waisman, K. B. McCall and C. A. Elvehjem, *J. Nutrition*, 1945, **29,** 1.
8. T. J. Cunha, D. C. Lindley and M. E. Ensminger, *J. Animal Sci.*, 1946, **5,** 219.
9. J. R. Couch, W. W. Cravens, C. A. Elvehjem and J. G. Halpin, *J. Nutrition*, 1948, **35,** 57.
10. V. P. Sydenstricker, S. A. Singal, A. P. Briggs, N. M. de Vaughn and H. Isbell, *Science*, 1942, **95,** 176 ; *J. Amer. Med. Assoc.*, 1942, **118,** 1199.

14. PHARMACOLOGY OF BIOTIN

The intravenous injection of 250 μg. of biotin per kg. of bodyweight into anaesthetised cats had no effect on the blood-pressure, heart rate or respiration.$^{[1]}$ No effect was produced on strips of guinea pig uterus, rabbit uterus or on rabbit intestine when these were suspended in solutions containing up to 1 part in 40,000 of biotin or when a frog's heart was perfused *in situ* with a solution containing 200 µg. of biotin.

Feeding excess biotin caused fatty livers, which contained large amounts of cholesterol. The effect was inhibited by egg white, lipocaic or inositol when these were given at the same time as the biotin [2] (see page 572).

References to Section 14

1. J. L. Schmidt and M. Landy, *Proc. Soc. Exp. Biol. Med.*, 1942, **49**, 82.
2. G. Gavin and E. W. McHenry, *J. Biol. Chem.*, 1941, **141**, 619.

15. BIOTIN IN THE NUTRITION OF MICRO-ORGANISMS

Yeasts

Biotin is an important growth factor for a number of micro-organisms and can be detected by the yeast growth method (page 421) in as low a concentration as 1 part in 10,000,000,000.[1] It is essential for the growth of many strains of *Saccharomyces cerevisiae* [2] and for the vast majority of a large number of other yeasts tested.[3] Many yeasts can utilise instead of biotin, desthiobiotin (page 447) which is transformed into biotin within the cells.[4] Bacteria, however, cannot utilise desthiobiotin in this way. Biotin was the only member of the vitamin B complex that definitely increased the production of alcohol by yeast.[5]

The biotin content of different yeasts varies considerably, the lowest value found in a series tested being 0·23 µg. per g. and the highest 7·6 µg. per g.[5a] Some yeasts, e.g. *S. cerevisiae*, took up large amounts of biotin from the culture medium, whereas others, e.g. *Endomyces magnusii*, took up hardly any, although both require biotin for growth ; obviously the uptake is not correlated with the requirement in different species. *Torulopsis utilis* and *Hansenula anomala*, which synthesise biotin, also did not take up biotin from the medium.

Other Fungi

Biotin was necessary for the growth of a number of moulds including *Lophiodermum pinastri* and *Ashbya* (*Nematospora*) *gossypii*,[6] *Trichophyton album*,[7] *Eremothecium ashbyii*,[8] *Neurospora sitophila* and its " pyridoxineless " X-ray mutant,[9] *Hypholoma fasciculare* [7] and *Marasmius androsaceus*.[10] Biotin also stimulated the growth of

Penicillium digitatum, the effect being more pronounced above pH 6·5 than at pH 3·0.[11]   Other moulds which required biotin were *Ascoidea rubescens, Ophiostoma fagi, O. piliferum* and *Mitrula paludosa.*[12]

Some fungi, however, can synthesise biotin.   For example, *Phycomyces blakesleeanus* on a synthetic medium containing asparagine and glucose produced a good deal of biotin, the greater part of which accumulated in the medium.[13]   The yield of biotin increased with temperature, with the amount of asparagine and in presence of traces of certain metals.   *Penicillium chrysogenum* also synthesised biotin, although only in small amounts.[12]   Desthiobiotin was a normal intermediate in the biosynthesis of biotin by this mould.[14]

An organism that cannot synthesise biotin will grow in a synthetic medium if this is also inoculated with an organism that synthesises biotin, and it is even possible for each of the organisms to supply the other with an essential growth factor that it cannot itself produce. This is believed to account for the phenomenon of symbiosis.

Bacteria

Biotin was essential for the growth of *Lactobacillus helveticus* [15] and *L. arabinosus* [16] and indeed for all species of *Lactobacilli* tested by Rogosa *et al.*[17]   Unlike yeasts, however, these organisms cannot utilise desthiobiotin in place of biotin.[18]   *L. helveticus* can utilise the methyl ester of biotin, though growth and fermentation were slower than with free biotin.[19]   Three strains of *Leuconostoc, L. mesenteroides, L. dextranicum* and *L. dextranicum elai,* required biotin for growth when the medium contained invert sugar, glucose or fructose, but grew without biotin on a sucrose medium.[19a]   Biotin was also essential for *B. radicicola,*[20, 21] *Rhizobium trifolii,*[20, 21] *Staphylococcus aureus,*[22] *Streptobacterium plantarum,*[23] and four species of *Propionibacteria.*[24] It was also necessary for maximum growth of *Clostridium tetani,*[25] *Cl. botulinum,*[26] *Cl. kluyveri,*[27] three strains of *Cl. acetobutylicum,*[28] and about twenty other species of *Clostridia.*[29]   *B. polymyxa* required only biotin of the vitamin B complex, whilst *B. macerans* and *B. acetoaethylicus* required both biotin and aneurine.[30]   Biotin was apparently the only growth factor required by *Neisseria sicca.*[31]

The biotin requirements of bacteria can be observed by the effects of avidin on their growth.[32]

A biotin-deficient mutant of *E. coli* was isolated by C. H. Gray and E. L. Tatum.[33]

The amount of biotin present in the five bacteria, *Aerobacter aerogenes, Serratia marcescens, Pseudomonas fluorescens, Proteus vulgaris* and *Clostridium butylicum* ranged from 420 to 1800 molecules per cell and the rate of synthesis from 0·08 to 3·2 molecules per cell per second.[34]

References to Section 15

1. F. Kögl and B. Tönnis, *Z. physiol. Chem.*, 1936, **242**, 43.
2. R. J. Williams, R. E. Eakin and E. E. Snell, *J. Amer. Chem. Soc.*, 1940, **62**, 1204 ; L. H. Leonian and V. G. Lilly, *Amer. J. Bot.*, 1942, **29**, 459.
3. P. R. Burkholder, *ibid.*, 1943, **30**, 206 ; P. R. Burkholder and D. Moyer, *Bull. Torrey Bot. Club.*, 1943, **70**, 372 ; P. R. Burkholder, I. McVeigh and D. Moyer, *J. Bact.*, 1944, **48**, 385 ; A. S. Schultz and L. Atkin, *Arch. Biochem.*, 1947, **14**, 369.
4. J. L. Stokes and M. Gunness, *J. Biol. Chem.*, 1945, **157**, 121.
5. V. de Souza and M. Sreenivasaya, *J. Sci. Ind. Res., India*, 1945, **4**, 384.
5a. W. S. Chang and W. H. Peterson, *J. Bact.*, 1949, **58**, 33.
6. F. Kögl and N. Fries, *Z. physiol. Chem.*, 1937, **249**, 93.
7. W. H. Schopfer and S. Blumer, *Z. Vitaminforsch.*, 1942, **59**, 106 ; *Ber. Schweiz. Bot. Ges.*, 1943, **53**, 409.
8. W. H. Schopfer, *Helv. Chim. Acta*, 1944, **27**, 1017.
9. J. L. Stokes, J. W. Foster and C. R. Woodward, *Arch. Biochem.*, 1943, **2**, 235.
10. G. Lindeberg, *Symbol. bot. Upsalienses*, 1944, VIII, **2**, 1.
11. R. C. Wooster and V. H. Cheldelin, *Arch. Biochem.*, 1945, **8**, 311.
12. F. W. Tanner, S. E. Pfeiffer and J. M. van Lanen, *ibid.*, 29.
13. W. H. Schopfer, *Z. Vitaminforsch.*, 1943, **14**, 42.
14. E. L. Tatum, *J. Biol. Chem.*, 1945, **160**, 455.
15. G. M. Shull, B. L. Hutchings and W. H. Peterson, *ibid.*, 1942, **142**, 913.
16. L. D. Wright and H. R. Skeggs, *Proc. Soc. Exp. Biol. Med.*, 1944, **56**, 95.
17. M. Rogosa, R. P. Tittsler and D. S. Geib, *J. Bact.*, 1947, **54**, 13.
18. K. Dittmer, D. B. Melville and V. du Vigneaud, *Science*, 1944, **99**, 203.
19. J. L. Stokes and M. Gunness, *Proc. Soc. Exp. Biol. Med.*, 1943, **54**, 28.
19a. W. W. Carlson and V. Whiteside-Carlson, *ibid.*, 1949, **71**, 416.
20. P. M. West and P. W. Wilson, *Enzymologia*, 1939, **8**, 152.
21. R. Nilsson, G. Bjälfoe and D. Burström, *Naturwiss.*, 1939, **27**, 389.
22. F. Kögl and W. J. van Wagtendonk, *Rec. trav. chim.*, 1938, **57**, 747.
23. R. Kuhn and K. Schwartz, *Ber.*, 1941, **74**, 1617.
24. R. C. Thompson, *J. Bact.*, 1943, **46**, 99.
25. R. E. Feeney, J. H. Mueller and P. A. Miller, *ibid.*, 563.
26. C. Lamanna and C. Lewis, *ibid.*, 1946, **51**, 398.
27. B. T. Bornstein and H. A. Barker, *ibid.*, 1948, **55**, 222.
28. R. Reyes-Teodoro and M. N. Michelson, *Arch. Biochem.*, 1944, **4**, 291 ; 1945, **6**, 471.
29. J. O. Lampen and W. H. Peterson, *ibid.*, 1943, **2**, 443.

30. H. Katznelson, *J. Bact.*, 1944, **48**, 495.

31. Z. J. Ordal and R. K. Busch, *ibid.*, 1946, **51**, 791.

32. M. Landy, D. M. Dicken, M. M. Bicking and W. R. Mitchell, *Proc. Soc. Exp. Biol. Med.*, 1942, **49**, 441.

33. C. H. Gray and E. L. Tatum, *Proc. Nat. Acad. Sci.*, 1944, **30**, 404.

34. H. McIlwain, *Nature*, 1946, **158**, 898.

16. EFFECT OF BIOTIN ON PLANTS

Biotin and aneurine were claimed by F. Kögl and A. J. Haagen-Smit [1] to be phyto-hormones, since each increased the growth of pea embryos grown in a synthetic medium ; the effect of the two compounds together was greater than that of either alone. The amount of biotin, like that of other members of the vitamin B complex, increased during the germination of oats, wheat, barley and maize.[2]

References to Section 16

1. F. Kögl and A. J. Haagen-Smit, *Z. physiol. Chem.*, 1936, **243**, 209.

2. P. R. Burkholder, *Science*, 1943, **97**, 562.

17. BIOTIN REQUIREMENTS OF INSECTS

Biotin is essential for the optimal growth of *Tribolium confusum* [1,2] and of *Sitodrepa panicea*, *Lasioderma serricorne* and *Ptinus tectus*, but not of *Silvanus surinamensis*.[3] The diaminocarboxylic acid derived from biotin (page 407) could partially replace biotin for *Tribolium*. The sterilised larvae of *Lasioderma* showed less satisfactory growth than normal larvae without biotin, so that biotin may be a more important factor in the absence of symbionts [4] (see page 115). Biotin was necessary for the growth of mosquito larvae (*Aedes aegypti*) to the fourth instar.[5] It could be replaced by small amounts of oleic acid or lecithin.

Pollen and royal jelly are rich in biotin, as well as in pantothenic acid (page 364), and it has been suggested that these two members of the vitamin B complex may be concerned with the development of bee larvae into queen bees.[6]

The addition of raw egg white to the diet of the larvae of the rice-moth (*Corcyra cephalonica*) inhibited growth, and caused death in twenty-eight days. Avidin produced the same effect. When larvae fed on egg white for fourteen days were given a diet rich in biotin, growth was resumed and the increase in weight was approximately proportional to the amount of biotin added.[7]

References to Section 17

1. G. Fraenkel and M. Blewett, *Nature*, 1942, **149**, 301 ; 1942, **150,** 177 ; 1943, **151,** 703.
2. H. Rosenthal and T. Reichstein, *ibid.*, 1942, **150,** 546.
3. G. Fraenkel and M. Blewett, *Biochem. J.*, 1943, **37,** 686.
4. M. Blewett and G. Fraenkel, *Proc. Roy. Soc. B.*, 1944, **132,** 212.
5. L. Golberg, B. de Meillon and M. Lavoipierre, *J. Exp. Biol.*, 1945, **21,** 90 ; W. Trager, *J. Biol. Chem.*, 1949, **176,** 1211.
6. G. Kitzes, H. A. Schuette and C. A. Elvehjem, *J. Nutrition*, 1943, **26,** 241.
7. P. S. Sarma, *Indian J. Med. Res.*, 1944, **32,** 149.

18. FUNCTION OF BIOTIN

Miller *et al.*[1] sought to determine the function of biotin by esti-mating the amounts present in a number of enzyme preparations, but they failed to detect a single enzyme that contained more than one molecule of biotin per molecule, and accordingly concluded that biotin was only present as an impurity. D. Burk and R. J. Winzler[2] suggested that biotin was the prosthetic group of a coenzyme that catalysed the transfer of carbon dioxide, whilst Koser *et al.*[3] suggested that it was concerned with the synthesis of aspartic acid, since the latter stimulated the growth of *Torula cremoris* in the absence of biotin. This was confirmed five years later, when Stokes[4] *et al.* showed that *S. faecalis* R, *L. helveticus* and *L. arabinosus* failed to grow unless about 1 mμg. of biotin and 1 mg. of aspartic acid per 10 ml. were added to the medium but that if the biotin concentration were in-creased to 10 mμg. per 10 ml. the addition of aspartic acid was un-necessary. Aspartic acid was therefore synthesised by organisms grown in presence of excess biotin. Oxybiotin and the diaminocar-boxylic acid (page 407) could replace biotin for this purpose, but larger quantities were required. *L. arabinosus* was able to synthesise aspartic acid from glutamic acid plus oxaloacetic acid, fumaric acid, malic acid or succinic acid, and from alanine plus oxaloacetic acid, but biotin did not play any part in these reactions. Apparently, therefore, the enzyme system containing biotin was not concerned with the final stage in the synthesis of aspartic acid, but with one of the intermediate stages.

Carboxylation and Decarboxylation

Using *E. coli*, H. C. Lichstein and W. W. Umbreit[5] showed that aspartic acid was degraded according to the following scheme :

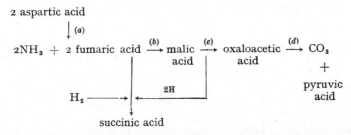

Since biotin restored the ability of *E. coli* to produce carbon dioxide from aspartic acid, malic acid and oxaloacetic acid after the bacterial cells had lost this ability on standing, they concluded that biotin was concerned with the coenzyme of oxaloacetic acid decarboxylase.

This suggestion was supported by Lardy *et al.*,[6] who demonstrated that biotin-deficient *L. arabinosus* could convert oxaloacetic acid to aspartic acid by transamination and therefore suggested that the inability of biotin-deficient organisms to synthesise aspartic acid lay in their failure to condense pyruvic acid with carbon dioxide to produce oxaloacetic acid, *i.e.*, the reverse of reaction (*d*). In a medium devoid of aspartic acid the addition of bicarbonate stimulated growth in the presence but not in the absence of biotin.

The hypothesis was in part supported by the work of W. Shive and L. L. Rogers [7] on biotin antagonists. They found that in *E. coli* α-ketoglutaric acid effected a 3-fold increase in the antibacterial index for the competitive inhibition of biotin by desthiobiotin (page 452) and that L-glutamic acid had a similar effect. Aspartic acid, succinic acid, fumaric acid, malic acid and *cis*-aconitic acid, on the other hand, were inactive. This indicates that inhibition of the growth effect of biotin interferes with the biosynthesis of α-ketoglutaric acid which in *E. coli* is apparently involved in the biosynthesis of aspartic acid. Thus in this organism, biotin appears to function in the conversion of oxalosuccinic acid into α-ketoglutaric acid. In *L. arabinosus*, the antibacterial index for the competitive inhibition of biotin by γ-(3 : 4-ureylene-cyclohexyl)-butyric acid (see page 453) was increased 10-fold by the addition of aspartic or oxaloacetic acid, so that in this instance biotin is apparently concerned in the synthesis of oxaloacetic acid. Similar results with biotin antagonists were reported by Axelrod *et al.*[7a], who found that a number of biotin analogues would neutralise the stimulatory effect of biotin on biotin-deficient yeast, but that the stimulatory effect of aspartic acid was not affected thereby. The analogues, therefore, presumably exert their effect by preventing the conversion of biotin into a form necessary for the synthesis of aspartic acid.

Some doubt was thrown on the association of biotin with the

decarboxylation of oxaloacetic acid, however, by the observations of Ochoa *et al.*,[8] who isolated from pigeon and turkey livers an enzyme that catalysed the reversible conversion of L-malic acid to pyruvic acid plus carbon dioxide and the decarboxylation of oxaloacetic acid to pyruvic acid. In biotin-deficient turkeys the amount of this enzyme, though not of other enzymes catalysing related reactions was markedly reduced but, unfortunately, the purified enzyme did not contain biotin.

H. A. Lardy and his co-workers,[9] however, have produced evidence suggesting that biotin may be associated with carbon dioxide fixation in several different enzyme reactions, not only in micro-organisms but also in animals. Thus, in presence of biotin, *L. arabinosus* fixed C^{14} from bicarbonate into cellular aspartic acid, but no fixation occurred when the medium contained less than 0·05 mμg. of biotin per ml., or when aspartic acid or an anti-biotin was added. Again, C^{14} fixation occurred to a greater extent in normal rats than in biotin-deficient animals, and the livers of biotin-deficient animals synthesised citrulline at half the rate of normal or vitamin B_6-deficient animals ; the rate was increased to normal by the intraperitoneal injection of biotin.

Biotin containing C^{14} was prepared by reacting the diaminocarboxylic acid (page 407) with radioactive phosgene. When added to cultures of *L. arabinosus* under conditions requiring its participation in carbon dioxide fixation, there was no replacement of C^{14} by C^{12}, so that the ureido carbonyl group is apparently not transferred during carbon dioxide fixation.[10]

Deamination

Carbon dioxide fixation does not appear to be the only function of biotin and according to H. C. Lichstein and W. W. Umbreit,[11] it can also restore the ability of *E. coli* to deaminate aspartic acid, serine and threonine when this is lost by the cells having been left at pH 4 for thirty minutes at 27 to 37° C. Thus biotin appeared to be connected with reaction (*a*) in the above scheme, as well as with reaction (*d*). Similar results were obtained with other bacterial species, and aspartic acid deaminase activity was restored by adenylic acid as well as by biotin. In no instance was the alanine, phenylalanine, methionine or glutamic acid deaminase activity affected by biotin.[12]

Axelrod *et al.*,[13] however, failed to confirm these results, but H. C. Lichstein[14] showed that this was due to their use of an unsuitable medium. Adenylic acid was shown to be necessary for the activation of biotin for the stimulation of cell-free aspartic acid deaminase,[15] and a deaminase activator that was neither biotin nor adenylic acid was isolated from yeast by paper partition chromatography.[16] It supported the growth of *S. cerevisiae* (Java strain) in a biotin-deficient medium and on hydrolysis biotin was liberated, supporting the growth of *S. cerevisiae* 139, which does not respond to the coenzyme.

Oxidation of Pyruvic and Lactic Acids

A suggestion by Summerson *et al.*[17] that biotin may be concerned with the oxidation of pyruvic acid and lactic acid indicates yet another possible function of biotin. The evidence for the suggestion was that carbon dioxide production was markedly increased when biotin was added to liver slices from biotin-deficient rats respiring in a solution containing lactate or pyruvate as substrate. These results are supported by similar observations made by Olson *et al.*[18] on the respiration of ventricle slices from biotin-deficient ducks. In presence of succinate the oxygen uptake was much less than normal and the accumulation of lactic acid decreased. In addition the production of C^{14} carbon dioxide from labelled succinate by ventricle slices was much less with tissue from biotin-deficient ducks than with tissue from controls.

References to Section 18

1. D. R. Miller, J. O. Lampen and W. H. Peterson, *J. Amer. Chem. Soc.*, 1943, **65**, 2369.
2. D. Burk and R. J. Winzler, *Science*, 1943, **97**, 57.
3. S. A. Koser, M. H. Wright and A. Dorfman, *Proc. Soc. Exp. Biol. Med.*, 1942, **51**, 204.
4. J. L. Stokes, A. Larsen and M. Gunness, *J. Bact.*, 1947, **54**, 19, 219 ; *J. Biol. Chem.*, 1947, **167**, 613.
5. H. C. Lichstein and W. W. Umbreit, *ibid.*, 1947, **170**, 329.
6. H. A. Lardy, R. L. Potter and C. A. Elvehjem, *ibid.*, 1947, **169**, 451.
7. W. Shive and L. L. Rogers, *ibid.*, 453.
7a. A. E. Axelrod, S. E. Purvis and K. Hofmann, *ibid.*, 1948, **176**, 695.
8. S. Ochoa, A. Mehler, M. L. Blanchard, T. H. Jukes, C. E. Hoffmann and M. A. Regan, *ibid.*, 1947, **170**, 413.
9. H. A. Lardy, R. L. Potter and R. H. Burris, *J. Biol. Chem.*, 1949, **179**, 721 ; P. R. MacLeod and H. A. Lardy, *ibid.*, 733 ; P. R. MacLeod, S. Grisolia, P. P. Cohen and H. A. Lardy, *ibid.*, 1949, **180**, 1003.
10. D. B. Melville, J. G. Pierce and C. W. H. Partridge, *ibid.*, 299.
11. H. C. Lichstein and W. W. Umbreit, *ibid.*, 1947, **170**, 423.
12. H. C. Lichstein and J. F. Christman, *ibid.*, 1948, **175**, 649.
13. A. E. Axelrod, K. Hofmann, S. E. Purvis and M. Mayhall, *ibid.*, 991.
14. H. C. Lichstein, *ibid.*, 1949, **177**, 487.
15. H. C. Lichstein, *ibid.*, 125.
16. H. C. Lichstein and J. F. Christman, *J. Bact.*, 1949, **58**, 565.
17. W. H. Summerson, J. M. Lee and C. W. H. Partridge, *Science*, 1944, **100**, 250.
18. R. E. Olson, O. N. Miller, Y. J. Topper and F. J. Stare, *J. Biol. Chem.*, 1948, **175**, 503.

19. ANALOGUES OF BIOTIN

Pimelic Acid

The nutritional requirements of *Corynebacterium diphtheriae* were studied by J. H. Mueller *et al.*,[1] who showed that the growth of this organism was stimulated by various fractions prepared from animal tissues, in addition to a number of amino acids. One of the constituents of these fractions was identified as pimelic acid,[2] and synthetic pimelic acid proved to be equally active. Mueller's observations were confirmed by Evans *et al.*[3] using *gravis*, *intermedius* and *mitis* strains of *C. diphtheriae*. Du Vigneaud *et al.*[4] showed that biotin could replace pimelic acid for the Allen strain of *C. diphtheriae*, although pimelic acid produced slightly more growth than biotin at the maximum level of 1.5 μg. ; biotin was more effective than pimelic acid, however, at low concentrations. Pimelic acid is probably utilised by some strains of this organism for the synthesis of biotin, much as some strains utilise β-alanine in place of pantothenic acid.

Thirteen different organisms tested by W. J. Robbins and R. Ma[5] failed to grow on an otherwise complete medium in which biotin was replaced by pimelic acid alone or accompanied by L-cystine, glutathione or methionine.

Isomers of Biotin

Synthetic *d*-biotin and natural biotin had identical growth-promoting activities for three bacteria, one yeast and a fungus. *l*-Biotin and *dl*-allobiotin supported the growth of bacteria only in large amounts and this slight activity was probably due to contamination with traces of *d*-biotin.[6]

On rats maintained on a diet containing egg white, *dl*-biotin was half as active as natural biotin,[7] whilst *l*-biotin was without effect at seven and a half times, and *dl*-allobiotin at ten times, the level of biotin.

Synthetic *d*-biotin was as effective as natural biotin[8] in promoting growth and preventing dermatitis in chicks fed a purified diet containing 15 % of raw egg white. *l*-Biotin and *dl*-biotin were inactive.

Homologues of Biotin

Rather surprisingly perhaps, increasing or decreasing the length of the valeric acid side-chain of biotin not only almost completely destroys the growth-promoting activity of the molecule but converts it into a growth-inhibitory substance. Although nor-biotin ($n = 3$) and homo-biotin ($n = 5$) can replace biotin for *Saccharomyces globosus* and one strain of *S. cerevisiae*, they and other homologues are potent antagonists of biotin for other strains of the latter and for *S. fragilis*, *Zygosaccharomyces barkeri* and *L. helveticus*[8a] (page 453).

Analogues of Biotin

2-γ-Hydroxypropyl-2'-ketoimidazolidino-(4' : 5' : 3 : 4)-thiophene [9] (I) and *dl*-tetradehydrobiotin [10] (II) :

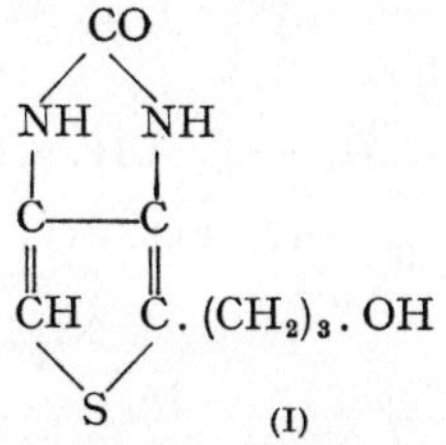

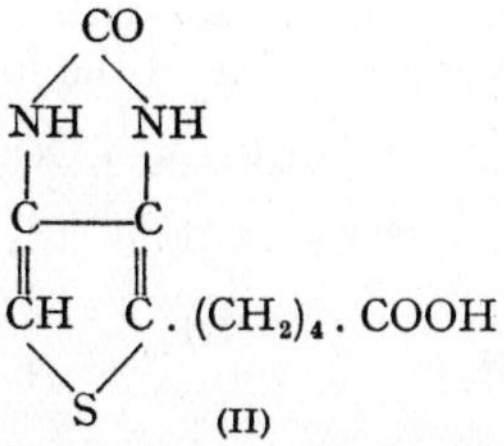

were inactive when tested on *S. cerevisiae* and on *L. arabinosus* or *L. helveticus*; neither had anti-biotin activity. Analogues of biotin in which the valeric acid side-chain was replaced by γ-phenoxy-, γ-benzyloxy- and γ-hydroxy-*n*-propyl groups were also without biotin activity for *L. arabinosus* or *S. cerevisiae* and without anti-biotin activity.[11]

Biotin Sulphone

Oxidation of biotin gave a sulphone (page 407) which stimulated the growth of yeast. Even with large amounts, however, growth did not increase beyond a relatively low maximum, which was only about one-third of that obtained with biotin.[12] The sulphone had only about 0·1 % the activity of biotin when the two were compared at a level that produced one-quarter of the maximal growth. Biotin sulphone, like desthiobiotin, has anti-biotin activity (see page 452).

Degradation Products of Biotin

The diamino-carboxylic acid, 3 : 4-diamino-tetrahydrothiophene-2-valeric acid, derived from biotin by treatment with alkali (page 407), was found to stimulate the growth of yeast in a biotin-free medium.[13] It possessed about one-tenth the activity of biotin and its action was not inhibited by avidin. It had 4 to 7 % of the activity of biotin for *Lactobacilli*.[6] Diaminopelargonic acid, which on treatment with phosgene yields desthiobiotin, had one-tenth the activity of desthiobiotin towards yeast.[14] The diamino-tetrahydrothiophene-2-valeric acids corresponding to *dl*-allo- and *dl*-epi-allo-biotin were inactive at levels 100 to 250 times that at which biotin was active.[7]

Desthiobiotin

When biotin was treated with Raney nickel an atom of sulphur is lost, giving desthiobiotin (page 410). This was found to stimulate the growth of yeast, but not of *L. helveticus*.[6, 15] This diverse effect on the two micro-organisms was shown to be due to the ability of yeast to convert desthiobiotin into biotin, since the former disappeared from the incubated culture and was replaced by a substance with growth-promoting properties for *L. helveticus*.[6, 16]

Desthiobiotin was synthesised in several ways. J. L. Wood and V. du Vigneaud[17] used the following method :

$$CH_2(COOC_2H_5)_2 \;+\; Br(CH_2)_5 . COOC_2H_5 \;\longrightarrow\; (C_2H_5OOC)_2 . CH . (CH_2)_5 . COOC_2$$

1. Saponification
2. Bromination
3. Amination
4. Decarboxylation

$$\xrightarrow{\hspace{2cm}} \quad HOOC . CH . (CH_2)_5 . COOH \underset{|}{\overset{}{}} NH_2 \quad \xrightarrow{Ac_2O} \quad CH_3 . CO . CH . (CH_2)_5 . CO \underset{|}{\overset{}{}} NH . CO . CH_3$$

$$\xrightarrow{HCl} \quad CH_3 . CO . CH . (CH_2)_5 . COOH \underset{|}{\overset{}{}} NH_2 \quad \xrightarrow{KCNO} \quad \begin{array}{c} CO \\ NH \quad NH \\ CH_3 . C{=\!=}C . (CH_2)_5 . COO \end{array}$$

$$\xrightarrow{H_2} \quad \begin{array}{c} CO \\ NH \quad NH \\ CH_3 . CH{-\!-}CH . (CH_2)_5 . COOH \end{array}$$

Melville[18] prepared it by the action of phosgene in alkaline solution on its degradation product, $\zeta\eta$-diaminopelargonic acid, whilst R. Duschinsky and L. A. Dolan[19] synthesised it by the following route :

$$CH_3 . CO . CH_2 . COOC_2H_5 \quad \xrightarrow{HNO_2} \quad CH_3 . CO . C . COOC_2H_5 \;\| \; N . OH$$

$$\downarrow{\tiny KOH\;HNO_2} \qquad\qquad\qquad \downarrow{\tiny H_2}$$

$$CH_3 . CO . CH{=}N . OH \qquad CH_3 . CO . CH . COOC_2H_5 \underset{|}{\overset{}{}} NH_2$$

$$\downarrow{\tiny H_2} \qquad\qquad\qquad \downarrow{\tiny HCNO}$$

$$CH_3 . CO . CH_2 . NH_2$$

$$\downarrow{\tiny HCNO}$$

$$\begin{array}{c} CO \\ NH \quad NH \\ CH_3 . C{=\!=}CH \end{array} \quad \xleftarrow{NaOH} \quad \begin{array}{c} CO \\ NH \quad NH \\ CH_3 . C{=\!=}C . COOC_2H_5 \end{array}$$

$$\downarrow{\tiny Cl . CO . (CH_2)_4 . COOC_2H_5}$$

$$\begin{array}{c} CO \\ NH \quad NH \\ CH_3 . C{=\!=}C . CO . (CH_2)_4 . COOC_2H_5 \end{array} \quad \xrightarrow[H_2O]{H_2} \quad \begin{array}{c} CO \\ NH \quad NH \\ CH_3 . CH{-\!-}CH . (CH_2)_5 . COOH \end{array}$$

Another route was used by Bourquin et al.[20]:

$$CH_3 . CO . CHNa . COOC_2H_5 + Br . (CH_2)_5 . COOC_2H_5 \longrightarrow$$

$$CH_3 . CO . CH . (CH_2)_5 . COOC_2H_5 \xrightarrow{KOH} CH_3 . CO . CH_2 . (CH_2)_5 . COOH$$
$$\underset{COOC_2H_5}{|}$$

$$\xrightarrow{C_6H_5 . N_2 . Cl} CH_3 . CO . \underset{\overset{||}{N . NH . C_6H_5}}{C} . (CH_2)_5 . COOH \xrightarrow{H_2} CH_3 . CO . \underset{\overset{|}{NH_2}}{CH} . (CH_2)_5 . COOH$$

$$\xrightarrow{KCNO} \quad \underset{CH_3 . \overset{||}{C}\!\!-\!\!-\!\!CH . (CH_2)_5 . COOH}{\overset{\overset{\displaystyle CO}{\diagup\;\diagdown}}{N\quad NH}} \xrightarrow{H_2} \underset{CH_3 . CH\!\!-\!\!-\!\!CH . (CH_2)_5 . COOH}{\overset{\overset{\displaystyle CO}{\diagup\;\diagdown}}{NH\quad NH}}$$

dl-Nordesthiobiotin was prepared by an analogous series of reactions. Substantially the same method was used by G. Swain,[20a] except that the amino group was introduced by chlorination with sulphuryl chloride, followed by amination with potassium phthalimide.

Although dl-desthiobiotin was active towards Saccharomyces cerevisiae, dl-nordesthiobiotin was not, nor was dl-ψ-desthiobiotin, prepared by the action of Raney nickel on dl-ψ-β-biotin.

According to Rubin et al.[21] synthetic dl-desthiobiotin had half the activity of d-biotin towards S. cerevisiae, but only 0·01 to 0·1 % of the activity of biotin on rats made biotin-deficient by the addition of egg white or succinylsulphathiazole to the diet.

That desthiobiotin is converted by certain organisms into biotin was confirmed by L. H. Leonian and V. G. Lilly,[22] who showed that 12 yeasts and 4 filamentous fungi grown on desthiobiotin converted it into a substance active for L. arabinosus, L. helveticus, Rhizobium trifolii 205 and Sordaria fimicola, all of which are unable to utilise desthiobiotin. S. cerevisiae " old process ", however, when grown in presence of biotin and desthiobiotin, yielded substances with biotin activity for the two Lactobacilli, but not for R. trifolii.

Desthiobiotin had the same activity as biotin for Neurospora crassa, E. coli and Penicillium notatum, 21464 but was inactive for P. chrysogenum 62078.[23] This last organism apparently synthesises desthiobiotin and the addition of pimelic acid increased the amount produced. This gives further support to the view that desthiobiotin is an intermediate in the biosynthesis of biotin. Desthiobiotin could replace biotin as a growth factor for several Clostridia.[24]

The thiourea analogue of desthiobiotin, 5-methyl-2-thio-imidazolidone-4-n-hexoic acid, had a very slight growth-promoting activity towards yeast, and this was completely inhibited by avidin.[25] Towards L. helveticus it showed a low anti-biotin activity in comparison with that of desthiobiotin (page 452).

29   449

α-Isopropyl-5-methyl-2-imidazolidone-4-propionic acid, the structural isomer of desthiobiotin corresponding to Kögl's revised formula for α-biotin (page 412), had neither growth-promoting activity towards *S. cerevisiae* or *L. helveticus* nor anti-biotin activity towards *L. helveticus*.[26]

The higher homologue of desthiobiotin, homodesthiobiotin was synthesised by the following route : [27]

$$C_2H_5OOC . (CH_2)_7 . COCl \xrightarrow{Cd(CH_3)_2} C_2H_5OOC . (CH_2)_7 . CO . CH_3 \xrightarrow{C_2H_5NO_2}$$

$$C_2H_5OOC . (CH_2)_6 . \underset{\substack{\| \\ N . OH}}{C} . CO . CH_3 \xrightarrow{H_2} C_2H_5OOC . (CH_2)_6 . \underset{\substack{| \\ NH_2}}{CH} . CO . CH_3 \xrightarrow{KC}$$

$$CH_3 . C \underset{\substack{| \\ NH}}{=\!\!=} \underset{\substack{| \\ NH}}{\overset{\substack{CO \\ / \ \backslash}}{C}} (CH_2)_6 . COOC_2H_5 \xrightarrow[H_2]{H_2O} CH_3 . \underset{\substack{| \\ NH}}{CH} \!-\!\! \underset{\substack{| \\ NH}}{\overset{\substack{CO \\ / \ \backslash}}{CH}} . (CH_2)_6 . COOH$$

It was devoid of biotin activity when tested on *S. cerevisiae* but had anti-biotin activity (page 452). A method similar to the above was also used for the preparation of desthiobiotin.

Two other homologues of desthiobiotin, 2-imidazolidone-4-*n*-hexoic acid and 5-ethyl-2-imidazolidone-4-*n*-hexoic acid, were also without biotin activity towards *S. cerevisiae* and *L. helveticus*.[28] They antagonised the growth-promoting effect of biotin, however (page 452).

Oxybiotin

Oxybiotin[29] or O-heterobiotin, one of the four possible racemic forms of 2'-keto-imidazolidino-(4' : 5' : 3 : 4)-tetrahydrofuran-2-*n*-valeric acid was synthesised by the route[30] shown on opposite page.

According to Duschinsky *et al.*[31] oxybiotin had 25 % of the growth-promoting activity of *d*-biotin towards *L. helveticus* or *Saccharomyces cerevisiae* and, according to Pilgrim *et al.*,[32, 33] 50 % of the activity of *d*-biotin towards *L. arabinosus*, 40 % towards *L. helveticus*, 15 % towards *Rhizobium trifolii* and 25 and 8 % towards *S. cerevisiae* when compared at half maximal and maximal growth respectively.

Rubin *et al.*[34] found it to have 28 % of the activity of biotin for *S. cerevisiae* (5 strains) and *L. helveticus*, and 50 % for *L. arabinosus*. They also found that it was inactivated by avidin in the same stoichiometric proportions as was biotin, whilst its growth-promoting action on *L. helveticus* was inhibited by desthiobiotin. Oxybiotin could replace biotin as a growth factor for several *Clostridia*,[24] and for *Lactobacillus pentosus*.[24a]

Oxybiotin can be estimated by comparing the growth produced in

$$C_2H_5OOC \quad COOC_2H_5$$
$$C \!\equiv\! C$$
$$+$$
$$CH\!-\!CH$$
$$CH \quad C . (CH_2)_4 . CH_2OH \qquad \longrightarrow$$
$$\diagdown O \diagup$$

$$HOOC \quad COOH$$
$$C\!-\!C$$
$$\| \quad \|$$
$$CH \quad C . (CH_2)_4 . CH_2OH \qquad \longrightarrow$$
$$\diagdown O \diagup$$

$$OC \quad COCl$$
$$C\!-\!C$$
$$\| \quad \|$$
$$CH \quad C . (CH_2)_4 . CH_2OAc \qquad \longrightarrow$$
$$\diagdown O \diagup$$

$$C_2H_5OOC . NH \quad NH . COOC_2H_5$$
$$C\!-\!C$$
$$\| \quad \|$$
$$CH \quad C . (CH_2)_4 . CH_2OH \qquad \longrightarrow$$
$$\diagdown O \diagup$$

$$CO$$
$$NH \quad NH$$
$$C\!-\!C$$
$$H$$
$$CH_2 \quad CH . (CH_2)_4 . CH_2OH \qquad \longrightarrow$$
$$\diagdown O \diagup$$

$$CO$$
$$NH \quad NH$$
$$C\!-\!C$$
$$H \quad H$$
$$CH_2 \quad CH . (CH_2)_4 . COOH$$
$$\diagdown O \diagup$$

cultures of *L. arabinosus* and *S. faecalis*, [35] and subtracting the true biotin content, as indicated by the response of *S. faecalis*, from the apparent biotin content, as indicated by *L. arabinosus*. It can also be estimated by first destroying biotin with Raney nickel, which does not affect oxybiotin and then assaying the solution microbiologically.[36]

Oxybiotin cured egg-white injury in the rat, being 5 to 10 % as effective as *d*-biotin in this respect.[34, 37, 38] It also cured symptoms of biotin deficiency in chicks, having 17 to 33 % of the activity of *d*-biotin.[39, 40] Its activity fell off with increasing dosage, and oxybiotin was found in liver and muscle when large doses were given.[40]

The diamino-carboxylic acid, 3 : 4-diaminotetrahydrofuran-2-valeric acid, from oxybiotin was inactive for *S. cerevisiae* and for *L. arabinosus*.[33] Replacement of the carboxyl group of oxybiotin by a primary alcohol group gave a compound with 1/300 the activity of biotin. Oxybiotin, its methyl ester and the corresponding alcohol combined with avidin in the same molecular proportion as did biotin.[33]

Rubin *et al.*[34] assumed that oxybiotin was converted to biotin or a vitamer of similar activity, but it is now certain that oxybiotin does not owe its activity to conversion into biotin. K. Hofmann and T. Winnick [41] developed a method of estimating oxybiotin by first destroying any biotin present by oxidation with 0·01 N-potassium permanganate, which does not attack oxybiotin, and then testing the solution with yeast for growth-stimulating activity. They were thus able to show that *S. cerevisiae* and *R. trifolii* grown in presence of oxybiotin utilised the compound as such and not after conversion into biotin. Thus the sulphur atom is not essential for biological activity. This conclusion was confirmed by Axelrod *et al.*[42] for *S. cerevisiae*, by K. K. Krueger and W. H. Peterson [24a] for *L. pentosus* and by McCoy *et al.*[42a] for chicks.

epi-Oxybiotin was prepared from the second *cis*-isomer of 3 : 4-diaminotetrahydrofuran-2-valeric acid, but neither of the *trans*-isomers reacted with phosgene, in striking contrast to the corresponding thiophen compounds, all four of which reacted to give cyclic ureides.[42b]

A series of homologues of oxybiotin, in which the side-chain contained two to six methylene groups, were prepared by Hofmann *et al.*[43] None of the compounds had appreciable biotin activity, and none had any anti-biotin activity at a molar inhibition ratio of 500,000. The nor-($n = 3$), homo-($n = 5$) and bishomo-($n = 6$) analogues had anti-oxybiotin activity, however, at ratios of 143,000, 30,000, and 7400 respectively ; the bisnor-($n = 2$) analogue had no activity. With *L. arabinosus*, only the homo-compound had any activity, a ratio of 225,000.

Growth Inhibitors

A number of analogues related to biotin had an inhibitory effect on the growth of certain micro-organisms owing to their ability to compete with biotin for some metabolic process essential for the activity of the cell. Some of these substances functioned as growth promoters under some conditions.

Biotin sulphone, for instance, although a growth factor for yeast (page 447), inhibited the growth of *L. helveticus*, *L. arabinosus* and *Staphylococcus aureus*,[44] 280 moles of the sulphone antagonising 1 mole of biotin.[12] The addition of biotin counteracted the inhibitory effect of the sulphone.

Another substance that behaved both as a growth inhibitor and as a growth promoter was desthiobiotin (page 410). This had a molar inhibition ratio of 200,000 for *S. cerevisiae* and of 1,000,000 for *L. helveticus*.[17, 45] Homodesthiobiotin (page 450) and 5-methyl-2-imidazolidone had no anti-biotin activity,[27] but two other homologues of desthiobiotin, 2-imidazolidone-4-*n*-hexoic acid and 5-ethyl-2-imidazolidone-4-*n*-hexoic acid (page 450) antagonised the activity of biotin.[28] α-Isopropyl-5-methyl-2-imidazolidone-4-propionic acid had no anti-biotin activity,[26] whilst the thiourea analogue of desthiobiotin (page 449) exhibited only a slight growth inhibitory activity.[25]

A series of four imidazolidone aliphatic acids were synthesised by Dittmer *et al.*; [46] these differed from desthiobiotin and its homologues in the absence of the methyl group. These compounds inhibited *S. cerevisiae* and *L. helveticus* and the effect was counteracted by biotin.[47,48] Imidazolidone-*n*-hexoic acid was the most potent, with a molar inhibition ratio of 126,000 for *L. helveticus* and 760,000 for yeast; it also inhibited types II and III pneumococci and *E. coli*. It was much more effective with desthiobiotin as the growth stimulant so that it probably functions by competing with desthiobiotin for an enzyme system that synthesises biotin. The antibacterial index for the competitive inhibition of desthiobiotin by imidazolidone-caproic acid was increased from 100 to 300 by exogenous α-ketoglutaric acid. The significance of this observation has already been discussed (page 443).

Two other potent anti-biotins were γ-(3 : 4-ureylene cyclohexyl)-butyric acid and γ-(2 : 3-ureylene cyclohexyl)-butyric acid, which have a formal resemblance to biotin :

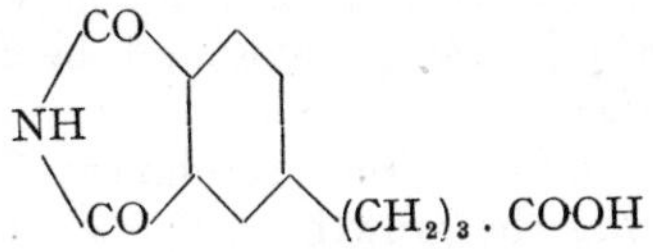

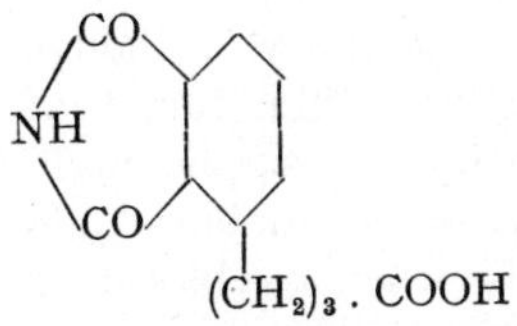

Rather surprisingly the former inhibited *L. helveticus*, but not *S. cerevisiae*, whereas the latter inhibited *S. cerevisiae* but not *L. helveticus*.[49]

γ-(3 : 4-Ureylene cyclohexyl)-butyric acid and also biotin sulphone were more potent antagonists of *dl*-oxybiotin with *L. arabinosus* than of *d*-biotin, for at certain levels the action of oxybiotin was completely counteracted, whereas that of *d*-biotin was scarcely affected.[50]

The following homologues of biotin and their derivatives were found to be antagonistic to biotin both for *S. cerevisiae* 139 and for *L. helveticus*: *dl*-norbiotin, *dl*-homobiotin, *dl*-bishomobiotin and *dl*-tris-homobiotin; *dl*-homobiotin sulphone, *dl*-bis-homobiotin sulphone and *dl*-tris-homobiotin sulphone.[51] Of these, homobiotin was the most potent, being probably the most potent anti-biotin known for *both* micro-organisms.

Some but not all of these compounds also inhibited *L. arabinosus*. With oxybiotin as growth factor, the homologues of biotin were more effective than the sulphones in inhibiting *L. helveticus* and *S. cerevisiae*, but the sulphones were more effective with *L. arabinosus*.[52] Homologues of oxybiotin containing 2, 3, 5 and 6 methylene groups in the side-chain were prepared, and tested as antagonists of biotin and

453

oxybiotin with *S. cerevisiae*, *L. arabinosus* and *Streptococcus haemolyticus* ; most of the compounds were extremely potent with oxybiotin as growth factor, but almost inactive with biotin.[53] Homo-oxybiotin (*n* = 5) had no protective effect on mice infected with *S. hæmolyticus*. The sulphonic acid analogues of oxybiotin and homo-oxybiotin :

$$
\begin{array}{c}
\mathrm{CO} \\
\diagup \; \diagdown \\
\mathrm{NH} \quad \mathrm{NH} \\
| \qquad | \\
\mathrm{CH}\!-\!\mathrm{CH} \\
| \qquad | \\
\mathrm{CH_2} \quad \mathrm{CH} \,.\, \mathrm{(CH_2)}_n \,.\, \mathrm{SO_3H} \\
\diagdown \; \diagup \\
\mathrm{O}
\end{array}
$$

were synthesised by Hofmann *et al.*[53, 54] The *dl*-oxybiotin sulphonic acid and the corresponding thiol and benzylthioether had pronounced antibiotin and anti-oxybiotin activity for a number of micro-organisms. The *dl*-homo-oxybiotin sulphonic acid, however, had slight growth-promoting activity, although the corresponding thiol and benzyl-thioether were inhibitory to *S. cerevisiae*.

4-Methyl-5-(ε-sulphoamyl)-2-imidazolidone, the sulphonic acid analogue of desthiobiotin also inhibited the growth of *S. cerevisiae*, especially when oxybiotin or desthiobiotin was the growth factor ; the compound had no effect on *L. helveticus*.[55]

References to Section 19

1. J. H. Mueller, K. S. Klise, E. F. Porter and A. Graybiel, *J. Bact.*, 1933, **25**, 509 ; J. H. Mueller, *ibid.*, 1935, **29**, 515 ; 1935, **30**, 513 ; J. H. Mueller and I. Kapnick, *ibid.*, 525 ; J. H. Mueller, *ibid.*, 1936, **32**, 207 ; J. H. Mueller and Y. SubbaRow, *ibid.*, 1937, **34**, 153.
2. J. H. Mueller, *Science*, 1937, **85**, 502 ; *J. Biol. Chem.*, 1937, **119**, 124 ; *J. Bact.*, 1937, **34**, 163.
3. W. C. Evans, F. C. Happold and W. R. C. Handley, *Brit. J. Exp. Path.*, 1939, **20**, 41.
4. V. du Vigneaud, K. Dittmer, E. Hague and B. Long, *Science*, 1942, **96**, 186.
5. W. J. Robbins and R. Ma, *ibid.*, 406.
6. J. L. Stokes and M. Gunness, *J. Biol. Chem.*, 1945, **157**, 121.
7. G. A. Emerson, *ibid.*, 127.
8. W. H. Ott, *ibid.*, 131.
8a. M. R. Belcher and H. C. Lichstein, *J. Bact.*, 1949, **58**, 565.
9. L. C. Cheney and J. R. Piening, *J. Amer. Chem. Soc.*, 1945, **67**, 729, 731, 2213.
10. S. R. Safir, S. Bernstein, B. R. Baker, W. L. McEwen and Y. SubbaRow, *J. Org. Chem.*, 1947, **12**, 475.

11. L. C. Cheney and J. R. Piening, *J. Amer. Chem. Soc.*, 1945, **67**, 2252.

12. K. Dittmer and V. du Vigneaud, *Science*, 1944, **100**, 129 ; *Arch. Biochem.*, 1944, **4**, 229.

13. V. du Vigneaud, K. Dittmer, K. Hofmann and D. B. Melville, *Proc. Soc. Exp. Biol. Med.*, 1942, **50**, 374.

14. D. B. Melville, *J. Amer. Chem. Soc.*, 1944, **66**, 1422.

15. D. B. Melville, K. Dittmer, G. B. Brown and V. du Vigneaud, *Science*, 1943, **98**, 497.

16. K. Dittmer, D. B. Melville, V. du Vigneaud, *Proc. Soc. Exp. Biol. Med.*, 1944, **99**, 203 ; *Science*, 1944, **99**, 203.

17. J. L. Wood and V. du Vigneaud, *J. Amer. Chem. Soc.*, 1945, **67**, 210.

18. D. B. Melville, *ibid.*, 1944, **66**, 1422.

19. R. Duschinsky and L. A. Dolan, *ibid.*, 1945, **67**, 2079.

20. J. P. Bourquin, O. Schnider and A. Grüssner, *Helv. Chim. Acta*, 1945, **28**, 528.

20a. G. Swain, *J. Chem. Soc.*, 1948, 1552.

21. S. H. Rubin, L. Drekter and E. H. Moyer, *Proc. Soc. Exp. Biol. Med.*, 1945, **58**, 352.

22. L. H. Leonian and V. G. Lilly, *J. Bact.*, 1945, **49**, 291.

23. E. L. Tatum, *J. Biol. Chem.*, 1945, **160**, 455.

24. D. Perlman, *Arch. Biochem.*, 1948, **16**, 79.

24a. K. K. Krueger and W. H. Peterson, *J. Bact.*, 1948, **55**, 693.

25. G. B. Brown and V. du Vigneaud, *J. Biol. Chem.*, 1946, **163**, 761.

26. G. B. Brown and M. F. Ferger, *J. Amer. Chem. Soc.*, 1946, **68**, 1507.

27. H. McKennis and V. du Vigneaud, *ibid.*, 832.

28. R. Duschinsky and L. A. Dolan, *ibid.*, 2350.

29. K. Hofmann and A. E. Axelrod, *Arch. Biochem.*, 1946, **11**, 375.

30. K. Hofmann, *J. Amer. Chem. Soc.*, 1945, **67**, 1459 ; B. P. 615901, 615908, 615909, 617260.

31. R. Duschinsky, L. A. Dolan, D. Flower and S. H. Rubin, *Arch. Biochem.*, 1945, **6**, 480.

32. F. J. Pilgrim, A. E. Axelrod, T. Winnick and K. Hofmann, *Science*, 1945, **102**, 35.

33. T. Winnick, K. Hofmann, F. J. Pilgrim and A. E. Axelrod, *J. Biol. Chem.*, 1945, **161**, 405.

34. S. H. Rubin, D. Flower, F. Rosen and L. Drekter, *Arch. Biochem.*, 1945, **8**, 79.

35. T. D. Luckey, P. R. Moore and C. A. Elvehjem, *Proc. Soc. Exp. Biol. Med.*, 1946, **61**, 97.

36. K. Hofmann, T. Winnick and A. E. Axelrod, *J. Biol. Chem.*, 1947, **169**, 191.

37. A. E. Axelrod, F. J. Pilgrim and K. Hofmann, *ibid.*, 1946, **163**, 191.

38. K. Hofmann, R. H. McCoy, J. R. Felton, A. E. Axelrod and F. J. Pilgrim, *Arch. Biochem.*, 1945, **7**, 393.

39. R. H. McCoy, J. R. Felton and K. Hofmann, *ibid.*, 1946, **9**, 141.

40. P. R. Moore, T. D. Luckey, C. A. Elvehjem and E. B. Hart, *Proc. Soc. Exp. Biol. Med.*, 1946, **61**, 185.

41. K. Hofmann and T. Winnick, *J. Biol. Chem.*, 1945, **160**, 449.

42. A. E. Axelrod, B. C. Flinn and K. Hofmann, *J. Biol. Chem.*, 1947, **169,** 195.

42a. R. H. McCoy, J. M. McKibbin, A. E. Axelrod and K. Hofmann, *ibid.*, 1949, **176,** 1319, 1327.

42b. K. Hofmann, *J. Amer. Chem. Soc.*, 1949, **71,** 164.

43. K. Hofmann, C. Chen, A. Bridgwater and A. E. Axelrod, *J. Amer. Chem. Soc.*, 1947, **69,** 191.

44. K. Hofmann, D. B. Melville and V. du Vigneaud, *J. Biol. Chem.*, 1941, **141,** 207.

45. V. G. Lilly and L. H. Leonian, *Science*, 1944, **99,** 203.

46. K. Dittmer, M. F. Ferger and V. du Vigneaud, *J. Biol. Chem.*, 1946, **163,** 19.

47. L. L. Rogers and W. Shive, *ibid.*, 1947, **169,** 57.

48. K. Dittmer and V. du Vigneaud, *ibid.*, 63.

49. J. P. English, R. C. Clapp, Q. P. Cole, I. F. Halverstadt, J. O. Lampen and R. O. Roblin, *J. Amer. Chem. Soc.*, 1945, **67,** 295.

50. A. E. Axelrod, J. De Woody and K. Hofmann, *J. Biol. Chem.*, 1946, **163,** 771.

51. M. W. Goldberg, L. H. Sternbach, S. Kaiser, S. D. Heineman, J. Scheiner and S. H. Rubin, *Arch. Biochem.*, 1947, **14,** 480.

52. S. H. Rubin and J. Scheiner, *ibid.*, 1949, **23,** 400.

53. A. E. Axelrod and K. Hofmann, *J. Biol. Chem.*, 1949, **180,** 525.

54. K. Hofmann, A. Bridgwater and A. E. Axelrod, *J. Amer. Chem. Soc.*, 1947, **69,** 1550 ; 1949, **71,** 1253.

55. R. Duschinsky and S. H. Rubin, *ibid.*, 1948, **70,** 2546.

CHAPTER VIII

THE FOLIC ACID COMPLEX

1. INTRODUCTION

Folic Acid

One of the most complicated chapters in the story of the vitamin B complex is that relating to folic acid. When certain fastidious micro-organisms, such as *Lactobacillus helveticus* (frequently referred to, especially in U.S.A., as *L. casei* ϵ) and *Streptococcus faecalis* R (previously called *S. lactis* R), are transferred to a synthetic medium containing, in addition to amino acids, all the members of the vitamin B complex so far discussed, little or no growth occurs. The addition of certain concentrates prepared from natural sources produces optimal growth, however, and folic acid is the name given to one such factor obtained in 1941 from spinach leaves (hence its name) by H. K. Mitchell, E. E. Snell and R. J. Williams.[1]

The two essential steps in the preparation of this substance were adsorption on charcoal and elution of the active principle from the adsorbate by means of aqueous ammonia, steps also used in the preparation of several other growth factors, since shown to be closely related, chemically and biologically, to folic acid. It is convenient, therefore, to discuss all these substances together and refer to them collectively as the folic acid complex.

Norit Eluate Factor or *L. casei* Factor

One of these substances is the factor first called the norit eluate factor and subsequently known as the *L. casei* factor. This was first described by E. E. Snell and W. H. Peterson,[2] who stated that certain lactic acid bacteria, when grown in a medium containing amino acids and all the known growth factors, required in addition two new growth factors isolated from liver, one adsorbed and the other not adsorbed, on norit. They were accordingly distinguished as the norit eluate factor and norit filtrate factor respectively. The former was concentrated by a series of additional steps, giving a product that resembled the naturally occurring purines in several respects.

The best source of the new factor was " solubilised liver ", which was also used by E. L. R. Stokstad[3] in making a somewhat purer preparation (see page 467). This had the properties of a purine-pyrimidine dinucleotide or a mixture of the two mononucleotides, and could be replaced as a growth factor by a mixture of guanine and thymine, although larger amounts of these were required in order to produce the same response (page 513). Compared with the folic acid of Mitchell, Snell and Williams, Snell and Peterson's factor and Stokstad's factor were relatively crude, and this in part accounts for the conclusion reached at the time by Mitchell *et al.* that folic acid was not identical with either of these factors.

The norit eluate factor from liver was still further purified by Hutchings *et al.*[4] who showed that it was essential for the nutrition of the chick, although there was an element of doubt as to the identity of the bacterial and chick factors, as the one preparation was not tested for both types of activity. The method of isolation and the behaviour towards inactivating agents were, however, identical with those reported by earlier workers, and it was subsequently observed [5] that purified preparations of this chick factor not only promoted growth, but also resulted in increased haemoglobin formation and normal feathering of chicks.

The picture then became a trifle confused, following the publication of a paper by E. L. R. Stokstad,[6] describing the preparation of a norit eluate factor from yeast. Although the product stimulated the growth of *L. helveticus* to the same extent as did the liver factor, it had only half the activity of the liver factor towards *S. faecalis* R. Stokstad, therefore, concluded that the two factors were different and suggested that the liver factor might be identical with the vitamin B_c of Pfiffner *et al.*[7] (see page 469). The intimate relationship between the *L. casei* factor (in its various forms) and vitamin B_c received further support from a report [8] that a pure preparation of the norit eluate factor made by fermentation (see page 468) had been found to stimulate the growth of *L. helveticus* and *S. faecalis* R and also to increase the growth rate of chicks. This fermentation product has sometimes been referred to as " the third *L. casei* factor ".

SLR Factor

A fourth factor, described by Keresztesy *et al.*[9], differed from the three *L. casei* factors in being inert towards *L. helveticus* (*L. casei*), although effective in stimulating the growth of *S. lactis* R (*S. faecalis* R). Accordingly it was named the *S. lactis* R factor, abbreviated to SLR factor. Subsequently, Stokes *et al.*[10] found that folic acid could replace the SLR factor for all bacteria that could utilise the latter and that folic acid was produced when *S. faecalis* R was grown on a folic acid-free medium containing the SLR factor. The SLR factor failed to produce folic acid when incubated with rat liver suspensions, however, whereas incubation of the *L. casei* factor with fresh chick liver caused a marked increase in the folic acid content as measured by *S. faecalis* R.[11] The increase was twice as great when pyracin (page 336) was present in the incubation mixture. This action of pyracin is believed to be due either to conjugation with the *L. casei* factor or to its incorporation into an enzyme system that brings about the conversion of the *L. casei* factor to folic acid.

Vitamin B$_c$

A fifth factor, closely related to both folic acid and the three *L. casei* factors, was described in 1939-40 by A. G. Hogan and E. M. Parrott.[12] This was prepared from liver by a process involving adsorption on fuller's earth followed by elution. It was found to correct a hyperchromic macrocytic anaemia in chicks, and, in consequence, was named " vitamin B$_c$ " the suffix indicating its association with the nutrition of the chick. Further purification of vitamin B$_c$ was effected by A. G. Hogan and his colleagues,[13] who pointed out that the factor had properties very similar to those of the liver *L. casei* factor. Isolation of the pure factor [14] and a comparison of its properties with those of the *L. casei* factor confirmed this close relationship. Moreover, crystalline vitamin B$_c$[15] maintained normal growth and feathering in chicks in addition to preventing the development of a macrocytic hyperchromic anaemia, leucopenia and thrombocytopenia, whilst the purified folic acid of H. K. Mitchell and R. J. Williams [16] also stimulated the growth of chicks.

Further work on vitamin B$_c$, however, revealed a state of affairs comparable with that obtaining in the case of the *L. casei* factor, vitamin B$_c$ concentrates differing in their biological activities according to whether they were produced from liver or from yeast. Binkley *et al.*,[17] for example, found that vitamin B$_c$ concentrates prepared from yeast almost completely failed to stimulate the growth of *L. helveticus*, but they became highly active following enzymatic digestion ; from such digests a crystalline compound was isolated that stimulated the growth of both *L. helveticus* and *S. faecalis* R and also cured the anaemia and increased the growth rate of chicks. They accordingly reserved the name vitamin B$_c$ for the liver factor, and gave the name vitamin B$_c$ conjugate to the factor present in yeast.

Later, this same group of workers reported [18] the isolation of vitamin B$_c$ conjugate in crystalline form and confirmed its ineffectiveness as a growth factor for *L. helveticus* and *S. faecalis* R and its ability to cure a nutritional macrocytic anaemia in chicks. After digestion with an enzyme preparation made from hog kidney, the crystalline factor, like the crude factor previously described, yielded microbiologically active vitamin B_c. K. K. Krueger and W. H. Peterson,[19] on the other hand, reported that vitamin B_c concentrates prepared from yeast were just as active towards *L. helveticus* and *S. faecalis* R as were similar preparations from liver.

O. D. Bird and M. Robbins [20] also found that both micro-organisms responded to vitamin B_c conjugate, although *L. helveticus* responded in an abnormal manner, not only to crude preparations of vitamin B_c and the conjugate, but also to the crystalline conjugate. The divergence from the standard curve was in fact particularly noticeable with the latter. After incubation with vitamin B_c conjugase (see page 479), all the preparations gave a response corresponding closely to that of the standard. With *S. faecalis* R the response fell almost on the standard curve even without incubation with vitamin B_c conjugase.

It was not unreasonable, therefore, on the basis of this evidence to suppose that folic acid, the three *L. casei* factors, the SLR factor and vitamin B_c and its conjugate were very closely related. Unfortunately, however, several other growth factors under investigation at about the same time also appeared to be closely related to the seven factors so far discussed, and it became difficult to determine the relationships of all these factors to one another.

Other Chick Factors

Other factors that appeared to be related in some way to the folic acid complex were the factor U of E. L. R. Stokstad and P. D. V. Manning,[21] factors R and S of A. E. Schumacher, G. F. Heuser and L. C. Norris,[22] and vitamins B_{10} and B_{11} of Briggs *et al.*[23] (see also page 614).

The guinea-pig factor, factor GPF 1, of D. W. Woolley and H. Sprince [24] also appeared to be closely related to the group.

Vitamin M and Xanthopterine

In 1932, L. Wills and H. S. Bilimoria [25] showed that monkeys developed anaemia, leucopenia and granulocytopenia when maintained on a diet similar to that associated with human tropical macrocytic anaemia in India. The anaemic monkeys were cured by administration of a yeast extract. Similar results were obtained by Langston *et al.*,[26] who also showed that the leucopenia and granulocytopenia were relieved by concentrates prepared from either liver or yeast ; they termed the responsible factor, vitamin M.

A year previously, R. Tschesche and R. J. Wolf [27] had reported that an anaemia induced in rats by the feeding of goats' milk could be cured by administration of xanthopterine, the yellow pigment isolated by C. Schöpf and E. Becker [28] from the wings of the brimstone butterfly (*Gonepteryx rhamni*) and, in 1941, R. W. Simmons and E. R. Norris [29] showed that both synthetic xanthopterine and xanthopterine isolated from liver could cure an anaemia observed in Chinook salmon. J. R. Totter and P. L. Day,[30] therefore, tested xanthopterine in anaemic monkeys and found that, whilst it relieved the blood changes in nutritional cytopenia, it failed to cure the other manifestations of vitamin M deficiency. They also claimed that xanthopterine cured the leucopenia and increased the growth rate of sulphasuxidine-treated rats, but this claim was not substantiated by the work of B. Ransone and C. A. Elvehjem [31] or of Day *et al.*[32]

Although xanthopterine had a definite beneficial effect on vitamin M-deficient monkeys, the effect of folic acid was even more striking,[33] the growth rate being increased and the leucopenia and granulocytopenia relieved. The loss of hair (alopecia) was not, however, remedied by folic acid, whereas biotin cured this condition but did not affect the blood picture. Pantothenic acid, choline, *p*-aminobenzoic acid, pyridoxine and inositol were without appreciable effect in vitamin M deficiency, but a highly purified sample of the *L. casei* factor relieved the granulocytopenia in this condition.[34] Folic acid also cured fish anaemia,[35] although it had only one-fifth the activity of xanthopterine. On the other hand, xanthopterine failed to cure anaemic vitamin B_c-deficient chicks.[36]

These data suggested that vitamin M was closely related to folic acid, vitamin B_c and the *L. casei* factors and possibly identical with one of them, whereas xanthopterine was a simpler type of substance altogether and an inadequate substitute for these factors in the treatment of vitamin M-deficient monkeys.

An objection to the hypothesis that folic acid might be identical with vitamin M was that the folic acid contents of various substances, as determined by the original microbiological method of assay using *L. helveticus* and *S. faecalis* R, completely failed to account for the vitamin M activities of the same substances when tested on monkeys. Totter *et al.*,[37] following up an observation of L. D. Wright and A. D. Welch [38] that fresh rat liver could synthesise folic acid from xanthopterine, incubated a preparation of brewers' yeast with fresh rat liver, fresh chicken liver and liver from a vitamin M-deficient monkey. On assaying the digests with *S. faecalis* R, they obtained a 15-fold or even larger increase in the folic acid content.

When synthetic xanthopterine was incubated with the liver preparations in the same way, considerable amounts of folic acid were found to have been produced, except in the case of chicken liver. These results appeared to indicate that yeast contained a precursor, which liver tissue could convert into folic acid, and that the amount

461

of potential rather than actual folic acid in a substance was a measure of its vitamin M activity. They also seemed to suggest that xanthopterine might be a precursor of vitamin M, although Wright et al.[39] offered another suggestion, namely, that free folic acid in rat liver was converted by liver enzymes into a substance having little or no microbiological activity and that the reaction was inhibited by xanthopterine. Although, on the basis of their experimental data, they could not exclude the possibility that folic acid might be synthesised from xanthopterine, they favoured the hypothesis of a metabolite-antimetabolite relationship.

That vitamin M is simply free plus combined folic acid appears to be a valid conclusion from the most recent paper on vitamin M deficiency, in which Day et al.[40] reported that intramuscular injection of a highly purified *L. casei* factor, which was relatively inert towards *S. faecalis* R, cured both the anaemia and leucopenia of vitamin M-deficient monkeys in a total dose of 3 mg. given over several days ; prompt remission of the blood dyscrasia and a dramatic improvement in the clinical condition of the animals occurred. Xanthopterine was only slightly active when given orally, and was inactive by injection, again suggesting that it might serve as a precursor of vitamin M. The *L. casei* factor became as active as a standard vitamin B_c preparation in stimulating *S. faecalis* R after treatment with vitamin B_c conjugase (page 479).

Anti-sulphonamide Factor

Totter and Day's unconfirmed observation on the effect of xanthopterine on sulphasuxidine-treated rats, although misleading at the time, served a useful purpose in directing attention to the close analogy between the effects of vitamin M deficiency in monkeys and sulphonamide administration in rats. Thus, although the response of sulphasuxidine-treated rats to xanthopterine was suspect, the response to folic acid was definite, and both G. J. Martin [41] and C. A. Elvehjem and his colleagues [42] found that folic acid plus biotin cured the symptoms caused by administration of sulphasuxidine to rats.

Pantothenic acid, inositol and *p*-aminobenzoic acid have at various times been claimed to cure the achromotrichia (greying of hair) and alopecia (loss of hair) resulting from the administration of sulphonamides, but the response to the combined effect of folic acid and biotin was more striking than any obtained with the other vitamins.

The results obtained by Martin and by Elvehjem and his colleagues were confirmed by F. S. Daft and W. H. Sebrell,[43] who found that crystalline folic acid cured the leucopenia and granulocytopenia caused by feeding sulphonamides to rats, whilst A. D. Welch and L. D. Wright [44] showed that the increase in prothrombin time caused by administration of sulphasuxidine was overcome by feeding a mixture of folic acid and biotin and, to a smaller extent, by giving each factor separately. This result strongly supports the view that the effect of folic acid and biotin is to stimulate bacterial growth in the intestine (page 487) ; the bacteria synthesise vitamin K as well as vitamin B factors. It is the reduction in vitamin K synthesis, of course, that results in the increased prothrombin time.

Mallory *et al.*,[45] in view of the similarity in behaviour of an enzymatic digest of yeast and of a liver extract on the growth and white blood cell counts of sulphasuxidine-treated rats, also favoured the hypothesis that the factor antagonistic to the effects of sulphonamides in rats was identical with vitamin M.

Further work confirmed the ability of various forms of folic acid to reverse the effects of sulphonamide treatment, and also indicated that this effect was probably due to stimulation of the growth of intestinal bacteria (page 487).

From this somewhat lengthy discussion of the biological properties of folic acid, the *L. casei* factors, the SLR factor, vitamin B_c, vitamin M, the anti-sulphonamide factor and xanthopterine, the general conclusion must be that all these factors are in some way related to one another and, although some may be identical, the differences are sufficiently marked in other instances to lead one to believe that they are not all identical. In the ultimate, the only real test of identity is an examination of the chemical properties of the pure substances themselves. These have recently been made available and the constitution of several of the factors has been determined and some of them have been synthesised.

The first announcement that the constitution of the *L. casei* factor had been determined and its synthesis accomplished was made by Angier *et al.*[46] Unfortunately, the note merely reported the synthesis of a compound identical with the *L. casei* factor of liver, and stated that it stimulated the growth of *L. helveticus* and *S. faecalis* R, and promoted growth and haemoglobin formation in the chick. Not until nearly twelve months later did Angier *et al.*[47] disclose the chemical constitution of the *L. casei* factor and the method of synthesis. The formula assigned to the liver *L. casei* factor was :

The systematic name of this substance is N-[4-{[(2-amino-4-hydroxy-6-pteridyl-)-methyl]-amino}-benzoyl]-glutamic acid. Fermentation *L. casei* factor, which was found to contain three glutamic acid residues, was converted into the racemic form of the liver *L. casei* factor by anaerobic alkaline hydrolysis. The name of the liver factor was abbreviated to pteroyl-glutamic acid, pteroic acid being the short name for 4-{[(2-amino-4-hydroxy-6-pteridyl)-methyl]-amino}-benzoic acid. The latter was synthesised by a method similar to that used for the synthesis of the *L. casei* factor (see page 474), and was found to be active for *S. faecalis* R, but inactive for *L. helveticus* and the chick. Its biological activity thus resembled that of the SLR factor, although the two are not identical (page 473). The fermentation *L. casei* factor, containing three glutamic acid residues, was given the name pteroyldiglutamylglutamic acid or, more briefly if less accurately, pteroyltriglutamic acid, whilst yeast vitamin B$_c$ conjugate, which contained seven glutamic acid residues,[48] was called pteroylhexaglutamylglutamic acid or pteroylheptaglutamic acid.

The heptaglutamate was essentially inactive on micro-organisms whereas the triglutamate was active. Since vitamin B$_c$ conjugase converted the conjugate into vitamin B$_c$, it must be classified as a peptidase and, since it did not liberate vitamin B$_c$ from the methyl ester of the conjugate, it must be a carboxypeptidase. Finally, since it liberated glutamic acid from *p*-aminobenzoyl-*γ*-glutamyl-*γ*-glutamylglutamic acid, from synthetic pteroyltriglutamate and from the natural fermentation factor, but not more than 1 molecular equivalent in each instance, it must be classified as a *γ*-glutamic acid carboxypeptidase, requiring at least two terminal glutamic acid molecules in a peptide chain.[49]

The constitution of folic acid itself has not been conclusively settled, as it has not been isolated in the pure state. According to D. A. Hall,[50] however, a folic acid concentrate prepared from spinach exerted a synergistic action on synthetic pteroylglutamic acid, so that folic acid cannot be identical with pteroylglutamic acid. Synergism was similarly observed between pteroylglutamic acid and a concentrate prepared from poppy-straw, but not a similar concentrate from liver. This is taken to indicate that " folic acid " from vegetable sources is different from " folic acid " of animal origin.

References to Section 1

1. H. K. Mitchell, E. E. Snell and R. J. Williams, *J. Amer. Chem. Soc.*, 1941, **63**, 2284.
2. E. E. Snell and W. H. Peterson, *J. Biol. Chem.*, 1939, **128**, xciv ; *J. Bact.*, 1940, **36**, 273.
3. E. L. R. Stokstad, *J. Biol. Chem.*, 1941, **139**, 475.

4. B. L. Hutchings, N. Bohonos, D. M. Hegsted, C. A. Elvehjem and W. H. Peterson, *ibid.*, 1941, **140**, 681 ; B. L. Hutchings, N. Bohonos and W. H. Peterson, *ibid.*, 1941, **141**, 521.

5. R. C. Mills, G. M. Briggs, C. A. Elvehjem and E. B. Hart, *Proc. Soc. Exp. Biol. Med.*, 1942, **49**, 186.

6. E. L. R. Stokstad, *J. Biol. Chem.*, 1943, **149**, 573.

7. J. J. Pfiffner, S. B. Binkley, E. S. Bloom, R. A. Brown, O. D. Bird, A. D. Emmett, A. G. Hogan and B. L. O'Dell, *Science*, 1943, **97**, 404.

8. B. L. Hutchings, E. L. R. Stokstad, N. Bohonos and N. H. Slobodkin, *ibid.*, 1944, **99**, 371.

9. J. C. Keresztesy, E. L. Rickes and J. L. Stokes, *ibid.*, 1943, **97**, 465.

10. J. L. Stokes, J. C. Keresztesy and J. W. Foster, *ibid.*, 1944, **100**, 522.

11. L. J. Daniel, M. L. Scott, L. C. Norris and G. F. Heuser, *J. Biol. Chem.*, 1945, **160**, 265.

12. A. G. Hogan and E. M. Parrott, *ibid.*, 1938, **128**, xlvi ; 1940, **132**, 507.

13. L. R. Richardson, A. G. Hogan and R. J. Karrasch, *J. Nutrition*, 1942, **24**, 65 ; B. L. O'Dell and A. G. Hogan, *J. Biol. Chem.*, 1943, **149**, 323.

14. J. J. Pfiffner, S. B. Binkley, E. S. Bloom, R. A. Brown, O. D. Bird, A. D. Emmett, A. G. Hogan and B. L. O'Dell, *Science*, 1943, **97**, 404.

15. C. J. Campbell, R. A. Brown and A. D. Emmett, *J. Biol. Chem.*, 1944, **152**, 483.

16. H. K. Mitchell and R. J. Williams, *J. Amer. Chem. Soc.*, 1944, **66**, 271.

17. S. B. Binkley, O. D. Bird, E. S. Bloom, R. A. Brown, D. G. Calkins, C. J. Campbell, A. D. Emmett and J. J. Pfiffner, *Science*, 1944, **100**, 36.

18. J. J. Pfiffner, D. G. Calkins, B. L. O'Dell, E. S. Bloom, R. A. Brown, C. J. Campbell and O. D. Bird, *ibid.*, 1945, **102**, 228.

19. K. K. Krueger and W. H. Peterson, *J. Biol. Chem.*, 1945, **158**, 145.

20. O. D. Bird and M. Robbins, *ibid.*, 1946, **163**, 661.

21. E. L. R. Stokstad and P. D. V. Manning, *ibid.*, 1938, **125**, 687.

22. A. E. Schumacher, G. F. Heuser and L. C. Norris, *ibid.*, 1940, **135**, 313.

23. G. M. Briggs, T. D. Luckey, C. A. Elvehjem and E. B. Hart, *ibid.*, 1943, **148**, 163.

24. D. W. Woolley and H. Sprince, *ibid.*, 1944, **153**, 687.

25. L. Wills and H. S. Bilimoria, *Indian J. Med. Res.*, 1932, **20**, 391.

26. W. C. Langston, W. J. Darby, C. F. Shukers and P. L. Day, *J. Exp. Med.*, 1938, **68**, 923.

27. R. Tschesche and R. J. Wolf, *Z. physiol. Chem.*, 1937, **248**, 34.

28. C. Schöpf and E. Becker, *Annalen*, 1936, **524**, 49, 124.

29. R. W. Simmons and E. R. Norris, *J. Biol. Chem.*, 1941, **140**, 679 ; 1945, **158**, 449.

30. J. R. Totter and P. L. Day, *J. Biol. Chem.*, 1943, **147,** 257.
31. B. Ransone and C. A. Elvehjem, *ibid.*, 1943, **151,** 109.
32. H. G. Day, K. G. Wakim, W. H. Zimmerman and L. S. McClung, *J. Nutrition*, 1946, **31,** 355.
33. H. A. Waisman and C. A. Elvehjem, *ibid.*, 1943, **26,** 361 ; S. Saslaw, H. E. Wilson, C. A. Doan and J. L. Schwab, *Science*, 1943, **97,** 514 ; J. R. Totter, C. F. Shukers, J. Kolson, V. Mims and P. L. Day, *Fed. Proc.*, 1943, **2,** 72 ; *J. Biol. Chem.*, 1944, **152,** 147.
34. P. L. Day, V. Mims, J. R. Totter, E. L. R. Stokstad, B. L. Hutchings and N. H. Sloane, *ibid.*, 1945, **157,** 423.
35. H. K. Mitchell and R. J. Williams, *J. Amer. Chem. Soc.*, 1944, **66,** 271.
36. B. L. O'Dell and A. G. Hogan, *J. Biol. Chem.*, 1943, **149,** 323.
37. J. R. Totter, V. Mims and P. L. Day, *Science*, 1944, **100,** 223.
38. L. D. Wright and A. D. Welch, *ibid.*, 1943, **98,** 179.
39. L. D. Wright, H. R. Skeggs and A. D. Welch, *Fed. Proc.*, 1944, **3,** 88.
40. P. L. Day, V. Mims and R. J. Totter, *J. Biol. Chem.*, 1945, **161,** 45.
41. G. J. Martin, *Proc. Soc. Exp. Biol. Med.*, 1942, **51,** 353.
42. E. Nielsen and C. A. Elvehjem, *J. Biol. Chem.*, 1942, **145,** 713 ; B. Ransone and C. A. Elvehjem, *ibid.*, 1943, **151,** 109.
43. F. S. Daft and W. H. Sebrell, *U.S. Publ. Health Rep.*, 1943, **58,** 1542.
44. A. D. Welch and L. D. Wright, *J. Nutrition*, 1943, **25,** 555.
45. M. E. Mallory, V. Mims, R. J. Totter and P. L. Day, *J. Biol. Chem.*, 1944, **156,** 317.
46. R. B. Angier, J. H. Boothe, B. L. Hutchings, J. H. Mowat, J. Semb, E. L. R. Stokstad, Y. SubbaRow, C. W. Waller, D. B. Cosulich, M. J. Fahrenbach, M. E. Hultquist, E. Kuh, E. H. Northey, D. R. Seeger, J. P. Sickels and J. M. Smith, *Science*, 1945, **102,** 227.
47. R. B. Angier, J. H. Boothe, B. L. Hutchings, J. H. Mowat, J. Semb, E. L. R. Stokstad, Y. SubbaRow, C. W. Waller, D. B. Cosulich, M. J. Fahrenbach, M. E. Hultquist, E. Kuh, E. H. Northey, D. R. Seeger, J. P. Sickels and J. M. Smith, *ibid.*, 1946, **103,** 667.
48. J. J. Pfiffner, D. G. Calkins, E. S. Bloom and B. L. O'Dell, *J. Amer. Chem. Soc.*, 1946, **68,** 1392.
49. A. Kazenko and M. Laskowski, *J. Biol. Chem.*, 1948, **173,** 217.
50. D. A. Hall, *Biochem. J.*, 1947, **41,** 287.

2. ISOLATION OF FOLIC ACID

A feature common to the isolation of all the factors comprising the folic acid complex is that all are adsorbed on charcoal and eluted more or less completely by aqueous or alcoholic ammonia.

Folic Acid

Folic acid was prepared from spinach leaves by H. K. Mitchell, E. E. Snell and R. J. Williams,[1] and purified to such an extent that the product was 137,000 times as active as a standard material (Wilson liver fraction B). The spinach was extracted with water, acidified to about pH 3 and the extract stirred with charcoal and filtered. The adsorbate was eluted with hot 2·8 % ammonia and the eluate re-adsorbed on charcoal. The second adsorbate was eluted with hot aqueous aniline, and the adsorption and elution repeated once more. The activity in the final eluate was precipitated first with lead acetate and then with ammoniacal silver nitrate solution, the precipitates being regenerated with ammonium sulphate and ammonium chloride respectively. The solution from the silver regeneration was adsorbed on fuller's earth and the adsorbate eluted with 5 % ammonia. Further purification was effected by fractional elution from ammonia and by precipitation of the acid from a concentrated solution of the ammonium salt.

Quantitative studies of the adsorption of folic acid on charcoal were described by Frieden et al.[2] They observed that folic acid was more easily eluted from adsorbates made from crude preparations than from adsorbates from relatively pure solutions. This difference is attributed to the presence in the cruder solutions of interfering substances that reduce the adsorption affinity of the charcoal for folic acid.

The *L. casei* Factors

The method used by E. E. Snell and W. H. Peterson[3] for the isolation of the norit eluate factor from " solubilised liver " was as follows : The extract was diluted 20-fold with water, the pH adjusted to 3·0 with sulphuric acid and the liquor filtered and stirred with norit. The adsorbate, after being washed with water, was stirred with 50 % ethanol, filtered and then eluted three times with a mixture of pyridine-ethanol water (1 : 2 : 1). In a modification of the method, elution was carried out with 2 % aqueous ammonia. Further purification was achieved by evaporating the eluate to dryness, dissolving the residue in water and precipitating with picric acid. The picrate fraction, which was insoluble in water and ether but soluble in alcohol, contained the bulk of the activity. Considerable losses attended this procedure.

A somewhat similar method was used by E. L. R. Stokstad.[4] " Solubilised liver " was adsorbed on norit and the adsorbate was eluted with 0·5 N-ammonia in 70 % methanol. Final purification was effected by fractionally precipitating the manganese salt of the factor with methanol. No further purification was effected by pre-cipitation with heavy metals or by fractional precipitation from a concentrated aqueous solution.

The method used in isolating the pure crystalline liver *L. casei* factor was described in detail by Stokstad *et al.*[5] A liver extract, prepared by precipitating an aqueous extract of liver with alcohol, was used as the starting material. It was adjusted to pH 8·5 and heated to coagulate impurities, and the filtrate was acidified to pH 3 and stirred with norit. The adsorbate was eluted with 0·5 N-ammonia in 60 % ethanol at 70° C., and the eluate was acidified to pH 1·3 and adsorbed on a column of Superfiltrol, which was eluted with 0·5 N-ammonia in 60 % ethanol. The eluate was concentrated and neutral-ised to pH 7·0, and the *L. casei* factor was precipitated as the barium salt by adding alcohol and barium chloride. The barium salt was dissolved in 0·2 N-methanolic hydrogen chloride, and the solution left at 25° C. for an hour to convert the factor into its methyl ester. The mixture was evaporated to dryness, the residue was dissolved in water, acidified to pH 6 to 7 and extracted with *n*-butanol. The solution was chromatographed on a column of Superfiltrol, which was washed with 92·5 % acetone and then eluted with 75 % acetone. The ester was precipitated several times from hot aqueous methanol un-til pure, and then hydrolysed with alkali to give the pure *L. casei* factor.

The fermentation *L. casei* factor was produced by aerobic fermen-tation with an unidentified bacterium belonging to the genus *Coryne-bacterium*. The fermentation liquor, which contained 3 to 5 μg. per ml.,[6] was acidified to pH 3·0 and stirred with norit. The adsorbate was washed with water and 50 % ethanol and eluted with aqueous alcoholic ammonia at 70° C. The eluate was neutralised and the barium salt of the *L. casei* factor was precipitated by adding alcohol and barium chloride solution. The barium salt was dissolved in methanolic hydrogen chloride and allowed to stand in order to convert the factor into its methyl ester. The mixture was neutralised and evaporated to dryness and the residue dissolved in water. The solution was extracted with *n*-butanol, and the extract evaporated to dryness. The residue was dissolved in hot methanol and precipitated by cooling, the process being repeated with modifications several times until pure. The purified ester was then hydrolysed with baryta solution and the hydrolysate treated with Florisil to remove impurities, and then with barium chloride and alcohol to precipitate the barium salt of the factor. This was dissolved in water, hydrochloric acid was added, and the solution was cooled to 0° C. The precipitate was re-dissolved in acidulated water containing a little calcium or sodium chloride and the solution was cooled, giving a crystalline precipitate of the pure *L. casei* factor.

Vitamin B_c and Vitamin B_c Conjugate

Vitamin B$_c$ was isolated from beef liver by the following procedure.[7] An extract was made with acidulated water and, after concentration, alcohol was added to 50 % by volume and filtered. The precipitate was washed with 50 % alcohol and the combined filtrate and washings were concentrated to a syrup. This was re-dissolved in water, acidified to pH 1 and stirred with fuller's earth. The adsorbate was eluted with 0·2 N-ammonium hydroxide and the eluate concentrated, acidified to pH 1 and stirred with Superfiltrol. The adsorbate was eluted with 1 % ammonia in 50 % alcohol and the eluate concentrated. Various purification procedures were tried out at this point, *e.g.*, norit adsorption at pH 3 and elution with 10% ammonia ; adsorption at pH 4·3 on Amberlite IR4 and elution with 10% ammonia ; and precipitation with barium hydroxide, zinc sulphate or phosphotungstic acid. The last method was the only one that gave a sufficient degree of purification together with a sufficiently high recovery to be of value.

The method used by Pfiffner *et al.*[8] for the isolation of vitamin B$_o$ (pteroylglutamic acid) from hog liver was as follows : The autolysed tissue was extracted with hot water, the extract was concentrated under reduced pressure and filtered through a column of Amberlite IR4. The adsorbate was eluted with aqueous ammonia, and the eluate concentrated and stirred with Superfiltrol. This adsorbate was eluted with aqueous alcoholic ammonia, and the eluate concentrated and stirred with norit. This third adsorbate was also eluted with aqueous alcoholic ammonia and the adsorption on norit and elution then repeated. The final concentrate was extracted first at pH 5·6 with butanol and the extract discarded and then at pH 3. This second extract, which contained the activity, was evaporated and the resulting solid was extracted four times with boiling 90 % methanol. The combined extracts were treated with baryta, and the insoluble barium salts were filtered off. The water-soluble barium salts were then precipitated by the addition of zinc acetate and the precipitate decomposed with ammonium oxalate. The zinc oxalate was filtered off and the filtrate was acidified to pH 2·8 when the crude vitamin separated out. It was leached out with baryta and re-precipitated by acidifying the solution to pH 2·8. It was then crystallised from hot water.

One process was simplified by esterifying the crude zinc salt with methanolic hydrogen chloride and precipitating the methyl ester by adjusting the concentrated solution to pH 3.

Horse liver was found to be a much richer source of vitamin B$_c$ than was hog liver and, using this as the starting material, the process could be still further simplified by omitting the butanol extraction and the precipitation of the barium salts from methanol.

One process used for the isolation of vitamin B_c conjugate from yeast was as follows : [8] A plasmolysed extract of brewers' yeast was dissolved in warm water and the liquor acidified to pH 3 and filtered. The filtrate was stirred with norit, and the adsorbate was eluted with hot aqueous alcoholic ammonia. The eluate was concentrated and re-adsorbed on norit and the adsorbate eluted as before. The concentrated eluate was extracted at pH 5·5 to 6 with butanol, the extract discarded, and the aqueous solution re-extracted at pH 3. The activity remaining in the aqueous solution was due almost entirely to vitamin B_c conjugate, the solution having scarcely any activity towards *L. helveticus* or *S. faecalis*. It was converted by digestion with hog kidney into vitamin B_c, which was isolated by the procedure described above.

Another method used to prepare vitamin B_c conjugate [8a] was to percolate dried brewers' yeast with 60 % alcohol, which extracted inert material, and then to percolate with slightly acid 45 to 50 % alcohol, which extracted the conjugate. A further quantity of inert material was removed from the extract by addition of alcohol to a concentration of 70 % and adjusting the pH to 3 ; the conjugate was then precipitated by adjusting the pH of the filtrate to 5·5 to 6·0.

SLR Factor

The best source of the SLR factor was the liquor from *Rhizopus nigricans* fumaric acid fermentations.[9] The factor was isolated by adsorption on charcoal, elution, chromatographic purification and crystallisation. It was shown to be a pterine for which the name rhizopterine was proposed.

Xanthopterine

Xanthopterine was isolated from a liver extract [10] by precipitation with silver hydroxide and silver nitrate, regeneration with hydrochloric acid, adsorption on fuller's earth, elution with 20 % pyridine, evaporation to dryness, precipitation of the barium salt, and regeneration with hydrochloric acid and sodium carbonate.

References to Section 2

1. H. K. Mitchell, E. E. Snell and R. J. Williams, *J. Amer. Chem. Soc.*, 1941, **63**, 2284 ; 1944, **66**, 267.
2. E. H. Frieden, H. K. Mitchell and R. J. Williams, *ibid.*, 269.
3. E. E. Snell and W. H. Peterson, *J. Bact.*, 1940, **36**, 273.
4. E. L. R. Stokstad, *J. Biol. Chem.*, 1941, **139**, 475.

5. E. L. R. Stokstad, B. L. Hutchings and Y. SubbaRow, *Ann. N.Y. Acad. Sci.*, 1946, **48**, 261 ; *J. Amer. Chem. Soc.*, 1948, **70**, 3.

6. B. L. Hutchings, E. L. R. Stokstad, N. Bohonos, N. H. Sloane, and Y. SubbaRow, *Ann. N.Y. Acad. Sci.*, 1946, **48**, 265 ; *J. Amer. Chem. Soc.*, 1948, **70**, 1.

7. B. L. O'Dell and A. G. Hogan, *J. Biol. Chem.*, 1943, **149**, 323.

8. J. J. Pfiffner, S. B. Binkley, E. S. Bloom and B. L. O'Dell, *J. Amer. Chem. Soc.*, 1947, **69**, 1476.

8a. R. D. Greene, *J. Biol. Chem.*, 1949, **179**, 1075.

9. E. L. Rickes, L. Chaiet and J. C. Keresztesy, *J. Amer. Chem. Soc.*, 1947, **69**, 2749.

10. R. W. Simmons and E. R. Norris, *J. Biol. Chem.*, 1941, **140**, 679.

3. CHEMICAL CONSTITUTION OF FOLIC ACID

L. casei Factors

The first formula to be assigned to a member of the folic acid group was that given by Angier et al.[1] to the liver *L. casei* factor (see page 463). This formula was based on the following evidence.[1, 2, 3, 4] The fermentation *L. casei* factor on anaerobic alkaline hydrolysis was converted into the *dl*-form of the liver *L. casei* factor, the activity towards *L. helveticus* (*L. casei*) decreasing and the activity towards *S. faecalis* R increasing markedly. At the same time, two moles of *d*-amino acid were liberated. When the fermentation factor was hydrolysed under aerobic alkaline conditions, rapid inactivation occurred and two fractions were formed in equimolar amounts ; the first was highly fluorescent, whilst the second gave a positive test for an aromatic amine.

The fluorescent compound was a dibasic acid, $C_7H_5N_5O_3$, which on heating lost carbon dioxide to give a monobasic acid. Oxidation of the fluorescent compound with chlorine water, followed by hydrolysis with 0·1 N-hydrochloric acid, resulted in the formation of guanidine. This fact, together with the ultra-violet absorption spectrum, fluorescence and other properties, suggested the presence of a 2-amino-pteridine derivative containing a hydroxyl and a carboxyl group.

The compound was shown to be 2-amino-4-hydroxypteridine-6-carboxylic acid by comparison with a synthetic specimen, prepared by the chlorination with phosphorus pentachloride of 2-amino-4 : 7-dihydroxypteridine-6-carboxylic acid,[5] followed by reduction with hydrogen iodide. The position of the unchanged hydroxyl group was established by decarboxylation and identification of the product as 2-amino-4-hydroxy-pteridine by comparison with a specimen synthesised from 2 : 4 : 5 : triamino-6-hydroxy-pyrimidine and glyoxal.

The aromatic amine fraction on acid hydrolysis yielded p-aminobenzoic acid and an α-amino acid, subsequently identified as glutamic acid. Microbiological assay indicated that three moles of the latter were liberated from each mole of amine.

When the fermentation L. *casei* factor was treated with sulphurous acid, a pteridine fraction and an aromatic amine were formed. The former contained a carbonyl group and, on standing in dilute alkali solution in the absence of air, underwent a type of Cannizzaro reaction, yielding 2-amino-4-hydroxypteridine-6-carboxylic acid and 2-amino-4-hydroxy-6-methyl-pteridine. The latter was identified by comparison with a sample prepared by decarboxylation of 2-amino-4-hydroxy-6-pteridine-acetic acid, which in turn was prepared from 2 : 4 : 5-triamino-6-hydroxy-pyrimidine and methyl $\gamma\gamma$-dimethoxyacetoacetate.

Final proof that the methyl group of 2-amino-4-hydroxy-6-methyl-pteridine was in the 6-position was obtained by degradation of the compound to 2-amino-5-methylpyrazine by the method of J. Weijlard *et al.*[6]

The liberation of the aromatic amine and the pteridine moiety indicated that the latter was attached to the amino group of p-aminobenzoic acid. The necessity for oxygen in the alkaline cleavage of the L. *casei* factor, with other considerations, suggested the presence of a methylene group, and this view was supported by the fact that cleavage of N-benzyl-p-aminobenzoic acid with alkali was accelerated by the presence of oxygen.

Proof of the above structure for the liver L. *casei* factor was obtained by synthesis (see page 474).

The evidence so far discussed throws no light on the manner in which the three glutamic acid residues are linked together in the fermentation L. *casei* factor. There are five theoretically possible isomers of the triglutamate and two possible isomers of pteroyldiglutamate. Mowat *et al.*[7] synthesised pteroyl-α-glutamylglutamic acid and pteroyl-$\alpha\gamma$-glutamyldiglutamic acid and showed that they had only a slight activity towards L. *helveticus* and S. *faecalis* R, so that the latter was not identical with the fermentation factor. Pteroyl-γ-glutamylglutamic acid, however, had 60 to 70 % of the activity of pteroylglutamic acid on S. *faecalis* R and L. *helveticus* whilst pteroyl-γ-glutamyl-γ-glutamylglutamic acid, prepared from the triethyl ester of pteroyl-γ-glutamylglutamic acid and the acid chloride of α-ethyl carbobenzoxy-glutamate (page 476), had a low activity for S. *faecalis* R and a high activity for L. *helveticus*, thus resembling the fermentation factor, with which it is probably identical.[8]

SLR Factor (Rhizopterine)

On treatment with alkali, rhizopterine yielded aporhizopterine, $C_{14}H_{10}N_6O_3Na_2$,[9] subsequently shown to be identical with pteroic acid,[10] since it liberated p-aminobenzoic acid on pyrolysis or hydrolysis, gave guanidine on oxidation and a dihydroxypteridine on treatment with nitrous acid. The other substance produced on hydrolysis was identified as formic acid. Rhizopterine is therefore formyl-pteroic acid with the structure :

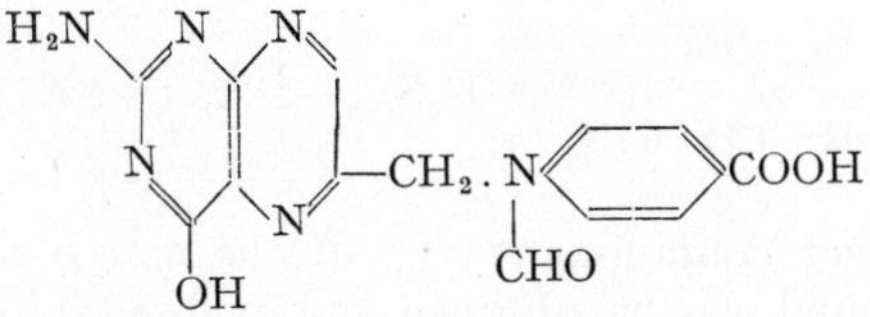

This structure was confirmed by treating synthetic pteroic acid with formic acid, when a substance identical with rhizopterine was obtained.

References to Section 3

1. R. B. Angier, J. H. Boothe, B. L. Hutchings, J. H. Mowat, J. Semb, E. L. R. Stokstad, Y. SubbaRow, C. W. Waller, D. B. Cosulich, M. J. Fahrenbach, M. E. Hultquist, E. Kuh, E. H. Northey, D. R. Seeger, J. P. Sickels and J. M. Smith, *Science*, 1946, **103**, 667.
2. E. L. R. Stokstad, B. L. Hutchings, J. H. Mowat, J. H. Boothe, C. W. Waller, R. B. Angier, J. Semb and Y. SubbaRow, *Ann. N.Y. Acad. Sci.*, 1946, **48**, 269 ; *J. Amer. Chem. Soc.*, 1948, **70**, 5.
3. J. H. Mowat, J. H. Boothe, B. L. Hutchings, E. L. R. Stokstad, C. W. Waller, R. B. Angier, J. Semb, D. B. Cosulich and Y. SubbaRow, *Ann. N.Y. Acad. Sci.*, 1946, **48**, 279 ; *J. Amer. Chem. Soc.*, 1948, **70**, 14.
4. B. L. Hutchings, E. L. R. Stokstad, J. H. Mowat, J. H. Boothe, C. W. Waller, R. B. Angier, J. Semb and Y. SubbaRow, *ibid.*, 10.
5. R. Purrmann, *Annalen*, 1941, **548**, 284.
6. J. Weijlard, M. Tishler and A. E. Erickson, *J. Amer. Chem. Soc.*, 1945, **67**, 802.
7. J. H. Mowat, B. L. Hutchings, R. B. Angier, E. L. R. Stokstad, J. H. Boothe, C. W. Waller, J. Semb and Y. SubbaRow, *ibid.*, 1948, **70**, 1096.
8. J. H. Boothe, J. H. Mowat, B. L. Hutchings, R. B. Angier, C. W. Waller, E. L. R. Stokstad, J. Semb, A. L. Gazzola and Y. SubbaRow, *ibid.*, 1099.
9. E. L. Rickes, N. R. Trenner, J. B. Conn and J. C. Keresztesy, *ibid.*, 1947, **69**, 2751.
10. D. E. Wolf, R. C. Anderson, E. A. Kaczka, S. A. Harris, G. E. Arth, P. L. Southwick, R. Mozingo and K. Folkers, *ibid.*, 2753.

4. SYNTHESIS OF FOLIC ACID

Liver *L. casei* Factor

Angier *et al.*,[1] synthesised the liver *L. casei* factor (pteroylglutamic acid) by four different methods. In the first,[1, 2] equimolecular amounts of 2 : 4 : 5-triamino-6-hydroxypyrimidine, *p*-aminobenzoyl-L-glutamic acid and 2 : 3-dibromopropionaldehyde were reacted together in presence of an acetate buffer:

$$\text{H}_2\text{N}.\overset{\displaystyle \text{N}\!-\!\text{C}.\text{OH}}{\underset{\displaystyle \text{N}\!-\!\text{C}.\text{NH}_2}{\text{C}\quad\text{C}.\text{NH}_2}} \;+\; \overset{\displaystyle \text{Br}.\text{CH}_2}{\underset{\displaystyle \text{Br}.\text{CH}.\text{CHO}}{|}} \;+\; \text{H}_2\text{N}\!\!\left\langle\!=\!\right\rangle\!\!\text{CO}.\text{NH}.\text{CH}.\text{CH}_2.\text{CH}_2.\text{CO}$$
$$\underset{\displaystyle \text{COOH}}{|}$$

giving a product containing 15 % of the active compound. The dihydro-compound was first formed and oxidised during the reaction to the aromatic compound. The crude preparation was dissolved in dilute alkali, impurities were precipitated by the addition of barium chloride, followed by ethanol to a concentration of 20 % and the solution was then freed from barium, adjusted to pH 7·0, filtered and extracted three times with 10-volume portions of butanol. The aqueous phase was concentrated, acidified to pH 3·0 and cooled to 0·5° C. The precipitate that formed was re-dissolved in dilute alkali, the solution treated with charcoal, acidified to pH 3·0 and the active compound crystallised from hot water. The product was identical in its chemical and physical properties with the *L. casei* factor isolated from liver.

The second method of synthesis was slightly different.[1, 3] 2 : 3-Dibromo-propionaldehyde was reacted with pyridine, and the product was condensed with 2 : 4 : 5-triamino-6-hydroxy-pyrimidine and potassium iodide to give N-[(2-amino-4-hydroxy-6-pteridyl)-methyl]-pyridinium iodide. This was then condensed with *p*-aminobenzoyl-L-glutamic acid by heating with sodium methoxide in ethylene glycol at 140° C. The product again contained 15 % of the active compound and was purified as described above.

Pteroic acid was synthesised by both the above methods, using *p*-aminobenzoic acid in place of *p*-aminobenzoyl-L-glutamic acid.[1, 2, 3]

A third method of synthesis [4] was to treat reductone (2 : 3-dihydroxyacrylaldehyde) with *p*-aminobenzoylglutamic acid, esterify the resulting *p*-(2 : 3-dihydroxy-2-ene-propylideneamino)-benzoylglutamic acid and condense the ester with 2 : 4 : 5-triamino-6-hydroxy-pyrimidine:—

$$\text{H}_2\text{N}.\overset{\displaystyle \text{N}\!=\!\text{C}.\text{OH}}{\underset{\displaystyle \text{N}\!-\!\text{C}.\text{NH}_2}{\text{C}\quad\text{C}.\text{NH}_2}} \;+\; \overset{\displaystyle \text{CHOH}}{\underset{\displaystyle \text{C(OH)}.\text{CHO}}{\|}} \;+\; \text{H}_2\text{N}\!\!\left\langle\!=\!\right\rangle\!\!\text{CO}.\text{NH}.\text{CH}.\text{CH}_2.\text{CH}_2.\text{C}$$
$$\underset{\displaystyle \text{COOH}}{|}$$

In a fourth method,[5] 2-amino-4-hydroxy-6-methylpteridine, prepared by reduction of 2-amino-4-hydroxy-6-pteridylmethyl pyridinium iodide, was either brominated or chlorinated and the product condensed with the diethyl ester of p-aminobenzoylglutamic acid.

All these and several similar methods were patented by the American Cyanamid Co.[6] Thus in place of 2 : 3-dibromopropionalde-hyde, there may be used 3-halogeno-2-isonitrosopropionaldehydes, 2 : 2 : 3-trihalogeno-propionaldehydes, 2-halogeno-3-alkoxypropion-aldehydes, 1 : 1 - dihalogeno - 2 : 3 - epoxypropanes, 1 : 1 : 3 - trihalo-genoacetones or 2 : 2 : 3-trihalogenoalkylaldehydes. In addition, a patent was filed by the same company to cover the preparation of pteroylglutamic acid from the corresponding diaminopteridine by heating in an aqueous solvent under alkaline conditions. 1 : 1-Dichloro-acetone and 1 : 1-dichloro-3-bromoacetone were used by F. E. King and P. C. Spensley.[7]

P. Karrer and R. Schwyzer [8] developed a new method of synthe-sising pteroylglutamic acid, in which 2 : 4 : 5-triamino-6-hydroxy-pyrimidine was condensed with glyceraldehyde or dihydroxyacetone giving a mixture of 2-amino-4-hydroxy-6-hydroxymethylpteridine and 2-amino-4-hydroxy-7-hydroxymethylpteridine. The former gave pteroylglutamic acid with p-aminobenzoylglutamic acid. Reaction of the pyrimidine with glyceraldehyde di-p-toluenesulphonate and p-aminobenzoylglutamic acid in presence of sodium iodide also yielded pteroylglutamic acid.

Roche Products Ltd.[9] patented processes for the preparation of pteroylglutamic acid by reacting 2-amino-4-hydroxy-6-hydroxy-methylpteridine with thionyl chloride and then treating the product with p-aminobenzoylglutamic acid, or by hydrogenating a mixture of the pteridine and p-nitrobenzoylglutamic acid. Hoffmann-La Roche & Co.[10] condensed 2 : 4 : 5-triamino-6-hydroxy-pyrimidine with a ketohexose and oxidised the resulting 2-amino-4-hydroxy-6-tetra-hydroxybutylpteridine with lead tetra-acetate or some similar reagent capable of effecting glycol cleavage. The 2-amino-4-hydroxy-6-pteridylaldehyde so formed was hydrogenated in an inert solvent or formic acid in presence of p-aminobenzoylglutamic acid and a catalyst, giving pteroylglutamic acid ; any formyl-pteroylglutamic acid pro-duced at the same time was converted into pteroylglutamic acid by treatment with ammonia. H. S. Forrest and J. Walker [11] found that in the presence of hydrazine, glucose and fructose reacted with 2 : 4 : 5-triamino-6-hydroxypyrimidine to give 2-amino-4-hydroxy-6-D-arabotetrahydroxybutylpteridine, whereas in the absence of hydra-zine, 2-amino-4-hydroxy-7-D-arabotetrahydroxybutylpteridine was formed.

Fermentation *L. casei* Factor

Pteroyl-γ-glutamyl-γ-glutamyl-glutamic acid was synthesised [12] by reacting diethyl glutamate with the acid chloride of α-ethyl carbobenzoxyglutamate to give the carbobenzoxy dipeptide, hydrogenating to remove the protective benzyl group giving triethyl γ-glutamylglutamate, and then repeating the series of reactions with another molecule of α-ethyl carbobenzoxy glutamate acid chloride, and finally hydrolysing the tetraethyl ester of γ-glutamyl-γ-glutamylglutamic acid and converting to the pteroyl derivative.

A simplified method was subsequently described.[13] The p-nitrobenzoyl derivative of γ-ethyl glutamate was converted *via* the γ-hydrazide into the γ-azide, which was reacted either with triethyl γ-glutamylglutamate, giving triethyl p-nitrobenzoyl-γ-glutamyl-γ-glutamylglutamic acid direct, or with γ-ethyl glutamate, giving γ-ethyl p-nitrobenzoyl-γ-glutamylglutamate which was converted into the tripeptide by a repetition of the same procedure. The p-nitrobenzoyl derivative was then reduced and the amino compound converted into pteroyltriglutamate.

SLR Factor (Rhizopterine)

Rhizopterine was synthesised by treating synthetic pteroic acid with formic acid.[14]

Xanthopterine

Xanthopterine was synthesised by R. Purrmann [15] by reacting 2 : 4 : 5-triamino-6-hydroxy-pyrimidine with dichloroacetic acid and then cyclising the resulting 2 : 4-diamino-5-dichloroacetylamino-6-hydroxy-pyrimidine by treatment with silver oxide :

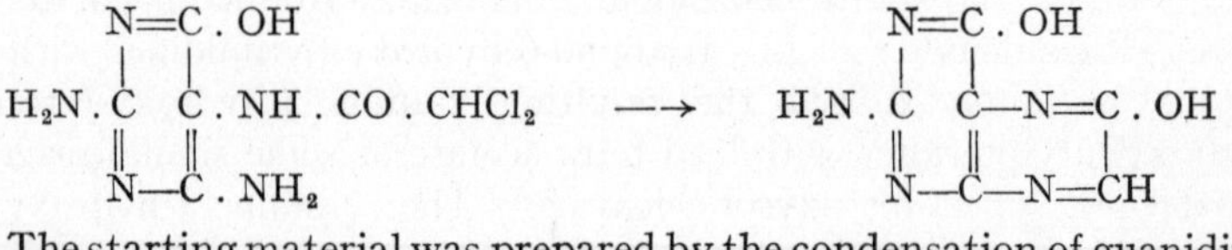

The starting material was prepared by the condensation of guanidine with phenylazocyanoacetic ester and reduction of the azo group in the product :

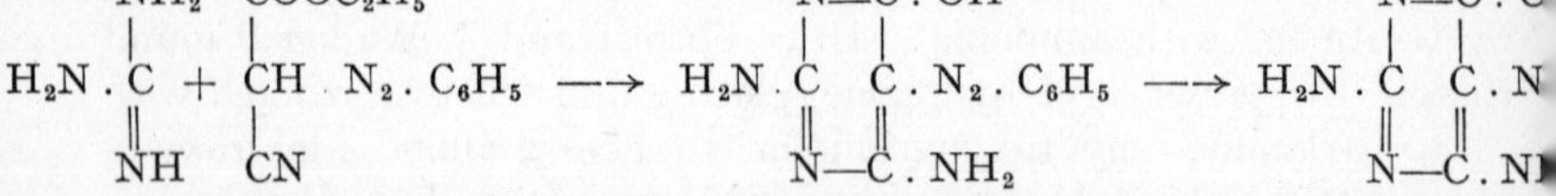

Xanthopterine can also be prepared in good yield by reduction of leucopterine ; [16] dihydroxanthopterine is formed on further reduction.

References to Section 4

1. R. B. Angier, J. H. Boothe, B. L. Hutchings, J. H. Mowat, J. Semb, E. L. R. Stokstad, Y. SubbaRow, C. W. Waller, D. B. Cosulich, M. J. Fahrenbach, M. E. Hultquist, E. Kuh, E. H. Northey, D. R. Seeger, J. P. Sickels and J. M. Smith, *Science*, 1946, **103**, 667 ; *Ann. N.Y. Acad. Sci.*, 1946, **48**, 283.
2. Waller *et al.*, *J. Amer. Chem. Soc.*, 1948, **70**, 19.
3. Hultquist *et al.*, *ibid.*, 23.
4. Angier *et al.*, *ibid.*, 25.
5. Boothe *et al.*, *ibid.*, 27.
6. American Cyanamid Co., U.S.P., 2442836-7, 2442867, 2443165, 2444002, 2444005, Brit. App., 12491/48, 14216/48, 24564/48, 25001-2/48, 3413/49.
7. F. E. King and P. C. Spensley, *Nature*, 1949, **164**, 574.
8. P. Karrer and R. Schwyzer, *Helv. Chim. Acta*, 1948, **31**, 777.
9. Roche Products Ltd., B.P. 624394, 630751.
10. Hoffmann-La Roche & Co., B.P. 626171, 628305 ; Roche Products Ltd., B.P. 631516.
11. H. S. Forrest and J. Walker, *J. Chem. Soc.*, 1949, 2077.
12. J. H. Boothe, J. H. Mowat, B. L. Hutchings, R. B. Angier, C. W. Waller, E. L. R. Stokstad, J. Semb, A. L. Gazzola and Y. SubbaRow, *J. Amer. Chem. Soc.*, 1948, **70**, 1099.
13. J. H. Boothe, J. Semb, C. W. Waller, R. B. Angier, J. H. Mowat, B. L. Hutchings, E. L. R. Stokstad and Y. SubbaRow, *ibid.*, 1949, **71**, 2304.
14. D. E. Wolf, R. C. Anderson, E. A. Kaczka, S. A. Harris, G. E. Arth, P. L. Southwick, R. Mozingo and K. Folkers, *ibid.*, 1947, **69**, 2753.
15. R. Purrmann, *Annalen*, 1940, **546**, 98.
16. J. R. Totter, *J. Biol. Chem.*, 1944, **154**, 105.

5. PROPERTIES OF FOLIC ACID

Folic Acid

H. K. Mitchell and R. J. Williams [1] assigned the formula, $C_{15}H_{15}O_8N_5$, to the folic acid isolated from spinach leaves, and stated that it was free from sugars or polyhydroxy compounds, but contained a xanthopterine-like moiety, since its absorption spectrum resembled that of xanthopterine.[2] The relationship of folic acid to other members of the group has not definitely been established, but there is some evidence to suggest that it is not identical with the liver *L. casei* factor.[3]

Liver *L. casei* Factor (Vitamin B$_c$)

Crystalline vitamin B$_c$ was isolated from liver by Pfiffner *et al.*[4] and E. L. R. Stokstad,[5] who obtained it from hot water in the form of yellow platelets which melted above 360° C. The empirical formula was $C_{21}H_{24}N_7O_8$. The solubility of the substance in water at pH 3 was approximately 10 μg. per ml. at 2° C. and 0·5 mg. per ml. at 100° C.[6] The factor was insoluble in the common organic solvents, but soluble in glacial acetic acid, phenol and methanol.[7] The extinction co-efficients in 0·1 N sodium hydroxide were :

$$E^{1\%}_{1\,cm.}\ 255\ m\mu.,\ 565\ ;\ \ 282\ m\mu.,\ 350\ ;\ \ 365\ m\mu.,\ 195.$$

Fermentation *L. casei* Factor

The fermentation *L. casei* factor differed from the liver factor in its biological activity ; whereas it was 60 to 80 % as active as the liver compound towards *L. helveticus*, it was only 4 to 6 % as active for *S. faecalis* R.[8] No reliable combustion figures could be obtained for the substance, which clearly had a composition different from that of liver factor, however.[8] The absorption spectrum was similar to that of the liver factor, but the extinction coefficients were lower, indicating that the fermentation factor had a higher molecular weight.[8]

Vitamin B$_c$ Conjugate

Vitamin B$_c$ conjugate, prepared from yeast by Pfiffner *et al.*[9] had a lower nitrogen content than had vitamin B$_c$, and, although the absorption spectra of the two substances were similar, the relative values of the extinction coefficients indicated that the molecule of the conjugate was nearly three times as big as that of vitamin B$_c$. It had practically no growth-promoting action for either *L. helveticus* or *S. lactis* R.

SLR Factor (Rhizopterine)

Rhizopterine had the empirical formula, $C_{15}H_{12}N_6O_4$, and was highly active towards *S. lactis* R, but substantially inactive towards *L. helveticus*. Unlike the *L. casei* factors, it did not stimulate growth or haemoglobin formation in chicks, and did not cure granulocytopenia in rats induced by feeding succinylsulphathiazole.[10]

It was a pale yellow solid which did not melt below 300° C. It was insoluble in the common organic solvents and water, but soluble in mineral acids and alkalis. It was therefore difficult to purify by crystallisation, but yielded a crystalline complex with luteo-ethylene-diaminocobaltic chloride and ammonia ;[11] treatment of the complex with dilute acetic acid yielded pure rhizopterine.

Xanthopterine

Xanthopterine is a yellow solid with a melting-point higher than 400° C., and it can be crystallised only with great difficulty. It is very sparingly soluble in organic solvents and cold water, but readily soluble in hot water and in hot ethylene glycol and glycerol.

References to Section 5

1. H. K. Mitchell and R. J. Williams, *J. Amer. Chem. Soc.*, 1944, **66**, 271.
2. H. K. Mitchell, *ibid.*, 274.
3. D. A. Hall *Biochem. J.*, 1947, **41**, 287.
4. J. J. Pfiffner, S. B. Binkley, E. S. Bloom, R. A. Brown, O. D. Bird, A. D. Emmett, A. G. Hogan and B. L. O'Dell, *Science*, 1943, **97**, 404.
5. E. L. R. Stokstad, *J. Biol. Chem.*, 1943, **149**, 573.
6. E. L. R. Stokstad, B. L. Hutchings and Y. SubbaRow, *J. Amer. Chem. Soc.*, 1948, **70**, 3.
7. B. L. O'Dell, *Univ. Microfilms Ann Arbor*, 1944, **5**, No. 2, 19.
8. B. L. Hutchings, E. L. R. Stokstad, N. Bohonos and N. H. Slobodkin, *Science*, 1944, **99**, 371 ; B. L. Hutchings, E. L. R. Stokstad, N. Bohonos, N. H. Sloane and Y. SubbaRow, *J. Amer. Chem. Soc.*, 1948, **70**, 1.
9. J. J. Pfiffner, D. G. Calkins, B. L. O'Dell, E. S. Bloom, R. A. Brown, C. J. Campbell and O. D. Bird, *Science*, 1945, **102**, 228.
10. E. L. Rickes, L. Chaiet and J. C. Keresztesy, *J. Amer. Chem. Soc.*, 1947, **69**, 2749.
11. D. E. Wolf, R. C. Anderson, E. A. Kaczka, S. A. Harris, G. E. Arth, P. L. Southwick, R. Mozingo and K. Folkers, *ibid.*, 2753.

6. STABILITY OF FOLIC ACID

Pteroylglutamic acid is labile to acid, 70 to 100 % of the activity being destroyed on autoclaving at pH 1.[1, 2] It becomes progressively more stable as the pH increases and is relatively stable to heat within the pH range 4 to 12. At pH 6·8, for instance, solutions can be sterilised by heating for thirty minutes without loss of potency.

Folic acid is partially inactivated by lead and mercury salts [1] and by treatment with sulphite.[2] Aeration at pH 10 also causes partial inactivation.[2]

In pure solutions, it is rapidly inactivated by light,[2, 3] with formation of p-aminobenzoylglutamic acid [3] and 2-amino-4-hydroxy-6-formyl-pteridine [3a] ; the latter is converted first into the corresponding acid and then into 2-amino-4-hydroxypteridine.

Vitamin Bc Conjugase

Vitamin B$_c$ conjugate (pteroylheptaglutamic acid) is converted into pteroylglutamic acid by the action of an enzyme, known as vitamin B$_c$ conjugase (page 460). This is present in pig kidney,[4] the liver and small intestine of the pig,[5, 6] in ox liver,[5, 6] chick pancreas,[5, 6] chick liver,[7] and almonds.[4] The enzyme also converts pteroyltriglutamic acid into pteroylglutamic acid, Day *et al.*[8] obtaining a 23-fold increase in the activity of a concentrate of the fermentation *L. casei* factor towards *S. faecalis* R on incubation with vitamin B_c conjugase.

Vitamin B_c conjugase is also produced, often in considerable amounts, by many micro-organisms,[6] but it does not appear to be present in moulds or yeasts and only in small amounts in potatoes.[4] The enzyme was shown to be different from kidney nucleosidase, the acid phosphatase of almond or potato, the alkaline phosphatase of the small intestine and the β-glucosidase of almond.

The activity of the enzyme was inhibited by nucleic acid and sulphydryl-combining reagents.[9]

The purification of vitamin B_c conjugase was described by Laskowski *et al.*[10] The process involved treatment with calcium phosphate gel, precipitation with alcohol and repeated concentration of the solution and salting-out with sodium sulphate. A method of estimating the enzyme in animal tissues was worked out, and this was used to ascertain its distribution. The enzyme was found to be widely distributed in the rat's body; the pancreas, brain, intestinal mucosa and bone showed much higher values than the liver. Chicken pancreas, intestinal mucosa and liver were very good sources. A similar distribution of the enzyme was observed by Bird *et al.*[11] They noted that the optimal pH for activity was generally 4·5, but that enzyme preparations from chick and turkey pancreas were most effective at pH 7·0 to 7·5. Yeast extract contained a potent inhibitor of the enzyme. The vitamin B_c contents of several preparations of vitamin B_c conjugate were estimated microbiologically after digestion with vitamin B_c conjugase.

References to Section 6

1. B. L. O'Dell and A. G. Hogan, *J. Biol. Chem.*, 1943, **149**, 323.
2. E. P. Daniel and O. L. Kline, *ibid.*, 1947, **170**, 739.
3. E. L. R. Stokstad, D. Fordham and A. de Grunigen, *ibid.*, 1947, **167**, 877.
3a. O. H. Lowry, O. A. Bessey and E. J. Crawford, *ibid.*, 1949, **180**, 389.
4. O. D. Bird, S. B. Binkley, E. S. Bloom, A. D. Emmett and J. J. Pfiffner, *ibid.*, 1945, **157**, 413.
5. V. Mims and M. Laskowski, *ibid.*, 1945, **160**, 493.
6. P. R. Burkholder, I. McVeigh and K. Wilson, *Arch. Biochem.*, 1945, **7**, 287.
7. L. J. Daniel, M. L. Scott, L. C. Norris and G. F. Heuser, *J. Biol. Chem.*, 1945, **160**, 265.
8. P. L. Day, V. Mims and J. R. Totter, *ibid.*, 1945, **161**, 45.
9. V. Mims, M. E. Swendseid and O. D. Bird, *ibid.*, 1947, **170**, 367.
10. M. Laskowski, V. Mims and P. L. Day, *ibid.*, 1945, **157**, 731.
11. O. D. Bird, M. Robbins, J. M. Vandenbelt and J. J. Pfiffner, *ibid.*, 1946, **163**, 649.

7. ESTIMATION OF FOLIC ACID

Microbiological Methods

Although chicks were used extensively in studying the relationship between different members of the folic acid group of factors, the methods used to assay preparations of these factors and foodstuffs containing them have invariably involved the use of micro-organisms, particularly *L. helveticus* and *S. faecalis* R. These, as already noted, respond to different degrees with the different factors. Pteroic acid and the SLR factor, for instance, stimulate *S. faecalis* R but not *L. helveticus*, pteroylglutamate stimulates both, pteroyltriglutamate (fermentation *L. casei* factor) stimulates *L. helveticus* but not *S. faecalis* R, and pteroylheptaglutamate (vitamin B_c conjugate) stimulates neither organism.

In their original method, Mitchell *et al.*[1] used *S. faecalis* R which was also used by Elvehjem and his colleagues,[2] who modified the medium in order to obtain greater acid production and thus increase the titre.

L. helveticus was used by M. Landy and D. M. Dicken.[3] The medium was the same as that used for the assay of five other members of the vitamin B complex, but had the disadvantage of requiring a large number of constituents.

As might be expected, the chief difficulty in assaying folic acid arises from the differences in the response elicited by the different forms of the factor. The object of assaying foodstuffs, for example, is to determine the total folic acid content, that is, the amount of material that could be utilised by the healthy animal for growth and haemopoiesis and, to this extent, a biological method using the chick or the monkey, would be superior to any microbiological assay method. Such a method does not appear to exist, however, and workers have therefore been forced to use microbiological methods in combination with some process of hydrolysis to convert the microbiologically inactive forms into forms that would produce a response. Cheldelin *et al.*[4] advocated digestion with takadiastase, which they claimed to give maximum folic acid values, whilst Laskowski *et al.*[5] recommended digestion with an extract of chick pancreas for yeast extracts and autoclaving at pH 4 for twelve hours for liver preparations.

Bird *et al.*[6] described a method of hydrolysing vitamin B_c conjugate by means of vitamin B_c conjugase prepared from hog kidney or almonds; the total folic acid was then estimated microbiologically with *L. helveticus*.

Although the conjugase from hog kidney is said to give satisfactory results with plant materials,[7] a combination of hog kidney and chick pancreas enzymes gave higher results than either alone.[8] Lower results were obtained by the microbiological assay of milk following digestion with chick pancreas than by assay with chicks.[9]

Chemical Methods

A chemical method of estimating folic acid was described by Hutchings *et al.*[10] It was based on the observation that pteroylglutamic acid and related compounds were cleaved by reduction with zinc and acid giving a pteridine and an aromatic amine. The latter was estimated colorimetrically by reaction with N-naphthylethylene diamine. Interference due to the presence of adenine, adenosine and nucleic acid was eliminated by reducing with titanous chloride instead of with zinc and acid.[11]

Pteroylglutamic acid can also be estimated fluorimetrically.[12] On oxidation with potassium permanganate it is converted into 2-amino-4-hydroxypteridine-6-carboxylic acid, which fluoresces strongly at 470 mμ. when irradiated with light of wave-length 365 mμ.; the intensity of the fluorescence is proportional to the concentration. When interfering pigments are present, the oxidation product is isolated chromatographically.

Pteroylglutamic acid can also be estimated polarographically, except when iron is present.[13] With 1 % tetramethylammonium hydroxide solution, pH 9·0 to 9·5, as the base solution, it has a half-wave potential *versus* the S.C.E. of 0·98 volt. With cadmium as an internal standard the error of the estimation is only $\pm$ 2 %.

References to Section 7

1. H. K. Mitchell, E. E. Snell and R. J. Williams, *J. Amer. Chem. Soc.*, 1941, **63**, 2284; H. K. Mitchell and E. E. Snell, *Univ. Texas Publ.*, 1941, No. 4137, 36.
2. T. D. Luckey, G. M. Briggs and C. A. Elvehjem, *J. Biol. Chem.*, 1944, **152**, 157; L. J. Teply and C. A. Elvehjem, *ibid.*, 1945, **157**, 303.
3. M. Landy and D. M. Dicken, *J. Lab. Clin. Med.*, 1942, **27**, 1086.
4. V. H. Cheldelin, M. A. Eppright, E. E. Snell and B. M. Guirard, *Univ. Texas Publ.*, 1942, No. 4237, 32.
5. M. Laskowski, V. Mims and P. L. Day, *J. Biol. Chem.*, 1945, **157**, 731.
6. O. D. Bird, B. Bressler, R. A. Brown, C. J. Campbell and A. D. Emmett, *ibid.*, 1945, **159**, 631.
7. O. E. Olson, E. E. C. Fager, R. H. Burris and C. A. Elvehjem, *Arch. Biochem.*, 1948, **18**, 261.
8. A. Sreenivasan, A. E. Harper, and C. A. Elvehjem, *J. Biol. Chem.*, 1949, **177**, 117.
9. A. Z. Hodson, *J. Nutrition*, 1949, **38**, 25.

10. B. L. Hutchings, E. L. R. Stokstad, J. H. Boothe, J. H. Mowat, C. W. Waller, R. B. Angier, J. Semb and Y. SubbaRow, *J. Biol. Chem.*, 1947, **168**, 705.

11. A. J. Glazko and L. M. Wolf, *Arch. Biochem.*, 1949, **21**, 241.

12. V. Allfrey, L. J. Teply, C. Geffen and C. G. King, *J. Biol. Chem.*, 1949, **178**, 465.

13. W. J. Mader and H. A. Frediani, *Anal. Chem.*, 1948, **12**, 1199.

8. OCCURRENCE OF FOLIC ACID COMPLEX

Folic acid has been reported to be present [1] in liver, kidney, yeast, mushrooms, grass and other green leaves.

Milk has a very low folic acid content, although A. D. Welch and L. D. Wright [2] failed to produce folic acid deficiency in rats when a milk diet was used in conjunction with a poorly-absorbed sulphonamide such as succinylsulphathiazole. Moreover, the hepatic tissues of such rats were found to contain more microbiologically active material than the livers of rats fed a purified diet supplemented with a comparable amount of folic acid. Welch and Wright suggested that milk contained a substance, itself microbiologically inactive, which served as a growth factor for rats. The presence of a conjugated form of folic acid was, in fact, confirmed by A. Z. Hodson,[2a] who assayed milk microbiologically after digestion with chick pancreas conjugase. Unfortunately inconsistent results were obtained with different test-organisms, *L. helveticus* giving a value of 11 to 74 μg. per g. and *S. faecalis* a value of 0·9 to 2·4 μg. per g. ; still higher results were obtained by a chick assay method. In spite of these inconsistencies, the results explain the observation of Cooperman *et al.*[3] that milk is a good source of the monkey anaemia factor. Most of this was present in the skim milk and hardly any in the cream ; raw whey was also a good source of the factor. Milk, as well as liver and certain grains, were good sources of the SLR factor, but leafy materials were, in general, poor sources of both.[4] Good correlation was observed between the effect of crude preparations on anaemic monkeys and their effect on *S. faecalis* R, but correlation was less satisfactory with purified materials.

Folic acid is also present [5] in many micro-organisms, the highest yields (0·25 to 1·67 mg. per ml.) being obtained from *B. subtilis*, *B. vulgatus*, *Serratia marcescens* and a Gram-negative bacillus from chick intestine.

The amount of monkey anti-anaemia factor [6] in fresh liver was greater than in whole liver powder, but lyophilised liver retained the total amount present in the fresh liver. Beef and pork livers were equally potent.

Xanthopterine has been shown to be present in liver [7] and in the eye of the dog fish, *Squalus acanthius* and of *Alligator mississipiensis*.[8]

References to Section 8

1. H. K. Mitchell, E. E. Snell and R. J. Williams, *J. Amer. Chem. Soc.*, 1941, **63**, 2284.
2. A. D. Welch and L. D. Wright, *Science*, 1944, **100**, 153.
2a. A. Z. Hodson, *J. Nutrition*, 1949, **38**, 25.
3. J. M. Cooperman, W. R. Ruegamer and C. A. Elvehjem, *Proc. Soc. Exp. Biol. Med.*, 1946, **62**, 101.
4. W. R. Ruegamer, J. M. Cooperman, E. M. Sporn, E. E. Snell and C. A. Elvehjem, *J. Biol. Chem.*, 1947, **167**, 861.
5. P. R. Burkholder, I. McVeigh and K. Wilson, *Arch. Biochem.*, 1945, **7**, 287.
6. L. D. Wright, H. R. Skeggs, A. D. Welch, K. L. Sprague and P. A. Mattis, *J. Nutrition*, 1945, **29**, 289.
7. R. W. Simmons and E. R. Norris, *J. Biol. Chem.*, 1941, **140**, 679 ; 1945, **158**, 449.
8. A. Pirie and D. M. Simpson; *Biochem. J.*, 1946, **40**, 14.

9. EFFECT OF FOLIC ACID DEFICIENCY IN ANIMALS

The effects of different members of the folic acid complex on different species of animals have already been described at some length in the introductory section, with the primary object of showing how the different factors are related to one another. In addition to their growth-promoting effects on micro-organisms, the compounds are characterised by their ability to cure anaemia, leucopenia and granulocytopenia in chicks and monkeys fed purified diets, and in rats treated with sulphaguanidine or sulphasuxidine.

Chicks

As already stated (page 459), crude specimens of vitamin B_c[1] and of the liver *L. casei* factor [2] prevented anaemia and promoted growth in chicks. The purified factors had similar effects. Crystalline vitamin B_c maintained normal growth and feathering in chicks and prevented the development of a macrocytic hyperchromic anaemia, leucopenia and thrombocytopenia,[3] whilst crystalline vitamin B_c conjugate cured a nutritional macrocytic anaemia in chicks.[4] A purified preparation of the fermentation *L. casei* factor [5] and purified folic acid [6] stimulated growth in chicks.

An apparently significant difference between the response of chicks to vitamin B_c and to the *L. casei* factor was, however, reported by

Petering *et al.*[7] Chicks were maintained on a purified diet, which resulted in poor growth, poor feathering, anaemia and high mortality. The symptoms were prevented by yeast or liver extract containing 22 to 44 μg. of vitamin B_c, but 4- or 5-pyridoxic acid (page 344) alone did not improve the condition of the birds, and the *L. casei* factor alone had only a slight effect. The *L. casei* factor and 4-pyridoxic acid together, however, increased the growth rate and haemoglobin formation, although to a smaller degree than did vitamin B_c.

Again, when only crude preparations were available, there was a difference of opinion as to whether vitamin B_c was the only anti-anaemic factor necessary for chicks. On the one hand, L. C. Norris and G. F. Heuser and their co-workers [8] maintained that it was only effective in presence of α- or β-pyracin (see page 344) and that a deficiency of vitamin B_c or of the *L. casei* factor caused a macrocytic, normochromic anaemia, whilst lack of β-pyracin caused a normocytic, hypochromic anaemia. They asserted that less β-pyracin and *L. casei* factor were required for growth than for the prevention of anaemia. Hutchings *et al.*[9] on the other hand, found that the addition of β-pyracin to the *L. casei* factor was not necessary for growth or haemoglobin formation in the chick. Subsequently, when the pure substance became available, they showed [10] that the effect of synthetic pteroylglutamic acid on the feathering of chicks was not enhanced by, *inter alia*, *p*-aminobenzoic acid, β-pyracin or *p*-aminophenyllactic acid, nor was it modified by the addition of intestinal antiseptics. Some of the inconsistent results obtained were doubtless due to the presence in the diet of variable amounts of vitamin B_{12}, which was not then known to be a factor essential for haemopoiesis (page 530).

Folic acid was twice as effective in the chick by injection as by oral administration.[11]

Consistent results were obtained with the synthetic factors, and chicks deprived of folic acid for the first four weeks of life responded dramatically to pteroylglutamic acid.[12, 13] Moreover, mole for mole, pteroylglutamic acid and pteroyltriglutamic acid were utilised equally well by the chick for growth and prevention of anaemia, and the addition of 4-pyridoxic acid lactone had no significant effect on the utilisation of pteroyltriglutamic acid.[14]

The response of chicks to folic acid, however, depended to a considerable extent on the diet.[15] The smallest response was obtained with high fat diets or with diets in which glucose, sucrose or starch was the sole carbohydrate, whilst the best response was obtained with diets rich in protein and with a low fat content or with maize meal or dextrin as carbohydrates. Whole liver added to a diet containing sucrose gave a greater response than could be accounted for by the folic acid present. This, of course, suggested the existence of other growth factors necessary for chicks ; since then vitamin B_{12} has been recognised to be such a factor (page 530).

In addition to its other effects, synthetic pteroylglutamic acid cured a perosis in chicks resulting from the feeding of a diet adequate in choline (page 590), biotin and manganese.[16] The condition was rendered more severe by sulphasuxidine, and it was therefore suggested that the effect was due to the folic acid stimulating the growth of intestinal bacteria, which in turn synthesised the antiperotic factor.

Pteroyl glutamic acid was also a chromotrichial factor for the chick.[12]

A biological property of folic acid apparently unconnected with the phenomena so far discussed is one concerned with the action of stilboestrol on the oviducts of chicks. Normally, the weight of these organs is increased on administration of the oestrogen, but this did not occur in folic acid-deficient chicks, although pantothenic acid-deficient birds behaved normally. Administration of the *L. casei* factor resulted in the response becoming normal. The response to stilboestrol was also reduced when chicks maintained on an adequate diet were given the folic acid antagonist, 7-methyl-folic acid (page 519), and the inhibition was reversed by folic acid.[17]

No nerve lesions were observed in folic acid-deficient chicks.[18] Folic acid-deficient chicks gave a response to some other factors besides the recognised members of the folic acid complex. Thus, an increase in growth, feathering and haemoglobin formation was observed with preparations of vitamins B_{10} and B_{11},[19] the precise nature of which is not yet known (page 614).

Similarly, the growth and haemoglobin response of chicks to factor R could not be accounted for by the amount of preformed folic acid in the preparation. The folic acid content was, however, increased by incubation with chick liver, rat liver or hog kidney,[20] the last-named being the most effective and liberating folic acid in amounts sufficient to account for the response obtained with chicks. It was therefore concluded that factor R was a mixture of folic acid conjugates. The response to factor R was not affected by succinyl sulphathiazole.

Turkeys

On a vitamin B_6-deficient diet, turkey poults developed a spastic cervical paralysis,[21] which terminated in death within twenty-four to thirty-six hours. In addition, growth was delayed, and a moderate degree of anaemia developed, the erythrocytes being larger in diameter, with less dense and larger nuclei.[22] Pteroylglutamic acid or the triglutamate were equally effective in curing the symptoms.[22a]

Rats

As already noted (page 462) folic acid, in conjunction with biotin, cured the achromotrichia caused by administration of sulphonamides to rats,[23, 24] whilst folic acid alone cured the leucopenia and granulocytopenia observed in such rats [25] and corrected the vitamin K-deficiency produced by sulphasuxidine.[26] These early observations were confirmed by subsequent investigations in which various forms of folic acid were used. Thus Higgins,[27] using the sulphones, promin and promizole, to produce an experimental hypochromic anaemia in young rats maintained on a purified high-carbohydrate diet, showed that vitamin B_c given at the rate of 80 μg. per day had a pronounced curative effect. Similarly, the *L. casei* factor cured a leucopenia and granulocytopenia produced in rats by administration of succinyl sulphathiazole, whilst the marrow responded with " spectacular myeloid proliferation ".[28]

Again, rats that had ceased to grow and in which characteristic deficiency symptoms had developed following administration of sulphaguanidine responded to liver extract or to a folic acid concentrate plus biotin [29] with a reduced mortality rate of 14 % and disappearance of liver and spleen lesions ; at the same time the bone-marrow became hyperplastic.

That the action of sulphonamides on haemopoiesis is probably mediated through the agency of intestinal bacteria appears to be a legitimate deduction from the work of B. L. O'Dell and A. G. Hogan,[30] who showed that reducing the level of pyridoxine or feeding sulphaguanidine increased the incidence of anaemia in chicks ; they suggested that in both instances growth of the intestinal bacteria that normally synthesised vitamin B_c was suppressed. The absence of other factors essential for the growth of the intestinal bacteria might equally well result in suppression of the intestinal flora, leading to a deficiency of vitamin B_c and so to an increase in the incidence of anaemia.

Further evidence on the nature of intestinal synthesis was advanced by A. K. Miller,[31] who confirmed the results obtained by previous workers that folic acid and biotin together corrected the deficiency symptoms caused by feeding 0·5 to 2·0 % of succinyl- or phthalyl-sulphathiazole with the diet. He also noted a marked decrease in the coliform count of the faeces, but no significant change in the total aerobes, total anaerobes or anaerobic spores. Neither sulphonamide-resistant nor sulphonamide-sensitive strains of *E. coli* were able to synthesise as much folic acid when grown in presence of a sulphonamide as when grown in its absence. He therefore concluded that *E. coli* or, at all events, coliform organisms, were responsible for the synthesis of folic acid in the gut (see page 505).

Still further confirmation of the part played by the intestinal bacteria of rats in preventing anaemia was provided by Sebrell and his colleagues,[32] who showed that rats fed a purified diet containing succinylsulphathiazole and subjected to repeated bleeding developed a severe anaemia, which was prevented or cured by the *L. casei* factor. The effect of the latter was enhanced by β-pyracin.[33]

The *L. casei* factor also corrected a granulocytopenia in rats fed a highly purified diet deficient in riboflavine, although riboflavine itself was ineffective.[34] Some of the rats, on the other hand, developed an anaemia that responded erratically to riboflavine, but not to the *L. casei* factor. The granulocytopenia was also cured by crystalline folic acid.

Schweigert *et al.*[35] found that rats fed on a basal dextrin diet with 1 % of succinylsulphathiazole failed to grow and that the vitamin B_c content of the livers decreased, though there was no effect on the riboflavine reserves. Addition of solubilised liver increased the vitamin B_c content of the livers 5- to 9-fold.

Rats with sulphonamide-induced leucopenia and granulocytopenia were also cured by a yeast concentrate, which possessed less than 0·4 % of the microbiological activity to be expected from its biological activity.[36] This was enhanced, however, by treatment with acid, alkali or enzyme. The properties of the yeast factor thus resembled those of vitamin B_c conjugate. Liver extracts also appeared to contain microbiologically inactive substances that were effective on rats, but they were not activated by treatment with acids, alkalis or enzymes. These substances may represent new forms of *L. casei* factor.

According to Wright *et al.*[37] the ease with which symptoms of folic acid deficiency develop in rats depends on the nature of the diet. Thus much larger quantities of succinylsulphathiazole (10 to 20 %) had to be added to a diet of powdered milk than to highly purified diets of comparable folic acid content in order to produce folic acid deficiency. They also observed that the folic acid-deficiency syndrome could co-exist with a high faecal elimination of folic acid (page 505). Rats fed exclusively on powdered milk excreted large amounts of folic acid in the faeces, and this was reduced by administration of the sulphonamide.

Day *et al.*[38] also reported that folic acid restored the growth rate of rats maintained on a milk diet to which sulphasuxidine had been added, and noted that the sulphonamide brought about a reduction in the number of coliform bacteria in the caecum and in the total bacterial count. These results suggest that the symptoms produced by administration of sulphonamides are connected with the reduction in the numbers of bacteria in the intestine, and that administration of folic acid in some way reverses this effect.

Pteroylglutamic acid did not affect the anaemia that resulted when rats on a purified diet were given thiourea, but it did correct the granulocytopenia that occasionally accompanied the anaemia and which was regularly produced when, in addition to thiourea, thyroid powder or thyroxine was given.[39] Pantothenic acid-deficient rats sometimes develop granulocytopenia or anaemia or both and, in this instance also, pteroylglutamic acid relieved the granulocytopenia (when alone), but not the anaemia.[40] The anaemia, when alone, was relieved by pantothenic acid. When both granulocytopenia and anaemia occurred together, both pantothenic acid and folic acid were required. Feeding protein-free or low-casein diets to rats also resulted in granulocytopenia and anaemia.[41] To rectify the granulocytopenia in this instance both casein and pteroylglutamic acid were necessary.

Synthetic pteroylglutamic acid at a level of 110 μg. per day increased the bodyweight and the leucocyte count of lactating rats, but no further increase was obtained by giving larger amounts.[42] Larger amounts (275 μg. per day) were necessary in order to effect a significant improvement in the weaning weights of the young, but doubling this amount did not bring about any further improvement. Pteroylglutamic acid has a beneficial effect on both lactation and reproduction, and rats fed on a diet containing succinylsulphathiazole and deficient only in pteroylglutamic acid for 1 to 3 months before breeding showed impaired reproduction,[43] whilst the addition of 0·5 % of an antagonist resulted in 100 % resorptions, even without prior deficiency.[44]

Crystalline pteroylheptaglutamate increased the total leucocytes and granulocytes in sulphasuxidine-treated rats as effectively as did pteroylglutamic acid when given orally and only slightly less effectively when injected ; the presence of an inhibitor of vitamin B_c conjugase did not affect the utilisation of the conjugate.[45]

Mice

Folic acid is also essential for mice and according to E. Nielsen and A. Black [46] the deficiency symptoms were rendered more acute when 0·6 % of sulphasuxidine was added to the diet. Franklin et al.,[47] however, failed to produce symptoms of pteroylglutamic acid deficiency in mice by giving sulphasuxidine. One of the symptoms apparently characteristic of folic acid deficiency in mice is poor lactation performance ; this was considerably improved by the administration of folic acid concentrates and of the pure factor.[48]

Pteroylglutamic acid–deficient mice also show a reduction in the counts of all the cellular elements of the circulating blood and maturation arrest of the bone marrow, suggesting that pteroylglutamic acid may not be necessary for the formation of the immature blood elements but is necessary for maturation after the primitive elements have been formed.[48a]

Guinea-pigs

D. W. Woolley and H. Sprince [49] identified folic acid as one of the growth factors required by the guinea-pig ; this had previously been designated GPF-1.

Dogs

W. A. Krehl and C. A. Elvehjem [50] found that young dogs maintained on a nicotinic acid-deficient diet until severe symptoms of blacktongue developed responded poorly to supplements of nicotinic acid and soon died despite the administration of what would normally have been adequate amounts of nicotinic acid. When the basal diet was supplemented with a folic acid concentrate (from " solubilised liver ") the response to nicotinic acid was consistently good.

Foxes

On a diet free from the vitamin B complex, but containing aneurine, riboflavine, pyridoxine, nicotinic acid, pantothenic acid and choline, foxes developed anaemia and anorexia, lost weight and eventually died.[51] Administration of folic acid resulted in immediate recovery with rapid regeneration of haemoglobin and red blood cells. Yeast folic acid conjugate was not utilised by foxes, but the substance was effective after hydrolysis with kidney enzyme. Folic acid was not the only factor required, however.

Mink

Absence of folic acid from the diet caused deficiency symptoms in the mink, characterised by irritability, weakness, bloody faecal discharge, anorexia, loss of weight, fall in the white cell count and, eventually, death.[52] Folic acid cured most of these symptoms promptly, but another factor appeared to be necessary for maintenance of weight and for haemoglobin regeneration.

Pigs

Folic acid alone or in combination with p-aminobenzoic acid, inositol or biotin appeared to have no beneficial effect on the growth or appearance of pigs, although haemoglobin formation was stimulated to a small extent.[53] On the contrary, symptoms of biotin deficiency were produced ; these were more acute when sulphasuxidine was also added to the diet.[53a] With sulphasuxidine alone, a normocytic anaemia was produced which was cured by the administration of pteroylglutamic acid. A more severe anaemia was produced by the addition of a crude folic acid antagonist to the diet,[53a, 53b] the effects of which were overcome more effectively by a mixture of pteroylglutamic acid and biotin than by the former alone.

Monkeys

Vitamin M was the name assigned by Langston et al.[54] to a factor in liver and yeast that relieved leucopenia and granulocytopenia in monkeys (see page 460). These symptoms were partially relieved by xanthopterine and completely by a pure specimen of the fermentation L. casei factor,[55] and by synthetic pteroylglutamic acid.[56]

Vitamin M deficiency is characterised by loss of weight, leucopenia, granulocytopenia, anaemia, bloody discharge, gingivitis, necrosis of the gums, loss of appetite and susceptibility to dysentery. Autopsy revealed ulcerated colon, liver damage and adrenal changes.[56]

Injection of 2 to 6 mg. of synthetic pteroylglutamic acid was followed by a dramatic increase in the leucocyte and reticulocyte counts. A prompt, but transient, increase in red blood cells occurred within twenty-four hours, followed by a return to the previous low levels and, several days later, by a more permanent increase.

Folic acid, however, may not be the only factor responsible for vitamin M deficiency, for Cooperman et al.,[57] in the course of an investigation into the effect of riboflavine deficiency, maintained rhesus monkeys on a diet containing all the other members of the vitamin B complex, including a norit eluate preparation from liver, and observed a fall in the red and white blood cell count which was not restored to normal by the administration of large doses of riboflavine. Addition of whole liver to the diet restored the normal blood picture. When monkeys were maintained on a similar diet containing adequate riboflavine but no folic acid, growth was slow and white blood cell counts become low. The addition to the diet of vitamin B_c, vitamin B_c conjugate or L. casei factor only partially remedied the deficiency symptoms. Concentrates of vitamin B_{10} and B_{11} had no effect. It appeared that a deficiency of folic acid precipitated a deficiency of the monkey anaemia factor ; this was characterised by lack of growth, a low level of haemoglobin and a reversal of the lymphocyte-neutrophile ratio. The animals were cured by treatment with whole liver, indicating the presence therein of an anti-anaemia factor additional to folic acid. This was also present in raw milk and stimulated the growth of S. faecalis R.[58] In this respect it resembled the SLR factor, but differed from it in being heat-labile.

R. Hertz [59] observed that sexually immature monkeys maintained on a synthetic diet deficient in folic acid failed to show the normal response to oestradiol benzoate, thus showing a similar response to that exhibited by folic acid-deficient chicks (page 486).

Fish

According to McLaren et al.,[60] young rainbow trout developed anaemia in the absence of folic acid. This was cured by the addition to the diet of 0·1 to 0·5 mg. of folic acid per 100 g. It is worth recording that p-aminobenzoic acid stimulated growth in the presence of folic acid, the only instance in animals where the two factors have distinctive effects.

Folic Acid and Resistance to Infection

Monkeys exhibited an increased resistance to experimental poliomyelitis when suffering from a chronic but not an acute folic acid deficiency.[61] Folic acid had no effect on experimental toxoplasmosis in mice, but the protection afforded by sulphathiazole was neutralised by folic acid.[62] Similarly, the chemotherapeutic action of sulphadiazine on psittacosis virus was antagonised by p-aminobenzoic acid and pteroylglutamic acid, competitively in the former instance and noncompetitively in the latter.[63] This suggests that the primary action of sulphadiazine in psittacosis is against the incorporation of p-aminobenzoic acid into pteroylglutamic acid by the virus. Large doses of sulphadiazine failed to inhibit the virus when pteroylglutamic acid was supplied, so that it evidently synthesises the vitamin in the absence of sulphonamide and utilises it for growth.

Folic Acid and Cancer

Leuchtenberger et al.[64] claimed that a folic acid concentrate and the crystalline fermentation L. casei factor inhibited the growth of transplanted sarcomas in mice. Later [65] they found that whereas the liver L. casei factor did not produce regression of spontaneous breast cancer in mice, the fermentation L. casei factor was effective in eleven out of twenty-eight mice. Synthetic pteroyltriglutamic acid, " Teropterin ", did not, however, produce regeneration of $6C_3HED$ tumours in C_3H mice, although it partially inhibited the effect of mustard gas on lymphosarcoma $6C_3HED$.[66]

Synthetic folic acid has been tested, with not very encouraging results, on various forms of malignant disease in humans (see page 501).

References to Section 9

1. A. G. Hogan and E. M. Parrott, *J. Biol. Chem.*, 1939, **128**, xlvi ; 1940, **132**, 507.
2. B. L. Hutchings, N. Bohonos, D. M. Hegsted, C. A. Elvehjem and W. H. Peterson, *ibid.*, 1941, **140**, 681 ; B. L. Hutchings, N. Bohonos and W. H. Peterson, *ibid.*, 1941, **141**, 521.
3. C. J. Campbell, R. A. Brown and A. D. Emmett, *ibid.*, 1944, **152**, 483.
4. J. J. Pfiffner, D. G. Calkins, B. L. O'Dell, E. S. Bloom, R. A. Brown, C. J. Campbell and O. D. Bird, *Science*, 1945, **102**, 228.
5. B. L. Hutchings, E. L. R. Stokstad, N. Bohonos and N. H. Slobodkin, *ibid.*, 1944, **99**, 371.
6. H. K. Mitchell and R. J. Williams, *J. Amer. Chem. Soc.*, 1944, **66**, 271.
7. H. G. Petering, J. P. Marvel, C. E. Glausier and J. Waddell, *J. Biol. Chem.*, 1946, **162**, 477.
8. F. W. Hill, L. C. Norris and G. F. Heuser, *J. Nutrition*, 1944, **28**, 175 ; M. L. Scott, L. C. Norris, G. F. Heuser and W. F. Bruce, *J. Biol. Chem.*, 1945, **158**, 291.
9. B. L. Hutchings, J. J. Oleson and E. L. R. Stokstad, *ibid.*, 1946, **163**, 447.
10. J. J. Oleson, B. L. Hutchings and N. H. Sloane, *ibid.*, 1946, **165**, 371.
11. D. V. Frost and F. P. Dann, *Science*, 1946, **104**, 492.
12. D. V. Frost, F. P. Dann and F. C. McIntire, *Proc. Soc. Exp. Biol. Med.*, 1946, **61**, 65.
13. E. I. Robertson, G. F. Fiala, M. L. Scott, L. C. Norris and G. F. Heuser, *ibid.*, 1947, **64**, 441.
14. T. H. Jukes and E. L. R. Stokstad, *J. Biol. Chem.*, 1947, **168**, 563.
15. T. D. Luckey, P. R. Moore, C. A. Elvehjem and E. B. Hart, *Proc. Soc. Exp. Biol. Med.*, 1946, **62**, 307.
16. L. J. Daniel, F. A. Farmer and L. C. Norris, *J. Biol. Chem.*, 1941, **163**, 349.
17. R. Hertz and W. H. Sebrell, *Science*, 1944, **100**, 293 ; R. Hertz, *Endocrinology*, 1945, **37**, 1 ; *Science*, 1948, **107**, 300.
18. J. H. Shaw and P. H. Phillips, *J. Nutrition*, 1945, **29**, 107.
19. T. D. Luckey, P. R. Moore, C. A. Elvehjem and E. B. Hart, *Science*, 1946, **103**, 682.
20. L. W. Charkey, L. J. Daniel, F. A. Farmer, L. C. Norris and G. F. Heuser, *Proc. Soc. Exp. Biol. Med.*, 1947, **64**, 102.
21. L. R. Richardson, A. G. Hogan and H. L. Kempster, *J. Nutrition*, 1945, **30**, 151.
22. T. H. Jukes, E. L. R. Stokstad and M. Belt, *ibid.*, 1947, **33**, 1.
22a. B. S. Schweigert, *Arch. Biochem.*, 1949, **20**, 41.
23. G. J. Martin, *Proc. Soc. Exp. Biol. Med.*, 1942, **51**, 353.
24. E. Nielsen and C. A. Elvehjem, *J. Biol. Chem.*, 1942, **145**, 713 ; B. Ransone and C. A. Elvehjem, *ibid.*, 1943, **151**, 109.

25. F. S. Daft and W. H. Sebrell, *U.S. Publ. Health Rep.*, 1943, **58,** 1542.
26. A. D. Welch and L. D. Wright, *J. Nutrition*, 1943, **25,** 555.
27. G. M. Higgins, *Proc. Staff. Meetings, Mayo Clinic*, 1944, **19,** 329.
28. K. M. Endicott, F. S. Daft and M. Ott, *Arch. Path.*, 1945, **40,** 364.
29. P. Gross, A. E. Axelrod and M. D. Bosse, *Amer. J. Med. Sci.*, 1944, **208,** 642.
30. B. L. O'Dell and A. G. Hogan, *J. Biol. Chem.*, 1943, **149,** 323.
31. A. K. Miller, *J. Nutrition*, 1945, **29,** 143.
32. A. Kornberg, H. Tabor and W. H. Sebrell, *Amer. J. Physiol.*, 1944, **142,** 604.
33. M. L. Scott, L. C. Norris and G. F. Heuser, *Science*, 1946, **103,** 303.
34. A. Kornberg, F. S. Daft and W. H. Sebrell, *Proc. Soc. Exp. Biol. Med.*, 1945, **58,** 46 ; *Arch. Biochem.*, 1945, **8,** 431.
35. B. S. Schweigert, L. J. Teply, I. T. Greenhut and C. A. Elvehjem, *Amer. J. Physiol.*, 1945, **144,** 74.
36. L. C. Stewart, F. S. Daft and W. H. Sebrell, *Arch. Biochem.*, 1946, **9,** 451.
37. L. D. Wright, H. R. Skeggs, A. D. Welch, K. L. Sprague and P. A. Mattis, *J. Nutrition*, 1945, **29,** 289.
38. H. G. Day, K. G. Wakim, W. H. Zimmerman and L. S. McClung, *ibid.*, 1946, **31,** 355.
39. F. S. Daft, A. Kornberg, L. L. Ashburn and W. H. Sebrell, *Proc. Soc. Exp. Biol. Med.*, 1946, **61,** 154.
40. F. S. Daft, A. Kornberg, L. L. Ashburn and W. H. Sebrell, *U.S. Publ. Health Rep.*, 1945, **60,** 1201.
41. A. Kornberg, F. S. Daft and W. H. Sebrell, *Science*, 1946, **103,** 646.
42. M. M. Nelson and H. M. Evans, *Arch. Biochem.*, 1947, **13,** 265.
43. A. J. Sica, A. M. Allgeier and L. R. Cerecedo, *ibid.*, 1948, **18,** 119.
44. M. M. Nelson and H. M. Evans, *Proc. Soc. Exp. Biol. Med.*, 1947, **66,** 289 ; *J. Nutrition*, 1949, **38,** 11.
45. M. E. Swendseid, R. A. Brown, O. D. Bird and R. A. Heinrich, *Arch. Biochem.*, 1948, **16,** 767.
46. E. Nielsen and A. Black, *J. Nutrition*, 1944, **28,** 203.
47. A. L. Franklin, E. L. R. Stokstad and T. H. Jukes, *Proc. Soc. Exp. Biol. Med.*, 1947, **65,** 368.
48. L. R. Cerecedo and L. J. Vinson, *Arch. Biochem.*, 1944, **5,** 157 ; L. R. Cerecedo and L. Mirone, *ibid.*, 1947, **12,** 154.
48a. D. R. Weir, R. W. Heinle and A. D. Welch, *Proc. Soc. Exp. Biol. Med.*, 1948, **69,** 211.
49. D. W. Woolley and H. Sprince, *J. Biol. Chem.*, 1944, **153,** 687 ; 1945, **157,** 447.
50. W. A. Krehl and C. A. Elvehjem, *ibid.*, 1948, **158,** 173.
51. A. E. Shaefer, C. K. Whitehair and C. A. Elvehjem, *Arch. Biochem.*, 1947, **12,** 349.
52. A. E. Schaefer, C. K. Whitehair and C. A. Elvehjem, *Proc. Soc. Exp. Biol. Med.*, 1946, **62,** 169.

53. T. J. Cunha, L. K. Bustad, W. E. Ham, D. R. Cordy, E. C. McCulloch, L. F. Woods, G. H. Conner and M. A. McGregor, *J. Nutrition*, 1947, **34**, 173.

53a. T. J. Cunha, R. W. Colby, L. K. Bustad and J. F. Bone, *ibid.*, 1948, **36**, 215.

53b. G. E. Cartwright, J. Fay, B. Tatting and M. M. Wintrobe, *J. Lab. Clin. Med.*, 1948, **33**, 397.

54. W. C. Langston, W. J. Darby, C. P. Shukers and P. L. Day, *J. Exp. Med.*, 1938, **68**, 923.

55. P. L. Day, V. Mims, J. R. Totter, E. L. R. Stokstad, B. L. Hutchings and N. H. Sloane, *J. Biol. Chem.*, 1945, **157**, 423.

56. J. R. Totter, *Ann. N. Y. Acad. Sci.*, 1946, **48**, 309.

57. J. M. Cooperman, K. B. McCall and C. A. Elvehjem, *Science*, 1945, **102**, 645 ; J. M. Cooperman, H. A. Waisman, K. B. McCall and C. A. Elvehjem, *J. Nutrition*, 1945, **30**, 45 ; J. M. Cooperman, C. A. Elvehjem, K. B. McCall and W. R. Ruegamer, *Proc. Soc. Exp. Biol. Med.*, 1946, **61**, 92.

58. J. M. Cooperman, W. R. Ruegamer, E. E. Snell and C. A. Elvehjem, *J. Biol. Chem.*, 1946, **163**, 769.

59. R. Hertz, *Proc. Soc. Exp. Biol. Med.*, 1948, **67**, 113.

60. B. A. McLaren, E. Keller, D. J. O'Donnell and C. A. Elvehjem, *Arch. Biochem.*, 1947, **15**, 169.

61. H. C. Lichstein, K. B. McCall, C. A. Elvehjem and P. F. Clark, *J. Bact.*, 1946, **52**, 105.

62. W. K. Summers, *Proc. Soc. Exp. Biol. Med.*, 1947, **66**, 509.

63. H. R. Morgan, *ibid.*, 1948, **67**, 29.

64. C. Leuchtenberger, R. Lewisohn, D. Laszlo and R. Leuchtenberger, *ibid.*, 1944, **55**, 204.

65. R. Leuchtenberger, C. Leuchtenberger, D. Laszlo and R. Lewisohn, *Science*, 1945, **101**, 16 ; R. Lewisohn, C. Leuchtenberger, R. Leuchtenberger and J. C. Keresztesy, *ibid.*, 1946, **104**, 436.

66. A. D. Bass and M. L. H. Freeman, *Proc. Soc. Exp. Biol. Med.*, 1947, **66**, 523.

10. EFFECT OF FOLIC ACID DEFICIENCY IN MAN

Folic Acid in the Treatment of Anaemia and Related Conditions

The first account of the effect of folic acid in human anaemia was given by T. D. Spies and his colleagues,[1, 2] who showed that the synthetic crystalline *L. casei* factor produced a sharp reticulocyte response in patients with nutritional macrocytic anaemia in relapse, followed by a rise in the red blood cells and haemoglobin. What was at the time particularly surprising was that an equally good response was obtained whether the preparation was given parenterally or by mouth. Later it was reported [3] that a number of cases of pernicious anaemia had been successfully treated with folic acid ; 50 mg. given intravenously resulted in an increase in the red blood cells, whilst 20 mg. daily for eighteen days gave a still bigger increase. Nine patients given 50 mg. by mouth twice daily for twenty days also responded with a reticulocyte peak and an increase in red blood cells and haemoglobin. The patients were maintained satisfactorily on 100 mg. orally twice a week. Total amounts ranging from 2 to 4·5 g. were used. Cases of sprue, nutritional anaemia of pregnancy and pellagra also responded satisfactorily, and the cases showed the same striking increase in strength, vigour and appetite as with liver therapy.[4] Iron-deficiency anaemia, aplastic anaemia and leukaemia did not respond.

Support for these initial results was quickly forthcoming. Two cases of Addisonian pernicious anaemia responded to 30 and 100 mg., and one case of macrocytic anaemia of non-tropical sprue to 20 mg. ; [5] two cases of tropical sprue were improved by 15 mg.[6] given intravenously, whilst other cases were restored almost to normal by 100 mg. given orally twice daily.[7] Macrocytic anaemias of infancy, in which the bone marrow showed megaloblastic changes and the presence of abnormal young granulocytes of the type found in pernicious anaemia, were cured by daily oral administration of folic acid, but it was ineffective in all other forms of megaloblastic anaemia.[8]

A case of tropical sprue was reported [9] in which a rapid response to synthetic folic acid was obtained with a dose of only 10 mg. per day for five days although the case had previously failed to respond to liver extract. Similarly, satisfactory responses were obtained [10] in cases of pernicious anaemia with 10 mg. per day given orally or parenterally. At the same time it was pointed out that folic acid was not identical with the factor responsible for the anti-pernicious anaemia activity of liver extracts.[10] Indeed, such extracts contained very little pteroylglutamic acid [11] and the small amounts present were not correlated with anti-anaemia activity.[12, 13] The rate of bone-marrow changes following a single oral dose of 50 mg. of folic acid was equal to that produced by intramuscular injection of liver extract.[14] T. D. Spies [15] reported successful results in nutritional anaemia, in the macrocytic anaemias of pregnancy, pellagra and sprue as well as in pernicious anaemia ; a daily dose of 10 mg. produced the maximum haemopoietic response.

In spite of these striking claims, however, a note of caution began to appear in some of the subsequent publications, drawing attention to the limitations of the new agent. It gradually became clear, in fact, that folic acid was inferior in many respects to liver extracts. Difficulty was experienced, for example, in maintaining pernicious anaemia patients on folic acid alone.[16] Again, synthetic folic acid neither prevented nor relieved subacute combined degeneration of the cord in pernicious anaemia, whereas certain types of liver extract did both.[17] A lack of response was also obtained [18] in aplastic and hypoplastic anaemia, leucopenia, thrombocytopenia and ulcerative colitis, whilst in refractory anaemias folic acid alone was not able to restore the blood picture to normal, proteolysed liver being necessary, and many pernicious anaemia cases responded sub-optimally. Diarrhoea was controlled and clinical improvement was observed in cases of tropical sprue and idiopathic steatorrhoea, but not in cases of coeliac disease ; folic acid did not, however, improve fat absorption. Even in macrocytic anaemia, the blood picture was often incompletely restored.[19] Again, in two cases of tropical sprue contracted in India, the response to synthetic folic acid was dramatic, whereas in two other cases no response was obtained.[20] Synthetic folic acid was found to have no effect in four severe cases of hypochromic anaemia contracted in India,[21] although it produced rapid improvement in the character of the stools in six cases of chronic diarrhoea, possibly of nutritional origin.[22]

Thus, the chief limitation of folic acid is its inability to improve the nervous symptoms in anaemia, and patients whose blood pictures were apparently adequately controlled by folic acid developed signs of posterolateral cord sclerosis, which rapidly became intensified. Increasing the dose of folic acid failed to improve the nervous symptoms, but these disappeared if liver or desiccated stomach extract was administered.

Ross *et al.*[23] observed that in some cases of pernicious anaemia treatment with folic acid actually made pre-existing signs of nervous disturbance worse, and better results were obtained with liver extract alone than with liver extract plus folic acid. J. F. Wilkinson [24] confirmed these results and summarised his experience with folic acid in the following words : " I am fully of the opinion that pteroylglutamic acid is neither the best nor the cheapest form of treatment for pernicious anaemia and must not be given alone to patients with neurological symptoms." Folic acid does not induce neurological symptoms in patients without anaemia.[24a]

L. S. P. Davidson and R. H. Girdwood [25] recorded a somewhat different, though possibly related, limitation of folic acid. Two patients with pernicious anaemia and three with sprue developed signs of vitamin B complex deficiency when treated with folic acid, and these did not improve until the folic acid was supplemented by liver extract. As yet there are no means of determining whether the phenomenon is caused by a deficiency of one or more unknown factors or by an imbalance of vitamins. In any event, combined treatment with folic acid and liver extract is advocated in cases of sprue.

Folic acid gives perfectly satisfactory results in the treatment of nutritional anaemias, including pernicious anaemia of pregnancy, nutritional macrocytic anaemia, and the sprue syndromes, because in these conditions there is no danger of spinal cord disease.[26] The variable results obtained in sprue may be due to the fact that the disease assumes different forms in different places ; thus contrasting results were obtained with Asiatic and non-tropical sprue.

Etiology of Pernicious Anaemia

Although the use of liver and liver extracts in the treatment of pernicious anaemia has long been known, the treatment is quite empirical and until recently nothing was known about the way in which liver extracts worked or, indeed, what was the nature of the physiological or biochemical lesion responsible for pernicious anaemia. The theory most generally favoured was that of W. B. Castle,[27] who suggested that " the haemopoietic factor effective in Addisonian pernicious anaemia is normally formed by the interaction of a gastric (intrinsic) and a food (extrinsic) factor. . . . In Addisonian pernicious anaemia, the intrinsic factor is usually absent. . . . In other types of macrocytic anaemia also the specific factor in liver extract is lacking as a result of absence of food (extrinsic) or of gastric (intrinsic) factor ; of defective absorption of their reaction products from the gastro-intestinal tract ; or of some combination of these pathogenic factors. "[28]

Castle's theory was re-examined by several workers after the effect of folic acid in haemopoiesis had been discovered. According to Welch *et al.*,[29] pteroylheptaglutamic acid was ineffective in the treatment of pernicious anaemia when given orally and did not become effective when administered simultaneously with or after normal human gastric juice so that it appears unlikely that the conjugated form of folic acid can be Castle's extrinsic factor. The heptaglutamate was likewise ineffective when given intramuscularly, and the amount of folic acid excreted in the urine was not increased, as it was when pteroylglutamic acid, liver extract, or conjugate incubated with conjugase was injected.[30] On the other hand, normal subjects exhibited an increased urinary excretion of folic acid following injection of the conjugate, whence it was concluded that normal subjects but not pernicious anaemia patients can utilise the conjugate. Since purified liver extracts added to bone-marrow extracts appeared to bring about the formation of pteroylglutamic acid from the heptaglutamate, it was suggested that liver extract may contain either a component of a conjugase system or a substance capable of counteracting inhibitors of conjugase activity. Similar observations were made and similar conclusions were reached by L. S. P. Davidson and R. H. Girdwood,[31] who made the further suggestion that the anti-anaemia factor in liver might be the product formed by the interaction of Castle's extrinsic factor with the intrinsic factor of the alimentary tract. This may be absorbed from the intestine and stored in the livers of normal individuals, but not in the livers of patients with pernicious anaemia.

Although the heptaglutamate is not converted into free folic acid by the action of normal gastric juice, it is altered thereby and the digested material did not yield free folic acid when incubated with liver homogenate.[31a] Gastric juice from pernicious anaemia patients, on the other hand, had no effect on the heptaglutamate, whilst juice from sprue patients behaved like normal gastric juice. Since pteroyl-triglutamate produced reticulocytosis in cases of pernicious anaemia,[31b] the effect of normal gastric juice on the heptaglutamate cannot be simply to convert it into the triglutamate. It has also been shown [31c] that the normal gastric juice combines with vitamin B_{12} to give a microbiologically inactive complex (page 543), whereas the gastric juice from pernicious anaemia patients is inactive ; the latter appears to be deficient in two respects therefore. It has been suggested that apoerythrein, the factor in normal gastric juice that combines with vitamin B_{12}, is Castle's intrinsic factor and vitamin B_{12} the extrinsic factor and, in that event, it is possible that this reaction is essential for the absorption and storage of vitamin B_{12}, in the absence of which folic acid is not liberated from the diet.

That pteroylglutamic acid is necessary for the normal production of red blood cells and the real operative agent that transforms a pathological megaloblastic bone marrow into the physiological normo-blastic state is suggested by the observations of Meyer et al.[31d] on the effect of folic acid antagonists. They found that when a sufficient amount of an antagonist was administered, together with liver extract, the anticipated rise in red blood cells and haemoglobin did not occur ; reticulocytosis was repressed and megaloblasts remained in the bone marrow. The effect of vitamin B_{12} was also inhibited.

Although the liberation of folic acid is therefore one of the functions of vitamin B_{12}, it does not appear to be the only one, since vitamin B_{12} and folic acid are not biologically equivalent. Thus, neither pteroyl-glutamic acid nor its conjugate had a direct action on primitive erythrocytes *in vitro*, whereas potent liver extracts caused them to mature.[32] Normal human and rat serum also contained the matura-tion factor, whereas serum from a pernicious anaemia patient did not. Pteroylglutamic acid also failed to increase the maturation of bone-marrow cells suspended in this deficient serum.

It has also been suggested as an alternative theory that the anti-pernicious anaemia factor is concerned with the synthesis of folic acid in the body, but an objection to this is that purified liver extracts were ineffective in the vitamin M-deficient monkey,[33] rat [34] and chick.[35] Furthermore, folic acid does not appear to be a precursor of the anti-pernicious anaemia factor, since the latter does not contain either a pterine nucleus or an aromatic amine such as p-aminobenzoic acid (page 533).

Patients with macrocytic anaemia (nutritional), sprue, pernicious anaemia of pregnancy and idiopathic refractory megaloblastic anaemia are, however, refractory to the injection of potent purified liver extracts, despite the presence of a megaloblastic bone-marrow. Such patients respond to orally administered whole liver, proteolysed liver, liver extract or folic acid. According to L. S. P. Davidson and R. H. Girdwood [31] these types of anaemia are due not to defective production of the factor responsible for liberating free folic acid from the conjugated form, but to the absence of conjugated folic acid either as the result of a dietary deficiency or of failure to absorb folic acid from the food. Hence injections of liver extract fail to cure these conditions, whereas free folic acid is effective. The efficacy of proteolysed or oral liver extracts may be due to the presence of folic acid conjugates.

Thus the most satisfactory theory that can be put forward at the present time to account for the different forms of anaemia is that free pteroylglutamic acid is essential for haemopoiesis, though not for the maintenance of a healthy central nervous system. If pteroylglutamic acid conjugates are absent from the diet or are not absorbed, a nutritional anaemia will result. If, on the other hand, they are present but the gastric juice is defective in apoerythrein, the absorption of vitamin B_{12} from the food is impaired and the conversion of folic acid conjugates into free folic acid and certain other transformations not at present characterised do not take place and pernicious anaemia supervenes. Folic acid or its conjugates given by mouth cure nutritional anaemias but not pernicious anaemia, whilst free folic acid but not its conjugates cure the haematological but not the neurological symptoms of pernicious anaemia. Vitamin B_{12} has no effect on nutritional anaemia, because in this condition the liver already has adequate supplies, whereas it is effective in pernicious anaemia by injection because it is then immediately available for effecting, amongst other reactions, the liberation of pteroylglutamic acid. It is ineffective by mouth because it requires apoerythrein before it can be absorbed and stored in the liver.

The theory that liver extracts contain a factor that liberates free folic acid from conjugates stored in the body, thus initiating the haemopoietic response, is not accepted by all workers, however. For instance, Suarez et al.[36] claimed that West Indian sprue responded to treatment with conjugates as well as to free folic acid, and that some pernicious anaemia patients also responded. T. D. Spies and his colleagues [37] also stated that pernicious anaemia, as well as sprue and nutritional macrocytic anaemia, responded satisfactorily to conjugates. On the other hand, it has been pointed out that conjugates are difficult to prepare and may well be contaminated with free folic acid. It has also been shown, as already noted, that the gastric juice in sprue resembles that in normal subjects and, in that event, it is not surprising that conjugates should be effective in sprue.

Effect of Folic Acid on Other Blood Disorders

Folic acid was used successfully on two cases of agranulocytosis, the granulocytes returning to the blood-stream within forty-eight hours.[38] When, however, folic acid was given, together with pyridoxine, to a group of patients suffering from granulocytopenia following treatment with sulphonamides, only half gave a response and this was not maintained in many of the cases.[39] In another series of cases of agranulocytosis,[39a] the apparent response to folic acid was actually proved to be due to spontaneous remission.

The liver *L. casei* factor was also used successfully in the treatment of leucopenia following radiation therapy,[40] although no response was obtained in patients with refractory macrocytic anaemias. Folic acid was also given to patients receiving deep X-ray treatment for various conditions ; many had less nausea, vomiting and depressive symptoms than a control group.[41] It has been stated,[41a] however, that folic acid has no effect on X-ray induced anaemia.

Folic Acid and Cancer

Although folic acid appeared to inhibit the growth of certain types of tumour in experimental animals, pteroyldiglutamic acid and pteroyltriglutamic acid had no effect on the cancer in cases of advanced neoplastic disease, although the patients experienced some subjective improvement.[42] This may be due to an analgesic effect, however, as the triglutamate is said to increase the pain threshold in man.[43]

References to Section 10

1. J. L. Berry, T. D. Spies and C. A. Doan, *Southern Med. J.*, 1945, **38**, 590.
2. T. D. Spies, C. F. Vilter, M. B. Koch and M. H. Caldwell, *ibid.*, 707.
3. C. F. Vilter, T. D. Spies and M. B. Koch, *ibid.*, 781.
4. T. D. Spies, *Lancet*, 1946, **1**, 225 ; *J. Amer. Med. Assoc.*, 1946, **130**, 474.
5. C. V. Moore, O. S. Bierbaum, A. D. Welch and L. D. Wright, *J. Lab. Clin. Med.*, 1945, **30**, 1056.

6. W. J. Darby and E. Jones, *Proc. Soc. Exp. Biol. Med.*, 1945, **60**, 259 ; W. J. Darby, E. Jones and H. C. Johnson, *Science*, 1946, **103**, 108 ; *J. Amer. Med. Assoc.*, 1946, **130**, 780.

7. T. D. Spies, F. Milanes, A. Menendez and M. B. Koch, *J. Lab. Clin. Med.*, 1946, **31**, 227 ; T. D. Spies, R. M. Suarez and F. Hernandez-Morales, *Science*, 1946, **104**, 75.

8. W. W. Zuelzer and F. N. Ogden, *Proc. Soc. Exp. Biol. Med.*, 1946, **61**, 176 ; *Amer. J. Dis. Child.*, 1946, **71**, 211 ; W. W. Zuelzer, *J. Amer. Med. Assoc.*, 1946, **131**, 7.

9. P. Manson-Bahr and O. Clarke, *Lancet*, 1946, **2**, 903.

10. J. F. Wilkinson, M. C. G. Israels and F. Fletcher, *ibid.*, 156.

11. E. L. R. Stokstad and T. H. Jukes, *Proc. Soc. Exp. Biol. Med.*, 1946, **62**, 112.

12. W. Jacobson and D. M. Simpson, *Biochem. J.*, 1946, **40**, 3, 9.

13. L. Golberg, B. de Meillon and J. F. Murray, *Nature*, 1947, **160**, 22.

14. H. Levy, *Brit. Med. J.*, 1947, **1**, 412.

15. T. D. Spies, *J. Amer. Med. Assoc.*, 1946, **130**, 474.

16. R. J. Harrison and J. C. White, *Lancet*, 1946, **2**, 787.

17. T. D. Spies and R. E. Stone, *ibid.*, 1947, **1**, 174.

18. L. S. P. Davidson and R. H. Girdwood, *ibid.*, 1946, **2**, 373 ; *Brit. Med. J.*, 1947, **1**, 587 ; L. S. P. Davidson, R. H. Girdwood and E. M. Innes, *Lancet*, 1947, **1**, 511.

19. G. A. Goldsmith, *Proc. Soc. Exp. Biol. Med.*, 1947, **64**, 115.

20. R. J. G. Morrison and C. R. St. Johnston, *Lancet*, 1947, **1**, 636.

21. L. B. Carruthers, *ibid.*, 1946, **1**, 849.

22. C. F. Vilter, R. W. Vilter and T. D. Spies, *J. Lab. Clin. Med.*, 1947, **32**, 262.

23. J. F. Ross, H. Belding and B. L. Pargel, *Blood*, 1948, **3**, 68.

24. J. F. Wilkinson, *Brit. Med. J.*, 1948, **1**, 771 ; M. C. G. Israels and J. F. Wilkinson, *ibid.*, 1949, **2**, 1073.

24a. H. Poliakoff, A. Sternbach, W. H. Walker, R. L. Kascht and L. M. Meyer, *Proc. Soc. Exp. Biol. Med.*, 1949, **72**, 392.

25. L. S. P. Davidson and R. H. Girdwood, *Lancet*, 1948, **1**, 360.

26. C. R. Das Gupta and J. B. Chatterjee, *Indian Med. Gaz.*, 1946, **81**, 402 ; T. D. Spies, G. G. Lopez, R. E. Stone, F. Milanes, R. L. Toca and T. Aramburu, *Lancet*, 1948, **1**, 239.

27. W. B. Castle, *Amer. J. Med. Sci.*, 1929, **178**, 748 ; W. B. Castle, W. C. Townsend and C. W. Heath, *ibid.*, 1930, **180**, 305.

28. J. Watson and W. B. Castle, *ibid.*, 1946, **211**, 513.

29. A. D. Welch, R. W. Heinle, E. M. Nelson and H. V. Nelson, *J. Biol. Chem.*, 1946, **164**, 787 ; *Ann. N.Y. Acad. Sci.*, 1946, **48**, 347 ; R. W. Heinle and A. D. Welch, *ibid.*, 343.

30. F. H. Bethell, M. C. Meyers, G. A. Andrews, M. E. Swendseid, O. D. Bird and R. A. Brown, *J. Lab. Clin. Med.*, 1947, **32**, 3.

31. L. S. P. Davidson and R. H. Girdwood, *Brit. Med. J.*, 1947, **1**, 567.

31a. H. G. Buyze and C. Engel, *Biochim. Biophys. Acta*, 1948, **2**, 217 ; *Nature*, 1949, **163**, 135.

31b. J. F. Wilkinson and M. C. G. Israels, *Lancet*, 1949, **2**, 689.

31c. J. L. Ternberg and R. E. Eakin, *J. Amer. Chem. Soc.*, 1949, **71**, 3858.

31d. L. M. Meyer, N. D. Ritz, A. Cuccese, J. Rutzky, A. Sawitsky and G. Bock, *Amer. J. Med. Sci.*, 1949, **218**, 197.

32. E. E. Hays, *Proc. Soc. Exp. Biol. Med.*, 1946, **62**, 558.

33. P. L. Day, V. Mims, J. R. Totter, E. L. R. Stokstad, B. L. Hutchings and N. H. Sloane, *J. Biol. Chem.*, 1945, **157**, 423.

34. F. S. Daft and W. H. Sebrell, *U.S. Publ. Health Rep.*, 1943, **58**, 1542.

35. T. H. Jukes and E. L. R. Stokstad, *J. Biol. Chem.*, 1947, **168**, 563.

36. R. M. Suarez, A. D. Welch, R. W. Heinle, R. M. Suarez, jnr. and E. M. Nelson, *J. Lab. Clin. Med.*, 1946, **31**, 1294.

37. T. D. Spies, *Southern Med. J.*, 1946, **39**, 634 ; T. D. Spies and R. E. Stone, *ibid.*, 1947, **40**, 46 ; T. D. Spies, G. G. Lopez, F. Milanes and T. Aramburu, *J. Amer. Med. Assoc.*, 1947, **134**, 18.

38. D. A. K. Black and S. W. Stanbury, *Lancet*, 1947, **1**, 827.

39. H. M. Denny, M. L. Menten and E. Graff, *Amer. J. Med. Sci.*, 1946, **211**, 672.

39a. J. H. Waelsch, *Lancet*, 1948, **2**, 888.

40. C. J. Watson, W. H. Sebrell, J. L. McKelvey and F. S. Daft, *Amer. J. Med. Sci.*, 1945, **210**, 463.

41. C. A. Doan, *ibid.*, 1946, **212**, 257.

41a. S. P. Stearnes, *Proc. Soc. Exp. Biol. Med.*, 1948, **69**, 518.

42. S. Farber, E. C. Cutler, J. W. Hawkins, J. H. Harrison, E. C. Peirce and G. G. Lenz, *Science*, 1947, **106**, 619 ; L. M. Meyer, *Trans. N.Y. Acad Sci.*, 1948, **10**, 99 ; M. J. Kleiner, *ibid.*, 71 ; S. P. Lehr, L. T. Wright, S. Weintraub and I. Arons, *ibid.*, 75.

43. D. Slaughter, *Science*, 1949, **109**, 286.

11. METABOLISM OF FOLIC ACID

According to Steinkamp *et al.*[1] normal subjects excreted in the urine 2 to 4 μg. per day of pteroylglutamic acid, as estimated microbiologically with *S. faecalis* R. Following oral administration of a test-dose, 15 to 75 %, with an average of 28·5 %, was recovered in the urine.

The amount excreted increased with the amount administered, being as much as 50 % with a 5 mg. oral dose ; nearly all was excreted within six hours.[1a, 1b] The di- and tri-glutamate, but not the heptaglutamate, were converted into pteroylglutamic acid.[1c] Monkeys reacted differently and the addition to a folic acid-deficient diet of various forms of pteroylglutamic acid failed to increase the urinary or faecal excretion appreciably ; the former only amounted to about 1 % and the latter to much less than 1 % of a 1 mg. dose.[1b]

In a patient with pernicious anaemia, receiving 0·85 mg. of synthetic folic acid daily, approximately 15 % was excreted in the urine. Following the intramuscular injection of 30 mg. of conjugate, no increase occurred in the amount of folic acid excreted, but the injection of a further 11 mg. resulted in the excretion of 4·1 mg. in the following 48 hours.[2] On the other hand, a normal individual, whose output of folic acid was consistently 3 μg. per day, excreted 10 to 22 % respectively of a dose of 800 μg. of synthetic folic acid given intramuscularly on each of two successive days and 8·4 and 8·2 % respectively of an equivalent dose (2800 μg.) of the conjugate similarly injected. This observation supports the theory that pernicious anaemia is characterised by inability to utilise folic acid conjugate (see page 500).

The effect of pteroic acid on the urinary excretion of folic acid was studied by Franklin et al.[3] Following the oral administration of 2 to 10 mg., only a small amount of pteroic acid was excreted in the urine, whereas after intravenous injection 15 to 46 % was recovered in the urine. Only about 1 % was recovered in the form of pteroylglutamic acid, however, so that pteroic acid was poorly absorbed from the gastro-intestinal tract and only a very small proportion of injected material was converted into pteroylglutamic acid.

Denko et al.[4] observed that more folic acid was excreted in the faeces than in the urine and that both together exceeded the dietary intake, confirming that a synthesis of folic acid takes place to a considerable extent in man, just as it does in animals. Other evidence indicates that this synthesis is effected by the intestinal flora (see page 505).

Humans excrete folic acid in the sweat,[5] and the amount may be 5- or 6-fold the amount eliminated per hour in the urine under conditions of profuse sweating.

Following the intravenous injection of pteroylglutamic acid or the triglutamate, an increase in the blood concentration took place which reached a maximum two hours later.[6] When the triglutamate was injected intramuscularly, two-thirds of the amount remaining in the blood-stream two hours later was present in the form of the monoglutamate.[7] The blood of many animals, including man, contains folic acid conjugase capable of releasing pteroylglutamic acid from the heptaglutamate.[8]

References to Section 11

1. R. Steinkamp, C. F. Shukers, J. R. Totter and P. L. Day, *Proc. Soc. Exp. Biol. Med.*, 1946, **62**, 556.
1a. T. H. Jukes, A. L. Franklin, E. L. R. Stokstad and J. W. Boehne, *J. Lab. Clin. Med.*, 1947, **32**, 1350.
1b. P. L. Day and J. R. Totter, *J. Nutrition*, 1948, **36**, 803.

1c. T. D. Spies, G. G. Lopez, R. E. Stone, F. Milanes, R. O. Brandenburg and T. Aramburu, *Int. Z. Vit. Forsch.*, 1947, **19**, 1.
2. A. D. Welch, R. W. Heinle, E. M. Nelson and H. V. Nelson, *Ann. N. Y. Acad. Sci.*, 1946, **48**, 347.
3. A. L. Franklin, E. L. R. Stokstad and T. H. Jukes, *Proc. Soc. Exp. Biol. Med.*, 1947, **66**, 576.
4. C. W. Denko, W. E. Grundy, J. W. Porter, G. H. Berryman, T. E. Friedemann and J. B. Youmans, *Arch. Biochem.*, 1946, **10**, 33.
5. B. C. Johnson, T. S. Hamilton and H. H. Mitchell, *J. Biol. Chem.*, 1945, **159**, 425.
6. B. S. Schweigert, *J. Lab. Clin. Med.*, 1948, **33**, 1271.
7. G. Toennies and D. L. Gallant, *ibid.*, 1949, **34**, 501.
8. R. E. Simpson and B. S. Schweigert, *Arch. Biochem.*, 1949, **20**, 32 ; R. Wolff, L. Drouet and R. Karlin, *Science*, 1949, **109**, 612.

12. INTESTINAL SYNTHESIS OF FOLIC ACID

Reference has already been made (page 461) to the production of folic acid deficiency in rats by administration of sulphasuxidine and other sulphonamides,[1-3] and to the fact that large amounts of folic acid are excreted in human faeces [4] (see page 504). The faecal excretion is largely independent of the dietary intake of folic acid and so, apparently, is the urinary excretion, which decreased only slightly on a restricted diet. This may be taken to indicate that some at least of the folic acid synthesised by the intestinal flora may be utilised in man. The rat may also be able to utilise the folic acid so produced [5] although, even in the rat, symptoms of folic acid deficiency can co-exist with a high faecal elimination of folic acid.[6] Rabbits can apparently utilise folic acid synthesised by the intestinal flora, as the administration of sulphasuxidine markedly reduced the urinary excretion of folic acid.[6a] If humans can, in fact, utilise folic acid from this source, then patients with pernicious anaemia are not only unable to utilise conjugated folic acid derived from the diet, but also folic acid produced by intestinal synthesis. Similarly, patients with nutritional macrocytic anaemia must be suffering not only from a dietary deficiency but also from an inability to absorb the vitamin from the gut.

In point of fact, the only direct evidence on the extent to which folic acid synthesised by the intestinal flora can be utilised in man is an observation by Grundy *et al.*[7] that absorption does not take place. These workers found that when phthalylsulphathiazole was given for several days to volunteers maintained on carefully controlled diets, the faecal excretion of *L. casei* factor fell to about 10 % of its original value and increased again when administration of the drug ceased. The amount of folic acid excreted in the urine did not fall with the decrease in the faecal excretion, as it certainly should have done if folic acid were being absorbed from the gut.

Chicks also appear unable to utilise folic acid produced by synthesis in the intestine, since the addition of succinylsulphathiazole to the diet did not affect growth, feathering or haemoglobin formation.[8]

References to Section 12

1. G. J. Martin, *Proc. Soc. Exp. Biol. Med.*, 1942, **51**, 353.
2. E. Nielsen and C. A. Elvehjem, *J. Biol. Chem.*, 1942, **145**, 713 ; B. Ransone and C. A. Elvehjem, *ibid.*, 1943, **151**, 109.
3. F. S. Daft and W. H. Sebrell, *U.S. Publ. Health Rep.*, 1943, **58**, 1542.
4. C. W. Denko, W. E. Grundy, J. W. Porter, G. H. Berryman, T. E. Friedemann and J. B. Youmans, *Arch. Biochem.*, 1946, **10**, 33 ; C. W. Denko, W. E. Grundy, N. C. Wheeler, C. R. Henderson, G. H. Berryman, T. E. Friedemann and J. B. Youmans, *ibid.*, 1946, **11**, 109.
5. B. L. O'Dell and A. G. Hogan, *J. Biol. Chem.*, 1943, **149**, 323.
6. L. D. Wright, H. R. Skeggs, A. D. Welch, K. L. Sprague and P. A. Mattis, *J. Nutrition*, 1945, **29**, 289.
6a. R. E. Simpson, B. S. Schweigert and P. B. Pearson, *Proc. Soc. Exp. Biol. Med.*, 1949, **70**, 611.
7. W. E. Grundy, M. Freed, H. C. Johnson, C. R. Henderson and G. H. Berryman, *Arch. Biochem.*, 1947, **15**, 187.
8. E. I. Robertson, L. J. Daniel, F. A. Farmer, L. C. Norris and G. F. Heuser, *Proc. Soc. Exp. Biol. Med.*, 1946, **62**, 97.

13. HUMAN AND ANIMAL REQUIREMENTS OF FOLIC ACID

Chicks

Chickens required 10 μg. per day of synthetic *L. casei* factor to promote normal feathering and pigmentation caused by folic acid deficiency.[1] Five μg. gave fair feathering but marked depigmentation, and 2·5 μg. were ineffective.

According to Robertson *et al.*,[2] chicks required 25 μg. per 100 g. of ration in order to survive up to six weeks of age, 45 μg. per 100 g. for growth and haemoglobin formation at four weeks, 45 μg. per 100 g. for growth at six weeks, 35 μg. per 100 g. for haemoglobin formation at six weeks, and not less than 55 μg. per 100 g. for feathering at six weeks. The addition of 1 to 2 % of sulphasuxidine did not affect growth, feathering or haemoglobin formation. A diet containing 42 μg. per 100 g. was adequate for egg production and hatchability,[2a] and storage of pteroylglutamic acid did not take place below this level.[2b]

Monkeys

In order to prevent vitamin M deficiency in monkeys, 100 μg. per day of liver vitamin B_c or of synthetic $L.$ $casei$ factor or 200 to 300 μg. per day of yeast vitamin B_c conjugate were required.[3]

Humans

No direct information is yet available as to the amount of folic acid that must be ingested in the diet in order to maintain a normal individual in full health, but an estimate of the probable folic acid requirements of humans can be made from a consideration of the amounts that have to be given to maintain a normal blood picture in patients with pernicious or other types of anaemia. Such estimates have been made by L. S. P. Davidson and R. H. Girdwood,[4] who stated that the daily requirement of folic acid was 0·5 to 1 mg., although the recommended dose for the initial treatment of pernicious anaemia is higher—5 to 10 mg. daily by mouth.

For the initial maintenance therapy of nutritional megaloblastic anaemia, pernicious anaemia of pregnancy, idiopathic refractory megaloblastic anaemia or the sprue syndrome, 5 to 10 mg. of folic acid per day are advocated. In the first two diseases, treatment can be stopped when the blood count is normal, but in idiopathic refractory megaloblastic anaemias treatment for life is necessary at a suggested dose level of 5 mg. daily. The maintenance treatment in sprue will vary according to the response, and folic acid may have to be supplemented by oral liver extract or proteolysed liver. From these data, therefore, the probable human requirement of folic acid is up to 5 mg. per day.

Rats

To cure all the symptoms of folic acid deficiency in rats, 5 μg. of pteroylglutamic acid were said to be required per day,[5] whereas to cure the granulocytopenia only 5·7 μg. were required per week.[6] Larger amounts were needed during pregnancy and, particularly, during lactation.[7]

References to Section 13

1. D. V. Frost, F. P. Dann and F. C. McIntire, $Proc.$ $Soc.$ $Exp.$ $Biol.$ $Med.$, 1946, **61,** 65.
2. E. J. Robertson, L. J. Daniel, F. A. Farmer, L. C. Norris and G. F. Heuser, $ibid.$, 1946, **62,** 97.
2a. B. S. Schweigert, H. L. German, P. B. Pearson and R. M. Sherwood, $J.$ $Nutrition$, 1948, **35,** 89 ; W. W. Cravens and J. G. Halpin, $ibid.$, 1949, **37,** 127.

2b. J. R. Totter, W. E. Martindale, M. McKee, C. K. Keith and P. L. Day, *Proc. Soc. Exp. Biol. Med.*, 1949, **70**, 435.

3. J. M. Cooperman, C. A. Elvehjem, K. B. McCall and W. R. Ruegamer, *ibid.*, 1946, **62**, 92.

4. L. S. P. Davidson and R. H. Girdwood, *Brit. Med. J.*, 1947, **1**, 587.

5. C. F. Asenjo, J. *Nutrition*, 1948, **36**, 601.

6. S. J. Darke and C. White, *Brit. J. Nutrition*, 1948, **2**, ix.

7. M. B. Williamson, *Proc. Soc. Exp. Biol. Med.*, 1949, **70**, 336.

14. PHARMACOLOGY OF FOLIC ACID

Pteroylglutamic Acid

The pharmacological properties of pteroylglutamic acid were described by Harned *et al.*[1] The acute intravenous toxicity was very low, the following values being obtained for LD50 : mice, 600 ; rat, 500 ; rabbit, 410 ; guinea-pig, 120 mg. per kg. of bodyweight. In the rat, most of the deaths occurred within thirty minutes of the injection, and followed a violent convulsion, which was mainly toxic. In rabbits and guinea-pigs many of the deaths were delayed and in these instances were due to renal damage, pteroylglutamic acid being precipitated in the tubules. Male mice tolerated dosages that were lethal to females.[2]

When rabbits were given 50 mg. per kg. per day intraperitoneally for ten weeks, there was a possible retardation of growth, but no difference between the treated and control group was observed as regards blood picture, number of deaths or general appearance. At autopsy, however, the treated group showed signs of renal injury. Similarly in rats given 75 mg. per kg. per day intraperitoneally, growth was slightly depressed but no other effect was observed except renal damage.

Pteroylglutamic acid did not affect the respiration of the dog or cat in doses up to 100 mg. per kg. intravenously, or the rabbit in doses up to 50 mg. per kg. A temporary rise in blood pressure occurred in the dogs following injection and a slight rise or fall in the cats. The substance had no appreciable effect on the rabbit ileum, it did not affect the blood sugar of fasted rats, produced no irritation when injected intracutaneously into guinea-pigs, and had no diuretic activity.

Xanthopterine

The pharmacological properties of xanthopterine were described by H. Hörlein.[3] He found it to be virtually non-toxic when administered orally, whilst the lethal dose of the sodium salt given intravenously was 50 mg. per kg. for mice, 30 mg. per kg. for rabbits and

7·5 mg. per kg. for cats. The toxicity of leucopterine was of the same order.

References to Section 14

1. B. K. Harned, R. W. Cunningham, H. D. Smith and M. C. Clark, *Ann. N.Y. Acad. Sci.*, 1946, **48,** 289.
2. A. Taylor and N. Carmichael, *Proc. Soc. Exp. Biol. Med.*, 1949, **71,** 544.
3. H. Hörlein, *Arch. Exp. Path. Pharmakol.*, 1941, **198,** 258.

15. FOLIC ACID IN THE NUTRITION OF MICRO-ORGANISMS

Essential Growth Factors

It has already been stated (page 457) that folic acid and the *L. casei* factor were originally recognised by virtue of their ability to stimulate the growth of *L. helveticus* (*L. casei* ϵ) and *S. faecalis* R, and that (page 459) vitamin B_c, now known to be identical with the liver *L. casei* factor, pteroylglutamic acid, although originally recognised as an anti-anaemia factor for the chick, also stimulated the growth of these two bacteria. The fermentation *L. casei* factor, pteroyltriglutamic acid, however, is a growth factor for *L. helveticus*. but not for *S. faecalis* R, whilst vitamin B_c conjugate, pteroylheptaglutamic acid, is not a growth factor for either, but has to be converted into the monoglutamate by the action of vitamin B_c conjugase before becoming effective (page 479). Pteroic acid and the SLR factor (rhizopterine), on the other hand, are growth factors for *S. faecalis* R, but not for *L. helveticus*. Finally, it is relevant to note that *p*-aminobenzoic acid is a growth factor in its own right, although its rôle in the nutrition of micro-organisms is to some extent bound up with that of folic acid (see page 563).

Folic acid is also a growth factor for *Clostridium tetani*[1] and for the ciliate, *Tetrahymena geleii*.[2] The latter is unique among micro-organisms in that its growth is stimulated by folic acid conjugate,[2a] which is twice as active as an equivalent weight of pteroylglutamic acid.

Synthesis of Folic Acid

Most organisms, however, appear to be capable of synthesising folic acid, although some will only do so if provided with a particular part of the molecule. For example, *Aerobacter aerogenes* was found[3] to synthesise folic acid, and the amount produced was materially increased when xanthopterine was added to the culture medium. It is not clear whether in this instance xanthopterine is a precursor of folic acid or an essential growth factor for the organism, or whether its similarity to a hypothetical intermediate enables it to inhibit the synthesis or utilisation of the intermediate. It has already been noted (page 461) that the folic acid content of incubated rat liver can be increased by addition of xanthopterine [4] and here again it is not clear whether xanthopterine is a precursor of folic acid or whether folic acid is converted by enzymes in the liver into a substance that is microbiologically inactive, xanthopterine inhibiting this transformation ; the latter explanation is that favoured by Wright *et al.*

Folic acid is also synthesised by *E. coli.* A. K. Miller [5] observed that less was synthesised *in vitro* by both sulphonamide-sensitive and sulphonamide-resistant strains when grown in presence of sulphanilamide than by the same strains when grown in a sulphonamide-free medium ; by contrast, the amount of biotin synthesised by the organisms was unaffected by the presence of the antibacterial drug. These results suggest that the sulphonamides may interfere with the synthesis of folic acid by some micro-organisms, the well-known antagonism between the sulphonamides and *p* aminobenzoic acid (page 546) extending to folic acid. The inhibitory action of sulphadiazine on *Plasmodium gallinaceum*, for example, is completely antagonised by pteroylglutamic acid,[5a] which also partially antagonised the antimalarial activity of chloroguanide.

The fermentation *L. casei* factor, pteroyltriglutamic acid, was isolated from a filtrate obtained by aerobic fermentation of an unidentified species of *Corynebacterium* [6] (page 468). Folic acid is probably synthesised in the intestinal tract by coliform organisms (page 487).[7]

L. arabinosus was shown [8] to synthesise pteroylglutamic acid when excess *p*-aminobenzoic acid was present. The amount so produced was dependent on the nature of the amino acids present. Pteroylglutamic acid and pteroic acid, however, were only a partial substitute for *p*-aminobenzoic acid for stimulating the growth of *L. arabinosus* and it is probable, therefore, that *p*-aminobenzoic acid has other functions in the bacterial cell besides that of serving as a precursor of pteroylglutamic acid.

Streptobacterium plantarum also synthesised pteroylglutamic acid.[9] Only glucose and *p*-aminobenzoic acid were essential, but glutamic acid had a stimulatory action. The synthesis of pteroylglutamic acid was inhibited by sulphonamides and the inhibition was antagonised competitively by *p*-aminobenzoic acid.

Flavobacterium buccalis converted pteroylglutamic acid into pteroic acid,[10] whilst *S. lactis* R, *S. faecalis* and *S. zymogenes* converted rhizopterine into folic acid or a substance with similar activity.[11]

Folic Acid Content of Micro-organisms

By microbiological assay with *L. helveticus*, Burkholder *et al.*[12] estimated the vitamin B_c contents of autolysed and enzyme-digested cultures of 82 strains of bacteria, 369 yeasts and 94 moulds. They found chicken pancreas to be the best agent for releasing the vitamin from its conjugate. No increase in the vitamin B_c content of bacteria and yeasts was obtained when xanthopterine was added to the culture media. Many of the organisms produced considerable amounts of vitamin B_c conjugase.

The amounts of folic acid present in the five bacteria, *Aerobacter aerogenes*, *Serratia marcescens*, *Pseudomonas fluorescens*, *Proteus vulgaris* and *Clostridium butylicum* ranged from 180 to 1200 molecules per cell and the rate of synthesis from 0·25 to 1·2 molecules per cell per second.[13]

Folic Acid in Viruses

The psittacosis virus can apparently synthesise pteroylglutamic acid, since *p*-aminobenzoic acid and pteroic acid competitively antagonised the inhibition of growth of the virus by sulphadiazine and pteroylglutamic acid antagonised the inhibition non-competitively.[14]

References to Section 15

1. J. H. Mueller and P. A. Miller, *Proc. Soc. Exp. Biol. Med.*, 1942, **49**, 211, 648 ; *J. Bact.*, 1942, **43**, 763.
2. G. W. Kidder and R. C. Fuller, *Science*, 1946, **104**, 160.
2a. G. W. Kidder and V. C. Dewey, *Proc. Nat. Acad. Sci.*, 1947, **33**, 95.
3. L. D. Wright and H. R. Skeggs, *Proc. Soc. Exp. Biol. Med.*, 1944, **55**, 92.
4. L. D. Wright, H. R. Skeggs and A. D. Welch, *Fed. Proc.*, 1944, **3**, 88.
5. A. K. Miller, *Proc. Soc. Exp. Biol. Med.*, 1944, **57**, 151.
5a. J. Greenberg, *Proc. Soc. Exp. Biol. Med.*, 1949, **71**, 306.
6. B. L. Hutchings, E. L. R. Stokstad, N. Bohonos, N. H. Sloane and Y. SubbaRow, *Ann. N. Y. Acad. Sci.*, 1946, **48**, 265.
7. A. K. Miller, *J. Nutrition*, 1945, **29**, 143.
8. H. P. Sarett, *J. Biol. Chem.*, 1947, **171**, 265.
9. R. H. Nimmo-Smith, J. Lascelles and D. D. Woods, *Brit. J. Exp. Path.*, 1948, **29**, 264.
10. L. Lemon, J. P. Sickels, B. L. Hutchings, M. E. Hultquist and J. M. Smith, *Arch. Biochem.*, 1948, **19**, 311.
11. Merck & Co. Inc., B.P. 613992.
12. P. R. Burkholder, I. McVeigh and K. Wilson, *Arch. Biochem.*, 1945, **7**, 287.
13. H. McIlwain, *Nature*, 1946, **158**, 898.
14. H. P. Morgan, *J. Exp. Med.*, 1948, **56**, 285.

16. FOLIC ACID IN HIGHER PLANTS

Nothing appears to be known concerning the importance of folic acid for higher plants. It is known to be present in some green leaves, spinach leaves being the source from which it was originally isolated (see page 457).

The amount of folic acid in oats, wheat, barley and maize [1] increased considerably during germination of the grain.

Reference to Section 16

1. P. R. Burkholder, *Science*, 1943, **97**, 562.

17. FOLIC ACID IN THE NUTRITION OF INSECTS

The suggestion that folic acid is essential for the development of insects was first made by Golberg *et al.*,[1] who found that, although larvae of the mosquito, *Aedes aegypti*, developed normally as far as the fourth instar on a diet that included aneurine, riboflavine, nicotinic acid, pantothenic acid and biotin, the larvae then died without pupating. A further factor was found necessary to bring about pupation, and this was identified as folic acid which, it was suggested, stimulated the formation of a pupation hormone. Neither xanthopterine nor thymine (page 513) was able to replace folic acid in promoting pupation. Subsequently it was found that,[2] although the liver *L. casei* factor (pteroylglutamic acid) could replace folic acid as a nutritional factor for mosquito larvae when water-extracted yeast residue was present in the basal diet, it gave unsatisfactory results when the yeast residue was absent. The lactone of 4-pyridoxic acid and, to a lesser extent, the lactone of 5-pyridoxic acid were able to supplement pteroylglutamic acid, although the rate of growth was lower than when the yeast residue was present. This result bears a striking analogy to that obtained by Scott *et al.* with chicks (see page 485).

The metamorphosis of mosquito larvae has been used as a test for pteroylglutamic acid in liver extracts and urine,[3] since the antipernicious anaemia factor had no effect on pupation.

Folic acid was also found to be essential for the growth of the larvae of the beetles, *Tenebrio molitor*,[5] *Tribolium confusum*,[4, 5] *Ptinus tectus*,[5] *Sitodrepa panicea*,[5] *Lasioderma serricorne* [5] and *Silvanus surinamensis* [5] and of the moth, *Ephestia kuehniella*.[5] With *Tribolium* and *Ephestia*, the absence of folic acid resulted in very slow growth, whilst with *Tenebrio*, growth ceased entirely. The mortality was very high with *Ephestia* and *Tenebrio*. Crystalline vitamin B$_c$ was as effective as synthetic folic acid in stimulating the growth of *Ephestia* larvae, whilst xanthopterine was also effective, but only in quantities approximately 1000-fold larger than folic acid. Xanthopterine was without effect on *Tenebrio*.

Pollen contains no folic acid, and royal jelly only 0·5 μg. per 100 g.[6] so that folic acid appears to be of no significance in the development of bee larvae as are apparently biotin and pantothenic acid (pages 390, 441).

References to Section 17

1. L. Golberg, B. de Meillon and M. Lavoipierre, *Nature*, 1944, **154**, 608 ; *J. Exp. Biol.*, 1945, **21**, 90.
2. L. Golberg and B. de Meillon, *Nature*, 1947, **160**, 582.
3. L. Golberg, B. de Meillon and J. F. Murray, *ibid.*, 22.
4. C. A. Grob, T. Reichstein and H. Rosenthal, *Experientia*, 1945, **1**, 275.
5. G. Fraenkel and M. Blewett, *Nature*, 1946, **157**, 697 ; *Biochem. J.*, 1947, **41**, 469.
6. G. Kitzes, H. A. Schuette and C. A. Elvehjem, *J. Nutrition*, 1943, **26**, 241.

18. ANALOGUES OF FOLIC ACID

Pyrimidines

J. L. Stokes [1] discovered that when *L. helveticus* was grown on a medium deficient in folic acid, thymine (5-methyluracil, I) and its nucleotide, thymidine, could be utilised instead, although a 5000-fold concentration of thymine was required to produce the same effect. According to K. K. Krueger and W. H. Peterson,[2] thymine did not completely replace vitamin B_c as a growth factor for *L. helveticus*, although it did for *S. faecalis* R. *Enterococci* also required folic acid for growth and these organisms likewise responded to thymine. With *S. faecalis* R,[1, 3, 4] thymine was the only substance capable of replacing folic acid, whereas with *L. helveticus* a response was obtained with some twenty compounds related to thymine (I).[5] Of these, the most effective, next to thymine itself, was 2-hydroxy-5-methyl-4-thiopyrimidine (II), whilst good responses were also obtained with 5-methyl-cytosine (III), 5-methyl-isocytosine (IV) and 2 : 4-diamino-5-methyl-pyrimidine (V).

Replacement of the 4-hydroxy group by the 4-thiol group did not appreciably reduce the activity, possibly on account of the lability of this group, but replacement of the 2-hydroxy group or of both hydroxy groups gave compounds of low activity. Replacement of either hydroxy group by an amino group weakened the activity, giving compounds with only one-tenth the potency. The amino compounds appeared to be effective *per se* and not by conversion into thymine.

Another derivative of uracil that stimulated the growth of *L. helveticus* was orotic acid, uracil-4-carboxylic acid.[6]

In addition to replacing folic acid in the nutrition of micro-organisms, thymine has also been shown [7] to bring about remissions in Addisonian pernicious anaemia and in macrocytic anaemia, provided very high doses (4·5 g. or more daily) were given. When attempts were made to relieve the symptoms of folic acid deficiency in animals by means of thymine, however, it was found to be completely ineffective,[8] nor did it increase growth or affect haemoglobin formation in the chick.[9]

Histidine could replace folic acid for growth and acid production of *S. faecalis* R, possibly by conversion into a pyrimidine compound.[10]

Pteridines and Analogues

A number of compounds have been prepared in which the pteridine ring is replaced by another heterocyclic ring. Most of these proved to be growth inhibitors (page 516), but N-{4-(4-quinazoline)-benzoyl}-glutamic acid [11] had 1/1000 to 1/10,000 the growth promoting activity of folic acid for *S. faecalis* R.

Formyl-folic acid, prepared by heating pteroylglutamic acid with formic acid and acetic anhydride (*cf.* the preparation of rhizopterine, page 476) was found to be as effective as folic acid in stimulating the growth of *S. faecalis* R *and L. helveticus*.[12] N^{10}-Nitrosopteroyl glutamic acid was as effective as the parent compound on *S. faecalis* and on chicks.[12a]

Daniel *et al.*[9] examined the effect of some sixty compounds, mainly substituted pteridines, on growth and haemoglobin formation in chicks. Several compounds, *e.g.* 2-amino-4 : 6-dihydroxy-7-carboxy-pteridine, 2 : 4-dihydroxy-6(or 7)-hydroxy-7(or 6)-carboxymethyl-pteridine, 2-amino-4-hydroxy-6(or 7)-hydroxy-7(or 6)-methyl pteridine and 2 : 4-dihydroxy-6(or 7)-hydroxy-7(or 6)-methylpteridine increased the weight of the chicks, but had no effect on haemoglobin formation. Other compounds, *e.g.* 2-amino-4-hydroxy-7-carboxypteridine, 2 : 4-diamino-7-carboxypteridine, 2 : 4-dihydroxy-7-carboxypteridine and 2-mercapto-4-hydroxy-7-carboxypteridine had little or no effect on growth but stimulated haemoglobin formation. Some compounds had an inhibitory effect on either growth or haemoglobin formation or both, whilst one compound increased weight but reduced haemoglobin formation (page 518).

Folic Acid, p-Aminobenzoic Acid and Sulphonamides

The discovery that p-aminobenzoic acid was present in the folic acid molecule directed attention to the relationship between the growth-promoting activities of the two substances and of compounds intermediate between them. p-Aminobenzoic acid stimulated the growth of organisms for which pteroylglutamic acid was not an essential growth factor (see page 556), and vice versa. The matter was of especial interest in view of the fact that sulphonamides owe their antibacterial properties to competition with p-aminobenzoic acid for an enzyme system essential for the life of the bacterial cell (page 546).

The first attempt to determine the relative functions of p-amino-benzoic acid and pteroylglutamic acid in the nutrition of micro-organisms was made by J. O. Lampen and M. J. Jones,[13] who found that L. helveticus and S. faecalis R were not inhibited by sulphadiazine in a basal medium free from p-aminobenzoic acid when either pteroyl-glutamic acid or thymine was added. The antagonism between sulphadiazine and p-aminobenzoyl-L-glutamic acid was competitive, whereas that between sulphadiazine and folic acid or thymine was not. These observations led the authors to suggest that sulphonamides owed their antibacterial action to their ability to interfere with the synthesis of pteroylglutamic acid from p-aminobenzoic acid.

Similar results were obtained with sulphanilamide, sulphathiazole and sulphapyridine. Inhibition of sulphonamide activity also occurred with L. arabinosus, but not with E. coli, S. aureus or D. pneumoniae. Pteroylglutamic acid would therefore be expected to interfere with sulphonamide therapy in relatively few infections.

A mutant of E. coli that required p-aminobenzoic acid for growth was not stimulated by folic acid or by thymine alone,[14] but a mixture of thymine, purines and amino acids was able to replace p-amino-benzoic acid for this strain.

The Ralston strain of S. faecalis was found to synthesise pteroyl-glutamic acid, although at a sub-optimal rate.[15] In this instance, inhibition by sulphonamides was antagonised non-competitively by pteroylglutamic acid, pteroyltriglutamic acid and thymine. The amount required for sulphonamide antagonism was approximately the same as that required by S. faecalis R for growth. Similarly, strains of Enterococcus that could not synthesise pteroylglutamic acid, but required the addition of the preformed factor, were insensitive to sulphonamides, whereas strains that were able to synthesise the factor were sensitive, except when pteroylglutamic acid was added to the medium. S. faecalis R and L. helveticus, grown in presence of pteroic acid, were resistant to sulphonamides, but pteroic acid had a slight anti-sulphonamide activity for *S. faecalis* (Ralston) and *S. zymogenes* 26C1. These observations were interpreted as confirming the theory that pteroylglutamic acid is synthesised from *p*-aminobenzoic acid.

Still further support for this theory was obtained by a comparison of the ability of various compounds related to *p*-aminobenzoic acid to replace it as a growth-promoter for *L. arabinosus*.[16] *p*-Amino-benzoylglutamic acid, pteroic acid, pteroylglutamic acid and pteroyl-triglutamic acid were all less active than *p*-aminobenzoic acid, mole for mole. High concentrations of thymine could replace *p*-amino-benzoic acid but with thymine the presence of a purine was necessary.

The inhibition of *L. arabinosus* by sulphanilamide was antagonised non-competitively by pteroylglutamic acid, pteroyltriglutamic acid and by thymine. *p*-Aminobenzoylglutamic acid was about as active as *p*-aminobenzoic acid in antagonising low concentrations of sulphon-amide, but much less active against higher concentrations. *p*-Amino-benzoylglutamic acid and pteroylglutamic acid were less active than *p*-aminobenzoic acid on *Streptobacterium plantarum*, and inhibition of this organism by sulphonamides was antagonised non-competitively by pteroylglutamic acid and by thymine. As with *L. arabinosus*, the activity of *p*-aminobenzoylglutamic acid approached that of *p*-amino-benzoic acid against low sulphonamide concentrations, but was much less against high concentrations.

It is suggested that pteroylglutamic acid, the purines and thymine are products of enzyme systems in which *p*-aminobenzoic acid functions. *p*-Aminobenzoylglutamic acid appears to be utilised by the two organisms only after conversion into *p*-aminobenzoic acid.

In view of these observations, the reported existence of a con-jugated form of *p*-aminobenzoic acid is of considerable significance. K. C. Blanchard [17] advanced evidence suggesting that, in yeast, *p*-aminobenzoic acid was combined with protein, and Ratner *et al.*[18] succeeded in isolating a polypeptide containing 8 % of *p*-aminobenzoic acid. This was subsequently shown to be linked through the carboxyl group with a chain of ten or eleven L-glutamic acid residues. This conjugate accounted for 20 to 30 % of the total *p*-aminobenzoic acid content of the yeast. Its constitution bears an obvious resemblance to that of vitamin B$_c$ conjugate.

Growth Inhibitors

Replacement of the methyl group of thymine (page 513) by an amino or hydroxy group resulted in the formation of compounds with inhibitory activity, *e.g.*, 5-hydroxyuracil, 5-aminouracil, 5-carb-amidouracil, and nearly all 2 : 4-diaminopyrimidines and their con-densed ring derivatives.[5] Growth was restored by the addition of more thymine or folic acid. This suggested that these substances displaced thymine from an active enzyme centre, thus supporting the hypothesis first advanced by J. L. Stokes [1] that thymine is the product of an enzyme system of which folic acid is the prosthetic group. Results with other compounds, however, were not consistent with this hypothesis. 5-Bromouracil, for example, completely inhibited the growth of *L. helveticus* in presence of thymine, but not of folic acid, whilst 5-nitrouracil prevented the growth of *L. helveticus* in presence of folic acid but not of thymine. It would appear therefore that thymine and folic acid act independently of one another and are not components of one and the same system.

A series of diaminopteridines with anti-folic acid properties was synthesised by Mallette *et al.*[19] These, with the general formula :

$$\text{H}_2\text{N} \underset{\text{NH}_2}{\overset{\text{N} \quad \text{N} \quad \text{R}_1}{\text{[pteridine structure]}}} \text{R}_2$$

were as follows :—

(1) 2 : 4-diamino-6 : 7-dimethylpyrimido(4 : 5-*b*)pyrazine,
(2) 2 : 4-diamino-6 : 7-dicarboxypyrimido(4 : 5-*b*)pyrazine,
(3) 2 : 4-diamino-7-carboxypyrimido(4 : 5-*b*)pyrazine,
(4) 2 : 4-diamino-6 : 7-diphenylpyrimido(4 : 5-*b*)pyrazine, and
(5) 2 : 4-diaminopyrimido(4 : 5-*b*)pyrazine.

The growth of *S. faecalis*, *L. helveticus* and *L. arabinosus* (without *p*-aminobenzoic acid) was inhibited by several of these compounds. Folic acid overcame this inhibition, the antagonism being competitive.[20] The inhibition indexes of compounds (1) and (4) were 5000 and 10 respectively with *S. faecalis* and 50,000 and 200,000 with *L. helveticus*.[20a] Against *E. coli* and *Staph. aureus*, compounds (1) and (4) were the most effective ; sulphathiazole exhibited a synergistic action with both.[21] The carboxypteridines, however, had little effect on *E. coli*, and only showed a synergistic effect with sulphathiazole when tested on *Staph. aureus*. Compound (5) had only a slight antibacterial action on either organism, but showed a considerable synergistic effect with sulphathiazole. The pteridines and sulphathiazole showed synergism with *L. arabinosus* also. Folic acid completely overcame the inhibition of growth brought about by low levels of pteridine and sulphonamide but with high levels the antagonism was only partial ; this antagonism was competitive. If, on the other hand, the inhibition of pteridine or sulphonamide were studied separately, the effect of added folic acid was non-competitive. High levels of folic acid antagonised the growth inhibition of *E. coli* and *S. aureus* caused by sulphonamides, although J. O. Lampen and M. J. Jones [15] had found that low levels of folic acid did not. With *L. arabinosus* the antagonism of sulphonamide inhibition by folic acid was non-competitive. This kind of synergism between the pteridines and sulphonamides is not unexpected as they are competing with two different parts of the folic acid molecule. The sulphonamides interfere with the functioning of an enzyme that synthesises folic acid, whilst the inhibitory pteridines presumably compete with the formation of an enzyme of which folic acid is the prosthetic group. Substitution of the amino groups in 2 : 4-diamino-6 : 7-diphenylpteridine by acetyl or methyl groups or the introduction of amino, acetylamino or hydroxyl groups into the phenyl nuclei considerably increased the inhibitory action on *S. faecalis*.[21a]

Several of the pteridine derivatives tested by Daniel *et al.*[9] (page 514) inhibited growth and haemoglobin formation in chicks, notably 2-amino-4-hydroxy-6 : 7-dimethylpteridine and 2-amino-4-hydroxy-6 : 7-diphenylpteridine. Several other compounds had no effect on growth but reduced the haemoglobin, and one compound, 2-amino-4-hydroxy-6(or 7)-hydroxy-7(or 6)-methylpteridine, increased the weight but depressed haemoglobin formation. The inhibitory compounds interfered with folic acid metabolism, for reduced levels of the vitamin were found in the liver and blood after administration of the substance.

The most important growth inhibitors related to pteroylglutamic acid, however, are either homologues or compounds derived from pteroylglutamic acid by the replacement of one or more substituent by some other group. To facilitate the description of these compounds, the atoms comprising the pteroyl radicle have been numbered as follows :

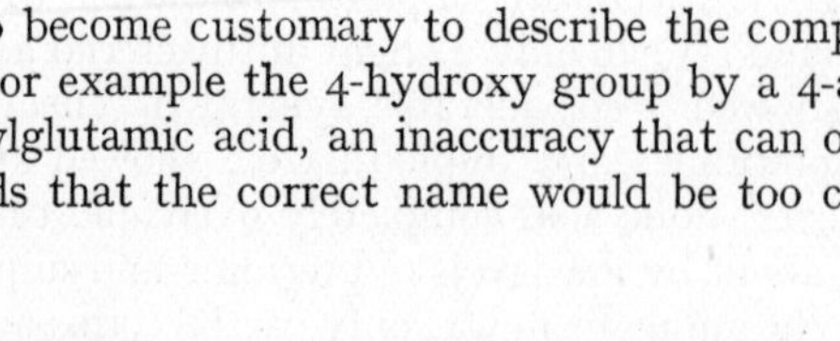

It has also become customary to describe the compound obtained by replacing for example the 4-hydroxy group by a 4-amino group as 4-aminopteroylglutamic acid, an inaccuracy that can only be excused on the grounds that the correct name would be too cumbersome for general use.

7-Methylfolic Acid

One close structural analogue of folic acid with growth-inhibitory properties is 7-methylfolic acid or, to give it its full chemical name,

N-(4-[{(2-amino-4-hydroxy-7-methyl-6-pteridyl)-methyl}-amino]-benzoyl)-L-glutamic acid.[22] This was prepared by the same reaction as that used to synthesise folic acid, except that 2 : 3-dibromobutyraldehyde was used in place of 2 : 3-dibromopropionaldehyde. It inhibited competitively the growth-promoting action of folic acid, the ratio of inhibitor to metabolite being 150, by a mechanism different from that involved in sulphonamide inhibition. Thus, the inhibitory action of sulphathiazole towards S. aureus was neutralised by p-aminobenzoic acid and by pteroic acid, but not by glutamic acid, p-aminobenzoylglutamic acid or pteroylglutamic acid, whereas the action of 7-methylfolic acid was neutralised by pteroylglutamic acid, pteroic acid and p-aminobenzoic acid but not by p-aminobenzoylglutamic acid.[23] This suggests that the synthesis of pteroic acid is the first step in the formation of pteroylglutamic acid, and that methylfolic acid prevents the synthesis of pteroylglutamic acid by interfering with the formation of pteroic acid and its union with glutamic acid. But methylfolic acid also displaced preformed pteroylglutamic acid and, like the sulphonamides, it interfered with the incorporation of p-aminobenzoic acid into pteroylglutamic acid. The effect of methylfolic acid was counteracted by sulphathiazole, this being an example of mutual interference by two antagonists.

The inhibitory action of 7-methylfolic acid was also antagonised by formylfolic acid (page 514) which was actually about thirty times as effective as folic acid, having an antibacterial index of 3000 with S. faecalis R.[12] Synthetic rhizopterine (page 476) was two to three times as effective as folic acid in preventing inhibition. The toxicity of 7-methylfolic acid was increased by heating with formic acid. These results suggest that rhizopterine may be converted directly into formylfolic acid.

7-Methylfolic acid also antagonised the growth-promoting action of pteroylglutamic acid on L. helveticus and on rats, and again the antagonism was competitive.[24] The effect in rats was to produce symptoms more acute than those produced by feeding a purified diet plus succinylsulphathiazole. 7-Methylfolic acid also produced symptoms of folic acid deficiency in mice, although such symptoms cannot normally be induced merely by feeding a purified diet plus succinylsulphathiazole. It also aggravated a folic acid deficiency in chicks maintained on a purified diet and reduced the response normally elicited in immature chicks by stilboestrol [25] (page 486).

The antagonist likewise interfered with the metabolism of pteroylglutamic acid in the pig, interrupting growth and significantly inhibiting the formation of erythrocytes and granulocytes.[26] This interference was overcome, even though administration of the antagonist was continued, by feeding normal human gastric juice together with a crude source of the extrinsic factor (page 498) from which pteroylglutamic acid had been eliminated.

The antibacterial index of 7-methylfolic acid was approximately 30 for *L. helveticus* in the absence of purines and pyrimidines.[27] The addition to the medium of adenine, guanine, hypoxanthine or xanthine increased the antibacterial index to about 100. Thymine alone had no effect but, in the presence of purines, the antibacterial index was increased to over 1000. This evidence appears to give further support to the theory of J. L. Stokes [1] that folic acid is concerned in the biosynthesis of thymine.

The inhibitory action of methylfolic acid for *L. helveticus* was antagonised by liver extracts to an extent 15 times greater than could be accounted for by their folic acid contents. A concentrate was prepared from hog liver that was somewhat more active than folic acid in antagonising the effect of methylfolic acid on *L. helveticus* and 10 to 100 times as effective with *S. faecalis* R. The new factor has been named folinic acid and proved to be as effective a growth factor for these two organisms as is folic acid. It also stimulated the growth of *Leuconostoc citrovorum*, an organism on which folic acid has no effect ; on mild acid hydrolysis folinic acid was apparently converted into folic acid.[27a]

9-Methylfolic Acid, N^{10}-Methylfolic Acid and 9 : N^{10}-Dimethylfolic Acid

9-Methylfolic acid also antagonises folic acid, but is much less potent than 7-methylfolic acid, having an antagonist activity of only 0·1 with *S. faecalis* R.[27b] N^{10}-Methylpteroylglutamic acid was much more potent, with an antagonist activity of 100 against *S. faecalis* R, but N^{10}-phenacylpteroylglutamic acid was much less active. 9 : N^{10}-Dimethylpteroylglutamic acid had an antagonist activity of 3·4.[27a]

Pteroylaspartic Acid

A homologue of a rather different type, which likewise had anti-folic acid properties was pteroylaspartic acid.[28] This has one methylene group less in the amino acid radicle than has folic acid, and it was shown to be antagonistic to folic acid both with *L. helveticus* and with the chick. With *S. faecalis* R, the inhibitor prevented the utilisation of pteroic acid, pteroylglutamic acid, pteroyl-γ-glutamylglutamic acid and pteroyl-γ-glutamyl-γ-glutamylglutamic acid. In all instances, the inhibition was competitive in nature.

Amino-folic Acids

A compound derived from pteroylglutamic acid by the replacement of the hydroxyl group by an amino group also had growth-inhibitory activity.[29] This was N-[4-{[(2 : 4-diamino-6-pteridyl)-methyl]-amino}-benzoyl]-glutamic acid, generally referred to as 4-aminopteroylglutamic acid or Aminopterin ; it was prepared from 2 : 4 : 5 : 6-tetraamino-pyrimidine by a reaction analogous to that used for the preparation of pteroylglutamic acid. The compound had inhibition ratios for half-maximum inhibition of the growth of *S. faecalis* R of 1·9, 0·7 and 0·4 at pteroylglutamic acid concentrations of 0·003, 0·005 and 0·01 μg. per 10 ml. respectively. The compound was highly toxic to mice and, at levels less than 0·3 mg. per kg. of diet, the toxicity was partially neutralised by pteroylglutamic acid, but this had no effect with amounts of 1 to 3 mg. per kg. of diet.[30]

4-Aminopteroylglutamic acid was also an antagonist for pteroylglutamic acid in rats and chickens, and here also the inhibition was not strictly competitive in nature.[31] It produced folic acid deficiency in rats, with loss of weight, hypoplasia of the bone-marrow and intestinal lesions with diarrhoea,[32] and abnormalities in chick embryos that were not prevented by large doses of folic acid.[33] In dogs, 4-aminopteroylglutamic acid produced a sprue-like syndrome with diarrhoea, peripheral leucopenia, depletion of the bone marrow and changes in the blood picture ;[34] haematological changes were also produced when the compounds were administered to guinea-pigs.[35] Pteroylaspartic acid and 7-methylfolic acid did not produce these changes, although they potentiated the effect of 4-aminopteroylglutamic acid.

4-Aminopteroylglutamic acid depressed the response of the oviducts of frogs to oestradiol, whereas folic acid potentiated the effect. The effect of Aminopterin was not reversed by folic acid in 100-fold concentration. It is suggested that folic acid antagonists may exert their inhibitory effects by interfering with folic acid utilisation, depressing nucleic acid synthesis and retarding the rate of cell division.[36] Aminopterin also interfered with the depressive influence of oestradiol on the rat prostate.[37]

4-Aminopteroylglutamic acid inhibited the growth of *E. coli*, but the inhibition was not reversed by pteroylglutamic acid, although it was reversed by thymidine or a liver extract. *Lactobacillus leichmannii* was also inhibited by 4-aminopteroylglutamic acid and in this instance the inhibition was reversed by pteroylglutamic acid at low concentrations of inhibitor and by thymidine at higher concentrations.[38]

Aminopterin had no effect on the growth of psittacosis virus.[39]

Aminopterin and several related compounds had an inhibitory action on tumour growth (page 523).

Other potent antagonists of folic acid are obtained by replacing the hydroxyl group in various homologues of pteroylglutamic acid by an amino-group. Thus 4-amino-N^{10}-methylpteroylglutamic acid was an antagonist of pteroylglutamic acid for rats, chicks and S. faecalis R; [40, 41] the inhibitory action on S. faecalis R was reversed by pteroylglutamic acid at all concentrations, but the toxic effect on rats was reversible only over a very narrow range.[40]

4-Amino-9 : N^{10}-dimethylpteroylglutamic acid had an antagonist activity of 1560 against S. faecalis.[27a] 4-Aminopteroylaspartic acid, made by condensing p-aminobenzoylaspartic acid with 1 : 3 : 3-tribromopropanone-2 and 2 : 4 : 5 : 6-tetraaminopyrimidine, was a competitive antagonist of pteroylglutamic acid in the chick, rat and certain bacteria.[42] It produced abnormalities in chick embryos, as did the corresponding alanine and threonine derivatives, but all were less active than 4-aminopteroylglutamic acid.[33] 4-Aminopteroyl derivatives of aminomalonic acid, ϵ-aminocaproic acid, isoleucine, phenylalanine, sarcosine, serine, tryptophan and valine have also been prepared.[43]

Xanthopterine and its Derivatives

Pure xanthopterine and dihydroxanthopterine inhibited the growth of L. helveticus, although impure xanthopterine has been stated to have slight growth-promoting activity.[44] According to J. A. Pritchard,[45] xanthopterine failed to cure the symptoms of folic acid deficiency induced in rats by the feeding of succinylsulphathiazole, whereas E. R. Norris and J. J. Majnarich [46] reported that it produced an immediate and rapid increase in the reticulocytes, red and white blood cells, blood-cell volume and haemoglobin in rats made anaemic by means of sulphathiazole. It also increased the rate of cell proliferation of erythrocytes in bone-marrow cultures and increased the numbers of nucleated cells and reticulocytes. A few other substances related to xanthopterine had a similar though less marked effect, but xanthopterine-7-carboxylic acid and 2-amino-4-hydroxy-7-methylpteridine were strongly inhibitory ; the effect of the latter was antagonised by xanthopterine.[47]

Miscellaneous Folic Acid Inhibitors

A number of substituted pteridine carboxylyl-p-aminobenzoylglutamic acids and related compounds were found to inhibit the growth of bacteria by competition with folic acid.[48] The most active compound was 2-amino-4:7-dihydroxypteridine-6-carboxylyl-p-aminobenzoylglutamic acid, but quinoxaline-2-carboxylyl-p-aminobenzoyl-glutamic acid and a substance formed by the reaction of dibromo-propionaldehyde with o-phenylene diamine and p-aminobenzoyl-glutamic acid were also markedly inhibitory. Quinoxaline itself inhibited the growth of *S. faecalis* R and the effect was reversed by pteroyl glutamic acid.[49]

According to Edwards *et al.*,[50] the benzimidazole corresponding to pteroylglutamic acid, namely N-{4-[(2-benzimidazolylmethyl)-amino]-benzoyl}-glutamic acid could replace folic acid as a growth factor for *S. faecalis* R, although N-{4-[(2-benzimidazolylmethyl)-amino]-benzene sulphonyl}-glutamic acid antagonised folic acid. King *et al*,[51] however, found the former to have a slight inhibitory action on the growth of both *S. faecalis* R and *L. helveticus* ; the 5-chloro-derivative was somewhat more active. Pteroylsulphoglutamic acid, N-[4-{[(2-amino-4-hydroxy-6-pteridyl)-methyl]-amino}-benzenesulphonyl]-glutamic acid slightly inhibited the growth of *S. faecalis*, but did not antagonise the action of folic acid on this organism or on *L. helveticus* or *S. aureus*.[52]

Folic Acid Antagonists and Cancer

It has already been noted (page 501) that pteroylglutamic acid and pteroyltriglutamic acid induce a sense of well-being in cancer patients without having any inhibitory action on the growth of the tumour. It was observed, however, that in animals a folic acid deficient diet protected experimental animals against Rous chicken sarcoma.[53, 54] This naturally led to tests being conducted with folic acid antagonists, and it was found that pteroylaspartic acid, 4-amino-N[10]-methylpteroic acid and 4-amino-N[10]-methylpteroylglutamic acid were slightly effective, 4-aminopteroylaspartic acid markedly effective and 4-aminopteroylglutamic acid most effective of all in preventing the development of sarcoma.[54] The lives of mice with transplanted leukemia were prolonged when large amounts of crude 7-methylfolic acid were given [55] or when 4-amino-N[10]-methylpteroylglutamic acid, 4-amino-9-methylpteroylglutamic acid, 4-amino-9 : N[10]-dimethyl-pteroylglutamic acid or 2 : 6-diaminopurine were administered.[56] The effect of 4-amino-N[10]-methylpteroylglutamic acid was blocked by prior administration of 10 to 20 times the amount of pteroylglutamic acid.[57]

One or two of these compounds, particularly Aminopterin, have been tested in human leukemia, but the results have proved disappointing. Occasional remissions were observed in some patients, but these were only temporary and toxic symptoms were produced in many patients.[58]

Several of the above folic acid antagonists inhibited the growth of crown gall tumour tissue on carrot fragments.[59]

References to Section 18

1. J. L. Stokes, *J. Bact.*, 1944, **47**, 433 ; 1944, **48**, 201.
2. K. K. Krueger and W. H. Peterson, *J. Biol. Chem.*, 1945, **158**, 145.
3. H. K. Mitchell and R. J. Williams, *J. Amer. Chem. Soc.*, 1944, **66**, 271.
4. T. D. Luckey, G. M. Briggs and C. A. Elvehjem, *J. Biol. Chem.*, 1944, **152**, 157.
5. G. H. Hitchings, E. A. Falco and H. B. Sherwood, *Science*, 1945, **102**, 251 ; G. H. Hitchings, G. B. Elion, H. Vander Werf, and E. A. Falco, *J. Biol. Chem.*, 1948, **174**, 765.
6. F. W. Chattaway, *Nature*, 1944, **153**, 250.
7. W. B. Frommeyer, T. D. Spies, C. F. Vilter and A. English, *J. Lab. Clin. Med.*, 1946, **31**, 643 ; T. D. Spies, W. B. Frommeyer, C. F. Vilter and A. English, *Blood*, 1946, **1**, 185.
8. H. G. Petering and R. A. Delor, *Science*, 1947, **105**, 547.
9. L. J. Daniel, M. L. Scott, L. C. Norris and G. F. Heuser, *J. Biol. Chem.*, 1948, **173**, 123.
10. D. A. Hall, *Proc. Biochem. Soc.*, 1946, **40**, lv.
11. G. J. Martin, J. Moss and S. Avakian, *J. Biol. Chem.*, 1947, **167**, 737.
12. M. Gordon, J. M. Ravel, R. E. Eakin and W. Shive, *J. Amer. Chem. Soc.*, 1948, **70**, 879.
12a. D. B. Cosulich and J. M. Smith, *ibid.*, 1949, **71**, 3574.
13. J. O. Lampen and M. J. Jones, *J. Biol. Chem.*, 1946, **164**, 485.
14. J. O. Lampen, R. R. Roepke and M. J. Jones, *ibid.*, 789.
15. J. O. Lampen and M. J. Jones, *ibid.*, 1946, **166**, 435.
16. J. O. Lampen and M. J. Jones, *ibid.*, 1947, **170**, 133.
17. K. C. Blanchard, *ibid.*, 1941, **140**, 919.
18. S. Ratner, M. Blanchard, A. F. Coburn and D. E. Green, *ibid.*, 1944, **155**, 689 ; S. Ratner, M. Blanchard and D. E. Green, *ibid.*, 1946, **164**, 691.
19. M. F. Mallette, E. C. Taylor and C. K. Cain, *J. Amer. Chem. Soc.*, 1947, **69**, 1814.
20. L. J. Daniel, L. C. Norris, M. L. Scott and G. F. Heuser, *J. Biol. Chem.*, 1947, **169**, 689.
20a. M. E. Swendseid, E. L. Wittle, G. W. Moersch, O. D. Bird and R. A. Brown, *ibid.*, 1949, **179**, 1175.
21. L. J. Daniel and L. C. Norris, *ibid.*, 1947, **170**, 747.
21a. C. K. Cain, E. C. Taylor and L. J. Daniel, *J. Amer. Chem. Soc.*, 1949, **71**, 892.
22. G. J. Martin, L. Tolman and J. Moss, *Arch. Biochem.*, 1947, **12**, 318.
23. G. J. Martin, L. Tolman and J. Moss, *Science*, 1947, **106**, 168.
24. A. L. Franklin, E. L. R. Stokstad, M. Belt and T. H. Jukes, *Proc. Soc. Exp. Biol. Med.*, 1947, **65**, 368 ; *J. Biol. Chem.*, 1947, **169**, 427.
25. R. Hertz, *Science*, 1948, **107**, 300.
26. A. D. Welch, R. W. Heinle, G. Sharpe, W. L. George and M. Epstein, *Proc. Soc. Exp. Biol. Med.*, 1947, **65**, 364.
27. L. L. Rogers and W. Shive, *J. Biol. Chem.*, 1948, **172**, 751.

27a. T. J. Bond, T. J. Bardos, M. Sibley and W. Shive, *J. Amer. Chem. Soc.*, 1949, **71**, 3852 ; T. J. Bardos, T. J. Bond, J. Humphreys and W. Shive, *ibid.*, 3852.

27b. D. B. Cosulich and J. M. Smith, *J. Amer. Chem. Soc.*, 1948, **70**, 1922 ; M. E. Hultquist, J. M. Smith, D. R. Seeger, D. B. Cosulich and E. Kuh, *ibid.*, 1949, **71**, 619 ; J. M. Smith, D. B. Cosulich, M. E. Hultquist and D. R. Seeger, *Trans. N.Y. Acad. Sci.*, 1948, **10**, 82.

28. B. L. Hutchings, J. H. Mowat, J. J. Oleson, E. L. R. Stokstad, J. H. Boothe, C. W. Waller, R. B. Angier, J. Semb and Y. SubbaRow, *J. Biol. Chem.*, 1947, **170**, 323.

29. D. R. Seeger, J. M. Smith and M. E. Hultquist, *J. Amer. Chem. Soc.*, 1947, **69**, 2567.

30. A. L. Franklin, E. L. R. Stokstad and T. H. Jukes, *Proc. Soc. Exp. Biol. Med.*, 1948, **67**, 399.

31. J. J. Oleson, B. L. Hutchings and Y. SubbaRow, *J. Biol. Chem.*, 1948, **175**, 359.

32. F. S. Philips and J. B. Thiersch, *J. Pharmacol.*, 1949, **95**, 303.

33. D. A. Karnofsky, P. A. Patterson and L. P. Ridgway, *Proc. Soc. Exp. Biol. Med.*, 1949, **71**, 447.

34. J. B. Thiersch and F. S. Philips, *ibid.*, 484.

35. J. Innes, E. M. Innes and C. V. Moore, *J. Lab. Clin. Med.*, 1949, **34**, 883.

36. E. D. Goldsmith, S. S. Schreiber and R. F. Nigrelli, *Proc. Soc. Exp. Biol. Med.*, 1948, **69**, 299 ; 1949, **71**, 461.

37. H. Brendler, *Science*, 1949, **110**, 119.

38. A. L. Franklin, E. L. R. Stokstad, C. E. Hoffmann, M. Belt and T. H. Jukes, *J. Amer. Chem. Soc.*, 1949, **71**, 3549.

39. H. R. Morgan, *J. Exp. Med.*, 1948, **88**, 285.

40. A. L. Franklin, M. Belt, E. L. R. Stokstad and T. H. Jukes, *J. Biol. Chem.*, 1949, **177**, 621.

41. D. R. Seeger, D. B. Cosulich, J. M. Smith and M. E. Hultquist, *J. Amer. Chem. Soc.*, 1949, **71**, 1753.

42. B. L. Hutchings, J. H. Mowat, J. J. Oleson, A. L. Gazzola, E. M. Boggiano, D. R. Seeger, J. H. Boothe, C. W. Waller, R. B. Angier, J. Semb and Y. SubbaRow, *J. Biol. Chem.*, 1949, **180**, 857.

43. W. B. Wright, D. B. Cosulich, M. J. Fahrenbach, C. W. Waller, J. M. Smith and M. E. Hultquist, *J. Amer. Chem. Soc.*, 1949, **71**, 3014.

44. G. B. Elion, A. E. Light and G. H. Hitchings, *ibid.*, 941.

45. J. A. Pritchard, *Proc. Soc. Exp. Biol. Med.*, 1948, **69**, 221.

46. E. R. Norris and J. J. Majnarich, *Amer. J. Physiol.*, 1948, **152**, 175, 179 ; 1948, **153**, 133.

47. E. R. Norris and J. J. Majnarich, *ibid.*, 1948, **152**, 652 ; 1948, **153**, 488.

48. D. W. Woolley and A. Pringle, *J. Biol. Chem.*, 1948, **174**, 327.

49. D. A. Hall, *Biochem. J.*, 1947, **41**, 294.

50. P. C. Edwards, D. Starling, A. M. Mattocks and H. E. Skipper, *Science*, 1948, **107**, 119.

51. F. E. King, P. C. Spensley and R. H. Nimmo-Smith, *Nature*, 1948, **162**, 153 ; F. E. King, R. M. Acheson and P. C. Spensley, *J. Chem. Soc.*, 1949, 1401.

52. H. S. Forrest and J. Walker, *ibid.*, 2002 ; M. Viscontini and J. Meier, *Helv. Chim. Acta*, 1949, **32**, 877 ; R. Gavard and M. Viscontini, *ibid.*, 2328.

53. E. Woll, *Trans. N.Y. Acad Sci.*, 1948, **10**, 83.

54. P. A. Little, A. Sampath, V. Paganelli, E. Locke and Y. SubbaRow, *ibid.*, 83 ; P. A. Little, A. Sampath and Y. SubbaRow, *J. Lab. Clin. Med.*, 1948, **33**, 1144.

55. D. R. Weir, A. D. Welch and R. W. Heinle, *Proc. Soc. Exp. Biol. Med.*, 1949, **71**, 107.

56. J. H. Burchenal, S. F. Johnston, J. R. Burchenal, M. N. Kushida, E. Robinson and C. C. Stock, *ibid.*, 381.

57. J. H. Burchenal, M. N. Kushida, S. F. Johnston and M. A. Cremer, *ibid.*, 559.

58. J. M. Stickney, A. B. Hagedorn, S. D. Mills and T. Cooper, *J. Lab. Clin. Med.*, 1948, **33**, 1481 ; W. Jacobson, W. C. Levin and G. Holt, *ibid.*, 1641 ; M. Pierce and H. Alt, *ibid.*, 1642 ; L. Berman, A. R. Axelrod, E. C. VonderHeide and E. A. Sharp, *ibid.*, 1643 ; S. G. Taylor, D. Slaughter, F. W. Preston, J. Crumrine and G. Hass, *ibid.*, 1643 ; S. Farber, L. K. Diamond, R. D. Mercer, R. F. Sylvester, and J. A. Wolff, *New England J. Med.*, 1948, **238**, 787 ; L. M. Meyer, H. Fink and A. Sawitsky, *Amer. J. Clin. Path.*, 1949, **29**, 119 ; P. L. de V. Hart, *Brit. Med. J.*, 1949, **2**, 363.

59. R. S. de Ropp, *Nature*, 1949, **164**, 954.

19. FUNCTION OF FOLIC ACID

In animals and man, folic acid is necessary for the proper functioning of the haemopoietic system. Nutritional anaemias are due to the absence of free or combined folic acid from the diet, whilst pernicious anaemia is probably due to an inability to utilise combined folic acid, owing to the absence of vitamin B_{12} from the liver (see page 498).

No satisfactory suggestion has yet been put forward to explain the mechanism whereby pteroylglutamic acid stimulates reticulocytosis, nor is it known why it is essential for the growth of bacteria. According to J. E. Davis[1] the action of folic acid is mediated through choline esterase. He claimed that subcutaneous injection of acetylcholine produced hyperchromic anaemia in dogs and that both liver extract and folic acid increased the number of reticulocytes and red blood cells, at the same time increasing the choline esterase activity. The choline esterase activity of dog serum was increased *in vitro* by incubation with folic acid or liver extract, and oral administration of folic acid to normal humans also increased the choline esterase activity.

These results have not been confirmed, and R. D. Hawkins [1a] could find no increase in the activity of either true cholinesterase or pseudo-cholinesterase on incubating the plasma of rats or dogs with folic acid or on administering folic acid to dogs or men. Dinning et al. [1b] suggest that pteroylglutamic acid may function in a choline oxidase system, since the livers and kidneys of Aminopterin-treated monkeys were virtually devoid of choline oxidase, as were the livers and kidneys of monkeys fed a pteroylglutamic acid-deficient diet.

Catalytic hydrogenation of vitamin B_6 yielded a dihydro-compound, which was readily oxidised to the parent compound, and it was suggested that vitamin B_6, like riboflavine, might function in an oxidation-reduction enzyme system. [2]

It appears probable, indeed, that pteroylglutamic acid influences tyrosine oxidation, because liver slices from pteroylglutamic acid-deficient rats showed a decreased ability to oxidise tyrosine compared with livers from normal rats, [3] and the reduced oxygen uptake was increased when pteroylglutamic acid was added in vitro. The ability to oxidise tyrosine was also lower than normal in liver slices from rats given Aminopterin, but in this instance no effect was observed on the addition of pteroylglutamic acid in vitro. Aminopterin in vitro had no effect on tyrosine oxidation by normal liver slices. It is known that the amount of phenolic compounds in the urine is increased in pernicious anaemia. [4] Scorbutic guinea-pigs also excreted large amounts of tyrosine-like compounds, up to 45 % of a 450-mg. dose of tyrosine being eliminated in the urine ; the administration of pteroylglutamic acid or ascorbic acid produced a marked drop in the amount of tyrosine excreted. [5] Premature infants fed cows' milk but no ascorbic acid excreted significant amounts of phenolic substances, and in some instances this was decreased on administration of pteroylglutamic acid, although the response was more marked and more regular when ascorbic acid was given. [5a]

7-Methylfolic acid inhibited tyrosine decarboxylase only in very high concentrations, although 7-methylfolic acid and pteroylaspartic acid inhibited dopa decarboxylase and the inhibition was nullified by folic acid. [6] On the assumption that folic acid was connected with the decarboxylation of tyrosine, which they presumed to be the first step in the formation of adrenaline, Martin et al. [7] tested the hypotensive action of 7-methylfolic acid. The fact that it proved to be a powerful depressor is presumptive evidence in favour of the view that folic acid is concerned with tyrosine decarboxylation.

On the other hand, folic acid appears to have other functions. Reference has already been made (page 517) to the theory, first advanced by J. L. Stokes, [8] that folic acid is responsible for the synthesis of thymine. This is supported, not only by the observation that thymine can replace folic acid in the nutrition of certain micro-organisms, but also by the observation that thymine reversed the antagonistic effect of some uracil derivatives on folic acid [9] and, in the presence of purine, increased many-fold the antibacterial index of "methylfolic acid" for *L. helveticus*.[10]

A partial deficiency of pteroylglutamic acid lowered the desoxy-ribonucleic acid content of *L. helveticus*, without affecting the ribo-nucleic acid, whereas a deficiency of riboflavine or biotin or an excess of thymine increased both.[10a]

It has also been suggested [11] that pteroylglutamic acid is involved in the synthesis of the porphyrin portions of metalporphyrin enzymes, since pteroylglutamic acid partially reversed the inhibitory action of cyanide, caffeine and hydrogen peroxide on *S. faecalis*.

Pteroylglutamic acid strongly inhibited the activity of xanthine oxidase and of a xanthopterine oxidase prepared from either milk or liver.[12] Pteroic acid also inhibited the latter enzyme, but pteroyldi- and tri-glutamic acid had no effect. Milk contained an enzyme that transformed pteroylglutamic acid into a substance that had no inhibitory action on xanthopterine oxidase.[13]

6-Pteridylaldehyde, obtained by the hydrolysis of pteroylglutamic acid in sulphurous acid, was found to be 200 to 400 times as active as folic acid in inhibiting xanthine oxidase, and also more active than folic acid in inhibiting xanthopterine oxidase.[14] It also inhibited quinine oxidase.

Thus folic acid and related compounds are capable of affecting a number of different enzyme systems, and it remains to be seen which of these are of physiological significance.

References to Section 19

1. J. E. Davis, *Science*, 1946, **104**, 37 ; *Amer. J. Physiol.*, 1946, **147**, 404.
1a. R. D. Hawkins, *Arch. Biochem.*, 1948, **17**, 97.
1b. J. S. Dinning, C. K. Keith and P. L. Day, *ibid.*, 1949, **24**, 463.
2. B. L. O'Dell, J. M. Vandenbelt, E. S. Bloom and J. J. Pfiffner, *J. Amer. Chem. Soc.*, 1947, **69**, 250.
3. G. Rodney, M. E. Swendseid and A. L. Swanson, *J. Biol. Chem.*, 1947, **168**, 395 ; 1949, **179**, 19.
4. M. E. Swendseid, I. F. Burton and F. H. Bethell, *Proc. Soc. Exp. Biol. Med.*, 1943, **52**, 202.
5. C. W. Woodruff and W. J. Darby, *J. Biol. Chem.*, 1948, **172**, 851 ; C. W. Woodruff, M. E. Charrington, A. K. Stockell and W. J. Darby, *ibid.*, 1949, **178**, 861.
5a. C. D. Govan and H. H. Gordon, *Science*, 1949, **109**, 332.
6. G. J. Martin and J. M. Beiler, *Arch. Biochem.*, 1947, **15**, 201.
7. G. J. Martin, L. Tolman and R. Brendel, *ibid.*, 323.

8. J. L. Stokes, *J. Bact.*, 1944, **47**, 433 ; 1944, **48**, 201.
9. G. H. Hitchings, E. A. Falco and H. B. Sherwood, *Science*, 1945, **102**, 251.
10. L. L. Rogers and W. Shive, *J. Biol. Chem.*, 1948, **172**, 751.
10a. W. H. Prussoff, L. J. Teply and C. G. King, *ibid.*, 1949, **176**, 1309.
11. J. R. Totter, E. Sims and P. L. Day, *Proc. Soc. Exp. Biol. Med.*, 1947, **66**, 7.
12. H. M. Kalckar and H. Klenow, *J. Biol. Chem.*, 1948, **172**, 349 ; B. H. J. Hofstee, *ibid.*, 1949, **179**, 633 ; J. N. Williams and C. A. Elvehjem, *Proc. Soc. Exp. Biol. Med.*, 1949, **71**, 303.
13. H. M. Kalckar and H. Klenow, *J. Biol. Chem.*, 1948, **172**, 351.
14. H. M. Kalckar, N. O. Kjeldgaard and H. Klenow, *ibid.*, 1948, **174**, 771.

VITAMIN B$_{12}$ (ERYTHROTIN)

1. INTRODUCTION

IN 1926, G. R. Minot and W. P. Murphy[1] demonstrated that patients with pernicious anaemia could be maintained in normal health by ingestion of liver. Subsequently it was discovered that the injection of liver extracts gave more reliable results with less inconvenience to the patients. Since that time, the use of liver extracts has become routine practice in the treatment not only of Addisonian pernicious anaemia, but also of pernicious anaemia due to tapeworm, pernicious anaemia of pregnancy, nutritional megaloblastic anaemia, megaloblastic anaemia of infancy and childhood and megaloblastic anaemia accompanying steatorrhoea. Three types of liver extracts are in use—" refined " extracts with a relatively low concentration of total solids derived from a large amount of liver, " crude " extracts with a much higher total solids content and " proteolysed " extracts in which the liver tissue is partially broken down before extraction in order to liberate more of the active principle. Some anaemias respond more readily to proteolysed and crude liver extracts than to refined extracts and there are many clinicians who maintain that refined extracts fail to keep the blood picture normal for more than a limited period.

Folic acid, as has already been pointed out (page 484), is an antianaemic factor that is only successful in megaloblastic forms of anaemia ; it has no effect in subacute combined degeneration of the cord, and may actually increase the severity of the nervous symptoms in pernicious anaemia. Clearly folic acid is different from the substance in liver extract that cures pernicious anaemia, and potent refined liver extracts do, in fact, contain negligible amounts of folic acid.

Attempts to fractionate liver extracts with the object of isolating the antipernicious anaemia factor have always been difficult because no chemical test for the factor exists, and no animal or micro-organism was known that would respond specifically to the factor. The isolation of more or less pure preparations of the anti-pernicious anaemia factor was announced in the same week by E. L. Smith[2] and Rickes et al.[3] The former obtained by chromatography two red pigments from an ox liver concentrate prepared by a method previously described by W. B. Emery and L. F. J. Parker.[4] Better yields were obtained from proteolysed liver extracts than from non-proteolysed extracts. One pigment appeared to be produced from the other by proteolysis. In the early stages of the fractionation, clinical tests with pernicious anaemia patients in relapse were used to follow the course of purification, but in the later stages the colour of the fractions was used for this purpose. The most active preparation gave a response with a dose containing only 0·3 mg. of total solids and, in addition to being anti-anaemic, was effective in sub-acute combined degeneration of the cord. The product was not pure and was not homogeneous when examined in the Tiselius apparatus. It contained neither folic acid nor xanthopterine, and had a molecular weight of about 3000.

Rickes et al.[3] claimed to have isolated the anti-pernicious anaemia factor in the pure state and gave it the name vitamin B_{12}. They gave no information about its properties or method of isolation beyond the fact that the substance formed red needles which did not melt below 300° C. and contained cobalt. Vitamin B_{12} was shown to be identical with one of two unidentified growth factors required by *Lactobacillus lactis* Dorner; both of these were present in refined liver extracts.[5] Crystalline vitamin B_{12} gave a positive response in three cases of Addisonian pernicious anaemia following single intramuscular injections of 3, 6 and 150 μg. respectively.[6]

Subsequently, E. L. Smith[7] crystallised the anti-pernicious anaemia factor from liver, and found it to contain 4 % of cobalt and, assuming this to represent one atom per molecule, three atoms of phosphorus per molecule. The phosphorus content of Smith's factor apparently differentiates it from the vitamin B_{12} of other workers, for both Ellis et al.[8] and Brink et al.[9] stated that the Co : P ratio was 1 : 1 and not 1 : 3. This discrepancy may perhaps be explained by the existence of several forms of vitamin B_{12}, all clinically active. A second form, known as vitamin B_{12a}, was obtained by catalytic hydrogenation of vitamin B_{12};[10] it was somewhat less active than the latter and had a similar but not identical absorption spectrum. A third form, vitamin B_{12b}, was isolated, together with vitamin B_{12}, from liver and a culture of *Streptomyces aureofaciens*;[11] it likewise differed from vitamin B_{12} in its absorption spectrum. Vitamin B_{12} has been isolated from *S. griseus*, which is now an important commercial source of this factor.[12]

It has also been claimed[13] that vitamin B_{12} exists in certain substances in the form of conjugates, inactive in pernicious anaemia until they have been digested with hogs' stomach mucosa or with pancreatic enzyme extracts. These conjugates, it is suggested, may be Castle's extrinsic factor (see page 498).

References to Section 1

1. G. R. Minot and W. P. Murphy, *J. Amer. Med. Assoc.*, 1926, **87,** 470.
2. E. L. Smith, *Nature*, 1948, **161,** 638.
3. E. L. Rickes, N. G. Brink, F. R. Koniuszy, T. R. Wood and K. Folkers, *Science*, 1948, **107,** 396; 1948, **108,** 135.
4. W. B. Emery and L. F. J. Parker, *Biochem. J. Proc.*, 1946, **40,** iv.
5. M. S. Shorb, *Science*, 1948, **107,** 397.
6. R. West, *ibid.*, 398.
7. E. L. Smith, *Nature*, 1948, **162,** 144.
8. B. Ellis, V. Petrow and G. F. Snook, *J. Pharm. Pharmacol.*, 1949, **1,** 60, 287.
9. N. G. Brink, D. E. Wolf, E. Kaczka, E. L. Rickes, F. R. Koniuszy, T. R. Wood and K. Folkers, *J. Amer. Chem. Soc.*, 1949, **71,** 1854.
10. E. Kaczka, D. E. Wolf and K. Folkers, *ibid.*, 1514.
11. J. V. Pierce, A. C. Page, E. L. R. Stokstad and T. H. Jukes, *ibid.*, 2952.
12. E. L. Rickes, N. G. Brink, F. R. Koniuszy, T. R. Wood and K. Folkers, *Science*, 1948, **108,** 634.
13. K. Hausmann, *Lancet*, 1949, **2,** 962.

2. ISOLATION, PURIFICATION AND PROPERTIES OF VITAMIN B$_{12}$

Isolation and Purification

Vitamin B$_{12}$ was prepared from either liver extract or a culture of *S. griseus* by chromatographic adsorption on activated alumina or charcoal.[1] The former was eluted with methanol or aqueous methanol and the latter with an aqueous solution of acetone, butanol or benzyl alcohol. In either instance, the eluate was evaporated, and the residue dissolved in alcohol. After filtration the solution was evaporated and the residue dissolved in methanol. Vitamin B$_{12}$ was precipitated from this solution by the addition of acetone or ether, the precipitate was dissolved in water and the solution treated with acetone. The resulting precipitate was dissolved in methanol and several volumes of acetone were added to precipitate the vitamin, which was then dissolved in water and acetone added until a turbidity formed. On standing, red crystals of vitamin B$_{12}$ separated out.

Concentrates of vitamin B$_{12}$ were also purified prior to crystallisation by counter-current distribution between water and a mixture (3 : 1) of toluene and *o*-cresol.

Partition chromatography has also been used to purify vitamin B$_{12}$. Strips of filter paper developed with wet *n*-butanol were used preparatory to microbiological assay [2] (page 534), whilst columns of starch developed with a mixture ($1 : 2 : 1$) of 0.1 N-hydrochloric acid, n-propanol and n-butanol were claimed [3] to effect a high degree of purification.

Properties

Vitamin B_{12} forms red needle-like birefringent crystals with no definite melting-point, but they darken at about $210°$ to $220°$ C. It is soluble in water, methanol, ethanol and phenol, but substantially insoluble in acetone, ether and chloroform. In aqueous solution it gives a characteristic absorption spectrum with maxima at 278, 361 and 550 mμ.; the values of $E_{1 cm.}^{1 \%}$ at these wave-lengths were 119, 187 and 59 respectively.[1] An aqueous solution of vitamin B_{12b} gave an absorption spectrum with maxima at 273, 351 and 525 mμ.[4]

Analysis of vitamin B_{12} indicated a formula approximating to C_{61-64} H_{86-92} N_{14} O_{13} PCo and a molecular weight of about 1490. Vitamin B_{12} is l-rotatory, and hydrolysis did not liberate α-amino acids.

Chemical Constitution

The chemical constitution of vitamin B_{12} is not yet known, but degradation experiments have revealed the structure of certain parts of the molecule. Alkaline fusion yielded substances which reacted in the same way as pyrroles with p-dimethylaminobenzaldehyde,[5] and acid hydrolysis gave $5 : 6$-dimethylbenzimidazole, the structure of which was confirmed by synthesis.[6] Thus the molecules of vitamin B_{12} and riboflavine contain the same nucleus. Acid hydrolysis also liberated ammonia and a ninhydrin-reacting substance, which appeared to be 2-aminopropanol.[7]

References to Section 2

1. Merck & Co., S. African Pat. 7724.
2. W. F. J. Cuthbertson and E. L. Smith, *Biochem. J. Proc.*, 1949, **44**, v ; 1949, **45**, xii ; G. E. Shaw, *ibid.*, 1949, **44**, liv ; W. A. Winsten and E. Eigen, *J. Biol. Chem.*, 1949, **181**, 109.
3. H. Borsook, C. L. Deasy, A. J. Haagen-Smit, G. Keighley and P. H. Lowy, *Science*, 1949, **110**, 528.
4. J. V. Pierce, A. C. Page, E. L. R. Stokstad and T. H. Jukes, *J. Amer. Chem. Soc.*, 1949, **71**, 2952.
5. N. G. Brink, D. E. Wolf, E. A. Kaczka, E. L. Rickes, F. R. Koniuszy, T. R. Wood and K. Folkers, *ibid.*, 1854.
6. N. G. Brink and K. Folkers, *ibid.*, 2951 ; E. R. Holliday and V. Petrow, *J. Pharm. Pharmacol.*, 1949, **1**, 734 ; G. R. Beaven, E. R. Holliday, E. A. Johnson, B. Ellis, P. Mamalis, V. Petrow and B. Sturgeon, *ibid.*, 957.
7. B. Ellis, V. Petrow and G. F. Snook, *ibid.*, 735, 950.

3. ESTIMATION OF VITAMIN B_{12}

Microbiological Methods

It has already been stated that vitamin B_{12} is identical with one of the factors necessary for the growth of *Lactobacillus lactis* Dorner, and this organism was the first to be used for the assay of vitamin B_{12},[1] the growth response being measured either turbidimetrically or by titration of the lactic acid produced. *L. lactis* responds to 0·01 mμg. per ml. of vitamin B_{12}. This organism is not entirely satisfactory, however. In the first place, it responds to thymidine in the absence of vitamin B_{12},[2] and in the second place it readily produces mutants that grow without vitamin B_{12}, and the composition of the medium and the conditions of growth have to be carefully standardised if consistent results are to be obtained.[3] The first of these objections is avoided by carrying out a preliminary separation of the vitamin B_{12} from other growth factors by paper partition chromatography (page 532). The filter paper strip can either be laid on an agar plate seeded with *L. lactis* and the zones of stimulation measured after incubation[4] or it can be cut into small pieces and each one separately assayed in test tubes in the ordinary way.[5]

A variety of media have been employed for the growth of *L. lactis* as several laboratories failed to obtain satisfactory results with Shorb's medium; [6, 7] the addition of tomato-juice and Tween 80 is said to be necessary.[3, 6] Inconsistent results can also be obtained if the amount of air in the tubes varies from one experiment to another. Thus under anaerobic conditions, produced by the addition of reducing substances or by the removal of oxygen, *L. lactis* will grow in the absence of vitamin B_{12}, whereas on aeration or addition of oxidising substances growth is inhibited and the inhibition can be overcome by vitamin B_{12}; carbon dioxide is essential for growth in any event.[8] Thus, assuming sufficient carbon dioxide to be present, the response will increase with the amount of oxygen in the atmosphere of the tubes or with the amount of oxidising substances, *e.g.* peroxides, in the tube itself. This presumably explains why in the absence of vitamin B_{12} the amount of growth varies with the diameter of the tubes,[9] and why the cup-plate method of assay gives more consistent results than assays using test-tubes; [6, 10] with the former the standard deviation (66 % confidence limits) is said to be ± 10 % and with the titrimetric method ± 21 %. Using the cup technique, *L. lactis* gave no response to thymidine, desoxyribonucleic acid or ascorbic acid.[10]

On the whole, more satisfactory results have been obtained with another *Lactobacillus*, *L. leichmannii*,[11] which is more stable and less exacting in its requirements than *L. lactis*.[12] This organism has also been used in conjunction with paper chromatography, the paper strips either being laid on agar plates seeded with the organism [13] or cut into pieces and each separately assayed.[14] The cup-plate assay method also gives good results with *L. leichmannii*.[10]

A study of the nutritional requirements of two strains of *L. leichmannii* was made by Hoffmann *et al*.[15] They used a basal medium containing glucose, sodium acetate, sodium citrate, trypsin-digested casein, acid-hydrolysed casein, salts, cystine, asparagine, tryptophan, Tween 80, pyrimidines and members of the vitamin B complex. It was found that a growth factor was formed on autoclaving and that some vitamin B_{12} was destroyed. The first difficulty was overcome either by replacing the glucose by sucrose or by the addition of thioglycolic acid or asparagus extract. Thioglycolic acid also protected the vitamin B_{12} from destruction during autoclaving. The growth-stimulating effect of thymidine and other desoxyribosides was measured and corrected for by assaying the samples before and after heating with 0·2N sodium hydroxide at 100° C. for 30 minutes, which destroys vitamin B_{12} but does not affect desoxyribosides.

An organism of a different type used for the assay of vitamin B_{12} was *Euglena gracilis* var. *bacillaris* which exhibited a quantitative response to the vitamin but was not stimulated by thymidine.[16] Whereas *L. leichmannii* required a concentration of at least 0·1 mμg. per ml. to produce a measurable growth response, *Euglena* required one-tenth of this amount.

Animal Assays

Vitamin B_{12} appears to be a component of the animal protein factor (page 539), which can be assayed by measuring the growth response of chicks or rats fed diets containing soya bean meal as the sole source of protein. Attempts have been made to use these methods for the assay of vitamin B_{12} concentrates, but they do not seem to be specific for vitamin B_{12}, as the results were sometimes inconsistent with those obtained by microbiological assay or clinical tests on pernicious anaemia patients. More consistent results were obtained when a thyrotoxic condition was first induced in the experimental animals by feeding iodinated casein, but it has been claimed that this test also is not specific for vitamin B_{12} (page 541). Thus liver extracts active in pernicious anaemia failed to stimulate the growth of chicks and crude liver extracts discarded from anti-pernicious anaemia fractions were highly active,[17] whereas vitamin B_{12} replaced the animal protein factor activity of injectible liver preparations when tested on thyrotoxic chicks.[18] With normal chicks, maximum growth was not obtained until other supplements were added.[19]

Mice have also been used for the assay of animal protein factor, one method being based on measuring the growth rate of mice born of mothers maintained on a purified diet, and the other on counteracting the growth retardation of mice fed thyroid-active material.[20] The growth of vitamin B$_{12}$-depleted rats was used by Frost et al.[21] for the assay of vitamin B$_{12}$ with apparently good correlation with the microbiological assay method, but crystalline vitamin B$_{12}$ according to B. H. Ershoff [22] was ineffective in counteracting the growth retardation of hyperthyroid rats.

References to Section 3

1. M. S. Shorb, *Science*, 1948, **107**, 397.
2. L. D. Wright, H. R. Skeggs and J. W. Huff, *J. Biol. Chem.*, 1948, **175**, 457.
3. M. S. Shorb and G. M. Briggs, *ibid.*, 1949, **176**, 1463.
4. W. F. J. Cuthbertson and E. L. Smith, *Biochem. J. Proc.*, 1949, **44**, v; 1949, **45**, xii.
5. G. E. Shaw, *ibid.*, 1949, **44**, liv; *J. Pharm. Pharmacol.*, 1949, **1**, 695.
6. W. F. J. Cuthbertson, *Biochem. J. Proc.*, 1949, **44**, v.
7. G. E. Shaw, *Nature*, 1949, **164**, 186.
8. L. K. Koditschek, D. Hendlin and H. B. Woodruff, *J. Biol. Chem.*, 1949, **179**, 1093; M. C. Caswell, L. K. Koditschek and D. Hendlin, *ibid.*, 1949, **180**, 125.
9. R. D. Greene, A. J. Brook and R. B. McCormack, *ibid.*, 1949, **178**, 999.
10. J. C. Foster, J. A. Lally and H. B. Woodruff, *Science*, 1949, **110**, 507.
11. H. R. Skeggs, J. W. Huff, L. D. Wright and D. K. Bosshardt, *J. Biol. Chem.*, 1949, **176**, 1459; C. E. Hoffmann, E. L. R. Stokstad, A. L. Franklin and T. H. Jukes, *ibid.*, 1465.
12. B. F. Capps, N. L. Hobbs and S. H. Fox, *J. Biol. Chem.*, 1949, **178**, 517.
13. W. A. Winsten and E. Eigen, *ibid.*, 1949, **177**, 989.
14. H. Yacowitz, L. C. Norris and G. F. Heuser, *Proc. Soc. Exp. Biol. Med.*, 1949, **71**, 372.
15. C. E. Hoffmann, E. L. R. Stokstad, B. L. Hutchings, A. C. Dornbush and T. H. Jukes, *J. Biol. Chem.*, 1949, **181**, 635.
16. S. H. Hutner, L. Provasoli, E. L. R. Stokstad, C. E. Hoffmann, M. Belt, A. L. Franklin and T. H. Jukes, *Proc. Soc. Exp. Biol. Med.*, 1949, **70**, 118.
17. C. A. Nichol, A. R. Robblee, W. W. Cravens and C. A. Elvehjem, *J. Biol. Chem.*, 1949, **177**, 631.
18. C. A. Nichol, L. S. Dietrich, W. W. Cravens and C. A. Elvehjem, *Proc. Soc. Exp. Biol. Med.*, 1949, **70**, 40.
19. E. L. R. Stokstad, T. H. Jukes, J. V. Pierce, A. C. Page and A. L. Franklin, *J. Biol. Chem.*, 1949, **180**, 647.
20. D. K. Bosshardt, W. J. Paul, K. O'Doherty, J. W. Huff and R. H. Barnes, *J. Nutrition*, 1949, **37**, 21.
21. D. V. Frost, H. H. Fricke and H. C. Spruth, *Proc. Soc. Exp. Biol. Med.*, 1949, **72**, 102.
22. B. H. Ershoff, *ibid.*, 1949, **71**, 209.

4. OCCURRENCE OF VITAMIN B₁₂

Comparatively few assays have yet been reported of the vitamin B_{12} content of natural materials and, in view of the divergent views as to the specificity of both microbiological methods and animal assays, such results as have been published should perhaps be accepted with reserve until confirmed.

Using a rat growth method, Lewis *et al.*[1] found desiccated sheep rumen contents, beef liver and kidney, chicken liver, condensed fish solubles and dried streptomycin slop to be the richest sources of vitamin B_{12}; these contained between 35 and 50 µg. per 100 g. Herring stickwater and desiccated pig adrenals contained about 15 µg. per 100 g. ; beef and mutton about 5 ; veal about 4 ; horsemeat, 7·5 ; pork, 1 to 3 ; casein, milk powder and cheese, 2 to 3 ; and egg yolk 2·8 µg. per 100 g. Plant materials showed no measurable activity.

Extracts prepared by digestion with pancreatin in the case of animal products and with pancreatin plus takadiastase in the case of plant materials gave the following values when assayed with *L. leichmannii* ;[2] liver extract, 39 ; fish meal and condensed fish solubles, 9 to 10 ; crude casein, 10 ; meat scraps, 4 ; alfalfa leaf meal, 4 ; soya bean meal and yellow corn, 1 ; dried brewers' yeast, 0·8 ; and wheat, 0·7 µg. per 100 g.

Pig liver gave active extracts only in summer and autumn, whereas calf liver showed no such seasonal variation.[3] There appeared to be no correlation between the microbiological response and the clinical potency of liver extracts,[2] though this, of course, may well be due to the extreme inaccuracy of the method used to assess clinical potency ; ten different liver extracts on sale in the U.S.A. gave values ranging from 0·087 to 2·17 µg. per U.S.P. unit of anti-pernicious anaemia activity, although 1 µg. of the pure vitamin had approximately 1 U.S.P. unit of activity. The vitamin B_{12} potency of a number of liver extracts tested in this country ranged from 0·2 to 22 µg. per ml.[4]

The liver, heart, small intestine and femoral muscles of vitamin B_{12}-depleted rats contained no vitamin B_{12}, whereas the kidney retained a substantial quantity.[5] Extracts active in pernicious anaemia were obtained from human livers, from the livers of twenty-six species of mammals and three species of fish, whereas inactive extracts were obtained from the livers of sea-lion, reptiles and amphibia.[6] A satisfactory extract was prepared from whale liver.[7]

References to Section 4

1. U. J. Lewis, U. D. Register, H. T. Thompson and C. A. Elvehjem, *Proc. Soc. Exp. Biol. Med.*, 1949, **72**, 479 ; 1949, **70**, 167.
2. H. T. Peeler, H. Yacowitz and L. C. Norris, *ibid.*, 515.

3. J. Dedichen, *Lancet*, 1949, **1**, 369.
4. W. F. J. Cuthbertson, J. F. Lloyd, W. B. Emery and K. A. Lees, *J. Pharm. Pharmacol.*, 1949, **1**, 705.
5. U. J. Lewis, U. D. Register and C. A. Elvehjem, *Proc. Soc. Exp. Biol. Med.*, 1949, **71**, 509.
6. J. F. Wilkinson, *Lancet*, 1949, **1**, 249, 336.
7. J. Innes and H. N. Robson, *ibid.*, 1949, **2**, 606.

5. EFFECT OF VITAMIN B$_{12}$ ON ANIMALS AND MAN

Effect on Man

Crystalline vitamin B$_{12}$ prepared from liver extracts gave a positive response when injected intramuscularly into patients with Addisonian pernicious anaemia in doses as small as 3 μg.,[1] although to produce a maximum reticulocyte response 6 to 10 μg. were required,[2] the actual amount varying with the individual. An average maintenance dose was 10 μg. every two weeks.[3] Vitamin B$_{12}$ was also effective in nutritional macrocytic anaemia and tropical sprue, and relieved sub-acute combined degeneration of the cord in pernicious anaemia.[4] The lingual manifestations of pernicious anaemia also responded,[5] although neither this condition nor the neurological symptoms responded to pteroylglutamic acid.

Vitamin B$_{12}$ prepared from *S. griseus* cultures [6] and vitamin B$_{12b}$ prepared from *S. aureofaciens* cultures [7] were apparently as effective in pernicious anaemia as vitamin B$_{12}$ prepared from liver extracts. A crude concentrate prepared from beef muscle was also effective when injected intramuscularly in pernicious anaemia patients in doses equivalent to 1 μg. of vitamin B$_{12}$ daily.[8] Concentrates of a cobalt-containing substance were prepared from cultures of *S. griseus* and from cow-dung; both were inactive in pernicious anaemia, but became active after digestion with hog-stomach mucosa or pancreatic enzyme.[9]

Vitamin B$_{12}$ was more effective by injection than by mouth, and most patients responded slowly to oral vitamin B$_{12}$ in amounts thirty to sixty times those required by the parenteral route.[10] Vitamin B$_{12b}$ gave no response orally unless given with normal human gastric juice, and an alcoholic extract of beef muscle also gave a good response only when given with normal gastric human juice.[11]

Vitamin B$_{12}$ is ineffective in nutritional anaemias due to a deficiency of folic acid (page 500), and cases have been reported where folic acid has to be administered before a response to vitamin B$_{12}$ can be obtained. The response to vitamin B$_{12}$ was delayed and sub-optimal when 1 mg. per day of the folic acid antagonist, Aminopterin, was given for two days prior to and for fourteen days during injection of vitamin B_{12},[12] supporting the hypothesis that vitamin B_{12} makes folic acid available to the organism ; when the Aminopterin was discontinued, a second reticulocyte response was obtained. Four patients with untreated pernicious anaemia excreted in the faeces a factor that stimulated *L. lactis* in an amount equivalent to 0·3 to 1·8 μg. per g. of vitamin B_{12}, an amount in excess of that required to cure pernicious anaemia. This was presumably produced by bacterial synthesis in the intestine.

That vitamin B_{12} has other functions than that of stimulating haemopoiesis is perhaps the conclusion to be drawn from the observations of Wetzel *et al.*,[13] who tested the effect of the vitamin on a group of eleven children in " varying states of recovery from simple growth failure ". Five were said to respond dramatically with increased physical vigour, alertness, better general behaviour and increase of appetite. In a case of severe allergic bronchitis, the symptoms vanished during the first week of treatment. These striking results may be connected with the effect of vitamin B_{12} on the utilisation of protein (see below).

Effect on the Growth of Animals

Cary *et al.*[14] described a factor, factor X, the absence of which resulted in a decline in the growth rate of rats, a decline that became more marked the higher the protein content of the diet. This factor appeared to be similar to the so-called animal protein factor (APF), which increased the hatchability of hens' eggs [15] and the growth rate of chicks maintained on an all-vegetable protein ration,[16] and to a factor in cow manure that stimulated the growth of chicks.[16, 17]

Crystalline vitamin B_{12} was found to exhibit animal protein factor activity on chicks fed soya bean meal as the sole source of protein ; it was as effective as the cow manure factor in stimulating the growth of chicks.[18] It also increased the growth rate of rats on a factor X-deficient diet, showing that vitamin B_{12} plays a fundamental role in the utilisation of protein.[19] In fact, evidence appears to be accumulating that vitamin B_{12} is concerned with transmethylation. In the first place, on a diet complete in the known vitamins, the growth of chicks was improved by supplementation with choline or betaine ; the addition of a liver paste containing little choline was even more effective and supplementation with choline or betaine then had little effect.[20] Secondly, crystalline vitamin B_{12} increased the growth rate of chicks on a diet low in choline, whilst renal injury in rats due to a low intake of choline and methionine was minimised by the addition of vitamin B_{12} to the diet, and the gain in weight was also increased, though not when adequate amounts of choline were fed.[21] Thirdly, vitamin B_{12}

had a marked lipotropic effect when injected into rats fed a high fat diet [22] and, finally, the administration of vitamin B_{12} to rats preceding acute carbon tetrachloride intoxication prevented liver injury.[23]

Stimulation of the growth of rats and chicks maintained on purified diets has been used for the assay of vitamin B_{12} with conflicting results (page 535). With the diets used, the response was presumably not always due solely to the vitamin B_{12} present.

Relation between Vitamin B_{12} and Folic Acid

As already pointed out (page 499), pteroylglutamic acid and vitamin B_{12} are not biologically equivalent. Thus, the administration of vitamin B_{12} to folic acid-deficient chicks increased the growth rate without any effect on feathering, whereas pteroylglutamic acid improved feathering but had no effect on growth.[24] The so-called vitamins B_{10} and B_{11} deficiencies (page 614) are probably deficiencies of vitamin B_{12} and folic acid respectively. Again, pteroylglutamic acid failed to increase the sub-optimal growth rate of rats fed a purified diet plus sulphasuxidine, but cured the leucocytopenia, whereas a liver extract produced good growth.[25] The effect of vitamin B_{12} on the growth of chicks was enhanced by ascorbic acid, and the amount of folic acid stored in the liver was higher when vitamin B_{12} and ascorbic acid were given together than with vitamin B_{12} alone.[26] Both pteroylglutamic acid and vitamin B_{12} were essential for pigs,[27] but vitamin B_{12} alone was not so effective as a concentrate of the animal protein factor, suggesting that the latter may contain another substance besides vitamin B_{12}.[28] Whereas the addition of pteroylglutamic acid to a diet deficient in both folic acid and vitamin B_{12} reduced the amount of D-amino acid oxidase present in the livers of chickens, the addition of vitamin B_{12} increased it ; [29] other enzymes were not affected.

Relation of Vitamin B_{12} to Thymine

Thymine has a haemopoietic action in tropical sprue similar to that produced by pteroylglutamic acid (page 514), though the clinical response was less dramatic.[30] It also brings about a response in nutritional macrocytic anaemia and pernicious anaemia, but several thousand parts of thymine were required to produce the same response as one part of pteroylglutamic acid, and several thousand parts of pteroylglutamic acid to produce the same response as one part of vitamin B_{12}.[31] Thymine also produced reticulocytosis in splenectomised rabbits.[32] Thymidine, however, failed to produce a reticulocyte response in a patient with pernicious anaemia,[33] so that care should be taken to eliminate thymidine in assaying vitamin B_{12} preparations microbiologically (page 534).

Other Biological Properties

Rats fed rations containing thyroid-active materials required a factor present in liver, fish solubles and tomatoes.[34] The factor was present in anti-pernicious anaemia active fractions but, whereas J. J. Betheil and H. A. Lardy [34] and G. A. Emerson [35] found vitamin B_{12} to be active, B. H. Ershoff [36] found it to be ineffective. Inconsistent results were obtained when attempts were made to use hyperthyroid rats for the assay of vitamin B_{12} (page 535).

Vitamin B_{12} did not produce a response in cobalt-deficient lambs either after injection of 125 μg. or after being fed orally for 6 weeks.[37]

Crystalline vitamin B_{12} prevented gizzard erosion in chicks.[38]

Vitamin B_{12}, like pteroylglutamic acid, increased the incidence and size of Rous tumour implants in chicks, and the effect of the two substances given together was greater than that of either alone.[39]

References to Section 5

1. R. West, *Science*, 1948, **107**, 398.
2. B. E. Hall and D. C. Campbell, *J. Lab. Clin. Med.*, 1948, **33**, 1646 ; C. C. Ungley, *Lancet*, 1948, **1**, 771 ; *Brit. Med. J.*, 1948, **2**, 154.
3. C. C. Ungley, *ibid.*, 1949, **2**, 1370.
4. J. C. Patel, *ibid.*, 1948, **2**, 934 ; T. D. Spies, R. E. Stone and T. Aramburu, *Southern Med. J.*, 1948, **41**, 487, 522 ; T. D. Spies, G. G. Lopez, F. Milanes, R. L. Toca and B. Culver, *ibid.*, 523 ; L. Berk, D. Denny-Brown, M. Finland and W. B. Castle, *New England J. Med.*, 1948, **239**, 328 ; T. D. Spies, R. E. Stone, G. G. Lopez, F. Milanes, T. Aramburu and R. L. Toca, *Postgrad. Med.*, 1948, **4**, 89 ; T. D. Spies, R. M. Suarez, G. G. Lopez, F. Milanes, R. E. Stone, R. L. Toca, T. Aramburu and S. Kartus, *J. Amer. Med. Assoc.*, 1949, **139**, 521 ; T. D. Spies and R. M. Suarez, *Blood*, 1948, **3**, 1213.
5. R. E. Stone and T. D. Spies, *J. Lab. Clin. Med.*, 1948, **33**, 1019 ; J. F. Schieve and R. W. Rundles, *ibid.*, 1949, **34**, 439.
6. D. M. Dunlop and W. M. Wilson, *Lancet*, 1949, **1**, 754 ; C. M. Miller and E. H. Moorhouse, *Brit. Med. J.*, 1949, **2**, 1511.
7. H. Lichtman, J. Watson, V. Ginsberg, J. V. Pierce, E. L. R. Stokstad and T. H. Jukes, *Proc. Soc. Exp. Biol. Med.*, 1949, **72**, 643.
8. E. H. Morgan, E. E. Hall and D. C. Campbell, *Proc. Staff Meetings Mayo Clinic*, 1949, **24**, 594.
9. K. Hausmann, *Lancet*, 1949, **2**, 962.
10. T. D. Spies, R. E. Stone, G. G. Lopez, F. Milanes, R. L. Toca and T. Aramburu, *ibid.*, 1454.
11. F. H. Gardner, J. W. Harris, R. F. Schilling and W. B. Castle, *J. Lab. Clin. Med.*, 1949, **34**, 1502.
12. F. H. Bethell, M. C. Meyers and R. B. Neligh, *ibid.*, 1948, **33**, 1477.

13. N. C. Wetzel, W. C. Fargo, I. H. Smith and J. Helikson, *Science*, 1949, **110**, 651.

14. C. A. Cary, A. M. Hartman, L. P. Dryden and G. D. Likely, *Fed. Proc.*, 1946, **5**, 128 ; A. M. Hartman, *ibid.*, 137.

15. R. B. Nestler, T. C. Byerly, N. R. Ellis and H. W. Titus, *Poultry Sci.*, 1936, **15**, 67.

16. J. C. Hammond, *ibid.*, 1944, **23**, 471.

17. M. Rubin and H. R. Bird, *J. Biol. Chem.*, 1946, **163**, 387 ; H. R. Bird, M. Rubin and A. C. Groschke, *ibid.*, 1948, **174**, 611.

18. W. H. Ott, E. L. Rickes and T. R. Wood, *ibid.*, 1047 ; R. J. Lillie, C. A. Denton and H. R. Bird, *ibid.*, 1949, **176**, 1477 ; R. J. Lillie, H. W. Olsen and H. R. Bird, *Proc. Soc. Exp. Biol. Med.*, 1949, **72**, 598.

19. A. M. Hartman, L. P. Dryden and C. A. Cary, *Arch. Biochem.*, 1949, **23**, 165.

20. M. B. Gillis and L. C. Norris, *J. Biol. Chem.*, 1949, **179**, 487.

21. A. E. Schaefer, W. D. Salmon and D. R. Strength, *Proc. Soc. Exp. Biol. Med.*, 1949, **71**, 193.

22. V. A. Drill and H. M. McCormick, *ibid.*, 1949, **72**, 388.

23. H. Popper, D. Koch-Weser and P. B. Szanto, *ibid.*, 1949, **71**, 688.

24. C. A. Nichol, L. S. Dietrich, C. A. Elvehjem and E. B. Hart, *J. Nutrition*, 1949, **39**, 287.

25. J. H. Jones, C. S. Rogers and C. H. Stone, *ibid.*, 579.

26. L. S. Dietrich, C. A. Nichol, W. J. Mouson and C. A. Elvehjem, *J. Biol. Chem.*, 1949, **181**, 915.

27. R. W. Heinle, A. D. Welch and J. A. Pritchard, *J. Lab. Clin. Med.*, 1948, **33**, 1647.

28. T. J. Cunha, J. E. Burnside, D. M. Buschman, R. S. Glasscock, A. M. Pearson and A. L. Shealy, *Arch. Biochem.*, 1949, **23**, 324.

29. J. N. Williams, C. A. Nichol and C. A. Elvehjem, *J. Biol. Chem.*, 1949, **180**, 689.

30. T. D. Spies, W. B. Frommeyer, G. G. Lopez, R. L. Toca and G. Gwinner, *Lancet*, 1946, **1**, 883.

31. T. D. Spies, R. E. Stone, G. G. Lopez, F. Milanes, R. L. Toca and T. Aramburu, *ibid.*, 1948, **2**, 519.

32. E. M. Bavin and T. R. Middleton, *Nature*, 1946, **158**, 627.

33. C. C. Ungley, *Lancet*, 1949, **1**, 164.

34. J. J. Betheil and H. A. Lardy, *J. Nutrition*, 1949, **37**, 495.

35. G. A. Emerson, *Proc. Soc. Exp. Biol. Med.*, 1949, **70**, 392.

36. B. H. Ershoff, *ibid.*, 1949, **71**, 209.

37. D. E. Becker, S. E. Smith and J. K. Loosli, *Science*, 1949, **110**, 71.

38. C. W. Mushett and W. H. Ott, *Poultry Science*, 1949, **28**, 850.

39. J. J. Oleson and P. A. Little, *Proc. Soc. Exp. Biol. Med.*, 1949, **71**, 226.

6. VITAMIN B₁₂ AND MICRO-ORGANISMS

Vitamin B₁₂ as Growth Factor

As already mentioned (page 534), vitamin B_{12} is an essential growth factor for *Lactobacillus lactis* Dorner and *L. leichmannii*, and both these organisms have been used for its assay. In the absence of vitamin B_{12}, thymidine and several purines stimulated the growth of both organisms, although only in much higher concentrations.[1] It has been suggested that vitamin B_{12} may function as a coenzyme in the conversion of thymine into thymidine, and that the biochemical lesion in pernicious anaemia may be an inability to synthesise certain nucleosides, especially thymidine, from purines or pyrimidines. The curative effects of pteroylglutamic acid may well be due to increased thymine synthesis (page 527), which by a mass action effect yields additional amounts of thymidine. The hypothesis that in *Lactobacilli* vitamin B_{12} is involved in nucleic acid synthesis is supported by the observation that it causes an increase in the phosphorus uptake of *L. leichmannii* and an increase in the desoxyribonucleic acid fraction.[2] Although ascorbic acid is not a growth factor for *L. leichmannii*, it augments the growth-promoting action of casein hydrolysate on this organism, an effect shared with other reducing agents such as thioglycolic acid and glutathione. It is believed that these substances protect the small amounts of vitamin B_{12} in trypsin and casein from destruction by oxidation during the autoclaving of the medium.[3] Vitamin B_{12} combines with a non-dialysable, heat-labile substance in normal gastric juice to form a complex, erythrein, which is non-dialysable and not dissociated by dialysis. In this form vitamin B_{12} is not available to *L. lactis*, *L. leichmannii* or *E. coli*, but is released by heat.[4] The heat labile factor, apoerythrein, also appears to be present in hog gastric mucosa and may be Castle's intrinsic factor (page 498). It can be assayed by measuring the growth inhibition of *E. coli* produced by the addition of known amounts of the juice to cultures containing vitamin B_{12}. Each ml. of normal gastric juice was found to be capable of combining with 15 to 60 mμg. of vitamin B_{12}, whereas each ml. of gastric juice from pernicious anaemia patients combined with only 1 to 5 mμg. of vitamin B_{12}.

Vitamin B_{12} is not essential for the growth of *S. faecalis* R or *Leuconostoc citrovorum*.[5]

Vitamin B_{12} is essential for the growth of the alga, *Euglena gracilis* var. *bacillaris*, another organism that has been used for the assay of vitamin B_{12}; it does not respond to thymidine.[6]

Vitamin B_{12} appears to be one of the rate-limiting factors in the synthesis of bacteriophage T4r, but it was not apparently utilised as a component of the virus, since there was not sufficient of the vitamin present to provide one molecule per virus particle.[7]

Synthesis of Vitamin B$_{12}$ by Micro-organisms

Vitamin B$_{12}$ is synthesised by the mould, *Streptomyces griseus*, and vitamin B$_{12b}$ by *S. aureofaciens* (page 531). It is also synthesised, apparently in the form of a complex inactive in human pernicious anaemia but active in chicks, by a non-motile, rod-shaped organism isolated from hen droppings.[8] It is probably synthesised by bacteria in the rumen of sheep [9] and, as might be expected, the synthesis is promoted by the ingestion of cobalt.[10]

The presence of a cobalt-containing substance similar to vitamin B$_{12}$ in cow-dung [11] is presumably due to bacterial synthesis in the rumen or intestine of cattle, and it has also been suggested that vitamin B$_{12}$ may be synthesised by the intestinal flora in humans, and even in patients suffering from pernicious anaemia (page 539).

References to Section 6

1. L. D. Wright, H. R. Skeggs and J. W. Huff, *J. Biol. Chem.*, 1948, **175**, 457; W. Shive, J. M. Ravel and W. M. Harding, *ibid.*, 1948, **175**, 991.
2. I. Z. Roberts, R. B. Roberts and P. H. Abelson, *J. Bact.*, 1949, **58**, 709.
3. A. D. Welch and M. F. Wilson, *Arch. Biochem.*, 1949, **22**, 486.
4. J. L. Ternberg and R. E. Eakin, *J. Amer. Chem. Soc.*, 1949, **71**, 3858.
5. M. H. Wright, *Science*, 1949, **110**, 257; H. E. Sauberlich, *Arch. Biochem.*, 1949, **24**, 224.
6. S. H. Hutner, L. Provasoli, E. L. R. Stokstad, C. E. Hoffmann, M. Belt, A. L. Franklin and T. H. Jukes, *Proc. Soc. Exp. Biol. Med.*, 1949, **70**, 118.
7. R. B. Roberts and M. Sands, *J. Bact.*, 1949, **58**, 710.
8. E. L. R. Stokstad, A. C. Page, J. V. Pierce, A. L. Franklin, T. H. Jukes, R. W. Heinle, M. Epstein and A. D. Welch, *J. Lab. Clin. Med.*, 1948, **33**, 860.
9. P. H. Abelson and H. H. Darby, *Science*, 1949, **110**, 566.
10. H. R. Marston and H. J. Lee, *Nature*, 1949, **164**, 529.
11. K. Hausmann, *Lancet*, 1949, **2**, 962.

p-AMINOBENZOIC ACID

1. INTRODUCTION

IN 1932, F. Mietzsch and J. Klarer [1] synthesised the substance, 4-sulphonamido-2′ : 4′-diaminoazobenzene dihydrochloride to which the name Prontosil rubrum was subsequently given :

$$H_2N\underset{=\!=}{\bigcirc}\overset{\overset{NH_2}{|}}{}N:N\underset{=\!=}{\bigcirc}SO_2NH_2 \ . \ 2HCl$$

This compound was shown by G. Domagk [2] and others to kill haemolytic streptococci in mice, although it had no activity *in vitro*. Tréfouel *et al.*[3] prepared other azo compounds of a similar type, and noted that the sulphonamide group appeared to be essential for antibacterial activity. They suggested that all these compounds were reduced in the body to *p*-aminobenzene-sulphonamide or, as it is now universally called, sulphanilamide

$$H_2N\underset{=\!=}{\bigcirc}SO_2NH_2$$

and that this was the curative agent. Tests on this substance, first prepared by P. Gelmo [4] in 1908, showed that it was in fact as active as Prontosil against streptococci, but in striking contrast to Prontosil it was highly active *in vitro* as well as *in vivo*.[5] The presence of sulphanilamide in the blood of patients under treatment with Prontosil was demonstrated by A. T. Fuller,[6] thus confirming the hypothesis of Tréfouel *et al*.

The discovery of the highly potent antibacterial activity of sulphanilamide was of the greatest importance in medicine. In the first place, it gave a new impetus to chemotherapy, for hitherto the search for antibacterial substances that could safely be used on patients and at the same time eliminate the infection had been singularly unsuccessful ; indeed, the use of antiseptics such as acriflavine in the treatment of wounds during the 1914-18 war had discredited chemotherapy because they damaged the tissues surrounding the wound. Secondly, it led to the preparation of thousands of derivatives of sulphanilamide, several of which were shown to be either more potent than the parent

35

substance or effective against organisms not inhibited by sulphanilamide.

It was only natural that many attempts should have been made to find an explanation of the striking antibacterial properties of sulphanilamide and its derivatives, and several plausible theories were put forward. The one that received most support and the one now generally accepted was based on the observation that the inhibitory effect of sulphanilamide could be prevented by various substances, such as peptone,[7] fractions from *Streptococcus* [8] and *Brucella abortus* [9] and certain enzymes [10] and tissue extracts.[11] D. D. Woods [12] fractionated the anti-sulphanilamide fraction of yeast, and found that the purified substance possessed many of the properties of *p*-aminobenzoic acid. On testing synthetic *p*-aminobenzoic acid he found that this, in fact, did neutralise the antibacterial action of sulphanilamide, and he therefore suggested that sulphanilamide inhibited the growth of bacteria by competing with *p*-aminobenzoic acid for certain enzymes essential for their growth. F. R. Selbie [13] confirmed Woods' observations by showing that mice succumbed to a streptococcal infection when *p*-aminobenzoic acid was administered simultaneously with sulphanilamide. On the basis of this evidence, P. Fildes [14] expressed Wood's theory in more general terms, and suggested that *p*-aminobenzoic acid was an essential metabolite, although not necessarily a growth factor, for all organisms that are inhibited by sulphanilamide.

Subsequently, S. D. Rubbo and J. M. Gillespie [15] succeeded in isolating pure *p*-aminobenzoic acid from yeast. They found that it could be titrated against sulphanilamide by using the growth of micro-organisms as the end-point, 1 mole antagonising 23,000 moles of sulphanilamide. Other workers [16] showed that *p*-aminobenzoic acid similarly antagonised the antibacterial effects of derivatives of sulphanilamide, *e.g.*, sulphathiazole, sulphapyridine and sulphadiazine.

Strauss *et al.*[17] made a careful study of the inhibition of the sulphonamides by *p*-aminobenzoic acid and found that : (*a*) the sulphonamides varied in the extent to which *p*-aminobenzoic acid affected them, the bacteriostatic action of 10 mg. % of sulphathiazole, sulphapyridine and sulphanilamide being inhibited by 0·04, 0·02 and 0·004 mg. % of *p*-aminobenzoic acid respectively ; (*b*) the addition of *p*-aminobenzoic acid to bacteria at different stages of growth could " revive a culture in the presence of sulphapyridine at any stage in the growth curve as long as there are any viable organisms " ; (*c*) after ingestion of *p*-aminobenzoic acid by humans, the urine interfered with the action of sulphathiazole on *Escherichia coli*, although to a smaller extent than did added *p*-aminobenzoic acid of the same concentration as measured colorimetrically, indicating that some change, such as conjugation or oxidation, had taken place in the excreted p-aminobenzoic acid ; (d) one hour after ingestion of p-amino-benzoic acid and sulphathiazole, the blood was not bacteriostatic to *Pneumococcus*, just as if p-aminobenzoic acid had been added *in vitro* ; and (e) although effective in preventing bacteriostasis, p-aminobenzoic acid did not prevent sulphonamide fever and rash whether given subsequently or simultaneously.

Further support to the theory of Woods and Fildes was given by S. D. Rubbo and J. M. Gillespie,[18] who found that *Clostridium aceto-butylicum* required p-aminobenzoic acid for growth, and that the amount of sulphanilamide required to inhibit growth was dependent on the amount of p-aminobenzoic acid present. One part by weight of p-aminobenzoic acid antagonised 26,000 parts of sulphanilamide.

The discovery of the antagonistic effect of sulphanilamide and p-aminobenzoic acid led to the discovery of other pairs of chemically related substances, one a growth stimulant and the other a growth inhibitor. S. D. Rubbo and J. M. Gillespie,[18] for example, reported that p-aminophenylacetic acid was a growth factor for *Clostridium acetobutylicum* and that p-aminophenylmethane sulphonic acid acted as a growth inhibitor for this organism. Other examples have already been discussed (pages 126, 292, 345, 397).

References to Section 1

1. F. Mietzsch and J. Klarer, D.R.P. 607537.
2. G. Domagk, *Deut. med. Woch.*, 1935, **61**, 250, 928.
3. J. Tréfouel, Mme. J. Tréfouel, F. Nitti and D. Bovet, *Compt. rend. Soc. Biol.*, 1935, **120**, 756.
4. P. Gelmo, *J. prakt. Chem.*, 1906 (2), **77**, 369.
5. L. Colebrook, G. A. H. Buttle and R. A. Q. O'Meara, *Lancet*, 1936, **2**, 1323.
6. A. T. Fuller, *ibid.*, 1937, **1**, 194.
7. J. S. Lockwood, *J. Immunology,* 1938, **35**, 155 ; J. S. Lockwood and H. M. Lynch, *J. Amer. Med. Assoc.*, 1940, **114**, 935.
8. T. C. Stamp, *Lancet*, 1939, **2**, 10.
9. H. N. Green, *Brit. J. Exp. Path.*, 1940, **21**, 38.
10. R. West and A. F. Coburn, *J. Exp. Med.*, 1940, **72**, 91.
11. C. M. MacLeod, *ibid.*, 217.
12. D. D. Woods, *Brit. J. Exp. Path.*, 1940, **21**, 74.
13. F. R. Selbie, *ibid.*, 90.
14. P. Fildes, *Lancet*, 1940, **1**, 956.
15. S. D. Rubbo and J. M. Gillespie, *Nature*, 1940, **146**, 838.
16. E. Strauss, J. H. Dingle and M. Finland, *Proc. Soc. Exp. Biol. Med.*, 1941, **46**, 131, 133 ; W. W. Spink and J. Jermsta, *ibid.*, 1941, **47**, 395.
17. E. Strauss, F. C. Lowell and M. Finland, *J. Clin. Invest.*, 1941, **20**, 189.
18. S. D. Rubbo and J. M. Gillespie, *Lancet*, 1942, **1**, 36.

2. ISOLATION OF p-AMINOBENZOIC ACID

As already mentioned (page 546), the isolation of p-aminobenzoic acid from yeast and its unequivocal identification was first accomplished by S. D. Rubbo and J. M. Gillespie,[1] but an improved method of isolation was described by K. C. Blanchard[2] in the following year. An aqueous alcoholic extract of yeast was extracted with ether, and the ethereal extract evaporated. The residue was made slightly alkaline with ammonia, treated with basic lead acetate, and the filtrate acidified and extracted with ether. The extract was re-treated with basic lead acetate and re-extracted with ether, when crystals of p-aminobenzoic acid, m.p. 186·4° C., separated from the final extract. On acetylation of the mother-liquors, crystals of p-acetylaminobenzoic acid (m.p. 259·5° C.) were obtained. Altogether the equivalent of 1·6 mg. of p-aminobenzoic acid was isolated from 1 kg. of yeast, about one-half that estimated to be present. The extraction was repeated on a sample of plasmolysed yeast heated at 80° C. to destroy enzymes and on another sample of the same yeast which had been allowed to autolyse. From these two samples, p-acetylaminobenzoic acid equivalent to 2·7 and 4·7 mg. of p-aminobenzoic acid per kg. was isolated, corresponding to 57 and 60 % of the amounts estimated to be present in these two preparations. Thus p-aminobenzoic acid appeared to exist in yeast in combined form, from which it was released on autolysis.

This was confirmed by Ratner et al.[3] who, by a process involving precipitation with a silver salt, fractionation of the lead and barium salts and precipitation from alcohol-ether or alcohol-acetone solutions, isolated from 50 kg. of dried yeast, 400 mg. of a polypeptide containing 8 % of p-aminobenzoic acid. This had no anti-sulphonamide activity, but free p-aminobenzoic acid was liberated on hydrolysis with acid or alkali. The peptide contained a chain of ten or eleven glutamic acid residues, to which the p-aminobenzoic acid was attached through its carboxyl group.[4] Thus the conjugate was analogous in structure to vitamin B_c conjugate (page 464). It accounted for 20 to 30 % of the total p-aminobenzoic acid content of yeast.

References to Section 2

1. S. D. Rubbo and J. M. Gillespie, *Nature*, 1940, **146**, 838.
2. K. C. Blanchard, *J. Biol. Chem.*, 1941, **140**, 919.
3. S. Ratner, M. Blanchard, A. F. Coburn and D. E. Green, *ibid.*, 1944, **155**, 689.
4. S. Ratner, M. Blanchard and D. E. Green, *ibid.*, 1946, **164**, 691.

3. ESTIMATION OF p-AMINOBENZOIC ACID

Chemical Methods

H. Tauber and S. Laufer [1] observed that when p-dimethylamino-benzaldehyde was reacted with p-aminobenzoic acid in glacial acetic acid, a yellow colour was produced, the intensity of which was proportional to the concentration of p-aminobenzoic acid. They suggested that the reaction might be used for the estimation of p-aminobenzoic acid. E. R. Kirch and O. Bergeim [2] proposed the use of a colour reaction with diazotised aneurine for the estimation of p-aminobenzoic acid in urine, whilst H. W. Eckert [3] used the colour formed with di-methyl-α-naphthylamine for its estimation in blood. Conjugated p-aminobenzoic acid was estimated after hydrolysis with acid. Another method of assay, which appears to be more in the nature of an identification and purity test, comprises the dissolution of the p-amino-benzoic acid in dilute hydrochloric acid and titration with bromine, as in the estimation of phenol. [4]

Microbiological Methods

Chemical methods of assay do not appear to have found favour in the estimation of p-aminobenzoic acid, and microbiological methods have been extensively used, just as they have in the case of other members of the vitamin B complex. The first method was due to M. Landy and D. M. Dicken, [5] who proposed the use of *Acetobacter suboxydans* as the test organism. The basal medium consisted of casein hydrolysate, glycerol, pantothenic acid, nicotinic acid, trypto-phan, cystine and salts, and the growth of the organism was measured turbidimetrically. The method was used for the estimation of p-aminobenzoic acid in animal tissues, blood, body-fluids, cereals and yeast, and appeared to be highly specific. J. C. Lewis [6] suggested the use of *Lactobacillus arabinosus* 17-5 with a basal medium similar to that of Landy and Dicken, but supplemented with additional members of the vitamin B complex. The growth response in this instance, however, was measured by titrating the lactic acid produced. Digestion with dilute alkali was used to liberate bound p-aminobenzoic acid, strong alkali or acids resulting in partial inactivation. The method was used to estimate p-aminobenzoic acid in foodstuffs and was said to be very specific.

According to Mitchell et al., [7] the method of Landy and Dicken gave a response equivalent to only a fraction of the total p-amino-benzoic acid present after acid or alkaline hydrolysis ; even after enzymic hydrolysis or autolysis, low results were obtained. They advocated hydrolysis with 6N-sulphuric acid at 115° C. for one hour.

Subsequently they [8] described a method of assaying *p*-aminobenzoic acid in a variety of foodstuffs and animal tissues by means of a mutant of *Neurospora crassa*. The use of yet another organism, *Clostridium acetobutylicum*, was proposed by J. O. Lampen and W. H. Peterson,[9] who recommended alkaline hydrolysis for the liberation of *p*-aminobenzoic acid. *Cl. acetobutylicum* had the advantage of requiring an incubation time of only twenty to twenty-four hours, and was capable of estimating dilutions of *p*-aminobenzoic acid as low as 0·00004 µg. per ml.[10]

References to Section 5

1. H. Tauber and S. Laufer, *J. Amer. Chem. Soc.*, 1941, **63**, 1488.
2. E. R. Kirch and O. Bergeim, *J. Biol. Chem.*, 1943, **148**, 445.
3. H. W. Eckert, *ibid.*, 197.
4. M. E. Martin and M. W. Green, *Bull. Nat. Formulary Comm.*, 1947, **15**, 106.
5. M. Landy and D. M. Dicken, *J. Biol. Chem.*, 1942, **146**, 109.
6. J. C. Lewis, *ibid.*, 441.
7. H. K. Mitchell, E. R. Isbell and R. C. Thompson, *ibid.*, 1943, **147**, 485.
8. R. C. Thompson, E. R. Isbell and H. K. Mitchell, *ibid.*, 1943, **148**, 281.
9. J. O. Lampen and W. H. Peterson, *ibid.*, 1944, **153**, 193.
10. R. D. Housewright and S. A. Koser, *J. Infect. Dis.*, 1944, **75**, 113.

4. OCCURRENCE OF *p*-AMINOBENZOIC ACID IN FOODSTUFFS

The occurrence of *p*-aminobenzoic acid in foodstuffs is obviously correlated to some extent with the occurrence of folic acid (page 483) but, whereas an estimate of the total (free and combined) *p*-aminobenzoic acid would include any *p*-aminobenzoic acid present as folic acid, *p*-aminobenzoic acid occurs in foodstuffs in the free state and in compounds other than folic acid. It has already been stated, for example (page 548), that in yeast 20 to 30 % of the *p*-aminobenzoic acid is present in combination with a polypeptide of glutamic acid.

A limited amount of information is available concerning the *p*-aminobenzoic acid contents of foodstuffs ; these invariably contain appreciably more *p*-aminobenzoic acid than the amount equivalent to the folic acid present.

The following values were obtained for cereals : wheat germ, 1·0 ;[1] wheat middlings, 0·52 ;[1] oats, 0·5 ;[2] rolled oats, 0·33 ;[1] maize meal, 0·3 ;[1] and alfalfa meal, 2·0 µg. per g.[1]

Fresh spinach contained 0·6 ;[3] dried carrots, 0·18 ;[4] and dried cabbage, 9·7 µg. per g.[4]

Fresh calf liver contained 0·2 ;[1] and ox liver, 2·5 μg. per g.[2] Dried whole egg contained 0·2 to 0·36 ; dried egg yolk, 0·8 ; and dried egg albumen, 0·055 μg. per g.[4] Skim milk contained 0·004 [4] and whole milk, 0·15 μg. per ml.[1]

As might be expected, yeast was the richest source of p-aminobenzoic acid, containing from 4 [2] to 100 [1] μg. per g. Mushrooms contained 1·3 μg. per g.[2]

References to Section 4

1. M. Landy and D. M. Dicken, *J. Biol. Chem.*, 1942, **146**, 109.
2. H. K. Mitchell, E. R. Isbell and R. C. Thompson, *ibid.*, 1943, **147**, 485.
3. R. C. Thompson, E. R. Isbell and H. K. Mitchell, *ibid.*, 1943, **148**, 281.
4. J. C. Lewis, *ibid.*, 1942, **146**, 441.

5. EFFECT OF p-AMINOBENZOIC ACID DEFICIENCY IN ANIMALS

The recognition of p-aminobenzoic acid as a growth factor for microorganisms (page 546) was soon followed by evidence of its biological importance for higher animals and man. S. Ansbacher[1] was the first to suggest that it might be a member of the vitamin B complex, following the discovery that it cured grey hair in rats, and also in mice,[2] when these were fed a synthetic diet. G. A. Emerson,[3] however, failed to confirm these observations, but they were substantiated by the subsequent work of G. J. Martin and S. Ansbacher,[4] who showed that p-aminobenzoic acid also counteracted the action of hydroquinone, which causes greying of hair in cats [5] and mice, and of sulphanilamide [6] and succinyl sulphathiazole,[7] which have a similar effect in rats. Moreover, the colour change normally produced by the action of tyrosinase on dihydroxyphenylalanine was modified by p-aminobenzoic acid *in vitro*, suggesting that it interfered with melanin formation.[8] The interference was not specific, however, since sulphanilamide and alanine, though not pantothenic acid (which has also been claimed to possess chromotrichial properties) behaved similarly.

According to B. Sure,[9] p-aminobenzoic acid was essential for reproduction and lactation in the rat.

Since the deficiency symptoms resulting from feeding a purified diet to rats were aggravated by succinylsulphathiazole and at least partially removed by p-aminobenzoic acid, Briggs *et al.*[10] suggested that the factor required to prevent these symptoms might be synthesised by bacteria in the gut. Apparently the symptoms were more or less completely cured by the addition of folic acid to the diet.[11] *p*-Aminobenzoic acid failed to cure the greying resulting from a deficiency of pantothenic acid.[12]

Grey hair has been claimed to be symptomatic not only of *p*-aminobenzoic acid deficiency, but also of pantothenic acid deficiency (see page 365), biotin deficiency (see page 424), folic acid deficiency (see page 487) and inositol deficiency (see page 572). It is possible that *p*-aminobenzoic acid is a chromotrichial factor because it is converted into folic acid, which is especially effective in stumulating the growth of the intestinal bacteria (see page 505), but such an explanation cannot apply to other members of the vitamin B complex, which are obviously not inter-convertible. The true explanation of the existence of several chromotrichial factors must be that many members of the vitamin B complex are capable of stimulating the growth of the intestinal flora, when this has been depressed either by feeding a purified diet or as the result of treatment with a sulphonamide, and that once the intestinal bacteria have regained their full vigour, they synthesise the factor nceessary for the formation of melanin.

Indirect confirmation of this hypothesis was provided by Coates *et al.*,[13] who found that refected rats (page 75) were entirely dependent on the symbiotic microflora for their supply of essential growth factors and were therefore particularly suitable for detecting interference with the activity of these organisms by growth inhibitors. They showed that sulphapyrazine, sulphathiazole, sulphaguanidine, sulphasuxidine and sulphathalidine reduced the excretion of aneurine and that the addition of *p*-aminobenzoic acid restored the excretion to normal.

The effect of *p*-aminobenzoic acid on the intestinal flora also accounts for its ability to cure a hypoprothrombinaemia produced in young rats by feeding sulphasuxidine.[14] The *p*-aminobenzoic acid stimulated the growth of the bacteria in the intestinal tract and these then synthesised the vitamin K necessary to restore the blood-clotting mechanism to normal.

p-Aminobenzoic acid was not apparently necessary for growth in the pig,[15] but it appeared to be essential for young trout.[16] In its absence these developed pale livers, 10 to 20 mg. per 100 g. of diet being necessary to prevent this condition.

References to Section 5

1. S. Ansbacher, *Science*, 1941, **93**, 164.
2. G. J. Martin and S. Ansbacher, *Proc. Soc. Exp. Biol. Med.*, 1941, **48**, 118.
3. G. A. Emerson, *ibid.*, 1941, **47**, 448.
4. G. J. Martin and S. Ansbacher, *J. Biol. Chem.*, 1941, **138**, 441.

5. H. Oettel, *Arch. Exp. Path. Pharmakol.*, 1936, **183**, 319.
6. G. J. Martin, *Proc. Soc. Exp. Biol. Med.*, 1942, **51**, 56.
7. L. D. Wright and A. D. Welch, *Science*, 1943, **97**, 426.
8. G. J. Martin, W. A. Wisansky and S. Ansbacher, *Proc. Soc. Exp. Biol. Med.*, 1941, **47**, 26.
9. B. Sure, *Science*, 1941, **94**, 167 ; *J. Nutrition*, 1943, **26**, 275.
10. G. M. Briggs, T. D. Luckey, R. C. Mills, C. A. Elvehjem and E. B. Hart, *Proc. Soc. Exp. Biol. Med.*, 1943, **52**, 7.
11. G. J. Martin, *ibid.*, 1942, **51**, 353.
12. L. M. Henderson, J. M. McIntire, H. A. Waisman and C. A. Elvehjem, *J. Nutrition*, 1942, **23**, 47.
13. M. E. Coates, R. M. Henry, P. M. Kon, S. K. Kon, E. H. Mawson, J. E. Stanier and S. Y. Thompson, *Nature*, 1946, **157**, 262.
14. H. G. Day, K. G. Wakim, M. M. Krider and E. E. O'Banion, *J. Nutrition*, 1943, **26**, 598.
15. T. J. Cunha, L. K. Bustad, W. E. Ham, D. R. Cordy, E. C. McCulloch, L. F. Woods, G. H. Conner and M. A. McGregor, *ibid.*, 1947, **34**, 173.
16. B. A. McLaren, E. Keller, D. J. O'Donnell and C. A. Elvehjem, *Arch. Biochem.*, 1947, **15**, 169.

6. EFFECT OF *p*-AMINOBENZOIC ACID DEFICIENCY IN MAN

The possibility that, by analogy with its effects in experimental animals, *p*-aminobenzoic acid might have a favourable effect in nutritional achromotrichia in man was first suggested by B. F. Sieve.[1] Attempts to restore the colour of grey hair in elderly men and women by means of *p*-aminobenzoic acid were unsuccessful, however. In one experiment,[2] only two out of nineteen subjects showed any improvement when given *p*-aminobenzoic acid together with calcium pantothenate and yeast. In another experiment,[3] only three out of eighty-eight cases of achromotrichia given 100 mg. of *p*-aminobenzoic acid three times daily for ten to twelve weeks showed any tendency to re-pigmentation, and in one of these the pigmentation disappeared again soon after treatment was stopped. Any claims, therefore, that preparations containing *p*-aminobenzoic acid are of value in restoring the grey hair of elderly patients to its former colour are completely unjustified, and there is no scientific evidence in support of them.

It has been claimed [4] that ointments containing *p*-aminobenzoic acid protect the skin against sunburn, and that *p*-aminobenzoic acid and local anaesthetics such as procaine derived from it protect the injected area from the erythema action of ultra-violet light when injected intracutaneously. Irradiated solutions of *p*-aminobenzoic acid were said to cause inflammation when injected intradermally in man.

Several workers observed that *p*-aminobenzoic acid had a leucopenic effect when given to patients infected with rickettsiae [5] (see page 557). It was therefore tried out in the treatment of patients with chronic lymphatic leukemia and chronic myeloid leukemia. It caused a profound fall in the leucocyte count when administered in doses of 50 g. a day. The haemoglobin content of the blood was reduced slightly.[6] The division of myeloid cells appeared to be stimulated at low concentrations and depressed at high concentrations.

References to Section 6

1. B. F. Sieve, *Science*, 1941, **94**, 257.
2. H. Brandalcone, E. Main and J. M. Steele, *Proc. Soc. Exp. Biol. Med.*, 1943, **53**, 47.
3. J. J. Eller and L. A. Diaz, *N.Y. Sta. J. Med.*, 1943, **43**, 1331.
4. S. Rothman and J. Rabin, *J. Invest. Dermat.*, 1942, **5**, 445.
5. A. Yeomans, J. C. Snyder, E. S. Murray, C. J. D. Zarafonetis and R. S. Ecke, *J. Amer. Med. Assoc.*, 1944, **126**, 349 ; P. K. Smith, *ibid.*, 1946, **131**, 1114 ; N. A. Tierney, *ibid.*, 280.
6. H. B. May and J. Vallence-Owen, *Lancet*, 1948, **2**, 607.

7. METABOLISM OF *p*-AMINOBENZOIC ACID

p-Aminobenzoic acid is excreted in human urine, probably in conjugated form, and in human faeces (see pages 77, 78).[1] By using *p*-aminobenzoic acid containing N^{15}, Lustig *et al.*[2] demonstrated that the substance was neither stored nor utilised by mice.

The average concentration of *p*-aminobenzoic acid in human sweat was 0·24 μg. per 100 ml.[3]

There is convincing evidence that *p*-aminobenzoic acid is synthesised by the intestinal flora of humans, for Denko *et al.*[1] found that the faecal excretion greatly exceeded the dietary intake. It is not known whether the *p*-aminobenzoic acid so formed is absorbed.

Administration of *p*-aminobenzoic acid to guinea-pigs resulted in a decrease of the bacterial population of the intestine and in the total disappearance of the Gram-negative lactose-fermenting bacilli.[4]

References to Section 7

1. E. Strauss, F. C. Lowell and M. Finland, *J. Clin. Invest.*, 1941, **20**, 189; C. W. Denko, W. E. Grundy, J. W. Porter, G. H. Berryman, T. E. Friedemann and J. B. Youmans, *Arch. Biochem.*, 1946, **10**, 33 ; C. W. Denko, W. E. Grundy, N. C. Wheeler, C. R. Henderson, G. H. Berryman, F. E. Friedemann and J. B. Youmans, *ibid.*, 1946, **11**, 109.
2. B. Lustig, A. R. Goldfarb and B. Gerstl, *Arch. Biochem.*, 1944, **5**, 59.
3. B. C. Johnson, H. H. Mitchell and T. S. Hamilton, *J. Biol. Chem.*, 1945, **161**, 357.
4. D. M. Whitney and L. Anigstein, *J. Bact.*, 1946, **52**, 400.

8. PHARMACOLOGY OF p-AMINOBENZOIC ACID

The toxicity of p-aminobenzoic acid was studied by C. C. Scott and E. B. Robbins,[1] who found that it was more toxic to mice and dogs than to rats when given orally, but more toxic to rats than to mice when the sodium salt was given intravenously. The values of LD50 were 2·85, 1·3 and 7·6 g. per kg. for mice, dogs and rats respectively by the oral route, and 4·6 and 2·8 g. per kg. for mice and rats respectively by the intravenous route. Oral doses in excess of 1 g. per kg. generally caused death in dogs, following acute gastro-enteritis and haemorrhage into the small intestine. Acute necrosis of the liver was produced by 2 g. per kg. or more. Rats tolerated 1·4 g. per kg. per day by mouth for a month without ill effects.

It has been stated,[2] however, that adult rats fed a diet containing 3 % of p-aminobenzoic acid developed enlarged thyroid glands after about a month, but this was not confirmed by C. D. Sullivan and J. W. Archdeacon,[3] who gave 7·5 mg. of p-aminobenzoic acid daily for forty-eight days by the intraperitoneal route and could observe no change in the weight of the thyroid glands. Body growth was inhibited, however, and the adrenals were slightly enlarged.

References to Section 8

1. C. C. Scott and E. B. Robbins, *Proc. Soc. Exp. Biol. Med.*, 1942, **49**, 184.
2. A. S. Gordon, E. D. Goldsmith and H. A. Charipper, *Endocrinology*, 1945, **37**, 223.
3. C. D. Sullivan and J. W. Archdeacon, *ibid.*, 1947, **41**, 325.

9. p-AMINOBENZOIC ACID IN THE NUTRITION OF MICRO-ORGANISMS

Bacteria requiring p-Aminobenzoic Acid

The Woods-Fildes theory (page 546) postulated that p-aminobenzoic acid was an essential metabolite of all micro-organisms susceptible to the action of the sulphonamides. Although some of these organisms can synthesise it for themselves others require it pre-formed in the medium before they can grow ; in such instances, p-aminobenzoic acid is also an essential growth factor. The first micro-organisms shown to require p-aminobenzoic acid were *Clostridium acetobutylicum* [1] and *Streptobacterium plantarum.*[2]

Clostridium acetobutylicum has been used for the microbiological assay of p-aminobenzoic acid (page 550) and so have *Acetobacter suboxydans* and *Lactobacillus arabinosus*, which also fail to grow in the absence of *p*-aminobenzoic acid.[3, 4] Other *Clostridia* for which *p*-aminobenzoic acid is essential are : *Cl. butylicum*,[5] *Cl. felsineum*,[5] and *Cl. kluyveri*.[6] It was also essential for *Lactobacillus helveticus* and *L. pentosus*,[7] and an X-ray mutant of *Escherichia coli*.[8]

Bacterial Synthesis of *p*-Aminobenzoic Acid

p-Aminobenzoic acid is synthesised by many bacteria.[9] Sulphathiazole-resistant strains of *Staph. aureus* produced more than susceptible strains,[9, 10] and the additional *p*-aminobenzoic acid was sufficient to account for the fastness of these strains to sulphathiazole.[11] H. McIlwain [12] showed that some of the *p*-aminobenzoic acid present in the cells of haemolytic streptococci could readily be removed by washing with saline and that only the tightly bound portion was responsible for sulphonamide-fastness. Sulphonamide-resistant strains of *D. pneumoniae* and *Shigella paradysenteriae* showed no increase in the ability to synthesise *p*-aminobenzoic acid.

The amounts of *p*-aminobenzoic acid in *Aerobacter aerogenes, Serratia marcescens, Pseudomonas aeruginosa, Streptococcus haemolyticus* and *Escherichia coli* were calculated by H. McIlwain [13] to be 7700, 3100, 4700, 3800 and 17,000 molecules per cell respectively. The corresponding rates of synthesis were 4·0, 1·2, 5·5, 1·1 and 3·9 molecules per cell per second.

Three X-ray mutants of *E. coli*, however, required *p*-aminobenzoic acid for growth, but this could be replaced by a combination of amino acids, a purine and thymine ; the presence of methionine in the amino acid mixture was essential.[13a] In a medium containing these supplements, the mutants were resistant to the action of sulphonamides. The evidence suggests that *p*-aminobenzoic acid plays a part in the synthesis of purines and thymine, methionine and possibly other amino acids, thus resembling vitamin B_{12} and folic acid (pages 515, 539, 543). Pteroylglutamic acid did not replace *p*-aminobenzoic acid, however, as a growth factor for the mutants.

A soil bacillus belonging to the *Pseudomoneaceae* was isolated which developed an enzyme specific for the oxidation of *p*-aminobenzoic acid to carbon dioxide, water and ammonia.[14] The growth of this organism was inhibited by sulphapyridine, and *p*-aminobenzoic acid counteracted the inhibition. The organism could be used to identify *p*-aminobenzoic acid in amounts as small as 10 μg. It was used by Spink *et al.*[15] to demonstrate that a sulphonamide-resistant strain of *Staph. aureus* produced more *p*-aminobenzoic acid than a non-resistant strain, confirming the result obtained by Landy *et al.*[11]

Antibacterial Action of p-Aminobenzoic Acid

The growth of certain gram-negative organisms e.g. *E. coli* was inhibited by a 1 in 150 solution of sodium p-aminobenzoate, and the growth of *M. tuberculosis* by a 1 in 1000 solution. Gram-positive organisms were not affected by a 1 in 100 solution.[15a] The severity of experimental tuberculosis in guinea-pigs was mitigated by the oral administration of about 100 mg. daily of p-aminobenzoic acid, and the survival time of the animals was increased, but neither the development of the infection nor the eventual fatal outcome was prevented.[15b] On the other hand, p-aminobenzoic acid accelerated the onset of experimental typhoid in mice and shortened the survival time.[15c]

Moulds and Yeasts

p-Aminobenzoic acid was essential for the growth of an X-ray mutant of *Neurospora crassa* [16] and of *Rhodotorula aurantiaca*.[17] It accelerated the growth of *Penicillium roquefortii* and *Byssochlamys fulva* but inhibited the growth of *Aspergillus niger*.[18] It neutralised the inhibitory action of sulphanilamide on *Penicillium digitatum*, *Fusarium coeruleum* and *Botrytis allii*.[19] One mutant of *N. crassa* actually required sulphonamides for growth and was inhibited by p-aminobenzoic acid; the inhibition was completely antagonised by sulphonamides.[19a] A double mutant, carrying the gene for sulphonamide requirement and a gene for failure to synthesise p-aminobenzoic acid, required both substances for growth.

Other Micro-organisms

The growth of *Strigomonas oncopelti* was inhibited by sulphanilamide and the inhibition was counteracted by p-aminobenzoic acid in concentrations 264,000 times that of the sulphanilamide.[20] p-Aminobenzoic acid had no effect on experimental toxoplasmosis in mice, but it nullified the protection afforded by sulphathiazole.[21] Clinical improvement in cases of amoebiasis followed the administration of p-aminobenzoic acid.[21a]

Viruses and Rickettsiae

p-Aminobenzoic acid was remarkably effective in murine typhus infection in mice when added to the food in a concentration of 3 %.[22] It was also effective against some rickettsial infections of chick embryos when injected into the yolk-sac and was twice as effective against Rocky Mountain spotted fever as against typhus, but it had no effect on the organisms of lymphogranuloma venereum or psittacosis.[23] *p*-Aminobenzoic acid had an anti-rickettsial activity in the guinea-pig in a dose of 0·3 g. per 100 g. of diet [24] and has been tried out with considerable success in rickettsial infections in man.[25] Thus in twenty cases of louse-borne typhus, an initial dose of 4 to 8 g. of *p*-aminobenzoic acid was given, followed by 2 g. every two hours ; this maintained a blood concentration of between 10 and 20 mg. per 100 ml. The symptoms were less severe in the treated patients than in the untreated controls, and the duration of the fever was considerably shorter. Similar beneficial results were obtained in twenty-nine patients with endemic (murine) typhus and in eighteen patients with tsutsugamushi disease. A large number of cases of Rocky Mountain spotted fever have been successfully treated with *p*-aminobenzoic acid, which is now regarded as the drug of choice. The dose for children is 0·9 g. per kg. of bodyweight.[26]

The chemotherapeutic activity of sulphadiazine on psittacosis virus was antagonised competitively by *p*-aminobenzoic acid and non-competitively by pteroylglutamic acid, suggesting that the sulphonamide exerted its effect by interfering with the incorporation of *p*-aminobenzoic acid into pteroylglutamic acid by the virus.[27] *p*-Aminobenzoic acid also reversed the action of sulphadiazine on the viruses of mouse pneumonitis and lymphogranuloma venereum.[28]

References to Section 9

1. S. D. Rubbo and J. M. Gillespie, *Nature*, 1940, **146,** 838 ; *Lancet*, 1942, **1,** 36.
2. R. Kuhn and K. Schwartz, *Ber.*, 1941, **74B,** 1617.
3. M. Landy and D. M. Dicken, *J. Biol. Chem.*, 1942, **146,** 109.
4. J. C. Lewis, *ibid.*, 441.
5. J. O. Lampen and W. H. Peterson, *Arch. Biochem.*, 1943, **2,** 443.
6. B. T. Bornstein and H. A. Barker, *J. Bact.*, 1948, **55,** 222.
7. E. E. Snell and H. K. Mitchell, *Arch. Biochem.*, 1942, **1,** 93.
8. J. O. Lampen, R. R. Roepke and M. J. Jones, *J. Biol. Chem.*, 1946, **164,** 789.
9. M. Landy, N. W. Larkum and E. J. Oswald, *Proc. Soc. Exp. Biol. Med.*, 1943, **52,** 338.
10. R. D. Housewright and S. A. Koser, *J. Infect. Dis.*, 1944, **75,** 113.
11. M. Landy, N. W. Larkum, E. J. Oswald and E. Streightoff, *Science*, 1943, **97,** 295.
12. H. McIlwain, *Biochem. J.*, 1945, **39,** 329.
13. H. McIlwain, *Nature*, 1946, **158,** 898.
13*a*. J. O. Lampen, M. J. Jones and R. R. Roepke, *J. Biol. Chem.*, 1949, **180,** 423.

14. G. S. Mirick, *J. Exp. Med.*, 1943, **78**, 255.
15. W. W. Spink, L. D. Wright, J. J. Vivino and H. R. Skeggs, *ibid.*, 1944, **79**, 331.
15a. R. Lecoq and J. Solomides, *C. R. Acad. Sci.*, 1947, **225**, 1392 ; 1948, **226**, 846.
15b. B. M. Bloomberg, *S. Afr. J. Med. Sci.*, 1947, **12**, 1.
15c. B. M. Bloomberg, *ibid.*, 5.
16. R. C. Thompson, E. R. Isbell and H. K. Mitchell, *J. Biol. Chem.*, 1943, **148**, 281.
17. W. J. Robbins and R. Ma, *Science*, 1944, **100**, 85.
18. G. W. K. Cavill and J. M. Vincent, *Nature*, 1945, **155**, 301 ; *J. Soc. Chem. Ind.*, 1948, **67**, 25.
19. P. W. Brian, *Nature*, 1944, **153**, 83.
19a. S. Emerson, *J. Bact.*, 1947, **54**, 195.
20. M. Lwoff and A. Lwoff, *Ann. Inst. Pasteur*, 1945, **71**, 206.
21. W. K. Summers, *Proc. Soc. Exp. Biol. Med.*, 1947, **66**, 509.
21a. K. G. Dwork, *Bull. N.Y. Acad. Med.*, 1948, **24**, 391.
22. D. Greiff, H. Pinkerton and V. Moragues, *J. Exp. Med.*, 1944, **80**, 561.
23. H. L. Hamilton, H. Plotz and J. E. Smadel, *Proc. Soc. Exp. Biol. Med.*, 1945, **58**, 255 ; H. L. Hamilton, *ibid.*, 1945, **59**, 220.
24. L. Anigstein and D. M. Whitney, *J. Bact.*, 1946, **52**, 402.
25. A. Yeomans, J. C. Snyder, E. S. Murray, C. J. D. Zarafonetis and R. S. Ecke, *J. Amer. Med. Assoc.*, 1944, **126**, 349 ; P. K. Smith, *ibid.*, 1946, **131**, 1114 ; N. A. Tierney, *ibid.*, 280.
26. W. J. Hendricks and M. Peters, *J. Pediat.*, 1947, **30**, 72. C. J. Tichenor, S. Ross and P. A. McLendon, *ibid.*, 1947, **31**, 1 ; S. Ross, P. A. McLendon and H. J. Davis, *Pediatrics*, 1948, **2**, 163 ; L. E. Fraser, H. Rosenblum and J. A. Daneiger, *Amer. J. Dis. Child.*, 1948, **75**, 493 ; C. G. Hooten, W. S. Hooten and J. E. Mitchell, *Virginia Med. Monthly*, 1949, **76**, 121.
27. H. R. Morgan, *Proc. Soc. Exp. Biol. Med.*, 1948, **67**, 29.
28. C.-T. Huang and M. D. Eaton, *J. Bact.*, 1949, **58**, 73.

10. EFFECT OF *p*-AMINOBENZOIC ACID ON HIGHER PLANTS

p-Aminobenzoic acid has not been shown to have any specific effect on the growth of plants, but it neutralised the inhibitory effect of sulphanilamide on the growth of oat roots.[1]

p-Aminobenzoic acid, in company with aneurine, biotin and pyridoxine, was found to be present in soil and natural manures.[2]

References to Section 10

1. P. W. Brian, *Nature*, 1944, **153**, 83.
2. M. A. Roulet, *Experientia*, 1948, **4**, 149.

11. *p*-AMINOBENZOIC ACID REQUIREMENTS OF INSECTS

p-Aminobenzoic acid may have some effect on the growth of the larvae of *Tribolium confusum* and *Ptinus tectus*, but it is not essential in the same way as are other members of the vitamin B complex.[1]

Reference to Section 11

1. G. Fraenkel and M. Blewett, *Nature*, 1942, **150**, 177 ; 1943, **151**, 703.

12. ANALOGUES OF *p*-AMINOBENZOIC ACID

Very few compounds related to *p*-aminobenzoic acid have growth-promoting properties. Thus, the methyl and ethyl esters were reported to have only o·1 % of the activity of the acid against *Cl. acetobutylicum*[1, 2] and *Streptobacterium plantarum*, whilst procaine had 10 to 20 % of the activity against the former organism,[1, 2] but only 1 % of the activity against the latter.[3] Tutocaine also had about 1 % of the activity of *p*-aminobenzoic acid against *S. plantarum*, whilst pantocaine was even less effective.[1, 3] N-Acyl-*p*-aminobenzoic acids were only slightly active, but *p*-nitrobenzoic acid and the N-glycosides were as active as the acid itself towards *Cl. acetobutylicum*.[1] *p*-Amino-phenylacetic acid had only o·1 % of the activity of *p*-aminobenzoic acid against this organism, whilst *o*-aminobenzoic acid, isonicotinic acid, *p*-hydroxybenzoic acid and folic acid were inactive.[1] *p*-Amino-, *p*-nitro- and *p*-chloroacetylbenzoylglycine had between 10 and 100 % of the activity of *p*-aminobenzoic acid.[2]

p-Nitrobenzoic acid does not invariably stimulate the growth of micro-organisms, however, for, according to Rosenthal *et al.*,[4] it inhibited the growth of certain bacteria. *p*-Aminobenzamide[5] and some other sulphur-free analogues of *p*-aminobenzoic acid have similar properties. Thus, according to E. Auhagen,[6] the growth-promoting effect of *p*-aminobenzoic acid on *S. plantarum* was counteracted by *p*-aminobenzophenone, *p*-aminoacetophenone and *pp'*-diaminobenzo-phenone. The last-named was the most active of the three, being one-fifth to one-third as effective as sulphanilamide ; it exhibited a slight antibacterial action in mice infected with streptococci, gonococci and meningococci.

The bacteriostasis induced by *p*-nitrobenzoic acid and *p*-amino-benzamide was examined further by Johnson *et al.*,[7] who found that the compounds were not effective against all bacteria inhibited by the sulphonamides. Thus they inhibited the growth of *E. coli* but not of *S. haemolyticus* ; furthermore, with *E. coli* inhibition lasted only for a short time, the organisms beginning to grow again after forty-eight hours. It would appear, therefore, that some organisms are able to convert these two substances readily into p-aminobenzoic acid, whereas others can do so only with difficulty. Johnson *et al.* prepared thirty-five other compounds related to p-aminobenzoic acid and tested their effect on the growth of *E. coli*, *S. haemolyticus* and *D. pneumoniae*. The results of their work can be summarised as follows : Substitution of p-aminobenzoic acid in the 2- or 3-position with, for example, a methyl or methoxy group or a halogen atom yielded bacteriostatic compounds, and the introduction of a second group destroyed the activity. Replacement of the amino group by any group other than the nitro group gave an inactive substance, whilst replacement of the carboxyl group had a variable result. Thus, p-aminoacetophenone and 3-methyl-4-aminobenzamide had bacteriostatic properties, whilst other compounds of this type showed growth-promoting activity and yet others were completely inactive. 4-Amino-4'-carboxydiphenylamine inhibited the growth of *Strep. haemolyticus*, *Staph. aureus* and *E. coli* to the same extent as sulphanilamide.[7a]

2-Chloro-4-aminobenzoic acid exhibited curious properties and was a growth factor for *S. haemolyticus* and *D. pneumoniae* but a growth inhibitor for *E. coli* at high concentrations and had anti-sulphanilamide properties at lower concentrations.

The only naphthalene compound tested, 4-amino-1-naphthoic acid, was bactericidal at high, but inactive at low, concentrations. Two thiophene compounds, 5-nitrothiophene-2-carboxamide and 5-nitrothiophene-2-carboxylic acid were highly inhibitory towards *S. haemolyticus*, but the former was ten times as active as the latter against *E. coli*. The only thiazole compound tested, 2-aminothiazole-5-carboxylic acid, was inactive and both 5-nitro-2-furoic acid and 5-acetylamino-furoic acid were inactive. 6-Aminopyridine-3-carboxylic acid, however, was as active as sulphanilamide against *S. haemolyticus* and eight times as active against *E. coli*, being about as active as sulphapyridine against both organisms.

p-Aminobenzoic acid reversed the activity of all the compounds that had bacteriostatic properties.

2-Aminopyrimidine-5-carboxylic acid had no antibacterial action on *Strep. pyogenes in vitro*, but had a slight antagonistic effect towards sulphanilamide, although inferior in this respect to p-aminobenzoic acid.[8] Of a series of derivatives of p-aminobenzoic acid substituted in the nucleus, the most potent antibacterial substances were 3-hydroxy- and 3-chloro-4-aminobenzoic acid and 3 : 4-diaminobenzoic acid.[9, 10] The first of these had one-third to one-ninth the activity of sulphanilamide and had a definite but feeble therapeutic effect in mice infected with haemolytic streptococci or pneumococci. Five other compounds, 3-methyl- and 2-chloro-4-aminobenzoic acid, 4-amino-isophthalic acid, 4-(4'-aminobenzamido)-benzoic acid and ethyl 4-aminobenzoate, completely antagonised the growth-inhibitory action of sulphanilamide.[10]

References to Section 12

1. J. O. Lampen and W. H. Peterson, *Arch. Biochem.*, 1943, **2**, 443.
2. R. D. Housewright and S. A. Koser, *J. Infect. Dis.*, 1944, **75**, 113.
3. E. F. Möller and K. Schwartz, *Ber.* 1941, **74B**, 1612 ; O. Dann and E. F. Möller, *Chem. Ber.*, 1947, **80**, 21.
4. S. Rosenthal, H. Bauer and E. Elvove, *U.S. Publ. Health Rep.*, 1939, **54**, 1317.
5. J. Hirsch, *Science*, 1942, **96**, 140.
6. E. Auhagen, *Z. physiol. Chem.*, 1942, **274**, 48.
7. O. H. Johnson, D. E. Green and R. Pauli, *J. Biol. Chem.*, 1944, **153**, 37.
7*a*. A. T. Fuller, C. R. Harington, R. Pitt Rivers and J. M. L. Stephen, *J. Chem. Soc.*, 1948, 241.
8. A. R. Martin, F. L. Rose and G. Swain, *Nature*, 1944, **154**, 639.
9. D. Wyss, M. Rubin and F. Strandskov, *Proc. Soc. Exp. Biol. Med.*, 1943, **52**, 155.
10. A. R. Martin and F. L. Rose, *Biochem. J.*, 1945, **39**, 91.

13. FUNCTION OF *p*-AMINOBENZOIC ACID

The relationship between *p*-aminobenzoic acid and sulphanilamide and the significance of the Woods-Fildes theory have already been discussed (page 546). If this theory is correct, *p*-aminobenzoic acid and sulphanilamide compete with one another for an enzyme system essential for the activity of the bacterial cell. This enzyme is probably concerned with the synthesis of folic acid (page 515), since pteroylglutamic acid non-competitively reverses the antibacterial action of sulphanilamide.

p-Aminobenzoic acid, however, is not the only antagonist for the sulphonamides for, in presence of sub-optimal amounts of *p*-aminobenzoic acid, adenine, guanine, xanthine and hypoxanthine nullified the bacteriostatic effect of sulphanilamide against *L. arabinosus* and *L. pentosus*.[1] Any of these purines antagonised the effect of sulphanilamide on *L. pentosus* or *L. helveticus* in the absence of *p*-aminobenzoic acid. With *L. pentosus*, the effect of the purines appeared to depend on the presence of a growth factor that was not *p*-aminobenzoic acid. In the absence of *p*-aminobenzoic acid, the growth of *Cl. acetobutylicum* was stimulated by adenine, guanine, xanthine and uracil.[2]

Methionine also antagonised the inhibitory action of sulphanil-amide on *E. coli*, having about one-third the activity of the purines in this respect.[3] It is possible therefore that *p*-aminobenzoic acid functions in the synthesis of methionine as well as of the purine bases, although folic acid is apparently concerned only with the latter. 4-Amino-2-chlorobenzoic acid was a specific inhibitor of methionine synthesis by *E. coli*. Methionine was also able to stimulate the growth of an X-ray mutant of *E. coli*, giving a response additional to that produced by *p*-aminobenzoic acid.[4] Thymine and other purines were inactive on this strain, and pteroylglutamic acid had less than 0·001 % of the activity of *p*-aminobenzoic acid, suggesting that the latter has a function independent of its association with folic acid.

On the other hand, the biological importance of *p*-aminobenzoic acid is undoubtedly associated in part with its conversion to folic acid. Thus *p*-aminobenzoylglutamic acid, pteroic acid, pteroyl-glutamic acid and pteroyltriglutamic acid could replace *p*-amino-benzoic acid as a growth factor for *L. arabinosus*, although they were all less active on a molar basis.[5] The inhibition of *L. arabinosus* by sulphanilamide was antagonised non-competitively by these sub-stances, with the exception of pteroic acid, as well as by thymine.

References to Section 13

1. E. E. Snell and H. K. Mitchell, *Arch. Biochem.*, 1942, **1**, 93.
2. R. D. Housewright and S. A. Koser, *J. Infect. Dis.*, 1944, **75**, 113.
3. W. Shive and E. C. Roberts, *J. Biol. Chem.*, 1946, **162**, 463.
4. J. O. Lampen, R. R. Roepke and M. J. Jones, *ibid.*, 1946, **164**, 789.
5. J. O. Lampen and M. J. Jones, *ibid.*, 1947, **170**, 133.

CHAPTER XI

INOSITOL

1. INTRODUCTION

THE discovery by E. Wildiers [1] of " bios ", the hypothetical substance necessary for the growth of certain yeasts, and its resolution into a number of individual factors, has already been discussed (page 404). The first of these substances to be identified was bios I, which was shown by E. V. Eastcott [2] to be identical with *meso*-inositol, one of the eight stereo-isomers of hexahydroxycyclohexane. This substance had been known since 1850 when it was discovered in muscle by D. Scherer.[3] It was shown to be a cyclic hexahydroxy-alcohol by L. Maquenne [4] in 1887 and synthesised by H. Wieland and R. S. Wishart [5] in 1914.

Although inositol thus became the first member of the bios complex, it was not recognised as a growth factor for animals until 1940, when D. W. Woolley [6] showed that mice reared on a diet deficient in inositol lost weight and became hairless. It was subsequently demonstrated that mice and other species of animals showed other characteristic symptoms besides alopecia when made inositol-deficient (see page 572).

Inositol was therefore added to the list of substances essential for the growth of micro-organisms and higher animals and was regarded by many workers as a member of the vitamin B complex.

There have been some misgivings, however, about the inclusion of inositol in the vitamin B complex, as the amount of inositol required by animals and micro-organisms is very considerably greater than their requirements for other members of the vitamin B complex.

Similarly, the amounts of inositol present in many foodstuffs far exceed their contents of other members of the complex. These considerations suggest that inositol must play a different rôle in the economy of living organisms from that of aneurine or nicotinic acid, for example, and that it is a structural component of living tissue rather than a catalyst of metabolic reactions. Indeed, inositol has some of the characteristics of the amino-acids, many of which are also essential for the growth of animals and micro-organisms. Inositol and choline (page 582) may, in fact, be regarded as a link between the vitamins and amino acids.

References to Section 1

1. E. Wildiers, *La Cellule*, 1901, **18**, 313.
2. E. V. Eastcott, *J. Phys. Chem.*, 1928, **32**, 1094.
3. D. Scherer, *Annalen*, 1850, **73**, 322.
4. L. Maquenne, *Ann. Chim.*, 1887, **12**, 80.
5. H. Wieland and R. S. Wishart, *Ber.*, 1914, **47**, 2082.
6. D. W. Woolley, *Science*, 1940, **92**, 384 ; *J. Biol. Chem.*, 1940, **136**, 113.

2. ISOLATION OF INOSITOL

D. W. Woolley [1] isolated inositol from the 70 % alcohol-insoluble fraction of an aqueous liver extract hydrolysed with concentrated hydrochloric acid. Impurities were removed by means of normal lead acetate solution and the inositol was then precipitated with basic lead acetate solution. After decomposing the precipitate with sulphuric acid, the inositol was precipitated by baryta in alcoholic solution and the precipitate decomposed with carbon dioxide. The inositol was dissolved in the minimum amount of water, and alcohol was added to the solution until crystallisation occurred.

Reference to Section 2

1. D. W. Woolley, *J. Biol. Chem.*, 1941, **139**, 29.

3. CHEMICAL CONSTITUTION AND SYNTHESIS OF INOSITOL

Inositol was shown to be a cyclic hexahydroxy-alcohol as long ago as 1887,[1] but its configuration was not established with certainty until 1942. One of the reasons for the slow progress in the elucidation of its structure was that reactions found to be of value in determining the structure of the sugars proved to be non-specific when applied to the cyclic alcohols.

The structure of *meso*-inositol was established by degradation of partly phosphorylated inositols by oxidation with potassium permanganate and the identification of the oxidation products. There are eight possible configurations of hexahydroxycyclohexane. By the action of phosphatase on phytin, an optically active tetraphosphoric ester [2] and an optically inactive monophosphoric ester of *meso*-inositol were obtained.[3] The formation of the former proved that *meso*-inositol could not have all its hydroxyl groups on one side of the ring, whilst the formation of the inactive monophosphoric ester excluded the formula with four adjacent hydroxyl groups on one side of the ring and the other two groups on the other side. Oxidation of a mixture of the mono- and di-phosphoric esters of *meso*-inositol yielded *meso*-tartaric acid and racemic tartaric acid. This result excluded the formula with alternate hydroxyl groups above and below the ring, since this contains only *trans*-hydroxyl groups and therefore cannot give rise to *meso*-tartaric acid on oxidation. Oxidation of *meso*-inositol itself by alkaline permanganate solution gave a mixture of trihydroxyglutaric acid, *d*- (III) and *l-talo*mucic acids and *d*- (IV) and *l*-saccharic acids. This evidence indicated that *meso*-inositol could have either formula I or formula II.

T. Posternak[4] decided between these formulae by studying the oxidation product obtained by the action of *Acetobacter suboxydans* on *meso*-inositol. This substance, inosose (V), gave on oxidation a mixture of *d*- (VI) and *l-ido*saccharic acid and, on reduction, regenerated *meso*-inositol and produced at the same time another naturally occurring cyclitol, scyllitol (VII). *meso*-Inositol must therefore have the structure represented by (I).

The structure assigned to *meso*-inositol by T. Posternak was confirmed by G. Dangschat and H. O. L. Fischer.[5] The tetra-acetate of *meso*inositol, obtained from the tetra-acetyl-monoacetone derivative by removal of acetone, was oxidised with lead tetra-acetate giving a dialdehyde, which on further oxidation gave a mixture of the tetra-acetyl derivatives of the diethyl esters of *d*- (VI) and *l-ido*saccharic acids.

meso-Inositol has been synthesised by hydrogenation of hexa-hydroxybenzene.[6] With Raney nickel as catalyst, a mixture of *meso*-inositol, scyllitol and other cyclitols was formed. Scyllitol crystallised out from a 50 % aqueous methanol solution and *meso*inositol from a 90 % aqueous methanol solution. Several attempts have been made to synthesise *meso*-inositol by other routes, but without success.[7, 8]

References to Section 3

1. L. Maquenne, *Ann. Chim.*, 1887, **12**, 80.
2. T. Posternak, *Helv. Chim. Acta*, 1935, **18**, 1283.
3. R. J. Anderson, *J. Biol. Chem.*, 1914, **18**, 441.
4. T. Posternak, *Helv. Chim. Acta*, 1942, **25**, 746.
5. G. Dangschat and H. O. L. Fischer, *Naturwiss*, 1942, **30**, 146.
6. H. Wieland and R. S. Wishart, *Ber.*, 1914, **47**, 2082 ; R. C. Anderson and E. S. Wallis, *J. Amer. Chem. Soc.*, 1948, **70**, 2931.
7. F. Micheel, *Annalen*, 1932, **496**, 77.
8. Y. Hamamura, *Proc. Imp. Acad. Tokyo*, 1934, **10**, 459.

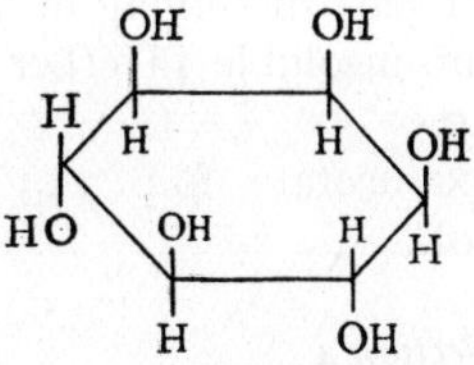

(I)

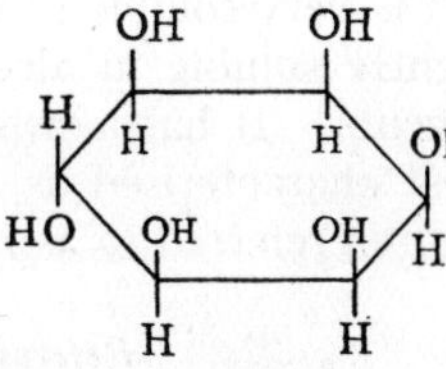

(II)

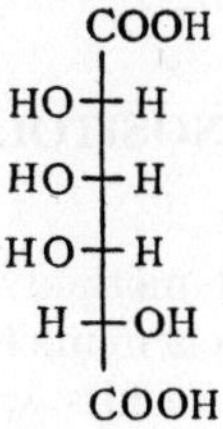

COOH
HO―H
HO―H
HO―H
H―OH
COOH

(III)

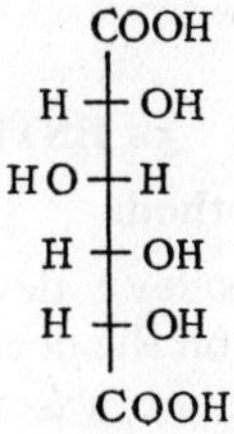

COOH
H―OH
HO―H
H―OH
H―OH
COOH

(IV)

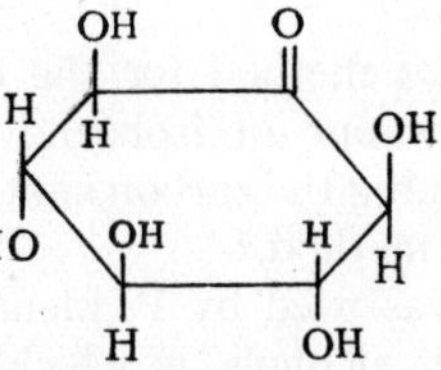

(V)

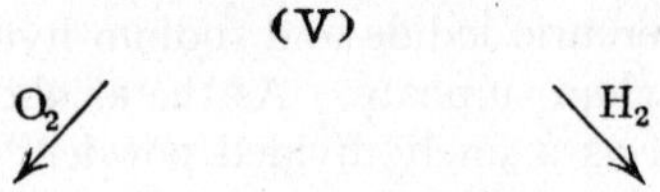

O_2 ↙   ↘ H_2

COOH
HO―H
H―OH
HO―H
H―OH
COOH

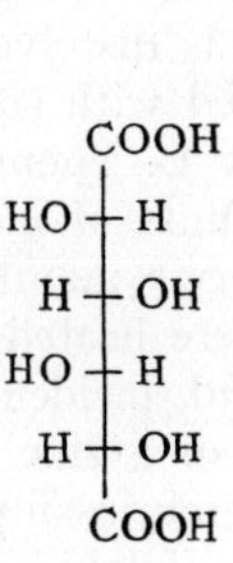

(VI)

+ meso-inositol

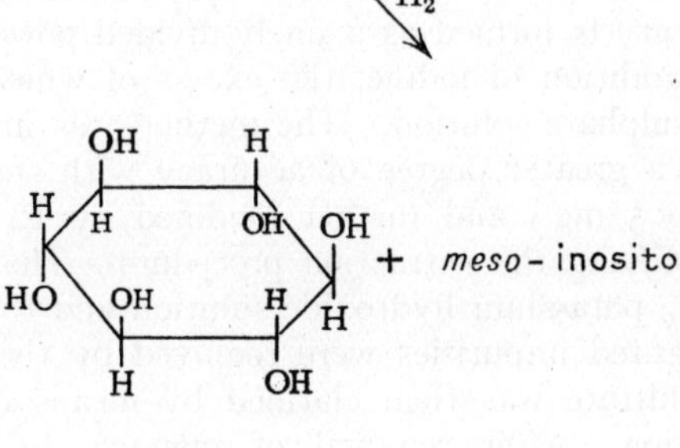

(VII)

4. PROPERTIES OF INOSITOL

meso-Inositol has m.p. 225 to 226° C. and forms a dihydrate, m.p. 218° C.[1] It is very soluble in water, 1 part dissolving in 5·7 parts at 24° C., slightly soluble in alcohol but insoluble in ether and other organic solvents. It has a sweet taste.

It is best characterised as the hexa-acetate, m.p. 213° C. *meso*-Inositol is often referred to as *i*-inositol.

Reference to Section 4

1. D. W. Woolley, *J. Biol. Chem.*, 1941, **139**, 29.

5. ESTIMATION OF INOSITOL

Biological Methods

D. W. Woolley[1] devised a biological method for the assay of inositol, based on the development of alopecia in mice. In the original diet yeast extract was used, but better results were subsequently obtained by replacing this with a mixture of synthetic vitamins.

Chemical Methods

The earliest chemical method for the estimation of inositol was the extremely laborious one of isolating the substance and either weighing it,[2] or determining the carbon content of the isolated material by a micro-combustion method.[3]

A simpler method was used by P. Fleury and J. Marque[4] for the estimation of polyhydric alcohols, in which the test solution is heated with potassium mercuric iodide and sodium hydroxide in presence of a suspension of barium sulphate. As the alcohol is oxidised, metallic mercury is formed as a finely-divided powder. This is dissolved by the addition of iodine, the excess of which is titrated with sodium thiosulphate solution. The method was improved by L. Young[5] to give a greater degree of accuracy with smaller amounts of inositol (1 to 5 mg.) and further modified by R. A. Gregory[6] mainly by simplifying the extraction procedure. The tissues were heated with 10 % potassium hydroxide solution and the alkali and, incidentally, unwanted impurities were removed by the addition of a zinc salt ; the filtrate was then clarified by means of acid mercuric sulphate solution. After removal of mercury by hydrogen sulphide, the inositol was precipitated with alcoholic baryta and barium removed from the precipitate. The purified inositol was then oxidised by potassium mercuric iodide.

A better chemical method of assay was developed by B. S. Platt and G. E. Glock.[7] The dried tissue was extracted with water and the fractions insoluble in 70 % acetone and soluble in ether were both removed from the extract. Glucose was then removed by fermentation with yeast and both acidic and basic substances were removed by adsorption on ion exchange materials. The free inositol in the solution was then quantitatively oxidised with periodic acid and the excess estimated iodometrically. Water-soluble combined inositol was estimated after acid hydrolysis of the aqueous extract.

Microbiological Methods

With inositol, as with so many other members of the vitamin B complex, biological and chemical methods of estimation have given place to microbiological methods, which are generally less tedious and more accurate than biological methods and more specific than chemical methods.

The first microbiological assay method was that of D. W. Woolley,[8] who used the Hansen No. 1 strain of Toronto yeast, *Saccharomyces cerevisiae*. This was grown on a basal medium consisting of glucose, casein hydrolysate, salts, other members of the vitamin B complex and an aqueous extract of malt sprouts to supply " bios II ". The response of the organism to graded doses of the test solution and of a standard inositol solution was measured turbidimetrically. The error was estimated to be not more than 5 or 6 %. A similar procedure was used by R. J. Williams *et al.*,[9] but in this instance the Gebruder-Meyer strain of yeast was employed. V. Jurist and J. R. Foy [10] also used yeast but in their basal medium the only constituents of uncertain composition were casein hydrolysate and a folic acid concentrate. Atkin *et al.*[11] used *S. carlsbergensis*.

G. W. Beadle [12] used a mutant of *Neurospora crassa*, which was claimed to have the advantage over yeast that the basal medium was simpler and the mould did not grow at all in the absence of inositol. Amounts of inositol ranging from 5 to 30 μg. per 20 ml. could be estimated with an error of $\pm$ 0·3 μg.

Burkholder *et al.*[13] used the yeast, *Kloeckera brevis*, for the assay of inositol, whilst Emery *et al.*,[14] compared the response obtained with this organism and that given by another yeast, *Schizosaccharomyces pombe*.

References to Section 5

1. D. W. Woolley, *J. Biol. Chem.*, 1940, **136**, 113 ; 1941, **139**, 29 ; *J. Nutrition*, 1941, **21**, Suppl., 17.
2. L. B. Winter, *Biochem. J.*, 1934, **28**, 6 ; 1940, **34**, 249.
3. J. Needham, *ibid.*, 1923, **17**, 422, 431.
4. P. Fleury and J. Marque, *Compt. rend.*, 1939, **188**, 1686 ; *J. Pharm. Chim.*, 1929, [8], **10**, 241.

5. L. Young, *Biochem. J.*, 1934, **28**, 1428, 1435.
6. R. A. Gregory, *ibid.*, 1935, **29**, 2798.
7. B. S. Platt and G. E. Glock, *ibid.*, 1943, **37**, 709.
8. D. W. Woolley, *J. Biol. Chem.*, 1941, **140**, 453 ; *J. Exp. Med.*, 1942, **75**, 277.
9. R. J. Williams, A. K. Stout, H. K. Mitchell and J. R. McMahan, *Univ. Texas Publ.*, 1941, No. 4137, 27.
10. V. Jurist and J. R. Foy, *J. Bact.*, 1944, **47**, 434.
11. L. Atkin, A. S. Schultz, W. L. Williams and C. N. Frey, *Ind. Eng. Chem., Anal. Ed.*, 1943, **15**, 141.
12. G. W. Beadle, *J. Biol. Chem.*, 1944, **156**, 683.
13. P. R. Burkholder, I. McVeigh and D. Moyer, *J. Bact.*, 1944, **48**, 385.
14. W. B. Emery, N. McLeod and F. A. Robinson, *Biochem. J.*, 1946, **40**, 426.

6. OCCURRENCE OF INOSITOL

Inositol occurs in most animal and plant tissues, fruits and cereal grains being especially good sources. Yeasts and certain other micro-organisms contain relatively large amounts,[1] and this is reflected in the relatively enormous amounts of inositol present in yeast extracts in comparison with their contents of other members of the vitamin B complex.[2] Thus, whereas the amounts of aneurine and pantothenic acid present in three different yeast extracts were of the order of 100 μg. per g., the amount of inositol present varied between 1000 and 3000 μg. per g. Relatively large amounts (2000 to 3000 μg. per g.) were also present in crude liver extracts.

Inositol was shown [3] to be present in liver in a water-soluble, alcohol-insoluble, non-dialysable form, presumably in combination with a protein. It was also shown to be present in the form of a complex in heart muscle,[4, 5] and was isolated from thyroid [6] and from kidneys, spleen and testes.[7] All the inositol present in brain cephalin was in the form of a phosphatide, diphosphoinositide.[7a]

In plants, inositol occurs in the form of its phosphoric esters. Inositol monophosphoric ester and triphosphoric ester have been shown to exist in wheat bran,[8] but the commonest inositol compound in cereals is the hexaphosphoric ester, phytic acid. The mixed calcium magnesium hydrogen salt of this acid, known as phytin, occurs in a large variety of plant materials, particularly cereals. Phytic acid forms a very stable calcium salt, in which neither the calcium nor the phosphorus can be utilised. Thus the phytic acid in oats renders non-available the whole of the calcium present in the cereal and, what is worse, immobilises much of the calcium present in other constituents of the diet, such as milk.[9] The phytic acid present accounts for the rachitogenic action of oatmeal, observed many years ago, the immobilisation of a part of the dietary calcium by the phytic acid reducing the calcium/phosphorus ration to such an extent that rickets may supervene. Phytic acid is also capable of immobilising other metals, for example iron but, in general, the results are less serious than with calcium.

Inositol was isolated from the phosphatides of the tubercle bacillus by R. J. Anderson,[10] whilst the phosphatides of soya-bean were shown to contain inositol monophosphoric ester.[11] Subsequently, D. W. Woolley,[12] showed that soya-bean phosphatide contained a complex of inositol monophosphoric ester with galactose, ethanolamine, tartaric acid, oleic acid and saturated fatty acids.

The chemical methods of estimating inositol have been used to only a very small extent for estimating inositol in foodstuffs, but L. Young,[13] using the iodomercurate method (page 568), obtained the following values for the inositol content of various animal tissues : ox brain, 149, 111 ; sheep brain, 172, 176 ; sheep heart muscle, 154 to 170 ; dog heart muscle, 156, 174 ; rabbit skeletal muscle, 16, 27 ; and ox skeletal muscle, less than 5 mg. per 100 g.

D. W. Woolley,[14] using a yeast growth method, obtained remarkably high values for ox liver and ox heart, namely, 340 and 1600 mg. per 100 g. The heart muscle of other species of animals contained considerably less inositol, however.[15]

The following values were obtained by D. W. Woolley [14] for various other natural substances : maize, 50 ; oats, 100 ; alfalfa leaf meal, 210 ; brewers' yeast, 500 ; and whole milk, 50 mg. per 100 g. Wheat flour contained 110 mg. of inositol per 100 g., and bread made from 98 % extraction flour, 64 mg. per 100 g.[16]

References to Section 6

1. F. Kögl and W. van Hasselt, *Z. physiol. Chem.*, 1936, **242**, 43.
2. W. B. Emery, N. McLeod and F. A. Robinson, *Biochem. J.*, 1946, **40**, 426.
3. D. W. Woolley, *J. Biol. Chem.*, 1941, **139**, 29.
4. F. Rosenberger, *Z. physiol. Chem.*, 1910, **64**, 341.
5. L. B. Winter, *Biochem. J.*, 1934, **28**, 6.
6. A. E. Meyer, *Proc. Soc. Exp. Biol. Med.*, 1946, **62**, 111.
7. P. B. Hawk, B. L. Oser and W. H. Summerson, *Practical Physiological Chemistry*, 1947.
7a. J. Folch, *J. Biol. Chem.*, 1949, **177**, 497, 505.
8. R. J. Anderson, *J. Biol. Chem.*, 1914, **18**, 425, 441 ; 1915, **20**, 463.
9. D. C. Harrison and E. Mellanby, *Biochem. J.*, 1939, **33**, 1660.
10. R. J. Anderson, *J. Amer. Chem. Soc.*, 1930, **52**, 1607.
11. E. Klenk and R. Sakal, *Z. physiol. Chem.*, 1939, **258**, 33.
12. D. W. Woolley, *J. Biol. Chem.*, 1943, **147**, 581.

13. L. Young, *Biochem. J.*, 1934, **28,** 1435.

14. D. W. Woolley, *J. Biol. Chem.*, 1941, **140,** 453.

15. A. N. Woods, J. Taylor, M. J. Hofer, G. A. Johnson, R. L. Kane and J. R. McMahan, *Univ. Texas Publ.*, 1942, No. 4237.

16. R. R. Sealock and A. H. Livermore, *J. Nutrition*, 1943, **25,** 265.

7. EFFECT OF INOSITOL DEFICIENCY IN ANIMALS

Mice and Rats

As already stated (page 564), the first symptoms of inositol deficiency to be recorded were alopecia and loss of weight.[1] These were observed in mice fed a ration of sucrose, purified casein, salts, cod liver oil, corn oil, yeast extract, aneurine, riboflavine, nicotinic acid, pyridoxine, pantothenic acid, β-alanine and choline. The hair was restored by administration of a non-dialysable fraction from liver, the responsible factor being subsequently isolated and identified as inositol (page 565). This was effective at a level of 10 mg. per g. of diet, whilst phytin (the calcium-magnesium salt of phytic acid) was effective at a level of 100 mg. per 100 g. D. W. Woolley[2] showed that the absence of pantothenic acid, as well as inositol, from the diet of mice produced alopecia and that the inositol-deficient mice, but not the pantothenic acid-deficient mice, recovered spontaneously. A deficiency of pantothenic acid had also a more marked effect on the weight of the animals than had a deficiency of inositol. The anti-alopecia activity of inositol in mice was confirmed by Martin *et al.*,[3] who also observed that it caused reddening of the skin. P. L. Pavcek and H. M. Baum[4] showed that the denudation around the eyes of rats, a symptom used by W. Halliday and H. M. Evans[5] for the assay of vitamin B_6, cleared up on administration of inositol, whilst Cunha *et al.*,[6] showed that loss of hair took place in rats maintained on a diet consisting of maize, soya bean, lucerne, minerals, halibut liver oil, folic acid and pyridoxine and that growth of the hair was restored by the addition of 0·3 % of inositol to the diet.

In contrast to p-aminobenzoic acid, inositol had an unfavourable effect on lactation in the rat ; the effect was counteracted by p-aminobenzoic acid.[7]

Lipotropic Effect

The production of fatty livers in rats by feeding a beef liver fraction was found to be prevented by the simultaneous administration of various tissues or cereal extracts[8] or of inositol,[9] whilst fatty livers produced by feeding biotin were also prevented by inositol.[8] Choline also had lipotropic properties (page 582) but, whereas it was effective in the treatment of fatty livers produced by aneurine and partially effective in the treatment of cholesterol fatty livers, it was said to have little effect on fatty livers produced by beef liver [9] or biotin.[10] Inositol, on the other hand, was said to have no effect on aneurine fatty livers.[10] That the two compounds probably operate by different mechanisms was confirmed by J. C. Forbes' observation [11] that the effect of inositol and choline together was greater than either alone. Choline reduced the liver cholesteryl esters more effectively than did inositol, whilst the lipotropic effect of inositol was abolished by corn oil.[12]

According to Best et al.,[13] however, there is no evidence that biotin produces a selective deposition of cholesteryl esters in the liver or that inositol has a specific effect on bound cholesterol or that the fatty livers observed after administration of biotin are particularly resistant to choline. On the contrary, the accumulation of cholesteryl esters in liver bore a constant relationship to the deposition of glyceride in the liver, and the administration of biotin did not affect this relationship. Best et al. confirmed the synergistic effect of choline and inositol on the liver lipins, and the greater efficacy of choline in reducing the liver glycerides and cholesteryl esters, but could find no evidence in support of any effect of choline, inositol or biotin on the absolute amount of phospholipin or free cholesterol in the liver or kidney lipides. They recommended that the term " biotin fatty livers " should be abandoned, and suggested that Gavin and McHenry's results were due to their having overlooked the presence of choline in beef liver.

Other Species of Animals

An increase in the growth rate was produced by the administration of inositol to cotton rats,[14] guinea-pigs,[15] and hamsters.[16] In hamsters, inositol counteracted a reproductive disorder produced by feeding an inositol-deficient diet.[17]

Chicks also exhibited an increased growth rate when given inositol,[18] which prevented an encephalomalacia and exudative diathesis due to vitamin E deficiency.[19]

Unlike rats and mice, inositol-deficient dogs did not develop alopecia, but exhibited decreased peristalsis of the stomach and small intestine with delayed gastric emptying, hypertonicity, hypomotility and formation of gas.[3, 20]

In pigs, inositol alleviated the symptoms produced by administration of sulphathalidine.[21] These symptoms resembled those of biotin deficiency and were prevented by giving biotin (page 426). Inositol had no beneficial effect, however, when given to pigs maintained on a diet containing the other members of the vitamin B complex.[21, 22]

Slow growth and a normocytic anaemia were produced in turkey poults by a deficiency of inositol.[23]

Inositol deficiency in young rainbow trout resulted in degeneration of the fins and in distended stomachs.[24] The symptoms were prevented by 25 to 50 mg. per 100 g. of diet.

Effect on Infected Animals

Inositol had no effect on the susceptibility of Swiss mice to experimental poliomyelitis.[25]

Inositol and Cancer

The inositol content of transplanted epidermal carcinoma in mice was more than twice that of normal epidermis, but methyl cholanthrene-treated epidermis contained only the normal amount.[26]

Inositol inhibited the growth of transplanted tumours in mice when given intravenously.[27] Its effect on transplanted sarcoma in mice was counteracted by p-aminobenzoic acid and other compounds.[28]

References to Section 7

1. D. W. Woolley, *Science*, 1940, **92**, 384 ; *J. Biol. Chem.*, 1940, **136**, 113 ; 1941, **139**, 29 ; *J. Nutrition*, 1941, **21**, *Suppl.* 17.
2. D. W. Woolley, *Proc. Soc. Exp. Biol. Med.*, 1941, **46**, 565 ; *J. Exp. Med.*, 1942, **75**, 277.
3. G. J. Martin, M. R. Thompson and J. de Carvajal-Forero, *Amer. J. Digest. Dis.*, 1941, **8**, 290.
4. P. L. Pavcek and H. M. Baum, *Science*, 1941, **93**, 502.
5. W. Halliday and H. M. Evans, *J. Nutrition*, 1937, **14**, 45.
6. T. J. Cunha, S. Kirkwood, P. H. Phillips and G. Bohstedt, *Proc. Soc. Exp. Biol. Med.*, 1943, **54**, 236.
7. B. Sure, *J. Nutrition*, 1943, **26**, 275.
8. G. Gavin and E. W. McHenry, *J. Biol. Chem.*, 1941, **139**, 485.
9. M. L. MacFarland and E. W. McHenry, *ibid.*, 1945, **159**, 605 ; 1948, **176**, 429.
10. G. Gavin, J. M. Patterson and E. W. McHenry, *ibid.*, 1943, **148**, 275.
11. J. C. Forbes, *Proc. Soc. Exp. Biol. Med.*, 1943, **54**, 89.
12. J. M. R. Beveridge and C. C. Lucas, *J. Biol. Chem.*, 1945, **157**, 311.
13. C. H. Best, C. C. Lucas, J. M. Patterson and J. H. Ridout, *Science*, 1946, **103**, 12 ; *Biochem. J.*, 1946, **40**, 368, 494.
14. J. M. McIntire, B. S. Schweigert and C. A. Elvehjem, *J. Nutrition*, 1944, **27**, 1.
15. A. G. Hogan and J. W. Hamilton, *ibid.*, 1942, **23**, 533.
16. J. M. Cooperman, H. A. Waisman and C. A. Elvehjem, *Proc. Soc. Exp. Biol. Med.*, 1943, **52**, 250.
17. J. W. Hamilton and A. G. Hogan, *J. Nutrition*, 1944, **27**, 213.

18. D. M. Hegsted, G. M. Briggs, R. C. Mills, C. A. Elvehjem and E. B. Hart, *Proc. Soc. Exp. Biol. Med.*, 1941, **47**, 376.
19. H. Dam, *J. Nutrition*, 1944, **27**, 193.
20. G. J. Martin, M. R. Thompson and J. de Carvajal-Forero, *Amer. J. Digest. Dis.*, 1942, **9**, 268.
21. D. C. Lindley and T. J. Cunha, *J. Nutrition*, 1946, **32**, 47.
22. T. J. Cunha, L. K. Bustad, W. E. Ham, D. R. Cordy, E. C. McCulloch, L. F. Woods, G. H. Conner and M. A. McGregor, *ibid.*, 1947, **34**, 173.
23. T. H. Jukes, E. L. R. Stokstad and M. Belt, *ibid.*, 1947, **33**, 1.
24. B. A. McLaren, E. Keller, D. J. O'Donnell and C. A. Elvehjem, *Arch. Biochem.*, 1947, **15**, 169.
25. H. C. Lichstein, H. A. Waisman, K. B. McCall, C. A. Elvehjem and P. F. Clark, *Proc. Soc. Exp. Biol. Med.*, 1945, **60**, 279.
26. E. L. Tatum, M. G. Ritchey, E. V. Cowdry and L. F. Wicks, *J. Biol. Chem.*, 1946, **163**, 675 ; M. G. Ritchey, L. F. Wicks and E. L. Tatum, *ibid.*, 1947, **171**, 51.
27. D. Laszlo and C. Leuchtenberger, *Science*, 1943, **97**, 515.
28. J. C. Keresztesy, D. Laszlo and C. Leuchtenberger, *Cancer Res.*, 1946, **6**, 128.

8. EFFECT OF INOSITOL DEFICIENCY IN MAN

Administration of inositol to patients with gastro-intestinal cancer reduced the characteristic fatty infiltration of the liver,[1] and it has been suggested [2] that the lipotropic action of inositol may be of value in the treatment of psoriasis. It has been stated [3] that a compound of α-tocopherol and inositol is of value in the treatment of muscular dystrophy, but the claim has not been substantiated by other workers.

Symptoms of uncomplicated inositol deficiency in man do not appear ever to have been encountered, nor have they apparently been artificially induced in volunteers.

References to Section 8

1. J. C. Abels, C. W. Kupel, G. T. Pack and C. P. Rhoads, *Proc. Soc. Exp. Biol. Med.*, 1943, **54**, 157.
2. P. Gross and B. M. Kesten, *Arch. Derm. Syph.*, 1941, **47**, 376.
3. A. T. Milhorat and W. E. Bartels, *Science*, 1945, **101**, 93.

9. HUMAN AND ANIMAL REQUIREMENTS OF INOSITOL

The importance of inositol in human and animal nutrition has not been established with the same degree of certainty as with other members of the vitamin B complex. It many ways, inositol exhibits anomalous behaviour, although not perhaps to the same extent as choline (page 582). As already pointed out (page 564), it exists in foodstuffs in far larger amounts than do other members of the vitamin B complex, and cases of inositol deficiency in man have never been recorded.

R. J. Williams [1] has estimated that humans require about 1 g. of inositol per day per 2500 cals. of diet compared with only about 1 mg. per day of aneurine or riboflavine.

Reference to Section 9

1. R. J. Williams, *J. Amer. Med. Assoc.*, 1942, **119**, 1.

10. METABOLISM OF INOSITOL

The inositol concentration of normal human blood plasma ranged from 0·37 to 0·76 mg. per 100 ml. The daily ingestion of 1·5 g. of inositol generally produced a moderate rise.[1]

Under normal conditions, human subjects excreted 0·626 mg. of inositol per hour in the urine and 0·027 mg. per hour in the sweat.[2] The average inositol content of human sweat was 21 μg. per 100 ml. and the value did not increase significantly after administration of 50 mg. of inositol per day. In a hot, moist atmosphere, the average amount of inositol excreted in the sweat during eight-hourly periods was 0·118 mg. per hour. The corresponding amount excreted in the urine during twenty-four hours was 0·494 mg. per hour.

When a solution containing 250 mg. of inositol was given orally to rats, about twenty-four hours were required for complete absorption. No increase in the liver glycogen occurred, although less than 1 % of the dose was excreted in the urine. Fasting did not affect the inositol content of the blood, liver, testis and heart of rats, and the oral administration of inositol to fasted animals did not increase the amount present in any of the tissues except the heart.[3] At least 7 % of inositol ingested by rats was converted into glucose.[4]

Rat tissues contained amounts of inositol ranging from 21 mg. per 100 g. in the muscle to 123 mg. per 100 g. in the kidney ; of these amounts, 13 and 88 mg. per 100 g. were present in the free state.[5] These amounts remained virtually unchanged after administration of inositol, confirming earlier observations [6] that the rat can synthesise inositol.

References to Section 10

1. S. Sonne and H. Sobotka, *Arch. Biochem.*, 1947, **14**, 93.
2. B. C. Johnson, H. H. Mitchell and T. S. Hamilton, *J. Biol. Chem.*, 1945, **161**, 357.

3. V. D. Wiebelhaus, J. J. Betheil and H. A. Lardy, *Arch. Biochem.*, 1947, **13**, 379.
4. M. R. Stetten and D. Stetten, *ibid.*, 1946, **164**, 85.
5. B. S. Platt and G. E. Glock, *Biochem. J.*, 1943, **37**, 709.
6. J. Needham, *ibid.*, 1924, **18**, 891.

11. INTESTINAL SYNTHESIS OF INOSITOL

What evidence there is supports the view that inositol is synthesised by the intestinal flora, for D. W. Woolley [1] showed that mice on a diet containing pantothenic acid synthesised inositol, and that bacteria isolated from the intestines of animals that had recovered spontaneously from alopecia (page 572) synthesised more inositol than micro-organisms from animals that did not recover spontaneously. Furthermore, E. Nielsen and A. Black [2] showed that inositol deficiency could be produced in rats by administration of a sulphonamide.

References to Section 11

1. D. W. Woolley, *J. Exp. Med.*, 1942, **75**, 277.
2. E. Nielsen and A. Black, *Proc. Soc. Exp. Biol. Med.*, 1944, **55**, 14.

12. INOSITOL IN THE NUTRITION OF MICRO-ORGANISMS

As already pointed out (page 564), *meso*-inositol is a constituent of the bios complex, and is essential for the growth of *Saccharomyces cerevisiae*.[1] It stimulates the growth of *Nematospora gossypii*,[2] *Rhizopus suinus*,[3] *Eremothecium ashbyii*[4] and *Trichophyton faviforme*,[5] but for most of these organisms it would appear to be a complementary rather than an essential growth factor. It also stimulated the growth of the following yeasts : [5] *Candida albicans, Kloeckera brevis, Mycoderma valida, M. vini, Pichia belgica, Saccharomyces bayanus, S. uvarum, Saccharomycodes ludwigii, Schizosaccharomyces pombe, Torulopsis stellata, Zygosaccharomyces japonicus* and *Z. priorianus*. It was also essential for *Saccharomyces carlsbergensis, S. chevalieri, S. logos, Torula colliculosa* and *Schizosaccharomyces versatilis*.[6]

References to Section 12

1. E. V. Eastcott, *J. Phys. Chem.*, 1928, **32**, 1094.
2. F. Kögl and N. Fries, *Z. physiol. Chem.*, 1937, **249**, 9.
3. W. H. Schopfer, *Compt. rend. Soc. Physique Hist. nat. Geneve*, 1942, **59**, 107 ; *Helv. Chim. Acta*, 1944, **27**, 468.
4. W. H. Schopfer, *ibid.*, 1017.

5. P. R. Burkholder and D. Moyer, *Bull Torrey Bot. Club.*, 1943, **70**, 372 ; P. R. Burkholder, *Amer. J. Bot.*, 1943, **30**, 206 ; P. R. Burkholder, I. McVeigh and D. Moyer, *J. Bact.*, 1944, **48**, 385.
6. A. S. Schultz and L. Atkin, *Arch. Biochem.*, 1947, **14**, 369.

13. INOSITOL IN HIGHER PLANTS

The inositol content of oats, wheat, barley and maize increased considerably during germination.[1]

Soil and natural manures were found to contain inositol, as well as aneurine, biotin, pyridoxine and p-aminobenzoic acid.[2]

References to Section 13

1. P. R. Burkholder, *Science*, 1943, **97**, 562.
2. M. A. Roulet, *Experientia*, 1948, **4**, 149.

14. INOSITOL REQUIREMENTS OF INSECTS

According to G. Fraenkel and M. Blewett,[1] inositol is of only slight value in the nutrition of *Tribolium confusum* and *Ptinus tectus* and of no importance in the nutrition of other beetles investigated. Nevertheless, inositol may be of significance in the economy of insects, for R. E. Slade[2] suggested that the potent insecticide, lindane (Gammexane), the active component of which is the γ-isomer of $1 : 2 : 3 : 4 : 5 : 6$-hexachlorocyclohexane, may be due to interference with a process involving *meso*-inositol, to which, of course, it bears a formal resemblance. S. Kirkwood and P. H. Phillips[3] did, in fact, show that the inhibition of yeast by lindane, but not of other inhibitory hexachlorocyclohexanes that were without insecticidal properties, was reversed by *meso*-inositol, and Burton *et al.*[4] showed that the growth of *Nematospora gossypii* was retarded by lindane in presence of small but not large amounts of *meso*-inositol. The results suggested that other compounds related to *meso*-inositol might have an insecticidal action, but neither the hexamethyl ether nor the mono-acetyl-pentamethyl ether of *meso*-inositol had more than a slight toxic action on flies.[5]

In addition to its toxic action on insects and micro-organisms, lindane produces mitosis in higher plants. Its mitotic action on *Allium Cepa* was inhibited by *meso*-inositol, but not by d-inositol or D-sorbitol.[6] On the other hand, so was the mitotic action of colchicine, so that the phenomenon can hardly be regarded as an example of a metabolite-anti-metabolite relationship. Again, W. H. Schopfer and his colleagues[7] were unable to confirm the existence of an antagonistic action of *meso*-inositol towards lindane, either with *E.*

ashbyii or *S. cerevisiae* or with pea roots, and it must therefore be concluded that the antagonistic action of inositol towards lindane, if it exists at all, is not comparable with the anti-vitamin activity of such substances as sulphanilamide and pantoyltaurine.

References to Section 14

1. G. Fraenkel and M. Blewett, *Nature*, 1943, **151**, 703.
2. R. E. Slade, *Chem. and Ind.*, 1945, 314.
3. S. Kirkwood and P. H. Phillips, *J. Biol. Chem.*, 1946, **163**, 251.
4. H. W. Burton, S. E. Jacobs and A. Goldstein, *Nature*, 1946, **158**, 22.
5. J. C. McGowan, *J. Soc. Chem. Ind.*, 1947, **66**, 446.
6. E. Chargaff, R. N. Stewart and B. Magasanik, *Science*, 1948, **108**, 556.
7. W. H. Schopfer, T. Posternak and M. L. Bossi, *Schweiz. Z. Path. Bakt.*, 1947, **10**, (4), 443 ; W. H. Schopfer and M. L. Bein, *Experientia*, 1948, **4**, 147.

15. ANALOGUES OF INOSITOL

The biological activity of *meso*-inositol (I) is not shared by its stereo-isomers, or by closely related compounds, with one or two exceptions. Thus *d*- (II) and *l*-inositol, pinitol and quebrachitol, the corresponding monomethyl ethers, and quercitol (III) were inactive in counteracting alopecia in mice and as growth factors for yeast, but mytilitol (IV), a cyclitol which occurs in mussels, exhibited some activity towards both organisms.[1] Scyllitol (V), as well as its homologue mytilitol, had some growth-promoting action on *Rhizopus suinus*, and *iso*mytilitol (VI), the methyl homologue of *meso*-inositol, was slightly more active ; oxy-mytilitol and oxy-*iso*mytilitol were inactive.[2] These results indicate that three *cis*-hydroxy groups are essential for biological activity.

The growth-stimulating action of *meso*-inositol on *Rhizopus suinus* and *Eremothecium ashbyii* was not shared by α-, β-, or γ-cyclohexane-1 : 2 : 3-triol.[3] Three diastereoisomeric inosamines, monoamino analogues of inositol, were prepared,[4] but their biological activity has not been recorded.

Phytin, the calcium magnesium hydrogen salt of inositol-phosphoric ester (page 570), cured alopecia in mice at a level of 100 mg. per 100 g. of diet, being about one-tenth as active as inositol itself, but it was inactive as a growth-factor for yeast.[5] Inositol hexa-acetate was active on mice, but inactive on yeast, whilst quinic acid (VII) and inosose (VIII) were inactive on yeast and had an uncertain effect in mice. Inositol mono- and tetra-phosphoric esters had 5 and 2 % of the potency of inositol for yeast.[5]

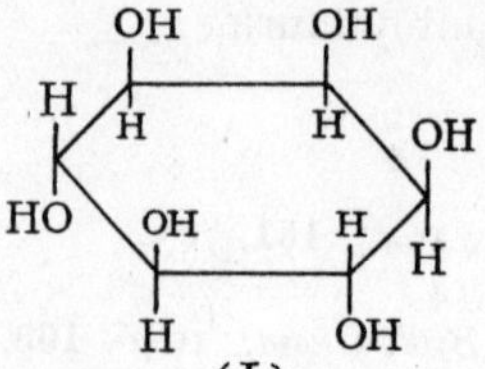

(I)

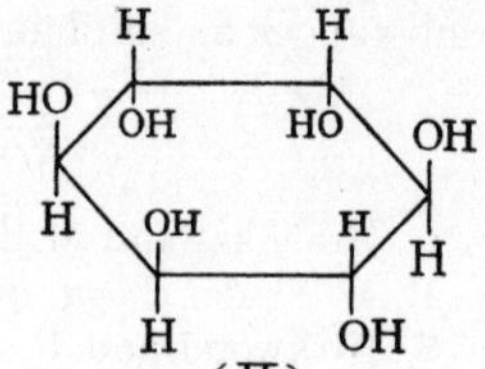

(II)

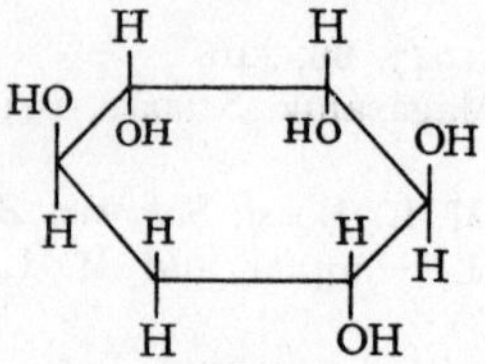

(III)

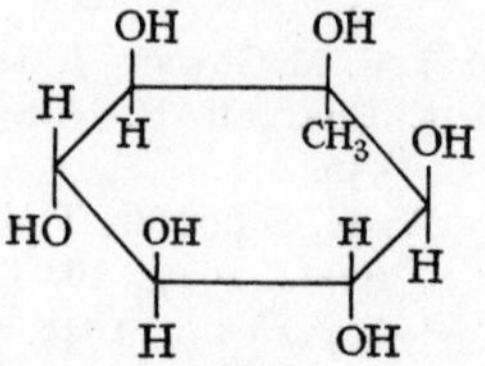

(IV)

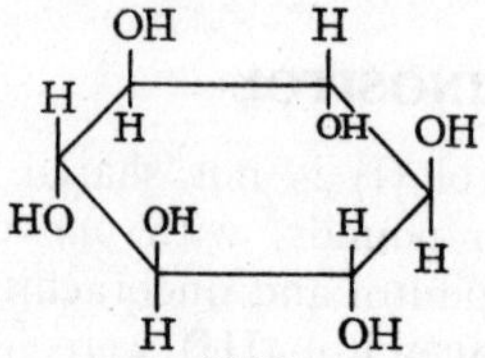

(V)

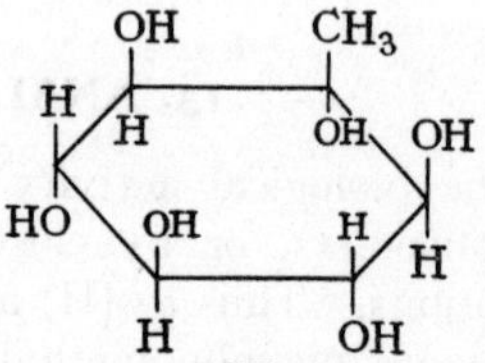

(VI)

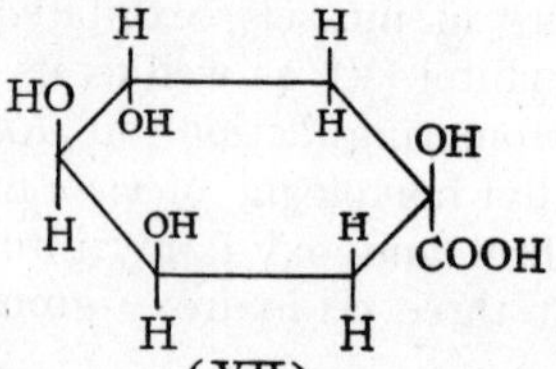

(VII)

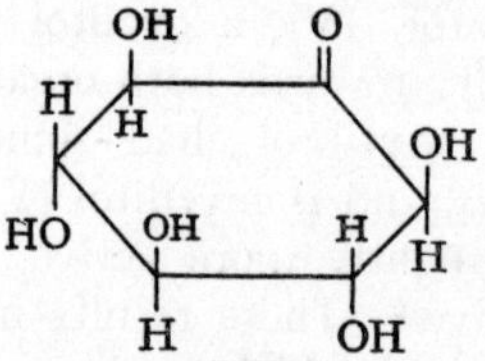

(VIII)

When the six hydroxyl groups of inositol were replaced by chlorine atoms to give hexachlorocyclohexane, the well-known insecticide, lindane (page 578), the growth-promoting activity of the molecule was lost completely and replaced by growth-inhibitory activity ; the chloro-compound inhibited the growth of both yeast [6] and fungi.[7]

References to Section 15

1. D. W. Woolley, *J. Biol. Chem.*, 1941, **140**, 461.
2. W. H. Schopfer, *Helv. Chim. Acta*, 1944, **27**, 468.
3. T. Posternak and F. Ravenna, *Helv. Chim. Acta*, 1947, **30**, 441.

4. H. E. Carter, R. K. Clarke, B. Lytle and G. E. McCasland, *J. Biol. Chem.*, 1948, **175**, 683.

5. D. W. Woolley, *Science*, 1940, **92**, 384 ; *J. Biol. Chem.*, 1940, **136**, 113 ; 1941, **139**, 29 ; *J. Nutrition*, 1941, **21**, *Suppl.* 17.

6. S. Kirkwood and P. H. Phillips, *J. Biol. Chem.*, 1946, **163**, 251.

7. H. W. Burton, S. E. Jacobs and A. Goldstein, *Nature*, 1946, **158**, 22.

16. FUNCTION OF INOSITOL

Nothing is yet known with certainty concerning the function of inositol. According to R. J. Williams *et al.*,[1] the amount of inositol in pancreatic amylase (4 mg. per g.) is sufficient to suggest that it may be an integral part of the enzyme, even if the molecular weight is no more than 44,000. The suggestion was strengthened by the observation that lindane inhibited the action of pancreatic α-amylase and the inhibition was competitively prevented by inositol.[2]

A. J. Rosenberg [3] observed that the growth of *Clostridium saccharobutyricum* was inhibited by malonate and that the inhibition was counteracted by boron and *meso*-inositol ; *d*- and *l*-inositol and quercitol were inactive. He therefore suggested that malonate inhibited the synthesis by the organism of the *meso*-inositol necessary for growth.

It is quite possible that inositol may not be a prosthetic group of an enzyme, as most other members of the vitamin B complex have proved to be, but merely a structural component of living tissue ; in this event inositol (and also choline) are anomalous members of the vitamin B complex possibly serving as a link between the vitamins, which act as metabolic catalysts, and the amino acids, which are essential in the building up of animal and plant tissues.

References to Section 16

1. R. J. Williams, F. Schlenk and M. A. Eppright, *J. Amer. Chem. Soc.*, 1944, **66**, 896.

2. R. L. Lane and R. J. Williams, *Arch. Biochem.*, 1948, **19**, 329.

3. A. J. Rosenberg, *Compt. rend.*, 1946, **222**, 1310.

Chapter XII

CHOLINE

1. INTRODUCTION

CHOLINE has been known since 1862, when it was discovered by A. Strecker [1] in bile. Its inclusion in the vitamin B complex requires even more justification than the inclusion of inositol, for it differs markedly from the other members of the complex.

In 1924, N. F. Fisher [2] and Allan et al. [3] independently discovered that depancreatised dogs maintained on insulin developed large fatty livers, the formation of which was prevented by feeding fresh beef pancreas ; a few years later, J. M. Hershey [4] found that egg yolk lecithin also prevented fatty liver formation. In 1932, C. H. Best and M. E. Huntsman [5] showed that the accumulation of fatty acids in the livers of rats maintained on a diet containing 40 % of beef fat was prevented by the inclusion of choline or betaine in the diet and, in the following year, C. H. Best and J. H. Ridout [6] showed that choline or betaine likewise prevented the deposition of fat in the liver resulting from the feeding of cholesterol. Best et al. [7] concluded that, since fatty liver formation caused by feeding fat was due to an increase in the neutral fat fraction and that caused by cholesterol was due to the formation of cholesteryl esters, choline and betaine were concerned with the metabolism of both fat and cholesterol. Choline was also found to prevent the formation of fatty livers due to the feeding of sucrose. [8] Thus, choline accelerated the removal of fat from rat's liver under a variety of dietetic conditions, whilst the amount of choline in the diet was an important factor in determining the level of fat in the liver.

Thus, superficially at all events, choline appeared to possess the essential characteristics of a vitamin in being necessary for the well-being of an experimental animal and having to be supplied pre-formed in the diet. In its absence, characteristic deficiency symptoms appeared and these were cured by administration of choline.

The suggestion that choline should be regarded as a member of the vitamin B complex was made independently by B. Sure [9] and P. György and H. Goldblatt [10] in 1940. The former showed that it was essential for the growth and lactation of rats and the latter confirmed the observations of previous workers that rats fed a diet low in choline, even though supplemented by aneurine and riboflavine, developed fatty infiltration of the liver. The addition of pyridoxine resulted in the formation of necrotic renal lesions, similar to those encountered in cystine intoxication. The severity of the lesions was reduced by substituting egg white for sucrose in the diet. This increased the methionine : cystine ratio, which had already been shown [11, 12] to affect fatty liver formation, an excess of cystine favouring and an excess of methionine preventing fatty livers. Administration of choline prevented the renal changes and also sometimes exerted a lipotropic effect.

Shortly afterwards, choline was shown [13] to be essential for growth and prevention of perosis in growing chicks, although choline-deficient chicks had not developed fatty livers at four weeks of age, and bone phosphatase values were normal in chicks suffering from perosis due to choline deficiency.

The formation of renal lesions in young rats on a choline-deficient diet was confirmed by W. H. Griffith and D. J. Mulford [14] who showed that the non-protein nitrogen of the blood was also increased. The possibility of survival and renal repair depended on the severity of the lesions. Most members of the vitamin B complex were without effect on the severity of the symptoms, but nicotinic acid had a slight beneficial effect.

In spite of the strong resemblance between the behaviour of choline and that of other vitamins in animals, there has been considerable hesitation about accepting choline as a vitamin. One difficulty is that it occurs in the body in such large amounts, compared with other members of the vitamin B complex (with the possible exception of inositol, page 564) as to suggest that it is a structural component of the body rather than a metabolic catalyst. Moreover, relatively enormous amounts are normally ingested by animals and humans, the daily requirement being estimated at 35 to 100 mg. per kg. of bodyweight for different species of animals (page 594) compared with a daily requirement of only 15 to 30 μg. per kg. of bodyweight per day of aneurine or riboflavine.

The demand for choline exceeds even that of inositol (page 576) and is actually of the same order as the requirement for certain amino acids. Inositol and choline may usefully be considered as links connecting the vitamin B complex proper with the amino acids, inositol being more closely related to the vitamin B complex and choline to the amino acids.

Another possible argument against the inclusion of choline in the vitamin B complex is that it has never been shown to be associated in man with a specific deficiency disease, this being frequently regarded as one of the essential criteria of a vitamin. This argument is not a very strong one, however, for as has already been pointed out several other substances that are undoubtedly vitamins are not associated with characteristic deficiency diseases in man. Actually, the existence of a deficiency disease " in Nature " is largely fortuitous, due first, to the existence of a foodstuff which either does not contain a substance essential for human nutrition or from which such a substance has been removed in some way and, secondly, the use of that foodstuff as a staple or at least as a major article of diet. Clearly, the accidental combination of these two factors would be less likely to occur with substances, such as choline or inositol or for that matter amino acids, which are present in virtually all foodstuffs and which are required in relatively large amounts. In such instances, there is such a wide margin between the amount normally present in foodstuffs and the minimum amount necessary to support life that the worst that can happen is a mild and often temporary deficiency state leading to vague symptoms of ill-health. Acute symptoms would only be observed in human volunteers maintained on diets from which the factor had been deliberately, and more or less completely, removed.

Another serious objection to the inclusion of choline in the vitamin B complex is its inability to stimulate the growth of micro-organisms, with one or two exceptions (page 596). It can hardly be regarded as a member of the bios complex and in this respect differs sharply from inositol, which it resembles in other ways.

References to Section 1

1. A. Strecker, *Annalen*, 1862, **123,** 353.
2. N. F. Fisher, *Amer. J. Physiol.*, 1924, **67,** 634.
3. F. N. Allan, D. J. Bowie, J. J. R. Macleod and W. L. Robinson, *Brit. J. Exp. Path.*, 1924, **5,** 75.
4. J. M. Hershey, *Amer. J. Physiol.*, 1930, **93,** 657.
5. C. H. Best and M. E. Huntsman, *J. Physiol.*, 1932, **75,** 405.
6. C. H. Best and J. H. Ridout, *ibid.*, 1933, **78,** 415.
7. C. H. Best, H. J. Channon and J. H. Ridout, *ibid.*, 1934, **81,** 409.
8. C. H. Best and M. E. Huntsman, *ibid.*, 1935, **83,** 255.
9. B. Sure, *J. Nutrition*, 1940, **19,** 71.
10. P. György and H. Goldblatt, *J. Exp. Med.*, 1940, **72,** 1.
11. V. du Vigneaud, *J. Biol. Chem.*, 1939, **131,** 57.
12. W. H. Griffith and N. J. Wade, *ibid.*, 567.
13. D. M. Hegsted, R. C. Mills, C. A. Elvehjem and E. B. Hart, *ibid.*, 1941, **138,** 459.
14. W. H. Griffith and D. J. Mulford, *J. Nutrition*, 1941, **21,** 633.

2. ISOLATION, CHEMICAL CONSTITUTION AND SYNTHESIS OF CHOLINE

Isolation

Choline was discovered in 1862 by A. Strecker,[1] who isolated it from the bile of cattle and pigs. It has also been isolated from a large variety of fungi and flowering plants, especially from the seeds of the latter. In animals, it is a constituent of phospholipids, *e.g.* brain and egg-yolk lecithin and sphingomyelin, and of acetylcholine, the mediator of nerve impulse transmission.

Choline was isolated from egg-yolk by the following method.[2] The yolks were extracted with ether, and the insoluble residue was extracted with hot alcohol. The combined extracts were evaporated to dryness and the residue was heated with methanolic barium hydroxide solution. After removal of the excess baryta with carbon dioxide the filtrate was evaporated and the residue taken up in water and filtered. The filtrate was again evaporated and the residue taken up in alcohol, filtered and the filtrate treated with mercuric chloride solution. The precipitate that formed was filtered off and dissolved in hot water, and hydrogen sulphide was passed into the solution. The mercury sulphide precipitate was filtered off and the filtrate evaporated. Dilute hydrochloric acid was added to the residue, and the solution was again evaporated. The residue was taken up in alcohol, the solution diluted with water and the choline precipitated with alcoholic cadmium chloride solution.

Constitution and Synthesis

Choline was shown to be β-hydroxyethyl-trimethyl-ammonium hydroxide :

$$(CH_3)_3N \cdot CH_2 \cdot CH_2OH$$
$$|$$
$$OH$$

by A. Baeyer[3] and A. Wurtz.[4] It was first synthesised by the action of trimethylamine on β-chloroethyl alcohol or ethylene oxide,[4] but it has also been prepared by heating β-bromoethyl-trimethyl-ammonium bromide in aqueous solution at 160° C.[5] or in alcoholic potassium hydroxide solution at 120° C.[6] It is more conveniently made, however, by hydrolysis of lecithin with acid[7] or alkali.[8]

References to Section 2

1. A. Strecker, *Annalen*, 1862, **123**, 353.
2. F. W. Schmidt, *Z. physiol. Chem.*, 1907, **53**, 428.
3. A. Baeyer, *Annalen*, 1866, **140**, 306 ; 1867, **142**, 322.
4. A. Wurtz, *ibid.*, 1868, *Suppl.* 6, 116, 197.

5. M. Krüger and P. Bergell, *Ber.*, 1903, **36,** 2901.
6. R. Lucius, *Arch. Pharm.*, 1907, **245,** 246.
7. G. Moruzzi, *Z. physiol. Chem.*, 1908, **55,** 352.
8. H. MacLean, *ibid.*, 360.

3. PROPERTIES OF CHOLINE

Choline is a strong base, which can be crystallised only with great difficulty. It is hygroscopic and very soluble in water and absolute alcohol, but insoluble in ether. It is generally made available as the chloride, which forms colourless needles of no definite m.p.

Choline chloride forms double salts with gold chloride, mercuric chloride, and platinic chloride, and these can be used for the characterisation of choline, although their melting-points vary with the rate of heating. Thus, W. Gulewitsch[1] recorded m.ps. of 241 to 243° C., 249 to 251° C. and 213 to 216° C. respectively, whilst M. Krüger and P. Bergell[2] obtained values of 233 to 234° C. and 245 to 246° C. for the m.ps. of the platinic chloride and gold chloride double salts.

References to Section 3

1. W. Gulewitsch, *Z. physiol. Chem.*, 1898, **24,** 513.
2. M. Krüger and P. Bergell, *Ber.*, 1903, **36,** 2901.

4. ESTIMATION OF CHOLINE

Chemical Estimation

All the chemical methods now in use for the estimation of choline depend on the precipitation of the sparingly soluble reineckate. This was first used by F. J. R. Beattie,[1] who dissolved the reineckate in acetone and measured the colour of the solution ; this was proportional to the amount of choline originally present. A. D. Marenzi and C. E. Cardini[2] also estimated choline by precipitation of the reineckate, but estimated the amount of chromium in the precipitate by means of Cazeneuve's reagent[3] (diphenylcarbazide), evaluating the colour so formed in a photometer. Beattie's method was used, with slight modifications, for the estimation of choline in foodstuffs by Jacobi *et al.*,[4] R. W. Engel[5] and D. Glick,[6] all of whom precipitated the reineckate from acid solution. Entenman *et al.*[7] used almost exactly the same method, but precipitated the reineckate from alkaline solution. The two methods gave similar results when applied to alcohol-ether extracts of plasma, but Glick's method gave lower results than that of Entenman *et al.* when applied to alcohol-ether extracts of liver.[8] The use of the cadmium chloride complex has also been suggested for the estimation of choline.[8a]

Microbiological Assays

For the microbiological assay of choline, the so-called *cholineless* strain of *Neurospora crassa* has been used. This was obtained by N. H. Horowitz and G. W. Beadle [9] by irradiation of *N. crassa* with ultra-violet light. It was used by R. W. Luecke and P. B. Pearson [10] for the estimation of choline in blood, urine and animal tissues. An improved medium was described by A. Z. Hodson.[11]

References to Section 4

1. F. J. R. Beattie, *Biochem. J.*, 1936, **30**, 1554.
2. A. D. Marenzi and C. E. Cardini, *Rev. Soc. argent. Biol.*, 1942, **18**, 265.
3. P. Cazeneuve, *Compt. rend.*, 1900, **131**, 346.
4. H. P. Jacobi, C. A. Baumann and W. J. Meek, *J. Biol. Chem.*, 1941, **138**, 571.
5. R. W. Engel, *ibid.*, 1942, **144**, 701.
6. D. Glick, *ibid.*, 1944, **156**, 643.
7. C. Entenman, A. Taurog and I. L. Chaikoff, *ibid.*, 1944, **155**, 13.
8. C. Entenman and I. L. Chaikoff, *ibid.*, 1945, **160**, 377.
8a. W. Seaman, J. J. Hugonet and W. Leibmann, *Anal. Chem.*, 1949, **21**, 411.
9. N. H. Horowitz and G. W. Beadle, *J. Biol. Chem.*, 1943, **150**, 325.
10. R. W. Luecke and P. B. Pearson, *ibid.*, 1944, **153**, 259 ; 1944, **155**, 507.
11. A. Z. Hodson, *ibid.*, 1945, **157**, 383.

5. OCCURRENCE OF CHOLINE IN FOODSTUFFS

Very complete information is available concerning the choline content of foodstuffs. Cereals and cereal products contain up to 1 mg. per g. and meat and fish up to 5 or 6 mg. per g., so that as has already been remarked (page 584) choline is present in these foodstuffs in much larger amounts than other members of the vitamin B complex. The only foodstuffs completely devoid of choline are fruits, whilst vegetables, with the exception of legumes, generally contain much less than do cereals and animal products.

Cereals

The following values were obtained by R. W. Engel [1] for the choline content of cereals : wheat, 0·92 ; wheat bran, 1·43 ; wheat germ, 4·1 ; oats, 0·94 ; rolled oats, 1·51 ; barley, 1·39 ; polished rice, 0·88 ; rice polishings, 1·26 ; yellow corn, 0·37 ; corn meal, 0·42 ; white flour, 0·52 ; and molasses (blackstrap), 0·86 mg. per g. of fresh weight. D. Glick [2] obtained the following values : hard spring wheat, 0·71 to

1·07 ; hard winter wheat, 0·58 to 0·96 ; soft winter wheat, 0·74 to 1·01 ; oats, 1·01 to 1·29 and barley, 0·96 to 1·20 mg. per g. ; whilst Willstaedt et al.[3] obtained results of the same order, namely : white bread, 0·625 ; black bread, 0·565 ; wheat grits, 0·75 ; oatmeal, 1·03 ; and rice, 1·07 mg. per g.

The choline contents of flours of different degrees of extraction and of offals ran parallel to the lipin phosphorus and lecithin contents. Commercial bleaching had no effect on the choline content of cereals.[2]

Vegetables

R .W. Engel [1] found the following amounts of choline in vegetables : snapbeans, 3·40 ; soya beans, 3·00 ; peas, 2·63 ; cowpeas, 2·57 ; asparagus, 1·28 ; cabbage, 2·51 and spinach, 2·38 mg. per g. of sun-dried material. Potatoes contained 1·06 ; carrots, 0·95 ; turnips, 0·94 and sweet potatoes, 0·35 mg. per g. of fresh material. Some-what different values were obtained by Willstaedt et al.,[3] who found in Brussels sprouts, 1·03 ; leek, 0·095 ; carrots, 0·04 ; spinach, 0·38 ; lettuce, 0·03 ; potato, nil ; beetroot, nil ; parsley, 0·16 ; celery, 0·17 ; parsnip, 0·41 ; horse-radish, 0·48 ; onion, nil ; tomato, nil ; peas, 0·55 ; peas (dried), 1·88 ; and beans (dried), 1·81 mg. per g. D. Glick [2] found soya beans to contain 2·37 mg. per g. Leguminous vegetables therefore contained appreciably more choline than did most other vegetables.

Fruits

According to Willstaedt et al.[3] apples, plums, melons and raisins contained no choline.

Meat

Meat is one of the richest sources of choline, and the following values were obtained by R. W. Engel : [1] pig liver, 5·52 ; pig kidneys, 2·56, 3·17 ; pig heart, 2·31 ; ham, 0·88 ; pork chops, 0·77 ; lamb kidney, 3·60 ; lamb shoulder, 1·19 ; lamb chops, 1·07 ; beef liver, 6.30 ; beef kidney, 3·33 ; beef roundsteak, 0·95 ; beef rib roast, 0·82 ; chicken liver, 3·42 ; and chicken kidney, 2·23 mg. per g. of fresh tissue.

According to McIntire et al.[4] the muscle tissue of veal, lamb, pork and beef contained 0·7 to 1·4 mg. of choline per g. and the kidney, liver and heart appreciably larger amounts—up to 5 mg. per g. No appreciable loss of choline occurred on cooking or curing meat. Some-what similar values were obtained by Willstaedt et al.,[3] namely : calf liver, 6.50 ; ox liver, 4·85 ; and pig kidneys, 3·31 mg. per g.

Fish

Fresh salmon contained 1·81 ; cod, 2·00 ; and herring 1·27 mg. of choline per g.,[3] whilst trout muscle contained 0·87 and fish meal 3·29 mg. per g.[1]

Miscellaneous

Fresh milk contained 0·147 mg. per ml., and dried skim milk powder and dried whole milk powder 1·59 and 1·07 mg. per g. respectively.[1]   According to R. W. Engel,[1] butter contained no choline, but Willstaedt et al.[3] found 0·40 mg. per g.   Cheese contained 0·48 [1] and 0·56 [3] mg. per g.   Egg white contained negligible amounts of choline, but the yolk contained 17·13 mg. per g.[1]

Several different species of edible fungi contained amounts of choline ranging from 0·2 to 0·7 mg. per g.[3]

References to Section 5

1. R. W. Engel, *J. Nutrition*, 1943, **25,** 441.
2. D. Glick, *Cereal Chem.*, 1945, **22,** 95.
3. H. Willstaedt, M. Borggard and H. Lieck, *Z. Vitaminforsch.*, 1946, **18,** 25.
4. J. M. McIntire, B. S. Schweigert and C. A. Elvehjem, *J. Nutrition*, 1944, **28,** 219.

6. EFFECT OF CHOLINE DEFICIENCY IN ANIMALS

Brief reference has already been made (page 582) to the association of choline deficiency with fatty liver formation in rats and with perosis in chicks, and to the fact that methionine and betaine have biological properties similar to those of choline.   The reason for the close resemblance between choline, betaine and methionine is discussed subsequently (page 598).

Rats

The symptoms of choline deficiency in the rat were fully described by J. M. Patterson and E. W. McHenry.[1]   The animals showed loss of weight, paralysis of the hind limbs, loss of hair and a hunched posture.   The kidneys were enlarged and haemorrhagic, whilst the livers were slightly larger than those of animals fed adequate amounts of choline, and showed fatty infiltration.   The kidneys contained less phospholipins than normal.   The renal haemorrhages were prevented by choline, an observation confirmed by R. W. Engel [2] who at the same time noted that the liver fat did not return to normal until inositol was added to the diet. Diets deficient in pyridoxine or essential fatty acids produced fatty livers even when supplied with adequate amounts of choline. The addition of choline to the diet reduced the incidence of lesions in the fore-stomach of rats receiving cystine and white flour.[3] The cirrhosis produced in rats by feeding a choline-deficient diet was prevented by hypothyroidism induced either by thyroidectomy or by feeding thiouracil, p-aminobenzoic acid or sulphonamides.[4]

Other symptoms produced by choline deficiency in rats were anaemia,[5] hypertension,[6] enlargement of the adrenal cortex and atrophy of the thymus.[7]

Chicks

According to T. H. Jukes,[8] the perosis that developed in chicks maintained on a purified diet was cured by choline when manganese was present, but L. R. Richardson and A. G. Hogan [9] found that the perosis was not cured by choline and manganese alone, requiring in addition an aqueous extract of liver or the eluate from a fuller's earth adsorbate of liver. Methionine did not cure the perosis.[8]

According to D. S. McKittrick,[10] the choline required by chicks may be divided into two parts. One part, the essential choline, is used in tissue formation, and the other part, the replaceable choline, in transmethylation (page 600).

Turkeys

Turkeys, like chicks, developed perosis on a choline-deficient diet. The symptoms were cured by choline, but not by betaine.[11, 12]

Dogs

A choline-deficient diet, devised by McKibbin et al.,[13] proved fatal to pups in three weeks. The animals showed fatty infiltration of the liver, an increase in the plasma phosphatase, impaired bromosulphonphthalein elimination and a fall in the plasma cholesterol and cholesteryl esters. In very severe cases, the prothrombin time was also increased, the blood haemoglobin was decreased and the haematocrit and plasma proteins were reduced. The total cholesterol content of the liver was unchanged, but the total lipins increased 3- to 4-fold. The ratio, liver weight/body weight, was not correlated with the choline content of the diet, but the morphological changes in the liver were correlated with the impairment of liver function.[14] The kidneys were not morphologically abnormal, and the only tissue affected besides the liver was the thymus, which showed atrophic changes. The addition of choline to the diet of choline-deficient pups resulted in a rapid increase in food consumption and weight, an improvement in liver function and the withdrawal of lipin from the liver ; [15] liver function was restored to normal within five to ten days.

Choline chloride cured fat embolism produced in dogs by bone marrow curettage.[16] The action of the pancreatic extract known as lipocaic,[17] which prevented fatty infiltration of the liver in depancreatised dogs, was shown to be due to its choline content.[18]

Other Animals

Fatty infiltration of the liver is not a symptom of choline deficiency in guinea-pigs, which appear to lack hepatic choline oxidase activity.[19] Hamsters develop fatty livers on a choline-deficient diet, but not to the same degree as rats.[20] Pigs also develop fatty livers, gain weight more slowly than normal animals, display inco-ordination and a lack of rigidity at the joints and suffer from renal glomerular occlusion and some tubular epithelial necrosis.[21]

Fish

Choline was essential for young rainbow trout, the fish developing haemorrhagic kidneys and intestines in its absence ; these symptoms were prevented by 5 to 10 mg. of choline per 100 g. of diet.[22]

Lipotropic Action of Choline and Inositol

The lipotropic action of choline and inositol together was greater than that of either alone.[23] Moreover, choline brought about a greater reduction in the cholesteryl ester content of the liver than did inositol.[24] According to Gavin et al.,[25] choline was effective in the treatment of fatty livers due to aneurine and partially effective for cholesterol fatty livers, but it had little effect on biotin fatty livers, whereas inositol was effective in the treatment of biotin fatty livers, but not of aneurine fatty livers. According to Best et al.,[26] however, there is no evidence for assuming that biotin fatty livers are unique or that inositol is more effective than choline in their treatment ; they suggested that Gavin et al. overlooked the fact that the beef liver fraction used by them to produce fatty livers contained choline, so that the response to treatment was due to the combined effect of choline and inositol and not to inositol alone as they apparently assumed. Best et al. furthermore showed that inositol had no preferential effect in reducing the amount of cholesteryl esters or glycerides in the liver ; on the contrary, it was less effective than choline in this respect, and it did not prevent, as did choline or methionine, the occurrence of haemorrhagic kidneys. They confirmed the synergistic effect of choline and inositol on liver lipins. Neither had any effect on the absolute amount of phospholipin or free cholesterol in the liver, nor on kidney lipids.

Choline and Cancer

The choline content of transplanted epidermal carcinoma in mice was two-and-a-half times that of the normal epidermis, but methyl cholanthrene-treated epidermis contained only the normal amounts.[27]

References to Section 6

1. J. M. Patterson and E. W. McHenry, *J. Biol. Chem.*, 1942, **145**, 207.
2. R. W. Engel, *J. Nutrition*, 1942, **24**, 175.
3. G. A. Sharpless and M. Sabol, *ibid.*, 1943, **25**, 113.
4. P. Handler, *J. Biol. Chem.*, 1948, **173**, 295.
5. R. W. Engel, *J. Nutrition*, 1948, **36**, 739.
6. W. S. Hartcroft and C. H. Best, *Brit. Med. J.*, 1949, **1**, 423.
7. R. E. Olson and H. W. Deane, *J. Nutrition*, 1949, **39**, 31.
8. T. H. Jukes, *J. Nutrition*, 1941, **21**, *Suppl.*, 13 ; 1941, **22**, 315.
9. L. R. Richardson and A. G. Hogan, *Proc. Soc. Exp. Biol. Med.*, 1941, **48**, 459.
10. D. S. McKittrick, *Arch. Biochem.*, 1948, **18**, 437.
11. T. H. Jukes, *J. Nutrition*, 1940, **20**, 445.
12. M. Rhian, R. J. Evans and J. L. St. John, *ibid.*, 1943, **25**, 1.
13. J. M. McKibbin, S. Thayer and F. J. Stare, *J. Lab. Clin. Med.*, 1944, **29**, 1109.
14. F. R. Dutra and J. M. McKibbin, *ibid.*, 1945, **30**, 301.
15. J. M. McKibbin, R. M. Ferry, S. Thayer, E. G. Patterson and F. J. Stare, *ibid.*, 422.
16. E. M. Monson and C. Dennis, *Proc. Soc. Exp. Biol. Med.*, 1949, **70**, 330.
17. J. van Prohaska, L. R. Dragstedt and H. P. Harms, *Amer. J. Physiol.*, 1936, **117**, 166, 175.
18. A. N. Wick, *Arch. Biochem.*, 1949, **20**, 113.
19. P. Handler, *Proc. Soc. Exp. Biol. Med.*, 1949, **70**, 70.
20. P. Handler and F. Bernheim, *ibid.*, 1949, **72**, 569.
21. B. C. Johnson and M. F. James, *J. Nutrition*, 1948, **36**, 339 ; A. L. Neumann, J. L. Krider, M. F. James and B. C. Johnson, *ibid.*, 1949, **38**, 195.
22. B. A. McLaren, E. F. Herman and C. A. Elvehjem, *Arch. Biochem.*, 1946, **10**, 433 ; B. A. McLaren, E. Keller, D. J. O'Donnell and C. A. Elvehjem, *ibid.*, 1947, **15**, 169.
23. J. C. Forbes, *Proc. Soc. Exp. Biol. Med.*, 1943, **54**, 89.
24. J. M. R. Beveridge and C. C. Lucas, *J. Biol. Chem.*, 1945, **157**, 311.
25. G. Gavin, J. M. Patterson and E. W. McHenry, *ibid.*, 1943, **148**, 275.
26. C. H. Best, C. C. Lucas, J. M. Patterson and J. H. Ridout, *Science*, 1946, **103**, 12 ; *Biochem. J.*, 1946, **40**, 368 ; J. H. Ridout, C. C. Lucas, J. M. Patterson and C. H. Best, *ibid.*, 494.

27. E. L. Tatum, M. G. Ritchey, E. V. Cowdry and L. F. Wicks, *J. Biol. Chem.*, 1946, **163**, 675 ; M. G. Ritchey, L. F. Wicks and E. L. Tatum, *ibid.*, 1947, **171**, 51.

7. EFFECT OF CHOLINE DEFICIENCY IN MAN

There appears to be no case on record of choline deficiency in man, but since choline exhibited such a marked lipotropic action in animals, it is not surprising that it should have been tried out in the treatment of acute and chronic diseases of the liver in man. Several therapeutic trials of choline in hepatic cirrhosis have been made but as none of the experiments was adequately controlled, they do not provide a conclusive answer to the question of how far choline deficiency is responsible for this condition. G. O. Broun and R. O. Muether [1] treated four cases with 1 g. of choline chloride daily for up to two years, whilst A. H. Russakoff and H. Blumberg [2] gave up to 6 g. per day to six cases, with ill-effects in only one case. J. S. Richardson [3] gave 1·5 g. of choline chloride per day for eight days to sixteen patients with infective hepatitis, but the treatment was ineffective.

Moosnick *et al.* [4] reported that a refractory case of pernicious anaemia was cured by the intravenous injection of 1 g. of choline chloride daily, and suggested that fatty infiltration of the liver had prevented the formation of the liver principle and that when the infiltration was removed by the choline the ability of the liver to produce the anti-pernicious anaemia principle was restored.

References to Section 7

1. G. O. Broun and R. O. Muether, *J. Amer. Med. Assoc.*, 1942, **118**, 1403.
2. A. H. Russakoff and H. Blumberg, *Ann. Int. Med.*, 1944, **21**, 848.
3. J. S. Richardson, *Brit. Med. J.*, 1945, **2**, 156.
4. F. B. Moosnick, E. M. Schleicher and W. E. Peterson, *J. Clin. Invest.*, 1945, **24**, 278.

8. METABOLISM OF CHOLINE

Very little choline is excreted in the urine or faeces. Thus, after administration of 40 g. of the chloride per day for six days to sheep, only 0·7 to 2·5 % of the ingested choline was recovered from the urine ; there was no accumulation of choline in the liver, kidney or plasma.[1] Similarly, dogs fed 5 g. of choline chloride per day for six days excreted only 0·5 % in the urine and there was no increase in the plasma concentration.

The total choline excreted by humans in the faeces, urine and sweat was only 0·7 to 1·5 % of the intake (624 to 899 mg.) and most of this was recovered from the urine.[2] A change in the temperature and relative humidity did not affect the total amount excreted, but more appeared in the sweat.

The concentration of choline in the plasma was reduced in depancreatised dogs maintained on insulin, and the fall was associated with the development of fatty livers.[3] The fall in the plasma choline could be prevented by a fraction prepared from pancreas, and this also prevented fatty formation in depancreatised dogs ; it did not contain choline. The average choline content of human serum was lowest in July ; five times as much was present in February and March.[4]

References to Section 8

1. R. W. Luecke and P. B. Pearson, *J. Biol. Chem.*, 1945, **158**, 561.
2. B. C. Johnson, T. S. Hamilton and H. H. Mitchell, *ibid.*, 1945, **159**, 5.
3. I. L. Chaikoff, C. Entenman and M. L. Montgomery, *ibid.*, 1945, **160**, 387.
4. J. A. Schlegel, *Proc. Soc. Exp. Biol. Med.*, 1949, **70**, 695.

9. HUMAN AND ANIMAL REQUIREMENTS OF CHOLINE

Estimates of the amount of choline chloride required by rats vary considerably. Thus, 10 to 20 mg.,[1] 4 to 6 mg.,[2] 10 mg.,[3] 3 mg.[4] and 12 to 15 mg.[5] per day are the amounts stated by different groups of workers to be necessary to prevent fatty liver formation. Another group of workers claimed that as much as 20 mg. per day were required to prevent rustiness in albino rats,[6] whilst Wistar (albino) rats were said to require only 4 to 6 mg. daily compared with 10 mg. daily found to be necessary to prevent fatty liver formation in hooded rats of the Wisconsin strain.[7] An average value for the choline requirement of rats could therefore be about 100 mg. per day per kg. of bodyweight. The amount of choline required increased with the temperature at which animals were kept, from 0·75 g. per kg. of diet at 68° F. to 5 g. per kg. at 90° F.[8]

According to one group of workers [9] dogs required 50 to 100 mg. of choline chloride per 100 g. of ration, or 25 to 100 mg. per kg. of bodyweight per day, whilst C. Entenman and I. L. Chaikoff [10] found the daily requirement to be about 35 mg. per kg. of bodyweight.

According to O. D. Abbott and C. U. de Masters,[11] chicks required about 75 mg. per kg. of bodyweight.

Willstaedt *et al.*[12] estimated the human requirement of choline by assaying the amounts present in a normal diet and found that the daily intake varied from 502 to 1047 mg. per day with an average value of 646 mg. According to this calculation, therefore, humans require proportionately less choline than animals, about 9 mg. per kg. of bodyweight.

As will be seen later (page 600), choline can be replaced to some extent by methionine, but the two substances are only partly biologically equivalent. Choline was a more effective supplement than methionine for the rat, 3·8 parts of the latter being equivalent to 1 part of the former.[5] The total methionine requirement of rats on a choline-free diet was 1·2 g. per 100 g. of diet ; half of this was required for growth and half for lipotropic purposes. Methionine did not increase the growth rate further when the diet contained 100 to 200 mg. of choline per 100 g.[13] Chicks required 1 % of methionine in the diet for optimal growth,[14] and young pigs 0·8 % of methionine and 0·1 % of choline.[15]

References to Section 9

1. H. J. Channon, J. V. Loach and G. R. Tristram, *Biochem. J.*, 1938, **32,** 1322.
2. W. H. Griffith, *J. Nutrition*, 1941, **22,** 239.
3. R. W. Engel, *ibid.*, 1942, **24,** 174.
4. H. Pfaltz, *Z. Vitaminforsch.*, 1942, **22,** 193.
5. G. C. Supplee, L. S. Gall and J. F. Caul, *J. Dairy Sci.*, 1945, **28,** 435.
6. H. S. Owens, M. Trautman and E. Woods, *Science*, 1941, **93,** 406.
7. D. H. Copeland, *Proc. Soc. Exp. Biol. Med.*, 1944, **57,** 33.
8. C. A. Mills, *Arch. Biochem.*, 1942, **1,** 73 ; *Proc. Soc. Exp. Biol. Med.*, 1943, **54,** 265.
9. A. E. Schaefer, J. M. McKibbin and C. A. Elvehjem, *ibid.*, 1941, **47,** 365 ; J. M. McKibbin, S. Thayer and F. J. Stare, *J. Lab. Clin. Med.*, 1944, **29,** 1109 ; F. R. Dutra and J. M. McKibbin, *ibid.*, 1945, **30,** 301.
10. C. Entenman and I. L. Chaikoff, *J. Biol. Chem.*, 1946, **138,** 477.
11. O. D. Abbott and C. U. de Masters, *J. Nutrition*, 1940, **19,** 47.
12. H. Willstaedt, M. Borggard and H. Lieck, *Z. Vitaminforsch.*, 1946, **18,** 25.
13. C. R. Treadwell, *J. Biol. Chem.*, 1945, **160,** 601.
14. A. A. Klose and H. J. Almquist, *ibid.*, 1941, **138,** 467.
15. A. L. Neumann, J. L. Krider, M. F. James and B. C. Johnson, *J. Nutrition*, 1949, **38,** 195.

10. PHARMACOLOGY OF CHOLINE

Choline chloride had a value of LD50 equal to 3·4 g. per kg. of bodyweight when given orally to rats in a concentration of 500 to 670 mg. per ml. and a value of 6·1 g. per kg. when given in a concentration of 200 to 400 mg. per ml.[1] The addition of 1 % of choline

chloride to the diet produced no toxic effect in 60-g. rats, but 10 %
stopped growth and intermediate amounts retarded growth.[2] No
pathological changes were observed at autopsy. The addition of 1, 2
and 4 % of choline to the diet reduced the growth rate of chicks by
12, 13·8 and 23·8 % respectively, but no other toxic effects were
observed.[3] The administration of 400 mg. of choline chloride per kg.
of bodyweight to dogs with experimentally induced fatty livers for
more than three weeks did not produce any adverse effects [4] but,
according to J. E. Davis,[5] prolonged administration of choline to dogs
caused a fall in the red blood cells. He attributed this to the vasodilator effect of choline and the consequent increased supply of blood
and oxygen to the bone marrow, since atropine, which blocks the
vasodilator action of choline but not its lipotropic effect, restored the
erythrocytes to normal. G. E. Cartwright and M. M. Wintrobe [6]
failed to observe any effect of choline on the red blood cells in man.

Choline has a vasodilator effect, but this is very much less marked
than that of acetyl choline.[7]

References to Section 10

1. M. W. Neuman and H. C. Hodge, *Proc. Soc. Exp. Biol. Med.*,
   1945, **58,** 87.
2. H. C. Hodge, *ibid.*, 212.
3. V. H. Melass, P. B. Pearson and R. M. Sherwood, *ibid.*, 1946, **62,**
   174.
4. A. Kaplan and I. L. Chaikoff, *J. Biol. Chem.*, 1937, **120,** 647.
5. J. E. Davis, *Amer. J. Physiol.*, 1944, **142,** 402; *Science*, 1947, **105,** 43.
6. G. E. Cartwright and M. M. Wintrobe, *J. Amer. Med. Assoc.*, 1945,
   127, 911.
7. F. W. Mott and W. D. Halliburton, *Proc. Roy. Soc.*, 1899, **65,** 91 ;
   A. Lohmann, *Arch. Physiol.*, 1906, **118,** 215 ; A. Desgrez and
   J. Chevalier, *Compt. rend.*, 1908, **146,** 89 ; J. Gautrelet, *ibid.*,
   1909, **148,** 995.

11. CHOLINE IN THE NUTRITION OF MICRO-ORGANISMS

Comparatively few organisms have been discovered that require
choline for growth. A Type III pneumococcus was reported as being
unable to grow in the absence of choline [1] and *Clostridium botulinum*
was found to require choline.[2]

Of thirty-five compounds related to choline only one, aminoethanol,
was able to support the growth of pneumococcus in the absence of
choline ; [1] this micro-organism is able, apparently, to convert aminoethanol into choline.

A clearer understanding of the biosynthesis of choline was obtained with the aid of mutants of *Neurospora crassa*, one of which has already been mentioned as having been used for the microbiological assay of choline (page 587). These *cholineless* mutants of *N. crassa*, although able to synthesise the methyl donator, methionine, were unable to synthesise the methyl acceptor, dimethylaminoethanol.[3]

Mutant 47904 produced a substance which was identified as mono-methylaminoethanol ; this replaced choline for another strain, 34486.[4] It was concluded that strain 47904 was unable to convert methyl-aminoethanol into choline, whereas in strain 34486 the synthesis of choline was blocked prior to the formation of methylaminoethanol, probably at the stage involving the formation of this substance from aminoethanol.

References to Section 11

1. E. Badger, *J. Biol. Chem.*, 1944, **153**, 183 ; *J. Bact.*, 1944, **47**, 509.
2. C. Lamanna and C. Lewis, *ibid.*, 1946, **51**, 398.
3. T. H. Jukes and A. C. Dornbush, *Proc. Soc. Exp. Biol. Med.*, 1945, **58**, 142.
4. N. H. Horowitz, *J. Biol. Chem.*, 1946, **162**, 413.

12. CHOLINE REQUIREMENTS OF INSECTS

Choline was essential for the growth of larvae of *Ptinus tectus* and *Lasioderma serricorne*, but not of the larvae of *Tribolium confusum* and *Sitodrepa panicea* under ordinary conditions.[1] When the larvae of the last-named beetle were sterilised, however, choline had to be added to the diet in order for growth to continue, so that this insect, and possibly also *Lasioderma*, contains symbionts that synthesise choline.

The cockroach, *Blattella germanica*, also required choline for growth.[2] This could not be replaced by either aminoethanol or methylamino-ethanol, but the addition of methionine, dimethylaminoethanol and betaine in that order stimulated growth on a choline-deficient diet. Insects fed betaine contained nearly as much choline as those fed an equivalent amount of choline.

References to Section 12

1. G. Fraenkel and M. Blewett, *Nature*, 1943, **151**, 703 ; 1943, **152**, 506 ; *Biochem. J.*, 1943, **37**, 686 ; *Proc. Roy. Soc.*, 1944, **132**, 212.
2. J. L. Noland and C. A. Baumann, *Proc. Soc. Exp. Biol. Med.*, 1949, **70**, 198.

13. FUNCTION OF CHOLINE

Reference has already been made to the prevention and cure of fatty livers in rats by administration of choline, betaine or methionine and to the fact that the compounds are not completely biologically equivalent.

Before discussing the part that choline plays in the economy of the animal body, it is necessary to examine more closely the relationship between choline, betaine and methionine.

Methionine

Methionine is a sulphur-containing amino acid with the formula (I).

$$CH_3S.CH_2.CH_2.CH.COOH \qquad HS.CH_2.CH_2.CH.COOH$$
$$\underset{\text{(I)}}{\overset{|}{NH_2}} \qquad\qquad \underset{\text{(II)}}{\overset{|}{NH_2}}$$

$$HS.CH_2.CH\ COOH$$
$$\underset{\text{(III)}}{\overset{|}{NH_2}}$$

Like choline, it has the property of preventing fatty liver formation in rats fed a high fat, low choline diet.[1] This property was not possessed by its demethyl derivative, homocysteine (II), the higher homologue of cysteine (III),[2] and this striking difference indicated that the lipotropic action of methionine was probably associated with the labile methyl group. This was confirmed, and additional light thrown on the connection between methionine and choline, when W. C. Rose and E. E. Rice[3] showed that homocysteine was lipotropic when given at the same time as tiki tiki or a milk concentrate to supply the vitamin B complex. It was inferred from this that these supplements contained an unknown factor necessary for the methylation of homocysteine. Du Vigneaud et al.[4] showed that the factor was choline (a) by acetylating the concentrates and demonstrating pharmacologically the presence of acetylcholine; (b) by actually isolating choline as the reineckate; and (c) by showing that homocysteine and choline chloride produced the same increase in weight as methionine and also—what is more significant perhaps—prevented the formation of fatty livers in precisely the same way as methionine. They therefore concluded that one of the functions of the methyl group of methionine was to make possible the synthesis of choline in the body.

In order to obtain direct evidence in support of this hypothesis methionine in which the hydrogen atoms of the methyl group had been replaced by deuterium atoms was fed to rats maintained on a diet deficient in methionine and choline.[5] Choline was isolated from the carcases as the chloroplatinate, and creatine as the creatinine zinc chloride complex. Prolonged feeding of deuterio-methionine yielded choline and creatine containing 85 % of the theoretical deuterium contents. Oxidation of the choline with permanganate yielded trimethylamine containing all the deuterium originally present in the choline, thus proving that the deuterium had been retained in the methyl groups.

In a similar experiment deuterio-choline was fed to animals on a methionine- and choline-free diet containing homocystine. Creatine isolated from the body tissues contained 24 to 29 % of the theoretical maximum proving that under certain conditions choline can function as a methyl donator. Aminoethanol was shown [6] to be the methyl acceptor in the formation of choline, since the administration of aminoethanol containing N^{15} led to the formation of choline containing N^{15}. Similarly, guanidinoacetic acid was shown [7, 8] to be the precursor of the amidine and glycine moieties of creatine by the use of compounds containing N^{15}. These experiments indicate that the following transformations can be effected in the rat :

$$I_2 . CH_2 . CH_2OH + 3CH_3S . (CH_2)_2 . CH . COOH \longrightarrow (CH_3)_3 \overset{+}{N} . CH_2 . CH_2OH$$
$$\underset{NH_2}{\vert}$$

$$\underset{I_2}{\overset{H}{\diagdown}} C . NH . CH_2 . COOH + CH_3S . (CH_2)_2 . \underset{\underset{NH_2}{\vert}}{CH} . COOH \longrightarrow \underset{NH_2 \diagup}{\overset{NH \diagdown}{}} C . N . \underset{\underset{CH_3}{\vert}}{CH_2} . COOH$$

$$\underset{I_2}{\overset{H}{\diagdown}} C . NH . CH_2 . COOH + (CH_3)_3 \overset{+}{N} . CH_2 . CH_2OH + HS . (CH_2)_2 . \underset{\underset{NH_2}{\vert}}{CH} . COOH \longrightarrow$$

$$\underset{NH_2 \diagup}{\overset{NH \diagdown}{}} C . N . \underset{\underset{CH_3}{\vert}}{CH_2} . CH_2OH$$

In this last reaction, homocystine and choline constituted a more effective methylating system for guanidinoacetic acid than did homocysteine and choline, suggesting that homocystine may be the carrier of methyl groups *in vivo*.[9]

When deuterio-creatinine was fed to rats and then ordinary methionine, the rate at which deuterium disappeared from the urinary creatinine was not affected by the level of methionine in the diet, showing that the rate of methyl transfer from methionine was not proportional to the methionine intake.[10]

A deficiency of choline cannot entirely be made good by the administration of methionine, nor can a deficiency of methionine be made good by giving choline, for a certain minimum amount of methionine is needed by both the rat [11] and the chick [12] for purposes unconnected with methylation. Similarly, when a severe choline deficiency was induced in chicks [13, 14] or turkeys,[15] methionine could not replace choline in preventing the characteristic perosis. This suggests that the anti-perotic action of choline is distinct from its growth-promoting and lipotropic actions.

A combined severe choline and partial methionine deficiency was induced in chicks by H. J. Almquist and C. R. Grau.[16] The addition of methionine to the diet increased the gain in weight to about two-thirds of the normal value. Better, but still limited, growth was obtained with a partial deficiency of methionine and ample amounts of choline. That choline and methionine were only partially biologically equivalent was confirmed by D. S. McKittrick,[17] who found that, for optimal growth, white Leghorn chicks required 0·5 % of methionine and 0·1 % of choline chloride, together with an additional 0·25 % of methionine or an additional 0·45 % of choline chloride, or an equivalent mixture of the two. Excess methionine depressed the growth and this could be counteracted by adding a methyl acceptor, such as glycocyamine, or serine.

In rat liver, choline is partly responsible for the conversion of glycine into serine.[17a]

Betaine and Sarcosine

Methionine is not the only substance that can serve as a substitute for choline for, under certain conditions, betaine

$$(CH_3)_3\overset{+}{N} . CH_2 . COO^-$$

is capable of exerting a growth effect in the chick equivalent to that of choline,[18] especially in presence of ethanolamine.[19] Like methionine, however, it did not cure perosis in chicks,[14, 16, 20] nor could it completely replace choline or methionine, but only that portion of the one that could be replaced by the other.[17]

Betaine containing deuterio-methyl groups and N^{15} was shown to be an effective methyl donator,[21] and the methyl groups appeared in the tissue choline as quickly as they did from dietary deuterio-choline. There was a discrepancy, however, between the amount of N^{15} and deuterium in the choline, indicating that betaine was not converted as a whole into choline. Dimethylglycine containing deuterium gave rise to choline and creatine only to a very limited extent. Sarcosine containing N^{15} and deuterium was also an effective methylating agent, but creatine was formed much more slowly from sarcosine than from choline.[22]

Two other substances which are able to replace the " replaceable choline "[17] are dimethylthetin (IV) and dimethyl-β-propiothetin (V).[22a]

$$(CH_3)_2\overset{+}{S}.CH_2.COO^- \qquad (CH_3)_2\overset{+}{S}.CH_2.CH_2.COO^-$$
$$\text{IV} \qquad\qquad\qquad \text{V}$$

The latter was isolated from algae, and may be present in pineapple.

Transmethylation Reactions

It is evident, therefore, that in the animal body, a number of substances exist that are capable of donating a methyl group to another substance, which serves as acceptor. These reactions are now referred to collectively as transmethylation reactions and are recognised to be of considerable importance in metabolism. The formation of choline and creatine from methionine, of methionine from choline and of choline from betaine are examples of transmethylation reactions, but other reactions are in competition with them for the available supplies of labile methyl groups. One of these is the methylation of nicotinamide to give N^1-methylnicotinamide (page 254), and the lipotropic effect of choline was reduced by the addition of nicotinic acid to the diet,[23, 24] because some of the additional methyl groups supplied by the choline were utilised in methylating nicotinamide. Other substances conceivably formed by methylation *in vivo* are adrenaline, ergothioneine, anserine and dimethyl sulphone.

Function of Choline

Choline is therefore essential for the functioning of the animal organism, and its partial replacement by methionine or betaine is simply due to the fact that these substances are able to promote the formation of choline from aminoethanol or from mono- or dimethyl-aminoethanol (page 599). They are not completely biologically equivalent because they are responsible for the methylation of other substances, and choline has other functions in addition to its methylating action.

The lipotropic action of choline is believed to be due to its incorporation into phospholipid molecules, which facilitate the transport and metabolism of fatty acids.[25] It seems probable, however, that choline acts by stimulating the formation and utilisation of fats in the liver rather than by increasing fat transport in the plasma, as it increased the turnover of liver lecithin, but not that of the plasma phosphatides.[26] Aminoethanol, methylaminoethanol and dimethyl-aminoethanol had a similar action, but diethanolamine reduced phosphorylation because it was incorporated into phospholipids that were less easily metabolised and thus accumulated in the liver.[27]   Inositol may likewise owe its lipotropic effect to its incorporation into phospholipids. The ethyl homologue of choline (page 603) is also lipotropic and can likewise be incorporated into phospholipid molecules. It has been suggested [28] that the action of insulin in depancreatised dogs may be to liberate bound methionine from the dietary protein, making it available for the synthesis of choline, which then exerts a lipotropic effect.

Choline is also responsible for certain *in vivo* methylations, it stimulates growth and it prevents perosis in chicks and turkeys. Little is known about the manner in which choline exerts these effects, but they appear to be independent properties of the choline molecule, since closely related analogues only possess one or, at most, two of these functions (page 603).

Finally, choline is the precursor of acetylcholine and, indeed, it has itself a vasodilator action, although much less marked than that of acetylcholine (page 596).

References to Section 13

1. H. F. Tucker and H. C. Eckstein, *J. Biol. Chem.*, 1937, **121,** 479.
2. S. A. Singal and H. C. Eckstein, *Proc. Soc. Exp. Biol. Med.*, 1939, **41,** 512.
3. W. C. Rose and E. E. Rice, *J. Biol. Chem.*, 1939, **130,** 305.
4. V. du Vigneaud, H. M. Dyer and M. W. Kies, *ibid.*, 1939, **130,** 325 ; V. du Vigneaud, J. P. Chandler, A. W. Moyer and D. M. Keppel, *ibid.*, 1939, **131,** 57.
5. V. du Vigneaud, M. Cohn, J. P. Chandler, J. R. Schenck and S. Simmonds, *ibid.*, 1941, **140,** 625.
6. D. Stetten, *ibid.*, 1941, **138,** 437.
7. K. Bloch and R. Schoenheimer, *ibid.*, 167.
8. H. Borsook and J. W. Dubnoff, *ibid.*, 1940, **132,** 559.
9. H. Borsook and J. W. Dubnoff, *ibid.*, 1945, **160,** 635.
10. M. Cohn, S. Simmonds, J. P. Chandler and V. du Vigneaud, *ibid.*, 1946, **162,** 343.
11. M. Womack and W. C. Rose, *ibid.*, 1941, **141,** 375.
12. H. J. Almquist and C. R. Grau, *J. Nutrition*, 1945, **29,** 219.
13. C. R. Grau and H. J. Almquist, *ibid.*, 1943, **26,** 631.
14. T. H. Jukes, *J. Biol. Chem.*, 1940, **134,** 789 ; *J. Nutrition*, 1941, **22,** 315.
15. T. H. Jukes, *ibid.*, 1941, **20,** 251.
16. H. J. Almquist and C. R. Grau, *ibid.*, 1944, **27,** 263 ; C. R. Grau and H. J. Almquist, *ibid.*, 1943, **26,** 631.
17. D. S. McKittrick, *Arch. Biochem.*, 1947, **15,** 133 ; 1948, **18,** 437.
17a. W. Sakami, *J. Biol. Chem.*, 1949, **179,** 495.
18. H. J. Almquist and C. R. Grau, *J. Biol. Chem.*, 1943, **149,** 575.

19. J. McGinnis, L. C. Norris and G. F. Heuser, *Proc. Soc. Exp. Biol. Med.*, 1942, **51**, 293.
20. J. McGinnis, L. C. Norris and G. F. Heuser, *ibid.*, 1944, **56**, 197.
21. V. du Vigneaud, S. Simmonds, J. F. Chandler and M. Cohn, *J. Biol. Chem.*, 1946, **165**, 639.
22. V. du Vigneaud, S. Simmonds and M. Cohn, *ibid.*, 1946, **166**, 47.
22a. J. W. Dubnoff and H. Borsook, *ibid.*, 1948, **176**, 789.
23. W. H. Griffith and D. J. Mulford, *J. Nutrition*, 1941, **21**, 633.
24. J. C. Forbes, *ibid.*, 1941, **22**, 359.
25. C. S. McArthur, *Science*, 1946, **104**, 222.
26. D. B. Zilversmit, C. Entenman and I. L. Chaikoff, *J. Biol. Chem.*, 1948, **176**, 193 ; C. Artom and W. E. Cornatzer, *ibid.*, 949.
27. C. Artom, W. E. Cornatzer and M. Crowder, *ibid.*, 1949, **180**, 495.
28. I. L. Chaikoff, C. Entenman and M. L. Montgomery, *J. Biol. Chem.*, 1945, **160**, 489.

14. ANALOGUES OF CHOLINE

The only compounds, other than choline or betaine, that supported the growth of young rats on a diet free from methionine but containing homocystine were simple derivatives of choline, such as lecithin and phosphorylcholine, and ethyl - β - hydroxyethyldimethylammonium chloride.[1] Another homologue of choline, diethyl-β-hydroxyethyl-methylammonium chloride prevented perosis in chicks, but did not promote growth, whilst the triethylanalogue, triethyl-β-hydroxyethyl-ammonium chloride, was neither anti-perotic nor growth-promoting.[2] Betaine was inactive in both respects, but the corresponding aldehyde had a weak growth-promoting and anti-perotic activity.[2] The triethyl compound, however, prevented renal haemorrhage in rats [3] and was lipotropic, being incorporated, like choline, into the phospholipid molecule.[4]

A particularly interesting analogue of choline is β-hydroxyethyl-trimethyl-arsonium chloride, the so-called arsenocholine :

$$(CH_3)_3As . CH_2 . CH_2OH$$
$$|$$
$$Cl$$

This compound was not able to methylate homocystine either in the rat [1] or the chick,[5] but it had lipotropic activity [6] and promoted growth and prevented perosis in chicks.[7, 8] Apparently, therefore, it could replace choline in every function except that of transmethylation. The result emphasises the variety of functions possessed by choline.

Sulfocholine, β-hydroxyethyl-dimethyl sulphonium chloride, be-haved in a similar way to arsenocholine and, although unable to methylate homocystine, it prevented fatty liver formation and renal haemorrhages in rats fed a methyl-free diet.[8a] Since dimethyl sulphide was isolated from the livers, it would appear that the lipo-tropic action of sulphocholine is due to its incorporation into liver phospholipids in place of choline. Dimethylthetin and dimethyl propiothetin were also lipotropic.

Although only the above compounds have a lipotropic effect in the absence of methionine and the presence of homocystine, both mono- and dimethylaminoethanol prevented perosis in chicks fed a basal diet deficient in choline and methionine whilst dimethylaminoethanol, but not the mono-derivative, increased the growth rate, though much less effectively than choline.[9] Both compounds stimulated growth to the same extent as choline when methionine was added. Using *cholineless* mutants of *Neurospora crassa*, Jukes *et al.*[10] and N. H. Horowitz [11] showed that aminoethanol was converted into choline in three steps, and feeding experiments with mono- and dimethylaminoethanol containing deuterio-methyl groups proved that these compounds were precursors of choline in animals.[12]

The low growth-promoting activity of dimethylaminoethanol is believed to be due to the inability of the animal to utilise the methyl groups present in the molecule, indicating that when choline takes part in transmethylation reactions, it releases only one methyl group, giving rise to dimethylaminoethanol which " would thus assume a pivotal position as both the immediate precursor and the principal demethylation product of choline ".

Although the triethyl analogue of choline had a slight lipotropic action in rats, it was toxic to mice and the toxicity was neutralised by an equal amount of choline. It also blocked the contraction of isolated frog muscle by choline, but not by acetylcholine, and it was therefore suggested that the compound interfered with the formation of acetylcholine from choline.[13]

References to Section 14

1. A. W. Moyer and V. du Vigneaud, *J. Biol. Chem.*, 1942, **143,** 373.
2. T. H. Jukes, *J. Nutrition*, 1941, **21,** *Suppl.*, 13.
3. J. M. Patterson and E. W. McHenry, *J. Biol. Chem.*, 1942, **145,** 207.
4. C. S. McArthur, *Science*, 1946, **104,** 222.
5. H. J. Almquist and T. H. Jukes, *Proc. Soc. Exp. Biol. Med.*, 1942, **51,** 243.
6. A. D. Welch, *J. Biol. Chem.*, 1941, **137,** 173 ; A. D. Welch and R. L. Landan, *ibid.*, 1942, **144,** 581.
7. H. J. Almquist and C. R. Grau, *J. Nutrition*, 1944, **27,** 263.
8. T. H. Jukes and A. D. Welch, *J. Biol. Chem.*, 1943, **146,** 19.
8a. G. A. Maw and V. du Vigneaud, *ibid.*, 1948, **176,** 1029, 1037.
9. T. H. Jukes and J. J. Oleson, *ibid.*, 1945, **157,** 419 ; T. H. Jukes, J. J. Oleson and A. C. Dornbush, *J. Nutrition*, 1945, **30,** 219.

10. T. H. Jukes, A. C. Dornbush and J. J. Oleson, *Fed. Proc.*, 1945, **4**, 157.
11. N. H. Horowitz, *J. Biol. Chem.*, 1946, **162**, 413.
12. V. du Vigneaud, J. P. Chandler, S. Simmonds, A. W. Moyer and M. Cohn, *ibid.*, 1946, **164**, 603.
13. A. S. Keston and S. B. Wortis, *Proc. Soc. Exp. Biol. Med.*, 1946, **61**, 439.

Chapter XIII

MISCELLANEOUS WATER-SOLUBLE GROWTH FACTORS

1. INTRODUCTION

There is no reason to believe that membership of the vitamin B complex is restricted to the compounds described in the preceding chapters, although it is doubtful if substances of such outstanding nutritional and therapeutic importance as aneurine and nicotinic acid remain to be discovered. This is perhaps a sweeping and unwise generalisation to make, but it appears to be warranted by evidence from clinical tests and animal experiments that the most serious symptoms of vitamin B complex deficiency are more or less completely relieved by aneurine, nicotinic acid and riboflavine.

For example, Elsom et al.[1] studied the clinical effects of a deficiency of the whole vitamin B complex and observed that many of the symptoms, including anorexia and mental symptoms, were improved by administration of aneurine alone, although other symptoms, such as delayed motility of the small intestine, a macrocytic anaemia and oedema of the upper and lower extremities, were not affected by either aneurine or riboflavine, but were relieved by administration of yeast. It is probable that many of these symptoms could have been relieved by other members of the vitamin B complex had these been available in 1940 when the work was carried out. From this point of view the results of Keys et al.,[2] carried out in 1945, are perhaps of greater significance. They maintained eight normal young men on a diet providing 33,000 cals. and 75 g. of protein a day together with 0·18 mg. of aneurine, 0·25 mg. of riboflavine and 3·5 mg. of nicotinic acid per 1000 cals. Another four men were given in addition 1 mg. of aneurine, 1 mg. of riboflavine and 10 mg. of nicotinamide daily. The only difference between the two groups after 161 days was that the first had a slightly higher concentration of pyruvic acid in the blood than the second group. At the end of this time, two men from the first group were given a diet containing negligible amounts of all three B vitamins; they showed increasing anorexia from the seventh to the twenty-first day and other signs of "subjective distress" but no objective signs of vitamin deficiency.

These two papers seem to indicate that the earliest symptoms of a vitamin B complex deficiency are due to a deficiency of aneurine, which appears to be the most critical of the B vitamins in human nutrition. The second paper suggests, in addition, that human subjects can be maintained in apparently normal health by the addition of aneurine, riboflavine and nicotinic acid to a diet deficient in the vitamin B complex, and this conclusion is supported by the fact that excellent results have been obtained in the treatment of vitamin B complex deficiency with these three factors only. A. G. Clarke and F. Prescott,[3] for instance, successfully treated seventeen cases which exhibited symptoms such as depression, psychoneurosis, anxiety, polyneuritis, glossitis, angular stomatitis and cheilosis, with 3 to 9 mg. of aneurine, 3 to 9 mg. of riboflavine and 100 to 500 mg. of nicotinic acid daily.

From the standpoint of human nutrition, therefore, it is doubtful whether any other members of the vitamin B complex of fundamental importance remain to be discovered. There is also strong evidence for believing that aneurine is the most important member of the vitamin B complex in animal nutrition, for a deficiency of this factor is the first of the B vitamin deficiencies to manifest itself, and it gives rise to the most serious symptoms. Thus, E. C. Miller and C. A. Baumann [4] found that rats died within three weeks on a vitamin B_1-deficient diet containing all the other members of the vitamin B complex, but suffered no ill-effects when deprived of nicotinic acid or choline only. On a riboflavine-deficient diet, they ceased to grow but apparently remained otherwise normal for four months, when they developed deficiency symptoms and died after seven to twelve months. On a pantothenic acid-free diet, growth ceased within a month and about half the animals died within five months.

The impression gained from animal experiments and clinical experience is that a vitamin B complex deficiency can be largely, though not completely, remedied by administration of aneurine, riboflavine and nicotinic acid ; some of the other B vitamins may of course be supplied by intestinal synthesis. In any event, it appears unsound in theory and possibly dangerous in practice to treat a multiple deficiency with one B vitamin only, for A. F. Morgan [5] using dogs and Supplee et al.[6] using rats obtained evidence that this sometimes precipitated a deficiency of another factor, although K. Unna and J. D. Clark [7] found that prolonged administration of large amounts of individual vitamins to rats on a diet deficient in one or more factors did not aggravate the deficiency state.

References to Section 1

1. K. O'S. Elsom, F. H. Lewy and G. W. Heublein, *Amer. J. Med. Sci.*, 1940, **200**, 757.
2. A. Keys, A. F. Henschel, H. L. Taylor, O. Mickelsen and J. Brozek, *Amer. J. Physiol.*, 1945, **144**, 5.
3. A. G. Clarke and F. Prescott, *Brit. Med. J.*, 1943, **2**, 503.
4. E. C. Miller and C. A. Baumann, *J. Nutrition*, 1944, **27**, 319.
5. A. F. Morgan, *Science*, 1941, **93**, 261.
6. G. C. Supplee, R. C. Bender and Z. M. Hanford, *J. Amer. Pharm. Assoc.*, 1942, **31**, 194.
7. K. Unna and J. D. Clark, *Amer. J. Med. Sci.*, 1942, **204**, 364.

2. INADEQUACY OF KNOWN VITAMINS FOR ANIMALS

Although aneurine, riboflavine and nicotinic acid are undoubtedly the most important of the B vitamins for both animals and humans, there is abundant evidence from animal experiments that other water-soluble nutritional factors exist in addition to the recognised members of the vitamin B complex, vitamin C and vitamin P. These are not of major importance in human or animal nutrition and their absence generally results in comparatively trivial disturbances in the well-being of experimental animals, although a prolonged deficiency may sometimes result in death.

Mice and Rats

E. R. Norris and J. Hauschildt [1] claimed that another factor in addition to aneurine, nicotinic acid, riboflavine, pyridoxine and " filtrate factor " was necessary to prevent skin lesions and loss of hair in mice fed a purified diet. Similarly, K. Schwartz [2] claimed that a new factor was necessary to increase the weight of pantothenic acid-deficient rats beyond the limit reached by administration of pantothenic acid alone ; the factor was termed " factor 125 " because with pantothenic acid alone the growth rate began to decrease when the rats weighed 125 g.

Dogs

Dogs manifested symptoms of deficiency when fed a purified diet supplemented by a mixture of synthetic B vitamins. Schaefer *et al.* [3] found that a factor in liver restored the growth and prevented anorexia in dogs maintained on a casein-sucrose diet supplemented by aneurine, riboflavine, nicotinic acid, pyridoxine, pantothenic acid and choline, whilst Smith *et al.* [4] found that a factor in yeast supplemented pyridoxine in improving the blood picture and general health of dogs maintained on a diet containing seven synthetic B vitamins, but no pyridoxine. P. J. Fouts [5] observed that dogs receiving a low protein diet supplemented with aneurine, riboflavine, pyridoxine, nicotinic acid and pantothenic acid developed a deficiency syndrome characterised by loss of weight, moderate anaemia, dermal and peptic ulcers and fatty cirrhotic livers ; ultimately most of the animals died. A high protein diet prevented the condition, but the growth rate was sub-optimal. A partial improvement resulted from the feeding of choline, liver extract or a filtrate factor preparation from rice bran, and complete improvement, except for a fibrosis of the liver, from administration of the liver extract together with large amounts of choline. A somewhat similar result was obtained by D. V. Frost and F. P. Dann,[6] who fed pups on a synthetic diet, supplemented by aneurine, riboflavine, nicotinic acid, pantothenic acid, pyridoxine and choline and noted that they developed deficiency symptoms. These were relieved by administration of yeast, liver paste or a liver extract fraction insoluble in 70 % alcohol.

Fox pups and mink kits also developed deficiency symptoms on a purified diet. These were relieved by feeding fresh liver.[6a]

Pigs

Russell et al.[7] maintained weanling pigs for up to 469 days on a purified diet supplemented with aneurine, riboflavine, nicotinic acid, pyridoxine, pantothenic acid, p-aminobenzoic acid and choline. The animals grew as well during the first three months as did pigs on a commercial feed, but later growth was slower, although there was nothing in the behaviour or appearance of the " deficient " animals to differentiate them from their more adequately nourished litter-mates. They failed to reproduce on mating, however, and the addition of dried liver to the ration did not restore the reproductive function.

Chicks and Pigeons

That " synthetic " rations are not completely adequate for chicks has been demonstrated by several workers. Gillis et al.,[8] for example, reported that liver extracts contained a heat-stable factor essential for reproduction in hens, although it did not increase the hatchability of eggs, whilst a growth factor for chicks was reported to be present in cow manure by M. Rubin and H. R. Bird.[9] It was heat-stable and non-dialysable, soluble in water and 50 % and 90 % ethyl alcohol, but insoluble in chloroform and ether. It was differentiated from folic acid, factors U, R and S and from vitamins B_{10} and B_{11}, but appears to be related to vitamin B_{12} (see page 544). Pigeons also developed deficiency symptoms, including a severe anaemia, when maintained on a purified diet supplemented by aneurine, riboflavine, nicotinic acid, pyridoxine and pantothenic acid ; [10] the anaemia was cured by extracts of yeast, liver or rice bran. Pigeons have also been said to require a weight restoration factor (page 611).

The inference underlying all this work is, of course, that new factors essential for the well-being of animals, and distinct from the known members of the vitamin B complex are present in the supplements used to relieve the deficiency symptoms. It will be noted that in most instances, the material used as the supplement was an extract prepared from either liver or yeast, both of which, as already noted, are excellent sources of most members of the vitamin B complex. In none of this work, however, was any serious attempt made to isolate and purify the responsible factor. Such attempts have been made with certain other factors, however, and the concentrates so obtained have been shown to produce the same effect in animals as the original crude extracts. Many of these concentrates, although still relatively impure, have been given specific names, some implying that the active principle is a vitamin or even a member of the vitamin B complex.

Claims for the isolation of a new vitamin have often rested on very flimsy evidence, because the preparations originally obtained have been highly impure and no subsequent attempts have been made to purify them, much less to isolate the responsible factor in the pure state. For this reason many of the older " vitamins " are now to be regarded as of historical interest only (see page 613), although many factors described in the recent literature merit more serious attention and may ultimately achieve recognition as vitamins. These are factors now under active investigation, which appear to have a reasonable chance of being isolated in the pure state. Once this has been done their biological properties can be examined to confirm that the activity supposed to be characteristic of them really is a function of the pure substance and not of an impurity from which it has previously not been separated.

It is felt that a brief account of the factors to which specific names have been given is necessary to make this survey complete, whether the factors belong to the group that is now only of historical interest or whether they are strong favourites for ultimate recognition as members of the vitamin B complex.

References to Section 2

1. E. R. Norris and J. Hauschildt, *Science*, 1940, **92**, 316.
2. K. Schwartz, *Z. physiol. Chem.*, 1942, **275**, 232.
3. A. E. Schaefer, J. M. McKibbin and C. A. Elvehjem, *J. Nutrition*, 1942, **23**, 491.

4. S. G. Smith, H. Hawfield, R. Curry, R. Connar and J. Collins, *J. Elisha Mitchell Sci. Soc.*, 1943, **59**, 117.
5. P. J. Fouts, *J. Nutrition*, 1943, **25**, 217.
6. D. V. Frost and F. P. Dann, *ibid.*, 1944, **27**, 355.
6a. A. E. Schaefer, C. K. Whitehair and C. A. Elvehjem, *ibid.*, 1948, **35**, 147 ; A. E. Schaefer, S. B. Tove, C. K. Whitehair and C. A. Elvehjem, *ibid.*, 157.
7. W. C. Russell, A. E. Teeri and K. Unna, *ibid.*, 1948, **35**, 321.
8. M. B. Gillis, G. F. Heuser and L. C. Norris, *ibid.*, 1942, **23**, 153.
9. M. Rubin and H. R. Bird, *J. Biol. Chem.*, 1946, **163**, 387, 393.
10. H. R. Street, *J. Nutrition*, 1944, **28**, 395.

3. VITAMINS B_3, B_4 and B_5

Vitamins B_3 and B_5

Vitamin B_3 is the name given to a factor present in yeast which, according to R. R. Williams and R. E. Waterman,[1] was necessary to restore to normal the weight of pigeons maintained on a vitamin B complex-deficient diet, after the polyneuritic symptoms had been cured by administration of vitamin B_1 ; it was unstable to heat. L. Randoin and R. Lecoq [2] had earlier reported the existence of a similar factor destroyed by alkaline autoclaving.

Evidence for the existence of a third alkali-labile factor in addition to vitamins B_1 and B_3 was obtained by Carter *et al.*,[3] who found that a fraction from liver, alleged to contain this factor, vitamin B_5, cured heart block in pigeons fed on polished rice ; they also found that large amounts of vitamin B_1 did not fully restore the weight of pigeons, thus apparently confirming the existence of vitamin B_3. Vitamin B_3 was shown to be necessary for the chick as well as for the pigeon by Eddy *et al.*[4]

Further support for the existence of vitamin B_3 was provided by J. R. O'Brien [5] who, like Carter *et al.*, showed that a vitamin B_1 concentrate administered at a level equivalent to forty times the antineuritic dose failed to restore fully the weight of pigeons fed a diet of autoclaved polished rice. An alcoholic extract of wheat or yeast was effective in restoring the weight to normal and an extract made after acid hydrolysis was still more effective, but an aqueous extract was quite inactive. J. R. O'Brien confirmed the instability of vitamin B_3, not only to heat, but also on storage or exposure to air.

The first note of doubt regarding the *bona fides* of vitamin B_3 was struck by C. W. Carter,[6] who observed that the weight of pigeons was fully restored when caseinogen was added to the diet, suggesting that the so-called vitamin B_3 deficiency was due to an inadequate intake of protein. The cardiac arrythmia previously attributed to vitamin B_5 deficiency was not affected by the caseinogen and was only cured by the addition of an extract prepared from wheat germ. As the result of subsequent work carried out jointly, C. W. Carter and J. R. O'Brien [7] reached the conclusion that caseinogen only fully restored the weight of pigeons under certain special conditions, and that vitamin B_3 was needed in addition. They described the preparation of a concentrate from liver and attempts to purify the factor. They found that most of the activity was adsorbed on fuller's earth. Their results appeared to substantiate the earlier claims for the existence of vitamin B_5.

Unfortunately, neither vitamin B_3 nor vitamin B_5 has ever been isolated in the pure state, and it is therefore impossible to decide whether they ought to be recognised as distinctive factors or not. In the light of more recent work, which has indicated the large number of water-soluble factors that are required by the chick (page 613), and presumably by pigeons also, it is reasonable to suppose that the concentrates of vitamins B_3 and B_5, which the Oxford workers used, owed their activity to the presence of these other factors. J. G. Lee and A. G. Hogan,[8] for instance, concluded that vitamins B_3 and B_5 were multiple in nature, the former being a source of pantothenic acid and the latter of pyridoxine, but doubtless choline, biotin, folic acid and vitamin B_{12} also contributed to the effects produced.

Vitamin B_4

Vitamin B_4 is the name given to a heat-labile factor claimed by V. Reader [9] to be necessary for rats when maintained on a diet of autoclaved cereals. In the absence of vitamin B_4 the rats not only ceased to grow but developed a hunched back, protruding jowls and a wobbly gait. Administration of a vitamin B_1 concentrate brought about a gradual recovery which was believed to be due to the relief of anorexia and a corresponding increase in the vitamin B_4 intake.[10]

Kline et al.[11] produced a vitamin B_4 deficiency in rats by using purified caseinogen and dextrin, crystalline vitamin B_1 and a highly purified concentrate of "vitamin B_2". The deficiency symptoms were relieved by feeding peanuts, which were assumed to be rich in vitamin B_4. Subsequently they observed [12] that brain, kidney and liver tissue also relieved the symptoms.

Subsequent workers failed to confirm the existence of vitamin B_4 and according to R. L. Swank and O. A. Bessey,[13] for example, a deficiency of vitamin B_1 would account for the paralysis in deficient rats making it unnecessary to postulate the existence of vitamin B_4, whilst Briggs et al.,[14] using a diet with which they had previously produced vitamin B_4 deficiency in rats, found that the typical paralysis was prevented and growth was promoted by the addition to the diet of arginine, glycine and cystine. There seems to be little justification, therefore, for retaining " vitamin B_4 " as a legitimate component of the vitamin B complex, and we may therefore regard vitamins B_3, B_4 and B_5 as of historical interest only.

References to Section 3

1. R. R. Williams and R. E. Waterman, *J. Biol. Chem.*, 1928, **78**, 311.
2. L. Randoin and R. Lecoq, *Compt. rend.*, 1926, **182**, 1408.
3. C. W. Carter, H. W. Kinnersley and R. A. Peters, *Biochem. J.*, 1930, **24**, 1764.
4. W. H. Eddy, S. Gurin and J. C. Keresztesy, *J. Biol. Chem.*, 1930, **87**, 729.
5. J. R. O'Brien, *Biochem. J.*, 1934, **28**, 926.
6. C. W. Carter, *ibid.*, 933.
7. C. W. Carter and J. R. O'Brien, *ibid.*, 1935, **29**, 2746 ; 1936, **30**, 43 ; 1937, **31**, 2270.
8. J. G. Lee and A. G. Hogan, *Missouri Agric. Exp. Stat. Bull.*, 1942, 342.
9. V. Reader, *Biochem. J.*, 1929, **23**, 689 ; 1930, **24**, 77, 1827 ; H. W. Kinnersley, J. R. O'Brien, R. A. Peters and V. Reader, *ibid.*, 1933, **27**, 225.
10. C. A. Elvehjem and A. Arnold, *Nature*, 1936, **137**, 109.
11. O. L. Kline, C. A. Elvehjem and E. B. Hart, *Biochem. J.*, 1936, **30**, 780.
12. O. L. Kline, H. R. Bird, C. A. Elvehjem and E. B. Hart, *J. Nutrition*, 1936, **11**, 515.
13. R. L. Swank and O. A. Bessey, *ibid.*, 1941, **22**, 77.
14. G. M. Briggs, T. D. Luckey, C. A. Elvehjem and E. B. Hart, *J. Biol. Chem.*, 1943, **150**, 11.

4. VITAMINS B_{10}, B_{11}, B_{13} AND B_{14}

In a paper published in 1943, Briggs *et al.*[1] stated that chicks required two new factors for proper feathering and growth, in addition to those already recognised. These were named vitamins B_{10} and B_{11} respectively, these numbers being selected " because there are at the present time nine vitamins of the B complex concerned in chick nutrition, seven of which have been well established as necessary, namely, thiamine, riboflavine, pantothenic acid, choline, nicotinic acid, pyridoxine and biotin. The two other members, inositol and folic acid, appear to be necessary for the chick."

This explains the absence of any information in the literature about vitamins B_7, B_8 and B_9 which may have puzzled a good many people ; these vitamins have never, in fact, existed ! There is thus a gap between vitamin B_6, which has been fully discussed in Chapter V, and vitamin B_{10}.

Vitamins B_{10} and B_{11}

Concentrates of vitamins B_{10} and B_{11}[1] were prepared from liver. Both factors were soluble in water, and were adsorbed on norit and superfiltrol at pH 3 and eluted from the adsorbates by means of aqueous alcoholic ammonia. Both factors were synthesised by a certain strain of *Mycobacterium tuberculosis* in presence of p-aminobenzoic acid.[2]

The existence of vitamins B_{10} and B_{11} was apparently confirmed by the observation of McGinnis *et al.*[3] that growth and feather pigmentation were impaired when chicks were reared on a diet of maize, peanut meal, casein, soya bean oil, cod liver oil and salts, supplemented by aneurine, riboflavine, pyridoxine, pantothenic acid and glycine.

The symptoms said to be characteristic of a deficiency of vitamins B_{10} and B_{11}, however, have been shown to be produced by a diet deficient in folic acid and vitamin B_{12}. The addition of vitamin B_{12} increased the growth rate, but did not improve feathering, whereas the addition of folic acid improved feathering but the growth rate still remained sub-optimal.[4] Clearly, therefore, vitamins B_{10} and B_{11} cannot be regarded as established members of the vitamin B complex.

Vitamin B_{13}

An unidentified growth factor was isolated from distillers' dried solubles by A. F. Novak and S. M. Hauge.[5] This factor, termed provisionally vitamin B_{13}, stimulated the growth of rats at a level of 2 μg. and gave a maximal response at 10 μg. per day. It was isolated by a process that included extraction with acid, precipitation of inert material with alcohol, chromatographic adsorption of impurities on fuller's earth, precipitation of the active fraction with phosphotungstic acid and separation by chloroform extraction.

Vitamin B_{14}

E. R. Norris and J. J. Majnarich[6] isolated a crystalline compound from urine that was highly active on cell proliferation *in vitro* and on haemopoiesis *in vivo* ; 33 mg. were isolated from 100 l. of urine. Its effect on bone-marrow proliferation was counteracted by 2-amino-4-hydroxy-7-methylpteridine, which also antagonises the effect of xanthopterine. Vitamin B_{14} was several million times as active as xanthopterine, however. A single injection of 0·01 μg. alleviated anaemia and leucopenia in rats treated with sulphasuxidine.

Whereas the activity of xanthopterine and pteroylglutamic acid on cell proliferation and haemopoiesis was enhanced by certain enzyme preparations, such as xanthine oxidase from milk, rat liver homogenate and rat gastric mucosa extract, the activity of vitamin B_{14} was not affected. The enzyme-treated pterines had about the same activity as vitamin B_{14}.

References to Section 4

1. G. M. Briggs, T. D. Luckey, C. A. Elvehjem and E. B. Hart, *J. Biol. Chem.*, 1943, **148**, 163.
2. R. C. Mills, G. M. Briggs, T. D. Luckey and C. A. Elvehjem, *Proc. Soc. Exp. Biol. Med.*, 1944, **56**, 240.
3. J. McGinnis, L. C. Norris and G. F. Heuser, *J. Biol. Chem.*, 1942, **145**, 341.
4. C. A. Nichol, L. S. Dietrich, C. A. Elvehjem and E. B. Hart, *J. Nutrition*, 1949, **39**, 287.
5. A. F. Novak and S. M. Hauge, *J. Biol. Chem.*, 1948, **174**, 235, 647.
6. E. R. Norris and J. J. Majnarich, *Science*, 1949, **109**, 32, 33.

5. VITAMIN L AND FACTORS U, W, R AND S

Vitamin L

Vitamin L is the name given by Nakahara *et al.*[1] to a factor said to be essential for the lactation of rats. Its name represents a return to the original system of naming the vitamins, in which successive letters of the alphabet are used. Its " discovery " occurred shortly after that of the fat-soluble anti-haemorrhagic vitamin K, and was followed in turn by the discovery of vitamin M which, as already observed, is now regarded as a conjugate of folic acid.

Nakahara *et al.*[2] subsequently claimed to have separated vitamin L into two fractions, vitamin L_1 and vitamin L_2, neither of which could replace the other. Unfortunately, although these factors were claimed to be distinct from the filtrate factor and factor W, they appear not to have been isolated in the pure state, and so their relationship to other members of the vitamin B complex cannot be determined. Folley *et al.*[3] failed to confirm the existence of a lactation factor for rats.

Factor U

Another factor of doubtful status is the factor U of E. L. R. Stokstad and P. D. V. Manning.[4] This was said to be required by chicks on a diet of polished rice and washed fish meal, supplemented by riboflavine and the chick antidermatitis factor. In a later paper,[5] a factor U concentrate was shown to contain vitamin B_6, which would have accounted for some of its activity.

Factor W

The factor W of D. V. Frost and C. A. Elvehjem [6] has already been discussed (page 349). It would appear to be an impure preparation of the filtrate factor. Another filtrate factor, possibly identical with factor W, is factor B_W, claimed by H. Kringstad and G. Lunde [7] to be essential for the growth of rats. This factor was present in both liver and yeast and differed from pantothenic acid in being stable to alkali and not extracted at pH 1 by ether. Liver and yeast also contained a closely related factor, termed factor B_X, which prevented grey hair in rats. The precise status of these factors has never been determined.

Factors R and S

Schumacher et al. [8] designated as factors R and S two unidentified factors necessary for the growth of chicks. Extracts of these factors were prepared by Hill et al. [9] from dried brewers' yeast by aqueous extraction at 80 to 85° C., by extraction with acid or by digestion with takadiastase. The extracts were concentrated under reduced pressure, the pH was adjusted to 1·6 and factor S precipitated by the addition of ten volumes of alcohol. After adjusting the pH of the filtrate to 7·0, factor R separated on standing ; the filtrate contained folic acid. Thus neither factor was identical with pteroylglutamic acid but factor R is possibly a conjugated form of folic acid. Factor S is now known to be identical with strepogenin. [10]

Strepogenin

In 1944, H. Sprince and D. W. Woolley [11] prepared concentrates from solubilised liver extract by six different methods and tested them as growth factors for haemolytic streptococcus, *Streptococcus lactis* and *L. helveticus*. Since the relative activities of the concentrates towards these organisms were substantially the same, it was concluded that one and the same factor was probably responsible for the growth stimulation in each instance. It was given the name of " strepogenin " since " its presence is necessary for streptococci of group A to generate ". Tryptic digests of many pure proteins, *e.g.* insulin, trypsinogen, trypsin, chymotrypsin and chymotrypsinogen, ribonuclease, tobacco mosaic virus, haemoglobin and casein, were found to be good sources of strepogenin. [12] Not only was strepogenin a growth factor for micro-organisms, but it also stimulated the growth of mice. [13] The growth rate of mice was reduced when the animals were fed on a diet containing hydrolysed casein together with cystine and tryptophan and restored either by replacing these substances by intact casein or by supplementing them with a tryptic digest of casein. [14] This indicated that strepogenin was associated with a protein molecule, and this was confirmed by the increased growth rates of mice fed proteins rich in strepogenin ; proteins such as egg white that contained little strepogenin had little growth-promoting activity.[15] D. W. Woolley[16] showed that strepogenin was a peptide of glutamic acid. He observed that it neutralised the effect of the tomato wilting agent, lycomarasmin, which is elaborated by *Fusarium lycopersici*. On hydrolysis, this substance yields aspartic acid, glycine and pyruvic acid, and is probably a tripeptide of serine, glycine and aspartic acid.[17] D. W. Woolley therefore synthesised serylglycylaspartic acid and glycylserylaspartic acid, and showed that they had a wilting action on tomato leaves equal to one-sixth, and one-half to one-quarter the activity of lycomarasmin. Arguing that strepogenin might have glutamic acid in place of the aspartic acid of lycomarasmin, D. W. Woolley synthesised L-serylglycyl-L-glutamic acid and found that it had one-fortieth the activity of strepogenin towards *L. helveticus*, and antagonised the wilting action of serylglycylaspartic acid. Strepogenin activity was also observed in glycylserylglutamic acid, alanylglycylglutamic acid, glycylalanylglutamic acid and glycylglutamic acid. Serylglycylaspartic acid was antagonistic to the growth-promoting activity of strepogenin. The strepogenin activity of serylglycylglutamic acid was confirmed by W. A. Krehl and J. S. Fruton.[18]

Further investigation showed, however, that lycomarasmin contained a new amino acid, α-hydroxyalanine, attached by a common nitrogen atom to the amino group of glycylasparagine.[19] Additional peptides were synthesised and, of these, α-hydroxy-α-acetylaminopropionylglycylaspartic acid, was as active as lycomarasmin.[20]

The position occupied by strepogenin in protein molecules was investigated.[21] In insulin it apparently occurs at the end of the peptide chain, with glycine as the end group. It occupies a similar position in trypsinogen, but probably not in casein.

A factor that may be identical with strepogenin was found to be necessary for normal growth and survival of the mealworm, *Tenebrio molitor*, in addition to eight known vitamins ; it was named vitamin B_T provisionally.[22]

References to Section 5

1. N. Nakahara and F. Inukai, *Sci. Papers Inst. Phys. Chem. Research Tokyo*, 1933, **22**, 301 ; 1934, **24**, 33 ; W. Nakahara, F. Inukai and S. Kato, *Proc. Imp. Acad. Tokyo*, 1934, **10**, 268.

2. W. Nakahara, F. Inukai, S. Kato and S. Ugami, *Sci. Papers Inst. Phys. Chem. Research Tokyo*, 1936, **29**, 47 ; W. Nakahara, F. Inukai and S. Ugami, *ibid.*, 1935, **28**, 152 ; 1937, **31**, 42 ; 1938, **34**, 250 ; 1939, **36**, 312 ; 1940, **38**, 24 ; *Proc. Imp. Acad. Tokyo*, 1936, **12**, 289 ; 1938, **14**, 9 ; *Science*, 1938, **87**, 372 ; 1940, **91**, 431.

3. S. J. Folley, E. W. Ikin, S. K. Kon and H. M. S. Watson, *Biochem. J.*, 1938, **32**, 1988.
4. E. L. R. Stokstad and P. D. V. Manning, *J. Biol. Chem.*, 1938, **125**, 687.
5. E. L. R. Stokstad, P. D. V. Manning and R. E. Rogers, *ibid.*, 1940, **132**, 463.
6. D. V. Frost and C. A. Elvehjem, *ibid.*, 1937, **119**, xxxiv.
7. H. Kringstad and G. Lunde, *Z. physiol. Chem.*, 1939, **261**, 110 ; G. Lunde and H. Kringstad, *Naturwiss.*, 1940, **28**, 157 ; *J. Nutrition*, 1940, **19**, 321.
8. A. E. Schumacher, G. F. Heuser and L. C. Norris, *J. Biol. Chem.*, 1940, **135**, 313.
9. F. W. Hill, L. C. Norris and G. F. Heuser, *J. Nutrition*, 1944, **28**, 175.
10. M. L. Scott, L. C. Norris and G. F. Heuser, *J. Biol. Chem.*, 1947, **167**, 261.
11. H. Sprince and D. W. Woolley, *J. Exp. Med.*, 1944, **80**, 213.
12. H. Sprince and D. W. Woolley, *J. Amer. Chem. Soc.*, 1945, **67**, 1734.
13. D. W. Woolley and H. Sprince, *Fed. Proc.*, 1945, **4**, 164.
14. D. W. Woolley, *J. Biol. Chem.*, 1945, **159**, 753.
15. D. W. Woolley, *ibid.*, 1946, **162**, 383.
16. D. W. Woolley, *ibid.*, 1946, **166**, 783 ; 1948, **172**, 71.
17. P. A. Plattner and N. Clauson-Kaas, *Helv. Chim. Acta*, 1944, **28**, 188.
18. W. A. Krehl and J. S. Fruton, *J. Biol. Chem.*, 1948, **173**, 479.
19. D. W. Woolley, *ibid.*, 1949, **176**, 1291.
20. D. W. Woolley, *ibid.*, 1299.
21. D. W. Woolley, *ibid.*, 1947, **171**, 443.
22. G. Fraenkel, M. Blewett and M. Coles, *Nature*, 1948, **161**, 981 ; G. Fraenkel, *Brit. J. Nutrition*, 1948, **2**, i.

6. MISCELLANEOUS GROWTH FACTORS FOR ANIMALS

Grass Juice Factor

The " grass juice factor " is a relatively labile vitamin, said by Kohler *et al.*[1] to be necessary for normal growth in rats and guinea-pigs. It was obtained from grass juice by shaking with a mixture of chloroform and amyl alcohol, removing proteins and then treating with charcoal. The activity was present in the filtrate.

A substance apparently identical with it was reported by M. D. Cannon and G. A. Emerson,[2] who found that guinea-pigs failed to thrive on a highly purified diet, supplemented by vitamins in amounts adequate for rats, unless either lettuce or grass was given. The factor was water-soluble and stable at 100° C. for one hour. The same factor was isolated from the fraction of an aqueous liver extract that was precipitated by 70 % alcohol and then solubilised by the action of enzymes.[3] It was said to be different from folic acid.

Guinea-pigs required two other factors not essential for rats or chicks. These were present in yeast and winter milk respectively,[4] and also in linseed oil meal.[3, 5] What may or may not have been the same three factors were termed by D. W. Woolley and H. Sprince,[6] factors GPF1, GPF2 and GPF3. The first of these was probably identical with folic acid and the second with a mixture of cellulose and casein. K. A. Kuiken[7] also claimed that guinea-pigs required unknown factors in rice polish, brewers' yeast, dried grass or liver, and that commercial casein contained a further factor absent from vitamin-free casein.

Cartilage Factors

Hegsted et al.[8] claimed that a factor present in cartilage, kidney and rice was necessary for chicks, which in the absence of this factor developed a dermatitis similar to that observed in pantothenic acid deficiency. Robinson et al.[9] reported that chondroitin sulphuric acid could serve as a growth factor for both the rat and the chick, and that its effect was different from that of the anti-dermatitis factor found in a filtrate from rice polishings, that is, presumably, pantothenic acid.

According to a later paper by Hegsted et al.,[10] the cartilage factor is a combination of chondroitin, glycine and arginine ; each alone failed to stimulate the growth of chicks, and even when combined the weight restoration was not equal to that obtained with cartilage. Chondroitin alone, however, gave a marked response when the amount of casein in the diet was increased. Subsequently it was shown [11] that cystine must also be present if growth equivalent to that produced by cartilage was to be obtained.

A combination of these four factors prevented gizzard erosion, which had been attributed to the absence of a specific factor by H. J. Almquist and his colleagues,[12] and by C. A. Elvehjem and his colleagues.[13] H. R. Bird and J. J. Oleson [14] believed that the anti-gizzard erosion factor was present in a chondroitin fraction from cartilage, whilst H. J. Almquist [15] believed that it was cholic acid. It has now been shown that vitamin B_{12} prevents gizzard erosion in chicks.[15a]

Zoopherin

A factor similar to the chick factor from cow manure (page 544) was termed " nutritional factor X " by Cary et al.[16] Both factors may be identical with the factor termed by Zucker et al.[17] zoopherin. Zoopherin deficiency revealed itself in rats after the natural lactation period by a marked growth restraint, high mortality, high blood urea and a low white cell count. The chick factor from cow manure completely relieved symptoms of zoopherin deficiency in rats, and fractions from crude, but not " vitamin-free " casein, liver extract powder and " fish solubles ", had similar properties. Zoopherin was not present in dried yeast. It appears to be related to vitamin B_{12}.

References to Section 6

1. G. O. Kohler, C. A. Elvehjem and E. B. Hart, *J. Nutrition*, 1938, **15,** 445.
2. M. D. Cannon and G. A. Emerson, *ibid.*, 1939, **18,** 155.
3. G. J. Mannering, M. D. Cannon, H. V. Barki, C. A. Elvehjem and E. B. Hart, *J. Biol. Chem.*, 1943, **151,** 101.
4. H. A. Sober, G. J. Mannering, M. D. Cannon, C. A. Elvehjem and E. B. Hart, *J. Nutrition*, 1942, **24,** 503.
5. D. W. Woolley, *J. Biol. Chem.*, 1942, **143,** 679.
6. D. W. Woolley and H. Sprince, *ibid.*, 1945, **157,** 447.
7. K. A. Kuiken, *Univ. Pittsburgh Bull.*, 1944, **40,** 142.
8. D. M. Hegsted, J. J. Oleson, C. A. Elvehjem and E. B. Hart, *J. Biol. Chem.*, 1940, **133,** xli.
9. H. E. Robinson, R. E. Gray, F. F. Chesley and L. A. Crandall, *J. Nutrition*, 1939, **17,** 227.
10. D. M. Hegsted, S. W. Hier, C. A. Elvehjem and E. B. Hart, *J. Biol. Chem.*, 1941, **139,** 863.
11. G. M. Briggs, R. C. Mills, C. A. Elvehjem and E. B. Hart, *ibid.*, 1942, **144,** 47.
12. H. J. Almquist and E. L. R. Stokstad, *Nature*, 1936, **137,** 581 ; *J. Nutrition*, 1937, **13,** 339 ; H. J. Almquist, *ibid.*, 1937, **14,** 241 ; *Poultry Sci.*, 1938, **17,** 155.
13. H. R. Bird, C. A. Elvehjem and E. B. Hart, *J. Biol. Chem.*, 1936, **114,** x ; H. R. Bird, O. L. Kline, C. A. Elvehjem, E. B. Hart and J. G. Halpin, *J. Nutrition*, 1936, **12,** 571.
14. H. R. Bird and J. J. Oleson, *J. Biol. Chem.*, 1938, **123,** xi.
15. H. J. Almquist, *Science*, 1938, **87,** 538 ; H. J. Almquist and E. Mecchi, *J. Biol. Chem.*, 1938, **126,** 407.
15a. C. W. Mushett and W. H. Ott, *Poultry Sci.*, 1949, **28,** 850.
16. C. A. Cary, A. M. Hartman, L. P. Dryden and G. D. Likely, *Fed. Proc.*, 1946, **5,** 128.
17. L. M. Zucker, T. F. Zucker, V. Babcock and P. Hollester, *Arch. Biochem.*, 1948, **16,** 115.

7. MISCELLANEOUS GROWTH FACTORS FOR MICRO-ORGANISMS

The factors so far discussed were discovered as the result of feeding tests on laboratory animals. There are other factors, however, the existence of which has been revealed by their ability to stimulate the growth of micro-organisms. One or two of the factors already discussed, for example, strepogenin (page 616) and vitamin B_{12} (page 530), are growth factors for micro-organisms as well as for animals, but there are in addition factors that have been recognised solely by virtue of their action on micro-organisms, and have not yet been tested for growth-promoting activity in animals.

The exacting organism, *Lactobacillus helveticus*, has been used by a large number of workers to test for the presence of new factors. Thus, M. A. Pollack and M. Lindner [1] obtained a fraction which was active on this organism and which resembled folic acid in some respects ; it was not very soluble in organic solvents, for instance, and was stable in weakly acidic or alkaline solution but not in presence of strong acid or alkali. It appeared to be amphoteric, however, and was not readily adsorbed from solution and was precipitated by flavianic acid and heavy metals. The activity of this factor was attributed by E. J.-H. Chu and R. J. Williams,[2] to the presence of *p*-aminobenzoic acid, material with vitamin B_6 activity and various amino acids and peptides.

Other growth factors for *L. helveticus* were isolated from whole liver by Chattaway *et al.*[3] One, Factor 1, was also required for the growth of *gravis* and *intermedius* strains of *Corynebacterium diphtheriae*, and was present in casein hydrolysate as well as in liver. It was not precipitated by saturation with ammonium sulphate ; not extracted from aqueous solution by butyl or amyl alcohol, nor by phenol or *p*-cresol ; it gave no precipitate with lead, silver or phosphotungstic acid ; it was not adsorbed on fuller's earth at pH 3, but was adsorbed on norit at pH 3 and eluted by alcoholic ammonia. Another factor, Factor 2, accelerated the initial growth of *L. helveticus*, and was similar to Pollack and Lindner's factor ; it was partially precipitated by ammonium sulphate and was soluble in butyl alcohol. A third factor, Factor 3, was principally responsible for acid production by *L. helveticus* ; it was soluble in butyl alcohol, phenol and *p*-cresol, but not in amyl alcohol, and was precipitated by lead, silver and phosphotungstic acid. Factor 3 also appears to exist in a combined form, insoluble in organic solvents. A number of synthetic glutamic acid peptides had growth-promoting activity.

A number of growth factors for *L. helveticus* were isolated from liver by Barton-Wright *et al.*[4] in the course of attempts to prepare a concentrate of folic acid. Various fractions were obtained that stimulated the growth of *L. helveticus* and *S. lactis* R ; these differed from folic acid in being soluble in chloroform. Two, designated Factors HL1 and HL3, were adsorbed on Decalso, but differed from one another in their growth promoting activity, whilst the third Factor HL4, was not adsorbed on Decalso. It was possible that

Factor HL1 was a mixture of Factors HL3 and HL4, but these were certainly different from one another, since they exerted a synergistic action. Another growth factor for *L. helveticus* and *S. lactis* R exists in malt-sprouts.[4a]

F. R. Smith [5] obtained evidence for the existence of a new factor in yeast extract. This was essential for the growth of certain strains of *S. lactis*, and could not be replaced by any known vitamin or combination of amino acids. The factor was not precipitated by lead, silver, mercury, copper or zinc salts, and was not adsorbed on fuller's earth or activated carbon. It was insoluble in organic solvents and was destroyed by heating to 210° C. under reduced pressure.

V. H. Cheldelin and T. R. Riggs [6] isolated a factor essential for the growth of *L. gayoni* 8289 from yeast and liver extracts by adsorption on norit and elution with ammonia. It was amphoteric but apparently not a protein, although it appeared to be combined with a protein in natural materials.

Metcalf *et al.*[7] observed that certain vegetables, particularly tomato juice, contained a growth factor for *L. fermentum*. The new factor, which could be partially replaced by aneurine, was named the T factor.

Claims have also been made for the existence of growth factors for *Clostridium sporogenes* in partially digested proteins ; [8] for *Lactobacillus bulgaricus* in yeast ; [9] and for *Leuconostoc citrovorum* in liver, peptone and yeast extract.[10] This last factor was distinguished from vitamin B_{12} by the fact that it was stable to alkali and did not stimulate the growth of *L. leichmannii*.

The growth requirements of the protozoan, *Tetrahymena geleii* have been referred to several times before, but in addition to requiring certain recognised B vitamins for growth, this organism also appears to need other factors, termed factor IIA or " protogen " and factors IIB ' and IIB ". Some of these may be identical with factors required by *L. helveticus* and *S. faecalis*.[11]

Finally, reference should be made to the fact that many purines and pyrimidines stimulate the growth of micro-organisms, and some of the new factors recently described may ultimately prove to be identical with some of these. Thus factor Z, which promotes the growth of *Phycomyces blakesleeanus*, is probably identical with hypoxanthine, which is a growth factor for this organism in presence of aneurine.[12, 13] Hypoxanthine also stimulated the growth of *Spirillum serpens*, whilst guanine and adenine, although inactive when added separately, together increased the growth of the organism.[14]

Uracil stimulated the growth of *S. aureus*,[15] *S. pyogenes*,[16] *S. salivarius*,[17] certain species of *Lactobacillus*,[18] *Clostridium tetani* [19] and *Shigella paradysenteriae*.[20]

References to Section 7

1. M. A. Pollack and M. Lindner, *J. Biol. Chem.*, 1943, **147**, 183.
2. E. J.-H. Chu and R. J. Williams, *ibid.*, 1944, **155**, 9.
3. F. W. Chattaway, F. C. Happold, M. Sandford, B. Lythgoe and A. R. Todd, *Nature*, 1943, **151**, 559 ; F. W. Chattaway, F. C. Happold and M. Sandford, *Biochem. J.*, 1944, **38**, 111 ; F. W. Chattaway, D. E. Dolby and F. C. Happold, *ibid.*, 1948, **43**, 567 ; F. W. Chattaway, D. E. Dolby, D. E. Hall and F. C. Happold, *ibid.*, 1949, **45**, 592 ; D. E. Dolby, F. C. Happold and M. Sandford, *Nature*, 1944, **153**, 619.
4. E. C. Barton-Wright, W. B. Emery and F. A. Robinson, *ibid.*, 771 ; *Biochem. J.*, 1945, **39**, 334.
4*a*. L. G. Colio and V. Babb, *J. Biol. Chem.*, 1948, **174**, 405.
5. F. R. Smith, *J. Bact.*, 1943, **46**, 369.
6. V. H. Cheldelin and T. R. Riggs, *Arch. Biochem.*, 1946, **10**, 19.
7. D. Metcalf, G. J. Hucker and D. C. Carpenter, *J. Bact.*, 1946, **51**, 381.
8. G. M. Shull and W. H. Peterson, *Arch. Biochem.*, 1948, **18**, 97.
9. W. L. Williams, E. Hoff-Jørgensen and E. E. Snell, *J. Biol. Chem.*, 1949, **177**, 933.
10. H. E. Sauberlich and C. A. Baumann, *ibid.*, 1948, **176**, 165 ; 1949, **181**, 871 ; H. P. Broquist, E. L. R. Stokstad, C. E. Hoffmann, M. Belt and T. H. Jukes, *Proc. Soc. Exp. Biol. Med.*, 1949, **71**, 549.
11. E. L. R. Stokstad, C. E. Hoffmann, M. A. Regan, D. Fordham and T. H. Jukes, *Arch. Biochem.*, 1949, **20**, 75 ; G. W. Kidder and V. C. Dewey, *ibid.*, 433 ; E. E. Snell and H. P. Broquist, *ibid.*, 1949, **23**, 326.
12. W. J. Robbins and F. Kavanagh, *Proc. Nat. Acad. Sci.*, 1942, **28**, 65.
13. H. Hurni, *Z. Vitaminforsch.*, 1945, **16**, 69.
14. D. Pennington, *Proc. Nat. Acad. Sci.*, 1942, **28**, 272.
15. G. M. Richardson, *Biochem. J.*, 1936, **30**, 2184.
16. D. W. Woolley, *J. Exp. Med.*, 1941, **73**, 487 ; A. W. Bernheimer, W. Gillman, G. A. Hottle and A. M. Pappenheimer, *J. Bact.*, 1942, **43**, 494.
17. K. L. Smiley, C. F. Niven and J. M. Sharman, *ibid.*, 1943, **45**, 445 ; C. F. Niven and K. L. Smiley, *J. Biol. Chem.*, 1943, **150**, 1.
18. E. E. Snell and H. K. Mitchell, *U.S. Proc. Nat. Acad. Sci.*, 1941, **27**, 1.
19. R. E. Feeney, J. H. Mueller and P. A. Miller, *J. Bact.*, 1943, **46**, 563.
20. S. H. Hutner, *Arch. Biochem.*, 1944, **4**, 119.

CHAPTER XIV

CONCLUSION

In the preceding pages, the story of the vitamin B complex has been told in considerable detail. From the point of view of human and animal nutrition, the survey has indicated the paramount importance of aneurine, riboflavine and nicotinic acid, notwithstanding the fact that these substances may sometimes be synthesised in the intestine by the bacterial flora. Pyridoxine and pantothenic acid would appear to be of less importance, whilst the other members of the complex are probably never responsible for serious deficiency diseases in man or, for that matter, in animals, except under very artificial conditions.

As has already been pointed out, however, the association with deficiency diseases, although of great importance for the physical welfare of mankind, is by no means the most important characteristic of the vitamin B complex when an attempt is made to assess its significance in biochemistry ; for the appearance of a deficiency disease depends on an unusual combination of circumstances (page 584).

The real significance of the vitamin B complex was appreciated more fully when its importance in the nutrition of micro-organisms came to be recognised, although the presence of the whole vitamin B complex in yeast and liver, both centres of intense metabolic activity, was suggestive, and work on the stimulation of tissue respiration by the B vitamins had already indicated their close association with enzyme reactions. The stimulatory action of these substances on the growth of micro-organisms, however, revealed their fundamental importance for living organisms of all types.

It is now clear that the vitamin B complex is an assemblage of biologically related substances that are essential for the metabolic activity of all living cells, and that their close association in yeast and liver is no mere accident. The fundamental rôle of riboflavine and nicotinic acid in effecting the transfer of hydrogen from substrates to molecular oxygen has already been discussed in Chapters III and IV. In the absence of these two substances, the dehydrogenation of a large number of substances cannot take place. Just what this means can best be appreciated by a consideration of the processes whereby glucose is transformed into carbon dioxide and water.

The first stage in this transformation takes place in the absence of oxygen by a process referred to as anaerobic glycolysis. This is represented as follows :

Glucose
↓
Glucose-6-phosphate
↓
Fructose-1-phosphate
↓
Fructose-1 : 6-diphosphate
↓
Glyceraldehyde phosphate
↓
Glyceraldehyde diphosphate
↓
Diphosphoglyceric acid
↓
α-Phosphoglyceric acid
↓
Phosphopyruvic acid
↓
Pyruvic acid
↓
Lactic acid

The presence of cozymase and diaphorase I is essential for the dehydrogenation of glyceraldehyde diphosphate to diphosphoglyceric acid and of pyruvic acid to lactic acid.

This series of changes represents the biochemical reactions that occur during the contraction of muscle, but the recovery of muscle to its original state involves another series of changes, which provides the energy necessary for the reconversion of most of the lactic acid back to glucose and thence into glycogen, in which form carbohydrate is stored in the muscle tissue. This energy is derived from the complete oxidation of the remainder of the lactic acid to carbon dioxide and water. This apparently simple transformation, known as respiration, which occurs in bacteria, yeast and protozoa as well as in animal tissues, is in reality exceedingly complex, and again involves riboflavine- and nicotinic acid-containing coenzymes at several stages. The lactic acid is first oxidised back to pyruvic acid, which is then further oxidised by one of two routes.

The first of these is known as the " oxaloacetic acid cycle " and was discovered by A. Szent-Györgyi in 1936. This process comprises the fixation of carbon dioxide to pyruvic acid to give oxaloacetic acid, which then takes up hydrogen to yield a mixture of fumaric and malic acids. These subsequently give up the hydrogen again with regeneration of oxaloacetic acid :

$$CH_3 . CO . COOH \xrightarrow{+ CO_2} HOOC . CH_2 . CO . COOH$$

$$+ H_2 \Big\uparrow \Big\downarrow - H_2$$

$$HOOC . CH_2 . CHOH . COOH$$

$$+ H_2O \Big\uparrow \Big\downarrow - H_2O$$

$$HOOC . CH : CH . COOH$$

The second route whereby pyruvic acid is dehydrogenated was discovered by H. A. Krebs and was originally called the " citric acid cycle ", because the formation of citric acid was believed to be one of the stages involved. It was subsequently shown, however, that *iso*-citric acid is actually the intermediate product, and that citric acid is only a by-product. Consequently, the name, " citric acid cycle ", has been abandoned in favour of the term, " tricarboxylic acid cycle ". In its present form this can be represented as follows :

$$CH_3 . CO . COOH$$
pyruvic acid

$$\Big\downarrow +CO_2$$

$$CH_3 . CO . COOH \qquad HOOC . CH_2 . CO . COOH$$
pyruvic acid $\qquad\qquad$ oxaloacetic acid

$$-H_2$$

$$CH . COOH \qquad\qquad HOOC . CH_2 . CHOH . COOH$$
$$\|$$
$$C . COOH \qquad\qquad\qquad\qquad\qquad malic\ acid$$
$$|$$
$$CH_2 . COOH$$
cis-aconitic acid

$$+H_2O$$

$$HOOC . CH : CH . COOH$$
fumaric acid

$$\Big\downarrow +H_2O$$

$$-H_2$$

$$CH_2 . COOH \qquad CHOH . COOH$$
$$| \qquad\qquad\qquad |$$
$$C(OH) . COOH \qquad CH . COOH$$
$$| \qquad\qquad\qquad |$$
$$CH_2 . COOH \qquad CH_2 . COOH \qquad HOOC . CH_2 . CH_2 . COOH$$
citric acid $\qquad\quad$ *iso*citric acid $\qquad\qquad\qquad$ succinic acid

$$\Big\downarrow -H_2 \qquad\qquad\qquad\qquad -CO_2$$

$$CO . COOH \qquad\qquad\qquad CO . COOH$$
$$| \qquad\qquad\qquad\qquad\qquad |$$
$$CH . COOH \qquad -CO_2 \qquad CH_2$$
$$| \qquad\qquad\qquad\qquad\qquad |$$
$$CH_2 . COOH \qquad\qquad\qquad CH_2 . COOH$$
oxalosuccinic acid $\qquad\qquad\qquad$ α-ketoglutaric acid

The conversion of *iso*citric acid into oxalosuccinic acid involves triphosphopyridine nucleotide and diaphorase II, whilst the dehydrogenation of malic acid to oxaloacetic acid requires the presence of cozymase and diaphorase I. Nor is this all, for the tricarboxylic acid cycle is now known to be intimately linked with fatty acid metabolism through oxaloacetic acid, which is the pivot around which both fat and carbohydrate metabolism revolve. It has been shown that fatty acids with an even number of carbon atoms undergo β-oxidation to acetoacetic acid or a homologue, and that these are then converted into acetyl phosphate which condenses with oxaloacetic acid to give *cis*-aconitic acid. This is transformed into *iso*citric acid which then passes through the tricarboxylic acid cycle. Propionic acid is oxidised to pyruvic acid, which is either converted into acetyl phosphate or metabolised through the tricarboxylic acid cycle. These changes are represented as follows :

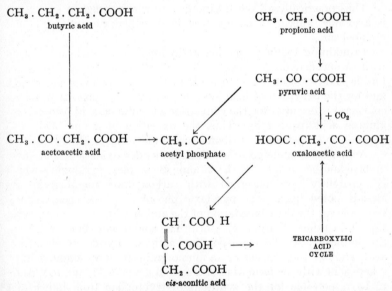

$CH_3 . CH_2 . CH_2 . COOH$
butyric acid

$CH_3 . CH_2 . COOH$
propionic acid

$CH_3 . CO . COOH$
pyruvic acid

$+ CO_2$

$CH_3 . CO . CH_2 . COOH \longrightarrow CH_3 . CO'$
acetoacetic acid   acetyl phosphate

$HOOC . CH_2 . CO . COOH$
oxaloacetic acid

$$CH . COO H$$
$$\| $$
$$C . COOH \longrightarrow$$
$$| $$
$$CH_2 . COOH$$
cis-aconitic acid

TRICARBOXYLIC ACID CYCLE

In the absence of enzymes containing nicotinic acid or riboflavine the metabolism of both fatty acids and carbohydrates is blocked, and this explains why the presence of these two substances is vital for the continued existence of all living cells.

Riboflavine and nicotinic acid are not the only B vitamins essential for fatty acid and carbohydrate metabolism, however. Aneurine pyrophosphate is a coenzyme necessary for the conversion of pyruvic acid into lactic acid, acetic acid, acetoacetic acid and oxaloacetic acid ; probably it activates the molecule preparatory to its oxidation or condensation with another molecule (page 102). This adequately explains the importance of aneurine in nutrition, for pyruvic acid occupies one of the key positions in both fat and carbohydrate metabolism. The conversion of pyruvic acid into acetic acid, however, also involves pantothenic acid (page 391), without which biological acetylations cannot take place. It is possible that the link between fatty acid metabolism and the tricarboxylic acid cycle may also be broken in its absence, although this has not yet been proved.

Another member of the vitamin B complex concerned with fat and carbohydrate metabolism is biotin, which appears to be a constituent of the coenzyme of oxaloacetic acid decarboxylase (page 443). This is responsible for the conversion of oxaloacetic acid into pyruvic acid and, presumably, for the fixation of carbon dioxide by pyruvic acid. It may also be concerned with the conversion of oxalosuccinic acid into α-ketoglutaric acid.

Thus practically all the B vitamins, of which sufficient knowledge is available, appear to be involved in carbohydrate and fatty acid metabolism.

In addition to their function as hydrogen carriers in association with various dehydrogenases, the flavine nucleotides are also necessary for the oxidation of D-amino acids to the corresponding keto-acids, and for the oxidation of diamino acids and glycine (page 195), whilst cozymase is essential for the conversion of glutamic acid into α-ketoglutaric acid (page 278). Thus the oxidation of amino acids also depends on the presence of riboflavine and nicotinic acid.

Amino acids undergo other changes besides oxidation, and these involve another member of the vitamin B complex, pyridoxine, which is apparently not concerned with carbohydrate metabolism. As already noted (page 331), pyridoxal phosphate is the coenzyme responsible for the decarboxylation of the amino acids, L-lysine, L-tyrosine, L-histidine, L-arginine, L-ornithine and L-glutamic acid, with the formation of the corresponding amines. Pyridoxal phosphate also catalyses the transfer of an amino group from an amino acid to a keto acid with the formation of a second amino acid, and it appears to be responsible for the synthesis of tryptophan from indole and serine.

A considerable amount of research work is at present being carried out on the mechanism of enzyme reactions, and the next few years will doubtless provide many further examples of reactions in which known members of the vitamin B complex are involved. In addition, it is not unlikely that other substances having analogous properties will be discovered and that these will have all the characteristics that we have come to associate with the components of the vitamin B complex. Thus, they should produce characteristic deficiency symptoms in suitable experimental animals when these are maintained on a diet from which the factor is missing but which is otherwise complete, and they should cure these deficiency symptoms when added to the diet ; they should stimulate the growth of exacting strains of micro-organisms when grown on a medium deficient in the factor, but otherwise adequate for growth ; and their growth-promoting action on micro-organisms, and possibly on animals too, should be antagonised by substances that closely resemble them in chemical structure ; most important of all, they should be present in enzyme systems responsible for specific biochemical reactions.

It must not, of course, be assumed that all coenzymes have vitamins as their prosthetic groups. Cytochrome, for instance, contains iron-porphyrin, whilst peroxidase and catalase contain other iron compounds, and ascorbic acid oxidase contains copper. Again, glutathione is a coenzyme for glyoxalase and possibly for many other enzymes, for there is a long list of enzyme systems that appear to depend for their activity on the presence of sulphhydryl groups. The vitamin B complex, therefore, comprises only one special class of substances essential for the activity of coenzymes ; it is characterised by the fact that its members cannot, except in certain circumstances, be produced by the organisms that require them, but have to be supplied ready made in the diet.

In concluding this survey, I can only express the hope that my attempt to systematise the large mass of information now available will have given the reader a clear picture of the chemical and biological behaviour of each member of the vitamin B complex, and an appreciation of the important function the group as a whole performs in the economy of mammals and birds, insects, plants and micro-organisms. I hope, too, that I have conveyed something of the sense of confusion, almost chaos, that seemed to herald the discovery of each new vitamin. It was rather as though one were watching the weaving of some large tapestry without knowing anything of the ultimate design. At first, one saw only jumbled patches of colour, formless and meaningless, but as the work progressed these patches resolved themselves one by one into familiar objects that one recognised and that became of greater and greater significance as the picture grew, until finally one could perceive the meaning and purpose of the whole picture. Even now the tapestry is incomplete, and we do not fully understand its purport. Perhaps we never shall, though we may comprehend its meaning more fully as we watch the weaving of other tapestries related in some way to the one that has formed the subject of this book.

AUTHOR INDEX

ABBOTT Labs., 155, 156.
Abbott, O. D., 594, 595.
Abdel Kader, M. M., 251, 252, 257, 266, 273, 274, 283, 286, 293, 295.
Abderhalden, E., 119, 130.
—— R., 119, 130.
Abelin, J., 367, 370.
Abels, J. C., 69, 74, 429, 432, 575.
Abelson, P. H., 543, 544.
Abraham, E. P., 192, 194, 201, 250, 252.
Acheson, R. M., 523, 526.
Ackermann, W. W., 387, 389, 395, 402.
Adams, R., 214, 216.
—— R. R., 209, 210.
Adler, E., 134, 135, 194, 201, 276, 277, 279, 280, 292, 293, 295.
Agnew, L. R. C., 320, 322.
Ahlstrom, L., 128, 131.
Ahmad, B., 64, 73.
Albanese, A. A., 84, 85.
Albert, P. W., 251, 252.
Albury, M., 44, 45, 46, 165, 167, 235, 236.
Albus, H., 275, 279.
Alcayaga, R., 320, 322, 368, 371.
Alden, H. S., 179, 183.
Alderton, G., 427, 431.
Alexander, B., 38, 42, 66, 70, 72, 73, 74, 76, 78, 80, 81, 84, 85.
Alexopoulos, C. J., 110, 113.
Aline, E., 369, 371.
Allan, F. N., 582, 584.
Allbone, E. C., 66, 73.
Allen, D. I., 43, 45.
Allenson, M. J. C., 223, 231.
Allfrey, V., 482, 483.
Allgeier, A. M., 489, 494.
Allied Chemical and Dye Corp., 215, 217.
Allison, F. E., 405.
Almquist, H. J., 595, 600, 602, 603, 604, 619, 620.
Alt, H., 523, 526.
Altman, K. I., 276, 277, 280.
American Cyanamid Co., 8, 154, 156, 214, 216, 306, 307, 357, 358, 359, 399, 402, 475, 477.
Ames, S. R., 334, 337.
Amiard, G., 95, 104.
Andersag, H., 15, 19, 21, 22, 117, 130, 300, 301.
Anderson, R. C., 414, 415, 416, 420, 473, 476, 477, 478, 479, 566.

Anderson, R. J., 565, 566.
Andrews, G. A., 498, 502.
—— J. S., 161, 164.
—— M. B., 285, 286.
Andus, L. J., 286, 287.
Angelescu, C., 90, 103.
Angier, R. B., 463, 466, 471, 472, 473, 474, 475, 476, 477, 482, 483, 520, 522, 525.
Anigstein, L., 554, 558, 559.
Ansbacher, S., 133, 134, 159, 163, 425, 430, 551, 552, 553.
Anslow, W. P., 417, 420.
Antognini, R., 176, 177.
Antopol, W., 48, 54, 88, 89, 200, 203, 318, 321, 323, 324, 325, 327, 329, 330.
Aramburu, T., 498, 501, 502, 503, 505, 538, 540, 541, 542.
Archdeacon, J. W., 555.
Archer, W., 170, 173, 189, 190.
Aring, C. D., 274, 323, 324.
Arismendi, H. H., 83, 85, 179, 183, 187, 189.
Armour Research Foundation, 22, 23.
Armstrong, M. D., 417, 420.
Arnason, A., 44, 46, 165, 167.
Arnold, A., 396, 402, 612, 613.
Arons, I., 501, 503.
Arth, G. E., 414, 415, 416, 420, 473, 476, 477, 478, 479.
Artom, C., 601, 603.
Ascham, J. K., 315, 317.
Aschner, M., 115, 116.
Asenjo, C. F., 507, 508.
Ashburn, L. L., 48, 54, 366, 370, 434, 436, 489, 494.
Ashe, W. F., 323, 324.
Asher, S. P., 60, 61.
Asmundson, V. S., 318, 320, 321, 329.
Atkin, L., 33, 34, 36, 106, 112, 225, 227, 231, 281, 285, 311, 314, 315, 316, 317, 338, 340, 361, 362, 386, 389, 404, 405, 438, 440, 569, 570, 577, 578.
Atkinson, M., 247, 249.
—— W. B., 366, 370.
Auhagen, E., 293, 295, 560, 562.
Austin, C. R., 52, 55.
Avakian, S., 346, 347, 514, 524.
Aykroyd, W. R., 233, 236, 241, 243, 248.
Ayre, J. E., 61.

630

Macy, I. G., 182, 183, 264, 268, 374, 376, 433, 434.
Madden, R. J., 212, 213, 214, 262, 265, 267, 288, 294.
Mader, W. J., 482, 483.
Madinaveitia, J., 209, 210, 398, 402.
Madsen, H., 76, 80.
—— L. L., 52, 56.
Magasanik, B., 578, 579.
Magyar, I., 64, 68, 73.
Main, E., 372, 553, 554.
Mainzer, F., 245, 249.
Majnarich, J. J., 522, 525, 614, 615.
Major, R. T., 350, 351, 354, 358.
Makino, K., 15, 303, 307.
Mallette, M. F., 517, 524.
Mallory, M. E., 463, 466.
Malmberg, M., 138, 139, 156, 162, 206, 207, 209.
Malone, L., 282, 286.
Mamalis, P., 533.
Manchester, F., 216, 217.
Mann, I., 175, 177.
—— P. J. G., 279, 280.
—— T., 391, 393.
Mannering, G. J., 184, 186, 188, 189, 619, 620.
Manning, P. D. V., 460, 465, 615, 618.
Mano, C., 62, 63, 86, 87, 89.
Manson-Bahr, P., 243, 248, 496, 502.
Manz, W., 292, 295.
Maquenne, L., 564, 565, 566.
Marchant, C., 106, 112, 338, 340.
Marenzi, A. D., 586, 587.
Margolis, G., 288, 294.
—— L. H., 259, 266, 288, 294.
Mariella, R. P., 346, 347.
Marque, J., 568, 569.
Marquette, M. M., 68, 73, 166, 168, 251, 252.
Marston, H. R., 544.
Martin, A. J. P., 212, 213, 238, 240.
—— A. R., 398, 402, 561, 562.
—— B. B., 360, 362.
—— C. J., 212, 213, 238, 240.
—— D. W., 324, 325.
—— G. J., 169, 172, 319, 322, 345, 346, 347, 434, 436, 462, 466, 487, 493, 505, 506, 514, 519, 524, 527, 528, 551, 552, 553, 572, 573, 574, 575.
—— H. E., 115, 116, 205, 206, 341, 342, 389, 390.
—— M. E., 549, 550.
Martindale, W. E., 506, 508.
Martinek, R. G., 220, 230.
Marvel, J. P., 485, 493.
Marvin, J. F., 244, 248.
Mason, H. L., 39, 42, 58, 59, 61, 65, 73, 83, 85, 179, 183, 187, 189, 243, 248.
Masunaga, E., 52, 55.

Mather, K., 232, 236.
Mathews, A. P., 219, 221, 230.
Matrone, G., 35, 37.
Matsunaga, S., 213.
Mattick, A. T. R., 75, 80.
Mattis, P. A., 483, 484, 488, 494, 505, 506.
Mattocks, A. M., 523, 525.
Matukawa, T., 298.
Maw, G. A., 603, 604.
Mawson, E. H., 184, 186, 552, 553.
Maxfield, J. R., 324, 325.
May, E. L., 396, 402.
—— H. B., 554.
Mayer, R. L., 151, 153.
Mayfield, H. L., 97, 105, 195, 202.
Mayhall, M., 444, 445.
Maynard, J. T., 399, 401, 402, 403.
—— L. A., 165, 167, 233, 236, 363, 364, 423, 424.
Mazoué, H., 126, 131, 208, 210.
McArthur, C. S., 601, 603, 604.
McBurney, C. H., 351, 352.
McCall, K. B., 53, 56, 170, 172, 189, 190, 238, 240, 320, 321, 322, 368, 371, 426, 429, 431, 435, 436, 437, 491, 492, 495, 507, 508, 573, 575.
McCance, R. A., 164, 167.
McCartney, J. R., 44, 45, 46, 165, 167, 235, 236.
McCarty, M. A., 45, 166, 167.
McCasland, G. E., 346, 347, 579, 581.
McClung, L. S., 148, 152, 461, 466, 488, 494.
McClure, F. J., 48, 54.
McCollum, E. V., 37, 41, 90, 103, 134, 135.
McCormack, R. B., 534, 536.
McCormick, H. M., 540, 542.
McCoy, R. H., 320, 322, 369, 371, 451, 452, 455, 456.
McCreary, J. F., 175, 177.
McCulloch, E. C., 52, 55, 56, 490, 495, 552, 553, 573, 575.
McDonald, F. G., 289, 295.
—— P. R., 174, 176.
McElroy, L. W., 79, 81, 185, 186, 327, 328, 376, 377, 425, 430.
McElvain, S. M., 214, 216, 217.
McEwen, W. L., 417, 420, 447, 454.
McGibbon, W. H., 425, 430.
McGinnis, J., 600, 603, 614, 615.
McGowan, J. C., 578, 579.
McGregor, M. A., 435, 436, 490, 495, 552, 553, 573, 575.
McHenry, E. W., 49, 55, 318, 319, 322, 428, 431, 438, 572, 574, 590, 591, 592, 603, 604.
McIlwain, A. J., 324, 325.

Najjar, V. A., 39, 42, 52, 55, 64, 72, 73, 74, 76, 80, 160, 163, 179, 183, 184, 186, 226, 231, 249, 252, 254, 260, 266, 288, 294.
Nakahara, N., 615, 617.
—— W., 429, 431.
Nason, A., 287.
Nasset, E. S., 94, 104, 368, 371.
National Oil Products Co., 356, 358.
Neal, A. L., 394, 401.
Needham, D. M., 276, 280.
—— J., 568, 569, 576, 577.
Needles, W., 58, 61.
Negelein, E., 195, 202, 276, 277, 280.
Neilands, J. B., 361, 362.
Neligh, R. B., 539, 541.
Nelson, E. M., 50, 55, 498, 500, 502, 503, 504, 505.
—— H. V., 498, 502, 504, 505.
—— M. M., 345, 347, 367, 370, 375, 376, 377, 425, 430, 489, 494.
—— V. E., 404, 405.
Nemir, R. L., 84, 85.
Nencki, M., 244, 248.
Ness, H. T., 68, 73.
Nestler, R. B., 539, 542.
Neuberger, A., 195, 202.
Neuman, M. W., 595, 596.
Neumann, A. L., 591, 592, 595.
—— F. W., 434, 436.
Neuwahl, F. J., 247, 249.
Neuweiler, W., 64, 69, 71, 72, 73, 74, 181, 183.
Nevens, W. B., 53, 56, 170, 172, 237, 239, 426, 431.
Nichol, C. A., 283, 286, 535, 536, 540, 542, 614, 615.
Nicholls, J., 366, 370.
—— J. V. V., 175, 177.
Nicholson, J. T. L., 49, 55, 79, 81, 82, 85.
Nielsen, E., 326, 327, 423, 424, 425, 430, 434, 436, 437, 462, 466, 487, 489, 493, 494, 505, 506, 577.
—— N., 361, 362, 373, 376, 386, 389, 394, 396, 399, 401, 402, 422.
Nier, A. O., 96, 104.
Nigrelli, R. F., 521, 525.
Nilsson, R., 404, 405.
Nimmo-Smith, R. H., 510, 511, 523, 526.
Nitchals, R., 234, 236.
Nitti, F., 545, 547.
Nitzberg, T., 68, 73.
Nitzescu, L. I., 47, 54, 90, 103.
Niven, C. F., 35, 37, 111, 113, 622, 623.
Nobécourt, P., 114, 115.
Nocito, V., 196, 202, 334, 335, 337.
Noecker, N. L., 109, 113.
Noggle, G. R., 286, 287.
Noland, J. L., 597.
Nopco Chemical Co., 357, 358.

Norris, E. R., 461, 465, 470, 471, 484, 522, 525, 608, 610, 614, 615.
—— F. W., 220, 222, 230, 235, 236.
—— L. C., 128, 131, 159, 161, 163, 164, 165, 167, 320, 322, 337, 338, 344, 347, 368, 369, 371, 378, 379, 459, 460, 465, 479, 480, 485, 486, 488, 493, 494, 506, 507, 514, 517, 518, 524, 535, 536, 537, 539, 542, 600, 603, 609, 611, 614, 615, 616, 618.
Northey, E. H., 463, 466, 471, 473, 474, 475, 477.
Novak, A. F., 614, 615.
Novelli, G. D., 391, 392, 393.
Nyc, J. F., 251, 252, 281, 285.

O'Banion, E. E., 552, 553.
Obermeyer, H. G., 34, 36, 70, 74, 183, 186.
O'Brien, J. R., 367, 370, 611, 612, 613.
Ochoa, S., 95, 104, 193, 201, 444, 445.
O'Dell, B. L., 458, 459, 461, 464, 465, 466, 469, 470, 471, 477, 478, 479, 480, 484, 487, 493, 494, 505, 506, 527, 528.
Odintzova, E. N., 106, 107, 112.
O'Doherty, K., 536.
O'Donnell, D. J., 170, 173, 189, 190, 239, 240, 320, 322, 369, 371, 426, 431, 492, 495, 552, 553, 574, 575, 591, 592.
Odoriz, J. B., 47, 54.
Oettel, H., 551, 553.
Ogden, F. N., 496, 502.
Ogg, C. L., 289, 291, 294.
Ohlson, M. A., 178, 180, 182, 187, 189.
Okade, S., 10, 12, 46, 54, 213.
O'Kane, D. E., 334, 335, 337.
Okey, R., 428, 431.
Okunuki, K., 194, 201.
Olcese, O., 271, 272.
Olcott, C. T., 76, 80.
Oldham, H., 83, 85, 178, 179, 180, 182, 183, 187, 189.
—— H. G., 70, 74, 84, 85, 178, 180, 182.
Oleson, J. J., 282, 286, 349, 351, 365, 369, 405, 485, 493, 520, 521, 522, 525, 541, 542, 604, 605, 619, 620.
Olsen, H. W., 539, 542.
Olson, O. E., 481, 482.
—— R. E., 392, 393, 445, 590, 592.
O'Malley, C. M., 155, 156.
O'Meara, R. A. Q., 545, 547.
Omori, S., 37, 42, 44, 46.
Ondratschek, K., 112, 113.
Onstatt, R. H., 133.
Oppel, T. W., 433, 435, 436.
Ordal, Z. J., 439, 441.
Orent, E. R., 134, 135.
Organ, J. G., 39, 42.
Orimo, R., 92, 104.
Orla-Jensen, S., 203, 204.

Lipotropic action of inositol, 572, 591, 602.
Listerella monocytogenes, 204.
Liver, vitamin content of, 44, 166, 180, 234, 316, 363, 423, 483, 537, 551, 570, 571, 588.
— damage, riboflavine and, 200.
— extracts, comparative anti-pernicious anaemia activity of, 537.
— —, " crude ", 530.
— —, proteolysed, 530, 531.
— —, " refined ", 530.
— L casei factor, 457, 463, 467, 468, 471, 472, 477.
Lophiodermum pinastri, 109, 438.
Luciferin, 197.
Lumichrome, 137.
Lumiflavine, 134, 136, 209.
Luminescence, 197, 198.
Lupus erythematosus, 247.
Lutidine, 215.
Lycomarasmin, 617.
Lymphogranuloma venereum, 558.
Lyochrome, 134.
Lysine, 195, 628.
—, ε-acetyl-, 195.
—, ε-benzoyl-, 195.
—, ε-methyl-, 195.
—, pantoyl-, 396.
Lysine decarboxylase, 331, 332.
Lysozyme, 427.
Lyxoflavine, 267.

MACKEREL, vitamin content of, 165, 233.
Maize, association with pellagra, 211, 233, 240, 271.
—, vitamin content of, 43, 164, 232, 316, 363, 537, 550, 571, 587.
Maleic acid, 197.
Malic acid, 442, 443, 444, 625, 626, 627.
Man, aneurine requirements of, 82-84.
—, biotin requirements of, 437.
—, choline requirements of, 594-595.
—, effect of p-aminobenzoic acid deficiency in, 553-554.
—, — aneurine deficiency in, 56-61.
—, — biotin deficiency in, 432.
—, — choline deficiency in, 593.
—, — folic acid deficiency in, 495-503.
—, — inositol deficiency in, 575.
—, — nicotinic acid deficiency in, 240-249.
—, — pantothenic acid deficiency in, 372.
—, — pyridoxine deficiency in, 322-325.
—, — riboflavine deficiency in, 173-177.
—, folic acid requirements of, 507.
—, inositol requirements of, 576.

Man, nicotinic acid requirements of, 272-273.
—, riboflavine requirements of, 187-188.
—, vitamin B12 requirements of, 538-539.
Manure, vitamin content of, 114, 341, 424, 559, 578.
Marasmius androsaceus, 438.
Maté, vitamin content of, 44, 167.
Meat, vitamin content of, 44, 166, 234, 316, 363, 537, 567, 571, 587, 588.
Melanin, association with riboflavine, 166.
Melanospora destruens, 109.
Melons, vitamin content of, 588.
Meniere syndrome, 247.
Mepacrine, 209.
—, inhibition of enzyme action by, 196.
Mepacrine-resistant Pneumococci, 204.
Meso-inositol. See Inositol.
Methionine, 254, 260, 261, 446, 556, 563, 583, 590, 595, 597, 598-602.
—, N-methyl-, 195.
Methionine deaminase, 444.
Methionol, 119.
" Methoxy-pyridoxine ". See Pyridoxine, 4-methyl-.
Methyl pantothenone, 400.
Methylation in vivo, 254, 255, 258, 259, 260, 261, 288, 598-602.
Methylglyoxal, 91.
Methylglyoxalase, 92, 93.
Mice, effect of vitamin deficiency in, 169, 319, 424, 489, 490, 551, 572.
—, vitamin requirements of, 82, 188, 378, 608.
Microbiological assay of p-aminobenzoic acid, 549-550.
— — aneurine, 32-37.
— — biotin, 421-422.
— — choline, 587.
— — folic acid, 481.
— — inositol, 569.
— — nicotinic acid, 226-229.
— — pantothenic acid, 360.
— — pyridoxine, 311-313.
— — riboflavine, 157-159.
— — vitamin B12, 534-535.
Micrococcus lysodeikticus, 97.
Micro-organisms, p-aminobenzoic acid in nutrition of, 555-559.
—, aneurine in nutrition of, 105-113.
—, biotin in nutrition of, 438-441.
—, choline in nutrition of, 596-597.
—, folic acid in nutrition of, 509-511.
—, inositol in nutrition of, 577-578.
—, nicotinic acid in nutrition of, 281-286.
—, pantothenic acid in nutrition of, 380-389.